ALGEBRA

ARITHMETIC OPERATIONS

$$a(b + c) = ab + ac$$

$$\frac{a}{b} + \frac{c}{d} = \frac{ad + bc}{bd}$$

$$\frac{a + c}{b} = \frac{a}{b} + \frac{c}{b}$$

$$\frac{\frac{a}{b}}{\frac{c}{d}} = \frac{a}{b} \times \frac{d}{c} = \frac{ad}{bc}$$

EXPONENTS AND RADICALS

$$x^m x^n = x^{m+n}$$

$$\frac{x^m}{x^n} = x^{m-n}$$

$$(x^m)^n = x^{mn}$$

$$x^{-n} = \frac{1}{x^n}$$

$$(xy)^n = x^n y^n$$

$$\left(\frac{x}{y}\right)^n = \frac{x^n}{y^n}$$

$$x^{1/n} = \sqrt[n]{x}$$

$$x^{m/n} = \sqrt[n]{x^m} = (\sqrt[n]{x})^m$$

$$\sqrt[n]{xy} = \sqrt[n]{x}\,\sqrt[n]{y}$$

$$\sqrt[n]{\frac{x}{y}} = \frac{\sqrt[n]{x}}{\sqrt[n]{y}}$$

FACTORING SPECIAL POLYNOMIALS

$$x^2 - y^2 = (x + y)(x - y)$$

$$x^3 + y^3 = (x + y)(x^2 - xy + y^2)$$

$$x^3 - y^3 = (x - y)(x^2 + xy + y^2)$$

BINOMIAL THEOREM

$$(x + y)^2 = x^2 + 2xy + y^2 \qquad (x - y)^2 = x^2 - 2xy + y^2$$

$$(x + y)^3 = x^3 + 3x^2y + 3xy^2 + y^3$$

$$(x - y)^3 = x^3 - 3x^2y + 3xy^2 - y^3$$

$$(x + y)^n = x^n + nx^{n-1}y + \frac{n(n - 1)}{2}x^{n-2}y^2$$

$$+ \cdots + \binom{n}{k}x^{n-k}y^k + \cdots + nxy^{n-1} + y^n$$

$$\text{where } \binom{n}{k} = \frac{n(n - 1)\cdots(n - k + 1)}{1 \cdot 2 \cdot 3 \cdot \cdots \cdot k}$$

QUADRATIC FORMULA

If $ax^2 + bx + c = 0$, then $x = \dfrac{-b \pm \sqrt{b^2 - 4ac}}{2a}$.

INEQUALITIES AND ABSOLUTE VALUE

If $a < b$ and $b < c$, then $a < c$.

If $a < b$, then $a + c < b + c$.

If $a < b$ and $c > 0$, then $ca < cb$.

If $a < b$ and $c < 0$, then $ca > cb$.

If $a > 0$, then

$$|x| = a \quad \text{means} \quad x = a \quad \text{or} \quad x = -a$$

$$|x| < a \quad \text{means} \quad -a < x < a$$

$$|x| > a \quad \text{means} \quad x > a \quad \text{or} \quad x < -a$$

GEOMETRY

GEOMETRIC FORMULAS

Formulas for area A, circumference C, and volume V:

Triangle	Circle	Sector of Circle
$A = \frac{1}{2}bh$	$A = \pi r^2$	$A = \frac{1}{2}r^2\theta$
$\quad = \frac{1}{2}ab \sin\theta$	$C = 2\pi r$	$s = r\theta$ (θ in radians)

Sphere	Cylinder	Cone
$V = \frac{4}{3}\pi r^3$	$V = \pi r^2 h$	$V = \frac{1}{3}\pi r^2 h$
$A = 4\pi r^2$		$A = \pi r\sqrt{r^2 + h^2}$

DISTANCE AND MIDPOINT FORMULAS

Distance between $P_1(x_1, y_1)$ and $P_2(x_2, y_2)$:

$$d = \sqrt{(x_2 - x_1)^2 + (y_2 - y_1)^2}$$

Midpoint of $\overline{P_1P_2}$: $\left(\dfrac{x_1 + x_2}{2}, \dfrac{y_1 + y_2}{2}\right)$

LINES

Slope of line through $P_1(x_1, y_1)$ and $P_2(x_2, y_2)$:

$$m = \frac{y_2 - y_1}{x_2 - x_1}$$

Point-slope equation of line through $P_1(x_1, y_1)$ with slope m:

$$y - y_1 = m(x - x_1)$$

Slope-intercept equation of line with slope m and y-intercept b:

$$y = mx + b$$

CIRCLES

Equation of the circle with center (h, k) and radius r:

$$(x - h)^2 + (y - k)^2 = r^2$$

TRIGONOMETRY

ANGLE MEASUREMENT

π radians $= 180°$

$$1° = \frac{\pi}{180} \text{ rad} \qquad 1 \text{ rad} = \frac{180°}{\pi}$$

$s = r\theta$

(θ in radians)

RIGHT ANGLE TRIGONOMETRY

$$\sin\theta = \frac{\text{opp}}{\text{hyp}} \qquad \csc\theta = \frac{\text{hyp}}{\text{opp}}$$

$$\cos\theta = \frac{\text{adj}}{\text{hyp}} \qquad \sec\theta = \frac{\text{hyp}}{\text{adj}}$$

$$\tan\theta = \frac{\text{opp}}{\text{adj}} \qquad \cot\theta = \frac{\text{adj}}{\text{opp}}$$

TRIGONOMETRIC FUNCTIONS

$$\sin\theta = \frac{y}{r} \qquad \csc\theta = \frac{r}{y}$$

$$\cos\theta = \frac{x}{r} \qquad \sec\theta = \frac{r}{x}$$

$$\tan\theta = \frac{y}{x} \qquad \cot\theta = \frac{x}{y}$$

GRAPHS OF TRIGONOMETRIC FUNCTIONS

TRIGONOMETRIC FUNCTIONS OF IMPORTANT ANGLES

θ	radians	$\sin\theta$	$\cos\theta$	$\tan\theta$
0°	0	0	1	0
30°	$\pi/6$	$1/2$	$\sqrt{3}/2$	$\sqrt{3}/3$
45°	$\pi/4$	$\sqrt{2}/2$	$\sqrt{2}/2$	1
60°	$\pi/3$	$\sqrt{3}/2$	$1/2$	$\sqrt{3}$
90°	$\pi/2$	1	0	—

FUNDAMENTAL IDENTITIES

$$\csc\theta = \frac{1}{\sin\theta} \qquad \sec\theta = \frac{1}{\cos\theta}$$

$$\tan\theta = \frac{\sin\theta}{\cos\theta} \qquad \cot\theta = \frac{\cos\theta}{\sin\theta}$$

$$\cot\theta = \frac{1}{\tan\theta} \qquad \sin^2\theta + \cos^2\theta = 1$$

$$1 + \tan^2\theta = \sec^2\theta \qquad 1 + \cot^2\theta = \csc^2\theta$$

$$\sin(-\theta) = -\sin\theta \qquad \cos(-\theta) = \cos\theta$$

$$\tan(-\theta) = -\tan\theta \qquad \sin\left(\frac{\pi}{2} - \theta\right) = \cos\theta$$

$$\cos\left(\frac{\pi}{2} - \theta\right) = \sin\theta \qquad \tan\left(\frac{\pi}{2} - \theta\right) = \cot\theta$$

THE LAW OF SINES

$$\frac{\sin A}{a} = \frac{\sin B}{b} = \frac{\sin C}{c}$$

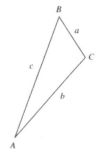

THE LAW OF COSINES

$$a^2 = b^2 + c^2 - 2bc\cos A$$

$$b^2 = a^2 + c^2 - 2ac\cos B$$

$$c^2 = a^2 + b^2 - 2ab\cos C$$

ADDITION AND SUBTRACTION FORMULAS

$$\sin(x + y) = \sin x \cos y + \cos x \sin y$$

$$\sin(x - y) = \sin x \cos y - \cos x \sin y$$

$$\cos(x + y) = \cos x \cos y - \sin x \sin y$$

$$\cos(x - y) = \cos x \cos y + \sin x \sin y$$

$$\tan(x + y) = \frac{\tan x + \tan y}{1 - \tan x \tan y}$$

$$\tan(x - y) = \frac{\tan x - \tan y}{1 + \tan x \tan y}$$

DOUBLE-ANGLE FORMULAS

$$\sin 2x = 2 \sin x \cos x$$

$$\cos 2x = \cos^2 x - \sin^2 x = 2\cos^2 x - 1 = 1 - 2\sin^2 x$$

$$\tan 2x = \frac{2\tan x}{1 - \tan^2 x}$$

HALF-ANGLE FORMULAS

$$\sin^2 x = \frac{1 - \cos 2x}{2} \qquad \cos^2 x = \frac{1 + \cos 2x}{2}$$

Multi - Variable Calculus

UC Irvine

James Stewart

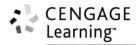

CENGAGE
Learning™

Australia • Brazil • Japan • Korea • Mexico • Singapore • Spain • United Kingdom • United States

CENGAGE
Learning™

Multi - Variable Calculus: UC Irvine

James Stewart

Executive Editors:
 Maureen Staudt
 Michael Stranz

Senior Project Development Manager:
 Linda DeStefano

Marketing Specialist:
 Sara Mercurio

Senior Production / Manufacturing Manager:
 Donna M. Brown

PreMedia Supervisor:
 Joel Brennecke

Rights & Permissions Specialist:
 Kalina Hintz
 Todd Osborne

Cover Image:
 Getty Images*

* Unless otherwise noted, all cover images used by Custom Solutions, a part of Cengage Learning, have been supplied courtesy of Getty Images with the exception of the Earthview cover image, which has been supplied by the National Aeronautics and Space Administration (NASA).

For product information and technology assistance, contact us at
Cengage Learning Customer & Sales Support, 1-800-354-9706

For permission to use material from this text or product, submit all requests online at **cengage.com/permissions**
Further permissions questions can be emailed to
permissionrequest@cengage.com

ISBN-13: 978-1-4266-3482-6

ISBN-10: 1-4266-3482-X

Cengage Learning
5191 Natorp Boulevard
Mason, Ohio 45040
USA

Cengage Learning is a leading provider of customized learning solutions with office locations around the globe, including Singapore, the United Kingdom, Australia, Mexico, Brazil, and Japan. Locate your local office at:
international.cengage.com/region

Cengage Learning products are represented in Canada by Nelson Education, Ltd.

For your lifelong learning solutions, visit **www.cengage.com/custom**

Visit our corporate website at **www.cengage.com**

Printed in the United States of America

Custom Contents

12

INFINITE SEQUENCES AND SERIES

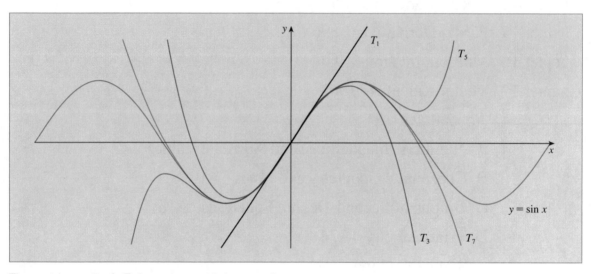

The partial sums T_n of a Taylor series provide better and better approximations to a function as n increases.

Infinite sequences and series were introduced briefly in *A Preview of Calculus* in connection with Zeno's paradoxes and the decimal representation of numbers. Their importance in calculus stems from Newton's idea of representing functions as sums of infinite series. For instance, in finding areas he often integrated a function by first expressing it as a series and then integrating each term of the series. We will pursue his idea in Section 12.10 in order to integrate such functions as e^{-x^2}. (Recall that we have previously been unable to do this.) Many of the functions that arise in mathematical physics and chemistry, such as Bessel functions, are defined as sums of series, so it is important to be familiar with the basic concepts of convergence of infinite sequences and series.

Physicists also use series in another way, as we will see in Section 12.11. In studying fields as diverse as optics, special relativity, and electromagnetism, they analyze phenomena by replacing a function with the first few terms in the series that represents it.

A **sequence** can be thought of as a list of numbers written in a definite order:

$$a_1, \ a_2, \ a_3, \ a_4, \ \ldots, \ a_n, \ldots$$

The number a_1 is called the *first term,* a_2 is the *second term,* and in general a_n is the *nth term.* We will deal exclusively with infinite sequences and so each term a_n will have a successor a_{n+1}.

Notice that for every positive integer n there is a corresponding number a_n and so a sequence can be defined as a function whose domain is the set of positive integers. But we usually write a_n instead of the function notation $f(n)$ for the value of the function at the number n.

> NOTATION The sequence $\{a_1, a_2, a_3, \ldots\}$ is also denoted by
>
> $$\{a_n\} \qquad \text{or} \qquad \{a_n\}_{n=1}^{\infty}$$

EXAMPLE 1 Some sequences can be defined by giving a formula for the nth term. In the following examples we give three descriptions of the sequence: one by using the preceding notation, another by using the defining formula, and a third by writing out the terms of the sequence. Notice that n doesn't have to start at 1.

(a) $\left\{ \dfrac{n}{n+1} \right\}_{n=1}^{\infty}$ $\qquad a_n = \dfrac{n}{n+1}$ $\qquad \left\{ \dfrac{1}{2}, \dfrac{2}{3}, \dfrac{3}{4}, \dfrac{4}{5}, \ldots, \dfrac{n}{n+1}, \ldots \right\}$

(b) $\left\{ \dfrac{(-1)^n(n+1)}{3^n} \right\}$ $\qquad a_n = \dfrac{(-1)^n(n+1)}{3^n}$ $\qquad \left\{ -\dfrac{2}{3}, \dfrac{3}{9}, -\dfrac{4}{27}, \dfrac{5}{81}, \ldots, \dfrac{(-1)^n(n+1)}{3^n}, \ldots \right\}$

(c) $\left\{ \sqrt{n-3} \right\}_{n=3}^{\infty}$ $\qquad a_n = \sqrt{n-3}, \ n \geqslant 3$ $\qquad \left\{ 0, 1, \sqrt{2}, \sqrt{3}, \ldots, \sqrt{n-3}, \ldots \right\}$

(d) $\left\{ \cos \dfrac{n\pi}{6} \right\}_{n=0}^{\infty}$ $\qquad a_n = \cos \dfrac{n\pi}{6}, \ n \geqslant 0$ $\qquad \left\{ 1, \dfrac{\sqrt{3}}{2}, \dfrac{1}{2}, 0, \ldots, \cos \dfrac{n\pi}{6}, \ldots \right\}$ $\qquad$ □

▼ **EXAMPLE 2** Find a formula for the general term a_n of the sequence

$$\left\{ \frac{3}{5}, -\frac{4}{25}, \frac{5}{125}, -\frac{6}{625}, \frac{7}{3125}, \ldots \right\}$$

assuming that the pattern of the first few terms continues.

SOLUTION We are given that

$$a_1 = \frac{3}{5} \qquad a_2 = -\frac{4}{25} \qquad a_3 = \frac{5}{125} \qquad a_4 = -\frac{6}{625} \qquad a_5 = \frac{7}{3125}$$

Notice that the numerators of these fractions start with 3 and increase by 1 whenever we go to the next term. The second term has numerator 4, the third term has numerator 5; in general, the nth term will have numerator $n+2$. The denominators are the powers of 5, so a_n has denominator 5^n. The signs of the terms are alternately positive and negative, so we need to multiply by a power of -1. In Example 1(b) the factor $(-1)^n$ meant we started with a negative term. Here we want to start with a positive term and so we use $(-1)^{n-1}$ or $(-1)^{n+1}$. Therefore

$$a_n = (-1)^{n-1} \frac{n+2}{5^n} \qquad \square$$

EXAMPLE 3 Here are some sequences that don't have a simple defining equation.
(a) The sequence $\{p_n\}$, where p_n is the population of the world as of January 1 in the year n.
(b) If we let a_n be the digit in the nth decimal place of the number e, then $\{a_n\}$ is a well-defined sequence whose first few terms are

$$\{7, 1, 8, 2, 8, 1, 8, 2, 8, 4, 5, \ldots\}$$

(c) The **Fibonacci sequence** $\{f_n\}$ is defined recursively by the conditions

$$f_1 = 1 \qquad f_2 = 1 \qquad f_n = f_{n-1} + f_{n-2} \qquad n \geqslant 3$$

Each term is the sum of the two preceding terms. The first few terms are

$$\{1, 1, 2, 3, 5, 8, 13, 21, \ldots\}$$

This sequence arose when the 13th-century Italian mathematician known as Fibonacci solved a problem concerning the breeding of rabbits (see Exercise 71). $\qquad \square$

A sequence such as the one in Example 1(a), $a_n = n/(n+1)$, can be pictured either by plotting its terms on a number line as in Figure 1 or by plotting its graph as in Figure 2. Note that, since a sequence is a function whose domain is the set of positive integers, its graph consists of isolated points with coordinates

$$(1, a_1) \qquad (2, a_2) \qquad (3, a_3) \qquad \ldots \qquad (n, a_n) \qquad \ldots$$

From Figure 1 or 2 it appears that the terms of the sequence $a_n = n/(n+1)$ are approaching 1 as n becomes large. In fact, the difference

$$1 - \frac{n}{n+1} = \frac{1}{n+1}$$

can be made as small as we like by taking n sufficiently large. We indicate this by writing

$$\lim_{n \to \infty} \frac{n}{n+1} = 1$$

In general, the notation

$$\lim_{n \to \infty} a_n = L$$

means that the terms of the sequence $\{a_n\}$ approach L as n becomes large. Notice that the following definition of the limit of a sequence is very similar to the definition of a limit of a function at infinity given in Section 4.4.

FIGURE 1

FIGURE 2

> **1 DEFINITION** A sequence $\{a_n\}$ has the **limit** L and we write
>
> $$\lim_{n \to \infty} a_n = L \qquad \text{or} \qquad a_n \to L \text{ as } n \to \infty$$
>
> if we can make the terms a_n as close to L as we like by taking n sufficiently large. If $\lim_{n \to \infty} a_n$ exists, we say the sequence **converges** (or is **convergent**). Otherwise, we say the sequence **diverges** (or is **divergent**).

Figure 3 illustrates Definition 1 by showing the graphs of two sequences that have the limit L.

 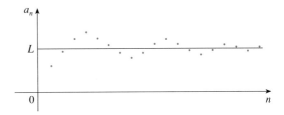

FIGURE 3
Graphs of two
sequences with
$\lim_{n \to \infty} a_n = L$

A more precise version of Definition 1 is as follows.

■ Compare this definition with Definition 4.4.5.

> **2 DEFINITION** A sequence $\{a_n\}$ has the **limit** L and we write
>
> $$\lim_{n \to \infty} a_n = L \qquad \text{or} \qquad a_n \to L \text{ as } n \to \infty$$
>
> if for every $\varepsilon > 0$ there is a corresponding integer N such that
>
> $$\text{if} \quad n > N \quad \text{then} \quad |a_n - L| < \varepsilon$$

Definition 2 is illustrated by Figure 4, in which the terms $a_1, a_2, a_3, \ldots$ are plotted on a number line. No matter how small an interval $(L - \varepsilon, L + \varepsilon)$ is chosen, there exists an N such that all terms of the sequence from a_{N+1} onward must lie in that interval.

FIGURE 4

Another illustration of Definition 2 is given in Figure 5. The points on the graph of $\{a_n\}$ must lie between the horizontal lines $y = L + \varepsilon$ and $y = L - \varepsilon$ if $n > N$. This picture must be valid no matter how small ε is chosen, but usually a smaller ε requires a larger N.

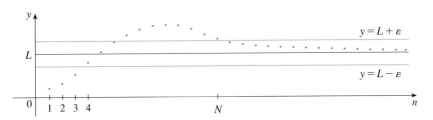

FIGURE 5

If you compare Definition 2 with Definition 4.4.5, you will see that the only difference between $\lim_{n\to\infty} a_n = L$ and $\lim_{x\to\infty} f(x) = L$ is that n is required to be an integer. Thus we have the following theorem, which is illustrated by Figure 6.

> **3 THEOREM** If $\lim_{x\to\infty} f(x) = L$ and $f(n) = a_n$ when n is an integer, then $\lim_{n\to\infty} a_n = L$.

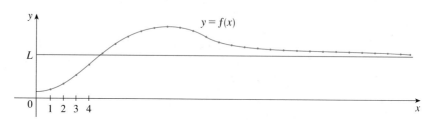

FIGURE 6

In particular, since we know that $\lim_{x\to\infty} (1/x^r) = 0$ when $r > 0$ (Theorem 4.4.4), we have

$$\boxed{4} \qquad \lim_{n\to\infty} \frac{1}{n^r} = 0 \qquad \text{if } r > 0$$

If a_n becomes large as n becomes large, we use the notation $\lim_{n\to\infty} a_n = \infty$. The following precise definition is similar to Definition 4.4.7.

> **5 DEFINITION** $\lim_{n\to\infty} a_n = \infty$ means that for every positive number M there is an integer N such that
>
> $$\text{if} \quad n > N \quad \text{then} \quad a_n > M$$

If $\lim_{n\to\infty} a_n = \infty$, then the sequence $\{a_n\}$ is divergent but in a special way. We say that $\{a_n\}$ diverges to ∞.

The Limit Laws given in Section 2.3 also hold for the limits of sequences and their proofs are similar.

LIMIT LAWS FOR SEQUENCES

If $\{a_n\}$ and $\{b_n\}$ are convergent sequences and c is a constant, then

$$\lim_{n\to\infty} (a_n + b_n) = \lim_{n\to\infty} a_n + \lim_{n\to\infty} b_n$$

$$\lim_{n\to\infty} (a_n - b_n) = \lim_{n\to\infty} a_n - \lim_{n\to\infty} b_n$$

$$\lim_{n\to\infty} ca_n = c \lim_{n\to\infty} a_n \qquad\qquad \lim_{n\to\infty} c = c$$

$$\lim_{n\to\infty} (a_n b_n) = \lim_{n\to\infty} a_n \cdot \lim_{n\to\infty} b_n$$

$$\lim_{n\to\infty} \frac{a_n}{b_n} = \frac{\lim_{n\to\infty} a_n}{\lim_{n\to\infty} b_n} \qquad \text{if } \lim_{n\to\infty} b_n \neq 0$$

$$\lim_{n\to\infty} a_n^p = \left[\lim_{n\to\infty} a_n\right]^p \qquad \text{if } p > 0 \text{ and } a_n > 0$$

The Squeeze Theorem can also be adapted for sequences as follows (see Figure 7).

SQUEEZE THEOREM FOR SEQUENCES

If $a_n \leq b_n \leq c_n$ for $n \geq n_0$ and $\lim\limits_{n \to \infty} a_n = \lim\limits_{n \to \infty} c_n = L$, then $\lim\limits_{n \to \infty} b_n = L$.

Another useful fact about limits of sequences is given by the following theorem, whose proof is left as Exercise 75.

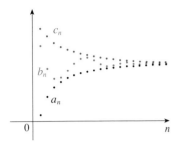

FIGURE 7
The sequence $\{b_n\}$ is squeezed between the sequences $\{a_n\}$ and $\{c_n\}$.

| 6 | **THEOREM** | If $\lim\limits_{n \to \infty} |a_n| = 0$, then $\lim\limits_{n \to \infty} a_n = 0$. |

EXAMPLE 4 Find $\lim\limits_{n \to \infty} \dfrac{n}{n + 1}$.

SOLUTION The method is similar to the one we used in Section 4.4: Divide numerator and denominator by the highest power of n and then use the Limit Laws.

$$\lim_{n \to \infty} \frac{n}{n + 1} = \lim_{n \to \infty} \frac{1}{1 + \dfrac{1}{n}} = \frac{\lim\limits_{n \to \infty} 1}{\lim\limits_{n \to \infty} 1 + \lim\limits_{n \to \infty} \dfrac{1}{n}}$$

$$= \frac{1}{1 + 0} = 1$$

■ This shows that the guess we made earlier from Figures 1 and 2 was correct.

Here we used Equation 4 with $r = 1$. □

EXAMPLE 5 Calculate $\lim\limits_{n \to \infty} \dfrac{\ln n}{n}$.

SOLUTION Notice that both numerator and denominator approach infinity as $n \to \infty$. We can't apply l'Hospital's Rule directly because it applies not to sequences but to functions of a real variable. However, we can apply l'Hospital's Rule to the related function $f(x) = (\ln x)/x$ and obtain

$$\lim_{x \to \infty} \frac{\ln x}{x} = \lim_{x \to \infty} \frac{1/x}{1} = 0$$

Therefore, by Theorem 3, we have

$$\lim_{n \to \infty} \frac{\ln n}{n} = 0$$ □

EXAMPLE 6 Determine whether the sequence $a_n = (-1)^n$ is convergent or divergent.

SOLUTION If we write out the terms of the sequence, we obtain

$$\{-1, 1, -1, 1, -1, 1, -1, \ldots\}$$

The graph of this sequence is shown in Figure 8. Since the terms oscillate between 1 and -1 infinitely often, a_n does not approach any number. Thus $\lim\limits_{n \to \infty} (-1)^n$ does not exist; that is, the sequence $\{(-1)^n\}$ is divergent. □

FIGURE 8

■ The graph of the sequence in Example 7 is shown in Figure 9 and supports our answer.

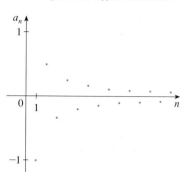

FIGURE 9

EXAMPLE 7 Evaluate $\lim\limits_{n\to\infty} \dfrac{(-1)^n}{n}$ if it exists.

SOLUTION

$$\lim_{n\to\infty} \left| \frac{(-1)^n}{n} \right| = \lim_{n\to\infty} \frac{1}{n} = 0$$

Therefore, by Theorem 6,

$$\lim_{n\to\infty} \frac{(-1)^n}{n} = 0$$

The following theorem says that if we apply a continuous function to the terms of a convergent sequence, the result is also convergent. The proof is left as Exercise 76.

---

7 THEOREM If $\lim\limits_{n\to\infty} a_n = L$ and the function f is continuous at L, then

$$\lim_{n\to\infty} f(a_n) = f(L)$$

EXAMPLE 8 Find $\lim\limits_{n\to\infty} \sin(\pi/n)$.

SOLUTION Because the sine function is continuous at 0, Theorem 7 enables us to write

$$\lim_{n\to\infty} \sin(\pi/n) = \sin\left(\lim_{n\to\infty} (\pi/n) \right) = \sin 0 = 0$$

▼ EXAMPLE 9 Discuss the convergence of the sequence $a_n = n!/n^n$, where $n! = 1 \cdot 2 \cdot 3 \cdot \cdots \cdot n$.

SOLUTION Both numerator and denominator approach infinity as $n \to \infty$, but here we have no corresponding function for use with l'Hospital's Rule ($x!$ is not defined when x is not an integer). Let's write out a few terms to get a feeling for what happens to a_n as n gets large:

$$a_1 = 1 \qquad a_2 = \frac{1 \cdot 2}{2 \cdot 2} \qquad a_3 = \frac{1 \cdot 2 \cdot 3}{3 \cdot 3 \cdot 3}$$

$$\boxed{8} \qquad a_n = \frac{1 \cdot 2 \cdot 3 \cdot \cdots \cdot n}{n \cdot n \cdot n \cdot \cdots \cdot n}$$

It appears from these expressions and the graph in Figure 10 that the terms are decreasing and perhaps approach 0. To confirm this, observe from Equation 8 that

$$a_n = \frac{1}{n} \left(\frac{2 \cdot 3 \cdot \cdots \cdot n}{n \cdot n \cdot \cdots \cdot n} \right)$$

Notice that the expression in parentheses is at most 1 because the numerator is less than (or equal to) the denominator. So

$$0 < a_n \leq \frac{1}{n}$$

We know that $1/n \to 0$ as $n \to \infty$. Therefore $a_n \to 0$ as $n \to \infty$ by the Squeeze Theorem.

■ CREATING GRAPHS OF SEQUENCES

Some computer algebra systems have special commands that enable us to create sequences and graph them directly. With most graphing calculators, however, sequences can be graphed by using parametric equations. For instance, the sequence in Example 9 can be graphed by entering the parametric equations

$$x = t \qquad y = t!/t^t$$

and graphing in dot mode, starting with $t = 1$ and setting the t-step equal to 1. The result is shown in Figure 10.

FIGURE 10

V EXAMPLE 10 For what values of r is the sequence $\{r^n\}$ convergent?

SOLUTION We know from Section 4.4 and the graphs of the exponential functions in Section 7.2 (or Section 7.4*) that $\lim_{x\to\infty} a^x = \infty$ for $a > 1$ and $\lim_{x\to\infty} a^x = 0$ for $0 < a < 1$. Therefore, putting $a = r$ and using Theorem 3, we have

$$\lim_{n\to\infty} r^n = \begin{cases} \infty & \text{if } r > 1 \\ 0 & \text{if } 0 < r < 1 \end{cases}$$

It is obvious that

$$\lim_{n\to\infty} 1^n = 1 \quad \text{and} \quad \lim_{n\to\infty} 0^n = 0$$

If $-1 < r < 0$, then $0 < |r| < 1$, so

$$\lim_{n\to\infty} |r^n| = \lim_{n\to\infty} |r|^n = 0$$

and therefore $\lim_{n\to\infty} r^n = 0$ by Theorem 6. If $r \leqslant -1$, then $\{r^n\}$ diverges as in Example 6. Figure 11 shows the graphs for various values of r. (The case $r = -1$ is shown in Figure 8.)

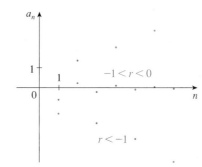

FIGURE 11
The sequence $a_n = r^n$

The results of Example 10 are summarized for future use as follows.

---

9 The sequence $\{r^n\}$ is convergent if $-1 < r \leqslant 1$ and divergent for all other values of r.

$$\lim_{n\to\infty} r^n = \begin{cases} 0 & \text{if } -1 < r < 1 \\ 1 & \text{if } r = 1 \end{cases}$$

---

10 DEFINITION A sequence $\{a_n\}$ is called **increasing** if $a_n < a_{n+1}$ for all $n \geqslant 1$, that is, $a_1 < a_2 < a_3 < \cdots$. It is called **decreasing** if $a_n > a_{n+1}$ for all $n \geqslant 1$. It is called **monotonic** if it is either increasing or decreasing.

EXAMPLE 11 The sequence $\left\{\dfrac{3}{n+5}\right\}$ is decreasing because

■ The right side is smaller because it has a larger denominator.

$$\frac{3}{n+5} > \frac{3}{(n+1)+5} = \frac{3}{n+6}$$

and so $a_n > a_{n+1}$ for all $n \geqslant 1$.

EXAMPLE 12 Show that the sequence $a_n = \dfrac{n}{n^2 + 1}$ is decreasing.

SOLUTION 1 We must show that $a_{n+1} < a_n$, that is,

$$\frac{n + 1}{(n + 1)^2 + 1} < \frac{n}{n^2 + 1}$$

This inequality is equivalent to the one we get by cross-multiplication:

$$\frac{n + 1}{(n + 1)^2 + 1} < \frac{n}{n^2 + 1} \iff (n + 1)(n^2 + 1) < n[(n + 1)^2 + 1]$$

$$\iff n^3 + n^2 + n + 1 < n^3 + 2n^2 + 2n$$

$$\iff 1 < n^2 + n$$

Since $n \geq 1$, we know that the inequality $n^2 + n > 1$ is true. Therefore $a_{n+1} < a_n$ and so $\{a_n\}$ is decreasing.

SOLUTION 2 Consider the function $f(x) = \dfrac{x}{x^2 + 1}$:

$$f'(x) = \frac{x^2 + 1 - 2x^2}{(x^2 + 1)^2} = \frac{1 - x^2}{(x^2 + 1)^2} < 0 \qquad \text{whenever } x^2 > 1$$

Thus f is decreasing on $(1, \infty)$ and so $f(n) > f(n + 1)$. Therefore $\{a_n\}$ is decreasing. ☐

---

11 **DEFINITION** A sequence $\{a_n\}$ is **bounded above** if there is a number M such that

$$a_n \leq M \qquad \text{for all } n \geq 1$$

It is **bounded below** if there is a number m such that

$$m \leq a_n \qquad \text{for all } n \geq 1$$

If it is bounded above and below, then $\{a_n\}$ is a **bounded sequence**.

For instance, the sequence $a_n = n$ is bounded below ($a_n > 0$) but not above. The sequence $a_n = n/(n + 1)$ is bounded because $0 < a_n < 1$ for all n.

We know that not every bounded sequence is convergent [for instance, the sequence $a_n = (-1)^n$ satisfies $-1 \leq a_n \leq 1$ but is divergent from Example 6] and not every monotonic sequence is convergent ($a_n = n \rightarrow \infty$). But if a sequence is both bounded *and* monotonic, then it must be convergent. This fact is proved as Theorem 12, but intuitively you can understand why it is true by looking at Figure 12. If $\{a_n\}$ is increasing and $a_n \leq M$ for all n, then the terms are forced to crowd together and approach some number L.

The proof of Theorem 12 is based on the **Completeness Axiom** for the set $\mathbb{R}$ of real numbers, which says that if S is a nonempty set of real numbers that has an upper bound M ($x \leq M$ for all x in S), then S has a **least upper bound** b. (This means that b is an upper bound for S, but if M is any other upper bound, then $b \leq M$.) The Completeness Axiom is an expression of the fact that there is no gap or hole in the real number line.

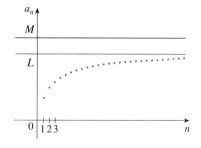

FIGURE 12

> **12 MONOTONIC SEQUENCE THEOREM** Every bounded, monotonic sequence is convergent.

PROOF Suppose $\{a_n\}$ is an increasing sequence. Since $\{a_n\}$ is bounded, the set $S = \{a_n \mid n \geq 1\}$ has an upper bound. By the Completeness Axiom it has a least upper bound L. Given $\varepsilon > 0$, $L - \varepsilon$ is *not* an upper bound for S (since L is the *least* upper bound). Therefore

$$a_N > L - \varepsilon \qquad \text{for some integer } N$$

But the sequence is increasing so $a_n \geq a_N$ for every $n > N$. Thus if $n > N$, we have

$$a_n > L - \varepsilon$$

so

$$0 \leq L - a_n < \varepsilon$$

since $a_n \leq L$. Thus

$$\left| L - a_n \right| < \varepsilon \qquad \text{whenever } n > N$$

so $\lim_{n \to \infty} a_n = L$.

A similar proof (using the greatest lower bound) works if $\{a_n\}$ is decreasing. □

The proof of Theorem 12 shows that a sequence that is increasing and bounded above is convergent. (Likewise, a decreasing sequence that is bounded below is convergent.) This fact is used many times in dealing with infinite series.

EXAMPLE 13 Investigate the sequence $\{a_n\}$ defined by the recurrence relation

$$a_1 = 2 \qquad a_{n+1} = \tfrac{1}{2}(a_n + 6) \qquad \text{for } n = 1, 2, 3, \ldots$$

SOLUTION We begin by computing the first several terms:

$$a_1 = 2 \qquad\qquad a_2 = \tfrac{1}{2}(2 + 6) = 4 \qquad a_3 = \tfrac{1}{2}(4 + 6) = 5$$

$$a_4 = \tfrac{1}{2}(5 + 6) = 5.5 \qquad a_5 = 5.75 \qquad\qquad a_6 = 5.875$$

$$a_7 = 5.9375 \qquad\qquad a_8 = 5.96875 \qquad\qquad a_9 = 5.984375$$

■ Mathematical induction is often used in dealing with recursive sequences. See page 55 for a discussion of the Principle of Mathematical Induction.

These initial terms suggest that the sequence is increasing and the terms are approaching 6. To confirm that the sequence is increasing, we use mathematical induction to show that $a_{n+1} > a_n$ for all $n \geq 1$. This is true for $n = 1$ because $a_2 = 4 > a_1$. If we assume that it is true for $n = k$, then we have

$$a_{k+1} > a_k$$

so

$$a_{k+1} + 6 > a_k + 6$$

and

$$\tfrac{1}{2}(a_{k+1} + 6) > \tfrac{1}{2}(a_k + 6)$$

Thus

$$a_{k+2} > a_{k+1}$$

We have deduced that $a_{n+1} > a_n$ is true for $n = k + 1$. Therefore the inequality is true for all n by induction.

Next we verify that $\{a_n\}$ is bounded by showing that $a_n < 6$ for all n. (Since the sequence is increasing, we already know that it has a lower bound: $a_n \geq a_1 = 2$ for all n.) We know that $a_1 < 6$, so the assertion is true for $n = 1$. Suppose it is true for $n = k$. Then

$$a_k < 6$$

so

$$a_k + 6 < 12$$

$$\tfrac{1}{2}(a_k + 6) < \tfrac{1}{2}(12) = 6$$

Thus

$$a_{k+1} < 6$$

This shows, by mathematical induction, that $a_n < 6$ for all n.

Since the sequence $\{a_n\}$ is increasing and bounded, Theorem 12 guarantees that it has a limit. The theorem doesn't tell us what the value of the limit is. But now that we know $L = \lim_{n \to \infty} a_n$ exists, we can use the recurrence relation to write

$$\lim_{n \to \infty} a_{n+1} = \lim_{n \to \infty} \tfrac{1}{2}(a_n + 6) = \tfrac{1}{2}\left(\lim_{n \to \infty} a_n + 6\right) = \tfrac{1}{2}(L + 6)$$

■ A proof of this fact is requested in Exercise 58.

Since $a_n \to L$, it follows that $a_{n+1} \to L$, too (as $n \to \infty$, $n + 1 \to \infty$ too). So we have

$$L = \tfrac{1}{2}(L + 6)$$

Solving this equation for L, we get $L = 6$, as predicted. ☐

12.1 EXERCISES

1. (a) What is a sequence?
(b) What does it mean to say that $\lim_{n \to \infty} a_n = 8$?
(c) What does it mean to say that $\lim_{n \to \infty} a_n = \infty$?

2. (a) What is a convergent sequence? Give two examples.
(b) What is a divergent sequence? Give two examples.

3–8 List the first five terms of the sequence.

3. $a_n = 1 - (0.2)^n$

4. $a_n = \dfrac{n + 1}{3n - 1}$

5. $a_n = \dfrac{3(-1)^n}{n!}$

6. $\{2 \cdot 4 \cdot 6 \cdot \ \cdots \ \cdot (2n)\}$

7. $a_1 = 3, \quad a_{n+1} = 2a_n - 1$

8. $a_1 = 4, \quad a_{n+1} = \dfrac{a_n}{a_n - 1}$

9–14 Find a formula for the general term a_n of the sequence, assuming that the pattern of the first few terms continues.

9. $\left\{1, \tfrac{1}{3}, \tfrac{1}{5}, \tfrac{1}{7}, \tfrac{1}{9}, \ldots\right\}$

10. $\left\{1, \tfrac{1}{3}, \tfrac{1}{9}, \tfrac{1}{27}, \tfrac{1}{81}, \ldots\right\}$

11. $\{2, 7, 12, 17, \ldots\}$

12. $\left\{-\tfrac{1}{4}, \tfrac{2}{9}, -\tfrac{3}{16}, \tfrac{4}{25}, \ldots\right\}$

13. $\left\{1, -\tfrac{2}{3}, \tfrac{4}{9}, -\tfrac{8}{27}, \ldots\right\}$

14. $\{5, 1, 5, 1, 5, 1, \ldots\}$

15. List the first six terms of the sequence defined by

$$a_n = \frac{n}{2n + 1}$$

Does the sequence appear to have a limit? If so, find it.

16. List the first nine terms of the sequence $\{\cos(n\pi/3)\}$. Does this sequence appear to have a limit? If so, find it. If not, explain why.

17–46 Determine whether the sequence converges or diverges. If it converges, find the limit.

17. $a_n = 1 - (0.2)^n$

18. $a_n = \dfrac{n^3}{n^3 + 1}$

19. $a_n = \dfrac{3 + 5n^2}{n + n^2}$

20. $a_n = \dfrac{n^3}{n + 1}$

21. $a_n = e^{1/n}$

22. $a_n = \dfrac{3^{n+2}}{5^n}$

23. $a_n = \tan\left(\dfrac{2n\pi}{1 + 8n}\right)$

24. $a_n = \sqrt{\dfrac{n + 1}{9n + 1}}$

25. $a_n = \dfrac{(-1)^{n-1}n}{n^2 + 1}$

26. $a_n = \dfrac{(-1)^n n^3}{n^3 + 2n^2 + 1}$

27. $a_n = \cos(n/2)$

28. $a_n = \cos(2/n)$

29. $\left\{\dfrac{(2n - 1)!}{(2n + 1)!}\right\}$

30. $\{\arctan 2n\}$

31. $\left\{\dfrac{e^n + e^{-n}}{e^{2n} - 1}\right\}$

32. $\left\{\dfrac{\ln n}{\ln 2n}\right\}$

33. $\{n^2 e^{-n}\}$

34. $\{n \cos n\pi\}$

35. $a_n = \dfrac{\cos^2 n}{2^n}$

36. $a_n = \ln(n + 1) - \ln n$

37. $a_n = n \sin(1/n)$

38. $a_n = \sqrt[n]{2^{1+3n}}$

39. $a_n = \left(1 + \dfrac{2}{n}\right)^n$

40. $a_n = \dfrac{\sin 2n}{1 + \sqrt{n}}$

41. $a_n = \ln(2n^2 + 1) - \ln(n^2 + 1)$

42. $a_n = \dfrac{(\ln n)^2}{n}$

43. $\{0, 1, 0, 0, 1, 0, 0, 0, 1, \ldots\}$

44. $\left\{1, \frac{1}{3}, \frac{1}{2}, \frac{1}{4}, \frac{1}{3}, \frac{1}{5}, \frac{1}{4}, \frac{1}{6}, \ldots\right\}$

45. $a_n = \dfrac{n!}{2^n}$

46. $a_n = \dfrac{(-3)^n}{n!}$

47–53 Use a graph of the sequence to decide whether the sequence is convergent or divergent. If the sequence is convergent, guess the value of the limit from the graph and then prove your guess. (See the margin note on page 716 for advice on graphing sequences.)

47. $a_n = 1 + (-2/e)^n$

48. $a_n = \sqrt{n} \sin(\pi/\sqrt{n})$

49. $a_n = \sqrt{\dfrac{3 + 2n^2}{8n^2 + n}}$

50. $a_n = \sqrt[n]{3^n + 5^n}$

51. $a_n = \dfrac{n^2 \cos n}{1 + n^2}$

52. $a_n = \dfrac{1 \cdot 3 \cdot 5 \cdot \cdots \cdot (2n - 1)}{n!}$

53. $a_n = \dfrac{1 \cdot 3 \cdot 5 \cdot \cdots \cdot (2n - 1)}{(2n)^n}$

---

54. (a) Determine whether the sequence defined as follows is convergent or divergent:

$$a_1 = 1 \qquad a_{n+1} = 4 - a_n \qquad \text{for } n \geqslant 1$$

(b) What happens if the first term is $a_1 = 2$?

55. If \$1000 is invested at 6% interest, compounded annually, then after n years the investment is worth $a_n = 1000(1.06)^n$ dollars.
(a) Find the first five terms of the sequence $\{a_n\}$.
(b) Is the sequence convergent or divergent? Explain.

56. Find the first 40 terms of the sequence defined by

$$a_{n+1} = \begin{cases} \frac{1}{2}a_n & \text{if } a_n \text{ is an even number} \\ 3a_n + 1 & \text{if } a_n \text{ is an odd number} \end{cases}$$

and $a_1 = 11$. Do the same if $a_1 = 25$. Make a conjecture about this type of sequence.

57. For what values of r is the sequence $\{nr^n\}$ convergent?

58. (a) If $\{a_n\}$ is convergent, show that

$$\lim_{n \to \infty} a_{n+1} = \lim_{n \to \infty} a_n$$

(b) A sequence $\{a_n\}$ is defined by $a_1 = 1$ and $a_{n+1} = 1/(1 + a_n)$ for $n \geqslant 1$. Assuming that $\{a_n\}$ is convergent, find its limit.

59. Suppose you know that $\{a_n\}$ is a decreasing sequence and all its terms lie between the numbers 5 and 8. Explain why the sequence has a limit. What can you say about the value of the limit?

60–66 Determine whether the sequence is increasing, decreasing, or not monotonic. Is the sequence bounded?

60. $a_n = (-2)^{n+1}$

61. $a_n = \dfrac{1}{2n + 3}$

62. $a_n = \dfrac{2n - 3}{3n + 4}$

63. $a_n = n(-1)^n$

64. $a_n = ne^{-n}$

65. $a_n = \dfrac{n}{n^2 + 1}$

66. $a_n = n + \dfrac{1}{n}$

---

67. Find the limit of the sequence

$$\left\{\sqrt{2}, \sqrt{2\sqrt{2}}, \sqrt{2\sqrt{2\sqrt{2}}}, \ldots\right\}$$

68. A sequence $\{a_n\}$ is given by $a_1 = \sqrt{2}$, $a_{n+1} = \sqrt{2 + a_n}$.
(a) By induction or otherwise, show that $\{a_n\}$ is increasing and bounded above by 3. Apply the Monotonic Sequence Theorem to show that $\lim_{n \to \infty} a_n$ exists.
(b) Find $\lim_{n \to \infty} a_n$.

69. Show that the sequence defined by

$$a_1 = 1 \qquad a_{n+1} = 3 - \frac{1}{a_n}$$

is increasing and $a_n < 3$ for all n. Deduce that $\{a_n\}$ is convergent and find its limit.

70. Show that the sequence defined by

$$a_1 = 2 \qquad a_{n+1} = \frac{1}{3 - a_n}$$

satisfies $0 < a_n \le 2$ and is decreasing. Deduce that the sequence is convergent and find its limit.

71. (a) Fibonacci posed the following problem: Suppose that rabbits live forever and that every month each pair produces a new pair which becomes productive at age 2 months. If we start with one newborn pair, how many pairs of rabbits will we have in the nth month? Show that the answer is f_n, where $\{f_n\}$ is the Fibonacci sequence defined in Example 3(c).
(b) Let $a_n = f_{n+1}/f_n$ and show that $a_{n-1} = 1 + 1/a_{n-2}$. Assuming that $\{a_n\}$ is convergent, find its limit.

72. (a) Let $a_1 = a$, $a_2 = f(a)$, $a_3 = f(a_2) = f(f(a))$, ..., $a_{n+1} = f(a_n)$, where f is a continuous function. If $\lim_{n \to \infty} a_n = L$, show that $f(L) = L$.
(b) Illustrate part (a) by taking $f(x) = \cos x$, $a = 1$, and estimating the value of L to five decimal places.

73. (a) Use a graph to guess the value of the limit

$$\lim_{n \to \infty} \frac{n^5}{n!}$$

(b) Use a graph of the sequence in part (a) to find the smallest values of N that correspond to $\varepsilon = 0.1$ and $\varepsilon = 0.001$ in Definition 2.

74. Use Definition 2 directly to prove that $\lim_{n \to \infty} r^n = 0$ when $|r| < 1$.

75. Prove Theorem 6.
[*Hint:* Use either Definition 2 or the Squeeze Theorem.]

76. Prove Theorem 7.

77. Prove that if $\lim_{n \to \infty} a_n = 0$ and $\{b_n\}$ is bounded, then $\lim_{n \to \infty} (a_n b_n) = 0$.

78. Let $a_n = \left(1 + \frac{1}{n}\right)^n$.
(a) Show that if $0 \le a < b$, then

$$\frac{b^{n+1} - a^{n+1}}{b - a} < (n + 1)b^n$$

(b) Deduce that $b^n[(n + 1)a - nb] < a^{n+1}$.
(c) Use $a = 1 + 1/(n + 1)$ and $b = 1 + 1/n$ in part (b) to show that $\{a_n\}$ is increasing.
(d) Use $a = 1$ and $b = 1 + 1/(2n)$ in part (b) to show that $a_{2n} < 4$.

(e) Use parts (c) and (d) to show that $a_n < 4$ for all n.
(f) Use Theorem 12 to show that $\lim_{n \to \infty} (1 + 1/n)^n$ exists. (The limit is e. See Equation 7.4.9 or 7.4*.9.)

79. Let a and b be positive numbers with $a > b$. Let a_1 be their arithmetic mean and b_1 their geometric mean:

$$a_1 = \frac{a + b}{2} \qquad b_1 = \sqrt{ab}$$

Repeat this process so that, in general,

$$a_{n+1} = \frac{a_n + b_n}{2} \qquad b_{n+1} = \sqrt{a_n b_n}$$

(a) Use mathematical induction to show that

$$a_n > a_{n+1} > b_{n+1} > b_n$$

(b) Deduce that both $\{a_n\}$ and $\{b_n\}$ are convergent.
(c) Show that $\lim_{n \to \infty} a_n = \lim_{n \to \infty} b_n$. Gauss called the common value of these limits the **arithmetic-geometric mean** of the numbers a and b.

80. (a) Show that if $\lim_{n \to \infty} a_{2n} = L$ and $\lim_{n \to \infty} a_{2n+1} = L$, then $\{a_n\}$ is convergent and $\lim_{n \to \infty} a_n = L$.
(b) If $a_1 = 1$ and

$$a_{n+1} = 1 + \frac{1}{1 + a_n}$$

find the first eight terms of the sequence $\{a_n\}$. Then use part (a) to show that $\lim_{n \to \infty} a_n = \sqrt{2}$. This gives the **continued fraction expansion**

$$\sqrt{2} = 1 + \cfrac{1}{2 + \cfrac{1}{2 + \cdots}}$$

81. The size of an undisturbed fish population has been modeled by the formula

$$p_{n+1} = \frac{bp_n}{a + p_n}$$

where p_n is the fish population after n years and a and b are positive constants that depend on the species and its environment. Suppose that the population in year 0 is $p_0 > 0$.
(a) Show that if $\{p_n\}$ is convergent, then the only possible values for its limit are 0 and $b - a$.
(b) Show that $p_{n+1} < (b/a)p_n$.
(c) Use part (b) to show that if $a > b$, then $\lim_{n \to \infty} p_n = 0$; in other words, the population dies out.
(d) Now assume that $a < b$. Show that if $p_0 < b - a$, then $\{p_n\}$ is increasing and $0 < p_n < b - a$. Show also that if $p_0 > b - a$, then $\{p_n\}$ is decreasing and $p_n > b - a$. Deduce that if $a < b$, then $\lim_{n \to \infty} p_n = b - a$.

LABORATORY
PROJECT

[CAS] LOGISTIC SEQUENCES

A sequence that arises in ecology as a model for population growth is defined by the **logistic difference equation**

$$p_{n+1} = kp_n(1 - p_n)$$

where p_n measures the size of the population of the nth generation of a single species. To keep the numbers manageable, p_n is a fraction of the maximal size of the population, so $0 \leq p_n \leq 1$. Notice that the form of this equation is similar to the logistic differential equation in Section 10.4. The discrete model—with sequences instead of continuous functions—is preferable for modeling insect populations, where mating and death occur in a periodic fashion.

An ecologist is interested in predicting the size of the population as time goes on, and asks these questions: Will it stabilize at a limiting value? Will it change in a cyclical fashion? Or will it exhibit random behavior?

Write a program to compute the first n terms of this sequence starting with an initial population p_0, where $0 < p_0 < 1$. Use this program to do the following.

1. Calculate 20 or 30 terms of the sequence for $p_0 = \frac{1}{2}$ and for two values of k such that $1 < k < 3$. Graph the sequences. Do they appear to converge? Repeat for a different value of p_0 between 0 and 1. Does the limit depend on the choice of p_0? Does it depend on the choice of k?

2. Calculate terms of the sequence for a value of k between 3 and 3.4 and plot them. What do you notice about the behavior of the terms?

3. Experiment with values of k between 3.4 and 3.5. What happens to the terms?

4. For values of k between 3.6 and 4, compute and plot at least 100 terms and comment on the behavior of the sequence. What happens if you change p_0 by 0.001? This type of behavior is called *chaotic* and is exhibited by insect populations under certain conditions.

12.2 SERIES

If we try to add the terms of an infinite sequence $\{a_n\}_{n=1}^{\infty}$ we get an expression of the form

$$\boxed{1} \qquad a_1 + a_2 + a_3 + \cdots + a_n + \cdots$$

which is called an **infinite series** (or just a **series**) and is denoted, for short, by the symbol

$$\sum_{n=1}^{\infty} a_n \qquad \text{or} \qquad \sum a_n$$

But does it make sense to talk about the sum of infinitely many terms?

It would be impossible to find a finite sum for the series

$$1 + 2 + 3 + 4 + 5 + \cdots + n + \cdots$$

because if we start adding the terms we get the cumulative sums 1, 3, 6, 10, 15, 21, ... and, after the nth term, we get $n(n + 1)/2$, which becomes very large as n increases.

However, if we start to add the terms of the series

$$\frac{1}{2} + \frac{1}{4} + \frac{1}{8} + \frac{1}{16} + \frac{1}{32} + \frac{1}{64} + \cdots + \frac{1}{2^n} + \cdots$$

n	Sum of first n terms
1	0.50000000
2	0.75000000
3	0.87500000
4	0.93750000
5	0.96875000
6	0.98437500
7	0.99218750
10	0.99902344
15	0.99996948
20	0.99999905
25	0.99999997

we get $\frac{1}{2}, \frac{3}{4}, \frac{7}{8}, \frac{15}{16}, \frac{31}{32}, \frac{63}{64}, \ldots, 1 - 1/2^n, \ldots$. The table shows that as we add more and more terms, these *partial sums* become closer and closer to 1. (See also Figure 11 in *A Preview of Calculus,* page 7.) In fact, by adding sufficiently many terms of the series we can make the partial sums as close as we like to 1. So it seems reasonable to say that the sum of this infinite series is 1 and to write

$$\sum_{n=1}^{\infty} \frac{1}{2^n} = \frac{1}{2} + \frac{1}{4} + \frac{1}{8} + \frac{1}{16} + \cdots + \frac{1}{2^n} + \cdots = 1$$

We use a similar idea to determine whether or not a general series (1) has a sum. We consider the **partial sums**

$$s_1 = a_1$$

$$s_2 = a_1 + a_2$$

$$s_3 = a_1 + a_2 + a_3$$

$$s_4 = a_1 + a_2 + a_3 + a_4$$

and, in general,

$$s_n = a_1 + a_2 + a_3 + \cdots + a_n = \sum_{i=1}^{n} a_i$$

These partial sums form a new sequence $\{s_n\}$, which may or may not have a limit. If $\lim_{n\to\infty} s_n = s$ exists (as a finite number), then, as in the preceding example, we call it the sum of the infinite series $\Sigma\, a_n$.

---

2 **DEFINITION** Given a series $\sum_{n=1}^{\infty} a_n = a_1 + a_2 + a_3 + \cdots$, let s_n denote its nth partial sum:

$$s_n = \sum_{i=1}^{n} a_i = a_1 + a_2 + \cdots + a_n$$

If the sequence $\{s_n\}$ is convergent and $\lim_{n\to\infty} s_n = s$ exists as a real number, then the series $\Sigma\, a_n$ is called **convergent** and we write

$$a_1 + a_2 + \cdots + a_n + \cdots = s \qquad \text{or} \qquad \sum_{n=1}^{\infty} a_n = s$$

The number s is called the **sum** of the series. Otherwise, the series is called **divergent**.

Thus the sum of a series is the limit of the sequence of partial sums. So when we write $\sum_{n=1}^{\infty} a_n = s$, we mean that by adding sufficiently many terms of the series we can get as close as we like to the number s. Notice that

$$\sum_{n=1}^{\infty} a_n = \lim_{n\to\infty} \sum_{i=1}^{n} a_i$$

■ Compare with the improper integral

$$\int_1^{\infty} f(x)\, dx = \lim_{t\to\infty} \int_1^t f(x)\, dx$$

To find this integral, we integrate from 1 to t and then let $t \to \infty$. For a series, we sum from 1 to n and then let $n \to \infty$.

EXAMPLE 1 An important example of an infinite series is the **geometric series**

$$a + ar + ar^2 + ar^3 + \cdots + ar^{n-1} + \cdots = \sum_{n=1}^{\infty} ar^{n-1} \qquad a \neq 0$$

Each term is obtained from the preceding one by multiplying it by the common ratio r. (We have already considered the special case where $a = \frac{1}{2}$ and $r = \frac{1}{2}$ on page 723.)

If $r = 1$, then $s_n = a + a + \cdots + a = na \to \pm\infty$. Since $\lim_{n\to\infty} s_n$ doesn't exist, the geometric series diverges in this case.

If $r \neq 1$, we have

$$s_n = a + ar + ar^2 + \cdots + ar^{n-1}$$

Figure 1 provides a geometric demonstration of the result in Example 1. If the triangles are constructed as shown and s is the sum of the series, then, by similar triangles,

$$\frac{s}{a} = \frac{a}{a - ar} \qquad \text{so} \qquad s = \frac{a}{1 - r}$$

and

$$rs_n = \qquad ar + ar^2 + \cdots + ar^{n-1} + ar^n$$

Subtracting these equations, we get

$$s_n - rs_n = a - ar^n$$

3

$$s_n = \frac{a(1 - r^n)}{1 - r}$$

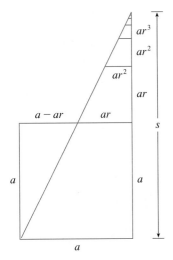

FIGURE 1

If $-1 < r < 1$, we know from (12.1.9) that $r^n \to 0$ as $n \to \infty$, so

$$\lim_{n\to\infty} s_n = \lim_{n\to\infty} \frac{a(1 - r^n)}{1 - r} = \frac{a}{1 - r} - \frac{a}{1 - r} \lim_{n\to\infty} r^n = \frac{a}{1 - r}$$

Thus when $|r| < 1$ the geometric series is convergent and its sum is $a/(1 - r)$.

If $r \leq -1$ or $r > 1$, the sequence $\{r^n\}$ is divergent by (12.1.9) and so, by Equation 3, $\lim_{n\to\infty} s_n$ does not exist. Therefore the geometric series diverges in those cases. $\square$

We summarize the results of Example 1 as follows.

> 4   The geometric series
>
> $$\sum_{n=1}^{\infty} ar^{n-1} = a + ar + ar^2 + \cdots$$
>
> is convergent if $|r| < 1$ and its sum is
>
> $$\sum_{n=1}^{\infty} ar^{n-1} = \frac{a}{1 - r} \qquad |r| < 1$$
>
> If $|r| \geq 1$, the geometric series is divergent.

In words: The sum of a convergent geometric series is

$$\frac{\text{first term}}{1 - \text{common ratio}}$$

▼ EXAMPLE 2 Find the sum of the geometric series

$$5 - \tfrac{10}{3} + \tfrac{20}{9} - \tfrac{40}{27} + \cdots$$

SOLUTION The first term is $a = 5$ and the common ratio is $r = -\frac{2}{3}$. Since $|r| = \frac{2}{3} < 1$, the series is convergent by (4) and its sum is

$$5 - \frac{10}{3} + \frac{20}{9} - \frac{40}{27} + \cdots = \frac{5}{1 - \left(-\frac{2}{3}\right)} = \frac{5}{\frac{5}{3}} = 3 \qquad \square$$

■ What do we really mean when we say that the sum of the series in Example 2 is 3? Of course, we can't literally add an infinite number of terms, one by one. But, according to Definition 2, the total sum is the limit of the sequence of partial sums. So, by taking the sum of sufficiently many terms, we can get as close as we like to the number 3. The table shows the first ten partial sums s_n and the graph in Figure 2 shows how the sequence of partial sums approaches 3.

n	s_n
1	5.000000
2	1.666667
3	3.888889
4	2.407407
5	3.395062
6	2.736626
7	3.175583
8	2.882945
9	3.078037
10	2.947975

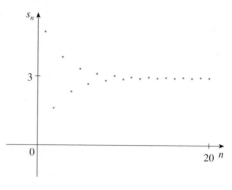

FIGURE 2

EXAMPLE 3 Is the series $\displaystyle\sum_{n=1}^{\infty} 2^{2n}3^{1-n}$ convergent or divergent?

SOLUTION Let's rewrite the nth term of the series in the form ar^{n-1}:

$$\sum_{n=1}^{\infty} 2^{2n}3^{1-n} = \sum_{n=1}^{\infty} (2^2)^n 3^{-(n-1)} = \sum_{n=1}^{\infty} \frac{4^n}{3^{n-1}} = \sum_{n=1}^{\infty} 4\left(\tfrac{4}{3}\right)^{n-1}$$

■ Another way to identify a and r is to write out the first few terms:

$$4 + \tfrac{16}{3} + \tfrac{64}{9} + \cdots$$

We recognize this series as a geometric series with $a = 4$ and $r = \tfrac{4}{3}$. Since $r > 1$, the series diverges by (4). ◻

▼ EXAMPLE 4 Write the number $2.3\overline{17} = 2.3171717\ldots$ as a ratio of integers.

SOLUTION

$$2.3171717\ldots = 2.3 + \frac{17}{10^3} + \frac{17}{10^5} + \frac{17}{10^7} + \cdots$$

After the first term we have a geometric series with $a = 17/10^3$ and $r = 1/10^2$. Therefore

$$2.3\overline{17} = 2.3 + \frac{\dfrac{17}{10^3}}{1 - \dfrac{1}{10^2}} = 2.3 + \frac{\dfrac{17}{1000}}{\dfrac{99}{100}}$$

$$= \frac{23}{10} + \frac{17}{990} = \frac{1147}{495}$$ ◻

EXAMPLE 5 Find the sum of the series $\displaystyle\sum_{n=0}^{\infty} x^n$, where $|x| < 1$.

SOLUTION Notice that this series starts with $n = 0$ and so the first term is $x^0 = 1$. (With series, we adopt the convention that $x^0 = 1$ even when $x = 0$.) Thus

$$\sum_{n=0}^{\infty} x^n = 1 + x + x^2 + x^3 + x^4 + \cdots$$

This is a geometric series with $a = 1$ and $r = x$. Since $|r| = |x| < 1$, it converges and (4) gives

TEC Module 12.2 explores a series that depends on an angle θ in a triangle and enables you to see how rapidly the series converges when θ varies.

$$\boxed{5} \qquad \sum_{n=0}^{\infty} x^n = \frac{1}{1-x}$$ ◻

EXAMPLE 6 Show that the series $\displaystyle\sum_{n=1}^{\infty} \frac{1}{n(n+1)}$ is convergent, and find its sum.

SOLUTION This is not a geometric series, so we go back to the definition of a convergent series and compute the partial sums.

$$s_n = \sum_{i=1}^{n} \frac{1}{i(i+1)} = \frac{1}{1 \cdot 2} + \frac{1}{2 \cdot 3} + \frac{1}{3 \cdot 4} + \cdots + \frac{1}{n(n+1)}$$

We can simplify this expression if we use the partial fraction decomposition

$$\frac{1}{i(i+1)} = \frac{1}{i} - \frac{1}{i+1}$$

(see Section 8.4). Thus we have

$$s_n = \sum_{i=1}^{n} \frac{1}{i(i+1)} = \sum_{i=1}^{n} \left(\frac{1}{i} - \frac{1}{i+1} \right)$$

$$= \left(1 - \frac{1}{2} \right) + \left(\frac{1}{2} - \frac{1}{3} \right) + \left(\frac{1}{3} - \frac{1}{4} \right) + \cdots + \left(\frac{1}{n} - \frac{1}{n+1} \right)$$

$$= 1 - \frac{1}{n+1}$$

■ Notice that the terms cancel in pairs. This is an example of a **telescoping sum**: Because of all the cancellations, the sum collapses (like a pirate's collapsing telescope) into just two terms.

and so

$$\lim_{n \to \infty} s_n = \lim_{n \to \infty} \left(1 - \frac{1}{n+1} \right) = 1 - 0 = 1$$

Therefore the given series is convergent and

$$\sum_{n=1}^{\infty} \frac{1}{n(n+1)} = 1$$

■ Figure 3 illustrates Example 6 by showing the graphs of the sequence of terms $a_n = 1/[n(n+1)]$ and the sequence $\{s_n\}$ of partial sums. Notice that $a_n \to 0$ and $s_n \to 1$. See Exercises 62 and 63 for two geometric interpretations of Example 6.

☑ EXAMPLE 7 Show that the **harmonic series**

$$\sum_{n=1}^{\infty} \frac{1}{n} = 1 + \frac{1}{2} + \frac{1}{3} + \frac{1}{4} + \cdots$$

is divergent.

SOLUTION For this particular series it's convenient to consider the partial sums $s_2, s_4, s_8, s_{16}, s_{32}, \ldots$ and show that they become large.

$$s_1 = 1$$

$$s_2 = 1 + \tfrac{1}{2}$$

$$s_4 = 1 + \tfrac{1}{2} + \left(\tfrac{1}{3} + \tfrac{1}{4} \right) > 1 + \tfrac{1}{2} + \left(\tfrac{1}{4} + \tfrac{1}{4} \right) = 1 + \tfrac{2}{2}$$

$$s_8 = 1 + \tfrac{1}{2} + \left(\tfrac{1}{3} + \tfrac{1}{4} \right) + \left(\tfrac{1}{5} + \tfrac{1}{6} + \tfrac{1}{7} + \tfrac{1}{8} \right)$$

$$> 1 + \tfrac{1}{2} + \left(\tfrac{1}{4} + \tfrac{1}{4} \right) + \left(\tfrac{1}{8} + \tfrac{1}{8} + \tfrac{1}{8} + \tfrac{1}{8} \right)$$

$$= 1 + \tfrac{1}{2} + \tfrac{1}{2} + \tfrac{1}{2} = 1 + \tfrac{3}{2}$$

$$s_{16} = 1 + \tfrac{1}{2} + \left(\tfrac{1}{3} + \tfrac{1}{4} \right) + \left(\tfrac{1}{5} + \cdots + \tfrac{1}{8} \right) + \left(\tfrac{1}{9} + \cdots + \tfrac{1}{16} \right)$$

$$> 1 + \tfrac{1}{2} + \left(\tfrac{1}{4} + \tfrac{1}{4} \right) + \left(\tfrac{1}{8} + \cdots + \tfrac{1}{8} \right) + \left(\tfrac{1}{16} + \cdots + \tfrac{1}{16} \right)$$

$$= 1 + \tfrac{1}{2} + \tfrac{1}{2} + \tfrac{1}{2} + \tfrac{1}{2} = 1 + \tfrac{4}{2}$$

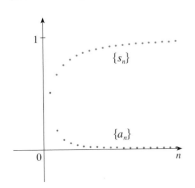

FIGURE 3

Similarly, $s_{32} > 1 + \frac{5}{2}$, $s_{64} > 1 + \frac{6}{2}$, and in general

$$s_{2^n} > 1 + \frac{n}{2}$$

This shows that $s_{2^n} \to \infty$ as $n \to \infty$ and so $\{s_n\}$ is divergent. Therefore the harmonic series diverges.

■ The method used in Example 7 for showing that the harmonic series diverges is due to the French scholar Nicole Oresme (1323–1382).

---

6 THEOREM If the series $\sum_{n=1}^{\infty} a_n$ is convergent, then $\lim_{n \to \infty} a_n = 0$.

PROOF Let $s_n = a_1 + a_2 + \cdots + a_n$. Then $a_n = s_n - s_{n-1}$. Since $\sum a_n$ is convergent, the sequence $\{s_n\}$ is convergent. Let $\lim_{n \to \infty} s_n = s$. Since $n - 1 \to \infty$ as $n \to \infty$, we also have $\lim_{n \to \infty} s_{n-1} = s$. Therefore

$$\lim_{n \to \infty} a_n = \lim_{n \to \infty} (s_n - s_{n-1}) = \lim_{n \to \infty} s_n - \lim_{n \to \infty} s_{n-1}$$
$$= s - s = 0$$

NOTE 1 With any *series* $\sum a_n$ we associate two *sequences:* the sequence $\{s_n\}$ of its partial sums and the sequence $\{a_n\}$ of its terms. If $\sum a_n$ is convergent, then the limit of the sequence $\{s_n\}$ is s (the sum of the series) and, as Theorem 6 asserts, the limit of the sequence $\{a_n\}$ is 0.

⊘ **NOTE 2** The converse of Theorem 6 is not true in general. If $\lim_{n \to \infty} a_n = 0$, we cannot conclude that $\sum a_n$ is convergent. Observe that for the harmonic series $\sum 1/n$ we have $a_n = 1/n \to 0$ as $n \to \infty$, but we showed in Example 7 that $\sum 1/n$ is divergent.

---

7 THE TEST FOR DIVERGENCE If $\lim_{n \to \infty} a_n$ does not exist or if $\lim_{n \to \infty} a_n \neq 0$, then the series $\sum_{n=1}^{\infty} a_n$ is divergent.

The Test for Divergence follows from Theorem 6 because, if the series is not divergent, then it is convergent, and so $\lim_{n \to \infty} a_n = 0$.

EXAMPLE 8 Show that the series $\sum_{n=1}^{\infty} \dfrac{n^2}{5n^2 + 4}$ diverges.

SOLUTION

$$\lim_{n \to \infty} a_n = \lim_{n \to \infty} \frac{n^2}{5n^2 + 4} = \lim_{n \to \infty} \frac{1}{5 + 4/n^2} = \frac{1}{5} \neq 0$$

So the series diverges by the Test for Divergence.

NOTE 3 If we find that $\lim_{n \to \infty} a_n \neq 0$, we know that $\sum a_n$ is divergent. If we find that $\lim_{n \to \infty} a_n = 0$, we know *nothing* about the convergence or divergence of $\sum a_n$. Remember the warning in Note 2: If $\lim_{n \to \infty} a_n = 0$, the series $\sum a_n$ might converge or it might diverge.

> **8 THEOREM** If $\Sigma\, a_n$ and $\Sigma\, b_n$ are convergent series, then so are the series $\Sigma\, ca_n$ (where c is a constant), $\Sigma\, (a_n + b_n)$, and $\Sigma\, (a_n - b_n)$, and
>
> (i) $\displaystyle\sum_{n=1}^{\infty} ca_n = c \sum_{n=1}^{\infty} a_n$
> (ii) $\displaystyle\sum_{n=1}^{\infty} (a_n + b_n) = \sum_{n=1}^{\infty} a_n + \sum_{n=1}^{\infty} b_n$
>
> (iii) $\displaystyle\sum_{n=1}^{\infty} (a_n - b_n) = \sum_{n=1}^{\infty} a_n - \sum_{n=1}^{\infty} b_n$

These properties of convergent series follow from the corresponding Limit Laws for Sequences in Section 12.1. For instance, here is how part (ii) of Theorem 8 is proved:

Let

$$s_n = \sum_{i=1}^{n} a_i \qquad s = \sum_{n=1}^{\infty} a_n \qquad t_n = \sum_{i=1}^{n} b_i \qquad t = \sum_{n=1}^{\infty} b_n$$

The nth partial sum for the series $\Sigma\, (a_n + b_n)$ is

$$u_n = \sum_{i=1}^{n} (a_i + b_i)$$

and, using Equation 5.2.10, we have

$$\lim_{n\to\infty} u_n = \lim_{n\to\infty} \sum_{i=1}^{n} (a_i + b_i) = \lim_{n\to\infty} \left(\sum_{i=1}^{n} a_i + \sum_{i=1}^{n} b_i \right)$$

$$= \lim_{n\to\infty} \sum_{i=1}^{n} a_i + \lim_{n\to\infty} \sum_{i=1}^{n} b_i = \lim_{n\to\infty} s_n + \lim_{n\to\infty} t_n = s + t$$

Therefore $\Sigma\, (a_n + b_n)$ is convergent and its sum is

$$\sum_{n=1}^{\infty} (a_n + b_n) = s + t = \sum_{n=1}^{\infty} a_n + \sum_{n=1}^{\infty} b_n$$

EXAMPLE 9 Find the sum of the series $\displaystyle\sum_{n=1}^{\infty} \left(\frac{3}{n(n+1)} + \frac{1}{2^n} \right)$.

SOLUTION The series $\Sigma\, 1/2^n$ is a geometric series with $a = \frac{1}{2}$ and $r = \frac{1}{2}$, so

$$\sum_{n=1}^{\infty} \frac{1}{2^n} = \frac{\frac{1}{2}}{1 - \frac{1}{2}} = 1$$

In Example 6 we found that

$$\sum_{n=1}^{\infty} \frac{1}{n(n+1)} = 1$$

So, by Theorem 8, the given series is convergent and

$$\sum_{n=1}^{\infty} \left(\frac{3}{n(n+1)} + \frac{1}{2^n} \right) = 3 \sum_{n=1}^{\infty} \frac{1}{n(n+1)} + \sum_{n=1}^{\infty} \frac{1}{2^n} = 3 \cdot 1 + 1 = 4$$

NOTE 4 A finite number of terms doesn't affect the convergence or divergence of a series. For instance, suppose that we were able to show that the series

$$\sum_{n=4}^{\infty} \frac{n}{n^3 + 1}$$

is convergent. Since

$$\sum_{n=1}^{\infty} \frac{n}{n^3+1} = \frac{1}{2} + \frac{2}{9} + \frac{3}{28} + \sum_{n=4}^{\infty} \frac{n}{n^3+1}$$

it follows that the entire series $\sum_{n=1}^{\infty} n/(n^3+1)$ is convergent. Similarly, if it is known that the series $\sum_{n=N+1}^{\infty} a_n$ converges, then the full series

$$\sum_{n=1}^{\infty} a_n = \sum_{n=1}^{N} a_n + \sum_{n=N+1}^{\infty} a_n$$

is also convergent.

12.2 EXERCISES

1. (a) What is the difference between a sequence and a series?
   (b) What is a convergent series? What is a divergent series?

2. Explain what it means to say that $\sum_{n=1}^{\infty} a_n = 5$.

3–8 Find at least 10 partial sums of the series. Graph both the sequence of terms and the sequence of partial sums on the same screen. Does it appear that the series is convergent or divergent? If it is convergent, find the sum. If it is divergent, explain why.

3. $\displaystyle\sum_{n=1}^{\infty} \frac{12}{(-5)^n}$

4. $\displaystyle\sum_{n=1}^{\infty} \frac{2n^2-1}{n^2+1}$

5. $\displaystyle\sum_{n=1}^{\infty} \tan n$

6. $\displaystyle\sum_{n=1}^{\infty} (0.6)^{n-1}$

7. $\displaystyle\sum_{n=1}^{\infty} \left(\frac{1}{\sqrt{n}} - \frac{1}{\sqrt{n+1}} \right)$

8. $\displaystyle\sum_{n=2}^{\infty} \frac{1}{n(n+2)}$

9. Let $a_n = \dfrac{2n}{3n+1}$.
   (a) Determine whether $\{a_n\}$ is convergent.
   (b) Determine whether $\sum_{n=1}^{\infty} a_n$ is convergent.

10. (a) Explain the difference between

$$\sum_{i=1}^{n} a_i \quad \text{and} \quad \sum_{j=1}^{n} a_j$$

   (b) Explain the difference between

$$\sum_{i=1}^{n} a_i \quad \text{and} \quad \sum_{i=1}^{n} a_j$$

11–20 Determine whether the geometric series is convergent or divergent. If it is convergent, find its sum.

11. $3 + 2 + \frac{4}{3} + \frac{8}{9} + \cdots$

12. $\frac{1}{8} - \frac{1}{4} + \frac{1}{2} - 1 + \cdots$

13. $3 - 4 + \frac{16}{3} - \frac{64}{9} + \cdots$

14. $1 + 0.4 + 0.16 + 0.064 + \cdots$

15. $\displaystyle\sum_{n=1}^{\infty} 6(0.9)^{n-1}$

16. $\displaystyle\sum_{n=1}^{\infty} \frac{10^n}{(-9)^{n-1}}$

17. $\displaystyle\sum_{n=1}^{\infty} \frac{(-3)^{n-1}}{4^n}$

18. $\displaystyle\sum_{n=0}^{\infty} \frac{1}{(\sqrt{2})^n}$

19. $\displaystyle\sum_{n=0}^{\infty} \frac{\pi^n}{3^{n+1}}$

20. $\displaystyle\sum_{n=1}^{\infty} \frac{e^n}{3^{n-1}}$

21–34 Determine whether the series is convergent or divergent. If it is convergent, find its sum.

21. $\displaystyle\sum_{n=1}^{\infty} \frac{1}{2n}$

22. $\displaystyle\sum_{n=1}^{\infty} \frac{n+1}{2n-3}$

23. $\displaystyle\sum_{k=2}^{\infty} \frac{k^2}{k^2-1}$

24. $\displaystyle\sum_{k=1}^{\infty} \frac{k(k+2)}{(k+3)^2}$

25. $\displaystyle\sum_{n=1}^{\infty} \frac{1+2^n}{3^n}$

26. $\displaystyle\sum_{n=1}^{\infty} \frac{1+3^n}{2^n}$

27. $\displaystyle\sum_{n=1}^{\infty} \sqrt[n]{2}$

28. $\displaystyle\sum_{n=1}^{\infty} [(0.8)^{n-1} - (0.3)^n]$

29. $\displaystyle\sum_{n=1}^{\infty} \ln\left(\frac{n^2+1}{2n^2+1} \right)$

30. $\displaystyle\sum_{k=1}^{\infty} (\cos 1)^k$

31. $\displaystyle\sum_{n=1}^{\infty} \arctan n$

32. $\displaystyle\sum_{n=1}^{\infty} \left(\frac{3}{5^n} + \frac{2}{n} \right)$

33. $\displaystyle\sum_{n=1}^{\infty} \left(\frac{1}{e^n} + \frac{1}{n(n+1)} \right)$

34. $\displaystyle\sum_{n=1}^{\infty} \frac{e^n}{n^2}$

35–40 Determine whether the series is convergent or divergent by expressing s_n as a telescoping sum (as in Example 6). If it is convergent, find its sum.

35. $\displaystyle\sum_{n=2}^{\infty} \frac{2}{n^2-1}$

36. $\displaystyle\sum_{n=1}^{\infty} \frac{2}{n^2+4n+3}$

37. $\displaystyle\sum_{n=1}^{\infty} \frac{3}{n(n+3)}$

38. $\displaystyle\sum_{n=1}^{\infty} \ln\frac{n}{n+1}$

39. $\displaystyle\sum_{n=1}^{\infty} \left(e^{1/n} - e^{1/(n+1)} \right)$

40. $\displaystyle\sum_{n=1}^{\infty} \left(\cos \frac{1}{n^2} - \cos \frac{1}{(n+1)^2} \right)$

41–46 Express the number as a ratio of integers.

41. $0.\overline{2} = 0.2222\ldots$

42. $0.\overline{73} = 0.73737373\ldots$

43. $3.\overline{417} = 3.417417417\ldots$

44. $6.2\overline{54} = 6.2545454\ldots$

45. $1.5\overline{342}$

46. $7.\overline{12345}$

47–51 Find the values of x for which the series converges. Find the sum of the series for those values of x.

47. $\displaystyle\sum_{n=1}^{\infty} \frac{x^n}{3^n}$

48. $\displaystyle\sum_{n=1}^{\infty} (x - 4)^n$

49. $\displaystyle\sum_{n=0}^{\infty} 4^n x^n$

50. $\displaystyle\sum_{n=0}^{\infty} \frac{(x + 3)^n}{2^n}$

51. $\displaystyle\sum_{n=0}^{\infty} \frac{\cos^n x}{2^n}$

---

52. We have seen that the harmonic series is a divergent series whose terms approach 0. Show that

$$\sum_{n=1}^{\infty} \ln\left(1 + \frac{1}{n} \right)$$

is another series with this property.

CAS 53–54 Use the partial fraction command on your CAS to find a convenient expression for the partial sum, and then use this expression to find the sum of the series. Check your answer by using the CAS to sum the series directly.

53. $\displaystyle\sum_{n=1}^{\infty} \frac{3n^2 + 3n + 1}{(n^2 + n)^3}$

54. $\displaystyle\sum_{n=2}^{\infty} \frac{1}{n^3 - n}$

---

55. If the nth partial sum of a series $\sum_{n=1}^{\infty} a_n$ is

$$s_n = \frac{n - 1}{n + 1}$$

find a_n and $\displaystyle\sum_{n=1}^{\infty} a_n$.

56. If the nth partial sum of a series $\sum_{n=1}^{\infty} a_n$ is $s_n = 3 - n\,2^{-n}$, find a_n and $\displaystyle\sum_{n=1}^{\infty} a_n$.

57. When money is spent on goods and services, those who receive the money also spend some of it. The people receiving some of the twice-spent money will spend some of that, and so on. Economists call this chain reaction the *multiplier effect*. In a hypothetical isolated community, the local government begins the process by spending D dollars. Suppose that each recipient of spent money spends $100c\%$ and saves $100s\%$ of the money that he or she receives. The values c and s are called the *marginal propensity to consume* and the *marginal propensity to save* and, of course, $c + s = 1$.
 (a) Let S_n be the total spending that has been generated after n transactions. Find an equation for S_n.
 (b) Show that $\lim_{n \to \infty} S_n = kD$, where $k = 1/s$. The number k is called the *multiplier*. What is the multiplier if the marginal propensity to consume is 80%?

Note: The federal government uses this principle to justify deficit spending. Banks use this principle to justify lending a large percentage of the money that they receive in deposits.

58. A certain ball has the property that each time it falls from a height h onto a hard, level surface, it rebounds to a height rh, where $0 < r < 1$. Suppose that the ball is dropped from an initial height of H meters.
 (a) Assuming that the ball continues to bounce indefinitely, find the total distance that it travels. (Use the fact that the ball falls $\frac{1}{2}gt^2$ meters in t seconds.)
 (b) Calculate the total time that the ball travels.
 (c) Suppose that each time the ball strikes the surface with velocity v it rebounds with velocity $-kv$, where $0 < k < 1$. How long will it take for the ball to come to rest?

59. Find the value of c if

$$\sum_{n=2}^{\infty} (1 + c)^{-n} = 2$$

60. Find the value of c such that

$$\sum_{n=0}^{\infty} e^{nc} = 10$$

61. In Example 7 we showed that the harmonic series is divergent. Here we outline another method, making use of the fact that $e^x > 1 + x$ for any $x > 0$. (See Exercise 7.2.93.)
  If s_n is the nth partial sum of the harmonic series, show that $e^{s_n} > n + 1$. Why does this imply that the harmonic series is divergent?

62. Graph the curves $y = x^n$, $0 \le x \le 1$, for $n = 0, 1, 2, 3, 4, \ldots$ on a common screen. By finding the areas between successive curves, give a geometric demonstration of the fact, shown in Example 6, that

$$\sum_{n=1}^{\infty} \frac{1}{n(n + 1)} = 1$$

63. The figure shows two circles C and D of radius 1 that touch at P. T is a common tangent line; C_1 is the circle that touches C, D, and T; C_2 is the circle that touches C, D, and C_1; C_3 is the circle that touches C, D, and C_2. This procedure can be continued indefinitely and produces an infinite sequence of circles $\{C_n\}$. Find an expression for the diameter of C_n and thus provide another geometric demonstration of Example 6.

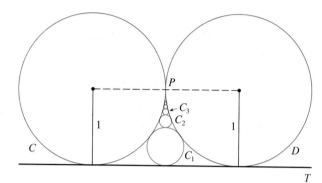

64. A right triangle ABC is given with $\angle A = \theta$ and $|AC| = b$. CD is drawn perpendicular to AB, DE is drawn perpendicular to BC, $EF \perp AB$, and this process is continued indefinitely, as shown in the figure. Find the total length of all the perpendiculars

$$|CD| + |DE| + |EF| + |FG| + \cdots$$

in terms of b and θ.

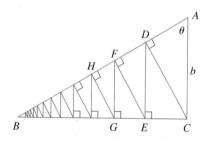

65. What is wrong with the following calculation?

$$0 = 0 + 0 + 0 + \cdots$$
$$= (1 - 1) + (1 - 1) + (1 - 1) + \cdots$$
$$= 1 - 1 + 1 - 1 + 1 - 1 + \cdots$$
$$= 1 + (-1 + 1) + (-1 + 1) + (-1 + 1) + \cdots$$
$$= 1 + 0 + 0 + 0 + \cdots = 1$$

(Guido Ubaldus thought that this proved the existence of God because "something has been created out of nothing.")

66. Suppose that $\sum_{n=1}^{\infty} a_n \ (a_n \neq 0)$ is known to be a convergent series. Prove that $\sum_{n=1}^{\infty} 1/a_n$ is a divergent series.

67. Prove part (i) of Theorem 8.

68. If $\sum a_n$ is divergent and $c \neq 0$, show that $\sum c a_n$ is divergent.

69. If $\sum a_n$ is convergent and $\sum b_n$ is divergent, show that the series $\sum (a_n + b_n)$ is divergent. [*Hint:* Argue by contradiction.]

70. If $\sum a_n$ and $\sum b_n$ are both divergent, is $\sum (a_n + b_n)$ necessarily divergent?

71. Suppose that a series $\sum a_n$ has positive terms and its partial sums s_n satisfy the inequality $s_n \leq 1000$ for all n. Explain why $\sum a_n$ must be convergent.

72. The Fibonacci sequence was defined in Section 12.1 by the equations

$$f_1 = 1, \quad f_2 = 1, \quad f_n = f_{n-1} + f_{n-2} \qquad n \geq 3$$

Show that each of the following statements is true.

(a) $\dfrac{1}{f_{n-1}f_{n+1}} = \dfrac{1}{f_{n-1}f_n} - \dfrac{1}{f_n f_{n+1}}$

(b) $\displaystyle\sum_{n=2}^{\infty} \dfrac{1}{f_{n-1}f_{n+1}} = 1$

(c) $\displaystyle\sum_{n=2}^{\infty} \dfrac{f_n}{f_{n-1}f_{n+1}} = 2$

73. The **Cantor set**, named after the German mathematician Georg Cantor (1845–1918), is constructed as follows. We start with the closed interval $[0, 1]$ and remove the open interval $\left(\frac{1}{3}, \frac{2}{3}\right)$. That leaves the two intervals $\left[0, \frac{1}{3}\right]$ and $\left[\frac{2}{3}, 1\right]$ and we remove the open middle third of each. Four intervals remain and again we remove the open middle third of each of them. We continue this procedure indefinitely, at each step removing the open middle third of every interval that remains from the preceding step. The Cantor set consists of the numbers that remain in $[0, 1]$ after all those intervals have been removed.

(a) Show that the total length of all the intervals that are removed is 1. Despite that, the Cantor set contains infinitely many numbers. Give examples of some numbers in the Cantor set.

(b) The **Sierpinski carpet** is a two-dimensional counterpart of the Cantor set. It is constructed by removing the center one-ninth of a square of side 1, then removing the centers of the eight smaller remaining squares, and so on. (The figure shows the first three steps of the construction.) Show that the sum of the areas of the removed squares is 1. This implies that the Sierpinski carpet has area 0.

74. (a) A sequence $\{a_n\}$ is defined recursively by the equation $a_n = \frac{1}{2}(a_{n-1} + a_{n-2})$ for $n \geqslant 3$, where a_1 and a_2 can be any real numbers. Experiment with various values of a_1 and a_2 and use your calculator to guess the limit of the sequence.

(b) Find $\lim_{n \to \infty} a_n$ in terms of a_1 and a_2 by expressing $a_{n+1} - a_n$ in terms of $a_2 - a_1$ and summing a series.

75. Consider the series
$$\sum_{n=1}^{\infty} \frac{n}{(n+1)!}$$

(a) Find the partial sums s_1, s_2, s_3, and s_4. Do you recognize the denominators? Use the pattern to guess a formula for s_n.

(b) Use mathematical induction to prove your guess.

(c) Show that the given infinite series is convergent, and find its sum.

76. In the figure there are infinitely many circles approaching the vertices of an equilateral triangle, each circle touching other circles and sides of the triangle. If the triangle has sides of length 1, find the total area occupied by the circles.

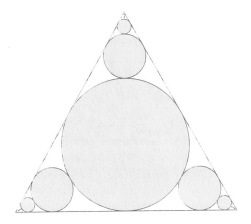

12.3 THE INTEGRAL TEST AND ESTIMATES OF SUMS

In general, it is difficult to find the exact sum of a series. We were able to accomplish this for geometric series and the series $\Sigma\, 1/[n(n+1)]$ because in each of those cases we could find a simple formula for the nth partial sum s_n. But usually it isn't easy to compute $\lim_{n \to \infty} s_n$. Therefore, in the next few sections, we develop several tests that enable us to determine whether a series is convergent or divergent without explicitly finding its sum. (In some cases, however, our methods will enable us to find good estimates of the sum.) Our first test involves improper integrals.

We begin by investigating the series whose terms are the reciprocals of the squares of the positive integers:

$$\sum_{n=1}^{\infty} \frac{1}{n^2} = \frac{1}{1^2} + \frac{1}{2^2} + \frac{1}{3^2} + \frac{1}{4^2} + \frac{1}{5^2} + \cdots$$

n	$s_n = \sum_{i=1}^{n} \dfrac{1}{i^2}$
5	1.4636
10	1.5498
50	1.6251
100	1.6350
500	1.6429
1000	1.6439
5000	1.6447

There's no simple formula for the sum s_n of the first n terms, but the computer-generated table of values given in the margin suggests that the partial sums are approaching a number near 1.64 as $n \to \infty$ and so it looks as if the series is convergent.

We can confirm this impression with a geometric argument. Figure 1 shows the curve $y = 1/x^2$ and rectangles that lie below the curve. The base of each rectangle is an interval of length 1; the height is equal to the value of the function $y = 1/x^2$ at the right endpoint of the interval. So the sum of the areas of the rectangles is

$$\frac{1}{1^2} + \frac{1}{2^2} + \frac{1}{3^2} + \frac{1}{4^2} + \frac{1}{5^2} + \cdots = \sum_{n=1}^{\infty} \frac{1}{n^2}$$

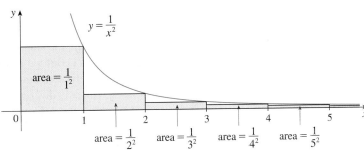

FIGURE 1

If we exclude the first rectangle, the total area of the remaining rectangles is smaller than the area under the curve $y = 1/x^2$ for $x \geqslant 1$, which is the value of the integral $\int_1^\infty (1/x^2)\, dx$. In Section 8.8 we discovered that this improper integral is convergent and has value 1. So the picture shows that all the partial sums are less than

$$\frac{1}{1^2} + \int_1^\infty \frac{1}{x^2}\, dx = 2$$

Thus the partial sums are bounded. We also know that the partial sums are increasing (because all the terms are positive). Therefore the partial sums converge (by the Monotonic Sequence Theorem) and so the series is convergent. The sum of the series (the limit of the partial sums) is also less than 2:

$$\sum_{n=1}^\infty \frac{1}{n^2} = \frac{1}{1^2} + \frac{1}{2^2} + \frac{1}{3^2} + \frac{1}{4^2} + \cdots < 2$$

[The exact sum of this series was found by the Swiss mathematician Leonhard Euler (1707–1783) to be $\pi^2/6$, but the proof of this fact is quite difficult. (See Problem 6 in the Problems Plus following Chapter 16.)]

Now let's look at the series

$$\sum_{n=1}^\infty \frac{1}{\sqrt{n}} = \frac{1}{\sqrt{1}} + \frac{1}{\sqrt{2}} + \frac{1}{\sqrt{3}} + \frac{1}{\sqrt{4}} + \frac{1}{\sqrt{5}} + \cdots$$

n	$s_n = \displaystyle\sum_{i=1}^{n} \frac{1}{\sqrt{i}}$
5	3.2317
10	5.0210
50	12.7524
100	18.5896
500	43.2834
1000	61.8010
5000	139.9681

The table of values of s_n suggests that the partial sums aren't approaching a finite number, so we suspect that the given series may be divergent. Again we use a picture for confirmation. Figure 2 shows the curve $y = 1/\sqrt{x}$, but this time we use rectangles whose tops lie *above* the curve.

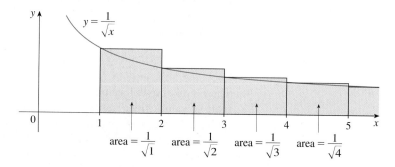

FIGURE 2

The base of each rectangle is an interval of length 1. The height is equal to the value of the function $y = 1/\sqrt{x}$ at the *left* endpoint of the interval. So the sum of the areas of all the rectangles is

$$\frac{1}{\sqrt{1}} + \frac{1}{\sqrt{2}} + \frac{1}{\sqrt{3}} + \frac{1}{\sqrt{4}} + \frac{1}{\sqrt{5}} + \cdots = \sum_{n=1}^\infty \frac{1}{\sqrt{n}}$$

This total area is greater than the area under the curve $y = 1/\sqrt{x}$ for $x \geqslant 1$, which is equal to the integral $\int_1^\infty (1/\sqrt{x})\, dx$. But we know from Section 8.8 that this improper integral is divergent. In other words, the area under the curve is infinite. So the sum of the series must be infinite; that is, the series is divergent.

The same sort of geometric reasoning that we used for these two series can be used to prove the following test. (The proof is given at the end of this section.)

THE INTEGRAL TEST Suppose f is a continuous, positive, decreasing function on $[1, \infty)$ and let $a_n = f(n)$. Then the series $\sum_{n=1}^{\infty} a_n$ is convergent if and only if the improper integral $\int_1^{\infty} f(x)\, dx$ is convergent. In other words:

(i) If $\int_1^{\infty} f(x)\, dx$ is convergent, then $\sum_{n=1}^{\infty} a_n$ is convergent.

(ii) If $\int_1^{\infty} f(x)\, dx$ is divergent, then $\sum_{n=1}^{\infty} a_n$ is divergent.

NOTE When we use the Integral Test, it is not necessary to start the series or the integral at $n = 1$. For instance, in testing the series

$$\sum_{n=4}^{\infty} \frac{1}{(n-3)^2} \qquad \text{we use} \qquad \int_4^{\infty} \frac{1}{(x-3)^2}\, dx$$

Also, it is not necessary that f be always decreasing. What is important is that f be *ultimately* decreasing, that is, decreasing for x larger than some number N. Then $\sum_{n=N}^{\infty} a_n$ is convergent, so $\sum_{n=1}^{\infty} a_n$ is convergent by Note 4 of Section 12.2.

EXAMPLE 1 Test the series $\displaystyle\sum_{n=1}^{\infty} \frac{1}{n^2 + 1}$ for convergence or divergence.

SOLUTION The function $f(x) = 1/(x^2 + 1)$ is continuous, positive, and decreasing on $[1, \infty)$ so we use the Integral Test:

$$\int_1^{\infty} \frac{1}{x^2 + 1}\, dx = \lim_{t \to \infty} \int_1^t \frac{1}{x^2 + 1}\, dx = \lim_{t \to \infty} \tan^{-1}x \Big]_1^t$$

$$= \lim_{t \to \infty} \left(\tan^{-1}t - \frac{\pi}{4} \right) = \frac{\pi}{2} - \frac{\pi}{4} = \frac{\pi}{4}$$

Thus $\int_1^{\infty} 1/(x^2 + 1)\, dx$ is a convergent integral and so, by the Integral Test, the series $\sum 1/(n^2 + 1)$ is convergent. □

■ In order to use the Integral Test we need to be able to evaluate $\int_1^{\infty} f(x)\, dx$ and therefore we have to be able to find an antiderivative of f. Frequently this is difficult or impossible, so we need other tests for convergence too.

▼ EXAMPLE 2 For what values of p is the series $\displaystyle\sum_{n=1}^{\infty} \frac{1}{n^p}$ convergent?

SOLUTION If $p < 0$, then $\lim_{n \to \infty} (1/n^p) = \infty$. If $p = 0$, then $\lim_{n \to \infty} (1/n^p) = 1$. In either case, $\lim_{n \to \infty} (1/n^p) \neq 0$, so the given series diverges by the Test for Divergence (12.2.7).

If $p > 0$, then the function $f(x) = 1/x^p$ is clearly continuous, positive, and decreasing on $[1, \infty)$. We found in Chapter 8 [see (8.8.2)] that

$$\int_1^{\infty} \frac{1}{x^p}\, dx \text{ converges if } p > 1 \text{ and diverges if } p \leq 1$$

It follows from the Integral Test that the series $\sum 1/n^p$ converges if $p > 1$ and diverges if $0 < p \leq 1$. (For $p = 1$, this series is the harmonic series discussed in Example 7 in Section 12.2.) □

The series in Example 2 is called the **p-series**. It is important in the rest of this chapter, so we summarize the results of Example 2 for future reference as follows.

⬚ The *p*-series $\sum_{n=1}^{\infty} \dfrac{1}{n^p}$ is convergent if $p > 1$ and divergent if $p \le 1$.	

EXAMPLE 3

(a) The series

$$\sum_{n=1}^{\infty} \frac{1}{n^3} = \frac{1}{1^3} + \frac{1}{2^3} + \frac{1}{3^3} + \frac{1}{4^3} + \cdots$$

is convergent because it is a *p*-series with $p = 3 > 1$.

(b) The series

$$\sum_{n=1}^{\infty} \frac{1}{n^{1/3}} = \sum_{n=1}^{\infty} \frac{1}{\sqrt[3]{n}} = 1 + \frac{1}{\sqrt[3]{2}} + \frac{1}{\sqrt[3]{3}} + \frac{1}{\sqrt[3]{4}} + \cdots$$

is divergent because it is a *p*-series with $p = \frac{1}{3} < 1$. ☐

⬚ **NOTE** We should *not* infer from the Integral Test that the sum of the series is equal to the value of the integral. In fact,

$$\sum_{n=1}^{\infty} \frac{1}{n^2} = \frac{\pi^2}{6} \qquad \text{whereas} \qquad \int_1^{\infty} \frac{1}{x^2}\, dx = 1$$

Therefore, in general,

$$\sum_{n=1}^{\infty} a_n \ne \int_1^{\infty} f(x)\, dx$$

☑ **EXAMPLE 4** Determine whether the series $\sum_{n=1}^{\infty} \dfrac{\ln n}{n}$ converges or diverges.

SOLUTION The function $f(x) = (\ln x)/x$ is positive and continuous for $x > 1$ because the logarithm function is continuous. But it is not obvious whether or not f is decreasing, so we compute its derivative:

$$f'(x) = \frac{(1/x)x - \ln x}{x^2} = \frac{1 - \ln x}{x^2}$$

Thus $f'(x) < 0$ when $\ln x > 1$, that is, $x > e$. It follows that f is decreasing when $x > e$ and so we can apply the Integral Test:

$$\int_1^{\infty} \frac{\ln x}{x}\, dx = \lim_{t \to \infty} \int_1^t \frac{\ln x}{x}\, dx = \lim_{t \to \infty} \frac{(\ln x)^2}{2} \Big]_1^t = \lim_{t \to \infty} \frac{(\ln t)^2}{2} = \infty$$

Since this improper integral is divergent, the series $\sum (\ln n)/n$ is also divergent by the Integral Test. ☐

ESTIMATING THE SUM OF A SERIES

Suppose we have been able to use the Integral Test to show that a series $\sum a_n$ is convergent and we now want to find an approximation to the sum s of the series. Of course, any partial sum s_n is an approximation to s because $\lim_{n \to \infty} s_n = s$. But how good is such an approximation? To find out, we need to estimate the size of the **remainder**

$$R_n = s - s_n = a_{n+1} + a_{n+2} + a_{n+3} + \cdots$$

FIGURE 3

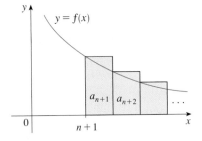

FIGURE 4

The remainder R_n is the error made when s_n, the sum of the first n terms, is used as an approximation to the total sum.

We use the same notation and ideas as in the Integral Test, assuming that f is decreasing on $[n, \infty)$. Comparing the areas of the rectangles with the area under $y = f(x)$ for $x > n$ in Figure 3, we see that

$$R_n = a_{n+1} + a_{n+2} + \cdots \leqslant \int_n^\infty f(x)\, dx$$

Similarly, we see from Figure 4 that

$$R_n = a_{n+1} + a_{n+2} + \cdots \geqslant \int_{n+1}^\infty f(x)\, dx$$

So we have proved the following error estimate.

> **2** **REMAINDER ESTIMATE FOR THE INTEGRAL TEST** Suppose $f(k) = a_k$, where f is a continuous, positive, decreasing function for $x \geqslant n$ and $\Sigma\, a_n$ is convergent. If $R_n = s - s_n$, then
>
> $$\int_{n+1}^\infty f(x)\, dx \leqslant R_n \leqslant \int_n^\infty f(x)\, dx$$

▼ **EXAMPLE 5**

(a) Approximate the sum of the series $\Sigma\, 1/n^3$ by using the sum of the first 10 terms. Estimate the error involved in this approximation.

(b) How many terms are required to ensure that the sum is accurate to within 0.0005?

SOLUTION In both parts (a) and (b) we need to know $\int_n^\infty f(x)\, dx$. With $f(x) = 1/x^3$, which satisfies the conditions of the Integral Test, we have

$$\int_n^\infty \frac{1}{x^3}\, dx = \lim_{t \to \infty} \left[-\frac{1}{2x^2} \right]_n^t = \lim_{t \to \infty} \left(-\frac{1}{2t^2} + \frac{1}{2n^2} \right) = \frac{1}{2n^2}$$

(a)

$$\sum_{n=1}^\infty \frac{1}{n^3} \approx s_{10} = \frac{1}{1^3} + \frac{1}{2^3} + \frac{1}{3^3} + \cdots + \frac{1}{10^3} \approx 1.1975$$

According to the remainder estimate in (2), we have

$$R_{10} \leqslant \int_{10}^\infty \frac{1}{x^3}\, dx = \frac{1}{2(10)^2} = \frac{1}{200}$$

So the size of the error is at most 0.005.

(b) Accuracy to within 0.0005 means that we have to find a value of n such that $R_n \leqslant 0.0005$. Since

$$R_n \leqslant \int_n^\infty \frac{1}{x^3}\, dx = \frac{1}{2n^2}$$

we want

$$\frac{1}{2n^2} < 0.0005$$

Solving this inequality, we get

$$n^2 > \frac{1}{0.001} = 1000 \qquad \text{or} \qquad n > \sqrt{1000} \approx 31.6$$

We need 32 terms to ensure accuracy to within 0.0005. $\qquad\qquad\qquad\qquad\qquad$ □

If we add s_n to each side of the inequalities in (2), we get

3

$$s_n + \int_{n+1}^{\infty} f(x)\,dx \leqslant s \leqslant s_n + \int_{n}^{\infty} f(x)\,dx$$

because $s_n + R_n = s$. The inequalities in (3) give a lower bound and an upper bound for s. They provide a more accurate approximation to the sum of the series than the partial sum s_n does.

EXAMPLE 6 Use (3) with $n = 10$ to estimate the sum of the series $\displaystyle\sum_{n=1}^{\infty} \frac{1}{n^3}$.

SOLUTION The inequalities in (3) become

$$s_{10} + \int_{11}^{\infty} \frac{1}{x^3}\,dx \leqslant s \leqslant s_{10} + \int_{10}^{\infty} \frac{1}{x^3}\,dx$$

From Example 5 we know that

$$\int_{n}^{\infty} \frac{1}{x^3}\,dx = \frac{1}{2n^2}$$

so

$$s_{10} + \frac{1}{2(11)^2} \leqslant s \leqslant s_{10} + \frac{1}{2(10)^2}$$

Using $s_{10} \approx 1.197532$, we get

$$1.201664 \leqslant s \leqslant 1.202532$$

If we approximate s by the midpoint of this interval, then the error is at most half the length of the interval. So

$$\sum_{n=1}^{\infty} \frac{1}{n^3} \approx 1.2021 \qquad \text{with error} < 0.0005 \qquad\qquad □$$

If we compare Example 6 with Example 5, we see that the improved estimate in (3) can be much better than the estimate $s \approx s_n$. To make the error smaller than 0.0005 we had to use 32 terms in Example 5 but only 10 terms in Example 6.

PROOF OF THE INTEGRAL TEST

We have already seen the basic idea behind the proof of the Integral Test in Figures 1 and 2 for the series $\Sigma \, 1/n^2$ and $\Sigma \, 1/\sqrt{n}$. For the general series $\Sigma \, a_n$, look at Figures 5 and 6. The area of the first shaded rectangle in Figure 5 is the value of f at the right endpoint of $[1, 2]$,

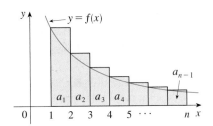

FIGURE 5

that is, $f(2) = a_2$. So, comparing the areas of the shaded rectangles with the area under $y = f(x)$ from 1 to n, we see that

$$\boxed{4} \qquad a_2 + a_3 + \cdots + a_n \leqslant \int_1^n f(x)\, dx$$

(Notice that this inequality depends on the fact that f is decreasing.) Likewise, Figure 6 shows that

$$\boxed{5} \qquad \int_1^n f(x)\, dx \leqslant a_1 + a_2 + \cdots + a_{n-1}$$

(i) If $\int_1^\infty f(x)\, dx$ is convergent, then (4) gives

$$\sum_{i=2}^n a_i \leqslant \int_1^n f(x)\, dx \leqslant \int_1^\infty f(x)\, dx$$

since $f(x) \geqslant 0$. Therefore

$$s_n = a_1 + \sum_{i=2}^n a_i \leqslant a_1 + \int_1^\infty f(x)\, dx = M, \text{ say}$$

Since $s_n \leqslant M$ for all n, the sequence $\{s_n\}$ is bounded above. Also

$$s_{n+1} = s_n + a_{n+1} \geqslant s_n$$

since $a_{n+1} = f(n+1) \geqslant 0$. Thus $\{s_n\}$ is an increasing bounded sequence and so it is convergent by the Monotonic Sequence Theorem (12.1.12). This means that $\Sigma\, a_n$ is convergent.

(ii) If $\int_1^\infty f(x)\, dx$ is divergent, then $\int_1^n f(x)\, dx \to \infty$ as $n \to \infty$ because $f(x) \geqslant 0$. But (5) gives

$$\int_1^n f(x)\, dx \leqslant \sum_{i=1}^{n-1} a_i = s_{n-1}$$

and so $s_{n-1} \to \infty$. This implies that $s_n \to \infty$ and so $\Sigma\, a_n$ diverges. $\qquad \square$

12.3 EXERCISES

1. Draw a picture to show that

$$\sum_{n=2}^\infty \frac{1}{n^{1.3}} < \int_1^\infty \frac{1}{x^{1.3}}\, dx$$

What can you conclude about the series?

2. Suppose f is a continuous positive decreasing function for $x \geqslant 1$ and $a_n = f(n)$. By drawing a picture, rank the following three quantities in increasing order:

$$\int_1^6 f(x)\, dx \qquad \sum_{i=1}^5 a_i \qquad \sum_{i=2}^6 a_i$$

3–8 Use the Integral Test to determine whether the series is convergent or divergent.

3. $\displaystyle\sum_{n=1}^\infty \frac{1}{\sqrt[5]{n}}$

4. $\displaystyle\sum_{n=1}^\infty \frac{1}{n^5}$

5. $\displaystyle\sum_{n=1}^\infty \frac{1}{(2n+1)^3}$

6. $\displaystyle\sum_{n=1}^\infty \frac{1}{\sqrt{n+4}}$

7. $\displaystyle\sum_{n=1}^\infty n e^{-n}$

8. $\displaystyle\sum_{n=1}^\infty \frac{n+2}{n+1}$

9–26 Determine whether the series is convergent or divergent.

9. $\sum_{n=1}^{\infty} \frac{2}{n^{0.85}}$

10. $\sum_{n=1}^{\infty} (n^{-1.4} + 3n^{-1.2})$

11. $1 + \frac{1}{8} + \frac{1}{27} + \frac{1}{64} + \frac{1}{125} + \cdots$

12. $1 + \frac{1}{2\sqrt{2}} + \frac{1}{3\sqrt{3}} + \frac{1}{4\sqrt{4}} + \frac{1}{5\sqrt{5}} + \cdots$

13. $1 + \frac{1}{3} + \frac{1}{5} + \frac{1}{7} + \frac{1}{9} + \cdots$

14. $\frac{1}{5} + \frac{1}{8} + \frac{1}{11} + \frac{1}{14} + \frac{1}{17} + \cdots$

15. $\sum_{n=1}^{\infty} \frac{5 - 2\sqrt{n}}{n^3}$

16. $\sum_{n=1}^{\infty} \frac{n^2}{n^3 + 1}$

17. $\sum_{n=1}^{\infty} \frac{1}{n^2 + 4}$

18. $\sum_{n=1}^{\infty} \frac{3n + 2}{n(n + 1)}$

19. $\sum_{n=1}^{\infty} \frac{\ln n}{n^3}$

20. $\sum_{n=1}^{\infty} \frac{1}{n^2 - 4n + 5}$

21. $\sum_{n=2}^{\infty} \frac{1}{n \ln n}$

22. $\sum_{n=2}^{\infty} \frac{1}{n(\ln n)^2}$

23. $\sum_{n=1}^{\infty} \frac{e^{1/n}}{n^2}$

24. $\sum_{n=3}^{\infty} \frac{n^2}{e^n}$

25. $\sum_{n=1}^{\infty} \frac{1}{n^3 + n}$

26. $\sum_{n=1}^{\infty} \frac{n}{n^4 + 1}$

27–30 Find the values of p for which the series is convergent.

27. $\sum_{n=2}^{\infty} \frac{1}{n(\ln n)^p}$

28. $\sum_{n=3}^{\infty} \frac{1}{n \ln n \, [\ln(\ln n)]^p}$

29. $\sum_{n=1}^{\infty} n(1 + n^2)^p$

30. $\sum_{n=1}^{\infty} \frac{\ln n}{n^p}$

---

31. The Riemann zeta-function ζ is defined by

$$\zeta(x) = \sum_{n=1}^{\infty} \frac{1}{n^x}$$

and is used in number theory to study the distribution of prime numbers. What is the domain of ζ?

32. (a) Find the partial sum s_{10} of the series $\sum_{n=1}^{\infty} 1/n^4$. Estimate the error in using s_{10} as an approximation to the sum of the series.
(b) Use (3) with $n = 10$ to give an improved estimate of the sum.
(c) Find a value of n so that s_n is within 0.00001 of the sum.

33. (a) Use the sum of the first 10 terms to estimate the sum of the series $\sum_{n=1}^{\infty} 1/n^2$. How good is this estimate?
(b) Improve this estimate using (3) with $n = 10$.
(c) Find a value of n that will ensure that the error in the approximation $s \approx s_n$ is less than 0.001.

34. Find the sum of the series $\sum_{n=1}^{\infty} 1/n^5$ correct to three decimal places.

35. Estimate $\sum_{n=1}^{\infty} (2n + 1)^{-6}$ correct to five decimal places.

36. How many terms of the series $\sum_{n=2}^{\infty} 1/[n(\ln n)^2]$ would you need to add to find its sum to within 0.01?

37. Show that if we want to approximate the sum of the series $\sum_{n=1}^{\infty} n^{-1.001}$ so that the error is less than 5 in the ninth decimal place, then we need to add more than $10^{11,301}$ terms!

CAS 38. (a) Show that the series $\sum_{n=1}^{\infty} (\ln n)^2/n^2$ is convergent.
(b) Find an upper bound for the error in the approximation $s \approx s_n$.
(c) What is the smallest value of n such that this upper bound is less than 0.05?
(d) Find s_n for this value of n.

39. (a) Use (4) to show that if s_n is the nth partial sum of the harmonic series, then

$$s_n \le 1 + \ln n$$

(b) The harmonic series diverges, but very slowly. Use part (a) to show that the sum of the first million terms is less than 15 and the sum of the first billion terms is less than 22.

40. Use the following steps to show that the sequence

$$t_n = 1 + \frac{1}{2} + \frac{1}{3} + \cdots + \frac{1}{n} - \ln n$$

has a limit. (The value of the limit is denoted by γ and is called Euler's constant.)
(a) Draw a picture like Figure 6 with $f(x) = 1/x$ and interpret t_n as an area [or use (5)] to show that $t_n > 0$ for all n.
(b) Interpret

$$t_n - t_{n+1} = [\ln(n + 1) - \ln n] - \frac{1}{n + 1}$$

as a difference of areas to show that $t_n - t_{n+1} > 0$. Therefore, $\{t_n\}$ is a decreasing sequence.
(c) Use the Monotonic Sequence Theorem to show that $\{t_n\}$ is convergent.

41. Find all positive values of b for which the series $\sum_{n=1}^{\infty} b^{\ln n}$ converges.

42. Find all values of c for which the following series converges.

$$\sum_{n=1}^{\infty} \left(\frac{c}{n} - \frac{1}{n + 1} \right)$$

12.4 THE COMPARISON TESTS

In the comparison tests the idea is to compare a given series with a series that is known to be convergent or divergent. For instance, the series

$$\boxed{1} \qquad \sum_{n=1}^{\infty} \frac{1}{2^n + 1}$$

reminds us of the series $\sum_{n=1}^{\infty} 1/2^n$, which is a geometric series with $a = \frac{1}{2}$ and $r = \frac{1}{2}$ and is therefore convergent. Because the series (1) is so similar to a convergent series, we have the feeling that it too must be convergent. Indeed, it is. The inequality

$$\frac{1}{2^n + 1} < \frac{1}{2^n}$$

shows that our given series (1) has smaller terms than those of the geometric series and therefore all its partial sums are also smaller than 1 (the sum of the geometric series). This means that its partial sums form a bounded increasing sequence, which is convergent. It also follows that the sum of the series is less than the sum of the geometric series:

$$\sum_{n=1}^{\infty} \frac{1}{2^n + 1} < 1$$

Similar reasoning can be used to prove the following test, which applies only to series whose terms are positive. The first part says that if we have a series whose terms are *smaller* than those of a known *convergent* series, then our series is also convergent. The second part says that if we start with a series whose terms are *larger* than those of a known *divergent* series, then it too is divergent.

THE COMPARISON TEST Suppose that $\Sigma\, a_n$ and $\Sigma\, b_n$ are series with positive terms.

(i) If $\Sigma\, b_n$ is convergent and $a_n \leq b_n$ for all n, then $\Sigma\, a_n$ is also convergent.

(ii) If $\Sigma\, b_n$ is divergent and $a_n \geq b_n$ for all n, then $\Sigma\, a_n$ is also divergent.

■ It is important to keep in mind the distinction between a sequence and a series. A sequence is a list of numbers, whereas a series is a sum. With every series $\Sigma\, a_n$ there are associated two sequences: the sequence $\{a_n\}$ of terms and the sequence $\{s_n\}$ of partial sums.

PROOF

(i) Let $\qquad s_n = \sum_{i=1}^{n} a_i \qquad t_n = \sum_{i=1}^{n} b_i \qquad t = \sum_{n=1}^{\infty} b_n$

Since both series have positive terms, the sequences $\{s_n\}$ and $\{t_n\}$ are increasing $(s_{n+1} = s_n + a_{n+1} \geq s_n)$. Also $t_n \to t$, so $t_n \leq t$ for all n. Since $a_i \leq b_i$, we have $s_n \leq t_n$. Thus $s_n \leq t$ for all n. This means that $\{s_n\}$ is increasing and bounded above and therefore converges by the Monotonic Sequence Theorem. Thus $\Sigma\, a_n$ converges.

(ii) If $\Sigma\, b_n$ is divergent, then $t_n \to \infty$ (since $\{t_n\}$ is increasing). But $a_i \geq b_i$ so $s_n \geq t_n$. Thus $s_n \to \infty$. Therefore $\Sigma\, a_n$ diverges. $\qquad\square$

In using the Comparison Test we must, of course, have some known series $\Sigma\, b_n$ for the purpose of comparison. Most of the time we use one of these series:

Standard Series for Use with the Comparison Test

■ A *p*-series $\left[\Sigma\, 1/n^p \text{ converges if } p > 1 \text{ and diverges if } p \leq 1; \text{ see (12.3.1)}\right]$

■ A geometric series $\left[\Sigma\, ar^{n-1} \text{ converges if } |r| < 1 \text{ and diverges if } |r| \geq 1; \text{ see (12.2.4)}\right]$

☑ **EXAMPLE 1** Determine whether the series $\displaystyle\sum_{n=1}^{\infty} \frac{5}{2n^2 + 4n + 3}$ converges or diverges.

SOLUTION For large n the dominant term in the denominator is $2n^2$ so we compare the given series with the series $\sum 5/(2n^2)$. Observe that

$$\frac{5}{2n^2 + 4n + 3} < \frac{5}{2n^2}$$

because the left side has a bigger denominator. (In the notation of the Comparison Test, a_n is the left side and b_n is the right side.) We know that

$$\sum_{n=1}^{\infty} \frac{5}{2n^2} = \frac{5}{2} \sum_{n=1}^{\infty} \frac{1}{n^2}$$

is convergent because it's a constant times a p-series with $p = 2 > 1$. Therefore

$$\sum_{n=1}^{\infty} \frac{5}{2n^2 + 4n + 3}$$

is convergent by part (i) of the Comparison Test. ☐

NOTE 1 Although the condition $a_n \leq b_n$ or $a_n \geq b_n$ in the Comparison Test is given for all n, we need verify only that it holds for $n \geq N$, where N is some fixed integer, because the convergence of a series is not affected by a finite number of terms. This is illustrated in the next example.

☑ **EXAMPLE 2** Test the series $\displaystyle\sum_{n=1}^{\infty} \frac{\ln n}{n}$ for convergence or divergence.

SOLUTION This series was tested (using the Integral Test) in Example 4 in Section 12.3, but it is also possible to test it by comparing it with the harmonic series. Observe that $\ln n > 1$ for $n \geq 3$ and so

$$\frac{\ln n}{n} > \frac{1}{n} \qquad n \geq 3$$

We know that $\sum 1/n$ is divergent (p-series with $p = 1$). Thus the given series is divergent by the Comparison Test. ☐

NOTE 2 The terms of the series being tested must be smaller than those of a convergent series or larger than those of a divergent series. If the terms are larger than the terms of a convergent series or smaller than those of a divergent series, then the Comparison Test doesn't apply. Consider, for instance, the series

$$\sum_{n=1}^{\infty} \frac{1}{2^n - 1}$$

The inequality

$$\frac{1}{2^n - 1} > \frac{1}{2^n}$$

is useless as far as the Comparison Test is concerned because $\sum b_n = \sum \left(\frac{1}{2}\right)^n$ is convergent and $a_n > b_n$. Nonetheless, we have the feeling that $\sum 1/(2^n - 1)$ ought to be convergent because it is very similar to the convergent geometric series $\sum \left(\frac{1}{2}\right)^n$. In such cases the following test can be used.

■ Exercises 40 and 41 deal with the cases $c = 0$ and $c = \infty$.

THE LIMIT COMPARISON TEST Suppose that $\Sigma\, a_n$ and $\Sigma\, b_n$ are series with positive terms. If

$$\lim_{n\to\infty} \frac{a_n}{b_n} = c$$

where c is a finite number and $c > 0$, then either both series converge or both diverge.

PROOF Let m and M be positive numbers such that $m < c < M$. Because a_n/b_n is close to c for large n, there is an integer N such that

$$m < \frac{a_n}{b_n} < M \qquad \text{when } n > N$$

and so $\qquad\qquad mb_n < a_n < Mb_n \qquad \text{when } n > N$

If $\Sigma\, b_n$ converges, so does $\Sigma\, Mb_n$. Thus $\Sigma\, a_n$ converges by part (i) of the Comparison Test. If $\Sigma\, b_n$ diverges, so does $\Sigma\, mb_n$ and part (ii) of the Comparison Test shows that $\Sigma\, a_n$ diverges. ☐

EXAMPLE 3 Test the series $\displaystyle\sum_{n=1}^{\infty} \frac{1}{2^n - 1}$ for convergence or divergence.

SOLUTION We use the Limit Comparison Test with

$$a_n = \frac{1}{2^n - 1} \qquad\qquad b_n = \frac{1}{2^n}$$

and obtain

$$\lim_{n\to\infty} \frac{a_n}{b_n} = \lim_{n\to\infty} \frac{1/(2^n - 1)}{1/2^n} = \lim_{n\to\infty} \frac{2^n}{2^n - 1} = \lim_{n\to\infty} \frac{1}{1 - 1/2^n} = 1 > 0$$

Since this limit exists and $\Sigma\, 1/2^n$ is a convergent geometric series, the given series converges by the Limit Comparison Test. ☐

EXAMPLE 4 Determine whether the series $\displaystyle\sum_{n=1}^{\infty} \frac{2n^2 + 3n}{\sqrt{5 + n^5}}$ converges or diverges.

SOLUTION The dominant part of the numerator is $2n^2$ and the dominant part of the denominator is $\sqrt{n^5} = n^{5/2}$. This suggests taking

$$a_n = \frac{2n^2 + 3n}{\sqrt{5 + n^5}} \qquad\qquad b_n = \frac{2n^2}{n^{5/2}} = \frac{2}{n^{1/2}}$$

$$\lim_{n\to\infty} \frac{a_n}{b_n} = \lim_{n\to\infty} \frac{2n^2 + 3n}{\sqrt{5 + n^5}} \cdot \frac{n^{1/2}}{2} = \lim_{n\to\infty} \frac{2n^{5/2} + 3n^{3/2}}{2\sqrt{5 + n^5}}$$

$$= \lim_{n\to\infty} \frac{2 + \dfrac{3}{n}}{2\sqrt{\dfrac{5}{n^5} + 1}} = \frac{2 + 0}{2\sqrt{0 + 1}} = 1$$

Since $\Sigma b_n = 2 \Sigma 1/n^{1/2}$ is divergent $\left(p\text{-series with } p = \frac{1}{2} < 1\right)$, the given series diverges by the Limit Comparison Test. $\qquad\qquad\qquad\qquad\qquad\qquad\qquad\qquad\qquad\qquad$ □

Notice that in testing many series we find a suitable comparison series Σb_n by keeping only the highest powers in the numerator and denominator.

ESTIMATING SUMS

If we have used the Comparison Test to show that a series Σa_n converges by comparison with a series Σb_n, then we may be able to estimate the sum Σa_n by comparing remainders. As in Section 12.3, we consider the remainder

$$R_n = s - s_n = a_{n+1} + a_{n+2} + \cdots$$

For the comparison series Σb_n we consider the corresponding remainder

$$T_n = t - t_n = b_{n+1} + b_{n+2} + \cdots$$

Since $a_n \leq b_n$ for all n, we have $R_n \leq T_n$. If Σb_n is a p-series, we can estimate its remainder T_n as in Section 12.3. If Σb_n is a geometric series, then T_n is the sum of a geometric series and we can sum it exactly (see Exercises 35 and 36). In either case we know that R_n is smaller than T_n.

☑ **EXAMPLE 5** Use the sum of the first 100 terms to approximate the sum of the series $\Sigma 1/(n^3 + 1)$. Estimate the error involved in this approximation.

SOLUTION Since

$$\frac{1}{n^3 + 1} < \frac{1}{n^3}$$

the given series is convergent by the Comparison Test. The remainder T_n for the comparison series $\Sigma 1/n^3$ was estimated in Example 5 in Section 12.3 using the Remainder Estimate for the Integral Test. There we found that

$$T_n \leq \int_n^\infty \frac{1}{x^3}\, dx = \frac{1}{2n^2}$$

Therefore the remainder R_n for the given series satisfies

$$R_n \leq T_n \leq \frac{1}{2n^2}$$

With $n = 100$ we have

$$R_{100} \leq \frac{1}{2(100)^2} = 0.00005$$

Using a programmable calculator or a computer, we find that

$$\sum_{n=1}^{\infty} \frac{1}{n^3 + 1} \approx \sum_{n=1}^{100} \frac{1}{n^3 + 1} \approx 0.6864538$$

with error less than 0.00005. $\qquad\qquad\qquad\qquad\qquad\qquad\qquad\qquad\qquad\qquad\qquad$ □

12.4 EXERCISES

1. Suppose $\Sigma\, a_n$ and $\Sigma\, b_n$ are series with positive terms and $\Sigma\, b_n$ is known to be convergent.
  (a) If $a_n > b_n$ for all n, what can you say about $\Sigma\, a_n$? Why?
  (b) If $a_n < b_n$ for all n, what can you say about $\Sigma\, a_n$? Why?

2. Suppose $\Sigma\, a_n$ and $\Sigma\, b_n$ are series with positive terms and $\Sigma\, b_n$ is known to be divergent.
  (a) If $a_n > b_n$ for all n, what can you say about $\Sigma\, a_n$? Why?
  (b) If $a_n < b_n$ for all n, what can you say about $\Sigma\, a_n$? Why?

3–32 Determine whether the series converges or diverges.

3. $\displaystyle\sum_{n=1}^{\infty} \frac{n}{2n^3 + 1}$ **4.** $\displaystyle\sum_{n=2}^{\infty} \frac{n^3}{n^4 - 1}$

5. $\displaystyle\sum_{n=1}^{\infty} \frac{n+1}{n\sqrt{n}}$ **6.** $\displaystyle\sum_{n=1}^{\infty} \frac{n-1}{n^2\sqrt{n}}$

7. $\displaystyle\sum_{n=1}^{\infty} \frac{9^n}{3 + 10^n}$ **8.** $\displaystyle\sum_{n=1}^{\infty} \frac{4 + 3^n}{2^n}$

9. $\displaystyle\sum_{n=1}^{\infty} \frac{\cos^2 n}{n^2 + 1}$ **10.** $\displaystyle\sum_{n=1}^{\infty} \frac{n^2 - 1}{3n^4 + 1}$

11. $\displaystyle\sum_{n=1}^{\infty} \frac{n-1}{n4^n}$ **12.** $\displaystyle\sum_{n=0}^{\infty} \frac{1 + \sin n}{10^n}$

13. $\displaystyle\sum_{n=1}^{\infty} \frac{\arctan n}{n^{1.2}}$ **14.** $\displaystyle\sum_{n=2}^{\infty} \frac{\sqrt{n}}{n - 1}$

15. $\displaystyle\sum_{n=1}^{\infty} \frac{2 + (-1)^n}{n\sqrt{n}}$ **16.** $\displaystyle\sum_{n=1}^{\infty} \frac{1}{\sqrt{n^3 + 1}}$

17. $\displaystyle\sum_{n=1}^{\infty} \frac{1}{\sqrt{n^2 + 1}}$ **18.** $\displaystyle\sum_{n=1}^{\infty} \frac{1}{2n + 3}$

19. $\displaystyle\sum_{n=1}^{\infty} \frac{1 + 4^n}{1 + 3^n}$ **20.** $\displaystyle\sum_{n=1}^{\infty} \frac{n + 4^n}{n + 6^n}$

21. $\displaystyle\sum_{n=1}^{\infty} \frac{\sqrt{n+2}}{2n^2 + n + 1}$ **22.** $\displaystyle\sum_{n=3}^{\infty} \frac{n + 2}{(n+1)^3}$

23. $\displaystyle\sum_{n=1}^{\infty} \frac{5 + 2n}{(1 + n^2)^2}$ **24.** $\displaystyle\sum_{n=1}^{\infty} \frac{n^2 - 5n}{n^3 + n + 1}$

25. $\displaystyle\sum_{n=1}^{\infty} \frac{1 + n + n^2}{\sqrt{1 + n^2 + n^6}}$ **26.** $\displaystyle\sum_{n=1}^{\infty} \frac{n + 5}{\sqrt[3]{n^7 + n^2}}$

27. $\displaystyle\sum_{n=1}^{\infty} \left(1 + \frac{1}{n}\right)^2 e^{-n}$ **28.** $\displaystyle\sum_{n=1}^{\infty} \frac{e^{1/n}}{n}$

29. $\displaystyle\sum_{n=1}^{\infty} \frac{1}{n!}$ **30.** $\displaystyle\sum_{n=1}^{\infty} \frac{n!}{n^n}$

31. $\displaystyle\sum_{n=1}^{\infty} \sin\left(\frac{1}{n}\right)$ **32.** $\displaystyle\sum_{n=1}^{\infty} \frac{1}{n^{1+1/n}}$

33–36 Use the sum of the first 10 terms to approximate the sum of the series. Estimate the error.

33. $\displaystyle\sum_{n=1}^{\infty} \frac{1}{\sqrt{n^4 + 1}}$ **34.** $\displaystyle\sum_{n=1}^{\infty} \frac{\sin^2 n}{n^3}$

35. $\displaystyle\sum_{n=1}^{\infty} \frac{1}{1 + 2^n}$ **36.** $\displaystyle\sum_{n=1}^{\infty} \frac{n}{(n+1)3^n}$

37. The meaning of the decimal representation of a number $0.d_1 d_2 d_3 \ldots$ (where the digit d_i is one of the numbers 0, 1, 2, $\ldots$, 9) is that

$$0.d_1 d_2 d_3 d_4 \ldots = \frac{d_1}{10} + \frac{d_2}{10^2} + \frac{d_3}{10^3} + \frac{d_4}{10^4} + \cdots$$

Show that this series always converges.

38. For what values of p does the series $\sum_{n=2}^{\infty} 1/(n^p \ln n)$ converge?

39. Prove that if $a_n \geq 0$ and $\Sigma\, a_n$ converges, then $\Sigma\, a_n^2$ also converges.

40. (a) Suppose that $\Sigma\, a_n$ and $\Sigma\, b_n$ are series with positive terms and $\Sigma\, b_n$ is convergent. Prove that if

$$\lim_{n\to\infty} \frac{a_n}{b_n} = 0$$

    then $\Sigma\, a_n$ is also convergent.
  (b) Use part (a) to show that the series converges.
    (i) $\displaystyle\sum_{n=1}^{\infty} \frac{\ln n}{n^3}$ (ii) $\displaystyle\sum_{n=1}^{\infty} \frac{\ln n}{\sqrt{n}\, e^n}$

41. (a) Suppose that $\Sigma\, a_n$ and $\Sigma\, b_n$ are series with positive terms and $\Sigma\, b_n$ is divergent. Prove that if

$$\lim_{n\to\infty} \frac{a_n}{b_n} = \infty$$

    then $\Sigma\, a_n$ is also divergent.
  (b) Use part (a) to show that the series diverges.
    (i) $\displaystyle\sum_{n=2}^{\infty} \frac{1}{\ln n}$ (ii) $\displaystyle\sum_{n=1}^{\infty} \frac{\ln n}{n}$

42. Give an example of a pair of series $\Sigma\, a_n$ and $\Sigma\, b_n$ with positive terms where $\lim_{n\to\infty} (a_n/b_n) = 0$ and $\Sigma\, b_n$ diverges, but $\Sigma\, a_n$ converges. (Compare with Exercise 40.)

43. Show that if $a_n > 0$ and $\lim_{n\to\infty} na_n \neq 0$, then $\Sigma\, a_n$ is divergent.

44. Show that if $a_n > 0$ and $\Sigma\, a_n$ is convergent, then $\Sigma\, \ln(1 + a_n)$ is convergent.

45. If $\Sigma\, a_n$ is a convergent series with positive terms, is it true that $\Sigma\, \sin(a_n)$ is also convergent?

46. If $\Sigma\, a_n$ and $\Sigma\, b_n$ are both convergent series with positive terms, is it true that $\Sigma\, a_n b_n$ is also convergent?

12.5 | ALTERNATING SERIES

The convergence tests that we have looked at so far apply only to series with positive terms. In this section and the next we learn how to deal with series whose terms are not necessarily positive. Of particular importance are *alternating series,* whose terms alternate in sign.

An **alternating series** is a series whose terms are alternately positive and negative. Here are two examples:

$$1 - \frac{1}{2} + \frac{1}{3} - \frac{1}{4} + \frac{1}{5} - \frac{1}{6} + \cdots = \sum_{n=1}^{\infty} \frac{(-1)^{n-1}}{n}$$

$$-\frac{1}{2} + \frac{2}{3} - \frac{3}{4} + \frac{4}{5} - \frac{5}{6} + \frac{6}{7} - \cdots = \sum_{n=1}^{\infty} (-1)^n \frac{n}{n+1}$$

We see from these examples that the nth term of an alternating series is of the form

$$a_n = (-1)^{n-1} b_n \qquad \text{or} \qquad a_n = (-1)^n b_n$$

where b_n is a positive number. $\left(\text{In fact, } b_n = |a_n|.\right)$

The following test says that if the terms of an alternating series decrease toward 0 in absolute value, then the series converges.

THE ALTERNATING SERIES TEST If the alternating series

$$\sum_{n=1}^{\infty} (-1)^{n-1} b_n = b_1 - b_2 + b_3 - b_4 + b_5 - b_6 + \cdots \qquad b_n > 0$$

satisfies

(i) $b_{n+1} \le b_n$ for all n

(ii) $\lim_{n \to \infty} b_n = 0$

then the series is convergent.

Before giving the proof let's look at Figure 1, which gives a picture of the idea behind the proof. We first plot $s_1 = b_1$ on a number line. To find s_2 we subtract b_2, so s_2 is to the left of s_1. Then to find s_3 we add b_3, so s_3 is to the right of s_2. But, since $b_3 < b_2$, s_3 is to the left of s_1. Continuing in this manner, we see that the partial sums oscillate back and forth. Since $b_n \to 0$, the successive steps are becoming smaller and smaller. The even partial sums $s_2, s_4, s_6, \ldots$ are increasing and the odd partial sums $s_1, s_3, s_5, \ldots$ are decreasing. Thus it seems plausible that both are converging to some number s, which is the sum of the series. Therefore we consider the even and odd partial sums separately in the following proof.

FIGURE 1

PROOF OF THE ALTERNATING SERIES TEST We first consider the even partial sums:

$$s_2 = b_1 - b_2 \geqslant 0 \qquad \text{since } b_2 \leqslant b_1$$

$$s_4 = s_2 + (b_3 - b_4) \geqslant s_2 \qquad \text{since } b_4 \leqslant b_3$$

In general $\qquad s_{2n} = s_{2n-2} + (b_{2n-1} - b_{2n}) \geqslant s_{2n-2} \qquad \text{since } b_{2n} \leqslant b_{2n-1}$

Thus $\qquad\qquad 0 \leqslant s_2 \leqslant s_4 \leqslant s_6 \leqslant \cdots \leqslant s_{2n} \leqslant \cdots$

But we can also write

$$s_{2n} = b_1 - (b_2 - b_3) - (b_4 - b_5) - \cdots - (b_{2n-2} - b_{2n-1}) - b_{2n}$$

Every term in brackets is positive, so $s_{2n} \leqslant b_1$ for all n. Therefore the sequence $\{s_{2n}\}$ of even partial sums is increasing and bounded above. It is therefore convergent by the Monotonic Sequence Theorem. Let's call its limit s, that is,

$$\lim_{n \to \infty} s_{2n} = s$$

Now we compute the limit of the odd partial sums:

$$\lim_{n \to \infty} s_{2n+1} = \lim_{n \to \infty} (s_{2n} + b_{2n+1})$$

$$= \lim_{n \to \infty} s_{2n} + \lim_{n \to \infty} b_{2n+1}$$

$$= s + 0 \qquad\qquad \text{[by condition (ii)]}$$

$$= s$$

Since both the even and odd partial sums converge to s, we have $\lim_{n \to \infty} s_n = s$ [see Exercise 80(a) in Section 12.1] and so the series is convergent. $\qquad\square$

Figure 2 illustrates Example 1 by showing the graphs of the terms $a_n = (-1)^{n-1}/n$ and the partial sums s_n. Notice how the values of s_n zigzag across the limiting value, which appears to be about 0.7. In fact, it can be proved that the exact sum of the series is $\ln 2 \approx 0.693$ (see Exercise 36).

V EXAMPLE 1 The alternating harmonic series

$$1 - \frac{1}{2} + \frac{1}{3} - \frac{1}{4} + \cdots = \sum_{n=1}^{\infty} \frac{(-1)^{n-1}}{n}$$

satisfies

(i) $b_{n+1} < b_n$ \qquad because $\qquad \dfrac{1}{n+1} < \dfrac{1}{n}$

(ii) $\lim\limits_{n \to \infty} b_n = \lim\limits_{n \to \infty} \dfrac{1}{n} = 0$

so the series is convergent by the Alternating Series Test. $\qquad\square$

V EXAMPLE 2 The series $\displaystyle\sum_{n=1}^{\infty} \frac{(-1)^n 3n}{4n-1}$ is alternating but

$$\lim_{n \to \infty} b_n = \lim_{n \to \infty} \frac{3n}{4n-1} = \lim_{n \to \infty} \frac{3}{4 - \dfrac{1}{n}} = \frac{3}{4}$$

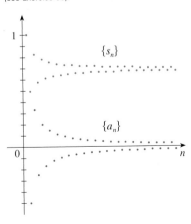

1

$\{s_n\}$

$\{a_n\}$

0

n

FIGURE 2

so condition (ii) is not satisfied. Instead, we look at the limit of the nth term of the series:

$$\lim_{n \to \infty} a_n = \lim_{n \to \infty} \frac{(-1)^n 3n}{4n - 1}$$

This limit does not exist, so the series diverges by the Test for Divergence. ◻

EXAMPLE 3 Test the series $\displaystyle\sum_{n=1}^{\infty} (-1)^{n+1} \frac{n^2}{n^3 + 1}$ for convergence or divergence.

SOLUTION The given series is alternating so we try to verify conditions (i) and (ii) of the Alternating Series Test.

Unlike the situation in Example 1, it is not obvious that the sequence given by $b_n = n^2/(n^3 + 1)$ is decreasing. However, if we consider the related function $f(x) = x^2/(x^3 + 1)$, we find that

$$f'(x) = \frac{x(2 - x^3)}{(x^3 + 1)^2}$$

Since we are considering only positive x, we see that $f'(x) < 0$ if $2 - x^3 < 0$, that is, $x > \sqrt[3]{2}$. Thus f is decreasing on the interval $(\sqrt[3]{2}, \infty)$. This means that $f(n + 1) < f(n)$ and therefore $b_{n+1} < b_n$ when $n \geq 2$. (The inequality $b_2 < b_1$ can be verified directly but all that really matters is that the sequence $\{b_n\}$ is eventually decreasing.)

Condition (ii) is readily verified:

■ Instead of verifying condition (i) of the Alternating Series Test by computing a derivative, we could verify that $b_{n+1} < b_n$ directly by using the technique of Solution 1 of Example 12 in Section 12.1.

$$\lim_{n \to \infty} b_n = \lim_{n \to \infty} \frac{n^2}{n^3 + 1} = \lim_{n \to \infty} \frac{\dfrac{1}{n}}{1 + \dfrac{1}{n^3}} = 0$$

Thus the given series is convergent by the Alternating Series Test. ◻

ESTIMATING SUMS

A partial sum s_n of any convergent series can be used as an approximation to the total sum s, but this is not of much use unless we can estimate the accuracy of the approximation. The error involved in using $s \approx s_n$ is the remainder $R_n = s - s_n$. The next theorem says that for series that satisfy the conditions of the Alternating Series Test, the size of the error is smaller than b_{n+1}, which is the absolute value of the first neglected term.

■ You can see geometrically why the Alternating Series Estimation Theorem is true by looking at Figure 1 (on page 746). Notice that $s - s_4 < b_5$, $|s - s_5| < b_6$, and so on. Notice also that s lies between any two consecutive partial sums.

ALTERNATING SERIES ESTIMATION THEOREM If $s = \Sigma (-1)^{n-1} b_n$ is the sum of an alternating series that satisfies

$$\text{(i) } 0 \leq b_{n+1} \leq b_n \qquad \text{and} \qquad \text{(ii) } \lim_{n \to \infty} b_n = 0$$

then

$$|R_n| = |s - s_n| \leq b_{n+1}$$

PROOF We know from the proof of the Alternating Series Test that s lies between any two consecutive partial sums s_n and s_{n+1}. It follows that

$$|s - s_n| \leq |s_{n+1} - s_n| = b_{n+1} \qquad\qquad ◻$$

V EXAMPLE 4 Find the sum of the series $\sum_{n=0}^{\infty} \frac{(-1)^n}{n!}$ correct to three decimal places. (By definition, $0! = 1$.)

SOLUTION We first observe that the series is convergent by the Alternating Series Test because

(i) $\quad \dfrac{1}{(n+1)!} = \dfrac{1}{n!\,(n+1)} < \dfrac{1}{n!}$

(ii) $\quad 0 < \dfrac{1}{n!} < \dfrac{1}{n} \to 0 \quad$ so $\quad \dfrac{1}{n!} \to 0$ as $n \to \infty$

To get a feel for how many terms we need to use in our approximation, let's write out the first few terms of the series:

$$s = \frac{1}{0!} - \frac{1}{1!} + \frac{1}{2!} - \frac{1}{3!} + \frac{1}{4!} - \frac{1}{5!} + \frac{1}{6!} - \frac{1}{7!} + \cdots$$

$$= 1 - 1 + \tfrac{1}{2} - \tfrac{1}{6} + \tfrac{1}{24} - \tfrac{1}{120} + \tfrac{1}{720} - \tfrac{1}{5040} + \cdots$$

Notice that $\qquad b_7 = \tfrac{1}{5040} < \tfrac{1}{5000} = 0.0002$

and $\qquad s_6 = 1 - 1 + \tfrac{1}{2} - \tfrac{1}{6} + \tfrac{1}{24} - \tfrac{1}{120} + \tfrac{1}{720} \approx 0.368056$

By the Alternating Series Estimation Theorem we know that

$$|s - s_6| \le b_7 < 0.0002$$

This error of less than 0.0002 does not affect the third decimal place, so we have $s \approx 0.368$ correct to three decimal places. $\qquad\square$

■ In Section 12.10 we will prove that $e^x = \sum_{n=0}^{\infty} x^n/n!$ for all x, so what we have obtained in Example 4 is actually an approximation to the number e^{-1}.

⊘ NOTE The rule that the error (in using s_n to approximate s) is smaller than the first neglected term is, in general, valid only for alternating series that satisfy the conditions of the Alternating Series Estimation Theorem. The rule does not apply to other types of series.

12.5 EXERCISES

1. (a) What is an alternating series?
  (b) Under what conditions does an alternating series converge?
  (c) If these conditions are satisfied, what can you say about the remainder after n terms?

2–20 Test the series for convergence or divergence.

2. $-\frac{1}{3} + \frac{2}{4} - \frac{3}{5} + \frac{4}{6} - \frac{5}{7} + \cdots$

3. $\frac{4}{7} - \frac{4}{8} + \frac{4}{9} - \frac{4}{10} + \frac{4}{11} - \cdots$

4. $\dfrac{1}{\sqrt{2}} - \dfrac{1}{\sqrt{3}} + \dfrac{1}{\sqrt{4}} - \dfrac{1}{\sqrt{5}} + \dfrac{1}{\sqrt{6}} - \cdots$

5. $\sum_{n=1}^{\infty} \dfrac{(-1)^{n-1}}{2n+1}$

6. $\sum_{n=1}^{\infty} \dfrac{(-1)^{n-1}}{\ln(n+4)}$

7. $\sum_{n=1}^{\infty} (-1)^n \dfrac{3n-1}{2n+1}$

8. $\sum_{n=1}^{\infty} (-1)^n \dfrac{n}{\sqrt{n^3+2}}$

9. $\sum_{n=1}^{\infty} (-1)^n \dfrac{n}{10^n}$

10. $\sum_{n=1}^{\infty} (-1)^n \dfrac{\sqrt{n}}{1+2\sqrt{n}}$

11. $\sum_{n=1}^{\infty} (-1)^{n+1} \dfrac{n^2}{n^3+4}$

12. $\sum_{n=1}^{\infty} (-1)^{n-1} \dfrac{e^{1/n}}{n}$

13. $\sum_{n=2}^{\infty} (-1)^n \dfrac{n}{\ln n}$

14. $\sum_{n=1}^{\infty} (-1)^{n-1} \dfrac{\ln n}{n}$

15. $\sum_{n=1}^{\infty} \dfrac{\cos n\pi}{n^{3/4}}$

16. $\sum_{n=1}^{\infty} \dfrac{\sin(n\pi/2)}{n!}$

17. $\sum_{n=1}^{\infty} (-1)^n \sin\left(\dfrac{\pi}{n}\right)$

18. $\sum_{n=1}^{\infty} (-1)^n \cos\left(\dfrac{\pi}{n}\right)$

19. $\sum_{n=1}^{\infty} (-1)^n \dfrac{n^n}{n!}$

20. $\sum_{n=1}^{\infty} \left(-\dfrac{n}{5}\right)^n$

21–22 Calculate the first 10 partial sums of the series and graph both the sequence of terms and the sequence of partial sums on the same screen. Estimate the error in using the 10th partial sum to approximate the total sum.

21. $\displaystyle\sum_{n=1}^{\infty} \frac{(-1)^{n-1}}{n^{3/2}}$

22. $\displaystyle\sum_{n=1}^{\infty} \frac{(-1)^{n-1}}{n^3}$

23–26 Show that the series is convergent. How many terms of the series do we need to add in order to find the sum to the indicated accuracy?

23. $\displaystyle\sum_{n=1}^{\infty} \frac{(-1)^{n+1}}{n^6}$ $(|\,\text{error}\,| < 0.00005)$

24. $\displaystyle\sum_{n=1}^{\infty} \frac{(-1)^{n}}{n\,5^n}$ $(|\,\text{error}\,| < 0.0001)$

25. $\displaystyle\sum_{n=0}^{\infty} \frac{(-1)^{n}}{10^n\,n!}$ $(|\,\text{error}\,| < 0.000005)$

26. $\displaystyle\sum_{n=1}^{\infty} (-1)^{n-1} n e^{-n}$ $(|\,\text{error}\,| < 0.01)$

27–30 Approximate the sum of the series correct to four decimal places.

27. $\displaystyle\sum_{n=1}^{\infty} \frac{(-1)^{n+1}}{n^5}$

28. $\displaystyle\sum_{n=1}^{\infty} \frac{(-1)^{n} n}{8^n}$

29. $\displaystyle\sum_{n=1}^{\infty} \frac{(-1)^{n-1} n^2}{10^n}$

30. $\displaystyle\sum_{n=1}^{\infty} \frac{(-1)^{n}}{3^n\,n!}$

31. Is the 50th partial sum s_{50} of the alternating series $\sum_{n=1}^{\infty} (-1)^{n-1}/n$ an overestimate or an underestimate of the total sum? Explain.

32–34 For what values of p is each series convergent?

32. $\displaystyle\sum_{n=1}^{\infty} \frac{(-1)^{n-1}}{n^p}$

33. $\displaystyle\sum_{n=1}^{\infty} \frac{(-1)^{n}}{n+p}$

34. $\displaystyle\sum_{n=2}^{\infty} (-1)^{n-1} \frac{(\ln n)^p}{n}$

35. Show that the series $\sum (-1)^{n-1} b_n$, where $b_n = 1/n$ if n is odd and $b_n = 1/n^2$ if n is even, is divergent. Why does the Alternating Series Test not apply?

36. Use the following steps to show that

$$\sum_{n=1}^{\infty} \frac{(-1)^{n-1}}{n} = \ln 2$$

Let h_n and s_n be the partial sums of the harmonic and alternating harmonic series.
(a) Show that $s_{2n} = h_{2n} - h_n$.
(b) From Exercise 40 in Section 12.3 we have

$$h_n - \ln n \to \gamma \qquad \text{as } n \to \infty$$

and therefore

$$h_{2n} - \ln(2n) \to \gamma \qquad \text{as } n \to \infty$$

Use these facts together with part (a) to show that $s_{2n} \to \ln 2$ as $n \to \infty$.

12.6 ABSOLUTE CONVERGENCE AND THE RATIO AND ROOT TESTS

Given any series $\sum a_n$, we can consider the corresponding series

$$\sum_{n=1}^{\infty} |a_n| = |a_1| + |a_2| + |a_3| + \cdots$$

whose terms are the absolute values of the terms of the original series.

■ We have convergence tests for series with positive terms and for alternating series. But what if the signs of the terms switch back and forth irregularly? We will see in Example 3 that the idea of absolute convergence sometimes helps in such cases.

> **1 DEFINITION** A series $\sum a_n$ is called **absolutely convergent** if the series of absolute values $\sum |a_n|$ is convergent.

Notice that if $\sum a_n$ is a series with positive terms, then $|a_n| = a_n$ and so absolute convergence is the same as convergence in this case.

EXAMPLE 1 The series

$$\sum_{n=1}^{\infty} \frac{(-1)^{n-1}}{n^2} = 1 - \frac{1}{2^2} + \frac{1}{3^2} - \frac{1}{4^2} + \cdots$$

is absolutely convergent because

$$\sum_{n=1}^{\infty} \left| \frac{(-1)^{n-1}}{n^2} \right| = \sum_{n=1}^{\infty} \frac{1}{n^2} = 1 + \frac{1}{2^2} + \frac{1}{3^2} + \frac{1}{4^2} + \cdots$$

is a convergent p-series ($p = 2$). □

EXAMPLE 2 We know that the alternating harmonic series

$$\sum_{n=1}^{\infty} \frac{(-1)^{n-1}}{n} = 1 - \frac{1}{2} + \frac{1}{3} - \frac{1}{4} + \cdots$$

is convergent (see Example 1 in Section 12.5), but it is not absolutely convergent because the corresponding series of absolute values is

$$\sum_{n=1}^{\infty} \left| \frac{(-1)^{n-1}}{n} \right| = \sum_{n=1}^{\infty} \frac{1}{n} = 1 + \frac{1}{2} + \frac{1}{3} + \frac{1}{4} + \cdots$$

which is the harmonic series (p-series with $p = 1$) and is therefore divergent. □

> **2 DEFINITION** A series $\Sigma\, a_n$ is called **conditionally convergent** if it is convergent but not absolutely convergent.

Example 2 shows that the alternating harmonic series is conditionally convergent. Thus it is possible for a series to be convergent but not absolutely convergent. However, the next theorem shows that absolute convergence implies convergence.

> **3 THEOREM** If a series $\Sigma\, a_n$ is absolutely convergent, then it is convergent.

PROOF Observe that the inequality

$$0 \leq a_n + |a_n| \leq 2|a_n|$$

is true because $|a_n|$ is either a_n or $-a_n$. If $\Sigma\, a_n$ is absolutely convergent, then $\Sigma\, |a_n|$ is convergent, so $\Sigma\, 2|a_n|$ is convergent. Therefore, by the Comparison Test, $\Sigma\, (a_n + |a_n|)$ is convergent. Then

$$\sum a_n = \sum (a_n + |a_n|) - \sum |a_n|$$

is the difference of two convergent series and is therefore convergent. □

■ Figure 1 shows the graphs of the terms a_n and partial sums s_n of the series in Example 3. Notice that the series is not alternating but has positive and negative terms.

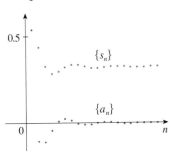

FIGURE I

▼ EXAMPLE 3 Determine whether the series

$$\sum_{n=1}^{\infty} \frac{\cos n}{n^2} = \frac{\cos 1}{1^2} + \frac{\cos 2}{2^2} + \frac{\cos 3}{3^2} + \cdots$$

is convergent or divergent.

SOLUTION This series has both positive and negative terms, but it is not alternating. (The first term is positive, the next three are negative, and the following three are positive: The signs change irregularly.) We can apply the Comparison Test to the series of absolute values

$$\sum_{n=1}^{\infty} \left| \frac{\cos n}{n^2} \right| = \sum_{n=1}^{\infty} \frac{|\cos n|}{n^2}$$

Since $|\cos n| \leq 1$ for all n, we have

$$\frac{|\cos n|}{n^2} \leq \frac{1}{n^2}$$

We know that $\Sigma \, 1/n^2$ is convergent (p-series with $p = 2$) and therefore $\Sigma \, |\cos n|/n^2$ is convergent by the Comparison Test. Thus the given series $\Sigma \, (\cos n)/n^2$ is absolutely convergent and therefore convergent by Theorem 3.   □

The following test is very useful in determining whether a given series is absolutely convergent.

THE RATIO TEST

(i) If $\displaystyle\lim_{n \to \infty} \left| \frac{a_{n+1}}{a_n} \right| = L < 1$, then the series $\displaystyle\sum_{n=1}^{\infty} a_n$ is absolutely convergent
(and therefore convergent).

(ii) If $\displaystyle\lim_{n \to \infty} \left| \frac{a_{n+1}}{a_n} \right| = L > 1$ or $\displaystyle\lim_{n \to \infty} \left| \frac{a_{n+1}}{a_n} \right| = \infty$, then the series $\displaystyle\sum_{n=1}^{\infty} a_n$
is divergent.

(iii) If $\displaystyle\lim_{n \to \infty} \left| \frac{a_{n+1}}{a_n} \right| = 1$, the Ratio Test is inconclusive; that is, no conclusion can be
drawn about the convergence or divergence of $\Sigma \, a_n$.

PROOF

(i) The idea is to compare the given series with a convergent geometric series. Since $L < 1$, we can choose a number r such that $L < r < 1$. Since

$$\lim_{n \to \infty} \left| \frac{a_{n+1}}{a_n} \right| = L \quad \text{and} \quad L < r$$

the ratio $|a_{n+1}/a_n|$ will eventually be less than r; that is, there exists an integer N such that

$$\left| \frac{a_{n+1}}{a_n} \right| < r \quad \text{whenever} \ n \geq N$$

or, equivalently,

$$\boxed{4} \qquad |a_{n+1}| < |a_n| r \quad \text{whenever} \ n \geq N$$

Putting n successively equal to N, $N + 1$, $N + 2$, ... in (4), we obtain

$$|a_{N+1}| < |a_N| r$$

$$|a_{N+2}| < |a_{N+1}| r < |a_N| r^2$$

$$|a_{N+3}| < |a_{N+2}| r < |a_N| r^3$$

and, in general,

$$\boxed{5} \qquad |a_{N+k}| < |a_N| r^k \quad \text{for all} \ k \geq 1$$

Now the series

$$\sum_{k=1}^{\infty} |a_N| r^k = |a_N| r + |a_N| r^2 + |a_N| r^3 + \cdots$$

is convergent because it is a geometric series with $0 < r < 1$. So the inequality (5), together with the Comparison Test, shows that the series

$$\sum_{n=N+1}^{\infty} |a_n| = \sum_{k=1}^{\infty} |a_{N+k}| = |a_{N+1}| + |a_{N+2}| + |a_{N+3}| + \cdots$$

is also convergent. It follows that the series $\sum_{n=1}^{\infty} |a_n|$ is convergent. (Recall that a finite number of terms doesn't affect convergence.) Therefore $\sum a_n$ is absolutely convergent.

(ii) If $|a_{n+1}/a_n| \to L > 1$ or $|a_{n+1}/a_n| \to \infty$, then the ratio $|a_{n+1}/a_n|$ will eventually be greater than 1; that is, there exists an integer N such that

$$\left| \frac{a_{n+1}}{a_n} \right| > 1 \qquad \text{whenever } n \geqslant N$$

This means that $|a_{n+1}| > |a_n|$ whenever $n \geqslant N$ and so

$$\lim_{n \to \infty} a_n \neq 0$$

Therefore $\sum a_n$ diverges by the Test for Divergence. □

NOTE Part (iii) of the Ratio Test says that if $\lim_{n \to \infty} |a_{n+1}/a_n| = 1$, the test gives no information. For instance, for the convergent series $\sum 1/n^2$ we have

$$\left| \frac{a_{n+1}}{a_n} \right| = \frac{\dfrac{1}{(n+1)^2}}{\dfrac{1}{n^2}} = \frac{n^2}{(n+1)^2} = \frac{1}{\left(1 + \dfrac{1}{n}\right)^2} \to 1 \qquad \text{as } n \to \infty$$

whereas for the divergent series $\sum 1/n$ we have

$$\left| \frac{a_{n+1}}{a_n} \right| = \frac{\dfrac{1}{n+1}}{\dfrac{1}{n}} = \frac{n}{n+1} = \frac{1}{1 + \dfrac{1}{n}} \to 1 \qquad \text{as } n \to \infty$$

Therefore, if $\lim_{n \to \infty} |a_{n+1}/a_n| = 1$, the series $\sum a_n$ might converge or it might diverge. In this case the Ratio Test fails and we must use some other test.

EXAMPLE 4 Test the series $\sum_{n=1}^{\infty} (-1)^n \dfrac{n^3}{3^n}$ for absolute convergence.

ESTIMATING SUMS
In the last three sections we used various methods for estimating the sum of a series—the method depended on which test was used to prove convergence. What about series for which the Ratio Test works? There are two possibilities: If the series happens to be an alternating series, as in Example 4, then it is best to use the methods of Section 12.5. If the terms are all positive, then use the special methods explained in Exercise 34.

SOLUTION We use the Ratio Test with $a_n = (-1)^n n^3 / 3^n$:

$$\left| \frac{a_{n+1}}{a_n} \right| = \left| \frac{\dfrac{(-1)^{n+1}(n+1)^3}{3^{n+1}}}{\dfrac{(-1)^n n^3}{3^n}} \right| = \frac{(n+1)^3}{3^{n+1}} \cdot \frac{3^n}{n^3}$$

$$= \frac{1}{3} \left(\frac{n+1}{n} \right)^3 = \frac{1}{3} \left(1 + \frac{1}{n} \right)^3 \to \frac{1}{3} < 1$$

Thus, by the Ratio Test, the given series is absolutely convergent and therefore convergent. □

▼ EXAMPLE 5 Test the convergence of the series $\sum_{n=1}^{\infty} \dfrac{n^n}{n!}$.

SOLUTION Since the terms $a_n = n^n/n!$ are positive, we don't need the absolute value signs.

$$\frac{a_{n+1}}{a_n} = \frac{(n+1)^{n+1}}{(n+1)!} \cdot \frac{n!}{n^n} = \frac{(n+1)(n+1)^n}{(n+1)n!} \cdot \frac{n!}{n^n}$$

$$= \left(\frac{n+1}{n}\right)^n = \left(1 + \frac{1}{n}\right)^n \to e \qquad \text{as } n \to \infty$$

(See Equation 7.4.9 or 7.4*.9.) Since $e > 1$, the given series is divergent by the Ratio Test. □

NOTE Although the Ratio Test works in Example 5, an easier method is to use the Test for Divergence. Since

$$a_n = \frac{n^n}{n!} = \frac{n \cdot n \cdot n \cdot \cdots \cdot n}{1 \cdot 2 \cdot 3 \cdot \cdots \cdot n} \geq n$$

it follows that a_n does not approach 0 as $n \to \infty$. Therefore the given series is divergent by the Test for Divergence.

The following test is convenient to apply when nth powers occur. Its proof is similar to the proof of the Ratio Test and is left as Exercise 37.

THE ROOT TEST

(i) If $\lim\limits_{n \to \infty} \sqrt[n]{|a_n|} = L < 1$, then the series $\sum_{n=1}^{\infty} a_n$ is absolutely convergent (and therefore convergent).

(ii) If $\lim\limits_{n \to \infty} \sqrt[n]{|a_n|} = L > 1$ or $\lim\limits_{n \to \infty} \sqrt[n]{|a_n|} = \infty$, then the series $\sum_{n=1}^{\infty} a_n$ is divergent.

(iii) If $\lim\limits_{n \to \infty} \sqrt[n]{|a_n|} = 1$, the Root Test is inconclusive.

If $\lim_{n \to \infty} \sqrt[n]{|a_n|} = 1$, then part (iii) of the Root Test says that the test gives no information. The series $\sum a_n$ could converge or diverge. (If $L = 1$ in the Ratio Test, don't try the Root Test because L will again be 1. And if $L = 1$ in the Root Test, don't try the Ratio Test because it will fail too.)

▼ EXAMPLE 6 Test the convergence of the series $\sum_{n=1}^{\infty} \left(\dfrac{2n+3}{3n+2}\right)^n$.

SOLUTION

$$a_n = \left(\frac{2n+3}{3n+2}\right)^n$$

$$\sqrt[n]{|a_n|} = \frac{2n+3}{3n+2} = \frac{2 + \dfrac{3}{n}}{3 + \dfrac{2}{n}} \to \frac{2}{3} < 1$$

Thus the given series converges by the Root Test. □

REARRANGEMENTS

The question of whether a given convergent series is absolutely convergent or conditionally convergent has a bearing on the question of whether infinite sums behave like finite sums.

If we rearrange the order of the terms in a finite sum, then of course the value of the sum remains unchanged. But this is not always the case for an infinite series. By a **rearrangement** of an infinite series $\Sigma\, a_n$ we mean a series obtained by simply changing the order of the terms. For instance, a rearrangement of $\Sigma\, a_n$ could start as follows:

$$a_1 + a_2 + a_5 + a_3 + a_4 + a_{15} + a_6 + a_7 + a_{20} + \cdots$$

It turns out that

if $\Sigma\, a_n$ is an absolutely convergent series with sum s,
then any rearrangement of $\Sigma\, a_n$ has the same sum s.

However, any conditionally convergent series can be rearranged to give a different sum. To illustrate this fact let's consider the alternating harmonic series

$$\boxed{6} \qquad 1 - \tfrac{1}{2} + \tfrac{1}{3} - \tfrac{1}{4} + \tfrac{1}{5} - \tfrac{1}{6} + \tfrac{1}{7} - \tfrac{1}{8} + \cdots = \ln 2$$

(See Exercise 36 in Section 12.5.) If we multiply this series by $\tfrac{1}{2}$, we get

$$\tfrac{1}{2} - \tfrac{1}{4} + \tfrac{1}{6} - \tfrac{1}{8} + \cdots = \tfrac{1}{2}\ln 2$$

Inserting zeros between the terms of this series, we have

■ Adding these zeros does not affect the sum of the series; each term in the sequence of partial sums is repeated, but the limit is the same.

$$\boxed{7} \qquad 0 + \tfrac{1}{2} + 0 - \tfrac{1}{4} + 0 + \tfrac{1}{6} + 0 - \tfrac{1}{8} + \cdots = \tfrac{1}{2}\ln 2$$

Now we add the series in Equations 6 and 7 using Theorem 12.2.8:

$$\boxed{8} \qquad 1 + \tfrac{1}{3} - \tfrac{1}{2} + \tfrac{1}{5} + \tfrac{1}{7} - \tfrac{1}{4} + \cdots = \tfrac{3}{2}\ln 2$$

Notice that the series in (8) contains the same terms as in (6), but rearranged so that one negative term occurs after each pair of positive terms. The sums of these series, however, are different. In fact, Riemann proved that

if $\Sigma\, a_n$ is a conditionally convergent series and r is any real number whatsoever, then there is a rearrangement of $\Sigma\, a_n$ that has a sum equal to r.

A proof of this fact is outlined in Exercise 40.

12.6 EXERCISES

1. What can you say about the series $\Sigma\, a_n$ in each of the following cases?

(a) $\displaystyle \lim_{n \to \infty} \left| \frac{a_{n+1}}{a_n} \right| = 8$ 　　(b) $\displaystyle \lim_{n \to \infty} \left| \frac{a_{n+1}}{a_n} \right| = 0.8$

(c) $\displaystyle \lim_{n \to \infty} \left| \frac{a_{n+1}}{a_n} \right| = 1$

2–28 Determine whether the series is absolutely convergent, conditionally convergent, or divergent.

2. $\displaystyle \sum_{n=1}^{\infty} \frac{n^2}{2^n}$

3. $\displaystyle \sum_{n=0}^{\infty} \frac{(-10)^n}{n!}$

4. $\displaystyle \sum_{n=1}^{\infty} (-1)^{n-1} \frac{2^n}{n^4}$

5. $\displaystyle \sum_{n=1}^{\infty} \frac{(-1)^{n+1}}{\sqrt[4]{n}}$

6. $\displaystyle \sum_{n=1}^{\infty} \frac{(-1)^n}{n^4}$

7. $\displaystyle \sum_{k=1}^{\infty} k\left(\tfrac{2}{3}\right)^k$

8. $\displaystyle \sum_{n=1}^{\infty} \frac{n!}{100^n}$

9. $\displaystyle \sum_{n=1}^{\infty} (-1)^n \frac{(1.1)^n}{n^4}$

10. $\displaystyle \sum_{n=1}^{\infty} (-1)^n \frac{n}{\sqrt{n^3 + 2}}$

11. $\displaystyle \sum_{n=1}^{\infty} \frac{(-1)^n e^{1/n}}{n^3}$

12. $\displaystyle \sum_{n=1}^{\infty} \frac{\sin 4n}{4^n}$

13. $\displaystyle \sum_{n=1}^{\infty} \frac{10^n}{(n+1)4^{2n+1}}$

14. $\displaystyle \sum_{n=1}^{\infty} (-1)^{n+1} \frac{n^2 2^n}{n!}$

15. $\displaystyle\sum_{n=1}^{\infty} \frac{(-1)^n \arctan n}{n^2}$

16. $\displaystyle\sum_{n=1}^{\infty} \frac{3 - \cos n}{n^{2/3} - 2}$

17. $\displaystyle\sum_{n=2}^{\infty} \frac{(-1)^n}{\ln n}$

18. $\displaystyle\sum_{n=1}^{\infty} \frac{n!}{n^n}$

19. $\displaystyle\sum_{n=1}^{\infty} \frac{\cos(n\pi/3)}{n!}$

20. $\displaystyle\sum_{n=1}^{\infty} \frac{(-2)^n}{n^n}$

21. $\displaystyle\sum_{n=1}^{\infty} \left(\frac{n^2 + 1}{2n^2 + 1}\right)^n$

22. $\displaystyle\sum_{n=2}^{\infty} \left(\frac{-2n}{n + 1}\right)^{5n}$

23. $\displaystyle\sum_{n=1}^{\infty} \left(1 + \frac{1}{n}\right)^{n^2}$

24. $\displaystyle\sum_{n=2}^{\infty} \frac{n}{(\ln n)^n}$

25. $1 - \dfrac{1 \cdot 3}{3!} + \dfrac{1 \cdot 3 \cdot 5}{5!} - \dfrac{1 \cdot 3 \cdot 5 \cdot 7}{7!} + \cdots$

$\quad + (-1)^{n-1} \dfrac{1 \cdot 3 \cdot 5 \cdot \cdots \cdot (2n - 1)}{(2n - 1)!} + \cdots$

26. $\dfrac{2}{5} + \dfrac{2 \cdot 6}{5 \cdot 8} + \dfrac{2 \cdot 6 \cdot 10}{5 \cdot 8 \cdot 11} + \dfrac{2 \cdot 6 \cdot 10 \cdot 14}{5 \cdot 8 \cdot 11 \cdot 14} + \cdots$

27. $\displaystyle\sum_{n=1}^{\infty} \frac{2 \cdot 4 \cdot 6 \cdot \cdots \cdot (2n)}{n!}$

28. $\displaystyle\sum_{n=1}^{\infty} (-1)^n \frac{2^n n!}{5 \cdot 8 \cdot 11 \cdot \cdots \cdot (3n + 2)}$

---

29. The terms of a series are defined recursively by the equations

$$a_1 = 2 \qquad a_{n+1} = \frac{5n + 1}{4n + 3} a_n$$

Determine whether $\Sigma\, a_n$ converges or diverges.

30. A series $\Sigma\, a_n$ is defined by the equations

$$a_1 = 1 \qquad a_{n+1} = \frac{2 + \cos n}{\sqrt{n}} a_n$$

Determine whether $\Sigma\, a_n$ converges or diverges.

31. For which of the following series is the Ratio Test inconclusive (that is, it fails to give a definite answer)?

(a) $\displaystyle\sum_{n=1}^{\infty} \frac{1}{n^3}$

(b) $\displaystyle\sum_{n=1}^{\infty} \frac{n}{2^n}$

(c) $\displaystyle\sum_{n=1}^{\infty} \frac{(-3)^{n-1}}{\sqrt{n}}$

(d) $\displaystyle\sum_{n=1}^{\infty} \frac{\sqrt{n}}{1 + n^2}$

32. For which positive integers k is the following series convergent?

$$\sum_{n=1}^{\infty} \frac{(n!)^2}{(kn)!}$$

33. (a) Show that $\sum_{n=0}^{\infty} x^n/n!$ converges for all x.
(b) Deduce that $\lim_{n \to \infty} x^n/n! = 0$ for all x.

34. Let $\Sigma\, a_n$ be a series with positive terms and let $r_n = a_{n+1}/a_n$. Suppose that $\lim_{n \to \infty} r_n = L < 1$, so $\Sigma\, a_n$ converges by the

Ratio Test. As usual, we let R_n be the remainder after n terms, that is,

$$R_n = a_{n+1} + a_{n+2} + a_{n+3} + \cdots$$

(a) If $\{r_n\}$ is a decreasing sequence and $r_{n+1} < 1$, show, by summing a geometric series, that

$$R_n \leq \frac{a_{n+1}}{1 - r_{n+1}}$$

(b) If $\{r_n\}$ is an increasing sequence, show that

$$R_n \leq \frac{a_{n+1}}{1 - L}$$

35. (a) Find the partial sum s_5 of the series $\sum_{n=1}^{\infty} 1/n2^n$. Use Exercise 34 to estimate the error in using s_5 as an approximation to the sum of the series.
(b) Find a value of n so that s_n is within 0.00005 of the sum. Use this value of n to approximate the sum of the series.

36. Use the sum of the first 10 terms to approximate the sum of the series

$$\sum_{n=1}^{\infty} \frac{n}{2^n}$$

Use Exercise 34 to estimate the error.

37. Prove the Root Test. [*Hint for part (i):* Take any number r such that $L < r < 1$ and use the fact that there is an integer N such that $\sqrt[n]{|a_n|} < r$ whenever $n \geq N$.]

38. Around 1910, the Indian mathematician Srinivasa Ramanujan discovered the formula

$$\frac{1}{\pi} = \frac{2\sqrt{2}}{9801} \sum_{n=0}^{\infty} \frac{(4n)!(1103 + 26390n)}{(n!)^4 396^{4n}}$$

William Gosper used this series in 1985 to compute the first 17 million digits of π.
(a) Verify that the series is convergent.
(b) How many correct decimal places of π do you get if you use just the first term of the series? What if you use two terms?

39. Given any series $\Sigma\, a_n$, we define a series $\Sigma\, a_n^+$ whose terms are all the positive terms of $\Sigma\, a_n$ and a series $\Sigma\, a_n^-$ whose terms are all the negative terms of $\Sigma\, a_n$. To be specific, we let

$$a_n^+ = \frac{a_n + |a_n|}{2} \qquad a_n^- = \frac{a_n - |a_n|}{2}$$

Notice that if $a_n > 0$, then $a_n^+ = a_n$ and $a_n^- = 0$, whereas if $a_n < 0$, then $a_n^- = a_n$ and $a_n^+ = 0$.
(a) If $\Sigma\, a_n$ is absolutely convergent, show that both of the series $\Sigma\, a_n^+$ and $\Sigma\, a_n^-$ are convergent.
(b) If $\Sigma\, a_n$ is conditionally convergent, show that both of the series $\Sigma\, a_n^+$ and $\Sigma\, a_n^-$ are divergent.

40. Prove that if $\Sigma\, a_n$ is a conditionally convergent series and r is any real number, then there is a rearrangement of $\Sigma\, a_n$ whose sum is r. [*Hints:* Use the notation of Exercise 39. Take just enough positive terms a_n^+ so that their sum is greater than r. Then add just enough negative terms a_n^- so that the cumulative sum is less than r. Continue in this manner and use Theorem 12.2.6.]

| 12.7 | STRATEGY FOR TESTING SERIES |

We now have several ways of testing a series for convergence or divergence; the problem is to decide which test to use on which series. In this respect, testing series is similar to integrating functions. Again there are no hard and fast rules about which test to apply to a given series, but you may find the following advice of some use.

It is not wise to apply a list of the tests in a specific order until one finally works. That would be a waste of time and effort. Instead, as with integration, the main strategy is to classify the series according to its *form*.

1. If the series is of the form $\sum 1/n^p$, it is a *p*-series, which we know to be convergent if $p > 1$ and divergent if $p \leqslant 1$.

2. If the series has the form $\sum ar^{n-1}$ or $\sum ar^n$, it is a geometric series, which converges if $|r| < 1$ and diverges if $|r| \geqslant 1$. Some preliminary algebraic manipulation may be required to bring the series into this form.

3. If the series has a form that is similar to a *p*-series or a geometric series, then one of the comparison tests should be considered. In particular, if a_n is a rational function or an algebraic function of *n* (involving roots of polynomials), then the series should be compared with a *p*-series. Notice that most of the series in Exercises 12.4 have this form. (The value of *p* should be chosen as in Section 12.4 by keeping only the highest powers of *n* in the numerator and denominator.) The comparison tests apply only to series with positive terms, but if $\sum a_n$ has some negative terms, then we can apply the Comparison Test to $\sum |a_n|$ and test for absolute convergence.

4. If you can see at a glance that $\lim_{n \to \infty} a_n \neq 0$, then the Test for Divergence should be used.

5. If the series is of the form $\sum (-1)^{n-1} b_n$ or $\sum (-1)^n b_n$, then the Alternating Series Test is an obvious possibility.

6. Series that involve factorials or other products (including a constant raised to the *n*th power) are often conveniently tested using the Ratio Test. Bear in mind that $|a_{n+1}/a_n| \to 1$ as $n \to \infty$ for all *p*-series and therefore all rational or algebraic functions of *n*. Thus the Ratio Test should not be used for such series.

7. If a_n is of the form $(b_n)^n$, then the Root Test may be useful.

8. If $a_n = f(n)$, where $\int_1^\infty f(x)\, dx$ is easily evaluated, then the Integral Test is effective (assuming the hypotheses of this test are satisfied).

In the following examples we don't work out all the details but simply indicate which tests should be used.

☑ EXAMPLE 1 $\displaystyle\sum_{n=1}^{\infty} \frac{n-1}{2n+1}$

Since $a_n \to \frac{1}{2} \neq 0$ as $n \to \infty$, we should use the Test for Divergence. ☐

EXAMPLE 2 $\displaystyle\sum_{n=1}^{\infty} \frac{\sqrt{n^3+1}}{3n^3+4n^2+2}$

Since a_n is an algebraic function of *n*, we compare the given series with a *p*-series. The comparison series for the Limit Comparison Test is $\Sigma\, b_n$, where

$$b_n = \frac{\sqrt{n^3}}{3n^3} = \frac{n^{3/2}}{3n^3} = \frac{1}{3n^{3/2}}$$

☐

☑ EXAMPLE 3 $\displaystyle\sum_{n=1}^{\infty} n e^{-n^2}$

Since the integral $\int_1^{\infty} x e^{-x^2}\, dx$ is easily evaluated, we use the Integral Test. The Ratio Test also works.

☐

EXAMPLE 4 $\displaystyle\sum_{n=1}^{\infty} (-1)^n \frac{n^3}{n^4 + 1}$

Since the series is alternating, we use the Alternating Series Test.

☐

☑ EXAMPLE 5 $\displaystyle\sum_{k=1}^{\infty} \frac{2^k}{k!}$

Since the series involves $k!$, we use the Ratio Test.

☐

EXAMPLE 6 $\displaystyle\sum_{n=1}^{\infty} \frac{1}{2 + 3^n}$

Since the series is closely related to the geometric series $\Sigma\, 1/3^n$, we use the Comparison Test.

☐

12.7 EXERCISES

1–38 Test the series for convergence or divergence.

1. $\displaystyle\sum_{n=1}^{\infty} \frac{1}{n + 3^n}$

2. $\displaystyle\sum_{n=1}^{\infty} \frac{(2n + 1)^n}{n^{2n}}$

3. $\displaystyle\sum_{n=1}^{\infty} (-1)^n \frac{n}{n + 2}$

4. $\displaystyle\sum_{n=1}^{\infty} (-1)^n \frac{n}{n^2 + 2}$

5. $\displaystyle\sum_{n=1}^{\infty} \frac{n^2\, 2^{n-1}}{(-5)^n}$

6. $\displaystyle\sum_{n=1}^{\infty} \frac{1}{2n + 1}$

7. $\displaystyle\sum_{n=2}^{\infty} \frac{1}{n\sqrt{\ln n}}$

8. $\displaystyle\sum_{k=1}^{\infty} \frac{2^k k!}{(k + 2)!}$

9. $\displaystyle\sum_{k=1}^{\infty} k^2 e^{-k}$

10. $\displaystyle\sum_{n=1}^{\infty} n^2 e^{-n^3}$

11. $\displaystyle\sum_{n=2}^{\infty} \frac{(-1)^{n+1}}{n \ln n}$

12. $\displaystyle\sum_{n=1}^{\infty} \sin n$

13. $\displaystyle\sum_{n=1}^{\infty} \frac{3^n n^2}{n!}$

14. $\displaystyle\sum_{n=1}^{\infty} \frac{\sin 2n}{1 + 2^n}$

15. $\displaystyle\sum_{n=0}^{\infty} \frac{n!}{2 \cdot 5 \cdot 8 \cdot \,\cdots\, \cdot (3n + 2)}$

16. $\displaystyle\sum_{n=1}^{\infty} \frac{n^2 + 1}{n^3 + 1}$

17. $\displaystyle\sum_{n=1}^{\infty} (-1)^n 2^{1/n}$

18. $\displaystyle\sum_{n=2}^{\infty} \frac{(-1)^{n-1}}{\sqrt{n} - 1}$

19. $\displaystyle\sum_{n=1}^{\infty} (-1)^n \frac{\ln n}{\sqrt{n}}$

20. $\displaystyle\sum_{k=1}^{\infty} \frac{k + 5}{5^k}$

21. $\displaystyle\sum_{n=1}^{\infty} \frac{(-2)^{2n}}{n^n}$

22. $\displaystyle\sum_{n=1}^{\infty} \frac{\sqrt{n^2 - 1}}{n^3 + 2n^2 + 5}$

23. $\displaystyle\sum_{n=1}^{\infty} \tan(1/n)$

24. $\displaystyle\sum_{n=1}^{\infty} n \sin(1/n)$

25. $\displaystyle\sum_{n=1}^{\infty} \frac{n!}{e^{n^2}}$

26. $\displaystyle\sum_{n=1}^{\infty} \frac{n^2 + 1}{5^n}$

27. $\displaystyle\sum_{k=1}^{\infty} \frac{k \ln k}{(k + 1)^3}$

28. $\displaystyle\sum_{n=1}^{\infty} \frac{e^{1/n}}{n^2}$

29. $\displaystyle\sum_{n=1}^{\infty} \frac{(-1)^n}{\cosh n}$

30. $\displaystyle\sum_{j=1}^{\infty} (-1)^j \frac{\sqrt{j}}{j + 5}$

31. $\displaystyle\sum_{k=1}^{\infty} \frac{5^k}{3^k + 4^k}$

32. $\displaystyle\sum_{n=1}^{\infty} \frac{(n!)^n}{n^{4n}}$

33. $\displaystyle\sum_{n=1}^{\infty} \frac{\sin(1/n)}{\sqrt{n}}$

34. $\displaystyle\sum_{n=1}^{\infty} \frac{1}{n + n \cos^2 n}$

35. $\displaystyle\sum_{n=1}^{\infty} \left(\frac{n}{n + 1}\right)^{n^2}$

36. $\displaystyle\sum_{n=2}^{\infty} \frac{1}{(\ln n)^{\ln n}}$

37. $\displaystyle\sum_{n=1}^{\infty} \left(\sqrt[n]{2} - 1\right)^n$

38. $\displaystyle\sum_{n=1}^{\infty} \left(\sqrt[n]{2} - 1\right)$

12.8 POWER SERIES

A **power series** is a series of the form

$$\boxed{1} \qquad \sum_{n=0}^{\infty} c_n x^n = c_0 + c_1 x + c_2 x^2 + c_3 x^3 + \cdots$$

where x is a variable and the c_n's are constants called the **coefficients** of the series. For each fixed x, the series (1) is a series of constants that we can test for convergence or divergence. A power series may converge for some values of x and diverge for other values of x. The sum of the series is a function

$$f(x) = c_0 + c_1 x + c_2 x^2 + \cdots + c_n x^n + \cdots$$

whose domain is the set of all x for which the series converges. Notice that f resembles a polynomial. The only difference is that f has infinitely many terms.

For instance, if we take $c_n = 1$ for all n, the power series becomes the geometric series

$$\sum_{n=0}^{\infty} x^n = 1 + x + x^2 + \cdots + x^n + \cdots$$

which converges when $-1 < x < 1$ and diverges when $|x| \geq 1$ (see Equation 12.2.5).

More generally, a series of the form

$$\boxed{2} \qquad \sum_{n=0}^{\infty} c_n(x - a)^n = c_0 + c_1(x - a) + c_2(x - a)^2 + \cdots$$

is called a **power series in $(x - a)$** or a **power series centered at a** or a **power series about a**. Notice that in writing out the term corresponding to $n = 0$ in Equations 1 and 2 we have adopted the convention that $(x - a)^0 = 1$ even when $x = a$. Notice also that when $x = a$, all of the terms are 0 for $n \geq 1$ and so the power series (2) always converges when $x = a$.

EXAMPLE 1 For what values of x is the series $\sum_{n=0}^{\infty} n! x^n$ convergent?

SOLUTION We use the Ratio Test. If we let a_n, as usual, denote the nth term of the series, then $a_n = n! x^n$. If $x \neq 0$, we have

$$\lim_{n \to \infty} \left| \frac{a_{n+1}}{a_n} \right| = \lim_{n \to \infty} \left| \frac{(n+1)! x^{n+1}}{n! x^n} \right| = \lim_{n \to \infty} (n+1)|x| = \infty$$

By the Ratio Test, the series diverges when $x \neq 0$. Thus the given series converges only when $x = 0$. □

EXAMPLE 2 For what values of x does the series $\sum_{n=1}^{\infty} \frac{(x-3)^n}{n}$ converge?

SOLUTION Let $a_n = (x - 3)^n/n$. Then

$$\left| \frac{a_{n+1}}{a_n} \right| = \left| \frac{(x-3)^{n+1}}{n+1} \cdot \frac{n}{(x-3)^n} \right|$$

$$= \frac{1}{1 + \dfrac{1}{n}} |x - 3| \to |x - 3| \qquad \text{as } n \to \infty$$

TRIGONOMETRIC SERIES

A power series is a series in which each term is a power function. A **trigonometric series**

$$\sum_{n=0}^{\infty} (a_n \cos nx + b_n \sin nx)$$

is a series whose terms are trigonometric functions. This type of series is discussed on the website

www.stewartcalculus.com

Click on **Additional Topics** and then on **Fourier Series**.

Notice that
$(n+1)! = (n+1)n(n-1) \cdots \cdots 3 \cdot 2 \cdot 1$
$= (n+1)n!$

By the Ratio Test, the given series is absolutely convergent, and therefore convergent, when $|x - 3| < 1$ and divergent when $|x - 3| > 1$. Now

$$|x - 3| < 1 \quad \Longleftrightarrow \quad -1 < x - 3 < 1 \quad \Longleftrightarrow \quad 2 < x < 4$$

so the series converges when $2 < x < 4$ and diverges when $x < 2$ or $x > 4$.

The Ratio Test gives no information when $|x - 3| = 1$ so we must consider $x = 2$ and $x = 4$ separately. If we put $x = 4$ in the series, it becomes $\Sigma \, 1/n$, the harmonic series, which is divergent. If $x = 2$, the series is $\Sigma \, (-1)^n/n$, which converges by the Alternating Series Test. Thus the given power series converges for $2 \leqslant x < 4$. □

We will see that the main use of a power series is that it provides a way to represent some of the most important functions that arise in mathematics, physics, and chemistry. In particular, the sum of the power series in the next example is called a **Bessel function**, after the German astronomer Friedrich Bessel (1784–1846), and the function given in Exercise 35 is another example of a Bessel function. In fact, these functions first arose when Bessel solved Kepler's equation for describing planetary motion. Since that time, these functions have been applied in many different physical situations, including the temperature distribution in a circular plate and the shape of a vibrating drumhead.

EXAMPLE 3 Find the domain of the Bessel function of order 0 defined by

$$J_0(x) = \sum_{n=0}^{\infty} \frac{(-1)^n x^{2n}}{2^{2n}(n!)^2}$$

SOLUTION Let $a_n = (-1)^n x^{2n}/[2^{2n}(n!)^2]$. Then

$$\left| \frac{a_{n+1}}{a_n} \right| = \left| \frac{(-1)^{n+1} x^{2(n+1)}}{2^{2(n+1)}[(n + 1)!]^2} \cdot \frac{2^{2n}(n!)^2}{(-1)^n x^{2n}} \right|$$

$$= \frac{x^{2n+2}}{2^{2n+2}(n + 1)^2(n!)^2} \cdot \frac{2^{2n}(n!)^2}{x^{2n}}$$

$$= \frac{x^2}{4(n + 1)^2} \to 0 < 1 \qquad \text{for all } x$$

■ Notice how closely the computer-generated model (which involves Bessel functions and cosine functions) matches the photograph of a vibrating rubber membrane.

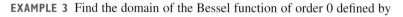

Thus, by the Ratio Test, the given series converges for all values of x. In other words, the domain of the Bessel function J_0 is $(-\infty, \infty) = \mathbb{R}$. □

Recall that the sum of a series is equal to the limit of the sequence of partial sums. So when we define the Bessel function in Example 3 as the sum of a series we mean that, for every real number x,

$$J_0(x) = \lim_{n \to \infty} s_n(x) \qquad \text{where} \qquad s_n(x) = \sum_{i=0}^{n} \frac{(-1)^i x^{2i}}{2^{2i}(i!)^2}$$

The first few partial sums are

$$s_0(x) = 1 \qquad s_1(x) = 1 - \frac{x^2}{4} \qquad s_2(x) = 1 - \frac{x^2}{4} + \frac{x^4}{64}$$

$$s_3(x) = 1 - \frac{x^2}{4} + \frac{x^4}{64} - \frac{x^6}{2304} \qquad s_4(x) = 1 - \frac{x^2}{4} + \frac{x^4}{64} - \frac{x^6}{2304} + \frac{x^8}{147{,}456}$$

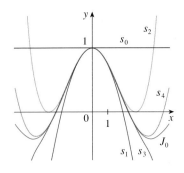

FIGURE 1

Partial sums of the Bessel function J_0

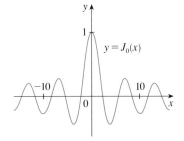

FIGURE 2

Figure 1 shows the graphs of these partial sums, which are polynomials. They are all approximations to the function J_0, but notice that the approximations become better when more terms are included. Figure 2 shows a more complete graph of the Bessel function.

For the power series that we have looked at so far, the set of values of x for which the series is convergent has always turned out to be an interval [a finite interval for the geometric series and the series in Example 2, the infinite interval $(-\infty, \infty)$ in Example 3, and a collapsed interval $[0, 0] = \{0\}$ in Example 1]. The following theorem, proved in Appendix F, says that this is true in general.

---

3   **THEOREM**   For a given power series $\sum_{n=0}^{\infty} c_n(x - a)^n$, there are only three possibilities:

  (i) The series converges only when $x = a$.

  (ii) The series converges for all x.

  (iii) There is a positive number R such that the series converges if $|x - a| < R$ and diverges if $|x - a| > R$.

The number R in case (iii) is called the **radius of convergence** of the power series. By convention, the radius of convergence is $R = 0$ in case (i) and $R = \infty$ in case (ii). The **interval of convergence** of a power series is the interval that consists of all values of x for which the series converges. In case (i) the interval consists of just a single point a. In case (ii) the interval is $(-\infty, \infty)$. In case (iii) note that the inequality $|x - a| < R$ can be rewritten as $a - R < x < a + R$. When x is an *endpoint* of the interval, that is, $x = a \pm R$, anything can happen—the series might converge at one or both endpoints or it might diverge at both endpoints. Thus in case (iii) there are four possibilities for the interval of convergence:

$$(a - R, a + R) \qquad (a - R, a + R] \qquad [a - R, a + R) \qquad [a - R, a + R]$$

The situation is illustrated in Figure 3.

FIGURE 3

We summarize here the radius and interval of convergence for each of the examples already considered in this section.

	Series	Radius of convergence	Interval of convergence
Geometric series	$\sum_{n=0}^{\infty} x^n$	$R = 1$	$(-1, 1)$
Example 1	$\sum_{n=0}^{\infty} n!\, x^n$	$R = 0$	$\{0\}$
Example 2	$\sum_{n=1}^{\infty} \dfrac{(x - 3)^n}{n}$	$R = 1$	$[2, 4)$
Example 3	$\sum_{n=0}^{\infty} \dfrac{(-1)^n x^{2n}}{2^{2n}(n!)^2}$	$R = \infty$	$(-\infty, \infty)$

In general, the Ratio Test (or sometimes the Root Test) should be used to determine the radius of convergence R. The Ratio and Root Tests always fail when x is an endpoint of the interval of convergence, so the endpoints must be checked with some other test.

EXAMPLE 4 Find the radius of convergence and interval of convergence of the series

$$\sum_{n=0}^{\infty} \frac{(-3)^n x^n}{\sqrt{n+1}}$$

SOLUTION Let $a_n = (-3)^n x^n / \sqrt{n+1}$. Then

$$\left| \frac{a_{n+1}}{a_n} \right| = \left| \frac{(-3)^{n+1} x^{n+1}}{\sqrt{n+2}} \cdot \frac{\sqrt{n+1}}{(-3)^n x^n} \right| = \left| -3x \sqrt{\frac{n+1}{n+2}} \right|$$

$$= 3 \sqrt{\frac{1 + (1/n)}{1 + (2/n)}} \, |x| \to 3|x| \qquad \text{as } n \to \infty$$

By the Ratio Test, the given series converges if $3|x| < 1$ and diverges if $3|x| > 1$. Thus it converges if $|x| < \frac{1}{3}$ and diverges if $|x| > \frac{1}{3}$. This means that the radius of convergence is $R = \frac{1}{3}$.

We know the series converges in the interval $\left(-\frac{1}{3}, \frac{1}{3}\right)$, but we must now test for convergence at the endpoints of this interval. If $x = -\frac{1}{3}$, the series becomes

$$\sum_{n=0}^{\infty} \frac{(-3)^n \left(-\frac{1}{3}\right)^n}{\sqrt{n+1}} = \sum_{n=0}^{\infty} \frac{1}{\sqrt{n+1}} = \frac{1}{\sqrt{1}} + \frac{1}{\sqrt{2}} + \frac{1}{\sqrt{3}} + \frac{1}{\sqrt{4}} + \cdots$$

which diverges. $\left(\text{Use the Integral Test or simply observe that it is a } p\text{-series with } p = \frac{1}{2} < 1.\right)$ If $x = \frac{1}{3}$, the series is

$$\sum_{n=0}^{\infty} \frac{(-3)^n \left(\frac{1}{3}\right)^n}{\sqrt{n+1}} = \sum_{n=0}^{\infty} \frac{(-1)^n}{\sqrt{n+1}}$$

which converges by the Alternating Series Test. Therefore the given power series converges when $-\frac{1}{3} < x \leq \frac{1}{3}$, so the interval of convergence is $\left(-\frac{1}{3}, \frac{1}{3}\right]$. ☐

▼ EXAMPLE 5 Find the radius of convergence and interval of convergence of the series

$$\sum_{n=0}^{\infty} \frac{n(x+2)^n}{3^{n+1}}$$

SOLUTION If $a_n = n(x+2)^n / 3^{n+1}$, then

$$\left| \frac{a_{n+1}}{a_n} \right| = \left| \frac{(n+1)(x+2)^{n+1}}{3^{n+2}} \cdot \frac{3^{n+1}}{n(x+2)^n} \right|$$

$$= \left(1 + \frac{1}{n}\right) \frac{|x+2|}{3} \to \frac{|x+2|}{3} \qquad \text{as } n \to \infty$$

Using the Ratio Test, we see that the series converges if $|x+2|/3 < 1$ and it diverges if $|x+2|/3 > 1$. So it converges if $|x+2| < 3$ and diverges if $|x+2| > 3$. Thus the radius of convergence is $R = 3$.

The inequality $|x + 2| < 3$ can be written as $-5 < x < 1$, so we test the series at the endpoints -5 and 1. When $x = -5$, the series is

$$\sum_{n=0}^{\infty} \frac{n(-3)^n}{3^{n+1}} = \tfrac{1}{3} \sum_{n=0}^{\infty} (-1)^n n$$

which diverges by the Test for Divergence $[(-1)^n n$ doesn't converge to $0]$. When $x = 1$, the series is

$$\sum_{n=0}^{\infty} \frac{n(3)^n}{3^{n+1}} = \tfrac{1}{3} \sum_{n=0}^{\infty} n$$

which also diverges by the Test for Divergence. Thus the series converges only when $-5 < x < 1$, so the interval of convergence is $(-5, 1)$. $\qquad\square$

12.8 EXERCISES

1. What is a power series?

2. (a) What is the radius of convergence of a power series? How do you find it?
(b) What is the interval of convergence of a power series? How do you find it?

3–28 Find the radius of convergence and interval of convergence of the series.

3. $\displaystyle\sum_{n=1}^{\infty} \frac{x^n}{\sqrt{n}}$

4. $\displaystyle\sum_{n=0}^{\infty} \frac{(-1)^n x^n}{n+1}$

5. $\displaystyle\sum_{n=1}^{\infty} \frac{(-1)^{n-1} x^n}{n^3}$

6. $\displaystyle\sum_{n=1}^{\infty} \sqrt{n}\, x^n$

7. $\displaystyle\sum_{n=0}^{\infty} \frac{x^n}{n!}$

8. $\displaystyle\sum_{n=1}^{\infty} n^n x^n$

9. $\displaystyle\sum_{n=1}^{\infty} (-1)^n \frac{n^2 x^n}{2^n}$

10. $\displaystyle\sum_{n=1}^{\infty} \frac{10^n x^n}{n^3}$

11. $\displaystyle\sum_{n=1}^{\infty} \frac{(-2)^n x^n}{\sqrt[4]{n}}$

12. $\displaystyle\sum_{n=1}^{\infty} \frac{x^n}{5^n n^5}$

13. $\displaystyle\sum_{n=2}^{\infty} (-1)^n \frac{x^n}{4^n \ln n}$

14. $\displaystyle\sum_{n=0}^{\infty} (-1)^n \frac{x^{2n}}{(2n)!}$

15. $\displaystyle\sum_{n=0}^{\infty} \frac{(x-2)^n}{n^2+1}$

16. $\displaystyle\sum_{n=0}^{\infty} (-1)^n \frac{(x-3)^n}{2n+1}$

17. $\displaystyle\sum_{n=1}^{\infty} \frac{3^n(x+4)^n}{\sqrt{n}}$

18. $\displaystyle\sum_{n=1}^{\infty} \frac{n}{4^n}(x+1)^n$

19. $\displaystyle\sum_{n=1}^{\infty} \frac{(x-2)^n}{n^n}$

20. $\displaystyle\sum_{n=1}^{\infty} \frac{(3x-2)^n}{n\,3^n}$

21. $\displaystyle\sum_{n=1}^{\infty} \frac{n}{b^n}(x-a)^n, \quad b>0$

22. $\displaystyle\sum_{n=1}^{\infty} \frac{n(x-4)^n}{n^3+1}$

23. $\displaystyle\sum_{n=1}^{\infty} n!(2x-1)^n$

24. $\displaystyle\sum_{n=1}^{\infty} \frac{n^2 x^n}{2 \cdot 4 \cdot 6 \cdot \,\cdots\, \cdot (2n)}$

25. $\displaystyle\sum_{n=1}^{\infty} \frac{(4x+1)^n}{n^2}$

26. $\displaystyle\sum_{n=2}^{\infty} \frac{x^{2n}}{n(\ln n)^2}$

27. $\displaystyle\sum_{n=1}^{\infty} \frac{x^n}{1 \cdot 3 \cdot 5 \cdot \,\cdots\, \cdot (2n-1)}$

28. $\displaystyle\sum_{n=1}^{\infty} \frac{n! x^n}{1 \cdot 3 \cdot 5 \cdot \,\cdots\, \cdot (2n-1)}$

29. If $\sum_{n=0}^{\infty} c_n 4^n$ is convergent, does it follow that the following series are convergent?

(a) $\displaystyle\sum_{n=0}^{\infty} c_n(-2)^n$

(b) $\displaystyle\sum_{n=0}^{\infty} c_n(-4)^n$

30. Suppose that $\sum_{n=0}^{\infty} c_n x^n$ converges when $x = -4$ and diverges when $x = 6$. What can be said about the convergence or divergence of the following series?

(a) $\displaystyle\sum_{n=0}^{\infty} c_n$

(b) $\displaystyle\sum_{n=0}^{\infty} c_n 8^n$

(c) $\displaystyle\sum_{n=0}^{\infty} c_n(-3)^n$

(d) $\displaystyle\sum_{n=0}^{\infty} (-1)^n c_n 9^n$

31. If k is a positive integer, find the radius of convergence of the series

$$\sum_{n=0}^{\infty} \frac{(n!)^k}{(kn)!} x^n$$

32. Let p and q be real numbers with $p < q$. Find a power series whose interval of convergence is
(a) (p, q) (b) $(p, q]$
(c) $[p, q)$ (d) $[p, q]$

33. Is it possible to find a power series whose interval of convergence is $[0, \infty)$? Explain.

34. Graph the first several partial sums $s_n(x)$ of the series $\sum_{n=0}^{\infty} x^n$, together with the sum function $f(x) = 1/(1 - x)$, on a common screen. On what interval do these partial sums appear to be converging to $f(x)$?

35. The function J_1 defined by

$$J_1(x) = \sum_{n=0}^{\infty} \frac{(-1)^n x^{2n+1}}{n!(n + 1)! 2^{2n+1}}$$

is called the *Bessel function of order 1*.
(a) Find its domain.
(b) Graph the first several partial sums on a common screen.
(CAS) (c) If your CAS has built-in Bessel functions, graph J_1 on the same screen as the partial sums in part (b) and observe how the partial sums approximate J_1.

36. The function A defined by

$$A(x) = 1 + \frac{x^3}{2 \cdot 3} + \frac{x^6}{2 \cdot 3 \cdot 5 \cdot 6} + \frac{x^9}{2 \cdot 3 \cdot 5 \cdot 6 \cdot 8 \cdot 9} + \cdots$$

is called the *Airy function* after the English mathematician and astronomer Sir George Airy (1801–1892).
(a) Find the domain of the Airy function.
(b) Graph the first several partial sums on a common screen.

(CAS) (c) If your CAS has built-in Airy functions, graph A on the same screen as the partial sums in part (b) and observe how the partial sums approximate A.

37. A function f is defined by

$$f(x) = 1 + 2x + x^2 + 2x^3 + x^4 + \cdots$$

that is, its coefficients are $c_{2n} = 1$ and $c_{2n+1} = 2$ for all $n \geqslant 0$. Find the interval of convergence of the series and find an explicit formula for $f(x)$.

38. If $f(x) = \sum_{n=0}^{\infty} c_n x^n$, where $c_{n+4} = c_n$ for all $n \geqslant 0$, find the interval of convergence of the series and a formula for $f(x)$.

39. Show that if $\lim_{n \to \infty} \sqrt[n]{|c_n|} = c$, where $c \neq 0$, then the radius of convergence of the power series $\sum c_n x^n$ is $R = 1/c$.

40. Suppose that the power series $\sum c_n(x - a)^n$ satisfies $c_n \neq 0$ for all n. Show that if $\lim_{n \to \infty} |c_n/c_{n+1}|$ exists, then it is equal to the radius of convergence of the power series.

41. Suppose the series $\sum c_n x^n$ has radius of convergence 2 and the series $\sum d_n x^n$ has radius of convergence 3. What is the radius of convergence of the series $\sum (c_n + d_n)x^n$?

42. Suppose that the radius of convergence of the power series $\sum c_n x^n$ is R. What is the radius of convergence of the power series $\sum c_n x^{2n}$?

12.9 | **REPRESENTATIONS OF FUNCTIONS AS POWER SERIES**

In this section we learn how to represent certain types of functions as sums of power series by manipulating geometric series or by differentiating or integrating such a series. You might wonder why we would ever want to express a known function as a sum of infinitely many terms. We will see later that this strategy is useful for integrating functions that don't have elementary antiderivatives, for solving differential equations, and for approximating functions by polynomials. (Scientists do this to simplify the expressions they deal with; computer scientists do this to represent functions on calculators and computers.)

We start with an equation that we have seen before:

$$\boxed{1} \qquad \frac{1}{1 - x} = 1 + x + x^2 + x^3 + \cdots = \sum_{n=0}^{\infty} x^n \qquad |x| < 1$$

We first encountered this equation in Example 5 in Section 12.2, where we obtained it by observing that it is a geometric series with $a = 1$ and $r = x$. But here our point of view is different. We now regard Equation 1 as expressing the function $f(x) = 1/(1 - x)$ as a sum of a power series.

■ A geometric illustration of Equation 1 is shown in Figure 1. Because the sum of a series is the limit of the sequence of partial sums, we have

$$\frac{1}{1 - x} = \lim_{n \to \infty} s_n(x)$$

where

$$s_n(x) = 1 + x + x^2 + \cdots + x^n$$

is the nth partial sum. Notice that as n increases, $s_n(x)$ becomes a better approximation to $f(x)$ for $-1 < x < 1$.

FIGURE 1

$f(x) = \dfrac{1}{1 - x}$ and some partial sums

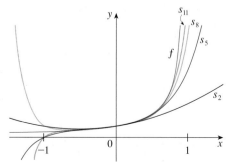

■ When a power series is asked for in this section, it is assumed that the series is centered at 0, unless otherwise specified.

V EXAMPLE 1 Express $1/(1 + x^2)$ as the sum of a power series and find the interval of convergence.

SOLUTION Replacing x by $-x^2$ in Equation 1, we have

$$\frac{1}{1 + x^2} = \frac{1}{1 - (-x^2)} = \sum_{n=0}^{\infty} (-x^2)^n$$

$$= \sum_{n=0}^{\infty} (-1)^n x^{2n} = 1 - x^2 + x^4 - x^6 + x^8 - \cdots$$

Because this is a geometric series, it converges when $|-x^2| < 1$, that is, $x^2 < 1$, or $|x| < 1$. Therefore the interval of convergence is $(-1, 1)$. (Of course, we could have determined the radius of convergence by applying the Ratio Test, but that much work is unnecessary here.) □

EXAMPLE 2 Find a power series representation for $1/(x + 2)$.

SOLUTION In order to put this function in the form of the left side of Equation 1 we first factor a 2 from the denominator:

$$\frac{1}{2 + x} = \frac{1}{2\left(1 + \dfrac{x}{2}\right)} = \frac{1}{2\left[1 - \left(-\dfrac{x}{2}\right)\right]}$$

$$= \frac{1}{2} \sum_{n=0}^{\infty} \left(-\frac{x}{2}\right)^n = \sum_{n=0}^{\infty} \frac{(-1)^n}{2^{n+1}} x^n$$

This series converges when $|-x/2| < 1$, that is, $|x| < 2$. So the interval of convergence is $(-2, 2)$. □

EXAMPLE 3 Find a power series representation of $x^3/(x + 2)$.

SOLUTION Since this function is just x^3 times the function in Example 2, all we have to do is to multiply that series by x^3:

■ It's legitimate to move x^3 across the sigma sign because it doesn't depend on n. [Use Theorem 12.2.8(i) with $c = x^3$.]

$$\frac{x^3}{x + 2} = x^3 \cdot \frac{1}{x + 2} = x^3 \sum_{n=0}^{\infty} \frac{(-1)^n}{2^{n+1}} x^n = \sum_{n=0}^{\infty} \frac{(-1)^n}{2^{n+1}} x^{n+3}$$

$$= \tfrac{1}{2} x^3 - \tfrac{1}{4} x^4 + \tfrac{1}{8} x^5 - \tfrac{1}{16} x^6 + \cdots$$

Another way of writing this series is as follows:

$$\frac{x^3}{x + 2} = \sum_{n=3}^{\infty} \frac{(-1)^{n-1}}{2^{n-2}} x^n$$

As in Example 2, the interval of convergence is $(-2, 2)$. □

DIFFERENTIATION AND INTEGRATION OF POWER SERIES

The sum of a power series is a function $f(x) = \sum_{n=0}^{\infty} c_n(x - a)^n$ whose domain is the interval of convergence of the series. We would like to be able to differentiate and integrate such functions, and the following theorem (which we won't prove) says that we can do so by differentiating or integrating each individual term in the series, just as we would for a polynomial. This is called **term-by-term differentiation and integration**.

> **2 THEOREM** If the power series $\sum c_n(x - a)^n$ has radius of convergence $R > 0$,
> then the function f defined by
>
> $$f(x) = c_0 + c_1(x - a) + c_2(x - a)^2 + \cdots = \sum_{n=0}^{\infty} c_n(x - a)^n$$
>
> is differentiable (and therefore continuous) on the interval $(a - R, a + R)$ and
>
> (i) $f'(x) = c_1 + 2c_2(x - a) + 3c_3(x - a)^2 + \cdots = \sum_{n=1}^{\infty} nc_n(x - a)^{n-1}$
>
> (ii) $\displaystyle\int f(x)\, dx = C + c_0(x - a) + c_1 \frac{(x - a)^2}{2} + c_2 \frac{(x - a)^3}{3} + \cdots$
>
> $$= C + \sum_{n=0}^{\infty} c_n \frac{(x - a)^{n+1}}{n + 1}$$
>
> The radii of convergence of the power series in Equations (i) and (ii) are both R.

■ In part (ii), $\int c_0\, dx = c_0 x + C_1$ is written as $c_0(x - a) + C$, where $C = C_1 + ac_0$, so all the terms of the series have the same form.

NOTE 1 Equations (i) and (ii) in Theorem 2 can be rewritten in the form

(iii) $\displaystyle\frac{d}{dx}\left[\sum_{n=0}^{\infty} c_n(x - a)^n\right] = \sum_{n=0}^{\infty} \frac{d}{dx}\left[c_n(x - a)^n\right]$

(iv) $\displaystyle\int\left[\sum_{n=0}^{\infty} c_n(x - a)^n\right] dx = \sum_{n=0}^{\infty} \int c_n(x - a)^n\, dx$

We know that, for finite sums, the derivative of a sum is the sum of the derivatives and the integral of a sum is the sum of the integrals. Equations (iii) and (iv) assert that the same is true for infinite sums, provided we are dealing with *power series*. (For other types of series of functions the situation is not as simple; see Exercise 36.)

NOTE 2 Although Theorem 2 says that the radius of convergence remains the same when a power series is differentiated or integrated, this does not mean that the *interval* of convergence remains the same. It may happen that the original series converges at an endpoint, whereas the differentiated series diverges there. (See Exercise 37.)

NOTE 3 The idea of differentiating a power series term by term is the basis for a powerful method for solving differential equations. We will discuss this method in Chapter 18.

EXAMPLE 4 In Example 3 in Section 12.8 we saw that the Bessel function

$$J_0(x) = \sum_{n=0}^{\infty} \frac{(-1)^n x^{2n}}{2^{2n}(n!)^2}$$

is defined for all x. Thus, by Theorem 2, J_0 is differentiable for all x and its derivative is found by term-by-term differentiation as follows:

$$J_0'(x) = \sum_{n=0}^{\infty} \frac{d}{dx} \frac{(-1)^n x^{2n}}{2^{2n}(n!)^2} = \sum_{n=1}^{\infty} \frac{(-1)^n 2n x^{2n-1}}{2^{2n}(n!)^2} \qquad \square$$

V EXAMPLE 5 Express $1/(1 - x)^2$ as a power series by differentiating Equation 1. What is the radius of convergence?

SOLUTION Differentiating each side of the equation

$$\frac{1}{1 - x} = 1 + x + x^2 + x^3 + \cdots = \sum_{n=0}^{\infty} x^n$$

we get

$$\frac{1}{(1 - x)^2} = 1 + 2x + 3x^2 + \cdots = \sum_{n=1}^{\infty} nx^{n-1}$$

If we wish, we can replace n by $n + 1$ and write the answer as

$$\frac{1}{(1 - x)^2} = \sum_{n=0}^{\infty} (n + 1)x^n$$

According to Theorem 2, the radius of convergence of the differentiated series is the same as the radius of convergence of the original series, namely, $R = 1$. □

EXAMPLE 6 Find a power series representation for $\ln(1 - x)$ and its radius of convergence.

SOLUTION We notice that, except for a factor of -1, the derivative of this function is $1/(1 - x)$. So we integrate both sides of Equation 1:

$$-\ln(1 - x) = \int \frac{1}{1 - x} dx = \int (1 + x + x^2 + \cdots) dx$$

$$= x + \frac{x^2}{2} + \frac{x^3}{3} + \cdots + C = \sum_{n=0}^{\infty} \frac{x^{n+1}}{n + 1} + C = \sum_{n=1}^{\infty} \frac{x^n}{n} + C \qquad |x| < 1$$

To determine the value of C we put $x = 0$ in this equation and obtain $-\ln(1 - 0) = C$. Thus $C = 0$ and

$$\ln(1 - x) = -x - \frac{x^2}{2} - \frac{x^3}{3} - \cdots = -\sum_{n=1}^{\infty} \frac{x^n}{n} \qquad |x| < 1$$

The radius of convergence is the same as for the original series: $R = 1$. □

Notice what happens if we put $x = \frac{1}{2}$ in the result of Example 6. Since $\ln\frac{1}{2} = -\ln 2$, we see that

$$\ln 2 = \frac{1}{2} + \frac{1}{8} + \frac{1}{24} + \frac{1}{64} + \cdots = \sum_{n=1}^{\infty} \frac{1}{n 2^n}$$

V EXAMPLE 7 Find a power series representation for $f(x) = \tan^{-1}x$.

SOLUTION We observe that $f'(x) = 1/(1 + x^2)$ and find the required series by integrating the power series for $1/(1 + x^2)$ found in Example 1.

$$\tan^{-1}x = \int \frac{1}{1 + x^2} dx = \int (1 - x^2 + x^4 - x^6 + \cdots) dx$$

$$= C + x - \frac{x^3}{3} + \frac{x^5}{5} - \frac{x^7}{7} + \cdots$$

■ The power series for $\tan^{-1}x$ obtained in Example 7 is called *Gregory's series* after the Scottish mathematician James Gregory (1638–1675), who had anticipated some of Newton's discoveries. We have shown that Gregory's series is valid when $-1 < x < 1$, but it turns out (although it isn't easy to prove) that it is also valid when $x = \pm 1$. Notice that when $x = 1$ the series becomes

$$\frac{\pi}{4} = 1 - \frac{1}{3} + \frac{1}{5} - \frac{1}{7} + \cdots$$

This beautiful result is known as the Leibniz formula for π.

To find C we put $x = 0$ and obtain $C = \tan^{-1}0 = 0$. Therefore

$$\tan^{-1}x = x - \frac{x^3}{3} + \frac{x^5}{5} - \frac{x^7}{7} + \cdots = \sum_{n=0}^{\infty} (-1)^n \frac{x^{2n+1}}{2n + 1}$$

Since the radius of convergence of the series for $1/(1 + x^2)$ is 1, the radius of convergence of this series for $\tan^{-1}x$ is also 1.   ☐

EXAMPLE 8

(a) Evaluate $\int [1/(1 + x^7)]\,dx$ as a power series.

(b) Use part (a) to approximate $\int_0^{0.5} [1/(1 + x^7)]\,dx$ correct to within 10^{-7}.

SOLUTION

(a) The first step is to express the integrand, $1/(1 + x^7)$, as the sum of a power series. As in Example 1, we start with Equation 1 and replace x by $-x^7$:

$$\frac{1}{1 + x^7} = \frac{1}{1 - (-x^7)} = \sum_{n=0}^{\infty} (-x^7)^n$$

$$= \sum_{n=0}^{\infty} (-1)^n x^{7n} = 1 - x^7 + x^{14} - \cdots$$

■ This example demonstrates one way in which power series representations are useful. Integrating $1/(1 + x^7)$ by hand is incredibly difficult. Different computer algebra systems return different forms of the answer, but they are all extremely complicated. (If you have a CAS, try it yourself.) The infinite series answer that we obtain in Example 8(a) is actually much easier to deal with than the finite answer provided by a CAS.

Now we integrate term by term:

$$\int \frac{1}{1 + x^7}\,dx = \int \sum_{n=0}^{\infty} (-1)^n x^{7n}\,dx = C + \sum_{n=0}^{\infty} (-1)^n \frac{x^{7n+1}}{7n + 1}$$

$$= C + x - \frac{x^8}{8} + \frac{x^{15}}{15} - \frac{x^{22}}{22} + \cdots$$

This series converges for $|-x^7| < 1$, that is, for $|x| < 1$.

(b) In applying the Fundamental Theorem of Calculus, it doesn't matter which antiderivative we use, so let's use the antiderivative from part (a) with $C = 0$:

$$\int_0^{0.5} \frac{1}{1 + x^7}\,dx = \left[x - \frac{x^8}{8} + \frac{x^{15}}{15} - \frac{x^{22}}{22} + \cdots \right]_0^{1/2}$$

$$= \frac{1}{2} - \frac{1}{8 \cdot 2^8} + \frac{1}{15 \cdot 2^{15}} - \frac{1}{22 \cdot 2^{22}} + \cdots + \frac{(-1)^n}{(7n + 1)2^{7n+1}} + \cdots$$

This infinite series is the exact value of the definite integral, but since it is an alternating series, we can approximate the sum using the Alternating Series Estimation Theorem. If we stop adding after the term with $n = 3$, the error is smaller than the term with $n = 4$:

$$\frac{1}{29 \cdot 2^{29}} \approx 6.4 \times 10^{-11}$$

So we have

$$\int_0^{0.5} \frac{1}{1 + x^7}\,dx \approx \frac{1}{2} - \frac{1}{8 \cdot 2^8} + \frac{1}{15 \cdot 2^{15}} - \frac{1}{22 \cdot 2^{22}} \approx 0.49951374$$ ☐

12.9 EXERCISES

1. If the radius of convergence of the power series $\sum_{n=0}^{\infty} c_n x^n$ is 10, what is the radius of convergence of the series $\sum_{n=1}^{\infty} n c_n x^{n-1}$? Why?

2. Suppose you know that the series $\sum_{n=0}^{\infty} b_n x^n$ converges for $|x| < 2$. What can you say about the following series? Why?

$$\sum_{n=0}^{\infty} \frac{b_n}{n+1} x^{n+1}$$

3–10 Find a power series representation for the function and determine the interval of convergence.

3. $f(x) = \dfrac{1}{1+x}$

4. $f(x) = \dfrac{3}{1-x^4}$

5. $f(x) = \dfrac{2}{3-x}$

6. $f(x) = \dfrac{1}{x+10}$

7. $f(x) = \dfrac{x}{9+x^2}$

8. $f(x) = \dfrac{x}{2x^2+1}$

9. $f(x) = \dfrac{1+x}{1-x}$

10. $f(x) = \dfrac{x^2}{a^3-x^3}$

11–12 Express the function as the sum of a power series by first using partial fractions. Find the interval of convergence.

11. $f(x) = \dfrac{3}{x^2-x-2}$

12. $f(x) = \dfrac{x+2}{2x^2-x-1}$

13. (a) Use differentiation to find a power series representation for

$$f(x) = \frac{1}{(1+x)^2}$$

What is the radius of convergence?
(b) Use part (a) to find a power series for

$$f(x) = \frac{1}{(1+x)^3}$$

(c) Use part (b) to find a power series for

$$f(x) = \frac{x^2}{(1+x)^3}$$

14. (a) Find a power series representation for $f(x) = \ln(1+x)$. What is the radius of convergence?
(b) Use part (a) to find a power series for $f(x) = x \ln(1+x)$.
(c) Use part (a) to find a power series for $f(x) = \ln(x^2+1)$.

15–18 Find a power series representation for the function and determine the radius of convergence.

15. $f(x) = \ln(5-x)$

16. $f(x) = \dfrac{x^2}{(1-2x)^2}$

17. $f(x) = \dfrac{x^3}{(x-2)^2}$

18. $f(x) = \arctan(x/3)$

19–22 Find a power series representation for f, and graph f and several partial sums $s_n(x)$ on the same screen. What happens as n increases?

19. $f(x) = \dfrac{x}{x^2+16}$

20. $f(x) = \ln(x^2+4)$

21. $f(x) = \ln\left(\dfrac{1+x}{1-x}\right)$

22. $f(x) = \tan^{-1}(2x)$

23–26 Evaluate the indefinite integral as a power series. What is the radius of convergence?

23. $\displaystyle\int \frac{t}{1-t^8}\, dt$

24. $\displaystyle\int \frac{\ln(1-t)}{t}\, dt$

25. $\displaystyle\int \frac{x-\tan^{-1}x}{x^3}\, dx$

26. $\displaystyle\int \tan^{-1}(x^2)\, dx$

27–30 Use a power series to approximate the definite integral to six decimal places.

27. $\displaystyle\int_0^{0.2} \frac{1}{1+x^5}\, dx$

28. $\displaystyle\int_0^{0.4} \ln(1+x^4)\, dx$

29. $\displaystyle\int_0^{0.1} x \arctan(3x)\, dx$

30. $\displaystyle\int_0^{0.3} \frac{x^2}{1+x^4}\, dx$

31. Use the result of Example 6 to compute $\ln 1.1$ correct to five decimal places.

32. Show that the function

$$f(x) = \sum_{n=0}^{\infty} \frac{(-1)^n x^{2n}}{(2n)!}$$

is a solution of the differential equation

$$f''(x) + f(x) = 0$$

33. (a) Show that J_0 (the Bessel function of order 0 given in Example 4) satisfies the differential equation

$$x^2 J_0''(x) + x J_0'(x) + x^2 J_0(x) = 0$$

(b) Evaluate $\int_0^1 J_0(x)\, dx$ correct to three decimal places.

34. The Bessel function of order 1 is defined by

$$J_1(x) = \sum_{n=0}^{\infty} \frac{(-1)^n x^{2n+1}}{n!(n+1)!2^{2n+1}}$$

(a) Show that J_1 satisfies the differential equation

$$x^2 J_1''(x) + x J_1'(x) + (x^2 - 1)J_1(x) = 0$$

(b) Show that $J_0'(x) = -J_1(x)$.

35. (a) Show that the function

$$f(x) = \sum_{n=0}^{\infty} \frac{x^n}{n!}$$

is a solution of the differential equation

$$f'(x) = f(x)$$

(b) Show that $f(x) = e^x$.

36. Let $f_n(x) = (\sin nx)/n^2$. Show that the series $\Sigma f_n(x)$ converges for all values of x but the series of derivatives $\Sigma f_n'(x)$ diverges when $x = 2n\pi$, n an integer. For what values of x does the series $\Sigma f_n''(x)$ converge?

37. Let

$$f(x) = \sum_{n=1}^{\infty} \frac{x^n}{n^2}$$

Find the intervals of convergence for f, f', and f''.

38. (a) Starting with the geometric series $\Sigma_{n=0}^{\infty} x^n$, find the sum of the series

$$\sum_{n=1}^{\infty} nx^{n-1} \qquad |x| < 1$$

(b) Find the sum of each of the following series.

(i) $\sum_{n=1}^{\infty} nx^n$, $|x| < 1$ (ii) $\sum_{n=1}^{\infty} \frac{n}{2^n}$

(c) Find the sum of each of the following series.

(i) $\sum_{n=2}^{\infty} n(n-1)x^n$, $|x| < 1$

(ii) $\sum_{n=2}^{\infty} \frac{n^2 - n}{2^n}$ (iii) $\sum_{n=1}^{\infty} \frac{n^2}{2^n}$

39. Use the power series for $\tan^{-1} x$ to prove the following expression for π as the sum of an infinite series:

$$\pi = 2\sqrt{3} \sum_{n=0}^{\infty} \frac{(-1)^n}{(2n+1)3^n}$$

40. (a) By completing the square, show that

$$\int_0^{1/2} \frac{dx}{x^2 - x + 1} = \frac{\pi}{3\sqrt{3}}$$

(b) By factoring $x^3 + 1$ as a sum of cubes, rewrite the integral in part (a). Then express $1/(x^3 + 1)$ as the sum of a power series and use it to prove the following formula for π:

$$\pi = \frac{3\sqrt{3}}{4} \sum_{n=0}^{\infty} \frac{(-1)^n}{8^n} \left(\frac{2}{3n+1} + \frac{1}{3n+2} \right)$$

12.10   TAYLOR AND MACLAURIN SERIES

In the preceding section we were able to find power series representations for a certain restricted class of functions. Here we investigate more general problems: Which functions have power series representations? How can we find such representations?

We start by supposing that f is any function that can be represented by a power series

$$\boxed{1} \quad f(x) = c_0 + c_1(x - a) + c_2(x - a)^2 + c_3(x - a)^3 + c_4(x - a)^4 + \cdots \qquad |x - a| < R$$

Let's try to determine what the coefficients c_n must be in terms of f. To begin, notice that if we put $x = a$ in Equation 1, then all terms after the first one are 0 and we get

$$f(a) = c_0$$

By Theorem 12.9.2, we can differentiate the series in Equation 1 term by term:

$$\boxed{2} \quad f'(x) = c_1 + 2c_2(x - a) + 3c_3(x - a)^2 + 4c_4(x - a)^3 + \cdots \qquad |x - a| < R$$

and substitution of $x = a$ in Equation 2 gives

$$f'(a) = c_1$$

Now we differentiate both sides of Equation 2 and obtain

$$\boxed{3} \quad f''(x) = 2c_2 + 2 \cdot 3c_3(x - a) + 3 \cdot 4c_4(x - a)^2 + \cdots \qquad |x - a| < R$$

Again we put $x = a$ in Equation 3. The result is

$$f''(a) = 2c_2$$

Let's apply the procedure one more time. Differentiation of the series in Equation 3 gives

$$\boxed{4} \quad f'''(x) = 2 \cdot 3c_3 + 2 \cdot 3 \cdot 4c_4(x - a) + 3 \cdot 4 \cdot 5c_5(x - a)^2 + \cdots \qquad |x - a| < R$$

and substitution of $x = a$ in Equation 4 gives

$$f'''(a) = 2 \cdot 3c_3 = 3!c_3$$

By now you can see the pattern. If we continue to differentiate and substitute $x = a$, we obtain

$$f^{(n)}(a) = 2 \cdot 3 \cdot 4 \cdot \cdots \cdot nc_n = n!c_n$$

Solving this equation for the nth coefficient c_n, we get

$$c_n = \frac{f^{(n)}(a)}{n!}$$

This formula remains valid even for $n = 0$ if we adopt the conventions that $0! = 1$ and $f^{(0)} = f$. Thus we have proved the following theorem.

$\boxed{5}$ **THEOREM** If f has a power series representation (expansion) at a, that is, if

$$f(x) = \sum_{n=0}^{\infty} c_n(x - a)^n \qquad |x - a| < R$$

then its coefficients are given by the formula

$$c_n = \frac{f^{(n)}(a)}{n!}$$

Substituting this formula for c_n back into the series, we see that *if f has a power series expansion at a, then it must be of the following form.*

$$\boxed{6} \quad f(x) = \sum_{n=0}^{\infty} \frac{f^{(n)}(a)}{n!}(x - a)^n$$

$$= f(a) + \frac{f'(a)}{1!}(x - a) + \frac{f''(a)}{2!}(x - a)^2 + \frac{f'''(a)}{3!}(x - a)^3 + \cdots$$

TAYLOR AND MACLAURIN

The Taylor series is named after the English mathematician Brook Taylor (1685–1731) and the Maclaurin series is named in honor of the Scottish mathematician Colin Maclaurin (1698–1746) despite the fact that the Maclaurin series is really just a special case of the Taylor series. But the idea of representing particular functions as sums of power series goes back to Newton, and the general Taylor series was known to the Scottish mathematician James Gregory in 1668 and to the Swiss mathematician John Bernoulli in the 1690s. Taylor was apparently unaware of the work of Gregory and Bernoulli when he published his discoveries on series in 1715 in his book *Methodus incrementorum directa et inversa.* Maclaurin series are named after Colin Maclaurin because he popularized them in his calculus textbook *Treatise of Fluxions* published in 1742.

The series in Equation 6 is called the **Taylor series of the function f at a** (or **about a** or **centered at a**). For the special case $a = 0$ the Taylor series becomes

$$\boxed{7} \qquad f(x) = \sum_{n=0}^{\infty} \frac{f^{(n)}(0)}{n!} x^n = f(0) + \frac{f'(0)}{1!} x + \frac{f''(0)}{2!} x^2 + \cdots$$

This case arises frequently enough that it is given the special name **Maclaurin series**.

NOTE   We have shown that *if f can be represented as a power series about a, then f is equal to the sum of its Taylor series.* But there exist functions that are not equal to the sum of their Taylor series. An example of such a function is given in Exercise 70.

☑ EXAMPLE 1 Find the Maclaurin series of the function $f(x) = e^x$ and its radius of convergence.

SOLUTION If $f(x) = e^x$, then $f^{(n)}(x) = e^x$, so $f^{(n)}(0) = e^0 = 1$ for all n. Therefore the Taylor series for f at 0 (that is, the Maclaurin series) is

$$\sum_{n=0}^{\infty} \frac{f^{(n)}(0)}{n!} x^n = \sum_{n=0}^{\infty} \frac{x^n}{n!} = 1 + \frac{x}{1!} + \frac{x^2}{2!} + \frac{x^3}{3!} + \cdots$$

To find the radius of convergence we let $a_n = x^n/n!$. Then

$$\left| \frac{a_{n+1}}{a_n} \right| = \left| \frac{x^{n+1}}{(n+1)!} \cdot \frac{n!}{x^n} \right| = \frac{|x|}{n+1} \to 0 < 1$$

so, by the Ratio Test, the series converges for all x and the radius of convergence is $R = \infty$.   □

The conclusion we can draw from Theorem 5 and Example 1 is that *if e^x has a power series expansion at 0, then*

$$e^x = \sum_{n=0}^{\infty} \frac{x^n}{n!}$$

So how can we determine whether e^x *does* have a power series representation?

Let's investigate the more general question: Under what circumstances is a function equal to the sum of its Taylor series? In other words, if f has derivatives of all orders, when is it true that

$$f(x) = \sum_{n=0}^{\infty} \frac{f^{(n)}(a)}{n!} (x - a)^n$$

As with any convergent series, this means that $f(x)$ is the limit of the sequence of partial sums. In the case of the Taylor series, the partial sums are

$$T_n(x) = \sum_{i=0}^{n} \frac{f^{(i)}(a)}{i!} (x - a)^i$$

$$= f(a) + \frac{f'(a)}{1!} (x - a) + \frac{f''(a)}{2!} (x - a)^2 + \cdots + \frac{f^{(n)}(a)}{n!} (x - a)^n$$

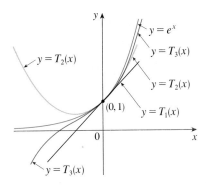

FIGURE I

■ As n increases, $T_n(x)$ appears to approach e^x in Figure 1. This suggests that e^x is equal to the sum of its Taylor series.

Notice that T_n is a polynomial of degree n called the **nth-degree Taylor polynomial of f at a**. For instance, for the exponential function $f(x) = e^x$, the result of Example 1 shows that the Taylor polynomials at 0 (or Maclaurin polynomials) with $n = 1, 2$, and 3 are

$$T_1(x) = 1 + x \qquad T_2(x) = 1 + x + \frac{x^2}{2!} \qquad T_3(x) = 1 + x + \frac{x^2}{2!} + \frac{x^3}{3!}$$

The graphs of the exponential function and these three Taylor polynomials are drawn in Figure 1.

In general, $f(x)$ is the sum of its Taylor series if

$$f(x) = \lim_{n \to \infty} T_n(x)$$

If we let

$$R_n(x) = f(x) - T_n(x) \qquad \text{so that} \qquad f(x) = T_n(x) + R_n(x)$$

then $R_n(x)$ is called the **remainder** of the Taylor series. If we can somehow show that $\lim_{n \to \infty} R_n(x) = 0$, then it follows that

$$\lim_{n \to \infty} T_n(x) = \lim_{n \to \infty} [f(x) - R_n(x)] = f(x) - \lim_{n \to \infty} R_n(x) = f(x)$$

We have therefore proved the following.

---

8 THEOREM If $f(x) = T_n(x) + R_n(x)$, where T_n is the nth-degree Taylor polynomial of f at a and

$$\lim_{n \to \infty} R_n(x) = 0$$

for $|x - a| < R$, then f is equal to the sum of its Taylor series on the interval $|x - a| < R$.

In trying to show that $\lim_{n \to \infty} R_n(x) = 0$ for a specific function f, we usually use the following fact.

---

9 TAYLOR'S INEQUALITY If $|f^{(n+1)}(x)| \leq M$ for $|x - a| \leq d$, then the remainder $R_n(x)$ of the Taylor series satisfies the inequality

$$|R_n(x)| \leq \frac{M}{(n + 1)!} |x - a|^{n+1} \qquad \text{for } |x - a| \leq d$$

To see why this is true for $n = 1$, we assume that $|f''(x)| \leq M$. In particular, we have $f''(x) \leq M$, so for $a \leq x \leq a + d$ we have

$$\int_a^x f''(t)\, dt \leq \int_a^x M\, dt$$

An antiderivative of f'' is f', so by Part 2 of the Fundamental Theorem of Calculus, we have

$$f'(x) - f'(a) \leq M(x - a) \qquad \text{or} \qquad f'(x) \leq f'(a) + M(x - a)$$

■ As alternatives to Taylor's Inequality, we have the following formulas for the remainder term. If $f^{(n+1)}$ is continuous on an interval I and $x \in I$, then

$$R_n(x) = \frac{1}{n!} \int_a^x (x - t)^n f^{(n+1)}(t)\, dt$$

This is called the *integral form of the remainder term*. Another formula, called *Lagrange's form of the remainder term*, states that there is a number z between x and a such that

$$R_n(x) = \frac{f^{(n+1)}(z)}{(n + 1)!} (x - a)^{n+1}$$

This version is an extension of the Mean Value Theorem (which is the case $n = 0$).

Proofs of these formulas, together with discussions of how to use them to solve the examples of Sections 12.10 and 12.11, are given on the website

www.stewartcalculus.com

Click on *Additional Topics* and then on *Formulas for the Remainder Term in Taylor series*.

Thus

$$\int_a^x f'(t)\, dt \leq \int_a^x [f'(a) + M(t - a)]\, dt$$

$$f(x) - f(a) \leq f'(a)(x - a) + M \frac{(x - a)^2}{2}$$

$$f(x) - f(a) - f'(a)(x - a) \leq \frac{M}{2}(x - a)^2$$

But $R_1(x) = f(x) - T_1(x) = f(x) - f(a) - f'(a)(x - a)$. So

$$R_1(x) \leq \frac{M}{2}(x - a)^2$$

A similar argument, using $f''(x) \geq -M$, shows that

$$R_1(x) \geq -\frac{M}{2}(x - a)^2$$

So

$$|R_1(x)| \leq \frac{M}{2}|x - a|^2$$

Although we have assumed that $x > a$, similar calculations show that this inequality is also true for $x < a$.

This proves Taylor's Inequality for the case where $n = 1$. The result for any n is proved in a similar way by integrating $n + 1$ times. (See Exercise 69 for the case $n = 2$.)

NOTE In Section 12.11 we will explore the use of Taylor's Inequality in approximating functions. Our immediate use of it is in conjunction with Theorem 8.

In applying Theorems 8 and 9 it is often helpful to make use of the following fact.

10

$$\lim_{n \to \infty} \frac{x^n}{n!} = 0 \qquad \text{for every real number } x$$

This is true because we know from Example 1 that the series $\Sigma\, x^n/n!$ converges for all x and so its nth term approaches 0.

☑ EXAMPLE 2 Prove that e^x is equal to the sum of its Maclaurin series.

SOLUTION If $f(x) = e^x$, then $f^{(n+1)}(x) = e^x$ for all n. If d is any positive number and $|x| \leq d$, then $|f^{(n+1)}(x)| = e^x \leq e^d$. So Taylor's Inequality, with $a = 0$ and $M = e^d$, says that

$$|R_n(x)| \leq \frac{e^d}{(n + 1)!}|x|^{n+1} \qquad \text{for } |x| \leq d$$

Notice that the same constant $M = e^d$ works for every value of n. But, from Equation 10, we have

$$\lim_{n \to \infty} \frac{e^d}{(n + 1)!}|x|^{n+1} = e^d \lim_{n \to \infty} \frac{|x|^{n+1}}{(n + 1)!} = 0$$

It follows from the Squeeze Theorem that $\lim_{n\to\infty} |R_n(x)| = 0$ and therefore $\lim_{n\to\infty} R_n(x) = 0$ for all values of x. By Theorem 8, e^x is equal to the sum of its Maclaurin series, that is,

$$\boxed{11} \qquad e^x = \sum_{n=0}^{\infty} \frac{x^n}{n!} \qquad \text{for all } x \qquad \square$$

■ In 1748 Leonard Euler used Equation 12 to find the value of e correct to 23 digits. In 2003 Shigeru Kondo, again using the series in (12), computed e to more than 50 billion decimal places. The special techniques employed to speed up the computation are explained on the web page

numbers.computation.free.fr

In particular, if we put $x = 1$ in Equation 11, we obtain the following expression for the number e as a sum of an infinite series:

$$\boxed{12} \qquad e = \sum_{n=0}^{\infty} \frac{1}{n!} = 1 + \frac{1}{1!} + \frac{1}{2!} + \frac{1}{3!} + \cdots$$

EXAMPLE 3 Find the Taylor series for $f(x) = e^x$ at $a = 2$.

SOLUTION We have $f^{(n)}(2) = e^2$ and so, putting $a = 2$ in the definition of a Taylor series (6), we get

$$\sum_{n=0}^{\infty} \frac{f^{(n)}(2)}{n!} (x - 2)^n = \sum_{n=0}^{\infty} \frac{e^2}{n!} (x - 2)^n$$

Again it can be verified, as in Example 1, that the radius of convergence is $R = \infty$. As in Example 2 we can verify that $\lim_{n\to\infty} R_n(x) = 0$, so

$$\boxed{13} \qquad e^x = \sum_{n=0}^{\infty} \frac{e^2}{n!} (x - 2)^n \qquad \text{for all } x \qquad \square$$

We have two power series expansions for e^x, the Maclaurin series in Equation 11 and the Taylor series in Equation 13. The first is better if we are interested in values of x near 0 and the second is better if x is near 2.

EXAMPLE 4 Find the Maclaurin series for $\sin x$ and prove that it represents $\sin x$ for all x.

SOLUTION We arrange our computation in two columns as follows:

$$f(x) = \sin x \qquad\qquad f(0) = 0$$
$$f'(x) = \cos x \qquad\qquad f'(0) = 1$$
$$f''(x) = -\sin x \qquad\qquad f''(0) = 0$$
$$f'''(x) = -\cos x \qquad\qquad f'''(0) = -1$$
$$f^{(4)}(x) = \sin x \qquad\qquad f^{(4)}(0) = 0$$

Since the derivatives repeat in a cycle of four, we can write the Maclaurin series as follows:

$$f(0) + \frac{f'(0)}{1!} x + \frac{f''(0)}{2!} x^2 + \frac{f'''(0)}{3!} x^3 + \cdots$$

$$= x - \frac{x^3}{3!} + \frac{x^5}{5!} - \frac{x^7}{7!} + \cdots = \sum_{n=0}^{\infty} (-1)^n \frac{x^{2n+1}}{(2n+1)!}$$

■ Figure 2 shows the graph of $\sin x$ together with its Taylor (or Maclaurin) polynomials

$$T_1(x) = x$$

$$T_3(x) = x - \frac{x^3}{3!}$$

$$T_5(x) = x - \frac{x^3}{3!} + \frac{x^5}{5!}$$

Notice that, as n increases, $T_n(x)$ becomes a better approximation to $\sin x$.

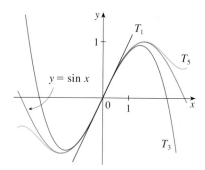

FIGURE 2

Since $f^{(n+1)}(x)$ is $\pm\sin x$ or $\pm\cos x$, we know that $\left| f^{(n+1)}(x) \right| \leq 1$ for all x. So we can take $M = 1$ in Taylor's Inequality:

$$\boxed{14} \qquad \left| R_n(x) \right| \leq \frac{M}{(n+1)!} \left| x^{n+1} \right| = \frac{|x|^{n+1}}{(n+1)!}$$

By Equation 10 the right side of this inequality approaches 0 as $n \to \infty$, so $\left| R_n(x) \right| \to 0$ by the Squeeze Theorem. It follows that $R_n(x) \to 0$ as $n \to \infty$, so $\sin x$ is equal to the sum of its Maclaurin series by Theorem 8.   □

We state the result of Example 4 for future reference.

$$\boxed{15} \qquad \sin x = x - \frac{x^3}{3!} + \frac{x^5}{5!} - \frac{x^7}{7!} + \cdots$$

$$= \sum_{n=0}^{\infty} (-1)^n \frac{x^{2n+1}}{(2n+1)!} \qquad \text{for all } x$$

EXAMPLE 5 Find the Maclaurin series for $\cos x$.

SOLUTION We could proceed directly as in Example 4 but it's easier to differentiate the Maclaurin series for $\sin x$ given by Equation 15:

$$\cos x = \frac{d}{dx}(\sin x) = \frac{d}{dx}\left(x - \frac{x^3}{3!} + \frac{x^5}{5!} - \frac{x^7}{7!} + \cdots \right)$$

$$= 1 - \frac{3x^2}{3!} + \frac{5x^4}{5!} - \frac{7x^6}{7!} + \cdots = 1 - \frac{x^2}{2!} + \frac{x^4}{4!} - \frac{x^6}{6!} + \cdots$$

■ The Maclaurin series for e^x, $\sin x$, and $\cos x$ that we found in Examples 2, 4, and 5 were discovered, using different methods, by Newton. These equations are remarkable because they say we know everything about each of these functions if we know all its derivatives at the single number 0.

Since the Maclaurin series for $\sin x$ converges for all x, Theorem 2 in Section 12.9 tells us that the differentiated series for $\cos x$ also converges for all x. Thus

$$\boxed{16} \qquad \cos x = 1 - \frac{x^2}{2!} + \frac{x^4}{4!} - \frac{x^6}{6!} + \cdots$$

$$= \sum_{n=0}^{\infty} (-1)^n \frac{x^{2n}}{(2n)!} \qquad \text{for all } x$$

□

EXAMPLE 6 Find the Maclaurin series for the function $f(x) = x \cos x$.

SOLUTION Instead of computing derivatives and substituting in Equation 7, it's easier to multiply the series for $\cos x$ (Equation 16) by x:

$$x \cos x = x \sum_{n=0}^{\infty} (-1)^n \frac{x^{2n}}{(2n)!} = \sum_{n=0}^{\infty} (-1)^n \frac{x^{2n+1}}{(2n)!} \qquad \square$$

EXAMPLE 7 Represent $f(x) = \sin x$ as the sum of its Taylor series centered at $\pi/3$.

SOLUTION Arranging our work in columns, we have

$$f(x) = \sin x \qquad f\left(\frac{\pi}{3}\right) = \frac{\sqrt{3}}{2}$$

$$f'(x) = \cos x \qquad f'\left(\frac{\pi}{3}\right) = \frac{1}{2}$$

$$f''(x) = -\sin x \qquad f''\left(\frac{\pi}{3}\right) = -\frac{\sqrt{3}}{2}$$

$$f'''(x) = -\cos x \qquad f'''\left(\frac{\pi}{3}\right) = -\frac{1}{2}$$

■ We have obtained two different series representations for $\sin x$, the Maclaurin series in Example 4 and the Taylor series in Example 7. It is best to use the Maclaurin series for values of x near 0 and the Taylor series for x near $\pi/3$. Notice that the third Taylor polynomial T_3 in Figure 3 is a good approximation to $\sin x$ near $\pi/3$ but not as good near 0. Compare it with the third Maclaurin polynomial T_3 in Figure 2, where the opposite is true.

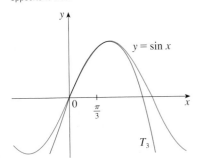

FIGURE 3

and this pattern repeats indefinitely. Therefore the Taylor series at $\pi/3$ is

$$f\left(\frac{\pi}{3}\right) + \frac{f'\left(\frac{\pi}{3}\right)}{1!}\left(x - \frac{\pi}{3}\right) + \frac{f''\left(\frac{\pi}{3}\right)}{2!}\left(x - \frac{\pi}{3}\right)^2 + \frac{f'''\left(\frac{\pi}{3}\right)}{3!}\left(x - \frac{\pi}{3}\right)^3 + \cdots$$

$$= \frac{\sqrt{3}}{2} + \frac{1}{2 \cdot 1!}\left(x - \frac{\pi}{3}\right) - \frac{\sqrt{3}}{2 \cdot 2!}\left(x - \frac{\pi}{3}\right)^2 - \frac{1}{2 \cdot 3!}\left(x - \frac{\pi}{3}\right)^3 + \cdots$$

The proof that this series represents $\sin x$ for all x is very similar to that in Example 4. [Just replace x by $x - \pi/3$ in (14).] We can write the series in sigma notation if we separate the terms that contain $\sqrt{3}$:

$$\sin x = \sum_{n=0}^{\infty} \frac{(-1)^n \sqrt{3}}{2(2n)!}\left(x - \frac{\pi}{3}\right)^{2n} + \sum_{n=0}^{\infty} \frac{(-1)^n}{2(2n+1)!}\left(x - \frac{\pi}{3}\right)^{2n+1} \qquad \square$$

The power series that we obtained by indirect methods in Examples 5 and 6 and in Section 12.9 are indeed the Taylor or Maclaurin series of the given functions because Theorem 5 asserts that, no matter how a power series representation $f(x) = \sum c_n(x - a)^n$ is obtained, it is always true that $c_n = f^{(n)}(a)/n!$. In other words, the coefficients are uniquely determined.

EXAMPLE 8 Find the Maclaurin series for $f(x) = (1 + x)^k$, where k is any real number.

SOLUTION Arranging our work in columns, we have

$$f(x) = (1 + x)^k \qquad\qquad f(0) = 1$$

$$f'(x) = k(1 + x)^{k-1} \qquad\qquad f'(0) = k$$

$$f''(x) = k(k - 1)(1 + x)^{k-2} \qquad\qquad f''(0) = k(k - 1)$$

$$f'''(x) = k(k - 1)(k - 2)(1 + x)^{k-3} \qquad\qquad f'''(0) = k(k - 1)(k - 2)$$

$$\vdots \qquad\qquad\qquad\qquad\qquad \vdots$$

$$f^{(n)}(x) = k(k - 1) \cdots (k - n + 1)(1 + x)^{k-n} \qquad f^{(n)}(0) = k(k - 1) \cdots (k - n + 1)$$

Therefore the Maclaurin series of $f(x) = (1 + x)^k$ is

$$\sum_{n=0}^{\infty} \frac{f^{(n)}(0)}{n!} x^n = \sum_{n=0}^{\infty} \frac{k(k - 1) \cdots (k - n + 1)}{n!} x^n$$

This series is called the **binomial series**. If its nth term is a_n, then

$$\left| \frac{a_{n+1}}{a_n} \right| = \left| \frac{k(k-1) \cdots (k-n+1)(k-n)x^{n+1}}{(n+1)!} \cdot \frac{n!}{k(k-1) \cdots (k-n+1)x^n} \right|$$

$$= \frac{|k-n|}{n+1} |x| = \frac{\left| 1 - \dfrac{k}{n} \right|}{1 + \dfrac{1}{n}} |x| \to |x| \qquad \text{as } n \to \infty$$

Thus, by the Ratio Test, the binomial series converges if $|x| < 1$ and diverges if $|x| > 1$. □

The traditional notation for the coefficients in the binomial series is

$$\binom{k}{n} = \frac{k(k-1)(k-2) \cdots (k-n+1)}{n!}$$

and these numbers are called the **binomial coefficients**.

The following theorem states that $(1 + x)^k$ is equal to the sum of its Maclaurin series. It is possible to prove this by showing that the remainder term $R_n(x)$ approaches 0, but that turns out to be quite difficult. The proof outlined in Exercise 71 is much easier.

---

17 **THE BINOMIAL SERIES** If k is any real number and $|x| < 1$, then

$$(1 + x)^k = \sum_{n=0}^{\infty} \binom{k}{n} x^n = 1 + kx + \frac{k(k-1)}{2!} x^2 + \frac{k(k-1)(k-2)}{3!} x^3 + \cdots$$

Although the binomial series always converges when $|x| < 1$, the question of whether or not it converges at the endpoints, ± 1, depends on the value of k. It turns out that the series converges at 1 if $-1 < k \le 0$ and at both endpoints if $k \ge 0$. Notice that if k is a positive integer and $n > k$, then the expression for $\binom{k}{n}$ contains a factor $(k - k)$, so $\binom{k}{n} = 0$ for $n > k$. This means that the series terminates and reduces to the ordinary Binomial Theorem when k is a positive integer. (See Reference Page 1.)

V EXAMPLE 9 Find the Maclaurin series for the function $f(x) = \dfrac{1}{\sqrt{4-x}}$ and its radius of convergence.

SOLUTION We write $f(x)$ in a form where we can use the binomial series:

$$\frac{1}{\sqrt{4-x}} = \frac{1}{\sqrt{4\left(1 - \dfrac{x}{4}\right)}} = \frac{1}{2\sqrt{1 - \dfrac{x}{4}}} = \frac{1}{2}\left(1 - \frac{x}{4}\right)^{-1/2}$$

Using the binomial series with $k = -\frac{1}{2}$ and with x replaced by $-x/4$, we have

$$\frac{1}{\sqrt{4-x}} = \frac{1}{2}\left(1 - \frac{x}{4}\right)^{-1/2} = \frac{1}{2}\sum_{n=0}^{\infty}\binom{-\frac{1}{2}}{n}\left(-\frac{x}{4}\right)^n$$

$$= \frac{1}{2}\left[1 + \left(-\frac{1}{2}\right)\left(-\frac{x}{4}\right) + \frac{\left(-\frac{1}{2}\right)\left(-\frac{3}{2}\right)}{2!}\left(-\frac{x}{4}\right)^2 + \frac{\left(-\frac{1}{2}\right)\left(-\frac{3}{2}\right)\left(-\frac{5}{2}\right)}{3!}\left(-\frac{x}{4}\right)^3 \right.$$

$$\left. + \cdots + \frac{\left(-\frac{1}{2}\right)\left(-\frac{3}{2}\right)\left(-\frac{5}{2}\right)\cdots\left(-\frac{1}{2} - n + 1\right)}{n!}\left(-\frac{x}{4}\right)^n + \cdots \right]$$

$$= \frac{1}{2}\left[1 + \frac{1}{8}x + \frac{1\cdot 3}{2!8^2}x^2 + \frac{1\cdot 3\cdot 5}{3!8^3}x^3 + \cdots + \frac{1\cdot 3\cdot 5\cdot\,\cdots\,\cdot(2n-1)}{n!8^n}x^n + \cdots \right]$$

We know from (17) that this series converges when $|-x/4| < 1$, that is, $|x| < 4$, so the radius of convergence is $R = 4$. $\square$

We collect in the following table, for future reference, some important Maclaurin series that we have derived in this section and the preceding one.

$\dfrac{1}{1-x} = \displaystyle\sum_{n=0}^{\infty} x^n = 1 + x + x^2 + x^3 + \cdots$	$R = 1$
$e^x = \displaystyle\sum_{n=0}^{\infty} \dfrac{x^n}{n!} = 1 + \dfrac{x}{1!} + \dfrac{x^2}{2!} + \dfrac{x^3}{3!} + \cdots$	$R = \infty$
$\sin x = \displaystyle\sum_{n=0}^{\infty} (-1)^n \dfrac{x^{2n+1}}{(2n+1)!} = x - \dfrac{x^3}{3!} + \dfrac{x^5}{5!} - \dfrac{x^7}{7!} + \cdots$	$R = \infty$
$\cos x = \displaystyle\sum_{n=0}^{\infty} (-1)^n \dfrac{x^{2n}}{(2n)!} = 1 - \dfrac{x^2}{2!} + \dfrac{x^4}{4!} - \dfrac{x^6}{6!} + \cdots$	$R = \infty$
$\tan^{-1}x = \displaystyle\sum_{n=0}^{\infty} (-1)^n \dfrac{x^{2n+1}}{2n+1} = x - \dfrac{x^3}{3} + \dfrac{x^5}{5} - \dfrac{x^7}{7} + \cdots$	$R = 1$
$(1+x)^k = \displaystyle\sum_{n=0}^{\infty} \binom{k}{n}x^n = 1 + kx + \dfrac{k(k-1)}{2!}x^2 + \dfrac{k(k-1)(k-2)}{3!}x^3 + \cdots$	$R = 1$

TEC Module 12.10/12.11 enables you to see how successive Taylor polynomials approach the original function.

One reason that Taylor series are important is that they enable us to integrate functions that we couldn't previously handle. In fact, in the introduction to this chapter we mentioned that Newton often integrated functions by first expressing them as power series and then integrating the series term by term. The function $f(x) = e^{-x^2}$ can't be integrated by techniques discussed so far because its antiderivative is not an elementary function (see Section 8.5). In the following example we use Newton's idea to integrate this function.

Ⅴ EXAMPLE 10

(a) Evaluate $\int e^{-x^2}\,dx$ as an infinite series.

(b) Evaluate $\int_0^1 e^{-x^2}\,dx$ correct to within an error of 0.001.

SOLUTION

(a) First we find the Maclaurin series for $f(x) = e^{-x^2}$. Although it's possible to use the direct method, let's find it simply by replacing x with $-x^2$ in the series for e^x given in Table 1. Thus, for all values of x,

$$e^{-x^2} = \sum_{n=0}^{\infty} \frac{(-x^2)^n}{n!} = \sum_{n=0}^{\infty} (-1)^n \frac{x^{2n}}{n!} = 1 - \frac{x^2}{1!} + \frac{x^4}{2!} - \frac{x^6}{3!} + \cdots$$

Now we integrate term by term:

$$\int e^{-x^2}\,dx = \int \left(1 - \frac{x^2}{1!} + \frac{x^4}{2!} - \frac{x^6}{3!} + \cdots + (-1)^n \frac{x^{2n}}{n!} + \cdots \right) dx$$

$$= C + x - \frac{x^3}{3 \cdot 1!} + \frac{x^5}{5 \cdot 2!} - \frac{x^7}{7 \cdot 3!} + \cdots + (-1)^n \frac{x^{2n+1}}{(2n+1)n!} + \cdots$$

This series converges for all x because the original series for e^{-x^2} converges for all x.

(b) The Fundamental Theorem of Calculus gives

$$\int_0^1 e^{-x^2}\,dx = \left[x - \frac{x^3}{3 \cdot 1!} + \frac{x^5}{5 \cdot 2!} - \frac{x^7}{7 \cdot 3!} + \frac{x^9}{9 \cdot 4!} - \cdots \right]_0^1$$

$$= 1 - \tfrac{1}{3} + \tfrac{1}{10} - \tfrac{1}{42} + \tfrac{1}{216} - \cdots$$

$$\approx 1 - \tfrac{1}{3} + \tfrac{1}{10} - \tfrac{1}{42} + \tfrac{1}{216} \approx 0.7475$$

■ We can take $C = 0$ in the antiderivative in part (a).

The Alternating Series Estimation Theorem shows that the error involved in this approximation is less than

$$\frac{1}{11 \cdot 5!} = \frac{1}{1320} < 0.001$$ □

Another use of Taylor series is illustrated in the next example. The limit could be found with l'Hospital's Rule, but instead we use a series.

EXAMPLE 11 Evaluate $\lim\limits_{x \to 0} \dfrac{e^x - 1 - x}{x^2}$.

SOLUTION Using the Maclaurin series for e^x, we have

$$\lim_{x \to 0} \frac{e^x - 1 - x}{x^2} = \lim_{x \to 0} \frac{\left(1 + \dfrac{x}{1!} + \dfrac{x^2}{2!} + \dfrac{x^3}{3!} + \cdots \right) - 1 - x}{x^2}$$

$$= \lim_{x \to 0} \frac{\dfrac{x^2}{2!} + \dfrac{x^3}{3!} + \dfrac{x^4}{4!} + \cdots}{x^2}$$

$$= \lim_{x \to 0} \left(\frac{1}{2} + \frac{x}{3!} + \frac{x^2}{4!} + \frac{x^3}{5!} + \cdots \right) = \frac{1}{2}$$

■ Some computer algebra systems compute limits in this way.

because power series are continuous functions. □

MULTIPLICATION AND DIVISION OF POWER SERIES

If power series are added or subtracted, they behave like polynomials (Theorem 12.2.8 shows this). In fact, as the following example illustrates, they can also be multiplied and divided like polynomials. We find only the first few terms because the calculations for the later terms become tedious and the initial terms are the most important ones.

EXAMPLE 12 Find the first three nonzero terms in the Maclaurin series for (a) $e^x \sin x$ and (b) $\tan x$.

SOLUTION

(a) Using the Maclaurin series for e^x and $\sin x$ in Table 1, we have

$$e^x \sin x = \left(1 + \frac{x}{1!} + \frac{x^2}{2!} + \frac{x^3}{3!} + \cdots\right)\left(x - \frac{x^3}{3!} + \cdots\right)$$

We multiply these expressions, collecting like terms just as for polynomials:

$$
\begin{array}{r}
1 + x + \tfrac{1}{2}x^2 + \tfrac{1}{6}x^3 + \cdots \\
\times \qquad\qquad x \qquad\quad - \tfrac{1}{6}x^3 + \cdots \\
\hline
x + \ x^2 + \tfrac{1}{2}x^3 + \tfrac{1}{6}x^4 + \cdots \\
+ \qquad\qquad\quad - \tfrac{1}{6}x^3 - \tfrac{1}{6}x^4 - \cdots \\
\hline
x + \ x^2 + \tfrac{1}{3}x^3 + \cdots
\end{array}
$$

Thus

$$e^x \sin x = x + x^2 + \tfrac{1}{3}x^3 + \cdots$$

(b) Using the Maclaurin series in Table 1, we have

$$\tan x = \frac{\sin x}{\cos x} = \frac{x - \dfrac{x^3}{3!} + \dfrac{x^5}{5!} - \cdots}{1 - \dfrac{x^2}{2!} + \dfrac{x^4}{4!} - \cdots}$$

We use a procedure like long division:

$$
\begin{array}{r}
x + \tfrac{1}{3}x^3 + \tfrac{2}{15}x^5 + \cdots \\
1 - \tfrac{1}{2}x^2 + \tfrac{1}{24}x^4 - \cdots \overline{\smash{)}\, x - \tfrac{1}{6}x^3 + \tfrac{1}{120}x^5 - \cdots} \\
x - \tfrac{1}{2}x^3 + \tfrac{1}{24}x^5 - \cdots \\
\hline
\tfrac{1}{3}x^3 - \tfrac{1}{30}x^5 + \cdots \\
\tfrac{1}{3}x^3 - \tfrac{1}{6}x^5 + \cdots \\
\hline
\tfrac{2}{15}x^5 + \cdots
\end{array}
$$

Thus

$$\tan x = x + \tfrac{1}{3}x^3 + \tfrac{2}{15}x^5 + \cdots \qquad\qquad \square$$

Although we have not attempted to justify the formal manipulations used in Example 12, they are legitimate. There is a theorem which states that if both $f(x) = \Sigma c_n x^n$ and $g(x) = \Sigma b_n x^n$ converge for $|x| < R$ and the series are multiplied as if they were polynomials, then the resulting series also converges for $|x| < R$ and represents $f(x)g(x)$. For division we require $b_0 \neq 0$; the resulting series converges for sufficiently small $|x|$.

12.10 EXERCISES

1. If $f(x) = \sum_{n=0}^{\infty} b_n(x-5)^n$ for all x, write a formula for b_8.

2. The graph of f is shown.

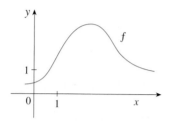

(a) Explain why the series

$$1.6 - 0.8(x-1) + 0.4(x-1)^2 - 0.1(x-1)^3 + \cdots$$

is *not* the Taylor series of f centered at 1.

(b) Explain why the series

$$2.8 + 0.5(x-2) + 1.5(x-2)^2 - 0.1(x-2)^3 + \cdots$$

is *not* the Taylor series of f centered at 2.

3. If $f^{(n)}(0) = (n+1)!$ for $n = 0, 1, 2, \ldots$, find the Maclaurin series for f and its radius of convergence.

4. Find the Taylor series for f centered at 4 if

$$f^{(n)}(4) = \frac{(-1)^n n!}{3^n(n+1)}$$

What is the radius of convergence of the Taylor series?

5–12 Find the Maclaurin series for $f(x)$ using the definition of a Maclaurin series. [Assume that f has a power series expansion. Do not show that $R_n(x) \to 0$.] Also find the associated radius of convergence.

5. $f(x) = (1-x)^{-2}$

6. $f(x) = \ln(1+x)$

7. $f(x) = \sin \pi x$

8. $f(x) = \cos 3x$

9. $f(x) = e^{5x}$

10. $f(x) = xe^x$

11. $f(x) = \sinh x$

12. $f(x) = \cosh x$

13–20 Find the Taylor series for $f(x)$ centered at the given value of a. [Assume that f has a power series expansion. Do not show that $R_n(x) \to 0$.]

13. $f(x) = x^4 - 3x^2 + 1$, $a = 1$

14. $f(x) = x - x^3$, $a = -2$

15. $f(x) = e^x$, $a = 3$

16. $f(x) = 1/x$, $a = -3$

17. $f(x) = \cos x$, $a = \pi$

18. $f(x) = \sin x$, $a = \pi/2$

19. $f(x) = 1/\sqrt{x}$, $a = 9$

20. $f(x) = x^{-2}$, $a = 1$

21. Prove that the series obtained in Exercise 7 represents $\sin \pi x$ for all x.

22. Prove that the series obtained in Exercise 18 represents $\sin x$ for all x.

23. Prove that the series obtained in Exercise 11 represents $\sinh x$ for all x.

24. Prove that the series obtained in Exercise 12 represents $\cosh x$ for all x.

25–28 Use the binomial series to expand the function as a power series. State the radius of convergence.

25. $\sqrt{1+x}$

26. $\dfrac{1}{(1+x)^4}$

27. $\dfrac{1}{(2+x)^3}$

28. $(1-x)^{2/3}$

29–38 Use a Maclaurin series in Table 1 to obtain the Maclaurin series for the given function.

29. $f(x) = \sin \pi x$

30. $f(x) = \cos(\pi x/2)$

31. $f(x) = e^x + e^{2x}$

32. $f(x) = e^x + 2e^{-x}$

33. $f(x) = x \cos(\tfrac{1}{2}x^2)$

34. $f(x) = x^2 \tan^{-1}(x^3)$

35. $f(x) = \dfrac{x}{\sqrt{4+x^2}}$

36. $f(x) = \dfrac{x^2}{\sqrt{2+x}}$

37. $f(x) = \sin^2 x$ $\left[\textit{Hint: Use } \sin^2 x = \tfrac{1}{2}(1 - \cos 2x).\right]$

38. $f(x) = \begin{cases} \dfrac{x - \sin x}{x^3} & \text{if } x \neq 0 \\ \dfrac{1}{6} & \text{if } x = 0 \end{cases}$

39–42 Find the Maclaurin series of f (by any method) and its radius of convergence. Graph f and its first few Taylor polynomials on the same screen. What do you notice about the relationship between these polynomials and f?

39. $f(x) = \cos(x^2)$

40. $f(x) = e^{-x^2} + \cos x$

41. $f(x) = xe^{-x}$

42. $f(x) = \ln(1+x^2)$

43. Use the Maclaurin series for e^x to calculate $e^{-0.2}$ correct to five decimal places.

44. Use the Maclaurin series for $\sin x$ to compute $\sin 3°$ correct to five decimal places.

45. (a) Use the binomial series to expand $1/\sqrt{1 - x^2}$.
(b) Use part (a) to find the Maclaurin series for $\sin^{-1}x$.

46. (a) Expand $1/\sqrt[4]{1 + x}$ as a power series.
(b) Use part (a) to estimate $1/\sqrt[4]{1.1}$ correct to three decimal places.

47–50 Evaluate the indefinite integral as an infinite series.

47. $\int x \cos(x^3)\, dx$

48. $\int \dfrac{e^x - 1}{x}\, dx$

49. $\int \dfrac{\cos x - 1}{x}\, dx$

50. $\int \arctan(x^2)\, dx$

51–54 Use series to approximate the definite integral to within the indicated accuracy.

51. $\int_0^1 x \cos(x^3)\, dx$ (three decimal places)

52. $\int_0^{0.2} [\tan^{-1}(x^3) + \sin(x^3)]\, dx$ (five decimal places)

53. $\int_0^{0.4} \sqrt{1 + x^4}\, dx$ ($|\text{error}| < 5 \times 10^{-6}$)

54. $\int_0^{0.5} x^2 e^{-x^2}\, dx$ ($|\text{error}| < 0.001$)

55–57 Use series to evaluate the limit.

55. $\displaystyle\lim_{x \to 0} \frac{x - \tan^{-1}x}{x^3}$

56. $\displaystyle\lim_{x \to 0} \frac{1 - \cos x}{1 + x - e^x}$

57. $\displaystyle\lim_{x \to 0} \frac{\sin x - x + \frac{1}{6}x^3}{x^5}$

58. Use the series in Example 12(b) to evaluate

$$\lim_{x \to 0} \frac{\tan x - x}{x^3}$$

We found this limit in Example 4 in Section 7.8 using l'Hospital's Rule three times. Which method do you prefer?

59–62 Use multiplication or division of power series to find the first three nonzero terms in the Maclaurin series for the function.

59. $y = e^{-x^2} \cos x$

60. $y = \sec x$

61. $y = \dfrac{x}{\sin x}$

62. $y = e^x \ln(1 - x)$

63–68 Find the sum of the series.

63. $\displaystyle\sum_{n=0}^{\infty} (-1)^n \frac{x^{4n}}{n!}$

64. $\displaystyle\sum_{n=0}^{\infty} \frac{(-1)^n \pi^{2n}}{6^{2n}(2n)!}$

65. $\displaystyle\sum_{n=0}^{\infty} \frac{(-1)^n \pi^{2n+1}}{4^{2n+1}(2n + 1)!}$

66. $\displaystyle\sum_{n=0}^{\infty} \frac{3^n}{5^n n!}$

67. $3 + \dfrac{9}{2!} + \dfrac{27}{3!} + \dfrac{81}{4!} + \cdots$

68. $1 - \ln 2 + \dfrac{(\ln 2)^2}{2!} - \dfrac{(\ln 2)^3}{3!} + \cdots$

69. Prove Taylor's Inequality for $n = 2$, that is, prove that if $|f'''(x)| \le M$ for $|x - a| \le d$, then

$$|R_2(x)| \le \frac{M}{6} |x - a|^3 \qquad \text{for } |x - a| \le d$$

70. (a) Show that the function defined by

$$f(x) = \begin{cases} e^{-1/x^2} & \text{if } x \ne 0 \\ 0 & \text{if } x = 0 \end{cases}$$

is not equal to its Maclaurin series.

(b) Graph the function in part (a) and comment on its behavior near the origin.

71. Use the following steps to prove (17).
(a) Let $g(x) = \sum_{n=0}^{\infty} \binom{k}{n} x^n$. Differentiate this series to show that

$$g'(x) = \frac{kg(x)}{1 + x} \qquad -1 < x < 1$$

(b) Let $h(x) = (1 + x)^{-k} g(x)$ and show that $h'(x) = 0$.
(c) Deduce that $g(x) = (1 + x)^k$.

72. In Exercise 53 in Section 11.2 it was shown that the length of the ellipse $x = a \sin \theta$, $y = b \cos \theta$, where $a > b > 0$, is

$$L = 4a \int_0^{\pi/2} \sqrt{1 - e^2 \sin^2 \theta}\, d\theta$$

where $e = \sqrt{a^2 - b^2}/a$ is the eccentricity of the ellipse. Expand the integrand as a binomial series and use the result of Exercise 46 in Section 8.1 to express L as a series in powers of the eccentricity up to the term in e^6.

<table>
<tr><td>

**LABORATORY
PROJECT**

</td></tr>
</table>

CAS AN ELUSIVE LIMIT

This project deals with the function

$$f(x) = \frac{\sin(\tan x) - \tan(\sin x)}{\arcsin(\arctan x) - \arctan(\arcsin x)}$$

1. Use your computer algebra system to evaluate $f(x)$ for $x = 1, 0.1, 0.01, 0.001$, and 0.0001. Does it appear that f has a limit as $x \to 0$?

2. Use the CAS to graph f near $x = 0$. Does it appear that f has a limit as $x \to 0$?

3. Try to evaluate $\lim_{x \to 0} f(x)$ with l'Hospital's Rule, using the CAS to find derivatives of the numerator and denominator. What do you discover? How many applications of l'Hospital's Rule are required?

4. Evaluate $\lim_{x \to 0} f(x)$ by using the CAS to find sufficiently many terms in the Taylor series of the numerator and denominator. (Use the command `taylor` in Maple or `Series` in Mathematica.)

5. Use the limit command on your CAS to find $\lim_{x \to 0} f(x)$ directly. (Most computer algebra systems use the method of Problem 4 to compute limits.)

6. In view of the answers to Problems 4 and 5, how do you explain the results of Problems 1 and 2?

**WRITING
PROJECT**

HOW NEWTON DISCOVERED THE BINOMIAL SERIES

The Binomial Theorem, which gives the expansion of $(a + b)^k$, was known to Chinese mathematicians many centuries before the time of Newton for the case where the exponent k is a positive integer. In 1665, when he was 22, Newton was the first to discover the infinite series expansion of $(a + b)^k$ when k is a fractional exponent (positive or negative). He didn't publish his discovery, but he stated it and gave examples of how to use it in a letter (now called the *epistola prior*) dated June 13, 1676, that he sent to Henry Oldenburg, secretary of the Royal Society of London, to transmit to Leibniz. When Leibniz replied, he asked how Newton had discovered the binomial series. Newton wrote a second letter, the *epistola posterior* of October 24, 1676, in which he explained in great detail how he arrived at his discovery by a very indirect route. He was investigating the areas under the curves $y = (1 - x^2)^{n/2}$ from 0 to x for $n = 0, 1, 2, 3, 4, \ldots$. These are easy to calculate if n is even. By observing patterns and interpolating, Newton was able to guess the answers for odd values of n. Then he realized he could get the same answers by expressing $(1 - x^2)^{n/2}$ as an infinite series.

Write a report on Newton's discovery of the binomial series. Start by giving the statement of the binomial series in Newton's notation (see the *epistola prior* on page 285 of [4] or page 402 of [2]). Explain why Newton's version is equivalent to Theorem 17 on page 778. Then read Newton's *epistola posterior* (page 287 in [4] or page 404 in [2]) and explain the patterns that Newton discovered in the areas under the curves $y = (1 - x^2)^{n/2}$. Show how he was able to guess the areas under the remaining curves and how he verified his answers. Finally, explain how these discoveries led to the binomial series. The books by Edwards [1] and Katz [3] contain commentaries on Newton's letters.

1. C. H. Edwards, *The Historical Development of the Calculus* (New York: Springer-Verlag, 1979), pp. 178–187.

2. John Fauvel and Jeremy Gray, eds., *The History of Mathematics: A Reader* (London: MacMillan Press, 1987).

3. Victor Katz, *A History of Mathematics: An Introduction* (New York: HarperCollins, 1993), pp. 463–466.

4. D. J. Struik, ed., *A Sourcebook in Mathematics, 1200–1800* (Princeton, NJ: Princeton University Press, 1969).

12.11 | APPLICATIONS OF TAYLOR POLYNOMIALS

In this section we explore two types of applications of Taylor polynomials. First we look at how they are used to approximate functions—computer scientists like them because polynomials are the simplest of functions. Then we investigate how physicists and engineers use them in such fields as relativity, optics, blackbody radiation, electric dipoles, the velocity of water waves, and building highways across a desert.

APPROXIMATING FUNCTIONS BY POLYNOMIALS

Suppose that $f(x)$ is equal to the sum of its Taylor series at a:

$$f(x) = \sum_{n=0}^{\infty} \frac{f^{(n)}(a)}{n!} (x - a)^n$$

In Section 12.10 we introduced the notation $T_n(x)$ for the nth partial sum of this series and called it the nth-degree Taylor polynomial of f at a. Thus

$$T_n(x) = \sum_{i=0}^{n} \frac{f^{(i)}(a)}{i!} (x - a)^i$$

$$= f(a) + \frac{f'(a)}{1!} (x - a) + \frac{f''(a)}{2!} (x - a)^2 + \cdots + \frac{f^{(n)}(a)}{n!} (x - a)^n$$

Since f is the sum of its Taylor series, we know that $T_n(x) \to f(x)$ as $n \to \infty$ and so T_n can be used as an approximation to f: $f(x) \approx T_n(x)$.

Notice that the first-degree Taylor polynomial

$$T_1(x) = f(a) + f'(a)(x - a)$$

is the same as the linearization of f at a that we discussed in Section 3.9. Notice also that T_1 and its derivative have the same values at a that f and f' have. In general, it can be shown that the derivatives of T_n at a agree with those of f up to and including derivatives of order n (see Exercise 38).

To illustrate these ideas let's take another look at the graphs of $y = e^x$ and its first few Taylor polynomials, as shown in Figure 1. The graph of T_1 is the tangent line to $y = e^x$ at $(0, 1)$; this tangent line is the best linear approximation to e^x near $(0, 1)$. The graph of T_2 is the parabola $y = 1 + x + x^2/2$, and the graph of T_3 is the cubic curve $y = 1 + x + x^2/2 + x^3/6$, which is a closer fit to the exponential curve $y = e^x$ than T_2. The next Taylor polynomial T_4 would be an even better approximation, and so on.

The values in the table give a numerical demonstration of the convergence of the Taylor polynomials $T_n(x)$ to the function $y = e^x$. We see that when $x = 0.2$ the convergence is very rapid, but when $x = 3$ it is somewhat slower. In fact, the farther x is from 0, the more slowly $T_n(x)$ converges to e^x.

When using a Taylor polynomial T_n to approximate a function f, we have to ask the questions: How good an approximation is it? How large should we take n to be in order to achieve a desired accuracy? To answer these questions we need to look at the absolute value of the remainder:

$$|R_n(x)| = |f(x) - T_n(x)|$$

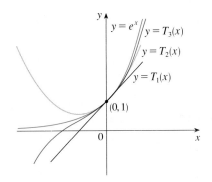

FIGURE 1

	$x = 0.2$	$x = 3.0$
$T_2(x)$	1.220000	8.500000
$T_4(x)$	1.221400	16.375000
$T_6(x)$	1.221403	19.412500
$T_8(x)$	1.221403	20.009152
$T_{10}(x)$	1.221403	20.079665
e^x	1.221403	20.085537

There are three possible methods for estimating the size of the error:

1. If a graphing device is available, we can use it to graph $|R_n(x)|$ and thereby estimate the error.

2. If the series happens to be an alternating series, we can use the Alternating Series Estimation Theorem.

3. In all cases we can use Taylor's Inequality (Theorem 12.10.9), which says that if $|f^{(n+1)}(x)| \leq M$, then

$$|R_n(x)| \leq \frac{M}{(n+1)!}|x - a|^{n+1}$$

Ⅴ EXAMPLE 1
(a) Approximate the function $f(x) = \sqrt[3]{x}$ by a Taylor polynomial of degree 2 at $a = 8$.
(b) How accurate is this approximation when $7 \leq x \leq 9$?

SOLUTION
(a)
$$f(x) = \sqrt[3]{x} = x^{1/3} \qquad f(8) = 2$$
$$f'(x) = \tfrac{1}{3}x^{-2/3} \qquad f'(8) = \tfrac{1}{12}$$
$$f''(x) = -\tfrac{2}{9}x^{-5/3} \qquad f''(8) = -\tfrac{1}{144}$$
$$f'''(x) = \tfrac{10}{27}x^{-8/3}$$

Thus the second-degree Taylor polynomial is

$$T_2(x) = f(8) + \frac{f'(8)}{1!}(x - 8) + \frac{f''(8)}{2!}(x - 8)^2$$
$$= 2 + \tfrac{1}{12}(x - 8) - \tfrac{1}{288}(x - 8)^2$$

The desired approximation is

$$\sqrt[3]{x} \approx T_2(x) = 2 + \tfrac{1}{12}(x - 8) - \tfrac{1}{288}(x - 8)^2$$

(b) The Taylor series is not alternating when $x < 8$, so we can't use the Alternating Series Estimation Theorem in this example. But we can use Taylor's Inequality with $n = 2$ and $a = 8$:

$$|R_2(x)| \leq \frac{M}{3!}|x - 8|^3$$

where $|f'''(x)| \leq M$. Because $x \geq 7$, we have $x^{8/3} \geq 7^{8/3}$ and so

$$f'''(x) = \frac{10}{27} \cdot \frac{1}{x^{8/3}} \leq \frac{10}{27} \cdot \frac{1}{7^{8/3}} < 0.0021$$

Therefore we can take $M = 0.0021$. Also $7 \leq x \leq 9$, so $-1 \leq x - 8 \leq 1$ and $|x - 8| \leq 1$. Then Taylor's Inequality gives

$$|R_2(x)| \leq \frac{0.0021}{3!} \cdot 1^3 = \frac{0.0021}{6} < 0.0004$$

Thus, if $7 \leq x \leq 9$, the approximation in part (a) is accurate to within 0.0004. ☐

2.5

FIGURE 2

0.0003

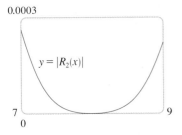

FIGURE 3

Let's use a graphing device to check the calculation in Example 1. Figure 2 shows that the graphs of $y = \sqrt[3]{x}$ and $y = T_2(x)$ are very close to each other when x is near 8. Figure 3 shows the graph of $|R_2(x)|$ computed from the expression

$$|R_2(x)| = |\sqrt[3]{x} - T_2(x)|$$

We see from the graph that

$$|R_2(x)| < 0.0003$$

when $7 \leqslant x \leqslant 9$. Thus the error estimate from graphical methods is slightly better than the error estimate from Taylor's Inequality in this case.

▼ EXAMPLE 2

(a) What is the maximum error possible in using the approximation

$$\sin x \approx x - \frac{x^3}{3!} + \frac{x^5}{5!}$$

when $-0.3 \leqslant x \leqslant 0.3$? Use this approximation to find $\sin 12°$ correct to six decimal places.

(b) For what values of x is this approximation accurate to within 0.00005?

SOLUTION

(a) Notice that the Maclaurin series

$$\sin x = x - \frac{x^3}{3!} + \frac{x^5}{5!} - \frac{x^7}{7!} + \cdots$$

is alternating for all nonzero values of x, and the successive terms decrease in size because $|x| < 1$, so we can use the Alternating Series Estimation Theorem. The error in approximating $\sin x$ by the first three terms of its Maclaurin series is at most

$$\left| \frac{x^7}{7!} \right| = \frac{|x|^7}{5040}$$

If $-0.3 \leqslant x \leqslant 0.3$, then $|x| \leqslant 0.3$, so the error is smaller than

$$\frac{(0.3)^7}{5040} \approx 4.3 \times 10^{-8}$$

To find $\sin 12°$ we first convert to radian measure.

$$\sin 12° = \sin\left(\frac{12\pi}{180}\right) = \sin\left(\frac{\pi}{15}\right)$$

$$\approx \frac{\pi}{15} - \left(\frac{\pi}{15}\right)^3 \frac{1}{3!} + \left(\frac{\pi}{15}\right)^5 \frac{1}{5!} \approx 0.20791169$$

Thus, correct to six decimal places, $\sin 12° \approx 0.207912$.

(b) The error will be smaller than 0.00005 if

$$\frac{|x|^7}{5040} < 0.00005$$

Solving this inequality for x, we get

$$|x|^7 < 0.252 \qquad \text{or} \qquad |x| < (0.252)^{1/7} \approx 0.821$$

So the given approximation is accurate to within 0.00005 when $|x| < 0.82$. $\qquad \square$

TEC Module 12.10/12.11 graphically shows the remainders in Taylor polynomial approximations.

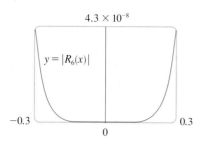

4.3×10^{-8}

$y = |R_6(x)|$

-0.3 0 0.3

FIGURE 4

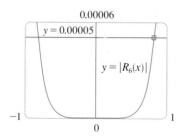

0.00006

$y = 0.00005$

$y = |R_6(x)|$

-1 0 1

FIGURE 5

What if we use Taylor's Inequality to solve Example 2? Since $f^{(7)}(x) = -\cos x$, we have $|f^{(7)}(x)| \leq 1$ and so

$$|R_6(x)| \leq \frac{1}{7!}|x|^7$$

So we get the same estimates as with the Alternating Series Estimation Theorem.

What about graphical methods? Figure 4 shows the graph of

$$|R_6(x)| = \left| \sin x - \left(x - \tfrac{1}{6}x^3 + \tfrac{1}{120}x^5 \right) \right|$$

and we see from it that $|R_6(x)| < 4.3 \times 10^{-8}$ when $|x| \leq 0.3$. This is the same estimate that we obtained in Example 2. For part (b) we want $|R_6(x)| < 0.00005$, so we graph both $y = |R_6(x)|$ and $y = 0.00005$ in Figure 5. By placing the cursor on the right intersection point we find that the inequality is satisfied when $|x| < 0.82$. Again this is the same estimate that we obtained in the solution to Example 2.

If we had been asked to approximate $\sin 72°$ instead of $\sin 12°$ in Example 2, it would have been wise to use the Taylor polynomials at $a = \pi/3$ (instead of $a = 0$) because they are better approximations to $\sin x$ for values of x close to $\pi/3$. Notice that $72°$ is close to $60°$ (or $\pi/3$ radians) and the derivatives of $\sin x$ are easy to compute at $\pi/3$.

Figure 6 shows the graphs of the Maclaurin polynomial approximations

$$T_1(x) = x \qquad\qquad T_3(x) = x - \frac{x^3}{3!}$$

$$T_5(x) = x - \frac{x^3}{3!} + \frac{x^5}{5!} \qquad T_7(x) = x - \frac{x^3}{3!} + \frac{x^5}{5!} - \frac{x^7}{7!}$$

to the sine curve. You can see that as n increases, $T_n(x)$ is a good approximation to $\sin x$ on a larger and larger interval.

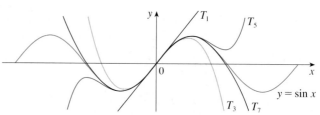

FIGURE 6

One use of the type of calculation done in Examples 1 and 2 occurs in calculators and computers. For instance, when you press the sin or e^x key on your calculator, or when a computer programmer uses a subroutine for a trigonometric or exponential or Bessel function, in many machines a polynomial approximation is calculated. The polynomial is often a Taylor polynomial that has been modified so that the error is spread more evenly throughout an interval.

APPLICATIONS TO PHYSICS

Taylor polynomials are also used frequently in physics. In order to gain insight into an equation, a physicist often simplifies a function by considering only the first two or three terms in its Taylor series. In other words, the physicist uses a Taylor polynomial as an approximation to the function. Taylor's Inequality can then be used to gauge the accuracy of the approximation. The following example shows one way in which this idea is used in special relativity.

◤ EXAMPLE 3 In Einstein's theory of special relativity the mass of an object moving with velocity v is

$$m = \frac{m_0}{\sqrt{1 - v^2/c^2}}$$

where m_0 is the mass of the object when at rest and c is the speed of light. The kinetic energy of the object is the difference between its total energy and its energy at rest:

$$K = mc^2 - m_0 c^2$$

(a) Show that when v is very small compared with c, this expression for K agrees with classical Newtonian physics: $K = \frac{1}{2} m_0 v^2$.
(b) Use Taylor's Inequality to estimate the difference in these expressions for K when $|v| \leq 100$ m/s.

SOLUTION
(a) Using the expressions given for K and m, we get

$$K = mc^2 - m_0 c^2 = \frac{m_0 c^2}{\sqrt{1 - v^2/c^2}} - m_0 c^2$$

$$= m_0 c^2 \left[\left(1 - \frac{v^2}{c^2} \right)^{-1/2} - 1 \right]$$

With $x = -v^2/c^2$, the Maclaurin series for $(1 + x)^{-1/2}$ is most easily computed as a binomial series with $k = -\frac{1}{2}$. (Notice that $|x| < 1$ because $v < c$.) Therefore we have

$$(1 + x)^{-1/2} = 1 - \frac{1}{2}x + \frac{(-\frac{1}{2})(-\frac{3}{2})}{2!} x^2 + \frac{(-\frac{1}{2})(-\frac{3}{2})(-\frac{5}{2})}{3!} x^3 + \cdots$$

$$= 1 - \frac{1}{2}x + \frac{3}{8}x^2 - \frac{5}{16}x^3 + \cdots$$

and

$$K = m_0 c^2 \left[\left(1 + \frac{1}{2}\frac{v^2}{c^2} + \frac{3}{8}\frac{v^4}{c^4} + \frac{5}{16}\frac{v^6}{c^6} + \cdots \right) - 1 \right]$$

$$= m_0 c^2 \left(\frac{1}{2}\frac{v^2}{c^2} + \frac{3}{8}\frac{v^4}{c^4} + \frac{5}{16}\frac{v^6}{c^6} + \cdots \right)$$

If v is much smaller than c, then all terms after the first are very small when compared with the first term. If we omit them, we get

$$K \approx m_0 c^2 \left(\frac{1}{2}\frac{v^2}{c^2} \right) = \frac{1}{2} m_0 v^2$$

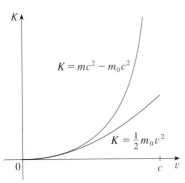

■ The upper curve in Figure 7 is the graph of the expression for the kinetic energy K of an object with velocity v in special relativity. The lower curve shows the function used for K in classical Newtonian physics. When v is much smaller than the speed of light, the curves are practically identical.

$K = mc^2 - m_0 c^2$

$K = \frac{1}{2} m_0 v^2$

FIGURE 7

(b) If $x = -v^2/c^2$, $f(x) = m_0 c^2 [(1 + x)^{-1/2} - 1]$, and M is a number such that $|f''(x)| \leq M$, then we can use Taylor's Inequality to write

$$|R_1(x)| \leq \frac{M}{2!} x^2$$

We have $f''(x) = \frac{3}{4} m_0 c^2 (1 + x)^{-5/2}$ and we are given that $|v| \leq 100$ m/s, so

$$|f''(x)| = \frac{3 m_0 c^2}{4(1 - v^2/c^2)^{5/2}} \leq \frac{3 m_0 c^2}{4(1 - 100^2/c^2)^{5/2}} \quad (= M)$$

Thus, with $c = 3 \times 10^8$ m/s,

$$|R_1(x)| \leq \frac{1}{2} \cdot \frac{3m_0 c^2}{4(1 - 100^2/c^2)^{5/2}} \cdot \frac{100^4}{c^4} < (4.17 \times 10^{-10})m_0$$

So when $|v| \leq 100$ m/s, the magnitude of the error in using the Newtonian expression for kinetic energy is at most $(4.2 \times 10^{-10})m_0$. $\qquad\square$

Another application to physics occurs in optics. Figure 8 is adapted from *Optics,* 4th ed., by Eugene Hecht (San Francisco: Addison-Wesley, 2002), page 153. It depicts a wave from the point source S meeting a spherical interface of radius R centered at C. The ray SA is refracted toward P.

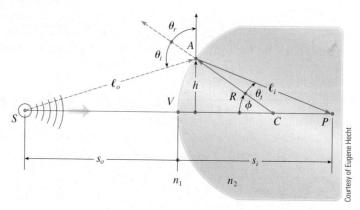

FIGURE 8
Refraction at a spherical interface

Courtesy of Eugene Hecht

Using Fermat's principle that light travels so as to minimize the time taken, Hecht derives the equation

$$\boxed{1} \qquad \frac{n_1}{\ell_o} + \frac{n_2}{\ell_i} = \frac{1}{R}\left(\frac{n_2 s_i}{\ell_i} - \frac{n_1 s_o}{\ell_o}\right)$$

where n_1 and n_2 are indexes of refraction and ℓ_o, ℓ_i, s_o, and s_i are the distances indicated in Figure 8. By the Law of Cosines, applied to triangles ACS and ACP, we have

■ Here we use the identity
$$\cos(\pi - \phi) = -\cos\phi$$

$$\boxed{2} \qquad \ell_o = \sqrt{R^2 + (s_o + R)^2 - 2R(s_o + R)\cos\phi}$$

$$\ell_i = \sqrt{R^2 + (s_i - R)^2 + 2R(s_i - R)\cos\phi}$$

Because Equation 1 is cumbersome to work with, Gauss, in 1841, simplified it by using the linear approximation $\cos\phi \approx 1$ for small values of ϕ. (This amounts to using the Taylor polynomial of degree 1.) Then Equation 1 becomes the following simpler equation [as you are asked to show in Exercise 34(a)]:

$$\boxed{3} \qquad \frac{n_1}{s_o} + \frac{n_2}{s_i} = \frac{n_2 - n_1}{R}$$

The resulting optical theory is known as *Gaussian optics,* or *first-order optics,* and has become the basic theoretical tool used to design lenses.

A more accurate theory is obtained by approximating $\cos\phi$ by its Taylor polynomial of degree 3 (which is the same as the Taylor polynomial of degree 2). This takes into account rays for which ϕ is not so small, that is, rays that strike the surface at greater distances h above the axis. In Exercise 34(b) you are asked to use this approximation to derive the more accurate equation

$$\boxed{4} \qquad \frac{n_1}{s_o} + \frac{n_2}{s_i} = \frac{n_2 - n_1}{R} + h^2\left[\frac{n_1}{2s_o}\left(\frac{1}{s_o} + \frac{1}{R}\right)^2 + \frac{n_2}{2s_i}\left(\frac{1}{R} - \frac{1}{s_i}\right)^2\right]$$

The resulting optical theory is known as *third-order optics*.

Other applications of Taylor polynomials to physics and engineering are explored in Exercises 32, 33, 35, 36, and 37 and in the Applied Project on page 793.

12.11 EXERCISES

1. (a) Find the Taylor polynomials up to degree 6 for $f(x) = \cos x$ centered at $a = 0$. Graph f and these polynomials on a common screen.
  (b) Evaluate f and these polynomials at $x = \pi/4$, $\pi/2$, and π.
  (c) Comment on how the Taylor polynomials converge to $f(x)$.

2. (a) Find the Taylor polynomials up to degree 3 for $f(x) = 1/x$ centered at $a = 1$. Graph f and these polynomials on a common screen.
  (b) Evaluate f and these polynomials at $x = 0.9$ and 1.3.
  (c) Comment on how the Taylor polynomials converge to $f(x)$.

3–10 Find the Taylor polynomial $T_n(x)$ for the function f at the number a. Graph f and T_3 on the same screen.

3. $f(x) = 1/x$, $a = 2$

4. $f(x) = x + e^{-x}$, $a = 0$

5. $f(x) = \cos x$, $a = \pi/2$

6. $f(x) = e^{-x}\sin x$, $a = 0$

7. $f(x) = \arcsin x$, $a = 0$

8. $f(x) = \dfrac{\ln x}{x}$, $a = 1$

9. $f(x) = xe^{-2x}$, $a = 0$

10. $f(x) = \tan^{-1}x$, $a = 1$

11–12 Use a computer algebra system to find the Taylor polynomials T_n centered at a for $n = 2, 3, 4, 5$. Then graph these polynomials and f on the same screen.

11. $f(x) = \cot x$, $a = \pi/4$

12. $f(x) = \sqrt[3]{1 + x^2}$, $a = 0$

13–22
(a) Approximate f by a Taylor polynomial with degree n at the number a.
(b) Use Taylor's Inequality to estimate the accuracy of the approximation $f(x) \approx T_n(x)$ when x lies in the given interval.

(c) Check your result in part (b) by graphing $|R_n(x)|$.

13. $f(x) = \sqrt{x}$, $a = 4$, $n = 2$, $4 \le x \le 4.2$

14. $f(x) = x^{-2}$, $a = 1$, $n = 2$, $0.9 \le x \le 1.1$

15. $f(x) = x^{2/3}$, $a = 1$, $n = 3$, $0.8 \le x \le 1.2$

16. $f(x) = \sin x$, $a = \pi/6$, $n = 4$, $0 \le x \le \pi/3$

17. $f(x) = \sec x$, $a = 0$, $n = 2$, $-0.2 \le x \le 0.2$

18. $f(x) = \ln(1 + 2x)$, $a = 1$, $n = 3$, $0.5 \le x \le 1.5$

19. $f(x) = e^{x^2}$, $a = 0$, $n = 3$, $0 \le x \le 0.1$

20. $f(x) = x \ln x$, $a = 1$, $n = 3$, $0.5 \le x \le 1.5$

21. $f(x) = x \sin x$, $a = 0$, $n = 4$, $-1 \le x \le 1$

22. $f(x) = \sinh 2x$, $a = 0$, $n = 5$, $-1 \le x \le 1$

23. Use the information from Exercise 5 to estimate $\cos 80°$ correct to five decimal places.

24. Use the information from Exercise 16 to estimate $\sin 38°$ correct to five decimal places.

25. Use Taylor's Inequality to determine the number of terms of the Maclaurin series for e^x that should be used to estimate $e^{0.1}$ to within 0.00001.

26. How many terms of the Maclaurin series for $\ln(1 + x)$ do you need to use to estimate $\ln 1.4$ to within 0.001?

27–29 Use the Alternating Series Estimation Theorem or Taylor's Inequality to estimate the range of values of x for which the given approximation is accurate to within the stated error. Check your answer graphically.

27. $\sin x \approx x - \dfrac{x^3}{6}$ $(|\text{error}| < 0.01)$

28. $\cos x \approx 1 - \dfrac{x^2}{2} + \dfrac{x^4}{24}$ $(|\text{error}| < 0.005)$

29. $\arctan x \approx x - \dfrac{x^3}{3} + \dfrac{x^5}{5}$ $(|\text{error}| < 0.05)$

30. Suppose you know that

$$f^{(n)}(4) = \frac{(-1)^n n!}{3^n(n+1)}$$

and the Taylor series of f centered at 4 converges to $f(x)$ for all x in the interval of convergence. Show that the fifth-degree Taylor polynomial approximates $f(5)$ with error less than 0.0002.

31. A car is moving with speed 20 m/s and acceleration 2 m/s² at a given instant. Using a second-degree Taylor polynomial, estimate how far the car moves in the next second. Would it be reasonable to use this polynomial to estimate the distance traveled during the next minute?

32. The resistivity ρ of a conducting wire is the reciprocal of the conductivity and is measured in units of ohm-meters (Ω-m). The resistivity of a given metal depends on the temperature according to the equation

$$\rho(t) = \rho_{20} e^{\alpha(t-20)}$$

where t is the temperature in °C. There are tables that list the values of α (called the temperature coefficient) and ρ_{20} (the resistivity at 20°C) for various metals. Except at very low temperatures, the resistivity varies almost linearly with temperature and so it is common to approximate the expression for $\rho(t)$ by its first- or second-degree Taylor polynomial at $t = 20$.
(a) Find expressions for these linear and quadratic approximations.
 (b) For copper, the tables give $\alpha = 0.0039$/°C and $\rho_{20} = 1.7 \times 10^{-8}$ Ω-m. Graph the resistivity of copper and the linear and quadratic approximations for $-250°C \leq t \leq 1000°C$.
(c) For what values of t does the linear approximation agree with the exponential expression to within one percent?

33. An electric dipole consists of two electric charges of equal magnitude and opposite sign. If the charges are q and $-q$ and are located at a distance d from each other, then the electric field E at the point P in the figure is

$$E = \frac{q}{D^2} - \frac{q}{(D+d)^2}$$

By expanding this expression for E as a series in powers of d/D, show that E is approximately proportional to $1/D^3$ when P is far away from the dipole.

34. (a) Derive Equation 3 for Gaussian optics from Equation 1 by approximating $\cos \phi$ in Equation 2 by its first-degree Taylor polynomial.
(b) Show that if $\cos \phi$ is replaced by its third-degree Taylor polynomial in Equation 2, then Equation 1 becomes

Equation 4 for third-order optics. [*Hint:* Use the first two terms in the binomial series for ℓ_o^{-1} and ℓ_i^{-1}. Also, use $\phi \approx \sin \phi$.]

35. If a water wave with length L moves with velocity v across a body of water with depth d, as in the figure, then

$$v^2 = \frac{gL}{2\pi} \tanh \frac{2\pi d}{L}$$

(a) If the water is deep, show that $v \approx \sqrt{gL/(2\pi)}$.
(b) If the water is shallow, use the Maclaurin series for tanh to show that $v \approx \sqrt{gd}$. (Thus in shallow water the velocity of a wave tends to be independent of the length of the wave.)
(c) Use the Alternating Series Estimation Theorem to show that if $L > 10d$, then the estimate $v^2 \approx gd$ is accurate to within $0.014gL$.

36. The period of a pendulum with length L that makes a maximum angle θ_0 with the vertical is

$$T = 4\sqrt{\frac{L}{g}} \int_0^{\pi/2} \frac{dx}{\sqrt{1 - k^2 \sin^2 x}}$$

where $k = \sin\left(\frac{1}{2}\theta_0\right)$ and g is the acceleration due to gravity. (In Exercise 40 in Section 8.7 we approximated this integral using Simpson's Rule.)
(a) Expand the integrand as a binomial series and use the result of Exercise 46 in Section 8.1 to show that

$$T = 2\pi\sqrt{\frac{L}{g}}\left[1 + \frac{1^2}{2^2}k^2 + \frac{1^2 3^2}{2^2 4^2}k^4 + \frac{1^2 3^2 5^2}{2^2 4^2 6^2}k^6 + \cdots\right]$$

If θ_0 is not too large, the approximation $T \approx 2\pi\sqrt{L/g}$, obtained by using only the first term in the series, is often used. A better approximation is obtained by using two terms:

$$T \approx 2\pi\sqrt{\frac{L}{g}}\left(1 + \tfrac{1}{4}k^2\right)$$

(b) Notice that all the terms in the series after the first one have coefficients that are at most $\frac{1}{4}$. Use this fact to compare this series with a geometric series and show that

$$2\pi\sqrt{\frac{L}{g}}\left(1 + \tfrac{1}{4}k^2\right) \leq T \leq 2\pi\sqrt{\frac{L}{g}}\frac{4 - 3k^2}{4 - 4k^2}$$

(c) Use the inequalities in part (b) to estimate the period of a pendulum with $L = 1$ meter and $\theta_0 = 10°$. How does it compare with the estimate $T \approx 2\pi\sqrt{L/g}$? What if $\theta_0 = 42°$?

37. If a surveyor measures differences in elevation when making plans for a highway across a desert, corrections must be made for the curvature of the earth.

(a) If R is the radius of the earth and L is the length of the highway, show that the correction is

$$C = R \sec(L/R) - R$$

(b) Use a Taylor polynomial to show that

$$C \approx \frac{L^2}{2R} + \frac{5L^4}{24R^3}$$

(c) Compare the corrections given by the formulas in parts (a) and (b) for a highway that is 100 km long. (Take the radius of the earth to be 6370 km.)

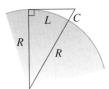

38. Show that T_n and f have the same derivatives at a up to order n.

39. In Section 4.8 we considered Newton's method for approximating a root r of the equation $f(x) = 0$, and from an initial approximation x_1 we obtained successive approximations $x_2, x_3, \ldots$, where

$$x_{n+1} = x_n - \frac{f(x_n)}{f'(x_n)}$$

Use Taylor's Inequality with $n = 1$, $a = x_n$, and $x = r$ to show that if $f''(x)$ exists on an interval I containing r, x_n, and x_{n+1}, and $|f''(x)| \leq M$, $|f'(x)| \geq K$ for all $x \in I$, then

$$|x_{n+1} - r| \leq \frac{M}{2K}|x_n - r|^2$$

[This means that if x_n is accurate to d decimal places, then x_{n+1} is accurate to about $2d$ decimal places. More precisely, if the error at stage n is at most 10^{-m}, then the error at stage $n + 1$ is at most $(M/2K)10^{-2m}$.]

APPLIED PROJECT

RADIATION FROM THE STARS

Any object emits radiation when heated. A *blackbody* is a system that absorbs all the radiation that falls on it. For instance, a matte black surface or a large cavity with a small hole in its wall (like a blastfurnace) is a blackbody and emits blackbody radiation. Even the radiation from the sun is close to being blackbody radiation.

Proposed in the late 19th century, the Rayleigh-Jeans Law expresses the energy density of blackbody radiation of wavelength λ as

$$f(\lambda) = \frac{8\pi kT}{\lambda^4}$$

where λ is measured in meters, T is the temperature in kelvins (K), and k is Boltzmann's constant. The Rayleigh-Jeans Law agrees with experimental measurements for long wavelengths but disagrees drastically for short wavelengths. [The law predicts that $f(\lambda) \to \infty$ as $\lambda \to 0^+$ but experiments have shown that $f(\lambda) \to 0$.] This fact is known as the *ultraviolet catastrophe*.

In 1900 Max Planck found a better model (known now as Planck's Law) for blackbody radiation:

$$f(\lambda) = \frac{8\pi hc\lambda^{-5}}{e^{hc/(\lambda kT)} - 1}$$

where λ is measured in meters, T is the temperature (in kelvins), and

$$h = \text{Planck's constant} = 6.6262 \times 10^{-34} \text{ J·s}$$

$$c = \text{speed of light} = 2.997925 \times 10^8 \text{ m/s}$$

$$k = \text{Boltzmann's constant} = 1.3807 \times 10^{-23} \text{ J/K}$$

1. Use l'Hospital's Rule to show that

$$\lim_{\lambda \to 0^+} f(\lambda) = 0 \quad \text{and} \quad \lim_{\lambda \to \infty} f(\lambda) = 0$$

for Planck's Law. So this law models blackbody radiation better than the Rayleigh-Jeans Law for short wavelengths.

2. Use a Taylor polynomial to show that, for large wavelengths, Planck's Law gives approximately the same values as the Rayleigh-Jeans Law.

3. Graph f as given by both laws on the same screen and comment on the similarities and differences. Use $T = 5700$ K (the temperature of the sun). (You may want to change from meters to the more convenient unit of micrometers: $1 \ \mu m = 10^{-6}$ m.)

4. Use your graph in Problem 3 to estimate the value of λ for which $f(\lambda)$ is a maximum under Planck's Law.

5. Investigate how the graph of f changes as T varies. (Use Planck's Law.) In particular, graph f for the stars Betelgeuse ($T = 3400$ K), Procyon ($T = 6400$ K), and Sirius ($T = 9200$ K) as well as the sun. How does the total radiation emitted (the area under the curve) vary with T? Use the graph to comment on why Sirius is known as a blue star and Betelgeuse as a red star.

12 REVIEW

CONCEPT CHECK

1. (a) What is a convergent sequence?
(b) What is a convergent series?
(c) What does $\lim_{n \to \infty} a_n = 3$ mean?
(d) What does $\sum_{n=1}^{\infty} a_n = 3$ mean?

2. (a) What is a bounded sequence?
(b) What is a monotonic sequence?
(c) What can you say about a bounded monotonic sequence?

3. (a) What is a geometric series? Under what circumstances is it convergent? What is its sum?
(b) What is a p-series? Under what circumstances is it convergent?

4. Suppose $\Sigma \, a_n = 3$ and s_n is the nth partial sum of the series. What is $\lim_{n \to \infty} a_n$? What is $\lim_{n \to \infty} s_n$?

5. State the following.
(a) The Test for Divergence
(b) The Integral Test
(c) The Comparison Test
(d) The Limit Comparison Test
(e) The Alternating Series Test
(f) The Ratio Test
(g) The Root Test

6. (a) What is an absolutely convergent series?
(b) What can you say about such a series?
(c) What is a conditionally convergent series?

7. (a) If a series is convergent by the Integral Test, how do you estimate its sum?

(b) If a series is convergent by the Comparison Test, how do you estimate its sum?
(c) If a series is convergent by the Alternating Series Test, how do you estimate its sum?

8. (a) Write the general form of a power series.
(b) What is the radius of convergence of a power series?
(c) What is the interval of convergence of a power series?

9. Suppose $f(x)$ is the sum of a power series with radius of convergence R.
(a) How do you differentiate f? What is the radius of convergence of the series for f'?
(b) How do you integrate f? What is the radius of convergence of the series for $\int f(x) \, dx$?

10. (a) Write an expression for the nth-degree Taylor polynomial of f centered at a.
(b) Write an expression for the Taylor series of f centered at a.
(c) Write an expression for the Maclaurin series of f.
(d) How do you show that $f(x)$ is equal to the sum of its Taylor series?
(e) State Taylor's Inequality.

11. Write the Maclaurin series and the interval of convergence for each of the following functions.
(a) $1/(1 - x)$ (b) e^x (c) $\sin x$
(d) $\cos x$ (e) $\tan^{-1} x$

12. Write the binomial series expansion of $(1 + x)^k$. What is the radius of convergence of this series?

TRUE-FALSE QUIZ

Determine whether the statement is true or false. If it is true, explain why. If it is false, explain why or give an example that disproves the statement.

1. If $\lim_{n \to \infty} a_n = 0$, then $\Sigma\, a_n$ is convergent.

2. The series $\sum_{n=1}^{\infty} n^{-\sin 1}$ is convergent.

3. If $\lim_{n \to \infty} a_n = L$, then $\lim_{n \to \infty} a_{2n+1} = L$.

4. If $\Sigma\, c_n 6^n$ is convergent, then $\Sigma\, c_n(-2)^n$ is convergent.

5. If $\Sigma\, c_n 6^n$ is convergent, then $\Sigma\, c_n(-6)^n$ is convergent.

6. If $\Sigma\, c_n x^n$ diverges when $x = 6$, then it diverges when $x = 10$.

7. The Ratio Test can be used to determine whether $\Sigma\, 1/n^3$ converges.

8. The Ratio Test can be used to determine whether $\Sigma\, 1/n!$ converges.

9. If $0 \le a_n \le b_n$ and $\Sigma\, b_n$ diverges, then $\Sigma\, a_n$ diverges.

10. $\displaystyle \sum_{n=0}^{\infty} \frac{(-1)^n}{n!} = \frac{1}{e}$

11. If $-1 < \alpha < 1$, then $\lim_{n \to \infty} \alpha^n = 0$.

12. If $\Sigma\, a_n$ is divergent, then $\Sigma\, |a_n|$ is divergent.

13. If $f(x) = 2x - x^2 + \frac{1}{3}x^3 - \cdots$ converges for all x, then $f'''(0) = 2$.

14. If $\{a_n\}$ and $\{b_n\}$ are divergent, then $\{a_n + b_n\}$ is divergent.

15. If $\{a_n\}$ and $\{b_n\}$ are divergent, then $\{a_n b_n\}$ is divergent.

16. If $\{a_n\}$ is decreasing and $a_n > 0$ for all n, then $\{a_n\}$ is convergent.

17. If $a_n > 0$ and $\Sigma\, a_n$ converges, then $\Sigma\, (-1)^n a_n$ converges.

18. If $a_n > 0$ and $\lim_{n \to \infty} (a_{n+1}/a_n) < 1$, then $\lim_{n \to \infty} a_n = 0$.

19. $0.99999 \ldots = 1$

20. If $\displaystyle \sum_{n=1}^{\infty} a_n = A$ and $\displaystyle \sum_{n=1}^{\infty} b_n = B$, then $\displaystyle \sum_{n=1}^{\infty} a_n b_n = AB$.

EXERCISES

1–8 Determine whether the sequence is convergent or divergent. If it is convergent, find its limit.

1. $a_n = \dfrac{2 + n^3}{1 + 2n^3}$

2. $a_n = \dfrac{9^{n+1}}{10^n}$

3. $a_n = \dfrac{n^3}{1 + n^2}$

4. $a_n = \cos(n\pi/2)$

5. $a_n = \dfrac{n \sin n}{n^2 + 1}$

6. $a_n = \dfrac{\ln n}{\sqrt{n}}$

7. $\{(1 + 3/n)^{4n}\}$

8. $\{(-10)^n/n!\}$

9. A sequence is defined recursively by the equations $a_1 = 1$, $a_{n+1} = \frac{1}{3}(a_n + 4)$. Show that $\{a_n\}$ is increasing and $a_n < 2$ for all n. Deduce that $\{a_n\}$ is convergent and find its limit.

10. Show that $\lim_{n \to \infty} n^4 e^{-n} = 0$ and use a graph to find the smallest value of N that corresponds to $\varepsilon = 0.1$ in the precise definition of a limit.

11–22 Determine whether the series is convergent or divergent.

11. $\displaystyle \sum_{n=1}^{\infty} \frac{n}{n^3 + 1}$

12. $\displaystyle \sum_{n=1}^{\infty} \frac{n^2 + 1}{n^3 + 1}$

13. $\displaystyle \sum_{n=1}^{\infty} \frac{n^3}{5^n}$

14. $\displaystyle \sum_{n=1}^{\infty} \frac{(-1)^n}{\sqrt{n+1}}$

15. $\displaystyle \sum_{n=2}^{\infty} \frac{1}{n\sqrt{\ln n}}$

16. $\displaystyle \sum_{n=1}^{\infty} \ln\left(\frac{n}{3n+1}\right)$

17. $\displaystyle \sum_{n=1}^{\infty} \frac{\cos 3n}{1 + (1.2)^n}$

18. $\displaystyle \sum_{n=1}^{\infty} \frac{n^{2n}}{(1 + 2n^2)^n}$

19. $\displaystyle \sum_{n=1}^{\infty} \frac{1 \cdot 3 \cdot 5 \cdot \cdots \cdot (2n - 1)}{5^n n!}$

20. $\displaystyle \sum_{n=1}^{\infty} \frac{(-5)^{2n}}{n^2 9^n}$

21. $\displaystyle \sum_{n=1}^{\infty} (-1)^{n-1} \frac{\sqrt{n}}{n + 1}$

22. $\displaystyle \sum_{n=1}^{\infty} \frac{\sqrt{n+1} - \sqrt{n-1}}{n}$

23–26 Determine whether the series is conditionally convergent, absolutely convergent, or divergent.

23. $\displaystyle \sum_{n=1}^{\infty} (-1)^{n-1} n^{-1/3}$

24. $\displaystyle \sum_{n=1}^{\infty} (-1)^{n-1} n^{-3}$

25. $\displaystyle \sum_{n=1}^{\infty} \frac{(-1)^n (n + 1)3^n}{2^{2n+1}}$

26. $\displaystyle \sum_{n=2}^{\infty} \frac{(-1)^n \sqrt{n}}{\ln n}$

27–31 Find the sum of the series.

27. $\displaystyle \sum_{n=1}^{\infty} \frac{(-3)^{n-1}}{2^{3n}}$

28. $\displaystyle \sum_{n=1}^{\infty} \frac{1}{n(n + 3)}$

29. $\displaystyle \sum_{n=1}^{\infty} [\tan^{-1}(n + 1) - \tan^{-1} n]$

30. $\displaystyle \sum_{n=0}^{\infty} \frac{(-1)^n \pi^n}{3^{2n}(2n)!}$

31. $1 - e + \dfrac{e^2}{2!} - \dfrac{e^3}{3!} + \dfrac{e^4}{4!} - \cdots$

32. Express the repeating decimal $4.17326326326 \ldots$ as a fraction.

33. Show that $\cosh x \geqslant 1 + \tfrac{1}{2}x^2$ for all x.

34. For what values of x does the series $\sum_{n=1}^{\infty} (\ln x)^n$ converge?

35. Find the sum of the series $\sum_{n=1}^{\infty} \dfrac{(-1)^{n+1}}{n^5}$ correct to four decimal places.

36. (a) Find the partial sum s_5 of the series $\sum_{n=1}^{\infty} 1/n^6$ and estimate the error in using it as an approximation to the sum of the series.
(b) Find the sum of this series correct to five decimal places.

37. Use the sum of the first eight terms to approximate the sum of the series $\sum_{n=1}^{\infty} (2 + 5^n)^{-1}$. Estimate the error involved in this approximation.

38. (a) Show that the series $\sum_{n=1}^{\infty} \dfrac{n^n}{(2n)!}$ is convergent.

(b) Deduce that $\lim\limits_{n \to \infty} \dfrac{n^n}{(2n)!} = 0$.

39. Prove that if the series $\sum_{n=1}^{\infty} a_n$ is absolutely convergent, then the series

$$\sum_{n=1}^{\infty} \left(\dfrac{n+1}{n} \right) a_n$$

is also absolutely convergent.

40–43 Find the radius of convergence and interval of convergence of the series.

40. $\sum_{n=1}^{\infty} (-1)^n \dfrac{x^n}{n^2 5^n}$

41. $\sum_{n=1}^{\infty} \dfrac{(x+2)^n}{n\,4^n}$

42. $\sum_{n=1}^{\infty} \dfrac{2^n(x-2)^n}{(n+2)!}$

43. $\sum_{n=0}^{\infty} \dfrac{2^n(x-3)^n}{\sqrt{n+3}}$

44. Find the radius of convergence of the series

$$\sum_{n=1}^{\infty} \dfrac{(2n)!}{(n!)^2} x^n$$

45. Find the Taylor series of $f(x) = \sin x$ at $a = \pi/6$.

46. Find the Taylor series of $f(x) = \cos x$ at $a = \pi/3$.

47–54 Find the Maclaurin series for f and its radius of convergence. You may use either the direct method (definition of a Maclaurin series) or known series such as geometric series, binomial series, or the Maclaurin series for e^x, $\sin x$, and $\tan^{-1}x$.

47. $f(x) = \dfrac{x^2}{1+x}$

48. $f(x) = \tan^{-1}(x^2)$

49. $f(x) = \ln(1-x)$

50. $f(x) = xe^{2x}$

51. $f(x) = \sin(x^4)$

52. $f(x) = 10^x$

53. $f(x) = 1/\sqrt[4]{16-x}$

54. $f(x) = (1-3x)^{-5}$

55. Evaluate $\displaystyle\int \dfrac{e^x}{x}\,dx$ as an infinite series.

56. Use series to approximate $\int_0^1 \sqrt{1+x^4}\,dx$ correct to two decimal places.

57–58
(a) Approximate f by a Taylor polynomial with degree n at the number a.
(b) Graph f and T_n on a common screen.
(c) Use Taylor's Inequality to estimate the accuracy of the approximation $f(x) \approx T_n(x)$ when x lies in the given interval.
(d) Check your result in part (c) by graphing $|R_n(x)|$.

57. $f(x) = \sqrt{x}$, $\quad a = 1$, $\quad n = 3$, $\quad 0.9 \leqslant x \leqslant 1.1$

58. $f(x) = \sec x$, $\quad a = 0$, $\quad n = 2$, $\quad 0 \leqslant x \leqslant \pi/6$

59. Use series to evaluate the following limit.

$$\lim_{x \to 0} \dfrac{\sin x - x}{x^3}$$

60. The force due to gravity on an object with mass m at a height h above the surface of the earth is

$$F = \dfrac{mgR^2}{(R+h)^2}$$

where R is the radius of the earth and g is the acceleration due to gravity.
(a) Express F as a series in powers of h/R.
(b) Observe that if we approximate F by the first term in the series, we get the expression $F \approx mg$ that is usually used when h is much smaller than R. Use the Alternating Series Estimation Theorem to estimate the range of values of h for which the approximation $F \approx mg$ is accurate to within one percent. (Use $R = 6400$ km.)

61. Suppose that $f(x) = \sum_{n=0}^{\infty} c_n x^n$ for all x.
(a) If f is an odd function, show that

$$c_0 = c_2 = c_4 = \cdots = 0$$

(b) If f is an even function, show that

$$c_1 = c_3 = c_5 = \cdots = 0$$

62. If $f(x) = e^{x^2}$, show that $f^{(2n)}(0) = \dfrac{(2n)!}{n!}$.

1. If $f(x) = \sin(x^3)$, find $f^{(15)}(0)$.

2. A function f is defined by

$$f(x) = \lim_{n \to \infty} \frac{x^{2n} - 1}{x^{2n} + 1}$$

Where is f continuous?

3. (a) Show that $\tan \frac{1}{2}x = \cot \frac{1}{2}x - 2 \cot x$.

(b) Find the sum of the series

$$\sum_{n=1}^{\infty} \frac{1}{2^n} \tan \frac{x}{2^n}$$

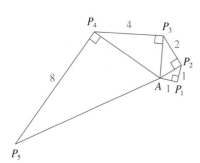

FIGURE FOR PROBLEM 4

4. Let $\{P_n\}$ be a sequence of points determined as in the figure. Thus $|AP_1| = 1$, $|P_n P_{n+1}| = 2^{n-1}$, and angle $AP_n P_{n+1}$ is a right angle. Find $\lim_{n \to \infty} \angle P_n AP_{n+1}$.

5. To construct the **snowflake curve**, start with an equilateral triangle with sides of length 1. Step 1 in the construction is to divide each side into three equal parts, construct an equilateral triangle on the middle part, and then delete the middle part (see the figure). Step 2 is to repeat step 1 for each side of the resulting polygon. This process is repeated at each succeeding step. The snowflake curve is the curve that results from repeating this process indefinitely.

(a) Let s_n, l_n, and p_n represent the number of sides, the length of a side, and the total length of the nth approximating curve (the curve obtained after step n of the construction), respectively. Find formulas for s_n, l_n, and p_n.

(b) Show that $p_n \to \infty$ as $n \to \infty$.

(c) Sum an infinite series to find the area enclosed by the snowflake curve.

Note: Parts (b) and (c) show that the snowflake curve is infinitely long but encloses only a finite area.

6. Find the sum of the series

$$1 + \frac{1}{2} + \frac{1}{3} + \frac{1}{4} + \frac{1}{6} + \frac{1}{8} + \frac{1}{9} + \frac{1}{12} + \cdots$$

where the terms are the reciprocals of the positive integers whose only prime factors are 2s and 3s.

7. (a) Show that for $xy \neq -1$,

$$\arctan x - \arctan y = \arctan \frac{x - y}{1 + xy}$$

if the left side lies between $-\pi/2$ and $\pi/2$.

(b) Show that

$$\arctan \tfrac{120}{119} - \arctan \tfrac{1}{239} = \frac{\pi}{4}$$

(c) Deduce the following formula of John Machin (1680–1751):

$$4 \arctan \tfrac{1}{5} - \arctan \tfrac{1}{239} = \frac{\pi}{4}$$

(d) Use the Maclaurin series for arctan to show that

$$0.197395560 < \arctan \tfrac{1}{5} < 0.197395562$$

(e) Show that

$$0.004184075 < \arctan \tfrac{1}{239} < 0.004184077$$

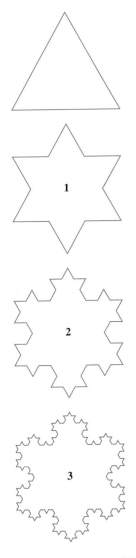

FIGURE FOR PROBLEM 5

(f) Deduce that, correct to seven decimal places,

$$\pi \approx 3.1415927$$

Machin used this method in 1706 to find π correct to 100 decimal places. Recently, with the aid of computers, the value of π has been computed to increasingly greater accuracy. Yasumada Kanada of the University of Tokyo recently computed the value of π to a trillion decimal places!

8. (a) Prove a formula similar to the one in Problem 7(a) but involving arccot instead of arctan.
   (b) Find the sum of the series

$$\sum_{n=0}^{\infty} \operatorname{arccot}(n^2 + n + 1)$$

9. Find the interval of convergence of $\sum_{n=1}^{\infty} n^3 x^n$ and find its sum.

10. If $a_0 + a_1 + a_2 + \cdots + a_k = 0$, show that

$$\lim_{n \to \infty} \left(a_0 \sqrt{n} + a_1 \sqrt{n+1} + a_2 \sqrt{n+2} + \cdots + a_k \sqrt{n+k} \right) = 0$$

If you don't see how to prove this, try the problem-solving strategy of *using analogy* (see page 55). Try the special cases $k = 1$ and $k = 2$ first. If you can see how to prove the assertion for these cases, then you will probably see how to prove it in general.

11. Find the sum of the series $\displaystyle\sum_{n=2}^{\infty} \ln\left(1 - \frac{1}{n^2} \right)$.

12. Suppose you have a large supply of books, all the same size, and you stack them at the edge of a table, with each book extending farther beyond the edge of the table than the one beneath it. Show that it is possible to do this so that the top book extends entirely beyond the table. In fact, show that the top book can extend any distance at all beyond the edge of the table if the stack is high enough. Use the following method of stacking: The top book extends half its length beyond the second book. The second book extends a quarter of its length beyond the third. The third extends one-sixth of its length beyond the fourth, and so on. (Try it yourself with a deck of cards.) Consider centers of mass.

FIGURE FOR PROBLEM 12

13. If the curve $y = e^{-x/10} \sin x$, $x \geq 0$, is rotated about the x-axis, the resulting solid looks like an infinite decreasing string of beads.
   (a) Find the exact volume of the nth bead. (Use either a table of integrals or a computer algebra system.)
   (b) Find the total volume of the beads.

14. If $p > 1$, evaluate the expression

$$\frac{1 + \dfrac{1}{2^p} + \dfrac{1}{3^p} + \dfrac{1}{4^p} + \cdots}{1 - \dfrac{1}{2^p} + \dfrac{1}{3^p} - \dfrac{1}{4^p} + \cdots}$$

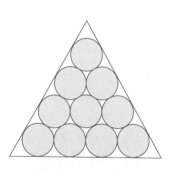

15. Suppose that circles of equal diameter are packed tightly in n rows inside an equilateral triangle. (The figure illustrates the case $n = 4$.) If A is the area of the triangle and A_n is the total area occupied by the n rows of circles, show that

$$\lim_{n \to \infty} \frac{A_n}{A} = \frac{\pi}{2\sqrt{3}}$$

FIGURE FOR PROBLEM 15

16. A sequence $\{a_n\}$ is defined recursively by the equations

$$a_0 = a_1 = 1 \qquad n(n-1)a_n = (n-1)(n-2)a_{n-1} - (n-3)a_{n-2}$$

Find the sum of the series $\sum_{n=0}^{\infty} a_n$.

17. Taking the value of x^x at 0 to be 1 and integrating a series term by term, show that

$$\int_0^1 x^x \, dx = \sum_{n=1}^{\infty} \frac{(-1)^{n-1}}{n^n}$$

18. Starting with the vertices $P_1(0, 1)$, $P_2(1, 1)$, $P_3(1, 0)$, $P_4(0, 0)$ of a square, we construct further points as shown in the figure: P_5 is the midpoint of P_1P_2, P_6 is the midpoint of P_2P_3, P_7 is the midpoint of P_3P_4, and so on. The polygonal spiral path $P_1P_2P_3P_4P_5P_6P_7 \ldots$ approaches a point P inside the square.
  (a) If the coordinates of P_n are (x_n, y_n), show that $\frac{1}{2}x_n + x_{n+1} + x_{n+2} + x_{n+3} = 2$ and find a similar equation for the y-coordinates.
  (b) Find the coordinates of P.

19. If $f(x) = \sum_{m=0}^{\infty} c_m x^m$ has positive radius of convergence and $e^{f(x)} = \sum_{n=0}^{\infty} d_n x^n$, show that

$$n d_n = \sum_{i=1}^{n} i c_i d_{n-i} \qquad n \geq 1$$

20. Right-angled triangles are constructed as in the figure. Each triangle has height 1 and its base is the hypotenuse of the preceding triangle. Show that this sequence of triangles makes indefinitely many turns around P by showing that $\Sigma \, \theta_n$ is a divergent series.

21. Consider the series whose terms are the reciprocals of the positive integers that can be written in base 10 notation without using the digit 0. Show that this series is convergent and the sum is less than 90.

22. (a) Show that the Maclaurin series of the function

$$f(x) = \frac{x}{1 - x - x^2} \qquad \text{is} \qquad \sum_{n=1}^{\infty} f_n x^n$$

where f_n is the nth Fibonacci number, that is, $f_1 = 1$, $f_2 = 1$, and $f_n = f_{n-1} + f_{n-2}$ for $n \geq 3$. [Hint: Write $x/(1 - x - x^2) = c_0 + c_1 x + c_2 x^2 + \cdots$ and multiply both sides of this equation by $1 - x - x^2$.]
  (b) By writing $f(x)$ as a sum of partial fractions and thereby obtaining the Maclaurin series in a different way, find an explicit formula for the nth Fibonacci number.

23. Let

$$u = 1 + \frac{x^3}{3!} + \frac{x^6}{6!} + \frac{x^9}{9!} + \cdots$$

$$v = x + \frac{x^4}{4!} + \frac{x^7}{7!} + \frac{x^{10}}{10!} + \cdots$$

$$w = \frac{x^2}{2!} + \frac{x^5}{5!} + \frac{x^8}{8!} + \cdots$$

Show that $u^3 + v^3 + w^3 - 3uvw = 1$.

24. Prove that if $n > 1$, the nth partial sum of the harmonic series is not an integer.
  Hint: Let 2^k be the largest power of 2 that is less than or equal to n and let M be the product of all odd integers that are less than or equal to n. Suppose that $s_n = m$, an integer. Then $M2^k s_n = M2^k m$. The right side of this equation is even. Prove that the left side is odd by showing that each of its terms is an even integer, except for the last one.

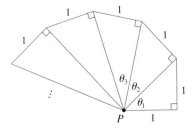

FIGURE FOR PROBLEM 18

FIGURE FOR PROBLEM 20

13

VECTORS AND THE GEOMETRY OF SPACE

Wind velocity is a vector because it has both magnitude and direction. Pictured are velocity vectors showing the wind pattern over the North Atlantic and Western Europe on February 28, 2007. Larger arrows indicate stronger winds.

In this chapter we introduce vectors and coordinate systems for three-dimensional space. This will be the setting for our study of the calculus of functions of two variables in Chapter 15 because the graph of such a function is a surface in space. In this chapter we will see that vectors provide particularly simple descriptions of lines and planes in space.

FIGURE 1
Coordinate axes

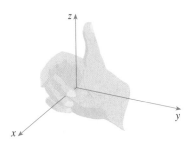

FIGURE 2
Right-hand rule

To locate a point in a plane, two numbers are necessary. We know that any point in the plane can be represented as an ordered pair (a, b) of real numbers, where a is the x-coordinate and b is the y-coordinate. For this reason, a plane is called two-dimensional. To locate a point in space, three numbers are required. We represent any point in space by an ordered triple (a, b, c) of real numbers.

In order to represent points in space, we first choose a fixed point O (the origin) and three directed lines through O that are perpendicular to each other, called the **coordinate axes** and labeled the x-axis, y-axis, and z-axis. Usually we think of the x- and y-axes as being horizontal and the z-axis as being vertical, and we draw the orientation of the axes as in Figure 1. The direction of the z-axis is determined by the **right-hand rule** as illustrated in Figure 2: If you curl the fingers of your right hand around the z-axis in the direction of a 90° counterclockwise rotation from the positive x-axis to the positive y-axis, then your thumb points in the positive direction of the z-axis.

The three coordinate axes determine the three **coordinate planes** illustrated in Figure 3(a). The xy-plane is the plane that contains the x- and y-axes; the yz-plane contains the y- and z-axes; the xz-plane contains the x- and z-axes. These three coordinate planes divide space into eight parts, called **octants**. The **first octant**, in the foreground, is determined by the positive axes.

FIGURE 3   (a) Coordinate planes   (b)

Because many people have some difficulty visualizing diagrams of three-dimensional figures, you may find it helpful to do the following [see Figure 3(b)]. Look at any bottom corner of a room and call the corner the origin. The wall on your left is in the xz-plane, the wall on your right is in the yz-plane, and the floor is in the xy-plane. The x-axis runs along the intersection of the floor and the left wall. The y-axis runs along the intersection of the floor and the right wall. The z-axis runs up from the floor toward the ceiling along the intersection of the two walls. You are situated in the first octant, and you can now imagine seven other rooms situated in the other seven octants (three on the same floor and four on the floor below), all connected by the common corner point O.

Now if P is any point in space, let a be the (directed) distance from the yz-plane to P, let b be the distance from the xz-plane to P, and let c be the distance from the xy-plane to P. We represent the point P by the ordered triple (a, b, c) of real numbers and we call a, b, and c the **coordinates** of P; a is the x-coordinate, b is the y-coordinate, and c is the z-coordinate. Thus, to locate the point (a, b, c), we can start at the origin O and move a units along the x-axis, then b units parallel to the y-axis, and then c units parallel to the z-axis as in Figure 4.

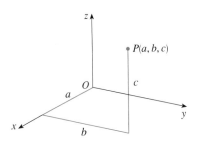

FIGURE 4

The point $P(a, b, c)$ determines a rectangular box as in Figure 5. If we drop a perpendicular from P to the xy-plane, we get a point Q with coordinates $(a, b, 0)$ called the **projection** of P on the xy-plane. Similarly, $R(0, b, c)$ and $S(a, 0, c)$ are the projections of P on the yz-plane and xz-plane, respectively.

As numerical illustrations, the points $(-4, 3, -5)$ and $(3, -2, -6)$ are plotted in Figure 6.

FIGURE 5

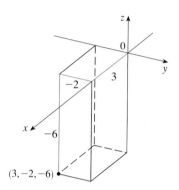

FIGURE 6

The Cartesian product $\mathbb{R} \times \mathbb{R} \times \mathbb{R} = \{(x, y, z) \mid x, y, z \in \mathbb{R}\}$ is the set of all ordered triples of real numbers and is denoted by $\mathbb{R}^3$. We have given a one-to-one correspondence between points P in space and ordered triples (a, b, c) in $\mathbb{R}^3$. It is called a **three-dimensional rectangular coordinate system**. Notice that, in terms of coordinates, the first octant can be described as the set of points whose coordinates are all positive.

In two-dimensional analytic geometry, the graph of an equation involving x and y is a curve in $\mathbb{R}^2$. In three-dimensional analytic geometry, an equation in x, y, and z represents a *surface* in $\mathbb{R}^3$.

◤ EXAMPLE 1 What surfaces in $\mathbb{R}^3$ are represented by the following equations?
(a) $z = 3$ (b) $y = 5$

SOLUTION

(a) The equation $z = 3$ represents the set $\{(x, y, z) \mid z = 3\}$, which is the set of all points in $\mathbb{R}^3$ whose z-coordinate is 3. This is the horizontal plane that is parallel to the xy-plane and three units above it as in Figure 7(a).

FIGURE 7

(a) $z = 3$, a plane in $\mathbb{R}^3$

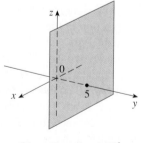

(b) $y = 5$, a plane in $\mathbb{R}^3$

(c) $y = 5$, a line in $\mathbb{R}^2$

(b) The equation $y = 5$ represents the set of all points in $\mathbb{R}^3$ whose y-coordinate is 5. This is the vertical plane that is parallel to the xz-plane and five units to the right of it as in Figure 7(b). ☐

NOTE When an equation is given, we must understand from the context whether it represents a curve in $\mathbb{R}^2$ or a surface in $\mathbb{R}^3$. In Example 1, $y = 5$ represents a plane in $\mathbb{R}^3$, but of course $y = 5$ can also represent a line in $\mathbb{R}^2$ if we are dealing with two-dimensional analytic geometry. See Figure 7(b) and (c).

In general, if k is a constant, then $x = k$ represents a plane parallel to the yz-plane, $y = k$ is a plane parallel to the xz-plane, and $z = k$ is a plane parallel to the xy-plane. In Figure 5, the faces of the rectangular box are formed by the three coordinate planes $x = 0$ (the yz-plane), $y = 0$ (the xz-plane), and $z = 0$ (the xy-plane), and the planes $x = a$, $y = b$, and $z = c$.

FIGURE 8

The plane $y = x$

☑ EXAMPLE 2 Describe and sketch the surface in $\mathbb{R}^3$ represented by the equation $y = x$.

SOLUTION The equation represents the set of all points in $\mathbb{R}^3$ whose x- and y-coordinates are equal, that is, $\{(x, x, z) \mid x \in \mathbb{R}, z \in \mathbb{R}\}$. This is a vertical plane that intersects the xy-plane in the line $y = x$, $z = 0$. The portion of this plane that lies in the first octant is sketched in Figure 8. ☐

The familiar formula for the distance between two points in a plane is easily extended to the following three-dimensional formula.

> **DISTANCE FORMULA IN THREE DIMENSIONS** The distance $|P_1P_2|$ between the points $P_1(x_1, y_1, z_1)$ and $P_2(x_2, y_2, z_2)$ is
>
> $$|P_1P_2| = \sqrt{(x_2 - x_1)^2 + (y_2 - y_1)^2 + (z_2 - z_1)^2}$$

To see why this formula is true, we construct a rectangular box as in Figure 9, where P_1 and P_2 are opposite vertices and the faces of the box are parallel to the coordinate planes. If $A(x_2, y_1, z_1)$ and $B(x_2, y_2, z_1)$ are the vertices of the box indicated in the figure, then

$$|P_1A| = |x_2 - x_1| \qquad |AB| = |y_2 - y_1| \qquad |BP_2| = |z_2 - z_1|$$

Because triangles P_1BP_2 and P_1AB are both right-angled, two applications of the Pythagorean Theorem give

$$|P_1P_2|^2 = |P_1B|^2 + |BP_2|^2$$

and

$$|P_1B|^2 = |P_1A|^2 + |AB|^2$$

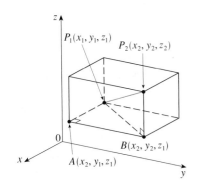

FIGURE 9

Combining these equations, we get

$$|P_1P_2|^2 = |P_1A|^2 + |AB|^2 + |BP_2|^2$$
$$= |x_2 - x_1|^2 + |y_2 - y_1|^2 + |z_2 - z_1|^2$$
$$= (x_2 - x_1)^2 + (y_2 - y_1)^2 + (z_2 - z_1)^2$$

Therefore $$|P_1P_2| = \sqrt{(x_2 - x_1)^2 + (y_2 - y_1)^2 + (z_2 - z_1)^2}$$

EXAMPLE 3 The distance from the point $P(2, -1, 7)$ to the point $Q(1, -3, 5)$ is

$$|PQ| = \sqrt{(1-2)^2 + (-3+1)^2 + (5-7)^2} = \sqrt{1+4+4} = 3 \qquad \square$$

☑ EXAMPLE 4 Find an equation of a sphere with radius r and center $C(h, k, l)$.

SOLUTION By definition, a sphere is the set of all points $P(x, y, z)$ whose distance from C is r. (See Figure 10.) Thus P is on the sphere if and only if $|PC| = r$. Squaring both sides, we have $|PC|^2 = r^2$ or

$$(x-h)^2 + (y-k)^2 + (z-l)^2 = r^2 \qquad \square$$

The result of Example 4 is worth remembering.

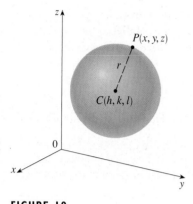

FIGURE 10

EQUATION OF A SPHERE An equation of a sphere with center $C(h, k, l)$ and radius r is

$$(x-h)^2 + (y-k)^2 + (z-l)^2 = r^2$$

In particular, if the center is the origin O, then an equation of the sphere is

$$x^2 + y^2 + z^2 = r^2$$

EXAMPLE 5 Show that $x^2 + y^2 + z^2 + 4x - 6y + 2z + 6 = 0$ is the equation of a sphere, and find its center and radius.

SOLUTION We can rewrite the given equation in the form of an equation of a sphere if we complete squares:

$$(x^2 + 4x + 4) + (y^2 - 6y + 9) + (z^2 + 2z + 1) = -6 + 4 + 9 + 1$$

$$(x+2)^2 + (y-3)^2 + (z+1)^2 = 8$$

Comparing this equation with the standard form, we see that it is the equation of a sphere with center $(-2, 3, -1)$ and radius $\sqrt{8} = 2\sqrt{2}$. $\qquad \square$

EXAMPLE 6 What region in $\mathbb{R}^3$ is represented by the following inequalities?

$$1 \leqslant x^2 + y^2 + z^2 \leqslant 4 \qquad z \leqslant 0$$

SOLUTION The inequalities

$$1 \leqslant x^2 + y^2 + z^2 \leqslant 4$$

can be rewritten as

$$1 \leqslant \sqrt{x^2 + y^2 + z^2} \leqslant 2$$

so they represent the points (x, y, z) whose distance from the origin is at least 1 and at most 2. But we are also given that $z \leqslant 0$, so the points lie on or below the xy-plane. Thus the given inequalities represent the region that lies between (or on) the spheres $x^2 + y^2 + z^2 = 1$ and $x^2 + y^2 + z^2 = 4$ and beneath (or on) the xy-plane. It is sketched in Figure 11. $\qquad \square$

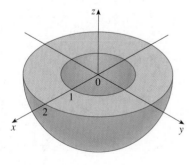

FIGURE 11

13.1 | EXERCISES

1. Suppose you start at the origin, move along the x-axis a distance of 4 units in the positive direction, and then move downward a distance of 3 units. What are the coordinates of your position?

2. Sketch the points $(0, 5, 2)$, $(4, 0, -1)$, $(2, 4, 6)$, and $(1, -1, 2)$ on a single set of coordinate axes.

3. Which of the points $P(6, 2, 3)$, $Q(-5, -1, 4)$, and $R(0, 3, 8)$ is closest to the xz-plane? Which point lies in the yz-plane?

4. What are the projections of the point $(2, 3, 5)$ on the xy-, yz-, and xz-planes? Draw a rectangular box with the origin and $(2, 3, 5)$ as opposite vertices and with its faces parallel to the coordinate planes. Label all vertices of the box. Find the length of the diagonal of the box.

5. Describe and sketch the surface in $\mathbb{R}^3$ represented by the equation $x + y = 2$.

6. (a) What does the equation $x = 4$ represent in $\mathbb{R}^2$? What does it represent in $\mathbb{R}^3$? Illustrate with sketches.
(b) What does the equation $y = 3$ represent in $\mathbb{R}^3$? What does $z = 5$ represent? What does the pair of equations $y = 3$, $z = 5$ represent? In other words, describe the set of points (x, y, z) such that $y = 3$ and $z = 5$. Illustrate with a sketch.

7–8 Find the lengths of the sides of the triangle PQR. Is it a right triangle? Is it an isosceles triangle?

7. $P(3, -2, -3)$, $Q(7, 0, 1)$, $R(1, 2, 1)$

8. $P(2, -1, 0)$, $Q(4, 1, 1)$, $R(4, -5, 4)$

9. Determine whether the points lie on straight line.
(a) $A(2, 4, 2)$, $B(3, 7, -2)$, $C(1, 3, 3)$
(b) $D(0, -5, 5)$, $E(1, -2, 4)$, $F(3, 4, 2)$

10. Find the distance from $(3, 7, -5)$ to each of the following.
(a) The xy-plane   (b) The yz-plane
(c) The xz-plane   (d) The x-axis
(e) The y-axis   (f) The z-axis

11. Find an equation of the sphere with center $(1, -4, 3)$ and radius 5. What is the intersection of this sphere with the xz-plane?

12. Find an equation of the sphere with center $(2, -6, 4)$ and radius 5. Describe its intersection with each of the coordinate planes.

13. Find an equation of the sphere that passes through the point $(4, 3, -1)$ and has center $(3, 8, 1)$.

14. Find an equation of the sphere that passes through the origin and whose center is $(1, 2, 3)$.

15–18 Show that the equation represents a sphere, and find its center and radius.

15. $x^2 + y^2 + z^2 - 6x + 4y - 2z = 11$

16. $x^2 + y^2 + z^2 + 8x - 6y + 2z + 17 = 0$

17. $2x^2 + 2y^2 + 2z^2 = 8x - 24z + 1$

18. $4x^2 + 4y^2 + 4z^2 - 8x + 16y = 1$

19. (a) Prove that the midpoint of the line segment from $P_1(x_1, y_1, z_1)$ to $P_2(x_2, y_2, z_2)$ is

$$\left(\frac{x_1 + x_2}{2}, \frac{y_1 + y_2}{2}, \frac{z_1 + z_2}{2} \right)$$

(b) Find the lengths of the medians of the triangle with vertices $A(1, 2, 3)$, $B(-2, 0, 5)$, and $C(4, 1, 5)$.

20. Find an equation of a sphere if one of its diameters has endpoints $(2, 1, 4)$ and $(4, 3, 10)$.

21. Find equations of the spheres with center $(2, -3, 6)$ that touch (a) the xy-plane, (b) the yz-plane, (c) the xz-plane.

22. Find an equation of the largest sphere with center $(5, 4, 9)$ that is contained in the first octant.

23–32 Describe in words the region of $\mathbb{R}^3$ represented by the equation or inequality.

23. $y = -4$ **24.** $x = 10$

25. $x > 3$ **26.** $y \geqslant 0$

27. $0 \leqslant z \leqslant 6$ **28.** $z^2 = 1$

29. $x^2 + y^2 + z^2 \leqslant 3$ **30.** $x = z$

31. $x^2 + z^2 \leqslant 9$ **32.** $x^2 + y^2 + z^2 > 2z$

33–36 Write inequalities to describe the region.

33. The region between the yz-plane and the vertical plane $x = 5$

34. The solid cylinder that lies on or below the plane $z = 8$ and on or above the disk in the xy-plane with center the origin and radius 2

35. The region consisting of all points between (but not on) the spheres of radius r and R centered at the origin, where $r < R$

36. The solid upper hemisphere of the sphere of radius 2 centered at the origin

37. The figure shows a line L_1 in space and a second line L_2, which is the projection of L_1 on the xy-plane. (In other words, the points on L_2 are directly beneath, or above, the points on L_1.)

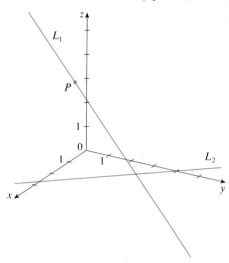

(a) Find the coordinates of the point P on the line L_1.

(b) Locate on the diagram the points A, B, and C, where the line L_1 intersects the xy-plane, the yz-plane, and the xz-plane, respectively.

38. Consider the points P such that the distance from P to $A(-1, 5, 3)$ is twice the distance from P to $B(6, 2, -2)$. Show that the set of all such points is a sphere, and find its center and radius.

39. Find an equation of the set of all points equidistant from the points $A(-1, 5, 3)$ and $B(6, 2, -2)$. Describe the set.

40. Find the volume of the solid that lies inside both of the spheres

$$x^2 + y^2 + z^2 + 4x - 2y + 4z + 5 = 0$$

and

$$x^2 + y^2 + z^2 = 4$$

13.2 VECTORS

The term **vector** is used by scientists to indicate a quantity (such as displacement or velocity or force) that has both magnitude and direction. A vector is often represented by an arrow or a directed line segment. The length of the arrow represents the magnitude of the vector and the arrow points in the direction of the vector. We denote a vector by printing a letter in boldface ($\mathbf{v}$) or by putting an arrow above the letter ($\vec{v}$).

For instance, suppose a particle moves along a line segment from point A to point B. The corresponding **displacement vector** $\mathbf{v}$, shown in Figure 1, has **initial point** A (the tail) and **terminal point** B (the tip) and we indicate this by writing $\mathbf{v} = \overrightarrow{AB}$. Notice that the vector $\mathbf{u} = \overrightarrow{CD}$ has the same length and the same direction as $\mathbf{v}$ even though it is in a different position. We say that $\mathbf{u}$ and $\mathbf{v}$ are **equivalent** (or **equal**) and we write $\mathbf{u} = \mathbf{v}$. The **zero vector**, denoted by $\mathbf{0}$, has length 0. It is the only vector with no specific direction.

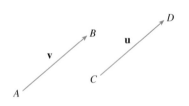

FIGURE 1
Equivalent vectors

COMBINING VECTORS

Suppose a particle moves from A to B, so its displacement vector is $\overrightarrow{AB}$. Then the particle changes direction and moves from B to C, with displacement vector $\overrightarrow{BC}$ as in Figure 2. The combined effect of these displacements is that the particle has moved from A to C. The resulting displacement vector $\overrightarrow{AC}$ is called the *sum* of $\overrightarrow{AB}$ and $\overrightarrow{BC}$ and we write

$$\overrightarrow{AC} = \overrightarrow{AB} + \overrightarrow{BC}$$

In general, if we start with vectors $\mathbf{u}$ and $\mathbf{v}$, we first move $\mathbf{v}$ so that its tail coincides with the tip of $\mathbf{u}$ and define the sum of $\mathbf{u}$ and $\mathbf{v}$ as follows.

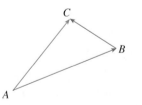

FIGURE 2

> **DEFINITION OF VECTOR ADDITION** If $\mathbf{u}$ and $\mathbf{v}$ are vectors positioned so the initial point of $\mathbf{v}$ is at the terminal point of $\mathbf{u}$, then the **sum** $\mathbf{u} + \mathbf{v}$ is the vector from the initial point of $\mathbf{u}$ to the terminal point of $\mathbf{v}$.

The definition of vector addition is illustrated in Figure 3. You can see why this definition is sometimes called the **Triangle Law**.

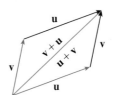

FIGURE 3 The Triangle Law

FIGURE 4 The Parallelogram Law

In Figure 4 we start with the same vectors **u** and **v** as in Figure 3 and draw another copy of **v** with the same initial point as **u**. Completing the parallelogram, we see that **u** + **v** = **v** + **u**. This also gives another way to construct the sum: If we place **u** and **v** so they start at the same point, then **u** + **v** lies along the diagonal of the parallelogram with **u** and **v** as sides. (This is called the **Parallelogram Law**.)

☑ **EXAMPLE 1** Draw the sum of the vectors **a** and **b** shown in Figure 5.

SOLUTION First we translate **b** and place its tail at the tip of **a**, being careful to draw a copy of **b** that has the same length and direction. Then we draw the vector **a** + **b** [see Figure 6(a)] starting at the initial point of **a** and ending at the terminal point of the copy of **b**.

Alternatively, we could place **b** so it starts where **a** starts and construct **a** + **b** by the Parallelogram Law as in Figure 6(b).

FIGURE 5

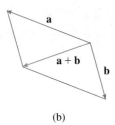

TEC Visual 13.2 shows how the Triangle and Parallelogram Laws work for various vectors **a** and **b**.

FIGURE 6

(a)

(b)

It is possible to multiply a vector by a real number c. (In this context we call the real number c a **scalar** to distinguish it from a vector.) For instance, we want $2\mathbf{v}$ to be the same vector as $\mathbf{v} + \mathbf{v}$, which has the same direction as **v** but is twice as long. In general, we multiply a vector by a scalar as follows.

> **DEFINITION OF SCALAR MULTIPLICATION** If c is a scalar and **v** is a vector, then the **scalar multiple** $c\mathbf{v}$ is the vector whose length is $|c|$ times the length of **v** and whose direction is the same as **v** if $c > 0$ and is opposite to **v** if $c < 0$. If $c = 0$ or $\mathbf{v} = \mathbf{0}$, then $c\mathbf{v} = \mathbf{0}$.

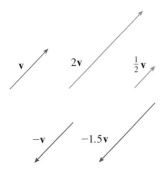

FIGURE 7
Scalar multiples of **v**

This definition is illustrated in Figure 7. We see that real numbers work like scaling factors here; that's why we call them scalars. Notice that two nonzero vectors are **parallel** if they are scalar multiples of one another. In particular, the vector $-\mathbf{v} = (-1)\mathbf{v}$ has the same length as **v** but points in the opposite direction. We call it the **negative** of **v**.

By the **difference u − v** of two vectors we mean

$$\mathbf{u} - \mathbf{v} = \mathbf{u} + (-\mathbf{v})$$

So we can construct $\mathbf{u} - \mathbf{v}$ by first drawing the negative of $\mathbf{v}$, $-\mathbf{v}$, and then adding it to $\mathbf{u}$ by the Parallelogram Law as in Figure 8(a). Alternatively, since $\mathbf{v} + (\mathbf{u} - \mathbf{v}) = \mathbf{u}$, the vector $\mathbf{u} - \mathbf{v}$, when added to $\mathbf{v}$, gives $\mathbf{u}$. So we could construct $\mathbf{u} - \mathbf{v}$ as in Figure 8(b) by means of the Triangle Law.

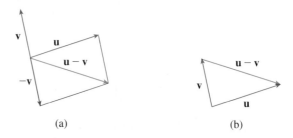

(a)　　　　　　(b)

FIGURE 8
Drawing $\mathbf{u} - \mathbf{v}$

EXAMPLE 2 If $\mathbf{a}$ and $\mathbf{b}$ are the vectors shown in Figure 9, draw $\mathbf{a} - 2\mathbf{b}$.

SOLUTION We first draw the vector $-2\mathbf{b}$ pointing in the direction opposite to $\mathbf{b}$ and twice as long. We place it with its tail at the tip of $\mathbf{a}$ and then use the Triangle Law to draw $\mathbf{a} + (-2\mathbf{b})$ as in Figure 10.

FIGURE 9　　　　　　**FIGURE 10**　　　　　□

COMPONENTS

For some purposes it's best to introduce a coordinate system and treat vectors algebraically. If we place the initial point of a vector $\mathbf{a}$ at the origin of a rectangular coordinate system, then the terminal point of $\mathbf{a}$ has coordinates of the form (a_1, a_2) or (a_1, a_2, a_3), depending on whether our coordinate system is two- or three-dimensional (see Figure 11). These coordinates are called the **components** of $\mathbf{a}$ and we write

$$\mathbf{a} = \langle a_1, a_2 \rangle \qquad \text{or} \qquad \mathbf{a} = \langle a_1, a_2, a_3 \rangle$$

We use the notation $\langle a_1, a_2 \rangle$ for the ordered pair that refers to a vector so as not to confuse it with the ordered pair (a_1, a_2) that refers to a point in the plane.

For instance, the vectors shown in Figure 12 are all equivalent to the vector $\overrightarrow{OP} = \langle 3, 2 \rangle$ whose terminal point is $P(3, 2)$. What they have in common is that the terminal point is reached from the initial point by a displacement of three units to the right and two upward. We can think of all these geometric vectors as **representations** of the

FIGURE 11

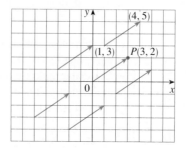

FIGURE 12
Representations of the vector $\mathbf{a} = \langle 3, 2 \rangle$

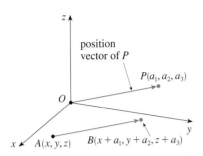

FIGURE 13

Representations of $\mathbf{a} = \langle a_1, a_2, a_3 \rangle$

algebraic vector $\mathbf{a} = \langle 3, 2 \rangle$. The particular representation $\overrightarrow{OP}$ from the origin to the point $P(3, 2)$ is called the **position vector** of the point P.

In three dimensions, the vector $\mathbf{a} = \overrightarrow{OP} = \langle a_1, a_2, a_3 \rangle$ is the **position vector** of the point $P(a_1, a_2, a_3)$. (See Figure 13.) Let's consider any other representation $\overrightarrow{AB}$ of $\mathbf{a}$, where the initial point is $A(x_1, y_1, z_1)$ and the terminal point is $B(x_2, y_2, z_2)$. Then we must have $x_1 + a_1 = x_2$, $y_1 + a_2 = y_2$, and $z_1 + a_3 = z_2$ and so $a_1 = x_2 - x_1$, $a_2 = y_2 - y_1$, and $a_3 = z_2 - z_1$. Thus we have the following result.

> $\boxed{1}$ Given the points $A(x_1, y_1, z_1)$ and $B(x_2, y_2, z_2)$, the vector $\mathbf{a}$ with representation $\overrightarrow{AB}$ is
> $$\mathbf{a} = \langle x_2 - x_1, y_2 - y_1, z_2 - z_1 \rangle$$

▼ EXAMPLE 3 Find the vector represented by the directed line segment with initial point $A(2, -3, 4)$ and terminal point $B(-2, 1, 1)$.

SOLUTION By (1), the vector corresponding to $\overrightarrow{AB}$ is

$$\mathbf{a} = \langle -2 - 2, 1 - (-3), 1 - 4 \rangle = \langle -4, 4, -3 \rangle \qquad \square$$

The **magnitude** or **length** of the vector $\mathbf{v}$ is the length of any of its representations and is denoted by the symbol $|\mathbf{v}|$ or $\|\mathbf{v}\|$. By using the distance formula to compute the length of a segment OP, we obtain the following formulas.

> The length of the two-dimensional vector $\mathbf{a} = \langle a_1, a_2 \rangle$ is
> $$|\mathbf{a}| = \sqrt{a_1^2 + a_2^2}$$
> The length of the three-dimensional vector $\mathbf{a} = \langle a_1, a_2, a_3 \rangle$ is
> $$|\mathbf{a}| = \sqrt{a_1^2 + a_2^2 + a_3^2}$$

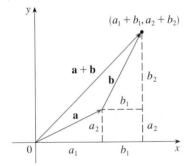

FIGURE 14

How do we add vectors algebraically? Figure 14 shows that if $\mathbf{a} = \langle a_1, a_2 \rangle$ and $\mathbf{b} = \langle b_1, b_2 \rangle$, then the sum is $\mathbf{a} + \mathbf{b} = \langle a_1 + b_1, a_2 + b_2 \rangle$, at least for the case where the components are positive. In other words, *to add algebraic vectors we add their components.* Similarly, *to subtract vectors we subtract components.* From the similar triangles in Figure 15 we see that the components of $c\mathbf{a}$ are ca_1 and ca_2. So *to multiply a vector by a scalar we multiply each component by that scalar.*

> If $\mathbf{a} = \langle a_1, a_2 \rangle$ and $\mathbf{b} = \langle b_1, b_2 \rangle$, then
> $$\mathbf{a} + \mathbf{b} = \langle a_1 + b_1, a_2 + b_2 \rangle \qquad\qquad \mathbf{a} - \mathbf{b} = \langle a_1 - b_1, a_2 - b_2 \rangle$$
> $$c\mathbf{a} = \langle ca_1, ca_2 \rangle$$
> Similarly, for three-dimensional vectors,
> $$\langle a_1, a_2, a_3 \rangle + \langle b_1, b_2, b_3 \rangle = \langle a_1 + b_1, a_2 + b_2, a_3 + b_3 \rangle$$
> $$\langle a_1, a_2, a_3 \rangle - \langle b_1, b_2, b_3 \rangle = \langle a_1 - b_1, a_2 - b_2, a_3 - b_3 \rangle$$
> $$c\langle a_1, a_2, a_3 \rangle = \langle ca_1, ca_2, ca_3 \rangle$$

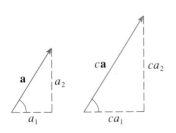

FIGURE 15

☑ **EXAMPLE 4** If $\mathbf{a} = \langle 4, 0, 3 \rangle$ and $\mathbf{b} = \langle -2, 1, 5 \rangle$, find $|\mathbf{a}|$ and the vectors $\mathbf{a} + \mathbf{b}$, $\mathbf{a} - \mathbf{b}$, $3\mathbf{b}$, and $2\mathbf{a} + 5\mathbf{b}$.

SOLUTION ·
$$|\mathbf{a}| = \sqrt{4^2 + 0^2 + 3^2} = \sqrt{25} = 5$$

$$\mathbf{a} + \mathbf{b} = \langle 4, 0, 3 \rangle + \langle -2, 1, 5 \rangle$$
$$= \langle 4 + (-2), 0 + 1, 3 + 5 \rangle = \langle 2, 1, 8 \rangle$$

$$\mathbf{a} - \mathbf{b} = \langle 4, 0, 3 \rangle - \langle -2, 1, 5 \rangle$$
$$= \langle 4 - (-2), 0 - 1, 3 - 5 \rangle = \langle 6, -1, -2 \rangle$$

$$3\mathbf{b} = 3\langle -2, 1, 5 \rangle = \langle 3(-2), 3(1), 3(5) \rangle = \langle -6, 3, 15 \rangle$$

$$2\mathbf{a} + 5\mathbf{b} = 2\langle 4, 0, 3 \rangle + 5\langle -2, 1, 5 \rangle$$
$$= \langle 8, 0, 6 \rangle + \langle -10, 5, 25 \rangle = \langle -2, 5, 31 \rangle \qquad \square$$

We denote by V_2 the set of all two-dimensional vectors and by V_3 the set of all three-dimensional vectors. More generally, we will later need to consider the set V_n of all n-dimensional vectors. An n-dimensional vector is an ordered n-tuple:

$$\mathbf{a} = \langle a_1, a_2, \ldots, a_n \rangle$$

where $a_1, a_2, \ldots, a_n$ are real numbers that are called the components of $\mathbf{a}$. Addition and scalar multiplication are defined in terms of components just as for the cases $n = 2$ and $n = 3$.

■ Vectors in n dimensions are used to list various quantities in an organized way. For instance, the components of a six-dimensional vector

$$\mathbf{p} = \langle p_1, p_2, p_3, p_4, p_5, p_6 \rangle$$

might represent the prices of six different ingredients required to make a particular product. Four-dimensional vectors $\langle x, y, z, t \rangle$ are used in relativity theory, where the first three components specify a position in space and the fourth represents time.

PROPERTIES OF VECTORS If $\mathbf{a}$, $\mathbf{b}$, and $\mathbf{c}$ are vectors in V_n and c and d are scalars, then

1. $\mathbf{a} + \mathbf{b} = \mathbf{b} + \mathbf{a}$ 2. $\mathbf{a} + (\mathbf{b} + \mathbf{c}) = (\mathbf{a} + \mathbf{b}) + \mathbf{c}$

3. $\mathbf{a} + \mathbf{0} = \mathbf{a}$ 4. $\mathbf{a} + (-\mathbf{a}) = \mathbf{0}$

5. $c(\mathbf{a} + \mathbf{b}) = c\mathbf{a} + c\mathbf{b}$ 6. $(c + d)\mathbf{a} = c\mathbf{a} + d\mathbf{a}$

7. $(cd)\mathbf{a} = c(d\mathbf{a})$ 8. $1\mathbf{a} = \mathbf{a}$

These eight properties of vectors can be readily verified either geometrically or algebraically. For instance, Property 1 can be seen from Figure 4 (it's equivalent to the Parallelogram Law) or as follows for the case $n = 2$:

$$\mathbf{a} + \mathbf{b} = \langle a_1, a_2 \rangle + \langle b_1, b_2 \rangle = \langle a_1 + b_1, a_2 + b_2 \rangle$$
$$= \langle b_1 + a_1, b_2 + a_2 \rangle = \langle b_1, b_2 \rangle + \langle a_1, a_2 \rangle$$
$$= \mathbf{b} + \mathbf{a}$$

We can see why Property 2 (the associative law) is true by looking at Figure 16 and applying the Triangle Law several times: The vector $\overrightarrow{PQ}$ is obtained either by first constructing $\mathbf{a} + \mathbf{b}$ and then adding $\mathbf{c}$ or by adding $\mathbf{a}$ to the vector $\mathbf{b} + \mathbf{c}$.

Three vectors in V_3 play a special role. Let

$$\mathbf{i} = \langle 1, 0, 0 \rangle \qquad \mathbf{j} = \langle 0, 1, 0 \rangle \qquad \mathbf{k} = \langle 0, 0, 1 \rangle$$

FIGURE 16

These vectors $\mathbf{i}$, $\mathbf{j}$, and $\mathbf{k}$ are called the **standard basis vectors**. They have length 1 and point in the directions of the positive x-, y-, and z-axes. Similarly, in two dimensions we define $\mathbf{i} = \langle 1, 0 \rangle$ and $\mathbf{j} = \langle 0, 1 \rangle$. (See Figure 17.)

FIGURE 17

Standard basis vectors in V_2 and V_3

(a)

(b)

If $\mathbf{a} = \langle a_1, a_2, a_3 \rangle$, then we can write

$$\mathbf{a} = \langle a_1, a_2, a_3 \rangle = \langle a_1, 0, 0 \rangle + \langle 0, a_2, 0 \rangle + \langle 0, 0, a_3 \rangle$$

$$= a_1 \langle 1, 0, 0 \rangle + a_2 \langle 0, 1, 0 \rangle + a_3 \langle 0, 0, 1 \rangle$$

$$\boxed{2} \qquad \mathbf{a} = a_1 \mathbf{i} + a_2 \mathbf{j} + a_3 \mathbf{k}$$

Thus any vector in V_3 can be expressed in terms of $\mathbf{i}$, $\mathbf{j}$, and $\mathbf{k}$. For instance,

$$\langle 1, -2, 6 \rangle = \mathbf{i} - 2\mathbf{j} + 6\mathbf{k}$$

Similarly, in two dimensions, we can write

$$\boxed{3} \qquad \mathbf{a} = \langle a_1, a_2 \rangle = a_1 \mathbf{i} + a_2 \mathbf{j}$$

See Figure 18 for the geometric interpretation of Equations 3 and 2 and compare with Figure 17.

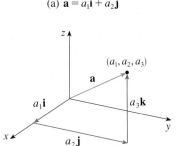

(a) $\mathbf{a} = a_1 \mathbf{i} + a_2 \mathbf{j}$

(b) $\mathbf{a} = a_1 \mathbf{i} + a_2 \mathbf{j} + a_3 \mathbf{k}$

FIGURE 18

EXAMPLE 5 If $\mathbf{a} = \mathbf{i} + 2\mathbf{j} - 3\mathbf{k}$ and $\mathbf{b} = 4\mathbf{i} + 7\mathbf{k}$, express the vector $2\mathbf{a} + 3\mathbf{b}$ in terms of $\mathbf{i}$, $\mathbf{j}$, and $\mathbf{k}$.

SOLUTION Using Properties 1, 2, 5, 6, and 7 of vectors, we have

$$2\mathbf{a} + 3\mathbf{b} = 2(\mathbf{i} + 2\mathbf{j} - 3\mathbf{k}) + 3(4\mathbf{i} + 7\mathbf{k})$$

$$= 2\mathbf{i} + 4\mathbf{j} - 6\mathbf{k} + 12\mathbf{i} + 21\mathbf{k} = 14\mathbf{i} + 4\mathbf{j} + 15\mathbf{k} \qquad \square$$

A **unit vector** is a vector whose length is 1. For instance, $\mathbf{i}$, $\mathbf{j}$, and $\mathbf{k}$ are all unit vectors. In general, if $\mathbf{a} \neq \mathbf{0}$, then the unit vector that has the same direction as $\mathbf{a}$ is

$$\boxed{4} \qquad \mathbf{u} = \frac{1}{|\mathbf{a}|} \mathbf{a} = \frac{\mathbf{a}}{|\mathbf{a}|}$$

In order to verify this, we let $c = 1/|\mathbf{a}|$. Then $\mathbf{u} = c\mathbf{a}$ and c is a positive scalar, so $\mathbf{u}$ has the same direction as $\mathbf{a}$. Also

$$|\mathbf{u}| = |c\mathbf{a}| = |c||\mathbf{a}| = \frac{1}{|\mathbf{a}|} |\mathbf{a}| = 1$$

EXAMPLE 6 Find the unit vector in the direction of the vector $2\mathbf{i} - \mathbf{j} - 2\mathbf{k}$.

SOLUTION The given vector has length

$$|2\mathbf{i} - \mathbf{j} - 2\mathbf{k}| = \sqrt{2^2 + (-1)^2 + (-2)^2} = \sqrt{9} = 3$$

so, by Equation 4, the unit vector with the same direction is

$$\tfrac{1}{3}(2\mathbf{i} - \mathbf{j} - 2\mathbf{k}) = \tfrac{2}{3}\mathbf{i} - \tfrac{1}{3}\mathbf{j} - \tfrac{2}{3}\mathbf{k}$$

APPLICATIONS

Vectors are useful in many aspects of physics and engineering. In Chapter 14 we will see how they describe the velocity and acceleration of objects moving in space. Here we look at forces.

A force is represented by a vector because it has both a magnitude (measured in pounds or newtons) and a direction. If several forces are acting on an object, the **resultant force** experienced by the object is the vector sum of these forces.

EXAMPLE 7 A 100-lb weight hangs from two wires as shown in Figure 19. Find the tensions (forces) $\mathbf{T}_1$ and $\mathbf{T}_2$ in both wires and their magnitudes.

SOLUTION We first express $\mathbf{T}_1$ and $\mathbf{T}_2$ in terms of their horizontal and vertical components. From Figure 20 we see that

[5] $$\mathbf{T}_1 = -|\mathbf{T}_1|\cos 50° \,\mathbf{i} + |\mathbf{T}_1|\sin 50° \,\mathbf{j}$$

[6] $$\mathbf{T}_2 = |\mathbf{T}_2|\cos 32° \,\mathbf{i} + |\mathbf{T}_2|\sin 32° \,\mathbf{j} \quad .$$

The resultant $\mathbf{T}_1 + \mathbf{T}_2$ of the tensions counterbalances the weight $\mathbf{w}$ and so we must have

$$\mathbf{T}_1 + \mathbf{T}_2 = -\mathbf{w} = 100\,\mathbf{j}$$

Thus

$$\left(-|\mathbf{T}_1|\cos 50° + |\mathbf{T}_2|\cos 32°\right)\mathbf{i} + \left(|\mathbf{T}_1|\sin 50° + |\mathbf{T}_2|\sin 32°\right)\mathbf{j} = 100\,\mathbf{j}$$

Equating components, we get

$$-|\mathbf{T}_1|\cos 50° + |\mathbf{T}_2|\cos 32° = 0$$

$$|\mathbf{T}_1|\sin 50° + |\mathbf{T}_2|\sin 32° = 100$$

Solving the first of these equations for $|\mathbf{T}_2|$ and substituting into the second, we get

$$|\mathbf{T}_1|\sin 50° + \frac{|\mathbf{T}_1|\cos 50°}{\cos 32°}\sin 32° = 100$$

So the magnitudes of the tensions are

$$|\mathbf{T}_1| = \frac{100}{\sin 50° + \tan 32° \cos 50°} \approx 85.64 \text{ lb}$$

and

$$|\mathbf{T}_2| = \frac{|\mathbf{T}_1|\cos 50°}{\cos 32°} \approx 64.91 \text{ lb}$$

Substituting these values in (5) and (6), we obtain the tension vectors

$$\mathbf{T}_1 \approx -55.05\,\mathbf{i} + 65.60\,\mathbf{j} \qquad \mathbf{T}_2 \approx 55.05\,\mathbf{i} + 34.40\,\mathbf{j}$$

FIGURE 19

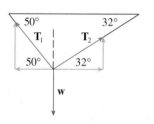

FIGURE 20

13.2 EXERCISES

1. Are the following quantities vectors or scalars? Explain.
(a) The cost of a theater ticket
(b) The current in a river
(c) The initial flight path from Houston to Dallas
(d) The population of the world

2. What is the relationship between the point $(4, 7)$ and the vector $\langle 4, 7 \rangle$? Illustrate with a sketch.

3. Name all the equal vectors in the parallelogram shown.

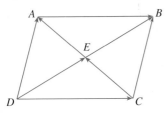

4. Write each combination of vectors as a single vector.
(a) $\overrightarrow{PQ} + \overrightarrow{QR}$ (b) $\overrightarrow{RP} + \overrightarrow{PS}$
(c) $\overrightarrow{QS} - \overrightarrow{PS}$ (d) $\overrightarrow{RS} + \overrightarrow{SP} + \overrightarrow{PQ}$

5. Copy the vectors in the figure and use them to draw the following vectors.
(a) $\mathbf{u} + \mathbf{v}$ (b) $\mathbf{u} - \mathbf{v}$
(c) $\mathbf{v} + \mathbf{w}$ (d) $\mathbf{w} + \mathbf{v} + \mathbf{u}$

6. Copy the vectors in the figure and use them to draw the following vectors.
(a) $\mathbf{a} + \mathbf{b}$ (b) $\mathbf{a} - \mathbf{b}$
(c) $2\mathbf{a}$ (d) $-\frac{1}{2}\mathbf{b}$
(e) $2\mathbf{a} + \mathbf{b}$ (f) $\mathbf{b} - 3\mathbf{a}$

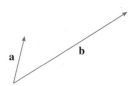

7–12 Find a vector $\mathbf{a}$ with representation given by the directed line segment $\overrightarrow{AB}$. Draw $\overrightarrow{AB}$ and the equivalent representation starting at the origin.

7. $A(2, 3)$, $B(-2, 1)$ **8.** $A(-2, -2)$, $B(5, 3)$

9. $A(-1, 3)$, $B(2, 2)$ **10.** $A(2, 1)$, $B(0, 6)$

11. $A(0, 3, 1)$, $B(2, 3, -1)$ **12.** $A(4, 0, -2)$, $B(4, 2, 1)$

13–16 Find the sum of the given vectors and illustrate geometrically.

13. $\langle -1, 4 \rangle$, $\langle 6, -2 \rangle$ **14.** $\langle -2, -1 \rangle$, $\langle 5, 7 \rangle$

15. $\langle 0, 1, 2 \rangle$, $\langle 0, 0, -3 \rangle$ **16.** $\langle -1, 0, 2 \rangle$, $\langle 0, 4, 0 \rangle$

17–20 Find $\mathbf{a} + \mathbf{b}$, $2\mathbf{a} + 3\mathbf{b}$, $|\mathbf{a}|$, and $|\mathbf{a} - \mathbf{b}|$.

17. $\mathbf{a} = \langle 5, -12 \rangle$, $\mathbf{b} = \langle -3, -6 \rangle$

18. $\mathbf{a} = 4\mathbf{i} + \mathbf{j}$, $\mathbf{b} = \mathbf{i} - 2\mathbf{j}$

19. $\mathbf{a} = \mathbf{i} + 2\mathbf{j} - 3\mathbf{k}$, $\mathbf{b} = -2\mathbf{i} - \mathbf{j} + 5\mathbf{k}$

20. $\mathbf{a} = 2\mathbf{i} - 4\mathbf{j} + 4\mathbf{k}$, $\mathbf{b} = 2\mathbf{j} - \mathbf{k}$

21–23 Find a unit vector that has the same direction as the given vector.

21. $-3\mathbf{i} + 7\mathbf{j}$ **22.** $\langle -4, 2, 4 \rangle$

23. $8\mathbf{i} - \mathbf{j} + 4\mathbf{k}$

24. Find a vector that has the same direction as $\langle -2, 4, 2 \rangle$ but has length 6.

25. If $\mathbf{v}$ lies in the first quadrant and makes an angle $\pi/3$ with the positive x-axis and $|\mathbf{v}| = 4$, find $\mathbf{v}$ in component form.

26. If a child pulls a sled through the snow on a level path with a force of 50 N exerted at an angle of $38°$ above the horizontal, find the horizontal and vertical components of the force.

27. A quarterback throws a football with angle of elevation $40°$ and speed 60 ft/s. Find the horizontal and vertical components of the velocity vector.

28–29 Find the magnitude of the resultant force and the angle it makes with the positive x-axis.

28.

29.

30. The magnitude of a velocity vector is called *speed.* Suppose that a wind is blowing from the direction N45°W at a speed of 50 km/h. (This means that the direction from which the wind blows is 45° west of the northerly direction.) A pilot is steering a plane in the direction N60°E at an airspeed (speed in still air) of 250 km/h. The *true course,* or *track,* of the plane is the direction of the resultant of the velocity vectors of the plane and the wind. The *ground speed* of the plane is the magnitude of the resultant. Find the true course and the ground speed of the plane.

31. A woman walks due west on the deck of a ship at 3 mi/h. The ship is moving north at a speed of 22 mi/h. Find the speed and direction of the woman relative to the surface of the water.

32. Ropes 3 m and 5 m in length are fastened to a holiday decoration that is suspended over a town square. The decoration has a mass of 5 kg. The ropes, fastened at different heights, make angles of 52° and 40° with the horizontal. Find the tension in each wire and the magnitude of each tension.

33. A clothesline is tied between two poles, 8 m apart. The line is quite taut and has negligible sag. When a wet shirt with a mass of 0.8 kg is hung at the middle of the line, the midpoint is pulled down 8 cm. Find the tension in each half of the clothesline.

34. The tension **T** at each end of the chain has magnitude 25 N. What is the weight of the chain?

35. Find the unit vectors that are parallel to the tangent line to the parabola $y = x^2$ at the point $(2, 4)$.

36. (a) Find the unit vectors that are parallel to the tangent line to the curve $y = 2 \sin x$ at the point $(\pi/6, 1)$.
(b) Find the unit vectors that are perpendicular to the tangent line.
(c) Sketch the curve $y = 2 \sin x$ and the vectors in parts (a) and (b), all starting at $(\pi/6, 1)$.

37. If A, B, and C are the vertices of a triangle, find $\overrightarrow{AB} + \overrightarrow{BC} + \overrightarrow{CA}$.

38. Let C be the point on the line segment AB that is twice as far from B as it is from A. If $\mathbf{a} = \overrightarrow{OA}$, $\mathbf{b} = \overrightarrow{OB}$, and $\mathbf{c} = \overrightarrow{OC}$, show that $\mathbf{c} = \frac{2}{3}\mathbf{a} + \frac{1}{3}\mathbf{b}$.

39. (a) Draw the vectors $\mathbf{a} = \langle 3, 2 \rangle$, $\mathbf{b} = \langle 2, -1 \rangle$, and $\mathbf{c} = \langle 7, 1 \rangle$.
(b) Show, by means of a sketch, that there are scalars s and t such that $\mathbf{c} = s\mathbf{a} + t\mathbf{b}$.
(c) Use the sketch to estimate the values of s and t.
(d) Find the exact values of s and t.

40. Suppose that **a** and **b** are nonzero vectors that are not parallel and **c** is any vector in the plane determined by **a** and **b**. Give a geometric argument to show that **c** can be written as $\mathbf{c} = s\mathbf{a} + t\mathbf{b}$ for suitable scalars s and t. Then give an argument using components.

41. If $\mathbf{r} = \langle x, y, z \rangle$ and $\mathbf{r}_0 = \langle x_0, y_0, z_0 \rangle$, describe the set of all points (x, y, z) such that $|\mathbf{r} - \mathbf{r}_0| = 1$.

42. If $\mathbf{r} = \langle x, y \rangle$, $\mathbf{r}_1 = \langle x_1, y_1 \rangle$, and $\mathbf{r}_2 = \langle x_2, y_2 \rangle$, describe the set of all points (x, y) such that $|\mathbf{r} - \mathbf{r}_1| + |\mathbf{r} - \mathbf{r}_2| = k$, where $k > |\mathbf{r}_1 - \mathbf{r}_2|$.

43. Figure 16 gives a geometric demonstration of Property 2 of vectors. Use components to give an algebraic proof of this fact for the case $n = 2$.

44. Prove Property 5 of vectors algebraically for the case $n = 3$. Then use similar triangles to give a geometric proof.

45. Use vectors to prove that the line joining the midpoints of two sides of a triangle is parallel to the third side and half its length.

46. Suppose the three coordinate planes are all mirrored and a light ray given by the vector $\mathbf{a} = \langle a_1, a_2, a_3 \rangle$ first strikes the xz-plane, as shown in the figure. Use the fact that the angle of incidence equals the angle of reflection to show that the direction of the reflected ray is given by $\mathbf{b} = \langle a_1, -a_2, a_3 \rangle$. Deduce that, after being reflected by all three mutually perpendicular mirrors, the resulting ray is parallel to the initial ray. (American space scientists used this principle, together with laser beams and an array of corner mirrors on the moon, to calculate very precisely the distance from the earth to the moon.)

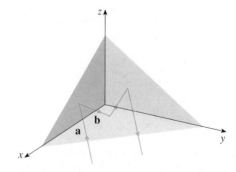

13.3 THE DOT PRODUCT

So far we have added two vectors and multiplied a vector by a scalar. The question arises: Is it possible to multiply two vectors so that their product is a useful quantity? One such product is the dot product, whose definition follows. Another is the cross product, which is discussed in the next section.

> **1 DEFINITION** If $\mathbf{a} = \langle a_1, a_2, a_3 \rangle$ and $\mathbf{b} = \langle b_1, b_2, b_3 \rangle$, then the **dot product** of $\mathbf{a}$ and $\mathbf{b}$ is the number $\mathbf{a} \cdot \mathbf{b}$ given by
>
> $$\mathbf{a} \cdot \mathbf{b} = a_1 b_1 + a_2 b_2 + a_3 b_3$$

Thus, to find the dot product of $\mathbf{a}$ and $\mathbf{b}$, we multiply corresponding components and add. The result is not a vector. It is a real number, that is, a scalar. For this reason, the dot product is sometimes called the **scalar product** (or **inner product**). Although Definition 1 is given for three-dimensional vectors, the dot product of two-dimensional vectors is defined in a similar fashion:

$$\langle a_1, a_2 \rangle \cdot \langle b_1, b_2 \rangle = a_1 b_1 + a_2 b_2$$

V EXAMPLE 1

$$\langle 2, 4 \rangle \cdot \langle 3, -1 \rangle = 2(3) + 4(-1) = 2$$
$$\langle -1, 7, 4 \rangle \cdot \langle 6, 2, -\tfrac{1}{2} \rangle = (-1)(6) + 7(2) + 4(-\tfrac{1}{2}) = 6$$
$$(\mathbf{i} + 2\mathbf{j} - 3\mathbf{k}) \cdot (2\mathbf{j} - \mathbf{k}) = 1(0) + 2(2) + (-3)(-1) = 7 \qquad \square$$

The dot product obeys many of the laws that hold for ordinary products of real numbers. These are stated in the following theorem.

> **2 PROPERTIES OF THE DOT PRODUCT** If $\mathbf{a}$, $\mathbf{b}$, and $\mathbf{c}$ are vectors in V_3 and c is a scalar, then
>
> 1. $\mathbf{a} \cdot \mathbf{a} = |\mathbf{a}|^2$
> 2. $\mathbf{a} \cdot \mathbf{b} = \mathbf{b} \cdot \mathbf{a}$
> 3. $\mathbf{a} \cdot (\mathbf{b} + \mathbf{c}) = \mathbf{a} \cdot \mathbf{b} + \mathbf{a} \cdot \mathbf{c}$
> 4. $(c\mathbf{a}) \cdot \mathbf{b} = c(\mathbf{a} \cdot \mathbf{b}) = \mathbf{a} \cdot (c\mathbf{b})$
> 5. $\mathbf{0} \cdot \mathbf{a} = 0$

These properties are easily proved using Definition 1. For instance, here are the proofs of Properties 1 and 3:

1. $\mathbf{a} \cdot \mathbf{a} = a_1^2 + a_2^2 + a_3^2 = |\mathbf{a}|^2$

3. $\mathbf{a} \cdot (\mathbf{b} + \mathbf{c}) = \langle a_1, a_2, a_3 \rangle \cdot \langle b_1 + c_1, b_2 + c_2, b_3 + c_3 \rangle$
$$= a_1(b_1 + c_1) + a_2(b_2 + c_2) + a_3(b_3 + c_3)$$
$$= a_1 b_1 + a_1 c_1 + a_2 b_2 + a_2 c_2 + a_3 b_3 + a_3 c_3$$
$$= (a_1 b_1 + a_2 b_2 + a_3 b_3) + (a_1 c_1 + a_2 c_2 + a_3 c_3)$$
$$= \mathbf{a} \cdot \mathbf{b} + \mathbf{a} \cdot \mathbf{c}$$

The proofs of the remaining properties are left as exercises. $\qquad \square$

The dot product $\mathbf{a} \cdot \mathbf{b}$ can be given a geometric interpretation in terms of the **angle θ between a and b**, which is defined to be the angle between the representations of $\mathbf{a}$ and

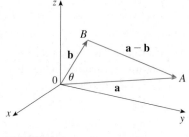

FIGURE I

b that start at the origin, where $0 \le \theta \le \pi$. In other words, θ is the angle between the line segments $\overrightarrow{OA}$ and $\overrightarrow{OB}$ in Figure 1. Note that if **a** and **b** are parallel vectors, then $\theta = 0$ or $\theta = \pi$.

The formula in the following theorem is used by physicists as the *definition* of the dot product.

---

3 THEOREM If θ is the angle between the vectors **a** and **b**, then

$$\mathbf{a} \cdot \mathbf{b} = |\mathbf{a}||\mathbf{b}| \cos \theta$$

PROOF If we apply the Law of Cosines to triangle OAB in Figure 1, we get

$$\boxed{4} \qquad |AB|^2 = |OA|^2 + |OB|^2 - 2|OA||OB| \cos \theta$$

(Observe that the Law of Cosines still applies in the limiting cases when $\theta = 0$ or π, or $\mathbf{a} = \mathbf{0}$ or $\mathbf{b} = \mathbf{0}$.) But $|OA| = |\mathbf{a}|$, $|OB| = |\mathbf{b}|$, and $|AB| = |\mathbf{a} - \mathbf{b}|$, so Equation 4 becomes

$$\boxed{5} \qquad |\mathbf{a} - \mathbf{b}|^2 = |\mathbf{a}|^2 + |\mathbf{b}|^2 - 2|\mathbf{a}||\mathbf{b}| \cos \theta$$

Using Properties 1, 2, and 3 of the dot product, we can rewrite the left side of this equation as follows:

$$|\mathbf{a} - \mathbf{b}|^2 = (\mathbf{a} - \mathbf{b}) \cdot (\mathbf{a} - \mathbf{b})$$
$$= \mathbf{a} \cdot \mathbf{a} - \mathbf{a} \cdot \mathbf{b} - \mathbf{b} \cdot \mathbf{a} + \mathbf{b} \cdot \mathbf{b}$$
$$= |\mathbf{a}|^2 - 2\mathbf{a} \cdot \mathbf{b} + |\mathbf{b}|^2$$

Therefore Equation 5 gives

$$|\mathbf{a}|^2 - 2\mathbf{a} \cdot \mathbf{b} + |\mathbf{b}|^2 = |\mathbf{a}|^2 + |\mathbf{b}|^2 - 2|\mathbf{a}||\mathbf{b}| \cos \theta$$

Thus

$$-2\mathbf{a} \cdot \mathbf{b} = -2|\mathbf{a}||\mathbf{b}| \cos \theta$$

or

$$\mathbf{a} \cdot \mathbf{b} = |\mathbf{a}||\mathbf{b}| \cos \theta \qquad \square$$

EXAMPLE 2 If the vectors **a** and **b** have lengths 4 and 6, and the angle between them is $\pi/3$, find $\mathbf{a} \cdot \mathbf{b}$.

SOLUTION Using Theorem 3, we have

$$\mathbf{a} \cdot \mathbf{b} = |\mathbf{a}||\mathbf{b}| \cos(\pi/3) = 4 \cdot 6 \cdot \tfrac{1}{2} = 12 \qquad \square$$

The formula in Theorem 3 also enables us to find the angle between two vectors.

---

6 COROLLARY If θ is the angle between the nonzero vectors **a** and **b**, then

$$\cos \theta = \frac{\mathbf{a} \cdot \mathbf{b}}{|\mathbf{a}||\mathbf{b}|}$$

▼ EXAMPLE 3 Find the angle between the vectors $\mathbf{a} = \langle 2, 2, -1 \rangle$ and $\mathbf{b} = \langle 5, -3, 2 \rangle$.

SOLUTION Since

$$|\mathbf{a}| = \sqrt{2^2 + 2^2 + (-1)^2} = 3 \qquad \text{and} \qquad |\mathbf{b}| = \sqrt{5^2 + (-3)^2 + 2^2} = \sqrt{38}$$

and since

$$\mathbf{a} \cdot \mathbf{b} = 2(5) + 2(-3) + (-1)(2) = 2$$

we have, from Corollary 6,

$$\cos \theta = \frac{\mathbf{a} \cdot \mathbf{b}}{|\mathbf{a}||\mathbf{b}|} = \frac{2}{3\sqrt{38}}$$

So the angle between **a** and **b** is

$$\theta = \cos^{-1}\left(\frac{2}{3\sqrt{38}}\right) \approx 1.46 \quad (\text{or } 84°) \qquad \square$$

Two nonzero vectors **a** and **b** are called **perpendicular** or **orthogonal** if the angle between them is $\theta = \pi/2$. Then Theorem 3 gives

$$\mathbf{a} \cdot \mathbf{b} = |\mathbf{a}||\mathbf{b}| \cos(\pi/2) = 0$$

and conversely if $\mathbf{a} \cdot \mathbf{b} = 0$, then $\cos \theta = 0$, so $\theta = \pi/2$. The zero vector **0** is considered to be perpendicular to all vectors. Therefore we have the following method for determining whether two vectors are orthogonal.

> [7]   Two vectors **a** and **b** are orthogonal if and only if $\mathbf{a} \cdot \mathbf{b} = 0$.

EXAMPLE 4 Show that $2\mathbf{i} + 2\mathbf{j} - \mathbf{k}$ is perpendicular to $5\mathbf{i} - 4\mathbf{j} + 2\mathbf{k}$.

SOLUTION Since

$$(2\mathbf{i} + 2\mathbf{j} - \mathbf{k}) \cdot (5\mathbf{i} - 4\mathbf{j} + 2\mathbf{k}) = 2(5) + 2(-4) + (-1)(2) = 0$$

these vectors are perpendicular by (7). $\qquad \square$

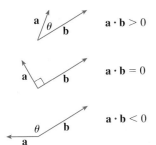

Because $\cos \theta > 0$ if $0 \le \theta < \pi/2$ and $\cos \theta < 0$ if $\pi/2 < \theta \le \pi$, we see that $\mathbf{a} \cdot \mathbf{b}$ is positive for $\theta < \pi/2$ and negative for $\theta > \pi/2$. We can think of $\mathbf{a} \cdot \mathbf{b}$ as measuring the extent to which **a** and **b** point in the same direction. The dot product $\mathbf{a} \cdot \mathbf{b}$ is positive if **a** and **b** point in the same general direction, 0 if they are perpendicular, and negative if they point in generally opposite directions (see Figure 2). In the extreme case where **a** and **b** point in exactly the same direction, we have $\theta = 0$, so $\cos \theta = 1$ and

$$\mathbf{a} \cdot \mathbf{b} = |\mathbf{a}||\mathbf{b}|$$

FIGURE 2

TEC Visual 13.3A shows an animation of Figure 2.

If **a** and **b** point in exactly opposite directions, then $\theta = \pi$ and so $\cos \theta = -1$ and $\mathbf{a} \cdot \mathbf{b} = -|\mathbf{a}||\mathbf{b}|$.

DIRECTION ANGLES AND DIRECTION COSINES

The **direction angles** of a nonzero vector **a** are the angles α, β, and γ (in the interval $[0, \pi]$) that **a** makes with the positive x-, y-, and z-axes. (See Figure 3.)

The cosines of these direction angles, $\cos \alpha$, $\cos \beta$, and $\cos \gamma$, are called the **direction cosines** of the vector **a**. Using Corollary 6 with **b** replaced by **i**, we obtain

FIGURE 3

$$[8] \qquad \cos \alpha = \frac{\mathbf{a} \cdot \mathbf{i}}{|\mathbf{a}||\mathbf{i}|} = \frac{a_1}{|\mathbf{a}|}$$

(This can also be seen directly from Figure 3.)

Similarly, we also have

$$\boxed{9} \qquad \cos \beta = \frac{a_2}{|\mathbf{a}|} \qquad \cos \gamma = \frac{a_3}{|\mathbf{a}|}$$

By squaring the expressions in Equations 8 and 9 and adding, we see that

$$\boxed{10} \qquad \cos^2\alpha + \cos^2\beta + \cos^2\gamma = 1$$

We can also use Equations 8 and 9 to write

$$\mathbf{a} = \langle a_1, a_2, a_3 \rangle = \langle |\mathbf{a}| \cos \alpha, |\mathbf{a}| \cos \beta, |\mathbf{a}| \cos \gamma \rangle$$
$$= |\mathbf{a}| \langle \cos \alpha, \cos \beta, \cos \gamma \rangle$$

Therefore

$$\boxed{11} \qquad \frac{1}{|\mathbf{a}|} \mathbf{a} = \langle \cos \alpha, \cos \beta, \cos \gamma \rangle$$

which says that the direction cosines of **a** are the components of the unit vector in the direction of **a**.

EXAMPLE 5 Find the direction angles of the vector $\mathbf{a} = \langle 1, 2, 3 \rangle$.

SOLUTION Since $|\mathbf{a}| = \sqrt{1^2 + 2^2 + 3^2} = \sqrt{14}$, Equations 8 and 9 give

$$\cos \alpha = \frac{1}{\sqrt{14}} \qquad \cos \beta = \frac{2}{\sqrt{14}} \qquad \cos \gamma = \frac{3}{\sqrt{14}}$$

and so

$$\alpha = \cos^{-1}\left(\frac{1}{\sqrt{14}}\right) \approx 74° \qquad \beta = \cos^{-1}\left(\frac{2}{\sqrt{14}}\right) \approx 58° \qquad \gamma = \cos^{-1}\left(\frac{3}{\sqrt{14}}\right) \approx 37°$$

$\square$

PROJECTIONS

Figure 4 shows representations $\overrightarrow{PQ}$ and $\overrightarrow{PR}$ of two vectors **a** and **b** with the same initial point P. If S is the foot of the perpendicular from R to the line containing $\overrightarrow{PQ}$, then the vector with representation $\overrightarrow{PS}$ is called the **vector projection** of **b** onto **a** and is denoted by $\text{proj}_\mathbf{a} \mathbf{b}$. (You can think of it as a shadow of **b**.)

TEC Visual 13.3B shows how Figure 4 changes when we vary **a** and **b**.

FIGURE 4
Vector projections

The **scalar projection** of **b** onto **a** (also called the **component of b along a**) is defined to be the signed magnitude of the vector projection, which is the number $|\mathbf{b}| \cos \theta$, where

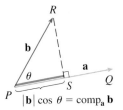

FIGURE 5
Scalar projection

θ is the angle between **a** and **b**. (See Figure 5.) This is denoted by $\text{comp}_a \mathbf{b}$. Observe that it is negative if $\pi/2 < \theta \leq \pi$. The equation

$$\mathbf{a} \cdot \mathbf{b} = |\mathbf{a}||\mathbf{b}| \cos \theta = |\mathbf{a}|(|\mathbf{b}| \cos \theta)$$

shows that the dot product of **a** and **b** can be interpreted as the length of **a** times the scalar projection of **b** onto **a**. Since

$$|\mathbf{b}| \cos \theta = \frac{\mathbf{a} \cdot \mathbf{b}}{|\mathbf{a}|} = \frac{\mathbf{a}}{|\mathbf{a}|} \cdot \mathbf{b}$$

the component of **b** along **a** can be computed by taking the dot product of **b** with the unit vector in the direction of **a**. We summarize these ideas as follows.

Scalar projection of **b** onto **a**: $\quad \text{comp}_a \mathbf{b} = \dfrac{\mathbf{a} \cdot \mathbf{b}}{|\mathbf{a}|}$

Vector projection of **b** onto **a**: $\quad \text{proj}_a \mathbf{b} = \left(\dfrac{\mathbf{a} \cdot \mathbf{b}}{|\mathbf{a}|} \right) \dfrac{\mathbf{a}}{|\mathbf{a}|} = \dfrac{\mathbf{a} \cdot \mathbf{b}}{|\mathbf{a}|^2} \mathbf{a}$

Notice that the vector projection is the scalar projection times the unit vector in the direction of **a**.

☑ EXAMPLE 6 Find the scalar projection and vector projection of $\mathbf{b} = \langle 1, 1, 2 \rangle$ onto $\mathbf{a} = \langle -2, 3, 1 \rangle$.

SOLUTION Since $|\mathbf{a}| = \sqrt{(-2)^2 + 3^2 + 1^2} = \sqrt{14}$, the scalar projection of **b** onto **a** is

$$\text{comp}_a \mathbf{b} = \frac{\mathbf{a} \cdot \mathbf{b}}{|\mathbf{a}|} = \frac{(-2)(1) + 3(1) + 1(2)}{\sqrt{14}} = \frac{3}{\sqrt{14}}$$

The vector projection is this scalar projection times the unit vector in the direction of **a**:

$$\text{proj}_a \mathbf{b} = \frac{3}{\sqrt{14}} \frac{\mathbf{a}}{|\mathbf{a}|} = \frac{3}{14} \mathbf{a} = \left\langle -\frac{3}{7}, \frac{9}{14}, \frac{3}{14} \right\rangle \qquad \square$$

One use of projections occurs in physics in calculating work. In Section 6.4 we defined the work done by a constant force F in moving an object through a distance d as $W = Fd$, but this applies only when the force is directed along the line of motion of the object. Suppose, however, that the constant force is a vector $\mathbf{F} = \overrightarrow{PR}$ pointing in some other direction, as in Figure 6. If the force moves the object from P to Q, then the **displacement vector** is $\mathbf{D} = \overrightarrow{PQ}$. The **work** done by this force is defined to be the product of the component of the force along **D** and the distance moved:

$$W = (|\mathbf{F}| \cos \theta)|\mathbf{D}|$$

But then, from Theorem 3, we have

$$W = |\mathbf{F}||\mathbf{D}| \cos \theta = \mathbf{F} \cdot \mathbf{D}$$

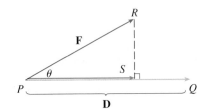

FIGURE 6

Thus the work done by a constant force **F** is the dot product **F** · **D**, where **D** is the displacement vector.

EXAMPLE 7 A wagon is pulled a distance of 100 m along a horizontal path by a constant force of 70 N. The handle of the wagon is held at an angle of 35° above the horizontal. Find the work done by the force.

SOLUTION If **F** and **D** are the force and displacement vectors, as pictured in Figure 7, then the work done is

$$W = \mathbf{F} \cdot \mathbf{D} = |\mathbf{F}||\mathbf{D}| \cos 35°$$

$$= (70)(100) \cos 35° \approx 5734 \text{ N·m} = 5734 \text{ J} \qquad \square$$

FIGURE 7

EXAMPLE 8 A force is given by a vector $\mathbf{F} = 3\mathbf{i} + 4\mathbf{j} + 5\mathbf{k}$ and moves a particle from the point $P(2, 1, 0)$ to the point $Q(4, 6, 2)$. Find the work done.

SOLUTION The displacement vector is $\mathbf{D} = \overrightarrow{PQ} = \langle 2, 5, 2 \rangle$, so by Equation 12, the work done is

$$W = \mathbf{F} \cdot \mathbf{D} = \langle 3, 4, 5 \rangle \cdot \langle 2, 5, 2 \rangle$$

$$= 6 + 20 + 10 = 36$$

If the unit of length is meters and the magnitude of the force is measured in newtons, then the work done is 36 joules. $\qquad \square$

13.3 EXERCISES

1. Which of the following expressions are meaningful? Which are meaningless? Explain.
(a) $(\mathbf{a} \cdot \mathbf{b}) \cdot \mathbf{c}$ (b) $(\mathbf{a} \cdot \mathbf{b})\mathbf{c}$
(c) $|\mathbf{a}|(\mathbf{b} \cdot \mathbf{c})$ (d) $\mathbf{a} \cdot (\mathbf{b} + \mathbf{c})$
(e) $\mathbf{a} \cdot \mathbf{b} + \mathbf{c}$ (f) $|\mathbf{a}| \cdot (\mathbf{b} + \mathbf{c})$

2. Find the dot product of two vectors if their lengths are 6 and $\frac{1}{3}$ and the angle between them is $\pi/4$.

3–10 Find $\mathbf{a} \cdot \mathbf{b}$.

3. $\mathbf{a} = \left\langle -2, \frac{1}{3} \right\rangle$, $\mathbf{b} = \langle -5, 12 \rangle$

4. $\mathbf{a} = \langle -2, 3 \rangle$, $\mathbf{b} = \langle 0.7, 1.2 \rangle$

5. $\mathbf{a} = \left\langle 4, 1, \frac{1}{4} \right\rangle$, $\mathbf{b} = \langle 6, -3, -8 \rangle$

6. $\mathbf{a} = \langle s, 2s, 3s \rangle$, $\mathbf{b} = \langle t, -t, 5t \rangle$

7. $\mathbf{a} = \mathbf{i} - 2\mathbf{j} + 3\mathbf{k}$, $\mathbf{b} = 5\mathbf{i} + 9\mathbf{k}$

8. $\mathbf{a} = 4\mathbf{j} - 3\mathbf{k}$, $\mathbf{b} = 2\mathbf{i} + 4\mathbf{j} + 6\mathbf{k}$

9. $|\mathbf{a}| = 6$, $|\mathbf{b}| = 5$, the angle between $\mathbf{a}$ and $\mathbf{b}$ is $2\pi/3$

10. $|\mathbf{a}| = 3$, $|\mathbf{b}| = \sqrt{6}$, the angle between $\mathbf{a}$ and $\mathbf{b}$ is $45°$

11–12 If $\mathbf{u}$ is a unit vector, find $\mathbf{u} \cdot \mathbf{v}$ and $\mathbf{u} \cdot \mathbf{w}$.

11.

12.

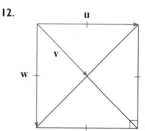

13. (a) Show that $\mathbf{i} \cdot \mathbf{j} = \mathbf{j} \cdot \mathbf{k} = \mathbf{k} \cdot \mathbf{i} = 0$.
(b) Show that $\mathbf{i} \cdot \mathbf{i} = \mathbf{j} \cdot \mathbf{j} = \mathbf{k} \cdot \mathbf{k} = 1$.

14. A street vendor sells a hamburgers, b hot dogs, and c soft drinks on a given day. He charges \$2 for a hamburger, \$1.50 for a hot dog, and \$1 for a soft drink. If $\mathbf{A} = \langle a, b, c \rangle$ and $\mathbf{P} = \langle 2, 1.5, 1 \rangle$, what is the meaning of the dot product $\mathbf{A} \cdot \mathbf{P}$?

15–20 Find the angle between the vectors. (First find an exact expression and then approximate to the nearest degree.)

15. $\mathbf{a} = \langle -8, 6 \rangle$, $\mathbf{b} = \left\langle \sqrt{7}, 3 \right\rangle$

16. $\mathbf{a} = \left\langle \sqrt{3}, 1 \right\rangle$, $\mathbf{b} = \langle 0, 5 \rangle$

17. $\mathbf{a} = \langle 3, -1, 5 \rangle$, $\quad \mathbf{b} = \langle -2, 4, 3 \rangle$

18. $\mathbf{a} = \langle 4, 0, 2 \rangle$, $\quad \mathbf{b} = \langle 2, -1, 0 \rangle$

19. $\mathbf{a} = \mathbf{j} + \mathbf{k}$, $\quad \mathbf{b} = \mathbf{i} + 2\mathbf{j} - 3\mathbf{k}$

20. $\mathbf{a} = \mathbf{i} + 2\mathbf{j} - 2\mathbf{k}$, $\quad \mathbf{b} = 4\mathbf{i} - 3\mathbf{k}$

21–22 Find, correct to the nearest degree, the three angles of the triangle with the given vertices.

21. $A(1, 0)$, $\quad B(3, 6)$, $\quad C(-1, 4)$

22. $D(0, 1, 1)$, $\quad E(-2, 4, 3)$, $\quad F(1, 2, -1)$

23–24 Determine whether the given vectors are orthogonal, parallel, or neither.

23. (a) $\mathbf{a} = \langle -5, 3, 7 \rangle$, $\quad \mathbf{b} = \langle 6, -8, 2 \rangle$
(b) $\mathbf{a} = \langle 4, 6 \rangle$, $\quad \mathbf{b} = \langle -3, 2 \rangle$
(c) $\mathbf{a} = -\mathbf{i} + 2\mathbf{j} + 5\mathbf{k}$, $\quad \mathbf{b} = 3\mathbf{i} + 4\mathbf{j} - \mathbf{k}$
(d) $\mathbf{a} = 2\mathbf{i} + 6\mathbf{j} - 4\mathbf{k}$, $\quad \mathbf{b} = -3\mathbf{i} - 9\mathbf{j} + 6\mathbf{k}$

24. (a) $\mathbf{u} = \langle -3, 9, 6 \rangle$, $\quad \mathbf{v} = \langle 4, -12, -8 \rangle$
(b) $\mathbf{u} = \mathbf{i} - \mathbf{j} + 2\mathbf{k}$, $\quad \mathbf{v} = 2\mathbf{i} - \mathbf{j} + \mathbf{k}$
(c) $\mathbf{u} = \langle a, b, c \rangle$, $\quad \mathbf{v} = \langle -b, a, 0 \rangle$

25. Use vectors to decide whether the triangle with vertices $P(1, -3, -2)$, $Q(2, 0, -4)$, and $R(6, -2, -5)$ is right-angled.

26. For what values of b are the vectors $\langle -6, b, 2 \rangle$ and $\langle b, b^2, b \rangle$ orthogonal?

27. Find a unit vector that is orthogonal to both $\mathbf{i} + \mathbf{j}$ and $\mathbf{i} + \mathbf{k}$.

28. Find two unit vectors that make an angle of $60°$ with $\mathbf{v} = \langle 3, 4 \rangle$.

29–33 Find the direction cosines and direction angles of the vector. (Give the direction angles correct to the nearest degree.)

29. $\langle 3, 4, 5 \rangle$

30. $\langle 1, -2, -1 \rangle$

31. $2\mathbf{i} + 3\mathbf{j} - 6\mathbf{k}$

32. $2\mathbf{i} - \mathbf{j} + 2\mathbf{k}$

33. $\langle c, c, c \rangle$, $\quad$ where $c > 0$

34. If a vector has direction angles $\alpha = \pi/4$ and $\beta = \pi/3$, find the third direction angle γ.

35–40 Find the scalar and vector projections of $\mathbf{b}$ onto $\mathbf{a}$.

35. $\mathbf{a} = \langle 3, -4 \rangle$, $\quad \mathbf{b} = \langle 5, 0 \rangle$

36. $\mathbf{a} = \langle 1, 2 \rangle$, $\quad \mathbf{b} = \langle -4, 1 \rangle$

37. $\mathbf{a} = \langle 3, 6, -2 \rangle$, $\quad \mathbf{b} = \langle 1, 2, 3 \rangle$

38. $\mathbf{a} = \langle -2, 3, -6 \rangle$, $\quad \mathbf{b} = \langle 5, -1, 4 \rangle$

39. $\mathbf{a} = 2\mathbf{i} - \mathbf{j} + 4\mathbf{k}$, $\quad \mathbf{b} = \mathbf{j} + \frac{1}{2}\mathbf{k}$

40. $\mathbf{a} = \mathbf{i} + \mathbf{j} + \mathbf{k}$, $\quad \mathbf{b} = \mathbf{i} - \mathbf{j} + \mathbf{k}$

41. Show that the vector $\text{orth}_{\mathbf{a}}\, \mathbf{b} = \mathbf{b} - \text{proj}_{\mathbf{a}}\, \mathbf{b}$ is orthogonal to $\mathbf{a}$. (It is called an **orthogonal projection** of $\mathbf{b}$.)

42. For the vectors in Exercise 36, find $\text{orth}_{\mathbf{a}}\, \mathbf{b}$ and illustrate by drawing the vectors $\mathbf{a}$, $\mathbf{b}$, $\text{proj}_{\mathbf{a}}\, \mathbf{b}$, and $\text{orth}_{\mathbf{a}}\, \mathbf{b}$.

43. If $\mathbf{a} = \langle 3, 0, -1 \rangle$, find a vector $\mathbf{b}$ such that $\text{comp}_{\mathbf{a}}\, \mathbf{b} = 2$.

44. Suppose that $\mathbf{a}$ and $\mathbf{b}$ are nonzero vectors.
(a) Under what circumstances is $\text{comp}_{\mathbf{a}}\, \mathbf{b} = \text{comp}_{\mathbf{b}}\, \mathbf{a}$?
(b) Under what circumstances is $\text{proj}_{\mathbf{a}}\, \mathbf{b} = \text{proj}_{\mathbf{b}}\, \mathbf{a}$?

45. Find the work done by a force $\mathbf{F} = 8\mathbf{i} - 6\mathbf{j} + 9\mathbf{k}$ that moves an object from the point $(0, 10, 8)$ to the point $(6, 12, 20)$ along a straight line. The distance is measured in meters and the force in newtons.

46. A tow truck drags a stalled car along a road. The chain makes an angle of $30°$ with the road and the tension in the chain is 1500 N. How much work is done by the truck in pulling the car 1 km?

47. A sled is pulled along a level path through snow by a rope. A 30-lb force acting at an angle of $40°$ above the horizontal moves the sled 80 ft. Find the work done by the force.

48. A boat sails south with the help of a wind blowing in the direction S36°E with magnitude 400 lb. Find the work done by the wind as the boat moves 120 ft.

49. Use a scalar projection to show that the distance from a point $P_1(x_1, y_1)$ to the line $ax + by + c = 0$ is

$$\frac{|ax_1 + by_1 + c|}{\sqrt{a^2 + b^2}}$$

Use this formula to find the distance from the point $(-2, 3)$ to the line $3x - 4y + 5 = 0$.

50. If $\mathbf{r} = \langle x, y, z \rangle$, $\mathbf{a} = \langle a_1, a_2, a_3 \rangle$, and $\mathbf{b} = \langle b_1, b_2, b_3 \rangle$, show that the vector equation $(\mathbf{r} - \mathbf{a}) \cdot (\mathbf{r} - \mathbf{b}) = 0$ represents a sphere, and find its center and radius.

51. Find the angle between a diagonal of a cube and one of its edges.

52. Find the angle between a diagonal of a cube and a diagonal of one of its faces.

53. A molecule of methane, CH_4, is structured with the four hydrogen atoms at the vertices of a regular tetrahedron and the carbon atom at the centroid. The *bond angle* is the angle formed by the H—C—H combination; it is the angle between the lines that join the carbon atom to two of the hydrogen atoms. Show that the bond angle is about 109.5°. [*Hint:* Take the vertices of the tetrahedron to be the points $(1, 0, 0)$, $(0, 1, 0)$,

(0, 0, 1), and (1, 1, 1) as shown in the figure. Then the centroid is $\left(\frac{1}{2}, \frac{1}{2}, \frac{1}{2}\right)$.]

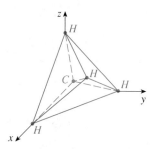

54. If $\mathbf{c} = |\mathbf{a}|\mathbf{b} + |\mathbf{b}|\mathbf{a}$, where $\mathbf{a}$, $\mathbf{b}$, and $\mathbf{c}$ are all nonzero vectors, show that $\mathbf{c}$ bisects the angle between $\mathbf{a}$ and $\mathbf{b}$.

55. Prove Properties 2, 4, and 5 of the dot product (Theorem 2).

56. Suppose that all sides of a quadrilateral are equal in length and opposite sides are parallel. Use vector methods to show that the diagonals are perpendicular.

57. Use Theorem 3 to prove the Cauchy-Schwarz Inequality:

$$|\mathbf{a} \cdot \mathbf{b}| \leq |\mathbf{a}|\,|\mathbf{b}|$$

58. The Triangle Inequality for vectors is

$$|\mathbf{a} + \mathbf{b}| \leq |\mathbf{a}| + |\mathbf{b}|$$

(a) Give a geometric interpretation of the Triangle Inequality.
(b) Use the Cauchy-Schwarz Inequality from Exercise 57 to prove the Triangle Inequality. [*Hint:* Use the fact that $|\mathbf{a} + \mathbf{b}|^2 = (\mathbf{a} + \mathbf{b}) \cdot (\mathbf{a} + \mathbf{b})$ and use Property 3 of the dot product.]

59. The Parallelogram Law states that

$$|\mathbf{a} + \mathbf{b}|^2 + |\mathbf{a} - \mathbf{b}|^2 = 2|\mathbf{a}|^2 + 2|\mathbf{b}|^2$$

(a) Give a geometric interpretation of the Parallelogram Law.
(b) Prove the Parallelogram Law. (See the hint in Exercise 58.)

60. Show that if $\mathbf{u} + \mathbf{v}$ and $\mathbf{u} - \mathbf{v}$ are orthogonal, then the vectors $\mathbf{u}$ and $\mathbf{v}$ must have the same length.

13.4 | THE CROSS PRODUCT

The **cross product** $\mathbf{a} \times \mathbf{b}$ of two vectors $\mathbf{a}$ and $\mathbf{b}$, unlike the dot product, is a vector. For this reason it is also called the **vector product**. Note that $\mathbf{a} \times \mathbf{b}$ is defined only when $\mathbf{a}$ and $\mathbf{b}$ are *three-dimensional* vectors.

> **1 DEFINITION** If $\mathbf{a} = \langle a_1, a_2, a_3 \rangle$ and $\mathbf{b} = \langle b_1, b_2, b_3 \rangle$, then the **cross product** of $\mathbf{a}$ and $\mathbf{b}$ is the vector
>
> $$\mathbf{a} \times \mathbf{b} = \langle a_2 b_3 - a_3 b_2, \, a_3 b_1 - a_1 b_3, \, a_1 b_2 - a_2 b_1 \rangle$$

This may seem like a strange way of defining a product. The reason for the particular form of Definition 1 is that the cross product defined in this way has many useful properties, as we will soon see. In particular, we will show that the vector $\mathbf{a} \times \mathbf{b}$ is perpendicular to both $\mathbf{a}$ and $\mathbf{b}$.

In order to make Definition 1 easier to remember, we use the notation of determinants. A **determinant of order 2** is defined by

$$\begin{vmatrix} a & b \\ c & d \end{vmatrix} = ad - bc$$

For example,

$$\begin{vmatrix} 2 & 1 \\ -6 & 4 \end{vmatrix} = 2(4) - 1(-6) = 14$$

A **determinant of order 3** can be defined in terms of second-order determinants as follows:

$$\boxed{2} \qquad \begin{vmatrix} a_1 & a_2 & a_3 \\ b_1 & b_2 & b_3 \\ c_1 & c_2 & c_3 \end{vmatrix} = a_1 \begin{vmatrix} b_2 & b_3 \\ c_2 & c_3 \end{vmatrix} - a_2 \begin{vmatrix} b_1 & b_3 \\ c_1 & c_3 \end{vmatrix} + a_3 \begin{vmatrix} b_1 & b_2 \\ c_1 & c_2 \end{vmatrix}$$

Observe that each term on the right side of Equation 2 involves a number a_i in the first row of the determinant, and a_i is multiplied by the second-order determinant obtained from the left side by deleting the row and column in which a_i appears. Notice also the minus sign in the second term. For example,

$$\begin{vmatrix} 1 & 2 & -1 \\ 3 & 0 & 1 \\ -5 & 4 & 2 \end{vmatrix} = 1 \begin{vmatrix} 0 & 1 \\ 4 & 2 \end{vmatrix} - 2 \begin{vmatrix} 3 & 1 \\ -5 & 2 \end{vmatrix} + (-1) \begin{vmatrix} 3 & 0 \\ -5 & 4 \end{vmatrix}$$

$$= 1(0 - 4) - 2(6 + 5) + (-1)(12 - 0) = -38$$

If we now rewrite Definition 1 using second-order determinants and the standard basis vectors $\mathbf{i}$, $\mathbf{j}$, and $\mathbf{k}$, we see that the cross product of the vectors $\mathbf{a} = a_1 \mathbf{i} + a_2 \mathbf{j} + a_3 \mathbf{k}$ and $\mathbf{b} = b_1 \mathbf{i} + b_2 \mathbf{j} + b_3 \mathbf{k}$ is

$$\boxed{3} \qquad \mathbf{a} \times \mathbf{b} = \begin{vmatrix} a_2 & a_3 \\ b_2 & b_3 \end{vmatrix} \mathbf{i} - \begin{vmatrix} a_1 & a_3 \\ b_1 & b_3 \end{vmatrix} \mathbf{j} + \begin{vmatrix} a_1 & a_2 \\ b_1 & b_2 \end{vmatrix} \mathbf{k}$$

In view of the similarity between Equations 2 and 3, we often write

$$\boxed{4} \qquad \mathbf{a} \times \mathbf{b} = \begin{vmatrix} \mathbf{i} & \mathbf{j} & \mathbf{k} \\ a_1 & a_2 & a_3 \\ b_1 & b_2 & b_3 \end{vmatrix}$$

Although the first row of the symbolic determinant in Equation 4 consists of vectors, if we expand it as if it were an ordinary determinant using the rule in Equation 2, we obtain Equation 3. The symbolic formula in Equation 4 is probably the easiest way of remembering and computing cross products.

◪ EXAMPLE 1 If $\mathbf{a} = \langle 1, 3, 4 \rangle$ and $\mathbf{b} = \langle 2, 7, -5 \rangle$, then

$$\mathbf{a} \times \mathbf{b} = \begin{vmatrix} \mathbf{i} & \mathbf{j} & \mathbf{k} \\ 1 & 3 & 4 \\ 2 & 7 & -5 \end{vmatrix}$$

$$= \begin{vmatrix} 3 & 4 \\ 7 & -5 \end{vmatrix} \mathbf{i} - \begin{vmatrix} 1 & 4 \\ 2 & -5 \end{vmatrix} \mathbf{j} + \begin{vmatrix} 1 & 3 \\ 2 & 7 \end{vmatrix} \mathbf{k}$$

$$= (-15 - 28) \mathbf{i} - (-5 - 8) \mathbf{j} + (7 - 6) \mathbf{k} = -43\mathbf{i} + 13\mathbf{j} + \mathbf{k} \qquad \square$$

◪ EXAMPLE 2 Show that $\mathbf{a} \times \mathbf{a} = \mathbf{0}$ for any vector $\mathbf{a}$ in V_3.

SOLUTION If $\mathbf{a} = \langle a_1, a_2, a_3 \rangle$, then

$$\mathbf{a} \times \mathbf{a} = \begin{vmatrix} \mathbf{i} & \mathbf{j} & \mathbf{k} \\ a_1 & a_2 & a_3 \\ a_1 & a_2 & a_3 \end{vmatrix}$$

$$= (a_2 a_3 - a_3 a_2) \mathbf{i} - (a_1 a_3 - a_3 a_1) \mathbf{j} + (a_1 a_2 - a_2 a_1) \mathbf{k}$$

$$= 0\mathbf{i} - 0\mathbf{j} + 0\mathbf{k} = \mathbf{0} \qquad \square$$

One of the most important properties of the cross product is given by the following theorem.

---

5 **THEOREM** The vector $\mathbf{a} \times \mathbf{b}$ is orthogonal to both $\mathbf{a}$ and $\mathbf{b}$.

PROOF   In order to show that $\mathbf{a} \times \mathbf{b}$ is orthogonal to $\mathbf{a}$, we compute their dot product as follows:

$$(\mathbf{a} \times \mathbf{b}) \cdot \mathbf{a} = \begin{vmatrix} a_2 & a_3 \\ b_2 & b_3 \end{vmatrix} a_1 - \begin{vmatrix} a_1 & a_3 \\ b_1 & b_3 \end{vmatrix} a_2 + \begin{vmatrix} a_1 & a_2 \\ b_1 & b_2 \end{vmatrix} a_3$$

$$= a_1(a_2b_3 - a_3b_2) - a_2(a_1b_3 - a_3b_1) + a_3(a_1b_2 - a_2b_1)$$

$$= a_1a_2b_3 - a_1b_2a_3 - a_1a_2b_3 + b_1a_2a_3 + a_1b_2a_3 - b_1a_2a_3$$

$$= 0$$

A similar computation shows that $(\mathbf{a} \times \mathbf{b}) \cdot \mathbf{b} = 0$. Therefore $\mathbf{a} \times \mathbf{b}$ is orthogonal to both $\mathbf{a}$ and $\mathbf{b}$.   ☐

If $\mathbf{a}$ and $\mathbf{b}$ are represented by directed line segments with the same initial point (as in Figure 1), then Theorem 5 says that the cross product $\mathbf{a} \times \mathbf{b}$ points in a direction perpendicular to the plane through $\mathbf{a}$ and $\mathbf{b}$. It turns out that the direction of $\mathbf{a} \times \mathbf{b}$ is given by the *right-hand rule:* If the fingers of your right hand curl in the direction of a rotation (through an angle less than 180°) from $\mathbf{a}$ to $\mathbf{b}$, then your thumb points in the direction of $\mathbf{a} \times \mathbf{b}$.

Now that we know the direction of the vector $\mathbf{a} \times \mathbf{b}$, the remaining thing we need to complete its geometric description is its length $|\mathbf{a} \times \mathbf{b}|$. This is given by the following theorem.

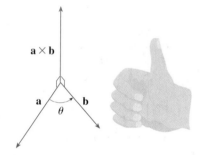

FIGURE 1

---

6 **THEOREM** If θ is the angle between $\mathbf{a}$ and $\mathbf{b}$ (so $0 \leqslant \theta \leqslant \pi$), then

$$|\mathbf{a} \times \mathbf{b}| = |\mathbf{a}|\,|\mathbf{b}|\,\sin\theta$$

TEC Visual 13.4 shows how $\mathbf{a} \times \mathbf{b}$ changes as $\mathbf{b}$ changes.

PROOF   From the definitions of the cross product and length of a vector, we have

$$|\mathbf{a} \times \mathbf{b}|^2 = (a_2b_3 - a_3b_2)^2 + (a_3b_1 - a_1b_3)^2 + (a_1b_2 - a_2b_1)^2$$

$$= a_2^2b_3^2 - 2a_2a_3b_2b_3 + a_3^2b_2^2 + a_3^2b_1^2 - 2a_1a_3b_1b_3 + a_1^2b_3^2$$

$$+ a_1^2b_2^2 - 2a_1a_2b_1b_2 + a_2^2b_1^2$$

$$= (a_1^2 + a_2^2 + a_3^2)(b_1^2 + b_2^2 + b_3^2) - (a_1b_1 + a_2b_2 + a_3b_3)^2$$

$$= |\mathbf{a}|^2|\mathbf{b}|^2 - (\mathbf{a} \cdot \mathbf{b})^2$$

$$= |\mathbf{a}|^2|\mathbf{b}|^2 - |\mathbf{a}|^2|\mathbf{b}|^2\cos^2\theta \qquad \text{(by Theorem 13.3.3)}$$

$$= |\mathbf{a}|^2|\mathbf{b}|^2(1 - \cos^2\theta)$$

$$= |\mathbf{a}|^2|\mathbf{b}|^2\sin^2\theta$$

Taking square roots and observing that $\sqrt{\sin^2\theta} = \sin\theta$ because $\sin\theta \geqslant 0$ when $0 \leqslant \theta \leqslant \pi$, we have

$$|\mathbf{a} \times \mathbf{b}| = |\mathbf{a}|\,|\mathbf{b}|\,\sin\theta$$ ☐

Geometric characterization of $\mathbf{a} \times \mathbf{b}$

Since a vector is completely determined by its magnitude and direction, we can now say that $\mathbf{a} \times \mathbf{b}$ is the vector that is perpendicular to both $\mathbf{a}$ and $\mathbf{b}$, whose orientation is determined by the right-hand rule, and whose length is $|\mathbf{a}||\mathbf{b}|\sin\theta$. In fact, that is exactly how physicists *define* $\mathbf{a}\times\mathbf{b}$.

> **7 COROLLARY** Two nonzero vectors $\mathbf{a}$ and $\mathbf{b}$ are parallel if and only if
>
> $$\mathbf{a}\times\mathbf{b}=\mathbf{0}$$

PROOF Two nonzero vectors $\mathbf{a}$ and $\mathbf{b}$ are parallel if and only if $\theta=0$ or π. In either case $\sin\theta=0$, so $|\mathbf{a}\times\mathbf{b}|=0$ and therefore $\mathbf{a}\times\mathbf{b}=\mathbf{0}$. ☐

The geometric interpretation of Theorem 6 can be seen by looking at Figure 2. If $\mathbf{a}$ and $\mathbf{b}$ are represented by directed line segments with the same initial point, then they determine a parallelogram with base $|\mathbf{a}|$, altitude $|\mathbf{b}|\sin\theta$, and area

$$A=|\mathbf{a}|(|\mathbf{b}|\sin\theta)=|\mathbf{a}\times\mathbf{b}|$$

Thus we have the following way of interpreting the magnitude of a cross product.

FIGURE 2

> The length of the cross product $\mathbf{a}\times\mathbf{b}$ is equal to the area of the parallelogram determined by $\mathbf{a}$ and $\mathbf{b}$.

EXAMPLE 3 Find a vector perpendicular to the plane that passes through the points $P(1,4,6)$, $Q(-2,5,-1)$, and $R(1,-1,1)$.

SOLUTION The vector $\overrightarrow{PQ}\times\overrightarrow{PR}$ is perpendicular to both $\overrightarrow{PQ}$ and $\overrightarrow{PR}$ and is therefore perpendicular to the plane through P, Q, and R. We know from (13.2.1) that

$$\overrightarrow{PQ}=(-2-1)\,\mathbf{i}+(5-4)\,\mathbf{j}+(-1-6)\,\mathbf{k}=-3\mathbf{i}+\mathbf{j}-7\mathbf{k}$$

$$\overrightarrow{PR}=(1-1)\,\mathbf{i}+(-1-4)\,\mathbf{j}+(1-6)\,\mathbf{k}=-5\mathbf{j}-5\mathbf{k}$$

We compute the cross product of these vectors:

$$\overrightarrow{PQ}\times\overrightarrow{PR}=\begin{vmatrix} \mathbf{i} & \mathbf{j} & \mathbf{k} \\ -3 & 1 & -7 \\ 0 & -5 & -5 \end{vmatrix}$$

$$=(-5-35)\,\mathbf{i}-(15-0)\,\mathbf{j}+(15-0)\,\mathbf{k}=-40\mathbf{i}-15\mathbf{j}+15\mathbf{k}$$

So the vector $\langle -40,-15,15\rangle$ is perpendicular to the given plane. Any nonzero scalar multiple of this vector, such as $\langle -8,-3,3\rangle$, is also perpendicular to the plane. ☐

EXAMPLE 4 Find the area of the triangle with vertices $P(1,4,6)$, $Q(-2,5,-1)$, and $R(1,-1,1)$.

SOLUTION In Example 3 we computed that $\overrightarrow{PQ}\times\overrightarrow{PR}=\langle -40,-15,15\rangle$. The area of the parallelogram with adjacent sides PQ and PR is the length of this cross product:

$$|\overrightarrow{PQ}\times\overrightarrow{PR}|=\sqrt{(-40)^2+(-15)^2+15^2}=5\sqrt{82}$$

The area A of the triangle PQR is half the area of this parallelogram, that is, $\frac{5}{2}\sqrt{82}$. ☐

If we apply Theorems 5 and 6 to the standard basis vectors $\mathbf{i}$, $\mathbf{j}$, and $\mathbf{k}$ using $\theta = \pi/2$, we obtain

$$\mathbf{i} \times \mathbf{j} = \mathbf{k} \qquad \mathbf{j} \times \mathbf{k} = \mathbf{i} \qquad \mathbf{k} \times \mathbf{i} = \mathbf{j}$$

$$\mathbf{j} \times \mathbf{i} = -\mathbf{k} \qquad \mathbf{k} \times \mathbf{j} = -\mathbf{i} \qquad \mathbf{i} \times \mathbf{k} = -\mathbf{j}$$

Observe that

$$\mathbf{i} \times \mathbf{j} \neq \mathbf{j} \times \mathbf{i}$$

⊘ Thus the cross product is not commutative. Also

$$\mathbf{i} \times (\mathbf{i} \times \mathbf{j}) = \mathbf{i} \times \mathbf{k} = -\mathbf{j}$$

whereas

$$(\mathbf{i} \times \mathbf{i}) \times \mathbf{j} = \mathbf{0} \times \mathbf{j} = \mathbf{0}$$

⊘ So the associative law for multiplication does not usually hold; that is, in general,

$$(\mathbf{a} \times \mathbf{b}) \times \mathbf{c} \neq \mathbf{a} \times (\mathbf{b} \times \mathbf{c})$$

However, some of the usual laws of algebra *do* hold for cross products. The following theorem summarizes the properties of vector products.

---

8 THEOREM If $\mathbf{a}$, $\mathbf{b}$, and $\mathbf{c}$ are vectors and c is a scalar, then

1. $\mathbf{a} \times \mathbf{b} = -\mathbf{b} \times \mathbf{a}$
2. $(c\mathbf{a}) \times \mathbf{b} = c(\mathbf{a} \times \mathbf{b}) = \mathbf{a} \times (c\mathbf{b})$
3. $\mathbf{a} \times (\mathbf{b} + \mathbf{c}) = \mathbf{a} \times \mathbf{b} + \mathbf{a} \times \mathbf{c}$
4. $(\mathbf{a} + \mathbf{b}) \times \mathbf{c} = \mathbf{a} \times \mathbf{c} + \mathbf{b} \times \mathbf{c}$
5. $\mathbf{a} \cdot (\mathbf{b} \times \mathbf{c}) = (\mathbf{a} \times \mathbf{b}) \cdot \mathbf{c}$
6. $\mathbf{a} \times (\mathbf{b} \times \mathbf{c}) = (\mathbf{a} \cdot \mathbf{c})\mathbf{b} - (\mathbf{a} \cdot \mathbf{b})\mathbf{c}$

These properties can be proved by writing the vectors in terms of their components and using the definition of a cross product. We give the proof of Property 5 and leave the remaining proofs as exercises.

PROOF OF PROPERTY 5 If $\mathbf{a} = \langle a_1, a_2, a_3 \rangle$, $\mathbf{b} = \langle b_1, b_2, b_3 \rangle$, and $\mathbf{c} = \langle c_1, c_2, c_3 \rangle$, then

$$\boxed{9} \qquad \mathbf{a} \cdot (\mathbf{b} \times \mathbf{c}) = a_1(b_2c_3 - b_3c_2) + a_2(b_3c_1 - b_1c_3) + a_3(b_1c_2 - b_2c_1)$$

$$= a_1b_2c_3 - a_1b_3c_2 + a_2b_3c_1 - a_2b_1c_3 + a_3b_1c_2 - a_3b_2c_1$$

$$= (a_2b_3 - a_3b_2)c_1 + (a_3b_1 - a_1b_3)c_2 + (a_1b_2 - a_2b_1)c_3$$

$$= (\mathbf{a} \times \mathbf{b}) \cdot \mathbf{c} \qquad\qquad \square$$

TRIPLE PRODUCTS

The product $\mathbf{a} \cdot (\mathbf{b} \times \mathbf{c})$ that occurs in Property 5 is called the **scalar triple product** of the vectors $\mathbf{a}$, $\mathbf{b}$, and $\mathbf{c}$. Notice from Equation 9 that we can write the scalar triple product as a determinant:

$$\boxed{10} \qquad\qquad \mathbf{a} \cdot (\mathbf{b} \times \mathbf{c}) = \begin{vmatrix} a_1 & a_2 & a_3 \\ b_1 & b_2 & b_3 \\ c_1 & c_2 & c_3 \end{vmatrix}$$

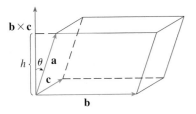

FIGURE 3

The geometric significance of the scalar triple product can be seen by considering the parallelepiped determined by the vectors **a**, **b**, and **c**. (See Figure 3.) The area of the base parallelogram is $A = |\mathbf{b} \times \mathbf{c}|$. If θ is the angle between **a** and $\mathbf{b} \times \mathbf{c}$, then the height h of the parallelepiped is $h = |\mathbf{a}||\cos\theta|$. (We must use $|\cos\theta|$ instead of $\cos\theta$ in case $\theta > \pi/2$.) Therefore the volume of the parallelepiped is

$$V = Ah = |\mathbf{b} \times \mathbf{c}||\mathbf{a}||\cos\theta| = |\mathbf{a} \cdot (\mathbf{b} \times \mathbf{c})|$$

Thus we have proved the following formula.

$\boxed{11}$ The volume of the parallelepiped determined by the vectors **a**, **b**, and **c** is the magnitude of their scalar triple product:

$$V = |\mathbf{a} \cdot (\mathbf{b} \times \mathbf{c})|$$

If we use the formula in (11) and discover that the volume of the parallelepiped determined by **a**, **b**, and **c** is 0, then the vectors must lie in the same plane; that is, they are **coplanar**.

☑ EXAMPLE 5 Use the scalar triple product to show that the vectors $\mathbf{a} = \langle 1, 4, -7 \rangle$, $\mathbf{b} = \langle 2, -1, 4 \rangle$, and $\mathbf{c} = \langle 0, -9, 18 \rangle$ are coplanar.

SOLUTION We use Equation 10 to compute their scalar triple product:

$$\mathbf{a} \cdot (\mathbf{b} \times \mathbf{c}) = \begin{vmatrix} 1 & 4 & -7 \\ 2 & -1 & 4 \\ 0 & -9 & 18 \end{vmatrix}$$

$$= 1 \begin{vmatrix} -1 & 4 \\ -9 & 18 \end{vmatrix} - 4 \begin{vmatrix} 2 & 4 \\ 0 & 18 \end{vmatrix} - 7 \begin{vmatrix} 2 & -1 \\ 0 & -9 \end{vmatrix}$$

$$= 1(18) - 4(36) - 7(-18) = 0$$

Therefore, by (11), the volume of the parallelepiped determined by **a**, **b**, and **c** is 0. This means that **a**, **b**, and **c** are coplanar. $\square$

The product $\mathbf{a} \times (\mathbf{b} \times \mathbf{c})$ that occurs in Property 6 is called the **vector triple product** of **a**, **b**, and **c**. Property 6 will be used to derive Kepler's First Law of planetary motion in Chapter 14. Its proof is left as Exercise 46.

TORQUE

The idea of a cross product occurs often in physics. In particular, we consider a force **F** acting on a rigid body at a point given by a position vector **r**. (For instance, if we tighten a bolt by applying a force to a wrench as in Figure 4, we produce a turning effect.) The **torque** τ (relative to the origin) is defined to be the cross product of the position and force vectors

$$\tau = \mathbf{r} \times \mathbf{F}$$

and measures the tendency of the body to rotate about the origin. The direction of the torque vector indicates the axis of rotation. According to Theorem 6, the magnitude of the

FIGURE 4

torque vector is

$$|\boldsymbol{\tau}| = |\mathbf{r} \times \mathbf{F}| = |\mathbf{r}||\mathbf{F}| \sin \theta$$

where θ is the angle between the position and force vectors. Observe that the only component of $\mathbf{F}$ that can cause a rotation is the one perpendicular to $\mathbf{r}$, that is, $|\mathbf{F}| \sin \theta$. The magnitude of the torque is equal to the area of the parallelogram determined by $\mathbf{r}$ and $\mathbf{F}$.

EXAMPLE 6 A bolt is tightened by applying a 40-N force to a 0.25-m wrench as shown in Figure 5. Find the magnitude of the torque about the center of the bolt.

SOLUTION The magnitude of the torque vector is

$$|\boldsymbol{\tau}| = |\mathbf{r} \times \mathbf{F}| = |\mathbf{r}||\mathbf{F}| \sin 75° = (0.25)(40) \sin 75°$$

$$= 10 \sin 75° \approx 9.66 \text{ N·m}$$

If the bolt is right-threaded, then the torque vector itself is

$$\boldsymbol{\tau} = |\boldsymbol{\tau}|\,\mathbf{n} \approx 9.66\,\mathbf{n}$$

where $\mathbf{n}$ is a unit vector directed down into the page. ☐

FIGURE 5

13.4 EXERCISES

1–7 Find the cross product $\mathbf{a} \times \mathbf{b}$ and verify that it is orthogonal to both $\mathbf{a}$ and $\mathbf{b}$.

1. $\mathbf{a} = \langle 6, 0, -2 \rangle$, $\quad \mathbf{b} = \langle 0, 8, 0 \rangle$

2. $\mathbf{a} = \langle 1, 1, -1 \rangle$, $\quad \mathbf{b} = \langle 2, 4, 6 \rangle$

3. $\mathbf{a} = \mathbf{i} + 3\mathbf{j} - 2\mathbf{k}$, $\quad \mathbf{b} = -\mathbf{i} + 5\mathbf{k}$

4. $\mathbf{a} = \mathbf{j} + 7\mathbf{k}$, $\quad \mathbf{b} = 2\mathbf{i} - \mathbf{j} + 4\mathbf{k}$

5. $\mathbf{a} = \mathbf{i} - \mathbf{j} - \mathbf{k}$, $\quad \mathbf{b} = \frac{1}{2}\mathbf{i} + \mathbf{j} + \frac{1}{2}\mathbf{k}$

6. $\mathbf{a} = \mathbf{i} + e^t\mathbf{j} + e^{-t}\mathbf{k}$, $\quad \mathbf{b} = 2\mathbf{i} + e^t\mathbf{j} - e^{-t}\mathbf{k}$

7. $\mathbf{a} = \langle t, t^2, t^3 \rangle$, $\quad \mathbf{b} = \langle 1, 2t, 3t^2 \rangle$

8. If $\mathbf{a} = \mathbf{i} - 2\mathbf{k}$ and $\mathbf{b} = \mathbf{j} + \mathbf{k}$, find $\mathbf{a} \times \mathbf{b}$. Sketch $\mathbf{a}$, $\mathbf{b}$, and $\mathbf{a} \times \mathbf{b}$ as vectors starting at the origin.

9–12 Find the vector, not with determinants, but by using properties of cross products.

9. $(\mathbf{i} \times \mathbf{j}) \times \mathbf{k}$

10. $\mathbf{k} \times (\mathbf{i} - 2\mathbf{j})$

11. $(\mathbf{j} - \mathbf{k}) \times (\mathbf{k} - \mathbf{i})$

12. $(\mathbf{i} + \mathbf{j}) \times (\mathbf{i} - \mathbf{j})$

13. State whether each expression is meaningful. If not, explain why. If so, state whether it is a vector or a scalar.
 (a) $\mathbf{a} \cdot (\mathbf{b} \times \mathbf{c})$
 (b) $\mathbf{a} \times (\mathbf{b} \cdot \mathbf{c})$
 (c) $\mathbf{a} \times (\mathbf{b} \times \mathbf{c})$
 (d) $(\mathbf{a} \cdot \mathbf{b}) \times \mathbf{c}$
 (e) $(\mathbf{a} \cdot \mathbf{b}) \times (\mathbf{c} \cdot \mathbf{d})$
 (f) $(\mathbf{a} \times \mathbf{b}) \cdot (\mathbf{c} \times \mathbf{d})$

14–15 Find $|\mathbf{u} \times \mathbf{v}|$ and determine whether $\mathbf{u} \times \mathbf{v}$ is directed into the page or out of the page.

14.

15.

16. The figure shows a vector $\mathbf{a}$ in the xy-plane and a vector $\mathbf{b}$ in the direction of $\mathbf{k}$. Their lengths are $|\mathbf{a}| = 3$ and $|\mathbf{b}| = 2$.
 (a) Find $|\mathbf{a} \times \mathbf{b}|$.
 (b) Use the right-hand rule to decide whether the components of $\mathbf{a} \times \mathbf{b}$ are positive, negative, or 0.

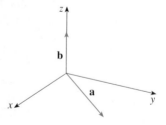

17. If $\mathbf{a} = \langle 1, 2, 1 \rangle$ and $\mathbf{b} = \langle 0, 1, 3 \rangle$, find $\mathbf{a} \times \mathbf{b}$ and $\mathbf{b} \times \mathbf{a}$.

18. If $\mathbf{a} = \langle 3, 1, 2 \rangle$, $\mathbf{b} = \langle -1, 1, 0 \rangle$, and $\mathbf{c} = \langle 0, 0, -4 \rangle$, show that $\mathbf{a} \times (\mathbf{b} \times \mathbf{c}) \neq (\mathbf{a} \times \mathbf{b}) \times \mathbf{c}$.

19. Find two unit vectors orthogonal to both $\langle 1, -1, 1 \rangle$ and $\langle 0, 4, 4 \rangle$.

20. Find two unit vectors orthogonal to both $\mathbf{i} + \mathbf{j} + \mathbf{k}$ and $2\mathbf{i} + \mathbf{k}$.

21. Show that $\mathbf{0} \times \mathbf{a} = \mathbf{0} = \mathbf{a} \times \mathbf{0}$ for any vector $\mathbf{a}$ in V_3.

22. Show that $(\mathbf{a} \times \mathbf{b}) \cdot \mathbf{b} = 0$ for all vectors $\mathbf{a}$ and $\mathbf{b}$ in V_3.

23. Prove Property 1 of Theorem 8.

24. Prove Property 2 of Theorem 8.

25. Prove Property 3 of Theorem 8.

26. Prove Property 4 of Theorem 8.

27. Find the area of the parallelogram with vertices $A(-2, 1)$, $B(0, 4)$, $C(4, 2)$, and $D(2, -1)$.

28. Find the area of the parallelogram with vertices $K(1, 2, 3)$, $L(1, 3, 6)$, $M(3, 8, 6)$, and $N(3, 7, 3)$.

29–32 (a) Find a nonzero vector orthogonal to the plane through the points P, Q, and R, and (b) find the area of triangle PQR.

29. $P(1, 0, 0)$, $Q(0, 2, 0)$, $R(0, 0, 3)$

30. $P(2, 1, 5)$, $Q(-1, 3, 4)$, $R(3, 0, 6)$

31. $P(0, -2, 0)$, $Q(4, 1, -2)$, $R(5, 3, 1)$

32. $P(-1, 3, 1)$, $Q(0, 5, 2)$, $R(4, 3, -1)$

33–34 Find the volume of the parallelepiped determined by the vectors $\mathbf{a}$, $\mathbf{b}$, and $\mathbf{c}$.

33. $\mathbf{a} = \langle 6, 3, -1 \rangle$, $\mathbf{b} = \langle 0, 1, 2 \rangle$, $\mathbf{c} = \langle 4, -2, 5 \rangle$

34. $\mathbf{a} = \mathbf{i} + \mathbf{j} - \mathbf{k}$, $\mathbf{b} = \mathbf{i} - \mathbf{j} + \mathbf{k}$, $\mathbf{c} = -\mathbf{i} + \mathbf{j} + \mathbf{k}$

35–36 Find the volume of the parallelepiped with adjacent edges PQ, PR, and PS.

35. $P(2, 0, -1)$, $Q(4, 1, 0)$, $R(3, -1, 1)$, $S(2, -2, 2)$

36. $P(3, 0, 1)$, $Q(-1, 2, 5)$, $R(5, 1, -1)$, $S(0, 4, 2)$

37. Use the scalar triple product to verify that the vectors $\mathbf{u} = \mathbf{i} + 5\mathbf{j} - 2\mathbf{k}$, $\mathbf{v} = 3\mathbf{i} - \mathbf{j}$, and $\mathbf{w} = 5\mathbf{i} + 9\mathbf{j} - 4\mathbf{k}$ are coplanar.

38. Use the scalar triple product to determine whether the points $A(1, 3, 2)$, $B(3, -1, 6)$, $C(5, 2, 0)$, and $D(3, 6, -4)$ lie in the same plane.

39. A bicycle pedal is pushed by a foot with a 60-N force as shown. The shaft of the pedal is 18 cm long. Find the magnitude of the torque about P.

40. Find the magnitude of the torque about P if a 36-lb force is applied as shown.

41. A wrench 30 cm long lies along the positive y-axis and grips a bolt at the origin. A force is applied in the direction $\langle 0, 3, -4 \rangle$ at the end of the wrench. Find the magnitude of the force needed to supply 100 N·m of torque to the bolt.

42. Let $\mathbf{v} = 5\mathbf{j}$ and let $\mathbf{u}$ be a vector with length 3 that starts at the origin and rotates in the xy-plane. Find the maximum and minimum values of the length of the vector $\mathbf{u} \times \mathbf{v}$. In what direction does $\mathbf{u} \times \mathbf{v}$ point?

43. (a) Let P be a point not on the line L that passes through the points Q and R. Show that the distance d from the point P to the line L is

$$ d = \frac{|\mathbf{a} \times \mathbf{b}|}{|\mathbf{a}|} $$

where $\mathbf{a} = \overrightarrow{QR}$ and $\mathbf{b} = \overrightarrow{QP}$.

(b) Use the formula in part (a) to find the distance from the point $P(1, 1, 1)$ to the line through $Q(0, 6, 8)$ and $R(-1, 4, 7)$.

44. (a) Let P be a point not on the plane that passes through the points Q, R, and S. Show that the distance d from P to the plane is

$$ d = \frac{|(\mathbf{a} \times \mathbf{b}) \cdot \mathbf{c}|}{|\mathbf{a} \times \mathbf{b}|} $$

where $\mathbf{a} = \overrightarrow{QR}$, $\mathbf{b} = \overrightarrow{QS}$, and $\mathbf{c} = \overrightarrow{QP}$.

(b) Use the formula in part (a) to find the distance from the point $P(2, 1, 4)$ to the plane through the points $Q(1, 0, 0)$, $R(0, 2, 0)$, and $S(0, 0, 3)$.

45. Prove that $(\mathbf{a} - \mathbf{b}) \times (\mathbf{a} + \mathbf{b}) = 2(\mathbf{a} \times \mathbf{b})$.

46. Prove Property 6 of Theorem 8, that is,

$$ \mathbf{a} \times (\mathbf{b} \times \mathbf{c}) = (\mathbf{a} \cdot \mathbf{c})\mathbf{b} - (\mathbf{a} \cdot \mathbf{b})\mathbf{c} $$

47. Use Exercise 46 to prove that

$$ \mathbf{a} \times (\mathbf{b} \times \mathbf{c}) + \mathbf{b} \times (\mathbf{c} \times \mathbf{a}) + \mathbf{c} \times (\mathbf{a} \times \mathbf{b}) = \mathbf{0} $$

48. Prove that

$$ (\mathbf{a} \times \mathbf{b}) \cdot (\mathbf{c} \times \mathbf{d}) = \begin{vmatrix} \mathbf{a} \cdot \mathbf{c} & \mathbf{b} \cdot \mathbf{c} \\ \mathbf{a} \cdot \mathbf{d} & \mathbf{b} \cdot \mathbf{d} \end{vmatrix} $$

49. Suppose that $\mathbf{a} \neq \mathbf{0}$.

(a) If $\mathbf{a} \cdot \mathbf{b} = \mathbf{a} \cdot \mathbf{c}$, does it follow that $\mathbf{b} = \mathbf{c}$?

(b) If $\mathbf{a} \times \mathbf{b} = \mathbf{a} \times \mathbf{c}$, does it follow that $\mathbf{b} = \mathbf{c}$?

(c) If $\mathbf{a} \cdot \mathbf{b} = \mathbf{a} \cdot \mathbf{c}$ and $\mathbf{a} \times \mathbf{b} = \mathbf{a} \times \mathbf{c}$, does it follow that $\mathbf{b} = \mathbf{c}$?

50. If $\mathbf{v}_1$, $\mathbf{v}_2$, and $\mathbf{v}_3$ are noncoplanar vectors, let

$$\mathbf{k}_1 = \frac{\mathbf{v}_2 \times \mathbf{v}_3}{\mathbf{v}_1 \cdot (\mathbf{v}_2 \times \mathbf{v}_3)} \qquad \mathbf{k}_2 = \frac{\mathbf{v}_3 \times \mathbf{v}_1}{\mathbf{v}_1 \cdot (\mathbf{v}_2 \times \mathbf{v}_3)}$$

$$\mathbf{k}_3 = \frac{\mathbf{v}_1 \times \mathbf{v}_2}{\mathbf{v}_1 \cdot (\mathbf{v}_2 \times \mathbf{v}_3)}$$

(These vectors occur in the study of crystallography. Vectors of the form $n_1 \mathbf{v}_1 + n_2 \mathbf{v}_2 + n_3 \mathbf{v}_3$, where each n_i is an integer, form a *lattice* for a crystal. Vectors written similarly in terms of $\mathbf{k}_1$, $\mathbf{k}_2$, and $\mathbf{k}_3$ form the *reciprocal lattice*.)

(a) Show that $\mathbf{k}_i$ is perpendicular to $\mathbf{v}_j$ if $i \neq j$.

(b) Show that $\mathbf{k}_i \cdot \mathbf{v}_i = 1$ for $i = 1, 2, 3$.

(c) Show that $\mathbf{k}_1 \cdot (\mathbf{k}_2 \times \mathbf{k}_3) = \dfrac{1}{\mathbf{v}_1 \cdot (\mathbf{v}_2 \times \mathbf{v}_3)}$.

DISCOVERY PROJECT

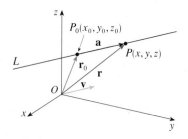

THE GEOMETRY OF A TETRAHEDRON

A tetrahedron is a solid with four vertices, P, Q, R, and S, and four triangular faces as shown in the figure.

1. Let $\mathbf{v}_1$, $\mathbf{v}_2$, $\mathbf{v}_3$, and $\mathbf{v}_4$ be vectors with lengths equal to the areas of the faces opposite the vertices P, Q, R, and S, respectively, and directions perpendicular to the respective faces and pointing outward. Show that

$$\mathbf{v}_1 + \mathbf{v}_2 + \mathbf{v}_3 + \mathbf{v}_4 = \mathbf{0}$$

2. The volume V of a tetrahedron is one-third the distance from a vertex to the opposite face, times the area of that face.

(a) Find a formula for the volume of a tetrahedron in terms of the coordinates of its vertices P, Q, R, and S.

(b) Find the volume of the tetrahedron whose vertices are $P(1, 1, 1)$, $Q(1, 2, 3)$, $R(1, 1, 2)$, and $S(3, -1, 2)$.

3. Suppose the tetrahedron in the figure has a trirectangular vertex S. (This means that the three angles at S are all right angles.) Let A, B, and C be the areas of the three faces that meet at S, and let D be the area of the opposite face PQR. Using the result of Problem 1, or otherwise, show that

$$D^2 = A^2 + B^2 + C^2$$

(This is a three-dimensional version of the Pythagorean Theorem.)

===== **13.5** EQUATIONS OF LINES AND PLANES

A line in the xy-plane is determined when a point on the line and the direction of the line (its slope or angle of inclination) are given. The equation of the line can then be written using the point-slope form.

Likewise, a line L in three-dimensional space is determined when we know a point $P_0(x_0, y_0, z_0)$ on L and the direction of L. In three dimensions the direction of a line is conveniently described by a vector, so we let $\mathbf{v}$ be a vector parallel to L. Let $P(x, y, z)$ be an arbitrary point on L and let $\mathbf{r}_0$ and $\mathbf{r}$ be the position vectors of P_0 and P (that is, they have representations $\overrightarrow{OP_0}$ and $\overrightarrow{OP}$). If $\mathbf{a}$ is the vector with representation $\overrightarrow{P_0P}$, as in Figure 1, then the Triangle Law for vector addition gives $\mathbf{r} = \mathbf{r}_0 + \mathbf{a}$. But, since $\mathbf{a}$ and $\mathbf{v}$ are parallel vectors, there is a scalar t such that $\mathbf{a} = t\mathbf{v}$. Thus

| 1 |

$$\boxed{\mathbf{r} = \mathbf{r}_0 + t\mathbf{v}}$$

FIGURE 1

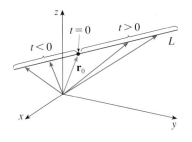

FIGURE 2

which is a **vector equation** of L. Each value of the **parameter** t gives the position vector **r** of a point on L. In other words, as t varies, the line is traced out by the tip of the vector **r**. As Figure 2 indicates, positive values of t correspond to points on L that lie on one side of P_0, whereas negative values of t correspond to points that lie on the other side of P_0.

If the vector **v** that gives the direction of the line L is written in component form as $\mathbf{v} = \langle a, b, c \rangle$, then we have $t\mathbf{v} = \langle ta, tb, tc \rangle$. We can also write $\mathbf{r} = \langle x, y, z \rangle$ and $\mathbf{r}_0 = \langle x_0, y_0, z_0 \rangle$, so the vector equation (1) becomes

$$\langle x, y, z \rangle = \langle x_0 + ta, y_0 + tb, z_0 + tc \rangle$$

Two vectors are equal if and only if corresponding components are equal. Therefore we have the three scalar equations:

$$\boxed{2} \qquad \boxed{\quad x = x_0 + at \qquad y = y_0 + bt \qquad z = z_0 + ct \quad}$$

where $t \in \mathbb{R}$. These equations are called **parametric equations** of the line L through the point $P_0(x_0, y_0, z_0)$ and parallel to the vector $\mathbf{v} = \langle a, b, c \rangle$. Each value of the parameter t gives a point (x, y, z) on L.

■ Figure 3 shows the line L in Example 1 and its relation to the given point and to the vector that gives its direction.

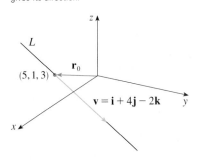

FIGURE 3

EXAMPLE I
(a) Find a vector equation and parametric equations for the line that passes through the point (5, 1, 3) and is parallel to the vector $\mathbf{i} + 4\mathbf{j} - 2\mathbf{k}$.
(b) Find two other points on the line.

SOLUTION
(a) Here $\mathbf{r}_0 = \langle 5, 1, 3 \rangle = 5\mathbf{i} + \mathbf{j} + 3\mathbf{k}$ and $\mathbf{v} = \mathbf{i} + 4\mathbf{j} - 2\mathbf{k}$, so the vector equation (1) becomes

$$\mathbf{r} = (5\mathbf{i} + \mathbf{j} + 3\mathbf{k}) + t(\mathbf{i} + 4\mathbf{j} - 2\mathbf{k})$$

or
$$\mathbf{r} = (5 + t)\mathbf{i} + (1 + 4t)\mathbf{j} + (3 - 2t)\mathbf{k}$$

Parametric equations are

$$x = 5 + t \qquad y = 1 + 4t \qquad z = 3 - 2t$$

(b) Choosing the parameter value $t = 1$ gives $x = 6$, $y = 5$, and $z = 1$, so (6, 5, 1) is a point on the line. Similarly, $t = -1$ gives the point (4, −3, 5). ☐

The vector equation and parametric equations of a line are not unique. If we change the point or the parameter or choose a different parallel vector, then the equations change. For instance, if, instead of (5, 1, 3), we choose the point (6, 5, 1) in Example 1, then the parametric equations of the line become

$$x = 6 + t \qquad y = 5 + 4t \qquad z = 1 - 2t$$

Or, if we stay with the point (5, 1, 3) but choose the parallel vector $2\mathbf{i} + 8\mathbf{j} - 4\mathbf{k}$, we arrive at the equations

$$x = 5 + 2t \qquad y = 1 + 8t \qquad z = 3 - 4t$$

In general, if a vector $\mathbf{v} = \langle a, b, c \rangle$ is used to describe the direction of a line L, then the numbers a, b, and c are called **direction numbers** of L. Since any vector parallel to **v** could also be used, we see that any three numbers proportional to a, b, and c could also be used as a set of direction numbers for L.

Another way of describing a line L is to eliminate the parameter t from Equations 2. If none of a, b, or c is 0, we can solve each of these equations for t, equate the results, and obtain

3

$$\frac{x - x_0}{a} = \frac{y - y_0}{b} = \frac{z - z_0}{c}$$

These equations are called **symmetric equations** of L. Notice that the numbers a, b, and c that appear in the denominators of Equations 3 are direction numbers of L, that is, components of a vector parallel to L. If one of a, b, or c is 0, we can still eliminate t. For instance, if $a = 0$, we could write the equations of L as

$$x = x_0 \qquad \frac{y - y_0}{b} = \frac{z - z_0}{c}$$

This means that L lies in the vertical plane $x = x_0$.

EXAMPLE 2

(a) Find parametric equations and symmetric equations of the line that passes through the points $A(2, 4, -3)$ and $B(3, -1, 1)$.
(b) At what point does this line intersect the xy-plane?

SOLUTION

(a) We are not explicitly given a vector parallel to the line, but observe that the vector $\mathbf{v}$ with representation $\overrightarrow{AB}$ is parallel to the line and

$$\mathbf{v} = \langle 3 - 2, -1 - 4, 1 - (-3) \rangle = \langle 1, -5, 4 \rangle$$

Thus direction numbers are $a = 1$, $b = -5$, and $c = 4$. Taking the point $(2, 4, -3)$ as P_0, we see that parametric equations (2) are

$$x = 2 + t \qquad y = 4 - 5t \qquad z = -3 + 4t$$

and symmetric equations (3) are

$$\frac{x - 2}{1} = \frac{y - 4}{-5} = \frac{z + 3}{4}$$

(b) The line intersects the xy-plane when $z = 0$, so we put $z = 0$ in the symmetric equations and obtain

$$\frac{x - 2}{1} = \frac{y - 4}{-5} = \frac{3}{4}$$

This gives $x = \frac{11}{4}$ and $y = \frac{1}{4}$, so the line intersects the xy-plane at the point $\left(\frac{11}{4}, \frac{1}{4}, 0\right)$. ☐

In general, the procedure of Example 2 shows that direction numbers of the line L through the points $P_0(x_0, y_0, z_0)$ and $P_1(x_1, y_1, z_1)$ are $x_1 - x_0$, $y_1 - y_0$, and $z_1 - z_0$ and so symmetric equations of L are

$$\frac{x - x_0}{x_1 - x_0} = \frac{y - y_0}{y_1 - y_0} = \frac{z - z_0}{z_1 - z_0}$$

■ Figure 4 shows the line L in Example 2 and the point P where it intersects the xy-plane.

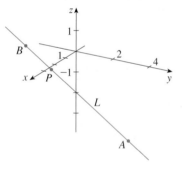

FIGURE 4

Often, we need a description, not of an entire line, but of just a line segment. How, for instance, could we describe the line segment AB in Example 2? If we put $t = 0$ in the parametric equations in Example 2(a), we get the point $(2, 4, -3)$ and if we put $t = 1$ we get $(3, -1, 1)$. So the line segment AB is described by the parametric equations

$$x = 2 + t \qquad y = 4 - 5t \qquad z = -3 + 4t \qquad 0 \le t \le 1$$

or by the corresponding vector equation

$$\mathbf{r}(t) = \langle 2 + t, 4 - 5t, -3 + 4t \rangle \qquad 0 \le t \le 1$$

In general, we know from Equation 1 that the vector equation of a line through the (tip of the) vector $\mathbf{r}_0$ in the direction of a vector $\mathbf{v}$ is $\mathbf{r} = \mathbf{r}_0 + t\mathbf{v}$. If the line also passes through (the tip of) $\mathbf{r}_1$, then we can take $\mathbf{v} = \mathbf{r}_1 - \mathbf{r}_0$ and so its vector equation is

$$\mathbf{r} = \mathbf{r}_0 + t(\mathbf{r}_1 - \mathbf{r}_0) = (1 - t)\mathbf{r}_0 + t\mathbf{r}_1$$

The line segment from $\mathbf{r}_0$ to $\mathbf{r}_1$ is given by the parameter interval $0 \le t \le 1$.

$\boxed{4}$ The line segment from $\mathbf{r}_0$ to $\mathbf{r}_1$ is given by the vector equation

$$\mathbf{r}(t) = (1 - t)\mathbf{r}_0 + t\mathbf{r}_1 \qquad 0 \le t \le 1$$

■ The lines L_1 and L_2 in Example 3, shown in Figure 5, are skew lines.

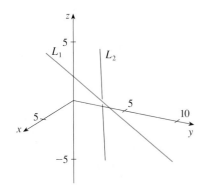

FIGURE 5

▽ EXAMPLE 3 Show that the lines L_1 and L_2 with parametric equations

$$x = 1 + t \qquad y = -2 + 3t \qquad z = 4 - t$$

$$x = 2s \qquad y = 3 + s \qquad z = -3 + 4s$$

are **skew lines**; that is, they do not intersect and are not parallel (and therefore do not lie in the same plane).

SOLUTION The lines are not parallel because the corresponding vectors $\langle 1, 3, -1 \rangle$ and $\langle 2, 1, 4 \rangle$ are not parallel. (Their components are not proportional.) If L_1 and L_2 had a point of intersection, there would be values of t and s such that

$$1 + t = 2s$$

$$-2 + 3t = 3 + s$$

$$4 - t = -3 + 4s$$

But if we solve the first two equations, we get $t = \frac{11}{5}$ and $s = \frac{8}{5}$, and these values don't satisfy the third equation. Therefore there are no values of t and s that satisfy the three equations, so L_1 and L_2 do not intersect. Thus L_1 and L_2 are skew lines. ☐

PLANES

Although a line in space is determined by a point and a direction, a plane in space is more difficult to describe. A single vector parallel to a plane is not enough to convey the "direction" of the plane, but a vector perpendicular to the plane does completely specify its direction. Thus a plane in space is determined by a point $P_0(x_0, y_0, z_0)$ in the plane and a vector $\mathbf{n}$ that is orthogonal to the plane. This orthogonal vector $\mathbf{n}$ is called a **normal vector**. Let $P(x, y, z)$ be an arbitrary point in the plane, and let $\mathbf{r}_0$ and $\mathbf{r}$ be the position vectors of P_0 and P. Then the vector $\mathbf{r} - \mathbf{r}_0$ is represented by $\overrightarrow{P_0 P}$. (See Figure 6.) The normal vector $\mathbf{n}$ is orthogonal to every vector in the given plane. In particular, $\mathbf{n}$ is orthogonal

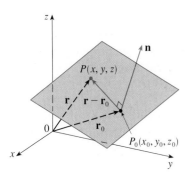

FIGURE 6

to $\mathbf{r} - \mathbf{r}_0$ and so we have

$\boxed{5}$

$$\mathbf{n} \cdot (\mathbf{r} - \mathbf{r}_0) = 0$$

which can be rewritten as

$\boxed{6}$

$$\mathbf{n} \cdot \mathbf{r} = \mathbf{n} \cdot \mathbf{r}_0$$

Either Equation 5 or Equation 6 is called a **vector equation of the plane**.

To obtain a scalar equation for the plane, we write $\mathbf{n} = \langle a, b, c \rangle$, $\mathbf{r} = \langle x, y, z \rangle$, and $\mathbf{r}_0 = \langle x_0, y_0, z_0 \rangle$. Then the vector equation (5) becomes

$$\langle a, b, c \rangle \cdot \langle x - x_0, y - y_0, z - z_0 \rangle = 0$$

or

$\boxed{7}$

$$a(x - x_0) + b(y - y_0) + c(z - z_0) = 0$$

Equation 7 is the **scalar equation of the plane through $P_0(x_0, y_0, z_0)$ with normal vector $\mathbf{n} = \langle a, b, c \rangle$**.

◻ **EXAMPLE 4** Find an equation of the plane through the point $(2, 4, -1)$ with normal vector $\mathbf{n} = \langle 2, 3, 4 \rangle$. Find the intercepts and sketch the plane.

SOLUTION Putting $a = 2$, $b = 3$, $c = 4$, $x_0 = 2$, $y_0 = 4$, and $z_0 = -1$ in Equation 7, we see that an equation of the plane is

$$2(x - 2) + 3(y - 4) + 4(z + 1) = 0$$

or

$$2x + 3y + 4z = 12$$

To find the x-intercept we set $y = z = 0$ in this equation and obtain $x = 6$. Similarly, the y-intercept is 4 and the z-intercept is 3. This enables us to sketch the portion of the plane that lies in the first octant (see Figure 7). ◻

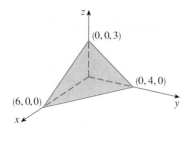

FIGURE 7

By collecting terms in Equation 7 as we did in Example 4, we can rewrite the equation of a plane as

$\boxed{8}$

$$ax + by + cz + d = 0$$

where $d = -(ax_0 + by_0 + cz_0)$. Equation 8 is called a **linear equation** in x, y, and z. Conversely, it can be shown that if a, b, and c are not all 0, then the linear equation (8) represents a plane with normal vector $\langle a, b, c \rangle$. (See Exercise 77.)

EXAMPLE 5 Find an equation of the plane that passes through the points $P(1, 3, 2)$, $Q(3, -1, 6)$, and $R(5, 2, 0)$.

SOLUTION The vectors $\mathbf{a}$ and $\mathbf{b}$ corresponding to $\overrightarrow{PQ}$ and $\overrightarrow{PR}$ are

$$\mathbf{a} = \langle 2, -4, 4 \rangle \qquad \mathbf{b} = \langle 4, -1, -2 \rangle$$

■ Figure 8 shows the portion of the plane in Example 5 that is enclosed by triangle *PQR*.

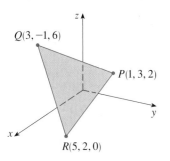

FIGURE 8

Since both **a** and **b** lie in the plane, their cross product **a** × **b** is orthogonal to the plane and can be taken as the normal vector. Thus

$$\mathbf{n} = \mathbf{a} \times \mathbf{b} = \begin{vmatrix} \mathbf{i} & \mathbf{j} & \mathbf{k} \\ 2 & -4 & 4 \\ 4 & -1 & -2 \end{vmatrix} = 12\,\mathbf{i} + 20\,\mathbf{j} + 14\,\mathbf{k}$$

With the point $P(1, 3, 2)$ and the normal vector **n**, an equation of the plane is

$$12(x - 1) + 20(y - 3) + 14(z - 2) = 0$$

or $6x + 10y + 7z = 50$ ☐

EXAMPLE 6 Find the point at which the line with parametric equations $x = 2 + 3t$, $y = -4t$, $z = 5 + t$ intersects the plane $4x + 5y - 2z = 18$.

SOLUTION We substitute the expressions for x, y, and z from the parametric equations into the equation of the plane:

$$4(2 + 3t) + 5(-4t) - 2(5 + t) = 18$$

This simplifies to $-10t = 20$, so $t = -2$. Therefore the point of intersection occurs when the parameter value is $t = -2$. Then $x = 2 + 3(-2) = -4$, $y = -4(-2) = 8$, $z = 5 - 2 = 3$ and so the point of intersection is $(-4, 8, 3)$.   ☐

FIGURE 9

Two planes are **parallel** if their normal vectors are parallel. For instance, the planes $x + 2y - 3z = 4$ and $2x + 4y - 6z = 3$ are parallel because their normal vectors are $\mathbf{n}_1 = \langle 1, 2, -3 \rangle$ and $\mathbf{n}_2 = \langle 2, 4, -6 \rangle$ and $\mathbf{n}_2 = 2\mathbf{n}_1$. If two planes are not parallel, then they intersect in a straight line and the angle between the two planes is defined as the acute angle between their normal vectors (see angle θ in Figure 9).

■ Figure 10 shows the planes in Example 7 and their line of intersection *L*.

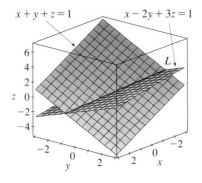

FIGURE 10

◪ EXAMPLE 7
(a) Find the angle between the planes $x + y + z = 1$ and $x - 2y + 3z = 1$.
(b) Find symmetric equations for the line of intersection L of these two planes.

SOLUTION
(a) The normal vectors of these planes are

$$\mathbf{n}_1 = \langle 1, 1, 1 \rangle \qquad \mathbf{n}_2 = \langle 1, -2, 3 \rangle$$

and so, if θ is the angle between the planes, Corollary 13.3.6 gives

$$\cos \theta = \frac{\mathbf{n}_1 \cdot \mathbf{n}_2}{|\mathbf{n}_1|\,|\mathbf{n}_2|} = \frac{1(1) + 1(-2) + 1(3)}{\sqrt{1 + 1 + 1}\,\sqrt{1 + 4 + 9}} = \frac{2}{\sqrt{42}}$$

$$\theta = \cos^{-1}\left(\frac{2}{\sqrt{42}}\right) \approx 72°$$

(b) We first need to find a point on L. For instance, we can find the point where the line intersects the xy-plane by setting $z = 0$ in the equations of both planes. This gives the equations $x + y = 1$ and $x - 2y = 1$, whose solution is $x = 1$, $y = 0$. So the point $(1, 0, 0)$ lies on L.

Now we observe that, since L lies in both planes, it is perpendicular to both of the normal vectors. Thus a vector $\mathbf{v}$ parallel to L is given by the cross product

$$\mathbf{v} = \mathbf{n}_1 \times \mathbf{n}_2 = \begin{vmatrix} \mathbf{i} & \mathbf{j} & \mathbf{k} \\ 1 & 1 & 1 \\ 1 & -2 & 3 \end{vmatrix} = 5\mathbf{i} - 2\mathbf{j} - 3\mathbf{k}$$

■ Another way to find the line of intersection is to solve the equations of the planes for two of the variables in terms of the third, which can be taken as the parameter.

and so the symmetric equations of L can be written as

$$\frac{x - 1}{5} = \frac{y}{-2} = \frac{z}{-3}$$

NOTE Since a linear equation in x, y, and z represents a plane and two nonparallel planes intersect in a line, it follows that two linear equations can represent a line. The points (x, y, z) that satisfy both $a_1 x + b_1 y + c_1 z + d_1 = 0$ and $a_2 x + b_2 y + c_2 z + d_2 = 0$ lie on both of these planes, and so the pair of linear equations represents the line of intersection of the planes (if they are not parallel). For instance, in Example 7 the line L was given as the line of intersection of the planes $x + y + z = 1$ and $x - 2y + 3z = 1$. The symmetric equations that we found for L could be written as

$$\frac{x - 1}{5} = \frac{y}{-2} \quad \text{and} \quad \frac{y}{-2} = \frac{z}{-3}$$

FIGURE 11

■ Figure 11 shows how the line L in Example 7 can also be regarded as the line of intersection of planes derived from its symmetric equations.

which is again a pair of linear equations. They exhibit L as the line of intersection of the planes $(x - 1)/5 = y/(-2)$ and $y/(-2) = z/(-3)$. (See Figure 11.)

In general, when we write the equations of a line in the symmetric form

$$\frac{x - x_0}{a} = \frac{y - y_0}{b} = \frac{z - z_0}{c}$$

we can regard the line as the line of intersection of the two planes

$$\frac{x - x_0}{a} = \frac{y - y_0}{b} \quad \text{and} \quad \frac{y - y_0}{b} = \frac{z - z_0}{c}$$

EXAMPLE 8 Find a formula for the distance D from a point $P_1(x_1, y_1, z_1)$ to the plane $ax + by + cz + d = 0$.

SOLUTION Let $P_0(x_0, y_0, z_0)$ be any point in the given plane and let $\mathbf{b}$ be the vector corresponding to $\overrightarrow{P_0 P_1}$. Then

$$\mathbf{b} = \langle x_1 - x_0, y_1 - y_0, z_1 - z_0 \rangle$$

From Figure 12 you can see that the distance D from P_1 to the plane is equal to the absolute value of the scalar projection of $\mathbf{b}$ onto the normal vector $\mathbf{n} = \langle a, b, c \rangle$. (See Section 13.3.) Thus

$$D = \left| \text{comp}_\mathbf{n} \mathbf{b} \right| = \frac{|\mathbf{n} \cdot \mathbf{b}|}{|\mathbf{n}|}$$

$$= \frac{|a(x_1 - x_0) + b(y_1 - y_0) + c(z_1 - z_0)|}{\sqrt{a^2 + b^2 + c^2}}$$

$$= \frac{|(ax_1 + by_1 + cz_1) - (ax_0 + by_0 + cz_0)|}{\sqrt{a^2 + b^2 + c^2}}$$

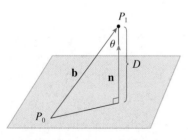

FIGURE 12

Since P_0 lies in the plane, its coordinates satisfy the equation of the plane and so we have $ax_0 + by_0 + cz_0 + d = 0$. Thus the formula for D can be written as

9

$$D = \frac{|ax_1 + by_1 + cz_1 + d|}{\sqrt{a^2 + b^2 + c^2}}$$

EXAMPLE 9 Find the distance between the parallel planes $10x + 2y - 2z = 5$ and $5x + y - z = 1$.

SOLUTION First we note that the planes are parallel because their normal vectors $\langle 10, 2, -2 \rangle$ and $\langle 5, 1, -1 \rangle$ are parallel. To find the distance D between the planes, we choose any point on one plane and calculate its distance to the other plane. In particular, if we put $y = z = 0$ in the equation of the first plane, we get $10x = 5$ and so $\left(\frac{1}{2}, 0, 0\right)$ is a point in this plane. By Formula 9, the distance between $\left(\frac{1}{2}, 0, 0\right)$ and the plane $5x + y - z - 1 = 0$ is

$$D = \frac{\left|5\left(\frac{1}{2}\right) + 1(0) - 1(0) - 1\right|}{\sqrt{5^2 + 1^2 + (-1)^2}} = \frac{\frac{3}{2}}{3\sqrt{3}} = \frac{\sqrt{3}}{6}$$

So the distance between the planes is $\sqrt{3}/6$.

EXAMPLE 10 In Example 3 we showed that the lines

$$L_1: \quad x = 1 + t \qquad y = -2 + 3t \qquad z = 4 - t$$

$$L_2: \quad x = 2s \qquad y = 3 + s \qquad z = -3 + 4s$$

are skew. Find the distance between them.

SOLUTION Since the two lines L_1 and L_2 are skew, they can be viewed as lying on two parallel planes P_1 and P_2. The distance between L_1 and L_2 is the same as the distance between P_1 and P_2, which can be computed as in Example 9. The common normal vector to both planes must be orthogonal to both $\mathbf{v}_1 = \langle 1, 3, -1 \rangle$ (the direction of L_1) and $\mathbf{v}_2 = \langle 2, 1, 4 \rangle$ (the direction of L_2). So a normal vector is

$$\mathbf{n} = \mathbf{v}_1 \times \mathbf{v}_2 = \begin{vmatrix} \mathbf{i} & \mathbf{j} & \mathbf{k} \\ 1 & 3 & -1 \\ 2 & 1 & 4 \end{vmatrix} = 13\mathbf{i} - 6\mathbf{j} - 5\mathbf{k}$$

If we put $s = 0$ in the equations of L_2, we get the point $(0, 3, -3)$ on L_2 and so an equation for P_2 is

$$13(x - 0) - 6(y - 3) - 5(z + 3) = 0 \qquad \text{or} \qquad 13x - 6y - 5z + 3 = 0$$

If we now set $t = 0$ in the equations for L_1, we get the point $(1, -2, 4)$ on P_1. So the distance between L_1 and L_2 is the same as the distance from $(1, -2, 4)$ to $13x - 6y - 5z + 3 = 0$. By Formula 9, this distance is

$$D = \frac{|13(1) - 6(-2) - 5(4) + 3|}{\sqrt{13^2 + (-6)^2 + (-5)^2}} = \frac{8}{\sqrt{230}} \approx 0.53$$

13.5 EXERCISES

1. Determine whether each statement is true or false.
(a) Two lines parallel to a third line are parallel.
(b) Two lines perpendicular to a third line are parallel.
(c) Two planes parallel to a third plane are parallel.
(d) Two planes perpendicular to a third plane are parallel.
(e) Two lines parallel to a plane are parallel.
(f) Two lines perpendicular to a plane are parallel.
(g) Two planes parallel to a line are parallel.
(h) Two planes perpendicular to a line are parallel.
(i) Two planes either intersect or are parallel.
(j) Two lines either intersect or are parallel.
(k) A plane and a line either intersect or are parallel.

2–5 Find a vector equation and parametric equations for the line.

2. The line through the point $(6, -5, 2)$ and parallel to the vector $\langle 1, 3, -\frac{2}{3} \rangle$

3. The line through the point $(2, 2.4, 3.5)$ and parallel to the vector $3\mathbf{i} + 2\mathbf{j} - \mathbf{k}$

4. The line through the point $(0, 14, -10)$ and parallel to the line $x = -1 + 2t, y = 6 - 3t, z = 3 + 9t$

5. The line through the point $(1, 0, 6)$ and perpendicular to the plane $x + 3y + z = 5$

6–12 Find parametric equations and symmetric equations for the line.

6. The line through the origin and the point $(1, 2, 3)$

7. The line through the points $(1, 3, 2)$ and $(-4, 3, 0)$

8. The line through the points $(6, 1, -3)$ and $(2, 4, 5)$

9. The line through the points $(0, \frac{1}{2}, 1)$ and $(2, 1, -3)$

10. The line through $(2, 1, 0)$ and perpendicular to both $\mathbf{i} + \mathbf{j}$ and $\mathbf{j} + \mathbf{k}$

11. The line through $(1, -1, 1)$ and parallel to the line $x + 2 = \frac{1}{2}y = z - 3$

12. The line of intersection of the planes $x + y + z = 1$ and $x + z = 0$

13. Is the line through $(-4, -6, 1)$ and $(-2, 0 -3)$ parallel to the line through $(10, 18, 4)$ and $(5, 3, 14)$?

14. Is the line through $(4, 1, -1)$ and $(2, 5, 3)$ perpendicular to the line through $(-3, 2, 0)$ and $(5, 1, 4)$?

15. (a) Find symmetric equations for the line that passes through the point $(1, -5, 6)$ and is parallel to the vector $\langle -1, 2, -3 \rangle$.
(b) Find the points in which the required line in part (a) intersects the coordinate planes.

16. (a) Find parametric equations for the line through $(2, 4, 6)$ that is perpendicular to the plane $x - y + 3z = 7$.
(b) In what points does this line intersect the coordinate planes?

17. Find a vector equation for the line segment from $(2, -1, 4)$ to $(4, 6, 1)$.

18. Find parametric equations for the line segment from $(10, 3, 1)$ to $(5, 6, -3)$.

19–22 Determine whether the lines L_1 and L_2 are parallel, skew, or intersecting. If they intersect, find the point of intersection.

19. L_1: $x = -6t$, $y = 1 + 9t$, $z = -3t$
L_2: $x = 1 + 2s$, $y = 4 - 3s$, $z = s$

20. L_1: $x = 1 + 2t$, $y = 3t$, $z = 2 - t$
L_2: $x = -1 + s$, $y = 4 + s$, $z = 1 + 3s$

21. L_1: $\dfrac{x}{1} = \dfrac{y - 1}{2} = \dfrac{z - 2}{3}$

L_2: $\dfrac{x - 3}{-4} = \dfrac{y - 2}{-3} = \dfrac{z - 1}{2}$

22. L_1: $\dfrac{x - 1}{2} = \dfrac{y - 3}{2} = \dfrac{z - 2}{-1}$

L_2: $\dfrac{x - 2}{1} = \dfrac{y - 6}{-1} = \dfrac{z + 2}{3}$

23–38 Find an equation of the plane.

23. The plane through the point $(6, 3, 2)$ and perpendicular to the vector $\langle -2, 1, 5 \rangle$

24. The plane through the point $(4, 0, -3)$ and with normal vector $\mathbf{j} + 2\mathbf{k}$

25. The plane through the point $(1, -1, 1)$ and with normal vector $\mathbf{i} + \mathbf{j} - \mathbf{k}$

26. The plane through the point $(-2, 8, 10)$ and perpendicular to the line $x = 1 + t, y = 2t, z = 4 - 3t$

27. The plane through the origin and parallel to the plane $2x - y + 3z = 1$

28. The plane through the point $(-1, 6, -5)$ and parallel to the plane $x + y + z + 2 = 0$

29. The plane through the point $(4, -2, 3)$ and parallel to the plane $3x - 7z = 12$

30. The plane that contains the line $x = 3 + 2t, y = t, z = 8 - t$ and is parallel to the plane $2x + 4y + 8z = 17$

31. The plane through the points $(0, 1, 1)$, $(1, 0, 1)$, and $(1, 1, 0)$

32. The plane through the origin and the points $(2, -4, 6)$ and $(5, 1, 3)$

33. The plane through the points $(3, -1, 2)$, $(8, 2, 4)$, and $(-1, -2, -3)$

34. The plane that passes through the point $(1, 2, 3)$ and contains the line $x = 3t$, $y = 1 + t$, $z = 2 - t$

35. The plane that passes through the point $(6, 0, -2)$ and contains the line $x = 4 - 2t$, $y = 3 + 5t$, $z = 7 + 4t$

36. The plane that passes through the point $(1, -1, 1)$ and contains the line with symmetric equations $x = 2y = 3z$

37. The plane that passes through the point $(-1, 2, 1)$ and contains the line of intersection of the planes $x + y - z = 2$ and $2x - y + 3z = 1$

38. The plane that passes through the line of intersection of the planes $x - z = 1$ and $y + 2z = 3$ and is perpendicular to the plane $x + y - 2z = 1$

39–42 Use intercepts to help sketch the plane.

39. $2x + 5y + z = 10$ **40.** $3x + y + 2z = 6$

41. $6x - 3y + 4z = 6$ **42.** $6x + 5y - 3z = 15$

43–45 Find the point at which the line intersects the given plane.

43. $x = 3 - t$, $y = 2 + t$, $z = 5t$; $x - y + 2z = 9$

44. $x = 1 + 2t$, $y = 4t$, $z = 2 - 3t$; $x + 2y - z + 1 = 0$

45. $x = y - 1 = 2z$; $4x - y + 3z = 8$

46. Where does the line through $(1, 0, 1)$ and $(4, -2, 2)$ intersect the plane $x + y + z = 6$?

47. Find direction numbers for the line of intersection of the planes $x + y + z = 1$ and $x + z = 0$.

48. Find the cosine of the angle between the planes $x + y + z = 0$ and $x + 2y + 3z = 1$.

49–54 Determine whether the planes are parallel, perpendicular, or neither. If neither, find the angle between them.

49. $x + 4y - 3z = 1$, $-3x + 6y + 7z = 0$

50. $2z = 4y - x$, $3x - 12y + 6z = 1$

51. $x + y + z = 1$, $x - y + z = 1$

52. $2x - 3y + 4z = 5$, $x + 6y + 4z = 3$

53. $x = 4y - 2z$, $8y = 1 + 2x + 4z$

54. $x + 2y + 2z = 1$, $2x - y + 2z = 1$

55–56 (a) Find parametric equations for the line of intersection of the planes and (b) find the angle between the planes.

55. $x + y + z = 1$, $x + 2y + 2z = 1$

56. $3x - 2y + z = 1$, $2x + y - 3z = 3$

57–58 Find symmetric equations for the line of intersection of the planes.

57. $5x - 2y - 2z = 1$, $4x + y + z = 6$

58. $z = 2x - y - 5$, $z = 4x + 3y - 5$

59. Find an equation for the plane consisting of all points that are equidistant from the points $(1, 0, -2)$ and $(3, 4, 0)$.

60. Find an equation for the plane consisting of all points that are equidistant from the points $(2, 5, 5)$ and $(-6, 3, 1)$.

61. Find an equation of the plane with x-intercept a, y-intercept b, and z-intercept c.

62. (a) Find the point at which the given lines intersect:

$$\mathbf{r} = \langle 1, 1, 0 \rangle + t\langle 1, -1, 2 \rangle$$
$$\mathbf{r} = \langle 2, 0, 2 \rangle + s\langle -1, 1, 0 \rangle$$

(b) Find an equation of the plane that contains these lines.

63. Find parametric equations for the line through the point $(0, 1, 2)$ that is parallel to the plane $x + y + z = 2$ and perpendicular to the line $x = 1 + t$, $y = 1 - t$, $z = 2t$.

64. Find parametric equations for the line through the point $(0, 1, 2)$ that is perpendicular to the line $x = 1 + t$, $y = 1 - t$, $z = 2t$ and intersects this line.

65. Which of the following four planes are parallel? Are any of them identical?

P_1: $4x - 2y + 6z = 3$ P_2: $4x - 2y - 2z = 6$

P_3: $-6x + 3y - 9z = 5$ P_4: $z = 2x - y - 3$

66. Which of the following four lines are parallel? Are any of them identical?

L_1: $x = 1 + t$, $y = t$, $z = 2 - 5t$

L_2: $x + 1 = y - 2 = 1 - z$

L_3: $x = 1 + t$, $y = 4 + t$, $z = 1 - t$

L_4: $\mathbf{r} = \langle 2, 1, -3 \rangle + t\langle 2, 2, -10 \rangle$

67–68 Use the formula in Exercise 43 in Section 13.4 to find the distance from the point to the given line.

67. $(4, 1, -2)$; $x = 1 + t$, $y = 3 - 2t$, $z = 4 - 3t$

68. $(0, 1, 3)$; $x = 2t$, $y = 6 - 2t$, $z = 3 + t$

69–70 Find the distance from the point to the given plane.

69. $(1, -2, 4)$, $3x + 2y + 6z = 5$

70. $(-6, 3, 5)$, $x - 2y - 4z = 8$

71–72 Find the distance between the given parallel planes.

71. $2x - 3y + z = 4$, $4x - 6y + 2z = 3$

72. $6z = 4y - 2x$, $9z = 1 - 3x + 6y$

73. Show that the distance between the parallel planes
$ax + by + cz + d_1 = 0$ and $ax + by + cz + d_2 = 0$ is

$$D = \frac{|d_1 - d_2|}{\sqrt{a^2 + b^2 + c^2}}$$

74. Find equations of the planes that are parallel to the plane
$x + 2y - 2z = 1$ and two units away from it.

75. Show that the lines with symmetric equations $x = y = z$ and
$x + 1 = y/2 = z/3$ are skew, and find the distance between
these lines.

76. Find the distance between the skew lines with parametric equations $x = 1 + t$, $y = 1 + 6t$, $z = 2t$, and
$x = 1 + 2s$, $y = 5 + 15s$, $z = -2 + 6s$.

77. If a, b, and c are not all 0, show that the equation
$ax + by + cz + d = 0$ represents a plane and $\langle a, b, c \rangle$ is
a normal vector to the plane.
  Hint: Suppose $a \neq 0$ and rewrite the equation in the form

$$a\left(x + \frac{d}{a}\right) + b(y - 0) + c(z - 0) = 0$$

78. Give a geometric description of each family of planes.
  (a) $x + y + z = c$ (b) $x + y + cz = 1$
  (c) $y \cos \theta + z \sin \theta = 1$

LABORATORY PROJECT

PUTTING 3D IN PERSPECTIVE

Computer graphics programmers face the same challenge as the great painters of the past: how
to represent a three-dimensional scene as a flat image on a two-dimensional plane (a screen or a
canvas). To create the illusion of perspective, in which closer objects appear larger than those
farther away, three-dimensional objects in the computer's memory are projected onto a rectangular screen window from a viewpoint where the eye, or camera, is located. The viewing
volume—the portion of space that will be visible—is the region contained by the four planes that
pass through the viewpoint and an edge of the screen window. If objects in the scene extend
beyond these four planes, they must be truncated before pixel data are sent to the screen. These
planes are therefore called *clipping planes*.

1. Suppose the screen is represented by a rectangle in the yz-plane with vertices $(0, \pm 400, 0)$
   and $(0, \pm 400, 600)$, and the camera is placed at $(1000, 0, 0)$. A line L in the scene passes
   through the points $(230, -285, 102)$ and $(860, 105, 264)$. At what points should L be clipped
   by the clipping planes?

2. If the clipped line segment is projected on the screen window, identify the resulting line
   segment.

3. Use parametric equations to plot the edges of the screen window, the clipped line segment,
   and its projection on the screen window. Then add sight lines connecting the viewpoint to
   each end of the clipped segments to verify that the projection is correct.

4. A rectangle with vertices $(621, -147, 206)$, $(563, 31, 242)$, $(657, -111, 86)$, and
   $(599, 67, 122)$ is added to the scene. The line L intersects this rectangle. To make the rectangle appear opaque, a programmer can use *hidden line rendering,* which removes portions
   of objects that are behind other objects. Identify the portion of L that should be removed.

13.6 CYLINDERS AND QUADRIC SURFACES

We have already looked at two special types of surfaces: planes (in Section 13.5) and
spheres (in Section 13.1). Here we investigate two other types of surfaces: cylinders and
quadric surfaces.

In order to sketch the graph of a surface, it is useful to determine the curves of intersection of the surface with planes parallel to the coordinate planes. These curves are called
traces (or cross-sections) of the surface.

CYLINDERS

A **cylinder** is a surface that consists of all lines (called **rulings**) that are parallel to a given line and pass through a given plane curve.

▼ **EXAMPLE 1** Sketch the graph of the surface $z = x^2$.

SOLUTION Notice that the equation of the graph, $z = x^2$, doesn't involve y. This means that any vertical plane with equation $y = k$ (parallel to the xz-plane) intersects the graph in a curve with equation $z = x^2$. So these vertical traces are parabolas. Figure 1 shows how the graph is formed by taking the parabola $z = x^2$ in the xz-plane and moving it in the direction of the y-axis. The graph is a surface, called a **parabolic cylinder**, made up of infinitely many shifted copies of the same parabola. Here the rulings of the cylinder are parallel to the y-axis. ☐

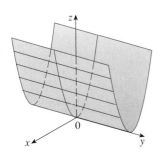

FIGURE 1
The surface $z = x^2$ is a parabolic cylinder.

We noticed that the variable y is missing from the equation of the cylinder in Example 1. This is typical of a surface whose rulings are parallel to one of the coordinate axes. If one of the variables x, y, or z is missing from the equation of a surface, then the surface is a cylinder.

EXAMPLE 2 Identify and sketch the surfaces.
(a) $x^2 + y^2 = 1$ (b) $y^2 + z^2 = 1$

SOLUTION
(a) Since z is missing and the equations $x^2 + y^2 = 1$, $z = k$ represent a circle with radius 1 in the plane $z = k$, the surface $x^2 + y^2 = 1$ is a circular cylinder whose axis is the z-axis. (See Figure 2.) Here the rulings are vertical lines.

(b) In this case x is missing and the surface is a circular cylinder whose axis is the x-axis. (See Figure 3.) It is obtained by taking the circle $y^2 + z^2 = 1$, $x = 0$ in the yz-plane and moving it parallel to the x-axis.

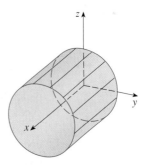

FIGURE 2 $x^2 + y^2 = 1$ **FIGURE 3** $y^2 + z^2 = 1$ ☐

⊘   NOTE   When you are dealing with surfaces, it is important to recognize that an equation like $x^2 + y^2 = 1$ represents a cylinder and not a circle. The trace of the cylinder $x^2 + y^2 = 1$ in the xy-plane is the circle with equations $x^2 + y^2 = 1$, $z = 0$.

QUADRIC SURFACES

A **quadric surface** is the graph of a second-degree equation in three variables x, y, and z. The most general such equation is

$$Ax^2 + By^2 + Cz^2 + Dxy + Eyz + Fxz + Gx + Hy + Iz + J = 0$$

where A, B, C, . . . , J are constants, but by translation and rotation it can be brought into one of the two standard forms

$$Ax^2 + By^2 + Cz^2 + J = 0 \qquad \text{or} \qquad Ax^2 + By^2 + Iz = 0$$

Quadric surfaces are the counterparts in three dimensions of the conic sections in the plane. (See Section 11.5 for a review of conic sections.)

EXAMPLE 3 Use traces to sketch the quadric surface with equation

$$x^2 + \frac{y^2}{9} + \frac{z^2}{4} = 1$$

SOLUTION By substituting $z = 0$, we find that the trace in the xy-plane is $x^2 + y^2/9 = 1$, which we recognize as an equation of an ellipse. In general, the horizontal trace in the plane $z = k$ is

$$x^2 + \frac{y^2}{9} = 1 - \frac{k^2}{4} \qquad z = k$$

which is an ellipse, provided that $k^2 < 4$, that is, $-2 < k < 2$.
   Similarly, the vertical traces are also ellipses:

$$\frac{y^2}{9} + \frac{z^2}{4} = 1 - k^2 \qquad x = k \qquad (\text{if } -1 < k < 1)$$

$$x^2 + \frac{z^2}{4} = 1 - \frac{k^2}{9} \qquad y = k \qquad (\text{if } -3 < k < 3)$$

Figure 4 shows how drawing some traces indicates the shape of the surface. It's called an **ellipsoid** because all of its traces are ellipses. Notice that it is symmetric with respect to each coordinate plane; this is a reflection of the fact that its equation involves only even powers of x, y, and z. □

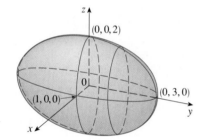

FIGURE 4

The ellipsoid $x^2 + \dfrac{y^2}{9} + \dfrac{z^2}{4} = 1$

EXAMPLE 4 Use traces to sketch the surface $z = 4x^2 + y^2$.

SOLUTION If we put $x = 0$, we get $z = y^2$, so the yz-plane intersects the surface in a parabola. If we put $x = k$ (a constant), we get $z = y^2 + 4k^2$. This means that if we slice the graph with any plane parallel to the yz-plane, we obtain a parabola that opens upward. Similarly, if $y = k$, the trace is $z = 4x^2 + k^2$, which is again a parabola that opens upward. If we put $z = k$, we get the horizontal traces $4x^2 + y^2 = k$, which we recognize as a family of ellipses. Knowing the shapes of the traces, we can sketch the graph in Figure 5. Because of the elliptical and parabolic traces, the quadric surface $z = 4x^2 + y^2$ is called an **elliptic paraboloid**.

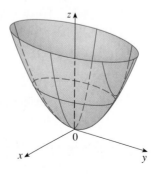

FIGURE 5

The surface $z = 4x^2 + y^2$ is an elliptic paraboloid. Horizontal traces are ellipses; vertical traces are parabolas.

▼ EXAMPLE 5 Sketch the surface $z = y^2 - x^2$.

SOLUTION The traces in the vertical planes $x = k$ are the parabolas $z = y^2 - k^2$, which open upward. The traces in $y = k$ are the parabolas $z = -x^2 + k^2$, which open downward. The horizontal traces are $y^2 - x^2 = k$, a family of hyperbolas. We draw the families of traces in Figure 6, and we show how the traces appear when placed in their correct planes in Figure 7.

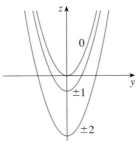

Traces in $x = k$ are $z = y^2 - k^2$

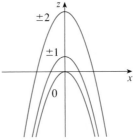

Traces in $y = k$ are $z = -x^2 + k^2$

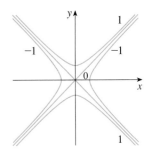

Traces in $z = k$ are $y^2 - x^2 = k$

FIGURE 6
Vertical traces are parabolas;
horizontal traces are hyperbolas.
All traces are labeled with the
value of k.

Traces in $x = k$

Traces in $y = k$

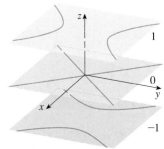

Traces in $z = k$

FIGURE 7
Traces moved to their
correct planes

TEC In Module 13.6A you can investigate how traces determine the shape of a surface.

In Figure 8 we fit together the traces from Figure 7 to form the surface $z = y^2 - x^2$, a **hyperbolic paraboloid**. Notice that the shape of the surface near the origin resembles that of a saddle. This surface will be investigated further in Section 15.7 when we discuss saddle points.

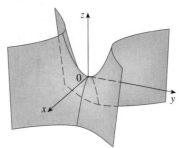

FIGURE 8
The surface $z = y^2 - x^2$ is a
hyperbolic paraboloid.

EXAMPLE 6 Sketch the surface $\dfrac{x^2}{4} + y^2 - \dfrac{z^2}{4} = 1$.

SOLUTION The trace in any horizontal plane $z = k$ is the ellipse

$$\frac{x^2}{4} + y^2 = 1 + \frac{k^2}{4} \qquad z = k$$

but the traces in the xz- and yz-planes are the hyperbolas

$$\frac{x^2}{4} - \frac{z^2}{4} = 1 \qquad y = 0 \qquad \text{and} \qquad y^2 - \frac{z^2}{4} = 1 \qquad x = 0$$

This surface is called a **hyperboloid of one sheet** and is sketched in Figure 9. □

FIGURE 9

The idea of using traces to draw a surface is employed in three-dimensional graphing software for computers. In most such software, traces in the vertical planes $x = k$ and $y = k$ are drawn for equally spaced values of k, and parts of the graph are eliminated using hidden line removal. Table 1 shows computer-drawn graphs of the six basic types of quadric surfaces in standard form. All surfaces are symmetric with respect to the z-axis. If a quadric surface is symmetric about a different axis, its equation changes accordingly.

TABLE I Graphs of quadric surfaces

Surface	Equation	Surface	Equation
Ellipsoid	$\dfrac{x^2}{a^2} + \dfrac{y^2}{b^2} + \dfrac{z^2}{c^2} = 1$ All traces are ellipses. If $a = b = c$, the ellipsoid is a sphere.	Cone	$\dfrac{z^2}{c^2} = \dfrac{x^2}{a^2} + \dfrac{y^2}{b^2}$ Horizontal traces are ellipses. Vertical traces in the planes $x = k$ and $y = k$ are hyperbolas if $k \neq 0$ but are pairs of lines if $k = 0$.
Elliptic Paraboloid	$\dfrac{z}{c} = \dfrac{x^2}{a^2} + \dfrac{y^2}{b^2}$ Horizontal traces are ellipses. Vertical traces are parabolas. The variable raised to the first power indicates the axis of the paraboloid.	Hyperboloid of One Sheet	$\dfrac{x^2}{a^2} + \dfrac{y^2}{b^2} - \dfrac{z^2}{c^2} = 1$ Horizontal traces are ellipses. Vertical traces are hyperbolas. The axis of symmetry corresponds to the variable whose coefficient is negative.
Hyperbolic Paraboloid	$\dfrac{z}{c} = \dfrac{x^2}{a^2} - \dfrac{y^2}{b^2}$ Horizontal traces are hyperbolas. Vertical traces are parabolas. The case where $c < 0$ is illustrated.	Hyperboloid of Two Sheets	$-\dfrac{x^2}{a^2} - \dfrac{y^2}{b^2} + \dfrac{z^2}{c^2} = 1$ Horizontal traces in $z = k$ are ellipses if $k > c$ or $k < -c$. Vertical traces are hyperbolas. The two minus signs indicate two sheets.

TEC In Module 13.6B you can see how changing a, b, and c in Table 1 affects the shape of the quadric surface.

V EXAMPLE 7 Identify and sketch the surface $4x^2 - y^2 + 2z^2 + 4 = 0$.

SOLUTION Dividing by -4, we first put the equation in standard form:

$$-x^2 + \frac{y^2}{4} - \frac{z^2}{2} = 1$$

Comparing this equation with Table 1, we see that it represents a hyperboloid of two sheets, the only difference being that in this case the axis of the hyperboloid is the y-axis. The traces in the xy- and yz-planes are the hyperbolas

$$-x^2 + \frac{y^2}{4} = 1 \qquad z = 0 \qquad \text{and} \qquad \frac{y^2}{4} - \frac{z^2}{2} = 1 \qquad x = 0$$

The surface has no trace in the xz-plane, but traces in the vertical planes $y = k$ for $|k| > 2$ are the ellipses

$$x^2 + \frac{z^2}{2} = \frac{k^2}{4} - 1 \qquad y = k$$

which can be written as

$$\frac{x^2}{\dfrac{k^2}{4} - 1} + \frac{z^2}{2\left(\dfrac{k^2}{4} - 1\right)} = 1 \qquad y = k$$

These traces are used to make the sketch in Figure 10. □

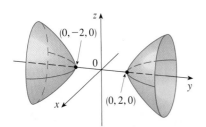

FIGURE 10
$4x^2 - y^2 + 2z^2 + 4 = 0$

EXAMPLE 8 Classify the quadric surface $x^2 + 2z^2 - 6x - y + 10 = 0$.

SOLUTION By completing the square we rewrite the equation as

$$y - 1 = (x - 3)^2 + 2z^2$$

Comparing this equation with Table 1, we see that it represents an elliptic paraboloid. Here, however, the axis of the paraboloid is parallel to the y-axis, and it has been shifted so that its vertex is the point $(3, 1, 0)$. The traces in the plane $y = k$ $(k > 1)$ are the ellipses

$$(x - 3)^2 + 2z^2 = k - 1 \qquad y = k$$

The trace in the xy-plane is the parabola with equation $y = 1 + (x - 3)^2$, $z = 0$. The paraboloid is sketched in Figure 11.

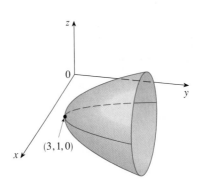

FIGURE 11
$x^2 + 2z^2 - 6x - y + 10 = 0$ □

APPLICATIONS OF QUADRIC SURFACES

Examples of quadric surfaces can be found in the world around us. In fact, the world itself is a good example. Although the earth is commonly modeled as a sphere, a more accurate model is an ellipsoid because the earth's rotation has caused a flattening at the poles. (See Exercise 47.)

Circular paraboloids, obtained by rotating a parabola about its axis, are used to collect and reflect light, sound, and radio and television signals. In a radio telescope, for instance, signals from distant stars that strike the bowl are reflected to the receiver at the focus and are therefore amplified. (The idea is explained in Problem 16 on page 202.) The same principle applies to microphones and satellite dishes in the shape of paraboloids.

Cooling towers for nuclear reactors are usually designed in the shape of hyperboloids of one sheet for reasons of structural stability. Pairs of hyperboloids are used to transmit rotational motion between skew axes. (The cogs of gears are the generating lines of the hyperboloids. See Exercise 49.)

A satellite dish reflects signals to the focus of a paraboloid.

© Corbis

Nuclear reactors have cooling towers in the shape of hyperboloids.

David Burnett / Photo Researchers, Inc

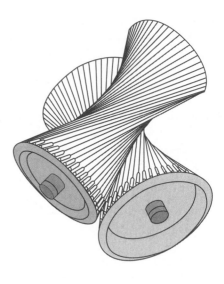

Hyperboloids produce gear transmission.

13.6 EXERCISES

1. (a) What does the equation $y = x^2$ represent as a curve in $\mathbb{R}^2$?
   (b) What does it represent as a surface in $\mathbb{R}^3$?
   (c) What does the equation $z = y^2$ represent?

2. (a) Sketch the graph of $y = e^x$ as a curve in $\mathbb{R}^2$.
   (b) Sketch the graph of $y = e^x$ as a surface in $\mathbb{R}^3$.
   (c) Describe and sketch the surface $z = e^y$.

3–8 Describe and sketch the surface.

3. $y^2 + 4z^2 = 4$

4. $z = 4 - x^2$

5. $x - y^2 = 0$

6. $yz = 4$

7. $z = \cos x$

8. $x^2 - y^2 = 1$

9. (a) Find and identify the traces of the quadric surface $x^2 + y^2 - z^2 = 1$ and explain why the graph looks like the graph of the hyperboloid of one sheet in Table 1.
   (b) If we change the equation in part (a) to $x^2 - y^2 + z^2 = 1$, how is the graph affected?
   (c) What if we change the equation in part (a) to $x^2 + y^2 + 2y - z^2 = 0$?

10. (a) Find and identify the traces of the quadric surface $-x^2 - y^2 + z^2 = 1$ and explain why the graph looks like the graph of the hyperboloid of two sheets in Table 1.
(b) If the equation in part (a) is changed to $x^2 - y^2 - z^2 = 1$, what happens to the graph? Sketch the new graph.

11–20 Use traces to sketch and identify the surface.

11. $x = y^2 + 4z^2$

12. $9x^2 - y^2 + z^2 = 0$

13. $x^2 = y^2 + 4z^2$

14. $25x^2 + 4y^2 + z^2 = 100$

15. $-x^2 + 4y^2 - z^2 = 4$

16. $4x^2 + 9y^2 + z = 0$

17. $36x^2 + y^2 + 36z^2 = 36$

18. $4x^2 - 16y^2 + z^2 = 16$

 19. $y = z^2 - x^2$

20. $x = y^2 - z^2$

21–28 Match the equation with its graph (labeled I–VIII). Give reasons for your choices.

21. $x^2 + 4y^2 + 9z^2 = 1$

22. $9x^2 + 4y^2 + z^2 = 1$

23. $x^2 - y^2 + z^2 = 1$

24. $-x^2 + y^2 - z^2 = 1$

25. $y = 2x^2 + z^2$

26. $y^2 = x^2 + 2z^2$

27. $x^2 + 2z^2 = 1$

28. $y = x^2 - z^2$

I

II

III

IV

V

VI

VII

VIII

29–36 Reduce the equation to one of the standard forms, classify the surface, and sketch it.

29. $z^2 = 4x^2 + 9y^2 + 36$

30. $x^2 = 2y^2 + 3z^2$

31. $x = 2y^2 + 3z^2$

32. $4x - y^2 + 4z^2 = 0$

33. $4x^2 + y^2 + 4z^2 - 4y - 24z + 36 = 0$

34. $4y^2 + z^2 - x - 16y - 4z + 20 = 0$

35. $x^2 - y^2 + z^2 - 4x - 2y - 2z + 4 = 0$

36. $x^2 - y^2 + z^2 - 2x + 2y + 4z + 2 = 0$

37–40 Use a computer with three-dimensional graphing software to graph the surface. Experiment with viewpoints and with domains for the variables until you get a good view of the surface.

37. $-4x^2 - y^2 + z^2 = 1$

38. $x^2 - y^2 - z = 0$

39. $-4x^2 - y^2 + z^2 = 0$

40. $x^2 - 6x + 4y^2 - z = 0$

41. Sketch the region bounded by the surfaces $z = \sqrt{x^2 + y^2}$ and $x^2 + y^2 = 1$ for $1 \le z \le 2$.

42. Sketch the region bounded by the paraboloids $z = x^2 + y^2$ and $z = 2 - x^2 - y^2$.

43. Find an equation for the surface obtained by rotating the parabola $y = x^2$ about the y-axis.

44. Find an equation for the surface obtained by rotating the line $x = 3y$ about the x-axis.

45. Find an equation for the surface consisting of all points that are equidistant from the point $(-1, 0, 0)$ and the plane $x = 1$. Identify the surface.

46. Find an equation for the surface consisting of all points P for which the distance from P to the x-axis is twice the distance from P to the yz-plane. Identify the surface.

47. Traditionally, the earth's surface has been modeled as a sphere, but the World Geodetic System of 1984 (WGS-84) uses an ellipsoid as a more accurate model. It places the center of the earth at the origin and the north pole on the positive z-axis. The distance from the center to the poles is 6356.523 km and the distance to a point on the equator is 6378.137 km.
(a) Find an equation of the earth's surface as used by WGS-84.
(b) Curves of equal latitude are traces in the planes $z = k$. What is the shape of these curves?
(c) Meridians (curves of equal longitude) are traces in planes of the form $y = mx$. What is the shape of these meridians?

48. A cooling tower for a nuclear reactor is to be constructed in the shape of a hyperboloid of one sheet (see the photo on page 846). The diameter at the base is 280 m and the minimum

diameter, 500 m above the base, is 200 m. Find an equation for the tower.

49. Show that if the point (a, b, c) lies on the hyperbolic paraboloid $z = y^2 - x^2$, then the lines with parametric equations $x = a + t$, $y = b + t$, $z = c + 2(b - a)t$ and $x = a + t$, $y = b - t$, $z = c - 2(b + a)t$ both lie entirely on this paraboloid. (This shows that the hyperbolic paraboloid is what is called a **ruled surface**; that is, it can be generated by the motion of a straight line. In fact, this exercise shows that through each point on the hyperbolic paraboloid there are two

generating lines. The only other quadric surfaces that are ruled surfaces are cylinders, cones, and hyperboloids of one sheet.)

50. Show that the curve of intersection of the surfaces $x^2 + 2y^2 - z^2 + 3x = 1$ and $2x^2 + 4y^2 - 2z^2 - 5y = 0$ lies in a plane.

51. Graph the surfaces $z = x^2 + y^2$ and $z = 1 - y^2$ on a common screen using the domain $|x| \leq 1.2$, $|y| \leq 1.2$ and observe the curve of intersection of these surfaces. Show that the projection of this curve onto the xy-plane is an ellipse.

---

13 REVIEW

CONCEPT CHECK

1. What is the difference between a vector and a scalar?

2. How do you add two vectors geometrically? How do you add them algebraically?

3. If **a** is a vector and c is a scalar, how is c**a** related to **a** geometrically? How do you find c**a** algebraically?

4. How do you find the vector from one point to another?

5. How do you find the dot product $\mathbf{a} \cdot \mathbf{b}$ of two vectors if you know their lengths and the angle between them? What if you know their components?

6. How are dot products useful?

7. Write expressions for the scalar and vector projections of **b** onto **a**. Illustrate with diagrams.

8. How do you find the cross product $\mathbf{a} \times \mathbf{b}$ of two vectors if you know their lengths and the angle between them? What if you know their components?

9. How are cross products useful?

10. (a) How do you find the area of the parallelogram determined by **a** and **b**?
(b) How do you find the volume of the parallelepiped determined by **a**, **b**, and **c**?

11. How do you find a vector perpendicular to a plane?

12. How do you find the angle between two intersecting planes?

13. Write a vector equation, parametric equations, and symmetric equations for a line.

14. Write a vector equation and a scalar equation for a plane.

15. (a) How do you tell if two vectors are parallel?
(b) How do you tell if two vectors are perpendicular?
(c) How do you tell if two planes are parallel?

16. (a) Describe a method for determining whether three points P, Q, and R lie on the same line.
(b) Describe a method for determining whether four points P, Q, R, and S lie in the same plane.

17. (a) How do you find the distance from a point to a line?
(b) How do you find the distance from a point to a plane?
(c) How do you find the distance between two lines?

18. What are the traces of a surface? How do you find them?

19. Write equations in standard form of the six types of quadric surfaces.

TRUE-FALSE QUIZ

Determine whether the statement is true or false. If it is true, explain why. If it is false, explain why or give an example that disproves the statement.

1. For any vectors **u** and **v** in V_3, $\mathbf{u} \cdot \mathbf{v} = \mathbf{v} \cdot \mathbf{u}$.

2. For any vectors **u** and **v** in V_3, $\mathbf{u} \times \mathbf{v} = \mathbf{v} \times \mathbf{u}$.

3. For any vectors **u** and **v** in V_3, $|\mathbf{u} \times \mathbf{v}| = |\mathbf{v} \times \mathbf{u}|$.

4. For any vectors **u** and **v** in V_3 and any scalar k, $k(\mathbf{u} \cdot \mathbf{v}) = (k\mathbf{u}) \cdot \mathbf{v}$.

5. For any vectors **u** and **v** in V_3 and any scalar k, $k(\mathbf{u} \times \mathbf{v}) = (k\mathbf{u}) \times \mathbf{v}$.

6. For any vectors **u**, **v**, and **w** in V_3, $(\mathbf{u} + \mathbf{v}) \times \mathbf{w} = \mathbf{u} \times \mathbf{w} + \mathbf{v} \times \mathbf{w}$.

7. For any vectors **u**, **v**, and **w** in V_3, $\mathbf{u} \cdot (\mathbf{v} \times \mathbf{w}) = (\mathbf{u} \times \mathbf{v}) \cdot \mathbf{w}$.

8. For any vectors **u**, **v**, and **w** in V_3, $\mathbf{u} \times (\mathbf{v} \times \mathbf{w}) = (\mathbf{u} \times \mathbf{v}) \times \mathbf{w}$.

9. For any vectors **u** and **v** in V_3, $(\mathbf{u} \times \mathbf{v}) \cdot \mathbf{u} = 0$.

10. For any vectors **u** and **v** in V_3, $(\mathbf{u} + \mathbf{v}) \times \mathbf{v} = \mathbf{u} \times \mathbf{v}$.

11. The cross product of two unit vectors is a unit vector.

12. A linear equation $Ax + By + Cz + D = 0$ represents a line in space.

13. The set of points $\{(x, y, z) \mid x^2 + y^2 = 1\}$ is a circle.

14. If $\mathbf{u} = \langle u_1, u_2 \rangle$ and $\mathbf{v} = \langle v_1, v_2 \rangle$, then $\mathbf{u} \cdot \mathbf{v} = \langle u_1 v_1, u_2 v_2 \rangle$.

15. If $\mathbf{u} \cdot \mathbf{v} = 0$, then $\mathbf{u} = \mathbf{0}$ or $\mathbf{v} = \mathbf{0}$.

16. If $\mathbf{u} \times \mathbf{v} = \mathbf{0}$, then $\mathbf{u} = \mathbf{0}$ or $\mathbf{v} = \mathbf{0}$.

17. If $\mathbf{u} \cdot \mathbf{v} = 0$, and $\mathbf{u} \times \mathbf{v} = \mathbf{0}$, then $\mathbf{u} = \mathbf{0}$ or $\mathbf{v} = \mathbf{0}$.

18. If $\mathbf{u}$ and $\mathbf{v}$ are in V_3, then $|\mathbf{u} \cdot \mathbf{v}| \leqslant |\mathbf{u}||\mathbf{v}|$.

EXERCISES

1. (a) Find an equation of the sphere that passes through the point $(6, -2, 3)$ and has center $(-1, 2, 1)$.
   (b) Find the curve in which this sphere intersects the yz-plane.
   (c) Find the center and radius of the sphere

$$x^2 + y^2 + z^2 - 8x + 2y + 6z + 1 = 0$$

2. Copy the vectors in the figure and use them to draw each of the following vectors.
   (a) $\mathbf{a} + \mathbf{b}$ (b) $\mathbf{a} - \mathbf{b}$ (c) $-\frac{1}{2}\mathbf{a}$ (d) $2\mathbf{a} + \mathbf{b}$

3. If $\mathbf{u}$ and $\mathbf{v}$ are the vectors shown in the figure, find $\mathbf{u} \cdot \mathbf{v}$ and $|\mathbf{u} \times \mathbf{v}|$. Is $\mathbf{u} \times \mathbf{v}$ directed into the page or out of it?

4. Calculate the given quantity if

$$\mathbf{a} = \mathbf{i} + \mathbf{j} - 2\mathbf{k} \qquad \mathbf{b} = 3\mathbf{i} - 2\mathbf{j} + \mathbf{k} \qquad \mathbf{c} = \mathbf{j} - 5\mathbf{k}$$

   (a) $2\mathbf{a} + 3\mathbf{b}$
   (b) $|\mathbf{b}|$
   (c) $\mathbf{a} \cdot \mathbf{b}$
   (d) $\mathbf{a} \times \mathbf{b}$
   (e) $|\mathbf{b} \times \mathbf{c}|$
   (f) $\mathbf{a} \cdot (\mathbf{b} \times \mathbf{c})$
   (g) $\mathbf{c} \times \mathbf{c}$
   (h) $\mathbf{a} \times (\mathbf{b} \times \mathbf{c})$
   (i) $\text{comp}_{\mathbf{a}} \mathbf{b}$
   (j) $\text{proj}_{\mathbf{a}} \mathbf{b}$
   (k) The angle between $\mathbf{a}$ and $\mathbf{b}$ (correct to the nearest degree)

5. Find the values of x such that the vectors $\langle 3, 2, x \rangle$ and $\langle 2x, 4, x \rangle$ are orthogonal.

6. Find two unit vectors that are orthogonal to both $\mathbf{j} + 2\mathbf{k}$ and $\mathbf{i} - 2\mathbf{j} + 3\mathbf{k}$.

7. Suppose that $\mathbf{u} \cdot (\mathbf{v} \times \mathbf{w}) = 2$. Find
   (a) $(\mathbf{u} \times \mathbf{v}) \cdot \mathbf{w}$
   (b) $\mathbf{u} \cdot (\mathbf{w} \times \mathbf{v})$
   (c) $\mathbf{v} \cdot (\mathbf{u} \times \mathbf{w})$
   (d) $(\mathbf{u} \times \mathbf{v}) \cdot \mathbf{v}$

8. Show that if $\mathbf{a}$, $\mathbf{b}$, and $\mathbf{c}$ are in V_3, then

$$(\mathbf{a} \times \mathbf{b}) \cdot [(\mathbf{b} \times \mathbf{c}) \times (\mathbf{c} \times \mathbf{a})] = [\mathbf{a} \cdot (\mathbf{b} \times \mathbf{c})]^2$$

9. Find the acute angle between two diagonals of a cube.

10. Given the points $A(1, 0, 1)$, $B(2, 3, 0)$, $C(-1, 1, 4)$, and $D(0, 3, 2)$, find the volume of the parallelepiped with adjacent edges AB, AC, and AD.

11. (a) Find a vector perpendicular to the plane through the points $A(1, 0, 0)$, $B(2, 0, -1)$, and $C(1, 4, 3)$.
    (b) Find the area of triangle ABC.

12. A constant force $\mathbf{F} = 3\mathbf{i} + 5\mathbf{j} + 10\mathbf{k}$ moves an object along the line segment from $(1, 0, 2)$ to $(5, 3, 8)$. Find the work done if the distance is measured in meters and the force in newtons.

13. A boat is pulled onto shore using two ropes, as shown in the diagram. If a force of 255 N is needed, find the magnitude of the force in each rope.

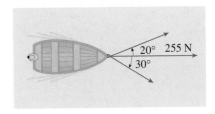

14. Find the magnitude of the torque about P if a 50-N force is applied as shown.

15–17 Find parametric equations for the line.

15. The line through $(4, -1, 2)$ and $(1, 1, 5)$

16. The line through $(1, 0, -1)$ and parallel to the line $\frac{1}{3}(x - 4) = \frac{1}{2}y = z + 2$

17. The line through $(-2, 2, 4)$ and perpendicular to the plane $2x - y + 5z = 12$

18–20 Find an equation of the plane.

18. The plane through $(2, 1, 0)$ and parallel to $x + 4y - 3z = 1$

19. The plane through $(3, -1, 1)$, $(4, 0, 2)$, and $(6, 3, 1)$

20. The plane through $(1, 2, -2)$ that contains the line $x = 2t, y = 3 - t, z = 1 + 3t$

21. Find the point in which the line with parametric equations $x = 2 - t, y = 1 + 3t, z = 4t$ intersects the plane $2x - y + z = 2$.

22. Find the distance from the origin to the line $x = 1 + t, y = 2 - t, z = -1 + 2t$.

23. Determine whether the lines given by the symmetric equations

$$\frac{x - 1}{2} = \frac{y - 2}{3} = \frac{z - 3}{4}$$

and

$$\frac{x + 1}{6} = \frac{y - 3}{-1} = \frac{z + 5}{2}$$

are parallel, skew, or intersecting.

24. (a) Show that the planes $x + y - z = 1$ and $2x - 3y + 4z = 5$ are neither parallel nor perpendicular.

(b) Find, correct to the nearest degree, the angle between these planes.

25. Find an equation of the plane through the line of intersection of the planes $x - z = 1$ and $y + 2z = 3$ and perpendicular to the plane $x + y - 2z = 1$.

26. (a) Find an equation of the plane that passes through the points $A(2, 1, 1)$, $B(-1, -1, 10)$, and $C(1, 3, -4)$.

(b) Find symmetric equations for the line through B that is perpendicular to the plane in part (a).

(c) A second plane passes through $(2, 0, 4)$ and has normal vector $\langle 2, -4, -3 \rangle$. Show that the acute angle between the planes is approximately $43°$.

(d) Find parametric equations for the line of intersection of the two planes.

27. Find the distance between the planes $3x + y - 4z = 2$ and $3x + y - 4z = 24$.

28–36 Identify and sketch the graph of each surface.

28. $x = 3$

29. $x = z$

30. $y = z^2$

31. $x^2 = y^2 + 4z^2$

32. $4x - y + 2z = 4$

33. $-4x^2 + y^2 - 4z^2 = 4$

34. $y^2 + z^2 = 1 + x^2$

35. $4x^2 + 4y^2 - 8y + z^2 = 0$

36. $x = y^2 + z^2 - 2y - 4z + 5$

37. An ellipsoid is created by rotating the ellipse $4x^2 + y^2 = 16$ about the x-axis. Find an equation of the ellipsoid.

38. A surface consists of all points P such that the distance from P to the plane $y = 1$ is twice the distance from P to the point $(0, -1, 0)$. Find an equation for this surface and identify it.

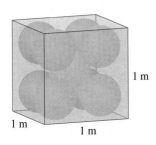

1 m

1 m   1 m

FIGURE FOR PROBLEM 1

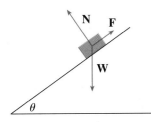

N   F

W

θ

FIGURE FOR PROBLEM 5

1. Each edge of a cubical box has length 1 m. The box contains nine spherical balls with the same radius r. The center of one ball is at the center of the cube and it touches the other eight balls. Each of the other eight balls touches three sides of the box. Thus the balls are tightly packed in the box. (See the figure.) Find r. (If you have trouble with this problem, read about the problem-solving strategy entitled *Use Analogy* on page 54.)

2. Let B be a solid box with length L, width W, and height H. Let S be the set of all points that are a distance at most 1 from some point of B. Express the volume of S in terms of L, W, and H.

3. Let L be the line of intersection of the planes $cx + y + z = c$ and $x - cy + cz = -1$, where c is a real number.
   (a) Find symmetric equations for L.
   (b) As the number c varies, the line L sweeps out a surface S. Find an equation for the curve of intersection of S with the horizontal plane $z = t$ (the trace of S in the plane $z = t$).
   (c) Find the volume of the solid bounded by S and the planes $z = 0$ and $z = 1$.

4. A plane is capable of flying at a speed of 180 km/h in still air. The pilot takes off from an airfield and heads due north according to the plane's compass. After 30 minutes of flight time, the pilot notices that, due to the wind, the plane has actually traveled 80 km at an angle 5° east of north.
   (a) What is the wind velocity?
   (b) In what direction should the pilot have headed to reach the intended destination?

5. Suppose a block of mass m is placed on an inclined plane, as shown in the figure. The block's descent down the plane is slowed by friction; if θ is not too large, friction will prevent the block from moving at all. The forces acting on the block are the weight $\mathbf{W}$, where $|\mathbf{W}| = mg$ (g is the acceleration due to gravity); the normal force $\mathbf{N}$ (the normal component of the reactionary force of the plane on the block), where $|\mathbf{N}| = n$; and the force $\mathbf{F}$ due to friction, which acts parallel to the inclined plane, opposing the direction of motion. If the block is at rest and θ is increased, $|\mathbf{F}|$ must also increase until ultimately $|\mathbf{F}|$ reaches its maximum, beyond which the block begins to slide. At this angle θ_s, it has been observed that $|\mathbf{F}|$ is proportional to n. Thus, when $|\mathbf{F}|$ is maximal, we can say that $|\mathbf{F}| = \mu_s n$, where μ_s is called the *coefficient of static friction* and depends on the materials that are in contact.
   (a) Observe that $\mathbf{N} + \mathbf{F} + \mathbf{W} = \mathbf{0}$ and deduce that $\mu_s = \tan(\theta_s)$.
   (b) Suppose that, for $\theta > \theta_s$, an additional outside force $\mathbf{H}$ is applied to the block, horizontally from the left, and let $|\mathbf{H}| = h$. If h is small, the block may still slide down the plane; if h is large enough, the block will move up the plane. Let $h_{\min}$ be the smallest value of h that allows the block to remain motionless (so that $|\mathbf{F}|$ is maximal).
      By choosing the coordinate axes so that $\mathbf{F}$ lies along the x-axis, resolve each force into components parallel and perpendicular to the inclined plane and show that
      $$h_{\min} \sin\theta + mg\cos\theta = n \quad \text{and} \quad h_{\min}\cos\theta + \mu_s n = mg\sin\theta$$
   (c) Show that
      $$h_{\min} = mg\tan(\theta - \theta_s)$$
      Does this equation seem reasonable? Does it make sense for $\theta = \theta_s$? As $\theta \to 90°$? Explain.
   (d) Let $h_{\max}$ be the largest value of h that allows the block to remain motionless. (In which direction is $\mathbf{F}$ heading?) Show that
      $$h_{\max} = mg\tan(\theta + \theta_s)$$
      Does this equation seem reasonable? Explain.

14

VECTOR FUNCTIONS

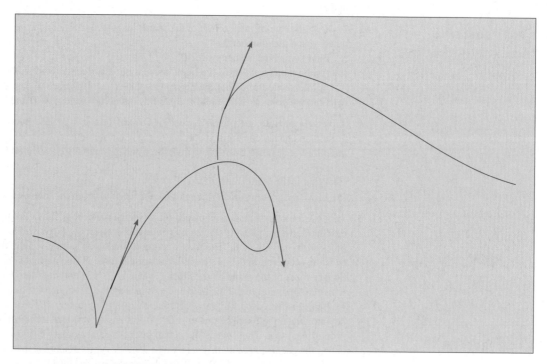

Tangent vectors show the direction in
which a space curve proceeds at any point.

The functions that we have been using so far have been real-valued functions. We now
study functions whose values are vectors because such functions are needed to describe
curves and surfaces in space. We will also use vector-valued functions to describe the
motion of objects through space. In particular, we will use them to derive Kepler's laws
of planetary motion.

In general, a function is a rule that assigns to each element in the domain an element in the range. A **vector-valued function**, or **vector function**, is simply a function whose domain is a set of real numbers and whose range is a set of vectors. We are most interested in vector functions $\mathbf{r}$ whose values are three-dimensional vectors. This means that for every number t in the domain of $\mathbf{r}$ there is a unique vector in V_3 denoted by $\mathbf{r}(t)$. If $f(t)$, $g(t)$, and $h(t)$ are the components of the vector $\mathbf{r}(t)$, then f, g, and h are real-valued functions called the **component functions** of $\mathbf{r}$ and we can write

$$\mathbf{r}(t) = \langle f(t), g(t), h(t) \rangle = f(t)\,\mathbf{i} + g(t)\,\mathbf{j} + h(t)\,\mathbf{k}$$

We usually use the letter t to denote the independent variable because it represents time in most applications of vector functions.

EXAMPLE 1 If

$$\mathbf{r}(t) = \left\langle t^3, \ln(3 - t), \sqrt{t} \right\rangle$$

then the component functions are

$$f(t) = t^3 \qquad g(t) = \ln(3 - t) \qquad h(t) = \sqrt{t}$$

By our usual convention, the domain of $\mathbf{r}$ consists of all values of t for which the expression for $\mathbf{r}(t)$ is defined. The expressions t^3, $\ln(3 - t)$, and $\sqrt{t}$ are all defined when $3 - t > 0$ and $t \geq 0$. Therefore the domain of $\mathbf{r}$ is the interval $[0, 3)$. ☐

The **limit** of a vector function $\mathbf{r}$ is defined by taking the limits of its component functions as follows.

> If $\lim_{t \to a} \mathbf{r}(t) = \mathbf{L}$, this definition is equivalent to saying that the length and direction of the vector $\mathbf{r}(t)$ approach the length and direction of the vector $\mathbf{L}$.

> **1** If $\mathbf{r}(t) = \langle f(t), g(t), h(t) \rangle$, then
>
> $$\lim_{t \to a} \mathbf{r}(t) = \left\langle \lim_{t \to a} f(t), \lim_{t \to a} g(t), \lim_{t \to a} h(t) \right\rangle$$
>
> provided the limits of the component functions exist.

Equivalently, we could have used an ε-δ definition (see Exercise 45). Limits of vector functions obey the same rules as limits of real-valued functions (see Exercise 43).

EXAMPLE 2 Find $\lim_{t \to 0} \mathbf{r}(t)$, where $\mathbf{r}(t) = (1 + t^3)\,\mathbf{i} + te^{-t}\,\mathbf{j} + \dfrac{\sin t}{t}\,\mathbf{k}$.

SOLUTION According to Definition 1, the limit of $\mathbf{r}$ is the vector whose components are the limits of the component functions of $\mathbf{r}$:

$$\lim_{t \to 0} \mathbf{r}(t) = \left[\lim_{t \to 0}(1 + t^3)\right]\mathbf{i} + \left[\lim_{t \to 0} te^{-t}\right]\mathbf{j} + \left[\lim_{t \to 0} \frac{\sin t}{t}\right]\mathbf{k}$$

$$= \mathbf{i} + \mathbf{k} \qquad \text{(by Equation 3.4.2)} \qquad ☐$$

A vector function **r** is **continuous at** a if

$$\lim_{t \to a} \mathbf{r}(t) = \mathbf{r}(a)$$

In view of Definition 1, we see that **r** is continuous at a if and only if its component functions f, g, and h are continuous at a.

There is a close connection between continuous vector functions and space curves. Suppose that f, g, and h are continuous real-valued functions on an interval I. Then the set C of all points (x, y, z) in space, where

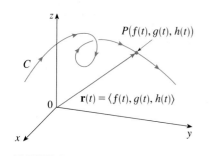

FIGURE 1
C is traced out by the tip of a moving position vector $\mathbf{r}(t)$.

$$\boxed{2} \qquad x = f(t) \qquad y = g(t) \qquad z = h(t)$$

and t varies throughout the interval I, is called a **space curve**. The equations in (2) are called **parametric equations of C** and t is called a **parameter**. We can think of C as being traced out by a moving particle whose position at time t is $\big(f(t), g(t), h(t)\big)$. If we now consider the vector function $\mathbf{r}(t) = \langle f(t), g(t), h(t) \rangle$, then $\mathbf{r}(t)$ is the position vector of the point $P\big(f(t), g(t), h(t)\big)$ on C. Thus any continuous vector function **r** defines a space curve C that is traced out by the tip of the moving vector $\mathbf{r}(t)$, as shown in Figure 1.

TEC Visual 14.1A shows several curves being traced out by position vectors, including those in Figures 1 and 2.

☑ **EXAMPLE 3** Describe the curve defined by the vector function

$$\mathbf{r}(t) = \langle 1 + t, 2 + 5t, -1 + 6t \rangle$$

SOLUTION The corresponding parametric equations are

$$x = 1 + t \qquad y = 2 + 5t \qquad z = -1 + 6t$$

which we recognize from Equations 13.5.2 as parametric equations of a line passing through the point $(1, 2, -1)$ and parallel to the vector $\langle 1, 5, 6 \rangle$. Alternatively, we could observe that the function can be written as $\mathbf{r} = \mathbf{r}_0 + t\mathbf{v}$, where $\mathbf{r}_0 = \langle 1, 2, -1 \rangle$ and $\mathbf{v} = \langle 1, 5, 6 \rangle$, and this is the vector equation of a line as given by Equation 13.5.1. ☐

Plane curves can also be represented in vector notation. For instance, the curve given by the parametric equations $x = t^2 - 2t$ and $y = t + 1$ (see Example 1 in Section 11.1) could also be described by the vector equation

$$\mathbf{r}(t) = \langle t^2 - 2t, t + 1 \rangle = (t^2 - 2t)\mathbf{i} + (t + 1)\mathbf{j}$$

where $\mathbf{i} = \langle 1, 0 \rangle$ and $\mathbf{j} = \langle 0, 1 \rangle$.

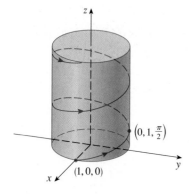

FIGURE 2

☑ **EXAMPLE 4** Sketch the curve whose vector equation is

$$\mathbf{r}(t) = \cos t\,\mathbf{i} + \sin t\,\mathbf{j} + t\,\mathbf{k}$$

SOLUTION The parametric equations for this curve are

$$x = \cos t \qquad y = \sin t \qquad z = t$$

Since $x^2 + y^2 = \cos^2 t + \sin^2 t = 1$, the curve must lie on the circular cylinder $x^2 + y^2 = 1$. The point (x, y, z) lies directly above the point $(x, y, 0)$, which moves counterclockwise around the circle $x^2 + y^2 = 1$ in the xy-plane. (See Example 2 in Section 11.1.) Since $z = t$, the curve spirals upward around the cylinder as t increases. The curve, shown in Figure 2, is called a **helix**. ☐

FIGURE 3

The corkscrew shape of the helix in Example 4 is familiar from its occurrence in coiled springs. It also occurs in the model of DNA (deoxyribonucleic acid, the genetic material of living cells). In 1953 James Watson and Francis Crick showed that the structure of the DNA molecule is that of two linked, parallel helixes that are intertwined as in Figure 3.

In Examples 3 and 4 we were given vector equations of curves and asked for a geometric description or sketch. In the next two examples we are given a geometric description of a curve and are asked to find parametric equations for the curve.

EXAMPLE 5 Find a vector equation and parametric equations for the line segment that joins the point $P(1, 3, -2)$ to the point $Q(2, -1, 3)$.

SOLUTION In Section 13.5 we found a vector equation for the line segment that joins the tip of the vector $\mathbf{r}_0$ to the tip of the vector $\mathbf{r}_1$:

$$\mathbf{r}(t) = (1 - t)\mathbf{r}_0 + t\mathbf{r}_1 \qquad 0 \leqslant t \leqslant 1$$

(See Equation 13.5.4.) Here we take $\mathbf{r}_0 = \langle 1, 3, -2 \rangle$ and $\mathbf{r}_1 = \langle 2, -1, 3 \rangle$ to obtain a vector equation of the line segment from P to Q:

$$\mathbf{r}(t) = (1 - t)\langle 1, 3, -2 \rangle + t\langle 2, -1, 3 \rangle \qquad 0 \leqslant t \leqslant 1$$

or $\qquad\qquad \mathbf{r}(t) = \langle 1 + t, 3 - 4t, -2 + 5t \rangle \qquad 0 \leqslant t \leqslant 1$

The corresponding parametric equations are

$$x = 1 + t \qquad y = 3 - 4t \qquad z = -2 + 5t \qquad 0 \leqslant t \leqslant 1 \qquad \square$$

■ Figure 4 shows the line segment PQ in Example 5.

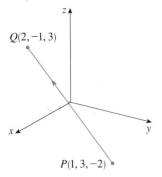

FIGURE 4

◥ EXAMPLE 6 Find a vector function that represents the curve of intersection of the cylinder $x^2 + y^2 = 1$ and the plane $y + z = 2$.

SOLUTION Figure 5 shows how the plane and the cylinder intersect, and Figure 6 shows the curve of intersection C, which is an ellipse.

FIGURE 5

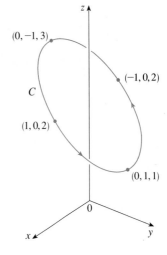

FIGURE 6

The projection of C onto the xy-plane is the circle $x^2 + y^2 = 1$, $z = 0$. So we know from Example 2 in Section 11.1 that we can write

$$x = \cos t \qquad y = \sin t \qquad 0 \leqslant t \leqslant 2\pi$$

From the equation of the plane, we have

$$z = 2 - y = 2 - \sin t$$

So we can write parametric equations for C as

$$x = \cos t \qquad y = \sin t \qquad z = 2 - \sin t \qquad 0 \leqslant t \leqslant 2\pi$$

The corresponding vector equation is

$$\mathbf{r}(t) = \cos t \,\mathbf{i} + \sin t \,\mathbf{j} + (2 - \sin t)\,\mathbf{k} \qquad 0 \leqslant t \leqslant 2\pi$$

This equation is called a *parametrization* of the curve C. The arrows in Figure 6 indicate the direction in which C is traced as the parameter t increases. ▢

USING COMPUTERS TO DRAW SPACE CURVES

Space curves are inherently more difficult to draw by hand than plane curves; for an accurate representation we need to use technology. For instance, Figure 7 shows a computer-generated graph of the curve with parametric equations

$$x = (4 + \sin 20t)\cos t \qquad y = (4 + \sin 20t)\sin t \qquad z = \cos 20t$$

It's called a **toroidal spiral** because it lies on a torus. Another interesting curve, the **trefoil knot**, with equations

$$x = (2 + \cos 1.5t)\cos t \qquad y = (2 + \cos 1.5t)\sin t \qquad z = \sin 1.5t$$

is graphed in Figure 8. It wouldn't be easy to plot either of these curves by hand.

Even when a computer is used to draw a space curve, optical illusions make it difficult to get a good impression of what the curve really looks like. (This is especially true in Figure 8. See Exercise 44.) The next example shows how to cope with this problem.

EXAMPLE 7 Use a computer to draw the curve with vector equation $\mathbf{r}(t) = \langle t, t^2, t^3 \rangle$. This curve is called a **twisted cubic**.

SOLUTION We start by using the computer to plot the curve with parametric equations $x = t$, $y = t^2$, $z = t^3$ for $-2 \leqslant t \leqslant 2$. The result is shown in Figure 9(a), but it's hard to see the true nature of the curve from that graph alone. Most three-dimensional computer graphing programs allow the user to enclose a curve or surface in a box instead of displaying the coordinate axes. When we look at the same curve in a box in Figure 9(b), we have a much clearer picture of the curve. We can see that it climbs from a lower corner of the box to the upper corner nearest us, and it twists as it climbs.

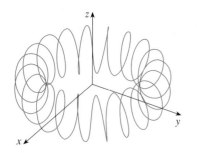

FIGURE 7 A toroidal spiral

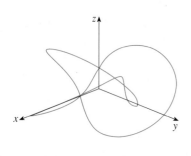

FIGURE 8 A trefoil knot

(a)

(b)

(c)

(d)

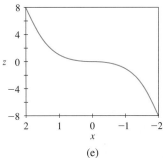

(e)

(f)

FIGURE 9 Views of the twisted cubic

TEC In Visual 14.1B you can rotate the box in Figure 9 to see the curve from any viewpoint.

We get an even better idea of the curve when we view it from different vantage points. Part (c) shows the result of rotating the box to give another viewpoint. Parts (d), (e), and (f) show the views we get when we look directly at a face of the box. In particular, part (d) shows the view from directly above the box. It is the projection of the curve on the xy-plane, namely, the parabola $y = x^2$. Part (e) shows the projection on the xz-plane, the cubic curve $z = x^3$. It's now obvious why the given curve is called a twisted cubic. ◻

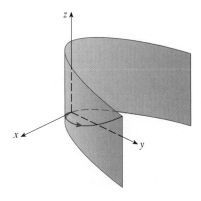

FIGURE 10

Another method of visualizing a space curve is to draw it on a surface. For instance, the twisted cubic in Example 7 lies on the parabolic cylinder $y = x^2$. (Eliminate the parameter from the first two parametric equations, $x = t$ and $y = t^2$.) Figure 10 shows both the cylinder and the twisted cubic, and we see that the curve moves upward from the origin along the surface of the cylinder. We also used this method in Example 4 to visualize the helix lying on the circular cylinder (see Figure 2).

A third method for visualizing the twisted cubic is to realize that it also lies on the cylinder $z = x^3$. So it can be viewed as the curve of intersection of the cylinders $y = x^2$ and $z = x^3$. (See Figure 11.)

TEC Visual 14.1C shows how curves arise as intersections of surfaces.

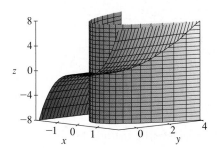

FIGURE 11

■ Some computer algebra systems provide us with a clearer picture of a space curve by enclosing it in a tube. Such a plot enables us to see whether one part of a curve passes in front of or behind another part of the curve. For example, Figure 13 shows the curve of Figure 12(b) as rendered by the tubeplot command in Maple.

We have seen that an interesting space curve, the helix, occurs in the model of DNA. Another notable example of a space curve in science is the trajectory of a positively charged particle in orthogonally oriented electric and magnetic fields **E** and **B**. Depending on the initial velocity given the particle at the origin, the path of the particle is either a space curve whose projection on the horizontal plane is the cycloid we studied in Section 11.1 [Figure 12(a)] or a curve whose projection is the trochoid investigated in Exercise 40 in Section 11.1 [Figure 12(b)].

(a) $\mathbf{r}(t) = \langle t - \sin t, 1 - \cos t, t \rangle$

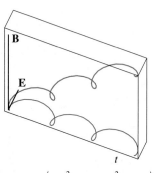

(b) $\mathbf{r}(t) = \langle t - \frac{3}{2}\sin t, 1 - \frac{3}{2}\cos t, t \rangle$

FIGURE 12
Motion of a charged particle in orthogonally oriented electric and magnetic fields

FIGURE 13

For further details concerning the physics involved and animations of the trajectories of the particles, see the following websites:

■ www.phy.ntnu.edu.tw/java/emField/emField.html

■ www.physics.ucla.edu/plasma-exp/Beam/

14.1 EXERCISES

1–2 Find the domain of the vector function.

1. $\mathbf{r}(t) = \langle \sqrt{4 - t^2}, e^{-3t}, \ln(t + 1) \rangle$

2. $\mathbf{r}(t) = \dfrac{t - 2}{t + 2}\mathbf{i} + \sin t\,\mathbf{j} + \ln(9 - t^2)\,\mathbf{k}$

3–6 Find the limit.

3. $\lim\limits_{t \to 0^+} \langle \cos t, \sin t, t \ln t \rangle$

4. $\lim\limits_{t \to 0} \left\langle \dfrac{e^t - 1}{t}, \dfrac{\sqrt{1 + t} - 1}{t}, \dfrac{3}{1 + t} \right\rangle$

5. $\lim\limits_{t \to 0} \left(e^{-3t}\mathbf{i} + \dfrac{t^2}{\sin^2 t}\mathbf{j} + \cos 2t\,\mathbf{k} \right)$

6. $\lim\limits_{t \to \infty} \left\langle \arctan t, e^{-2t}, \dfrac{\ln t}{t} \right\rangle$

7–14 Sketch the curve with the given vector equation. Indicate with an arrow the direction in which t increases.

7. $\mathbf{r}(t) = \langle \sin t, t \rangle$

8. $\mathbf{r}(t) = \langle t^3, t^2 \rangle$

9. $\mathbf{r}(t) = \langle t, \cos 2t, \sin 2t \rangle$

10. $\mathbf{r}(t) = \langle 1 + t, 3t, -t \rangle$

11. $\mathbf{r}(t) = \langle 1, \cos t, 2 \sin t \rangle$

12. $\mathbf{r}(t) = t^2\mathbf{i} + t\mathbf{j} + 2\mathbf{k}$

13. $\mathbf{r}(t) = t^2\mathbf{i} + t^4\mathbf{j} + t^6\mathbf{k}$

14. $\mathbf{r}(t) = \cos t\,\mathbf{i} - \cos t\,\mathbf{j} + \sin t\,\mathbf{k}$

15–18 Find a vector equation and parametric equations for the line segment that joins P to Q.

15. $P(0, 0, 0)$, $Q(1, 2, 3)$

16. $P(1, 0, 1)$, $Q(2, 3, 1)$

17. $P(1, -1, 2)$, $Q(4, 1, 7)$

18. $P(-2, 4, 0)$, $Q(6, -1, 2)$

19–24 Match the parametric equations with the graphs (labeled I–VI). Give reasons for your choices.

19. $x = \cos 4t$, $y = t$, $z = \sin 4t$

20. $x = t$, $y = t^2$, $z = e^{-t}$

21. $x = t$, $y = 1/(1 + t^2)$, $z = t^2$

22. $x = e^{-t} \cos 10t$, $y = e^{-t} \sin 10t$, $z = e^{-t}$

23. $x = \cos t$, $y = \sin t$, $z = \sin 5t$

24. $x = \cos t$, $y = \sin t$, $z = \ln t$

I

II

III

IV

V

VI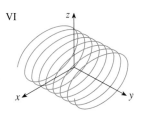

25. Show that the curve with parametric equations $x = t \cos t$, $y = t \sin t$, $z = t$ lies on the cone $z^2 = x^2 + y^2$, and use this fact to help sketch the curve.

26. Show that the curve with parametric equations $x = \sin t$, $y = \cos t$, $z = \sin^2 t$ is the curve of intersection of the surfaces $z = x^2$ and $x^2 + y^2 = 1$. Use this fact to help sketch the curve.

27. At what points does the curve $\mathbf{r}(t) = t\,\mathbf{i} + (2t - t^2)\,\mathbf{k}$ intersect the paraboloid $z = x^2 + y^2$?

28. At what points does the helix $\mathbf{r}(t) = \langle \sin t, \cos t, t \rangle$ intersect the sphere $x^2 + y^2 + z^2 = 5$?

29–32 Use a computer to graph the curve with the given vector equation. Make sure you choose a parameter domain and view-points that reveal the true nature of the curve.

29. $\mathbf{r}(t) = \langle \cos t \sin 2t, \sin t \sin 2t, \cos 2t \rangle$

30. $\mathbf{r}(t) = \langle t^2, \ln t, t \rangle$

31. $\mathbf{r}(t) = \langle t, t \sin t, t \cos t \rangle$

32. $\mathbf{r}(t) = \langle t, e^t, \cos t \rangle$

33. Graph the curve with parametric equations $x = (1 + \cos 16t) \cos t$, $y = (1 + \cos 16t) \sin t$, $z = 1 + \cos 16t$. Explain the appearance of the graph by showing that it lies on a cone.

34. Graph the curve with parametric equations

$$x = \sqrt{1 - 0.25 \cos^2 10t} \, \cos t$$
$$y = \sqrt{1 - 0.25 \cos^2 10t} \, \sin t$$
$$z = 0.5 \cos 10t$$

Explain the appearance of the graph by showing that it lies on a sphere.

35. Show that the curve with parametric equations $x = t^2$, $y = 1 - 3t$, $z = 1 + t^3$ passes through the points $(1, 4, 0)$ and $(9, -8, 28)$ but not through the point $(4, 7, -6)$.

36–38 Find a vector function that represents the curve of intersection of the two surfaces.

36. The cylinder $x^2 + y^2 = 4$ and the surface $z = xy$

37. The cone $z = \sqrt{x^2 + y^2}$ and the plane $z = 1 + y$

38. The paraboloid $z = 4x^2 + y^2$ and the parabolic cylinder $y = x^2$

39. Try to sketch by hand the curve of intersection of the circular cylinder $x^2 + y^2 = 4$ and the parabolic cylinder $z = x^2$. Then find parametric equations for this curve and use these equations and a computer to graph the curve.

40. Try to sketch by hand the curve of intersection of the parabolic cylinder $y = x^2$ and the top half of the ellipsoid $x^2 + 4y^2 + 4z^2 = 16$. Then find parametric equations for this curve and use these equations and a computer to graph the curve.

41. If two objects travel through space along two different curves, it's often important to know whether they will collide. (Will a missile hit its moving target? Will two aircraft collide?) The curves might intersect, but we need to know whether the objects are in the same position *at the same time*. Suppose the trajectories of two particles are given by the vector functions

$$\mathbf{r}_1(t) = \langle t^2, 7t - 12, t^2 \rangle \qquad \mathbf{r}_2(t) = \langle 4t - 3, t^2, 5t - 6 \rangle$$

for $t \geq 0$. Do the particles collide?

42. Two particles travel along the space curves

$$\mathbf{r}_1(t) = \langle t, t^2, t^3 \rangle \qquad \mathbf{r}_2(t) = \langle 1 + 2t, 1 + 6t, 1 + 14t \rangle$$

Do the particles collide? Do their paths intersect?

43. Suppose $\mathbf{u}$ and $\mathbf{v}$ are vector functions that possess limits as $t \to a$ and let c be a constant. Prove the following properties of limits.

(a) $\displaystyle \lim_{t \to a} [\mathbf{u}(t) + \mathbf{v}(t)] = \lim_{t \to a} \mathbf{u}(t) + \lim_{t \to a} \mathbf{v}(t)$

(b) $\lim_{t \to a} c\mathbf{u}(t) = c \lim_{t \to a} \mathbf{u}(t)$

(c) $\lim_{t \to a} [\mathbf{u}(t) \cdot \mathbf{v}(t)] = \lim_{t \to a} \mathbf{u}(t) \cdot \lim_{t \to a} \mathbf{v}(t)$

(d) $\lim_{t \to a} [\mathbf{u}(t) \times \mathbf{v}(t)] = \lim_{t \to a} \mathbf{u}(t) \times \lim_{t \to a} \mathbf{v}(t)$

44. The view of the trefoil knot shown in Figure 8 is accurate, but it doesn't reveal the whole story. Use the parametric equations

$$x = (2 + \cos 1.5t) \cos t$$

$$y = (2 + \cos 1.5t) \sin t$$

$$z = \sin 1.5t$$

to sketch the curve by hand as viewed from above, with gaps indicating where the curve passes over itself. Start by showing that the projection of the curve onto the xy-plane has polar coordinates $r = 2 + \cos 1.5t$ and $\theta = t$, so r varies between 1 and 3. Then show that z has maximum and minimum values when the projection is halfway between $r = 1$ and $r = 3$.

When you have finished your sketch, use a computer to draw the curve with viewpoint directly above and compare with your sketch. Then use the computer to draw the curve from several other viewpoints. You can get a better impression of the curve if you plot a tube with radius 0.2 around the curve. (Use the `tubeplot` command in Maple.)

45. Show that $\lim_{t \to a} \mathbf{r}(t) = \mathbf{b}$ if and only if for every $\varepsilon > 0$ there is a number $\delta > 0$ such that

$$\text{if } 0 < |t - a| < \delta \quad \text{then} \quad |\mathbf{r}(t) - \mathbf{b}| < \varepsilon$$

14.2 DERIVATIVES AND INTEGRALS OF VECTOR FUNCTIONS

Later in this chapter we are going to use vector functions to describe the motion of planets and other objects through space. Here we prepare the way by developing the calculus of vector functions.

DERIVATIVES

The **derivative** $\mathbf{r}'$ of a vector function $\mathbf{r}$ is defined in much the same way as for real-valued functions:

TEC Visual 14.2 shows an animation of Figure 1.

$$\boxed{1} \qquad \frac{d\mathbf{r}}{dt} = \mathbf{r}'(t) = \lim_{h \to 0} \frac{\mathbf{r}(t + h) - \mathbf{r}(t)}{h}$$

if this limit exists. The geometric significance of this definition is shown in Figure 1. If the points P and Q have position vectors $\mathbf{r}(t)$ and $\mathbf{r}(t + h)$, then $\overrightarrow{PQ}$ represents the vector $\mathbf{r}(t + h) - \mathbf{r}(t)$, which can therefore be regarded as a secant vector. If $h > 0$, the scalar multiple $(1/h)(\mathbf{r}(t + h) - \mathbf{r}(t))$ has the same direction as $\mathbf{r}(t + h) - \mathbf{r}(t)$. As $h \to 0$, it appears that this vector approaches a vector that lies on the tangent line. For this reason, the vector $\mathbf{r}'(t)$ is called the **tangent vector** to the curve defined by $\mathbf{r}$ at the point P, provided that $\mathbf{r}'(t)$ exists and $\mathbf{r}'(t) \neq \mathbf{0}$. The **tangent line** to C at P is defined to be the line through P parallel to the tangent vector $\mathbf{r}'(t)$. We will also have occasion to consider the **unit tangent vector**, which is

$$\mathbf{T}(t) = \frac{\mathbf{r}'(t)}{|\mathbf{r}'(t)|}$$

The following theorem gives us a convenient method for computing the derivative of a vector function $\mathbf{r}$: just differentiate each component of $\mathbf{r}$.

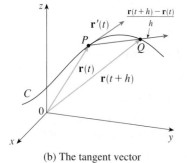

(a) The secant vector

(b) The tangent vector

FIGURE 1

$\boxed{2}$ **THEOREM** If $\mathbf{r}(t) = \langle f(t), g(t), h(t) \rangle = f(t)\,\mathbf{i} + g(t)\,\mathbf{j} + h(t)\,\mathbf{k}$, where f, g, and h are differentiable functions, then

$$\mathbf{r}'(t) = \langle f'(t), g'(t), h'(t) \rangle = f'(t)\,\mathbf{i} + g'(t)\,\mathbf{j} + h'(t)\,\mathbf{k}$$

PROOF

$$\mathbf{r}'(t) = \lim_{\Delta t \to 0} \frac{1}{\Delta t} [\mathbf{r}(t + \Delta t) - \mathbf{r}(t)]$$

$$= \lim_{\Delta t \to 0} \frac{1}{\Delta t} [\langle f(t + \Delta t), g(t + \Delta t), h(t + \Delta t) \rangle - \langle f(t), g(t), h(t) \rangle]$$

$$= \lim_{\Delta t \to 0} \left\langle \frac{f(t + \Delta t) - f(t)}{\Delta t}, \frac{g(t + \Delta t) - g(t)}{\Delta t}, \frac{h(t + \Delta t) - h(t)}{\Delta t} \right\rangle$$

$$= \left\langle \lim_{\Delta t \to 0} \frac{f(t + \Delta t) - f(t)}{\Delta t}, \lim_{\Delta t \to 0} \frac{g(t + \Delta t) - g(t)}{\Delta t}, \lim_{\Delta t \to 0} \frac{h(t + \Delta t) - h(t)}{\Delta t} \right\rangle$$

$$= \langle f'(t), g'(t), h'(t) \rangle \qquad \square$$

V EXAMPLE 1
(a) Find the derivative of $\mathbf{r}(t) = (1 + t^3)\mathbf{i} + te^{-t}\mathbf{j} + \sin 2t\,\mathbf{k}$.
(b) Find the unit tangent vector at the point where $t = 0$.

SOLUTION
(a) According to Theorem 2, we differentiate each component of $\mathbf{r}$:

$$\mathbf{r}'(t) = 3t^2\,\mathbf{i} + (1 - t)e^{-t}\mathbf{j} + 2\cos 2t\,\mathbf{k}$$

(b) Since $\mathbf{r}(0) = \mathbf{i}$ and $\mathbf{r}'(0) = \mathbf{j} + 2\mathbf{k}$, the unit tangent vector at the point $(1, 0, 0)$ is

$$\mathbf{T}(0) = \frac{\mathbf{r}'(0)}{|\mathbf{r}'(0)|} = \frac{\mathbf{j} + 2\mathbf{k}}{\sqrt{1 + 4}} = \frac{1}{\sqrt{5}}\mathbf{j} + \frac{2}{\sqrt{5}}\mathbf{k} \qquad \square$$

EXAMPLE 2 For the curve $\mathbf{r}(t) = \sqrt{t}\,\mathbf{i} + (2 - t)\mathbf{j}$, find $\mathbf{r}'(t)$ and sketch the position vector $\mathbf{r}(1)$ and the tangent vector $\mathbf{r}'(1)$.

SOLUTION We have

$$\mathbf{r}'(t) = \frac{1}{2\sqrt{t}}\mathbf{i} - \mathbf{j} \qquad \text{and} \qquad \mathbf{r}'(1) = \frac{1}{2}\mathbf{i} - \mathbf{j}$$

The curve is a plane curve and elimination of the parameter from the equations $x = \sqrt{t}$, $y = 2 - t$ gives $y = 2 - x^2$, $x \ge 0$. In Figure 2 we draw the position vector $\mathbf{r}(1) = \mathbf{i} + \mathbf{j}$ starting at the origin and the tangent vector $\mathbf{r}'(1)$ starting at the corresponding point $(1, 1)$. $\square$

FIGURE 2

V EXAMPLE 3 Find parametric equations for the tangent line to the helix with parametric equations

$$x = 2\cos t \qquad y = \sin t \qquad z = t$$

at the point $(0, 1, \pi/2)$.

SOLUTION The vector equation of the helix is $\mathbf{r}(t) = \langle 2\cos t, \sin t, t \rangle$, so

$$\mathbf{r}'(t) = \langle -2\sin t, \cos t, 1 \rangle$$

The parameter value corresponding to the point $(0, 1, \pi/2)$ is $t = \pi/2$, so the tangent vector there is $\mathbf{r}'(\pi/2) = \langle -2, 0, 1 \rangle$. The tangent line is the line through $(0, 1, \pi/2)$ parallel to the vector $\langle -2, 0, 1 \rangle$, so by Equations 13.5.2 its parametric equations are

$$x = -2t \qquad y = 1 \qquad z = \frac{\pi}{2} + t$$

◻

■ The helix and the tangent line in Example 3 are shown in Figure 3.

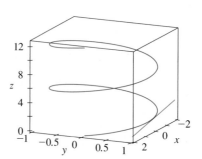

FIGURE 3

■ In Section 14.4 we will see how $\mathbf{r}'(t)$ and $\mathbf{r}''(t)$ can be interpreted as the velocity and acceleration vectors of a particle moving through space with position vector $\mathbf{r}(t)$ at time t.

Just as for real-valued functions, the **second derivative** of a vector function $\mathbf{r}$ is the derivative of $\mathbf{r}'$, that is, $\mathbf{r}'' = (\mathbf{r}')'$. For instance, the second derivative of the function in Example 3 is

$$\mathbf{r}''(t) = \langle -2 \cos t, -\sin t, 0 \rangle$$

DIFFERENTIATION RULES

The next theorem shows that the differentiation formulas for real-valued functions have their counterparts for vector-valued functions.

---

3 **THEOREM** Suppose $\mathbf{u}$ and $\mathbf{v}$ are differentiable vector functions, c is a scalar, and f is a real-valued function. Then

1. $\dfrac{d}{dt}[\mathbf{u}(t) + \mathbf{v}(t)] = \mathbf{u}'(t) + \mathbf{v}'(t)$

2. $\dfrac{d}{dt}[c\mathbf{u}(t)] = c\mathbf{u}'(t)$

3. $\dfrac{d}{dt}[f(t)\mathbf{u}(t)] = f'(t)\mathbf{u}(t) + f(t)\mathbf{u}'(t)$

4. $\dfrac{d}{dt}[\mathbf{u}(t) \cdot \mathbf{v}(t)] = \mathbf{u}'(t) \cdot \mathbf{v}(t) + \mathbf{u}(t) \cdot \mathbf{v}'(t)$

5. $\dfrac{d}{dt}[\mathbf{u}(t) \times \mathbf{v}(t)] = \mathbf{u}'(t) \times \mathbf{v}(t) + \mathbf{u}(t) \times \mathbf{v}'(t)$

6. $\dfrac{d}{dt}[\mathbf{u}(f(t))] = f'(t)\mathbf{u}'(f(t))$ (Chain Rule)

This theorem can be proved either directly from Definition 1 or by using Theorem 2 and the corresponding differentiation formulas for real-valued functions. The proof of Formula 4 follows; the remaining proofs are left as exercises.

PROOF OF FORMULA 4 Let

$$\mathbf{u}(t) = \langle f_1(t), f_2(t), f_3(t) \rangle \qquad \mathbf{v}(t) = \langle g_1(t), g_2(t), g_3(t) \rangle$$

Then
$$\mathbf{u}(t) \cdot \mathbf{v}(t) = f_1(t)\,g_1(t) + f_2(t)\,g_2(t) + f_3(t)\,g_3(t) = \sum_{i=1}^{3} f_i(t)\,g_i(t)$$

so the ordinary Product Rule gives

$$\frac{d}{dt}\,[\mathbf{u}(t) \cdot \mathbf{v}(t)] = \frac{d}{dt}\sum_{i=1}^{3} f_i(t)\,g_i(t) = \sum_{i=1}^{3}\frac{d}{dt}\,[f_i(t)\,g_i(t)]$$

$$= \sum_{i=1}^{3}\,[f_i'(t)\,g_i(t) + f_i(t)\,g_i'(t)]$$

$$= \sum_{i=1}^{3} f_i'(t)\,g_i(t) + \sum_{i=1}^{3} f_i(t)\,g_i'(t)$$

$$= \mathbf{u}'(t) \cdot \mathbf{v}(t) + \mathbf{u}(t) \cdot \mathbf{v}'(t) \qquad\qquad \square$$

▼ EXAMPLE 4 Show that if $|\mathbf{r}(t)| = c$ (a constant), then $\mathbf{r}'(t)$ is orthogonal to $\mathbf{r}(t)$ for all t.

SOLUTION Since

$$\mathbf{r}(t) \cdot \mathbf{r}(t) = |\mathbf{r}(t)|^2 = c^2$$

and c^2 is a constant, Formula 4 of Theorem 3 gives

$$0 = \frac{d}{dt}\,[\mathbf{r}(t) \cdot \mathbf{r}(t)] = \mathbf{r}'(t) \cdot \mathbf{r}(t) + \mathbf{r}(t) \cdot \mathbf{r}'(t) = 2\mathbf{r}'(t) \cdot \mathbf{r}(t)$$

Thus $\mathbf{r}'(t) \cdot \mathbf{r}(t) = 0$, which says that $\mathbf{r}'(t)$ is orthogonal to $\mathbf{r}(t)$.

Geometrically, this result says that if a curve lies on a sphere with center the origin, then the tangent vector $\mathbf{r}'(t)$ is always perpendicular to the position vector $\mathbf{r}(t)$. $\qquad \square$

INTEGRALS

The **definite integral** of a continuous vector function $\mathbf{r}(t)$ can be defined in much the same way as for real-valued functions except that the integral is a vector. But then we can express the integral of $\mathbf{r}$ in terms of the integrals of its component functions f, g, and h as follows. (We use the notation of Chapter 5.)

$$\int_a^b \mathbf{r}(t)\,dt = \lim_{n \to \infty} \sum_{i=1}^{n} \mathbf{r}(t_i^*)\,\Delta t$$

$$= \lim_{n \to \infty}\left[\left(\sum_{i=1}^{n} f(t_i^*)\,\Delta t\right)\mathbf{i} + \left(\sum_{i=1}^{n} g(t_i^*)\,\Delta t\right)\mathbf{j} + \left(\sum_{i=1}^{n} h(t_i^*)\,\Delta t\right)\mathbf{k}\right]$$

and so

$$\int_a^b \mathbf{r}(t)\,dt = \left(\int_a^b f(t)\,dt\right)\mathbf{i} + \left(\int_a^b g(t)\,dt\right)\mathbf{j} + \left(\int_a^b h(t)\,dt\right)\mathbf{k}$$

This means that we can evaluate an integral of a vector function by integrating each component function.

We can extend the Fundamental Theorem of Calculus to continuous vector functions as follows:

$$\int_a^b \mathbf{r}(t)\, dt = \mathbf{R}(t)\Big]_a^b = \mathbf{R}(b) - \mathbf{R}(a)$$

where $\mathbf{R}$ is an antiderivative of $\mathbf{r}$, that is, $\mathbf{R}'(t) = \mathbf{r}(t)$. We use the notation $\int \mathbf{r}(t)\, dt$ for indefinite integrals (antiderivatives).

EXAMPLE 5 If $\mathbf{r}(t) = 2\cos t\, \mathbf{i} + \sin t\, \mathbf{j} + 2t\, \mathbf{k}$, then

$$\int \mathbf{r}(t)\, dt = \left(\int 2\cos t\, dt \right) \mathbf{i} + \left(\int \sin t\, dt \right) \mathbf{j} + \left(\int 2t\, dt \right) \mathbf{k}$$

$$= 2\sin t\, \mathbf{i} - \cos t\, \mathbf{j} + t^2 \mathbf{k} + \mathbf{C}$$

where $\mathbf{C}$ is a vector constant of integration, and

$$\int_0^{\pi/2} \mathbf{r}(t)\, dt = \left[2\sin t\, \mathbf{i} - \cos t\, \mathbf{j} + t^2 \mathbf{k} \right]_0^{\pi/2} = 2\mathbf{i} + \mathbf{j} + \frac{\pi^2}{4}\mathbf{k} \qquad \square$$

14.2 EXERCISES

1. The figure shows a curve C given by a vector function $\mathbf{r}(t)$.
(a) Draw the vectors $\mathbf{r}(4.5) - \mathbf{r}(4)$ and $\mathbf{r}(4.2) - \mathbf{r}(4)$.
(b) Draw the vectors

$$\frac{\mathbf{r}(4.5) - \mathbf{r}(4)}{0.5} \quad \text{and} \quad \frac{\mathbf{r}(4.2) - \mathbf{r}(4)}{0.2}$$

(c) Write expressions for $\mathbf{r}'(4)$ and the unit tangent vector $\mathbf{T}(4)$.
(d) Draw the vector $\mathbf{T}(4)$.

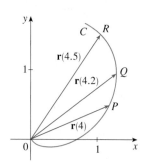

2. (a) Make a large sketch of the curve described by the vector function $\mathbf{r}(t) = \langle t^2, t \rangle$, $0 \le t \le 2$, and draw the vectors $\mathbf{r}(1)$, $\mathbf{r}(1.1)$, and $\mathbf{r}(1.1) - \mathbf{r}(1)$.

(b) Draw the vector $\mathbf{r}'(1)$ starting at $(1, 1)$ and compare it with the vector

$$\frac{\mathbf{r}(1.1) - \mathbf{r}(1)}{0.1}$$

Explain why these vectors are so close to each other in length and direction.

3–8
(a) Sketch the plane curve with the given vector equation.
(b) Find $\mathbf{r}'(t)$.
(c) Sketch the position vector $\mathbf{r}(t)$ and the tangent vector $\mathbf{r}'(t)$ for the given value of t.

3. $\mathbf{r}(t) = \langle t - 2, t^2 + 1 \rangle$, $t = -1$

4. $\mathbf{r}(t) = \langle 1 + t, \sqrt{t} \rangle$, $t = 1$

5. $\mathbf{r}(t) = \sin t\, \mathbf{i} + 2\cos t\, \mathbf{j}$, $t = \pi/4$

6. $\mathbf{r}(t) = e^t \mathbf{i} + e^{-t} \mathbf{j}$, $t = 0$

7. $\mathbf{r}(t) = e^t \mathbf{i} + e^{3t} \mathbf{j}$, $t = 0$

8. $\mathbf{r}(t) = (1 + \cos t)\, \mathbf{i} + (2 + \sin t)\, \mathbf{j}$, $t = \pi/6$

9–16 Find the derivative of the vector function.

9. $\mathbf{r}(t) = \langle t\sin t, t^2, t\cos 2t \rangle$

10. $\mathbf{r}(t) = \langle \tan t, \sec t, 1/t^2 \rangle$

11. $\mathbf{r}(t) = \mathbf{i} - \mathbf{j} + e^{4t}\mathbf{k}$

12. $\mathbf{r}(t) = \sin^{-1}t\,\mathbf{i} + \sqrt{1 - t^2}\,\mathbf{j} + \mathbf{k}$

13. $\mathbf{r}(t) = e^{t^2}\mathbf{i} - \mathbf{j} + \ln(1 + 3t)\mathbf{k}$

14. $\mathbf{r}(t) = at\cos 3t\,\mathbf{i} + b\sin^3 t\,\mathbf{j} + c\cos^3 t\,\mathbf{k}$

15. $\mathbf{r}(t) = \mathbf{a} + t\,\mathbf{b} + t^2\mathbf{c}$

16. $\mathbf{r}(t) = t\,\mathbf{a} \times (\mathbf{b} + t\,\mathbf{c})$

17–20 Find the unit tangent vector $\mathbf{T}(t)$ at the point with the given value of the parameter t.

17. $\mathbf{r}(t) = \langle te^{-t}, 2\arctan t, 2e^t \rangle, \quad t = 0$

18. $\mathbf{r}(t) = 4\sqrt{t}\,\mathbf{i} + t^2\mathbf{j} + t\,\mathbf{k}, \quad t = 1$

19. $\mathbf{r}(t) = \cos t\,\mathbf{i} + 3t\,\mathbf{j} + 2\sin 2t\,\mathbf{k}, \quad t = 0$

20. $\mathbf{r}(t) = 2\sin t\,\mathbf{i} + 2\cos t\,\mathbf{j} + \tan t\,\mathbf{k}, \quad t = \pi/4$

21. If $\mathbf{r}(t) = \langle t, t^2, t^3 \rangle$, find $\mathbf{r}'(t)$, $\mathbf{T}(1)$, $\mathbf{r}''(t)$, and $\mathbf{r}'(t) \times \mathbf{r}''(t)$.

22. If $\mathbf{r}(t) = \langle e^{2t}, e^{-2t}, te^{2t} \rangle$, find $\mathbf{T}(0)$, $\mathbf{r}''(0)$, and $\mathbf{r}'(t) \cdot \mathbf{r}''(t)$.

23–26 Find parametric equations for the tangent line to the curve with the given parametric equations at the specified point.

23. $x = 1 + 2\sqrt{t}, \quad y = t^3 - t, \quad z = t^3 + t; \quad (3, 0, 2)$

24. $x = e^t, \quad y = te^t, \quad z = te^{t^2}; \quad (1, 0, 0)$

25. $x = e^{-t}\cos t, \quad y = e^{-t}\sin t, \quad z = e^{-t}; \quad (1, 0, 1)$

26. $x = \ln t, \quad y = 2\sqrt{t}, \quad z = t^2; \quad (0, 2, 1)$

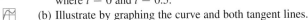 **27–29** Find parametric equations for the tangent line to the curve with the given parametric equations at the specified point. Illustrate by graphing both the curve and the tangent line on a common screen.

27. $x = t, \quad y = e^{-t}, \quad z = 2t - t^2; \quad (0, 1, 0)$

28. $x = 2\cos t, \quad y = 2\sin t, \quad z = 4\cos 2t; \quad (\sqrt{3}, 1, 2)$

29. $x = t\cos t, \quad y = t, \quad z = t\sin t; \quad (-\pi, \pi, 0)$

30. (a) Find the point of intersection of the tangent lines to the curve $\mathbf{r}(t) = \langle \sin \pi t, 2\sin \pi t, \cos \pi t \rangle$ at the points where $t = 0$ and $t = 0.5$.
 (b) Illustrate by graphing the curve and both tangent lines.

31. The curves $\mathbf{r}_1(t) = \langle t, t^2, t^3 \rangle$ and $\mathbf{r}_2(t) = \langle \sin t, \sin 2t, t \rangle$ intersect at the origin. Find their angle of intersection correct to the nearest degree.

32. At what point do the curves $\mathbf{r}_1(t) = \langle t, 1 - t, 3 + t^2 \rangle$ and $\mathbf{r}_2(s) = \langle 3 - s, s - 2, s^2 \rangle$ intersect? Find their angle of intersection correct to the nearest degree.

33–38 Evaluate the integral.

33. $\displaystyle\int_0^1 (16t^3\mathbf{i} - 9t^2\mathbf{j} + 25t^4\mathbf{k})\,dt$

34. $\displaystyle\int_0^1 \left(\frac{4}{1 + t^2}\,\mathbf{j} + \frac{2t}{1 + t^2}\,\mathbf{k}\right)dt$

35. $\displaystyle\int_0^{\pi/2} (3\sin^2 t\cos t\,\mathbf{i} + 3\sin t\cos^2 t\,\mathbf{j} + 2\sin t\cos t\,\mathbf{k})\,dt$

36. $\displaystyle\int_1^2 (t^2\mathbf{i} + t\sqrt{t - 1}\,\mathbf{j} + t\sin \pi t\,\mathbf{k})\,dt$

37. $\displaystyle\int (e^t\mathbf{i} + 2t\,\mathbf{j} + \ln t\,\mathbf{k})\,dt$

38. $\displaystyle\int (\cos \pi t\,\mathbf{i} + \sin \pi t\,\mathbf{j} + t\,\mathbf{k})\,dt$

39. Find $\mathbf{r}(t)$ if $\mathbf{r}'(t) = 2t\,\mathbf{i} + 3t^2\mathbf{j} + \sqrt{t}\,\mathbf{k}$ and $\mathbf{r}(1) = \mathbf{i} + \mathbf{j}$.

40. Find $\mathbf{r}(t)$ if $\mathbf{r}'(t) = t\,\mathbf{i} + e^t\mathbf{j} + te^t\mathbf{k}$ and $\mathbf{r}(0) = \mathbf{i} + \mathbf{j} + \mathbf{k}$.

41. Prove Formula 1 of Theorem 3.

42. Prove Formula 3 of Theorem 3.

43. Prove Formula 5 of Theorem 3.

44. Prove Formula 6 of Theorem 3.

45. If $\mathbf{u}(t) = \langle \sin t, \cos t, t \rangle$ and $\mathbf{v}(t) = \langle t, \cos t, \sin t \rangle$, use Formula 4 of Theorem 3 to find

$$\frac{d}{dt}[\mathbf{u}(t) \cdot \mathbf{v}(t)]$$

46. If $\mathbf{u}$ and $\mathbf{v}$ are the vector functions in Exercise 45, use Formula 5 of Theorem 3 to find

$$\frac{d}{dt}[\mathbf{u}(t) \times \mathbf{v}(t)]$$

47. Show that if $\mathbf{r}$ is a vector function such that $\mathbf{r}''$ exists, then

$$\frac{d}{dt}[\mathbf{r}(t) \times \mathbf{r}'(t)] = \mathbf{r}(t) \times \mathbf{r}''(t)$$

48. Find an expression for $\dfrac{d}{dt}[\mathbf{u}(t) \cdot (\mathbf{v}(t) \times \mathbf{w}(t))]$.

49. If $\mathbf{r}(t) \neq \mathbf{0}$, show that $\dfrac{d}{dt}\,|\mathbf{r}(t)| = \dfrac{1}{|\mathbf{r}(t)|}\,\mathbf{r}(t) \cdot \mathbf{r}'(t)$.

[*Hint:* $|\mathbf{r}(t)|^2 = \mathbf{r}(t) \cdot \mathbf{r}(t)$]

50. If a curve has the property that the position vector $\mathbf{r}(t)$ is always perpendicular to the tangent vector $\mathbf{r}'(t)$, show that the curve lies on a sphere with center the origin.

51. If $\mathbf{u}(t) = \mathbf{r}(t) \cdot [\mathbf{r}'(t) \times \mathbf{r}''(t)]$, show that

$$\mathbf{u}'(t) = \mathbf{r}(t) \cdot [\mathbf{r}'(t) \times \mathbf{r}'''(t)]$$

14.3 ARC LENGTH AND CURVATURE

In Section 11.2 we defined the length of a plane curve with parametric equations $x = f(t)$, $y = g(t)$, $a \leq t \leq b$, as the limit of lengths of inscribed polygons and, for the case where f' and g' are continuous, we arrived at the formula

$$\boxed{1} \qquad L = \int_a^b \sqrt{[f'(t)]^2 + [g'(t)]^2} \, dt = \int_a^b \sqrt{\left(\frac{dx}{dt}\right)^2 + \left(\frac{dy}{dt}\right)^2} \, dt$$

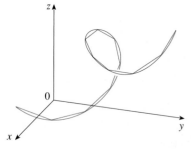

The length of a space curve is defined in exactly the same way (see Figure 1). Suppose that the curve has the vector equation $\mathbf{r}(t) = \langle f(t), g(t), h(t) \rangle$, $a \leq t \leq b$, or, equivalently, the parametric equations $x = f(t)$, $y = g(t)$, $z = h(t)$, where f', g', and h' are continuous. If the curve is traversed exactly once as t increases from a to b, then it can be shown that its length is

$$\boxed{2} \qquad L = \int_a^b \sqrt{[f'(t)]^2 + [g'(t)]^2 + [h'(t)]^2} \, dt$$
$$= \int_a^b \sqrt{\left(\frac{dx}{dt}\right)^2 + \left(\frac{dy}{dt}\right)^2 + \left(\frac{dz}{dt}\right)^2} \, dt$$

FIGURE I
The length of a space curve is the limit of lengths of inscribed polygons.

Notice that both of the arc length formulas (1) and (2) can be put into the more compact form

$$\boxed{3} \qquad L = \int_a^b |\mathbf{r}'(t)| \, dt$$

because, for plane curves $\mathbf{r}(t) = f(t)\mathbf{i} + g(t)\mathbf{j}$,

$$|\mathbf{r}'(t)| = |f'(t)\mathbf{i} + g'(t)\mathbf{j}| = \sqrt{[f'(t)]^2 + [g'(t)]^2}$$

and for space curves $\mathbf{r}(t) = f(t)\mathbf{i} + g(t)\mathbf{j} + h(t)\mathbf{k}$,

$$|\mathbf{r}'(t)| = |f'(t)\mathbf{i} + g'(t)\mathbf{j} + h'(t)\mathbf{k}| = \sqrt{[f'(t)]^2 + [g'(t)]^2 + [h'(t)]^2}$$

■ Figure 2 shows the arc of the helix whose length is computed in Example 1.

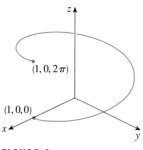

FIGURE 2

☑ **EXAMPLE I** Find the length of the arc of the circular helix with vector equation $\mathbf{r}(t) = \cos t\,\mathbf{i} + \sin t\,\mathbf{j} + t\,\mathbf{k}$ from the point $(1, 0, 0)$ to the point $(1, 0, 2\pi)$.

SOLUTION Since $\mathbf{r}'(t) = -\sin t\,\mathbf{i} + \cos t\,\mathbf{j} + \mathbf{k}$, we have

$$|\mathbf{r}'(t)| = \sqrt{(-\sin t)^2 + \cos^2 t + 1} = \sqrt{2}$$

The arc from $(1, 0, 0)$ to $(1, 0, 2\pi)$ is described by the parameter interval $0 \leq t \leq 2\pi$ and so, from Formula 3, we have

$$L = \int_0^{2\pi} |\mathbf{r}'(t)| \, dt = \int_0^{2\pi} \sqrt{2} \, dt = 2\sqrt{2}\,\pi \qquad \square$$

A single curve C can be represented by more than one vector function. For instance, the twisted cubic

$$\boxed{4} \qquad \mathbf{r}_1(t) = \langle t, t^2, t^3 \rangle \qquad 1 \leq t \leq 2$$

could also be represented by the function

$$\boxed{5} \qquad \mathbf{r}_2(u) = \langle e^u, e^{2u}, e^{3u} \rangle \qquad 0 \leqslant u \leqslant \ln 2$$

where the connection between the parameters t and u is given by $t = e^u$. We say that Equations 4 and 5 are **parametrizations** of the curve C. If we were to use Equation 3 to compute the length of C using Equations 4 and 5, we would get the same answer. In general, it can be shown that when Equation 3 is used to compute arc length, the answer is independent of the parametrization that is used.

Now we suppose that C is a curve given by a vector function

$$\mathbf{r}(t) = f(t)\mathbf{i} + g(t)\mathbf{j} + h(t)\mathbf{k} \qquad a \leqslant t \leqslant b$$

where $\mathbf{r}'$ is continuous and C is traversed exactly once as t increases from a to b. We define its **arc length function** s by

$$\boxed{6} \qquad s(t) = \int_a^t |\mathbf{r}'(u)|\, du = \int_a^t \sqrt{\left(\frac{dx}{du}\right)^2 + \left(\frac{dy}{du}\right)^2 + \left(\frac{dz}{du}\right)^2}\, du$$

Thus $s(t)$ is the length of the part of C between $\mathbf{r}(a)$ and $\mathbf{r}(t)$. (See Figure 3.) If we differentiate both sides of Equation 6 using Part 1 of the Fundamental Theorem of Calculus, we obtain

$$\boxed{7} \qquad \frac{ds}{dt} = |\mathbf{r}'(t)|$$

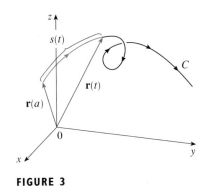

FIGURE 3

It is often useful to **parametrize a curve with respect to arc length** because arc length arises naturally from the shape of the curve and does not depend on a particular coordinate system. If a curve $\mathbf{r}(t)$ is already given in terms of a parameter t and $s(t)$ is the arc length function given by Equation 6, then we may be able to solve for t as a function of s: $t = t(s)$. Then the curve can be reparametrized in terms of s by substituting for t: $\mathbf{r} = \mathbf{r}(t(s))$. Thus, if $s = 3$ for instance, $\mathbf{r}(t(3))$ is the position vector of the point 3 units of length along the curve from its starting point.

EXAMPLE 2 Reparametrize the helix $\mathbf{r}(t) = \cos t\,\mathbf{i} + \sin t\,\mathbf{j} + t\,\mathbf{k}$ with respect to arc length measured from $(1, 0, 0)$ in the direction of increasing t.

SOLUTION The initial point $(1, 0, 0)$ corresponds to the parameter value $t = 0$. From Example 1 we have

$$\frac{ds}{dt} = |\mathbf{r}'(t)| = \sqrt{2}$$

and so

$$s = s(t) = \int_0^t |\mathbf{r}'(u)|\, du = \int_0^t \sqrt{2}\, du = \sqrt{2}\, t$$

Therefore $t = s/\sqrt{2}$ and the required reparametrization is obtained by substituting for t:

$$\mathbf{r}(t(s)) = \cos\!\left(s/\sqrt{2}\right)\mathbf{i} + \sin\!\left(s/\sqrt{2}\right)\mathbf{j} + \left(s/\sqrt{2}\right)\mathbf{k} \qquad\qquad \square$$

CURVATURE

A parametrization $\mathbf{r}(t)$ is called **smooth** on an interval I if $\mathbf{r}'$ is continuous and $\mathbf{r}'(t) \neq \mathbf{0}$ on I. A curve is called **smooth** if it has a smooth parametrization. A smooth curve has no sharp corners or cusps; when the tangent vector turns, it does so continuously.

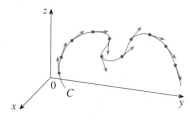

FIGURE 4

Unit tangent vectors at equally spaced points on C

TEC Visual 14.3A shows animated unit tangent vectors, like those in Figure 4, for a variety of plane curves and space curves.

If C is a smooth curve defined by the vector function $\mathbf{r}$, recall that the unit tangent vector $\mathbf{T}(t)$ is given by

$$\mathbf{T}(t) = \frac{\mathbf{r}'(t)}{|\mathbf{r}'(t)|}$$

and indicates the direction of the curve. From Figure 4 you can see that $\mathbf{T}(t)$ changes direction very slowly when C is fairly straight, but it changes direction more quickly when C bends or twists more sharply.

The curvature of C at a given point is a measure of how quickly the curve changes direction at that point. Specifically, we define it to be the magnitude of the rate of change of the unit tangent vector with respect to arc length. (We use arc length so that the curvature will be independent of the parametrization.)

---

8 DEFINITION The **curvature** of a curve is

$$\kappa = \left| \frac{d\mathbf{T}}{ds} \right|$$

where $\mathbf{T}$ is the unit tangent vector.

The curvature is easier to compute if it is expressed in terms of the parameter t instead of s, so we use the Chain Rule (Theorem 14.2.3, Formula 6) to write

$$\frac{d\mathbf{T}}{dt} = \frac{d\mathbf{T}}{ds}\frac{ds}{dt} \quad \text{and} \quad \kappa = \left| \frac{d\mathbf{T}}{ds} \right| = \left| \frac{d\mathbf{T}/dt}{ds/dt} \right|$$

But $ds/dt = |\mathbf{r}'(t)|$ from Equation 7, so

$$\boxed{\kappa(t) = \frac{|\mathbf{T}'(t)|}{|\mathbf{r}'(t)|}}$$

9

⊳ EXAMPLE 3 Show that the curvature of a circle of radius a is $1/a$.

SOLUTION We can take the circle to have center the origin, and then a parametrization is

$$\mathbf{r}(t) = a\cos t\,\mathbf{i} + a\sin t\,\mathbf{j}$$

Therefore $\mathbf{r}'(t) = -a\sin t\,\mathbf{i} + a\cos t\,\mathbf{j}$ and $|\mathbf{r}'(t)| = a$

so $$\mathbf{T}(t) = \frac{\mathbf{r}'(t)}{|\mathbf{r}'(t)|} = -\sin t\,\mathbf{i} + \cos t\,\mathbf{j}$$

and $$\mathbf{T}'(t) = -\cos t\,\mathbf{i} - \sin t\,\mathbf{j}$$

This gives $|\mathbf{T}'(t)| = 1$, so using Equation 9, we have

$$\kappa(t) = \frac{|\mathbf{T}'(t)|}{|\mathbf{r}'(t)|} = \frac{1}{a}$$ □

The result of Example 3 shows that small circles have large curvature and large circles have small curvature, in accordance with our intuition. We can see directly from the definition of curvature that the curvature of a straight line is always 0 because the tangent vector is constant.

Although Formula 9 can be used in all cases to compute the curvature, the formula given by the following theorem is often more convenient to apply.

[10] **THEOREM** The curvature of the curve given by the vector function $\mathbf{r}$ is

$$\kappa(t) = \frac{|\mathbf{r}'(t) \times \mathbf{r}''(t)|}{|\mathbf{r}'(t)|^3}$$

PROOF Since $\mathbf{T} = \mathbf{r}'/|\mathbf{r}'|$ and $|\mathbf{r}'| = ds/dt$, we have

$$\mathbf{r}' = |\mathbf{r}'|\mathbf{T} = \frac{ds}{dt}\mathbf{T}$$

so the Product Rule (Theorem 14.2.3, Formula 3) gives

$$\mathbf{r}'' = \frac{d^2s}{dt^2}\mathbf{T} + \frac{ds}{dt}\mathbf{T}'$$

Using the fact that $\mathbf{T} \times \mathbf{T} = \mathbf{0}$ (see Example 2 in Section 13.4), we have

$$\mathbf{r}' \times \mathbf{r}'' = \left(\frac{ds}{dt}\right)^2 (\mathbf{T} \times \mathbf{T}')$$

Now $|\mathbf{T}(t)| = 1$ for all t, so $\mathbf{T}$ and $\mathbf{T}'$ are orthogonal by Example 4 in Section 14.2. Therefore, by Theorem 13.4.6,

$$|\mathbf{r}' \times \mathbf{r}''| = \left(\frac{ds}{dt}\right)^2 |\mathbf{T} \times \mathbf{T}'| = \left(\frac{ds}{dt}\right)^2 |\mathbf{T}||\mathbf{T}'| = \left(\frac{ds}{dt}\right)^2 |\mathbf{T}'|$$

Thus
$$|\mathbf{T}'| = \frac{|\mathbf{r}' \times \mathbf{r}''|}{(ds/dt)^2} = \frac{|\mathbf{r}' \times \mathbf{r}''|}{|\mathbf{r}'|^2}$$

and
$$\kappa = \frac{|\mathbf{T}'|}{|\mathbf{r}'|} = \frac{|\mathbf{r}' \times \mathbf{r}''|}{|\mathbf{r}'|^3} \qquad \square$$

EXAMPLE 4 Find the curvature of the twisted cubic $\mathbf{r}(t) = \langle t, t^2, t^3 \rangle$ at a general point and at $(0, 0, 0)$.

SOLUTION We first compute the required ingredients:

$$\mathbf{r}'(t) = \langle 1, 2t, 3t^2 \rangle \qquad \mathbf{r}''(t) = \langle 0, 2, 6t \rangle$$

$$|\mathbf{r}'(t)| = \sqrt{1 + 4t^2 + 9t^4}$$

$$\mathbf{r}'(t) \times \mathbf{r}''(t) = \begin{vmatrix} \mathbf{i} & \mathbf{j} & \mathbf{k} \\ 1 & 2t & 3t^2 \\ 0 & 2 & 6t \end{vmatrix} = 6t^2\,\mathbf{i} - 6t\,\mathbf{j} + 2\,\mathbf{k}$$

$$|\mathbf{r}'(t) \times \mathbf{r}''(t)| = \sqrt{36t^4 + 36t^2 + 4} = 2\sqrt{9t^4 + 9t^2 + 1}$$

Theorem 10 then gives

$$\kappa(t) = \frac{|\mathbf{r}'(t) \times \mathbf{r}''(t)|}{|\mathbf{r}'(t)|^3} = \frac{2\sqrt{1 + 9t^2 + 9t^4}}{(1 + 4t^2 + 9t^4)^{3/2}}$$

At the origin, where $t = 0$, the curvature is $\kappa(0) = 2$.

For the special case of a plane curve with equation $y = f(x)$, we choose x as the parameter and write $\mathbf{r}(x) = x\,\mathbf{i} + f(x)\,\mathbf{j}$. Then $\mathbf{r}'(x) = \mathbf{i} + f'(x)\,\mathbf{j}$ and $\mathbf{r}''(x) = f''(x)\,\mathbf{j}$. Since $\mathbf{i} \times \mathbf{j} = \mathbf{k}$ and $\mathbf{j} \times \mathbf{j} = \mathbf{0}$, we have $\mathbf{r}'(x) \times \mathbf{r}''(x) = f''(x)\,\mathbf{k}$. We also have $|\mathbf{r}'(x)| = \sqrt{1 + [f'(x)]^2}$ and so, by Theorem 10,

11

$$\kappa(x) = \frac{|f''(x)|}{[1 + (f'(x))^2]^{3/2}}$$

EXAMPLE 5 Find the curvature of the parabola $y = x^2$ at the points $(0, 0)$, $(1, 1)$, and $(2, 4)$.

SOLUTION Since $y' = 2x$ and $y'' = 2$, Formula 11 gives

$$\kappa(x) = \frac{|y''|}{[1 + (y')^2]^{3/2}} = \frac{2}{(1 + 4x^2)^{3/2}}$$

The curvature at $(0, 0)$ is $\kappa(0) = 2$. At $(1, 1)$ it is $\kappa(1) = 2/5^{3/2} \approx 0.18$. At $(2, 4)$ it is $\kappa(2) = 2/17^{3/2} \approx 0.03$. Observe from the expression for $\kappa(x)$ or the graph of κ in Figure 5 that $\kappa(x) \to 0$ as $x \to \pm\infty$. This corresponds to the fact that the parabola appears to become flatter as $x \to \pm\infty$.

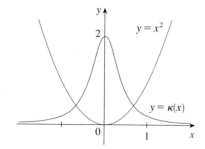

FIGURE 5
The parabola $y = x^2$ and its curvature function

THE NORMAL AND BINORMAL VECTORS

At a given point on a smooth space curve $\mathbf{r}(t)$, there are many vectors that are orthogonal to the unit tangent vector $\mathbf{T}(t)$. We single out one by observing that, because $|\mathbf{T}(t)| = 1$ for all t, we have $\mathbf{T}(t) \cdot \mathbf{T}'(t) = 0$ by Example 4 in Section 14.2, so $\mathbf{T}'(t)$ is orthogonal to $\mathbf{T}(t)$. Note that $\mathbf{T}'(t)$ is itself not a unit vector. But if $\mathbf{r}'$ is also smooth, we can define the **principal unit normal vector** $\mathbf{N}(t)$ (or simply **unit normal**) as

■ We can think of the normal vector as indicating the direction in which the curve is turning at each point.

$$\mathbf{N}(t) = \frac{\mathbf{T}'(t)}{|\mathbf{T}'(t)|}$$

The vector $\mathbf{B}(t) = \mathbf{T}(t) \times \mathbf{N}(t)$ is called the **binormal vector**. It is perpendicular to both $\mathbf{T}$ and $\mathbf{N}$ and is also a unit vector. (See Figure 6.)

FIGURE 6

EXAMPLE 6 Find the unit normal and binormal vectors for the circular helix

$$\mathbf{r}(t) = \cos t\,\mathbf{i} + \sin t\,\mathbf{j} + t\,\mathbf{k}$$

■ Figure 7 illustrates Example 6 by showing the vectors **T**, **N**, and **B** at two locations on the helix. In general, the vectors **T**, **N**, and **B**, starting at the various points on a curve, form a set of orthogonal vectors, called the **TNB** frame, that moves along the curve as t varies. This **TNB** frame plays an important role in the branch of mathematics known as differential geometry and in its applications to the motion of spacecraft.

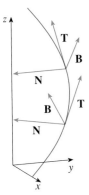

FIGURE 7

TEC Visual 14.3B shows how the TNB frame moves along several curves.

■ Figure 8 shows the helix and the osculating plane in Example 7.

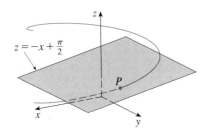

FIGURE 8

SOLUTION We first compute the ingredients needed for the unit normal vector:

$$\mathbf{r}'(t) = -\sin t\,\mathbf{i} + \cos t\,\mathbf{j} + \mathbf{k} \qquad |\mathbf{r}'(t)| = \sqrt{2}$$

$$\mathbf{T}(t) = \frac{\mathbf{r}'(t)}{|\mathbf{r}'(t)|} = \frac{1}{\sqrt{2}}(-\sin t\,\mathbf{i} + \cos t\,\mathbf{j} + \mathbf{k})$$

$$\mathbf{T}'(t) = \frac{1}{\sqrt{2}}(-\cos t\,\mathbf{i} - \sin t\,\mathbf{j}) \qquad |\mathbf{T}'(t)| = \frac{1}{\sqrt{2}}$$

$$\mathbf{N}(t) = \frac{\mathbf{T}'(t)}{|\mathbf{T}'(t)|} = -\cos t\,\mathbf{i} - \sin t\,\mathbf{j} = \langle -\cos t, -\sin t, 0 \rangle$$

This shows that the normal vector at a point on the helix is horizontal and points toward the z-axis. The binormal vector is

$$\mathbf{B}(t) = \mathbf{T}(t) \times \mathbf{N}(t) = \frac{1}{\sqrt{2}} \begin{bmatrix} \mathbf{i} & \mathbf{j} & \mathbf{k} \\ -\sin t & \cos t & 1 \\ -\cos t & -\sin t & 0 \end{bmatrix} = \frac{1}{\sqrt{2}} \langle \sin t, -\cos t, 1 \rangle \qquad \square$$

The plane determined by the normal and binormal vectors **N** and **B** at a point P on a curve C is called the **normal plane** of C at P. It consists of all lines that are orthogonal to the tangent vector **T**. The plane determined by the vectors **T** and **N** is called the **osculating plane** of C at P. The name comes from the Latin *osculum*, meaning "kiss." It is the plane that comes closest to containing the part of the curve near P. (For a plane curve, the osculating plane is simply the plane that contains the curve.)

The circle that lies in the osculating plane of C at P, has the same tangent as C at P, lies on the concave side of C (toward which **N** points), and has radius $\rho = 1/\kappa$ (the reciprocal of the curvature) is called the **osculating circle** (or the **circle of curvature**) of C at P. It is the circle that best describes how C behaves near P; it shares the same tangent, normal, and curvature at P.

▼ EXAMPLE 7 Find the equations of the normal plane and osculating plane of the helix in Example 6 at the point $P(0, 1, \pi/2)$.

SOLUTION The normal plane at P has normal vector $\mathbf{r}'(\pi/2) = \langle -1, 0, 1 \rangle$, so an equation is

$$-1(x - 0) + 0(y - 1) + 1\left(z - \frac{\pi}{2}\right) = 0 \qquad \text{or} \qquad z = x + \frac{\pi}{2}$$

The osculating plane at P contains the vectors **T** and **N**, so its normal vector is $\mathbf{T} \times \mathbf{N} = \mathbf{B}$. From Example 6 we have

$$\mathbf{B}(t) = \frac{1}{\sqrt{2}} \langle \sin t, -\cos t, 1 \rangle \qquad \mathbf{B}\left(\frac{\pi}{2}\right) = \left\langle \frac{1}{\sqrt{2}}, 0, \frac{1}{\sqrt{2}} \right\rangle$$

A simpler normal vector is $\langle 1, 0, 1 \rangle$, so an equation of the osculating plane is

$$1(x - 0) + 0(y - 1) + 1\left(z - \frac{\pi}{2}\right) = 0 \qquad \text{or} \qquad z = -x + \frac{\pi}{2} \qquad \square$$

EXAMPLE 8 Find and graph the osculating circle of the parabola $y = x^2$ at the origin.

SOLUTION From Example 5 the curvature of the parabola at the origin is $\kappa(0) = 2$. So the radius of the osculating circle at the origin is $1/\kappa = \frac{1}{2}$ and its center is $(0, \frac{1}{2})$. Its equation is therefore

$$x^2 + \left(y - \tfrac{1}{2}\right)^2 = \tfrac{1}{4}$$

For the graph in Figure 9 we use parametric equations of this circle:

$$x = \tfrac{1}{2} \cos t \qquad y = \tfrac{1}{2} + \tfrac{1}{2} \sin t$$

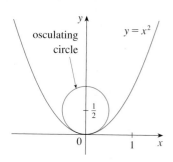

osculating circle

$y = x^2$

$\frac{1}{2}$

FIGURE 9

TEC Visual 14.3C shows how the osculating circle changes as a point moves along a curve.

We summarize here the formulas for unit tangent, unit normal and binormal vectors, and curvature.

$$\mathbf{T}(t) = \frac{\mathbf{r}'(t)}{|\mathbf{r}'(t)|} \qquad \mathbf{N}(t) = \frac{\mathbf{T}'(t)}{|\mathbf{T}'(t)|} \qquad \mathbf{B}(t) = \mathbf{T}(t) \times \mathbf{N}(t)$$

$$\kappa = \left|\frac{d\mathbf{T}}{ds}\right| = \frac{|\mathbf{T}'(t)|}{|\mathbf{r}'(t)|} = \frac{|\mathbf{r}'(t) \times \mathbf{r}''(t)|}{|\mathbf{r}'(t)|^3}$$

14.3 EXERCISES

1–6 Find the length of the curve.

1. $\mathbf{r}(t) = \langle 2 \sin t, 5t, 2 \cos t \rangle, \quad -10 \leqslant t \leqslant 10$

2. $\mathbf{r}(t) = \langle 2t, t^2, \frac{1}{3}t^3 \rangle, \quad 0 \leqslant t \leqslant 1$

3. $\mathbf{r}(t) = \sqrt{2}\,t\,\mathbf{i} + e^t\mathbf{j} + e^{-t}\mathbf{k}, \quad 0 \leqslant t \leqslant 1$

4. $\mathbf{r}(t) = \cos t\,\mathbf{i} + \sin t\,\mathbf{j} + \ln \cos t\,\mathbf{k}, \quad 0 \leqslant t \leqslant \pi/4$

5. $\mathbf{r}(t) = \mathbf{i} + t^2\mathbf{j} + t^3\mathbf{k}, \quad 0 \leqslant t \leqslant 1$

6. $\mathbf{r}(t) = 12t\,\mathbf{i} + 8t^{3/2}\,\mathbf{j} + 3t^2\mathbf{k}, \quad 0 \leqslant t \leqslant 1$

7–9 Find the length of the curve correct to four decimal places. (Use your calculator to approximate the integral.)

7. $\mathbf{r}(t) = \langle \sqrt{t}, t, t^2 \rangle, \quad 1 \leqslant t \leqslant 4$

8. $\mathbf{r}(t) = \langle t, \ln t, t \ln t \rangle, \quad 1 \leqslant t \leqslant 2$

9. $\mathbf{r}(t) = \langle \sin t, \cos t, \tan t \rangle, \quad 0 \leqslant t \leqslant \pi/4$

10. Graph the curve with parametric equations $x = \sin t$, $y = \sin 2t$, $z = \sin 3t$. Find the total length of this curve correct to four decimal places.

11. Let C be the curve of intersection of the parabolic cylinder $x^2 = 2y$ and the surface $3z = xy$. Find the exact length of C from the origin to the point $(6, 18, 36)$.

12. Find, correct to four decimal places, the length of the curve of intersection of the cylinder $4x^2 + y^2 = 4$ and the plane $x + y + z = 2$.

13–14 Reparametrize the curve with respect to arc length measured from the point where $t = 0$ in the direction of increasing t.

13. $\mathbf{r}(t) = 2t\,\mathbf{i} + (1 - 3t)\,\mathbf{j} + (5 + 4t)\,\mathbf{k}$

14. $\mathbf{r}(t) = e^{2t}\cos 2t\,\mathbf{i} + 2\,\mathbf{j} + e^{2t}\sin 2t\,\mathbf{k}$

15. Suppose you start at the point $(0, 0, 3)$ and move 5 units along the curve $x = 3 \sin t$, $y = 4t$, $z = 3 \cos t$ in the positive direction. Where are you now?

16. Reparametrize the curve

$$\mathbf{r}(t) = \left(\frac{2}{t^2 + 1} - 1\right)\mathbf{i} + \frac{2t}{t^2 + 1}\,\mathbf{j}$$

with respect to arc length measured from the point $(1, 0)$ in the direction of increasing t. Express the reparametrization in its simplest form. What can you conclude about the curve?

17–20
(a) Find the unit tangent and unit normal vectors $\mathbf{T}(t)$ and $\mathbf{N}(t)$.
(b) Use Formula 9 to find the curvature.

17. $\mathbf{r}(t) = \langle 2 \sin t, 5t, 2 \cos t \rangle$

18. $r(t) = \langle t^2, \sin t - t \cos t, \cos t + t \sin t \rangle, \quad t > 0$

19. $r(t) = \langle \sqrt{2}\, t, e^t, e^{-t} \rangle$

20. $r(t) = \langle t, \frac{1}{2} t^2, t^2 \rangle$

21–23 Use Theorem 10 to find the curvature.

21. $r(t) = t^2\, i + t\, k$

22. $r(t) = t\, i + t\, j + (1 + t^2)\, k$

23. $r(t) = 3t\, i + 4 \sin t\, j + 4 \cos t\, k$

24. Find the curvature of $r(t) = \langle e^t \cos t, e^t \sin t, t \rangle$ at the point $(1, 0, 0)$.

25. Find the curvature of $r(t) = \langle t, t^2, t^3 \rangle$ at the point $(1, 1, 1)$.

26. Graph the curve with parametric equations

$$x = t \qquad y = 4t^{3/2} \qquad z = -t^2$$

and find the curvature at the point $(1, 4, -1)$.

27–29 Use Formula 11 to find the curvature.

27. $y = 2x - x^2$ **28.** $y = \cos x$ **29.** $y = 4x^{5/2}$

30–31 At what point does the curve have maximum curvature? What happens to the curvature as $x \to \infty$?

30. $y = \ln x$ **31.** $y = e^x$

32. Find an equation of a parabola that has curvature 4 at the origin.

33. (a) Is the curvature of the curve C shown in the figure greater at P or at Q? Explain.
(b) Estimate the curvature at P and at Q by sketching the osculating circles at those points.

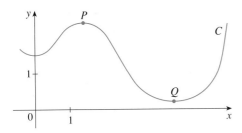

34–35 Use a graphing calculator or computer to graph both the curve and its curvature function $\kappa(x)$ on the same screen. Is the graph of κ what you would expect?

34. $y = x^4 - 2x^2$ **35.** $y = x^{-2}$

36–37 Two graphs, a and b, are shown. One is a curve $y = f(x)$ and the other is the graph of its curvature function $y = \kappa(x)$. Identify each curve and explain your choices.

36.   **37.**

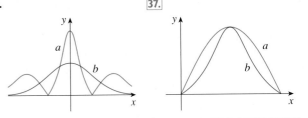

38. (a) Graph the curve $r(t) = \langle \sin 3t, \sin 2t, \sin 3t \rangle$. At how many points on the curve does it appear that the curvature has a local or absolute maximum?
(b) Use a CAS to find and graph the curvature function. Does this graph confirm your conclusion from part (a)?

39. The graph of $r(t) = \langle t - \frac{3}{2} \sin t, 1 - \frac{3}{2} \cos t, t \rangle$ is shown in Figure 12(b) in Section 14.1. Where do you think the curvature is largest? Use a CAS to find and graph the curvature function. For which values of t is the curvature largest?

40. Use Theorem 10 to show that the curvature of a plane parametric curve $x = f(t)$, $y = g(t)$ is

$$\kappa = \frac{|\dot{x}\ddot{y} - \dot{y}\ddot{x}|}{[\dot{x}^2 + \dot{y}^2]^{3/2}}$$

where the dots indicate derivatives with respect to t.

41–42 Use the formula in Exercise 40 to find the curvature.

41. $x = e^t \cos t, \quad y = e^t \sin t$

42. $x = 1 + t^3, \quad y = t + t^2$

43–44 Find the vectors T, N, and B at the given point.

43. $r(t) = \langle t^2, \frac{2}{3} t^3, t \rangle, \quad (1, \frac{2}{3}, 1)$

44. $r(t) = \langle \cos t, \sin t, \ln \cos t \rangle, \quad (1, 0, 0)$

45–46 Find equations of the normal plane and osculating plane of the curve at the given point.

45. $x = 2 \sin 3t, \quad y = t, \quad z = 2 \cos 3t; \quad (0, \pi, -2)$

46. $x = t, \quad y = t^2, \quad z = t^3; \quad (1, 1, 1)$

47. Find equations of the osculating circles of the ellipse $9x^2 + 4y^2 = 36$ at the points $(2, 0)$ and $(0, 3)$. Use a graphing calculator or computer to graph the ellipse and both osculating circles on the same screen.

48. Find equations of the osculating circles of the parabola $y = \frac{1}{2}x^2$ at the points $(0, 0)$ and $(1, \frac{1}{2})$. Graph both osculating circles and the parabola on the same screen.

49. At what point on the curve $x = t^3$, $y = 3t$, $z = t^4$ is the normal plane parallel to the plane $6x + 6y - 8z = 1$?

CAS 50. Is there a point on the curve in Exercise 49 where the osculating plane is parallel to the plane $x + y + z = 1$? [*Note:* You will need a CAS for differentiating, for simplifying, and for computing a cross product.]

51. Show that the curvature κ is related to the tangent and normal vectors by the equation

$$\frac{d\mathbf{T}}{ds} = \kappa \mathbf{N}$$

52. Show that the curvature of a plane curve is $\kappa = |d\phi/ds|$, where ϕ is the angle between $\mathbf{T}$ and $\mathbf{i}$; that is, ϕ is the angle of inclination of the tangent line. (This shows that the definition of curvature is consistent with the definition for plane curves given in Exercise 69 in Section 11.2.)

53. (a) Show that $d\mathbf{B}/ds$ is perpendicular to $\mathbf{B}$.
(b) Show that $d\mathbf{B}/ds$ is perpendicular to $\mathbf{T}$.
(c) Deduce from parts (a) and (b) that $d\mathbf{B}/ds = -\tau(s)\mathbf{N}$ for some number $\tau(s)$ called the **torsion** of the curve. (The torsion measures the degree of twisting of a curve.)
(d) Show that for a plane curve the torsion is $\tau(s) = 0$.

54. The following formulas, called the **Frenet-Serret formulas**, are of fundamental importance in differential geometry:

1. $d\mathbf{T}/ds = \kappa \mathbf{N}$
2. $d\mathbf{N}/ds = -\kappa \mathbf{T} + \tau \mathbf{B}$
3. $d\mathbf{B}/ds = -\tau \mathbf{N}$

(Formula 1 comes from Exercise 51 and Formula 3 comes from Exercise 53.) Use the fact that $\mathbf{N} = \mathbf{B} \times \mathbf{T}$ to deduce Formula 2 from Formulas 1 and 3.

55. Use the Frenet-Serret formulas to prove each of the following. (Primes denote derivatives with respect to t. Start as in the proof of Theorem 10.)
(a) $\mathbf{r}'' = s''\mathbf{T} + \kappa(s')^2\mathbf{N}$ (b) $\mathbf{r}' \times \mathbf{r}'' = \kappa(s')^3\mathbf{B}$
(c) $\mathbf{r}''' = [s''' - \kappa^2(s')^3]\mathbf{T} + [3\kappa s's'' + \kappa'(s')^2]\mathbf{N} + \kappa\tau(s')^3\mathbf{B}$
(d) $\tau = \dfrac{(\mathbf{r}' \times \mathbf{r}'') \cdot \mathbf{r}'''}{|\mathbf{r}' \times \mathbf{r}''|^2}$

56. Show that the circular helix $\mathbf{r}(t) = \langle a \cos t, a \sin t, bt \rangle$, where a and b are positive constants, has constant curvature and constant torsion. [Use the result of Exercise 55(d).]

57. Use the formula in Exercise 55(d) to find the torsion of the curve $\mathbf{r}(t) = \langle t, \frac{1}{2}t^2, \frac{1}{3}t^3 \rangle$.

58. Find the curvature and torsion of the curve $x = \sinh t$, $y = \cosh t$, $z = t$ at the point $(0, 1, 0)$.

59. The DNA molecule has the shape of a double helix (see Figure 3 on page 855). The radius of each helix is about 10 angstroms ($1 \, Å = 10^{-8}$ cm). Each helix rises about 34 Å during each complete turn, and there are about 2.9×10^8 complete turns. Estimate the length of each helix.

60. Let's consider the problem of designing a railroad track to make a smooth transition between sections of straight track. Existing track along the negative x-axis is to be joined smoothly to a track along the line $y = 1$ for $x \geqslant 1$.
(a) Find a polynomial $P = P(x)$ of degree 5 such that the function F defined by

$$F(x) = \begin{cases} 0 & \text{if } x \leqslant 0 \\ P(x) & \text{if } 0 < x < 1 \\ 1 & \text{if } x \geqslant 1 \end{cases}$$

is continuous and has continuous slope and continuous curvature.
(b) Use a graphing calculator or computer to draw the graph of F.

14.4 MOTION IN SPACE: VELOCITY AND ACCELERATION

In this section we show how the ideas of tangent and normal vectors and curvature can be used in physics to study the motion of an object, including its velocity and acceleration, along a space curve. In particular, we follow in the footsteps of Newton by using these methods to derive Kepler's First Law of planetary motion.

Suppose a particle moves through space so that its position vector at time t is $\mathbf{r}(t)$. Notice from Figure 1 that, for small values of h, the vector

$$\boxed{1} \qquad \frac{\mathbf{r}(t + h) - \mathbf{r}(t)}{h}$$

approximates the direction of the particle moving along the curve $\mathbf{r}(t)$. Its magnitude measures the size of the displacement vector per unit time. The vector (1) gives the average

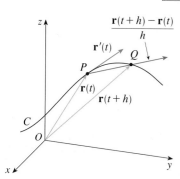

FIGURE I

velocity over a time interval of length h and its limit is the **velocity vector** $\mathbf{v}(t)$ at time t:

$$\boxed{\mathbf{v}(t) = \lim_{h \to 0} \frac{\mathbf{r}(t + h) - \mathbf{r}(t)}{h} = \mathbf{r}'(t)}$$

2

Thus the velocity vector is also the tangent vector and points in the direction of the tangent line.

The **speed** of the particle at time t is the magnitude of the velocity vector, that is, $|\mathbf{v}(t)|$. This is appropriate because, from (2) and from Equation 14.3.7, we have

$$|\mathbf{v}(t)| = |\mathbf{r}'(t)| = \frac{ds}{dt} = \text{rate of change of distance with respect to time}$$

As in the case of one-dimensional motion, the **acceleration** of the particle is defined as the derivative of the velocity:

$$\mathbf{a}(t) = \mathbf{v}'(t) = \mathbf{r}''(t)$$

EXAMPLE 1 The position vector of an object moving in a plane is given by $\mathbf{r}(t) = t^3\,\mathbf{i} + t^2\,\mathbf{j}$. Find its velocity, speed, and acceleration when $t = 1$ and illustrate geometrically.

SOLUTION The velocity and acceleration at time t are

$$\mathbf{v}(t) = \mathbf{r}'(t) = 3t^2\,\mathbf{i} + 2t\,\mathbf{j}$$

$$\mathbf{a}(t) = \mathbf{r}''(t) = 6t\,\mathbf{i} + 2\,\mathbf{j}$$

and the speed is

$$|\mathbf{v}(t)| = \sqrt{(3t^2)^2 + (2t)^2} = \sqrt{9t^4 + 4t^2}$$

When $t = 1$, we have

$$\mathbf{v}(1) = 3\,\mathbf{i} + 2\,\mathbf{j} \qquad \mathbf{a}(1) = 6\,\mathbf{i} + 2\,\mathbf{j} \qquad |\mathbf{v}(1)| = \sqrt{13}$$

These velocity and acceleration vectors are shown in Figure 2. ☐

EXAMPLE 2 Find the velocity, acceleration, and speed of a particle with position vector $\mathbf{r}(t) = \langle t^2, e^t, te^t \rangle$.

SOLUTION

$$\mathbf{v}(t) = \mathbf{r}'(t) = \langle 2t, e^t, (1 + t)e^t \rangle$$

$$\mathbf{a}(t) = \mathbf{v}'(t) = \langle 2, e^t, (2 + t)e^t \rangle$$

$$|\mathbf{v}(t)| = \sqrt{4t^2 + e^{2t} + (1 + t)^2 e^{2t}}$$ ☐

The vector integrals that were introduced in Section 14.2 can be used to find position vectors when velocity or acceleration vectors are known, as in the next example.

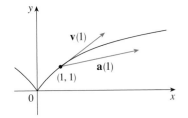

FIGURE 2

TEC Visual 14.4 shows animated velocity and acceleration vectors for objects moving along various curves.

■ Figure 3 shows the path of the particle in Example 2 with the velocity and acceleration vectors when $t = 1$.

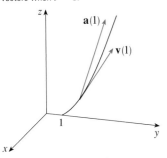

FIGURE 3

☑ EXAMPLE 3 A moving particle starts at an initial position $\mathbf{r}(0) = \langle 1, 0, 0 \rangle$ with initial velocity $\mathbf{v}(0) = \mathbf{i} - \mathbf{j} + \mathbf{k}$. Its acceleration is $\mathbf{a}(t) = 4t\,\mathbf{i} + 6t\,\mathbf{j} + \mathbf{k}$. Find its velocity and position at time t.

SOLUTION Since $\mathbf{a}(t) = \mathbf{v}'(t)$, we have

$$\mathbf{v}(t) = \int \mathbf{a}(t)\, dt = \int (4t\,\mathbf{i} + 6t\,\mathbf{j} + \mathbf{k})\, dt$$

$$= 2t^2\,\mathbf{i} + 3t^2\,\mathbf{j} + t\,\mathbf{k} + \mathbf{C}$$

To determine the value of the constant vector $\mathbf{C}$, we use the fact that $\mathbf{v}(0) = \mathbf{i} - \mathbf{j} + \mathbf{k}$. The preceding equation gives $\mathbf{v}(0) = \mathbf{C}$, so $\mathbf{C} = \mathbf{i} - \mathbf{j} + \mathbf{k}$ and

$$\mathbf{v}(t) = 2t^2\,\mathbf{i} + 3t^2\,\mathbf{j} + t\,\mathbf{k} + \mathbf{i} - \mathbf{j} + \mathbf{k}$$

$$= (2t^2 + 1)\,\mathbf{i} + (3t^2 - 1)\,\mathbf{j} + (t + 1)\,\mathbf{k}$$

Since $\mathbf{v}(t) = \mathbf{r}'(t)$, we have

$$\mathbf{r}(t) = \int \mathbf{v}(t)\, dt$$

$$= \int [(2t^2 + 1)\,\mathbf{i} + (3t^2 - 1)\,\mathbf{j} + (t + 1)\,\mathbf{k}]\, dt$$

$$= \left(\tfrac{2}{3}t^3 + t\right)\mathbf{i} + (t^3 - t)\,\mathbf{j} + \left(\tfrac{1}{2}t^2 + t\right)\mathbf{k} + \mathbf{D}$$

■ The expression for $\mathbf{r}(t)$ that we obtained in Example 3 was used to plot the path of the particle in Figure 4 for $0 \leqslant t \leqslant 3$.

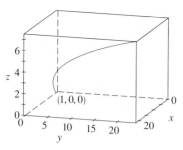

FIGURE 4

Putting $t = 0$, we find that $\mathbf{D} = \mathbf{r}(0) = \mathbf{i}$, so the position at time t is given by

$$\mathbf{r}(t) = \left(\tfrac{2}{3}t^3 + t + 1\right)\mathbf{i} + (t^3 - t)\,\mathbf{j} + \left(\tfrac{1}{2}t^2 + t\right)\mathbf{k}   \qquad \square$$

In general, vector integrals allow us to recover velocity when acceleration is known and position when velocity is known:

$$\mathbf{v}(t) = \mathbf{v}(t_0) + \int_{t_0}^{t} \mathbf{a}(u)\, du \qquad\qquad \mathbf{r}(t) = \mathbf{r}(t_0) + \int_{t_0}^{t} \mathbf{v}(u)\, du$$

If the force that acts on a particle is known, then the acceleration can be found from **Newton's Second Law of Motion**. The vector version of this law states that if, at any time t, a force $\mathbf{F}(t)$ acts on an object of mass m producing an acceleration $\mathbf{a}(t)$, then

$$\mathbf{F}(t) = m\mathbf{a}(t)$$

■ The angular speed of the object moving with position P is $\omega = d\theta/dt$, where θ is the angle shown in Figure 5.

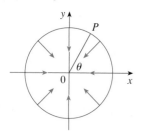

FIGURE 5

EXAMPLE 4 An object with mass m that moves in a circular path with constant angular speed ω has position vector $\mathbf{r}(t) = a \cos \omega t\,\mathbf{i} + a \sin \omega t\,\mathbf{j}$. Find the force acting on the object and show that it is directed toward the origin.

SOLUTION To find the force, we first need to know the acceleration:

$$\mathbf{v}(t) = \mathbf{r}'(t) = -a\omega \sin \omega t\,\mathbf{i} + a\omega \cos \omega t\,\mathbf{j}$$

$$\mathbf{a}(t) = \mathbf{v}'(t) = -a\omega^2 \cos \omega t\,\mathbf{i} - a\omega^2 \sin \omega t\,\mathbf{j}$$

Therefore Newton's Second Law gives the force as

$$\mathbf{F}(t) = m\mathbf{a}(t) = -m\omega^2(a \cos \omega t\,\mathbf{i} + a \sin \omega t\,\mathbf{j})$$

Notice that $\mathbf{F}(t) = -m\omega^2\mathbf{r}(t)$. This shows that the force acts in the direction opposite to the radius vector $\mathbf{r}(t)$ and therefore points toward the origin (see Figure 5). Such a force is called a *centripetal* (center-seeking) force. ◻

▼ EXAMPLE 5 A projectile is fired with angle of elevation α and initial velocity $\mathbf{v}_0$. (See Figure 6.) Assuming that air resistance is negligible and the only external force is due to gravity, find the position function $\mathbf{r}(t)$ of the projectile. What value of α maximizes the range (the horizontal distance traveled)?

SOLUTION We set up the axes so that the projectile starts at the origin. Since the force due to gravity acts downward, we have

$$\mathbf{F} = m\mathbf{a} = -mg\,\mathbf{j}$$

where $g = |\mathbf{a}| \approx 9.8 \text{ m/s}^2$. Thus

$$\mathbf{a} = -g\,\mathbf{j}$$

Since $\mathbf{v}'(t) = \mathbf{a}$, we have

$$\mathbf{v}(t) = -gt\,\mathbf{j} + \mathbf{C}$$

where $\mathbf{C} = \mathbf{v}(0) = \mathbf{v}_0$. Therefore

$$\mathbf{r}'(t) = \mathbf{v}(t) = -gt\,\mathbf{j} + \mathbf{v}_0$$

Integrating again, we obtain

$$\mathbf{r}(t) = -\tfrac{1}{2}gt^2\,\mathbf{j} + t\,\mathbf{v}_0 + \mathbf{D}$$

But $\mathbf{D} = \mathbf{r}(0) = \mathbf{0}$, so the position vector of the projectile is given by

$$\boxed{3} \qquad \mathbf{r}(t) = -\tfrac{1}{2}gt^2\,\mathbf{j} + t\,\mathbf{v}_0$$

If we write $|\mathbf{v}_0| = v_0$ (the initial speed of the projectile), then

$$\mathbf{v}_0 = v_0\cos\alpha\,\mathbf{i} + v_0\sin\alpha\,\mathbf{j}$$

and Equation 3 becomes

$$\mathbf{r}(t) = (v_0\cos\alpha)t\,\mathbf{i} + \left[(v_0\sin\alpha)t - \tfrac{1}{2}gt^2\right]\mathbf{j}$$

The parametric equations of the trajectory are therefore

$$\boxed{4} \qquad x = (v_0\cos\alpha)t \qquad y = (v_0\sin\alpha)t - \tfrac{1}{2}gt^2$$

The horizontal distance d is the value of x when $y = 0$. Setting $y = 0$, we obtain $t = 0$ or $t = (2v_0\sin\alpha)/g$. This second value of t then gives

$$d = x = (v_0\cos\alpha)\,\frac{2v_0\sin\alpha}{g} = \frac{v_0^2(2\sin\alpha\cos\alpha)}{g} = \frac{v_0^2\sin 2\alpha}{g}$$

Clearly, d has its maximum value when $\sin 2\alpha = 1$, that is, $\alpha = \pi/4$. ◻

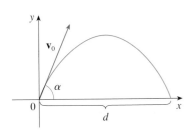

FIGURE 6

▪ If you eliminate t from Equations 4, you will see that y is a quadratic function of x. So the path of the projectile is part of a parabola.

☑ EXAMPLE 6 A projectile is fired with muzzle speed 150 m/s and angle of elevation 45° from a position 10 m above ground level. Where does the projectile hit the ground, and with what speed?

SOLUTION If we place the origin at ground level, then the initial position of the projectile is (0, 10) and so we need to adjust Equations 4 by adding 10 to the expression for y. With $v_0 = 150$ m/s, $\alpha = 45°$, and $g = 9.8$ m/s², we have

$$x = 150 \cos(\pi/4)t = 75\sqrt{2}\,t$$

$$y = 10 + 150 \sin(\pi/4)t - \tfrac{1}{2}(9.8)t^2 = 10 + 75\sqrt{2}\,t - 4.9t^2$$

Impact occurs when $y = 0$, that is, $4.9t^2 - 75\sqrt{2}t - 10 = 0$. Solving this quadratic equation (and using only the positive value of t), we get

$$t = \frac{75\sqrt{2} + \sqrt{11{,}250 + 196}}{9.8} \approx 21.74$$

Then $x \approx 75\sqrt{2}\,(21.74) \approx 2306$, so the projectile hits the ground about 2306 m away.

The velocity of the projectile is

$$v(t) = r'(t) = 75\sqrt{2}\,\mathbf{i} + \left(75\sqrt{2} - 9.8t\right)\mathbf{j}$$

So its speed at impact is

$$|v(21.74)| = \sqrt{(75\sqrt{2})^2 + (75\sqrt{2} - 9.8 \cdot 21.74)^2} \approx 151 \text{ m/s} \qquad \square$$

TANGENTIAL AND NORMAL COMPONENTS OF ACCELERATION

When we study the motion of a particle, it is often useful to resolve the acceleration into two components, one in the direction of the tangent and the other in the direction of the normal. If we write $v = |\mathbf{v}|$ for the speed of the particle, then

$$\mathbf{T}(t) = \frac{\mathbf{r}'(t)}{|\mathbf{r}'(t)|} = \frac{\mathbf{v}(t)}{|\mathbf{v}(t)|} = \frac{\mathbf{v}}{v}$$

and so

$$\mathbf{v} = v\mathbf{T}$$

If we differentiate both sides of this equation with respect to t, we get

$$\boxed{5} \qquad \mathbf{a} = \mathbf{v}' = v'\mathbf{T} + v\mathbf{T}'$$

If we use the expression for the curvature given by Equation 14.3.9, then we have

$$\boxed{6} \qquad \kappa = \frac{|\mathbf{T}'|}{|\mathbf{r}'|} = \frac{|\mathbf{T}'|}{v} \qquad \text{so} \qquad |\mathbf{T}'| = \kappa v$$

The unit normal vector was defined in the preceding section as $\mathbf{N} = \mathbf{T}'/|\mathbf{T}'|$, so (6) gives

$$\mathbf{T}' = |\mathbf{T}'|\mathbf{N} = \kappa v \mathbf{N}$$

and Equation 5 becomes

$$\boxed{7} \qquad \boxed{\mathbf{a} = v'\mathbf{T} + \kappa v^2 \mathbf{N}}$$

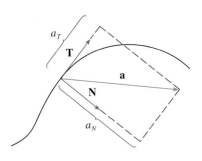

FIGURE 7

Writing a_T and a_N for the tangential and normal components of acceleration, we have

$$\mathbf{a} = a_T \mathbf{T} + a_N \mathbf{N}$$

where

$$\boxed{8} \qquad\qquad a_T = v' \quad \text{and} \quad a_N = \kappa v^2$$

This resolution is illustrated in Figure 7.

Let's look at what Formula 7 says. The first thing to notice is that the binormal vector **B** is absent. No matter how an object moves through space, its acceleration always lies in the plane of **T** and **N** (the osculating plane). (Recall that **T** gives the direction of motion and **N** points in the direction the curve is turning.) Next we notice that the tangential component of acceleration is v', the rate of change of speed, and the normal component of acceleration is κv^2, the curvature times the square of the speed. This makes sense if we think of a passenger in a car—a sharp turn in a road means a large value of the curvature κ, so the component of the acceleration perpendicular to the motion is large and the passenger is thrown against a car door. High speed around the turn has the same effect; in fact, if you double your speed, a_N is increased by a factor of 4.

Although we have expressions for the tangential and normal components of acceleration in Equations 8, it's desirable to have expressions that depend only on **r**, **r'**, and **r''**. To this end we take the dot product of $\mathbf{v} = v\mathbf{T}$ with **a** as given by Equation 7:

$$\mathbf{v} \cdot \mathbf{a} = v\mathbf{T} \cdot (v'\mathbf{T} + \kappa v^2 \mathbf{N})$$

$$= vv'\mathbf{T} \cdot \mathbf{T} + \kappa v^3 \mathbf{T} \cdot \mathbf{N}$$

$$= vv' \qquad\qquad \text{(since } \mathbf{T} \cdot \mathbf{T} = 1 \text{ and } \mathbf{T} \cdot \mathbf{N} = 0 \text{)}$$

Therefore

$$\boxed{9} \qquad\qquad a_T = v' = \frac{\mathbf{v} \cdot \mathbf{a}}{v} = \frac{\mathbf{r}'(t) \cdot \mathbf{r}''(t)}{|\mathbf{r}'(t)|}$$

Using the formula for curvature given by Theorem 14.3.10, we have

$$\boxed{10} \qquad a_N = \kappa v^2 = \frac{|\mathbf{r}'(t) \times \mathbf{r}''(t)|}{|\mathbf{r}'(t)|^3} |\mathbf{r}'(t)|^2 = \frac{|\mathbf{r}'(t) \times \mathbf{r}''(t)|}{|\mathbf{r}'(t)|}$$

EXAMPLE 7 A particle moves with position function $\mathbf{r}(t) = \langle t^2, t^2, t^3 \rangle$. Find the tangential and normal components of acceleration.

SOLUTION

$$\mathbf{r}(t) = t^2 \mathbf{i} + t^2 \mathbf{j} + t^3 \mathbf{k}$$

$$\mathbf{r}'(t) = 2t\,\mathbf{i} + 2t\,\mathbf{j} + 3t^2 \mathbf{k}$$

$$\mathbf{r}''(t) = 2\mathbf{i} + 2\mathbf{j} + 6t\,\mathbf{k}$$

$$|\mathbf{r}'(t)| = \sqrt{8t^2 + 9t^4}$$

Therefore Equation 9 gives the tangential component as

$$a_T = \frac{\mathbf{r}'(t) \cdot \mathbf{r}''(t)}{|\mathbf{r}'(t)|} = \frac{8t + 18t^3}{\sqrt{8t^2 + 9t^4}}$$

Since
$$\mathbf{r}'(t) \times \mathbf{r}''(t) = \begin{vmatrix} \mathbf{i} & \mathbf{j} & \mathbf{k} \\ 2t & 2t & 3t^2 \\ 2 & 2 & 6t \end{vmatrix} = 6t^2\,\mathbf{i} - 6t^2\,\mathbf{j}$$

Equation 10 gives the normal component as

$$a_N = \frac{|\mathbf{r}'(t) \times \mathbf{r}''(t)|}{|\mathbf{r}'(t)|} = \frac{6\sqrt{2}\,t^2}{\sqrt{8t^2 + 9t^4}}$$ □

KEPLER'S LAWS OF PLANETARY MOTION

We now describe one of the great accomplishments of calculus by showing how the material of this chapter can be used to prove Kepler's laws of planetary motion. After 20 years of studying the astronomical observations of the Danish astronomer Tycho Brahe, the German mathematician and astronomer Johannes Kepler (1571–1630) formulated the following three laws.

KEPLER'S LAWS

1. A planet revolves around the sun in an elliptical orbit with the sun at one focus.

2. The line joining the sun to a planet sweeps out equal areas in equal times.

3. The square of the period of revolution of a planet is proportional to the cube of the length of the major axis of its orbit.

In his book *Principia Mathematica* of 1687, Sir Isaac Newton was able to show that these three laws are consequences of two of his own laws, the Second Law of Motion and the Law of Universal Gravitation. In what follows we prove Kepler's First Law. The remaining laws are proved as exercises (with hints).

Since the gravitational force of the sun on a planet is so much larger than the forces exerted by other celestial bodies, we can safely ignore all bodies in the universe except the sun and one planet revolving about it. We use a coordinate system with the sun at the origin and we let $\mathbf{r} = \mathbf{r}(t)$ be the position vector of the planet. (Equally well, $\mathbf{r}$ could be the position vector of the moon or a satellite moving around the earth or a comet moving around a star.) The velocity vector is $\mathbf{v} = \mathbf{r}'$ and the acceleration vector is $\mathbf{a} = \mathbf{r}''$. We use the following laws of Newton:

Second Law of Motion: $\mathbf{F} = m\mathbf{a}$

Law of Gravitation: $\mathbf{F} = -\dfrac{GMm}{r^3}\,\mathbf{r} = -\dfrac{GMm}{r^2}\,\mathbf{u}$

where $\mathbf{F}$ is the gravitational force on the planet, m and M are the masses of the planet and the sun, G is the gravitational constant, $r = |\mathbf{r}|$, and $\mathbf{u} = (1/r)\mathbf{r}$ is the unit vector in the direction of $\mathbf{r}$.

We first show that the planet moves in one plane. By equating the expressions for $\mathbf{F}$ in Newton's two laws, we find that

$$\mathbf{a} = -\frac{GM}{r^3}\,\mathbf{r}$$

and so **a** is parallel to **r**. It follows that $\mathbf{r} \times \mathbf{a} = \mathbf{0}$. We use Formula 5 in Theorem 14.2.3 to write

$$\frac{d}{dt}(\mathbf{r} \times \mathbf{v}) = \mathbf{r}' \times \mathbf{v} + \mathbf{r} \times \mathbf{v}'$$

$$= \mathbf{v} \times \mathbf{v} + \mathbf{r} \times \mathbf{a} = \mathbf{0} + \mathbf{0} = \mathbf{0}$$

Therefore $$\mathbf{r} \times \mathbf{v} = \mathbf{h}$$

where **h** is a constant vector. (We may assume that $\mathbf{h} \neq \mathbf{0}$; that is, **r** and **v** are not parallel.) This means that the vector $\mathbf{r} = \mathbf{r}(t)$ is perpendicular to **h** for all values of t, so the planet always lies in the plane through the origin perpendicular to **h**. Thus the orbit of the planet is a plane curve.

To prove Kepler's First Law we rewrite the vector **h** as follows:

$$\mathbf{h} = \mathbf{r} \times \mathbf{v} = \mathbf{r} \times \mathbf{r}' = r\mathbf{u} \times (r\mathbf{u})'$$

$$= r\mathbf{u} \times (r\mathbf{u}' + r'\mathbf{u}) = r^2(\mathbf{u} \times \mathbf{u}') + rr'(\mathbf{u} \times \mathbf{u})$$

$$= r^2(\mathbf{u} \times \mathbf{u}')$$

Then

$$\mathbf{a} \times \mathbf{h} = \frac{-GM}{r^2}\mathbf{u} \times (r^2\mathbf{u} \times \mathbf{u}') = -GM\,\mathbf{u} \times (\mathbf{u} \times \mathbf{u}')$$

$$= -GM[(\mathbf{u} \cdot \mathbf{u}')\mathbf{u} - (\mathbf{u} \cdot \mathbf{u})\mathbf{u}'] \qquad \text{(by Theorem 13.4.8, Property 6)}$$

But $\mathbf{u} \cdot \mathbf{u} = |\mathbf{u}|^2 = 1$ and, since $|\mathbf{u}(t)| = 1$, it follows from Example 4 in Section 14.2 that $\mathbf{u} \cdot \mathbf{u}' = 0$. Therefore

$$\mathbf{a} \times \mathbf{h} = GM\,\mathbf{u}'$$

and so $$(\mathbf{v} \times \mathbf{h})' = \mathbf{v}' \times \mathbf{h} = \mathbf{a} \times \mathbf{h} = GM\,\mathbf{u}'$$

Integrating both sides of this equation, we get

$$\boxed{11} \qquad\qquad \mathbf{v} \times \mathbf{h} = GM\,\mathbf{u} + \mathbf{c}$$

where **c** is a constant vector.

At this point it is convenient to choose the coordinate axes so that the standard basis vector **k** points in the direction of the vector **h**. Then the planet moves in the xy-plane. Since both $\mathbf{v} \times \mathbf{h}$ and **u** are perpendicular to **h**, Equation 11 shows that **c** lies in the xy-plane. This means that we can choose the x- and y-axes so that the vector **i** lies in the direction of **c**, as shown in Figure 8.

If θ is the angle between **c** and **r**, then (r, θ) are polar coordinates of the planet. From Equation 11 we have

$$\mathbf{r} \cdot (\mathbf{v} \times \mathbf{h}) = \mathbf{r} \cdot (GM\,\mathbf{u} + \mathbf{c}) = GM\,\mathbf{r} \cdot \mathbf{u} + \mathbf{r} \cdot \mathbf{c}$$

$$= GMr\,\mathbf{u} \cdot \mathbf{u} + |\mathbf{r}||\mathbf{c}|\cos\theta = GMr + rc\cos\theta$$

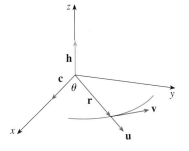

FIGURE 8

where $c = |\mathbf{c}|$. Then

$$r = \frac{\mathbf{r} \cdot (\mathbf{v} \times \mathbf{h})}{GM + c \cos \theta} = \frac{1}{GM} \frac{\mathbf{r} \cdot (\mathbf{v} \times \mathbf{h})}{1 + e \cos \theta}$$

where $e = c/(GM)$. But

$$\mathbf{r} \cdot (\mathbf{v} \times \mathbf{h}) = (\mathbf{r} \times \mathbf{v}) \cdot \mathbf{h} = \mathbf{h} \cdot \mathbf{h} = |\mathbf{h}|^2 = h^2$$

where $h = |\mathbf{h}|$. So

$$r = \frac{h^2/(GM)}{1 + e \cos \theta} = \frac{eh^2/c}{1 + e \cos \theta}$$

Writing $d = h^2/c$, we obtain the equation

$$\boxed{12} \qquad r = \frac{ed}{1 + e \cos \theta}$$

Comparing with Theorem 11.6.6, we see that Equation 12 is the polar equation of a conic section with focus at the origin and eccentricity e. We know that the orbit of a planet is a closed curve and so the conic must be an ellipse.

This completes the derivation of Kepler's First Law. We will guide you through the derivation of the Second and Third Laws in the Applied Project on page 884. The proofs of these three laws show that the methods of this chapter provide a powerful tool for describing some of the laws of nature.

14.4 EXERCISES

1. The table gives coordinates of a particle moving through space along a smooth curve.
   (a) Find the average velocities over the time intervals [0, 1], [0.5, 1], [1, 2], and [1, 1.5].
   (b) Estimate the velocity and speed of the particle at $t = 1$.

t	x	y	z
0	2.7	9.8	3.7
0.5	3.5	7.2	3.3
1.0	4.5	6.0	3.0
1.5	5.9	6.4	2.8
2.0	7.3	7.8	2.7

2. The figure shows the path of a particle that moves with position vector $\mathbf{r}(t)$ at time t.
   (a) Draw a vector that represents the average velocity of the particle over the time interval $2 \leqslant t \leqslant 2.4$.
   (b) Draw a vector that represents the average velocity over the time interval $1.5 \leqslant t \leqslant 2$.
   (c) Write an expression for the velocity vector $\mathbf{v}(2)$.

(d) Draw an approximation to the vector $\mathbf{v}(2)$ and estimate the speed of the particle at $t = 2$.

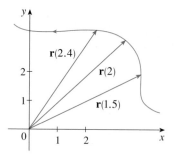

3–8 Find the velocity, acceleration, and speed of a particle with the given position function. Sketch the path of the particle and draw the velocity and acceleration vectors for the specified value of t.

3. $\mathbf{r}(t) = \langle -\frac{1}{2}t^2, t \rangle$, $t = 2$

4. $\mathbf{r}(t) = \langle 2 - t, 4\sqrt{t} \rangle$, $t = 1$

5. $\mathbf{r}(t) = 3 \cos t \, \mathbf{i} + 2 \sin t \, \mathbf{j}, \quad t = \pi/3$

6. $\mathbf{r}(t) = e^t \mathbf{i} + e^{2t} \mathbf{j}, \quad t = 0$

7. $\mathbf{r}(t) = t \, \mathbf{i} + t^2 \mathbf{j} + 2 \, \mathbf{k}, \quad t = 1$

8. $\mathbf{r}(t) = t \, \mathbf{i} + 2 \cos t \, \mathbf{j} + \sin t \, \mathbf{k}, \quad t = 0$

9–14 Find the velocity, acceleration, and speed of a particle with the given position function.

9. $\mathbf{r}(t) = \langle t^2 + 1, \, t^3, \, t^2 - 1 \rangle$

10. $\mathbf{r}(t) = \langle 2 \cos t, \, 3t, \, 2 \sin t \rangle$

11. $\mathbf{r}(t) = \sqrt{2} \, t \, \mathbf{i} + e^t \mathbf{j} + e^{-t} \mathbf{k}$

12. $\mathbf{r}(t) = t^2 \mathbf{i} + \ln t \, \mathbf{j} + t \, \mathbf{k}$

13. $\mathbf{r}(t) = e^t (\cos t \, \mathbf{i} + \sin t \, \mathbf{j} + t \, \mathbf{k})$

14. $\mathbf{r}(t) = t \sin t \, \mathbf{i} + t \cos t \, \mathbf{j} + t^2 \mathbf{k}$

15–16 Find the velocity and position vectors of a particle that has the given acceleration and the given initial velocity and position.

15. $\mathbf{a}(t) = \mathbf{i} + 2 \mathbf{j}, \quad \mathbf{v}(0) = \mathbf{k}, \quad \mathbf{r}(0) = \mathbf{i}$

16. $\mathbf{a}(t) = 2 \mathbf{i} + 6t \mathbf{j} + 12t^2 \mathbf{k}, \quad \mathbf{v}(0) = \mathbf{i}, \quad \mathbf{r}(0) = \mathbf{j} - \mathbf{k}$

17–18
(a) Find the position vector of a particle that has the given acceleration and the specified initial velocity and position.
(b) Use a computer to graph the path of the particle.

17. $\mathbf{a}(t) = 2t \mathbf{i} + \sin t \, \mathbf{j} + \cos 2t \, \mathbf{k}, \quad \mathbf{v}(0) = \mathbf{i}, \quad \mathbf{r}(0) = \mathbf{j}$

18. $\mathbf{a}(t) = t \mathbf{i} + e^t \mathbf{j} + e^{-t} \mathbf{k}, \quad \mathbf{v}(0) = \mathbf{k}, \quad \mathbf{r}(0) = \mathbf{j} + \mathbf{k}$

19. The position function of a particle is given by $\mathbf{r}(t) = \langle t^2, 5t, t^2 - 16t \rangle$. When is the speed a minimum?

20. What force is required so that a particle of mass m has the position function $\mathbf{r}(t) = t^3 \mathbf{i} + t^2 \mathbf{j} + t^3 \mathbf{k}$?

21. A force with magnitude 20 N acts directly upward from the xy-plane on an object with mass 4 kg. The object starts at the origin with initial velocity $\mathbf{v}(0) = \mathbf{i} - \mathbf{j}$. Find its position function and its speed at time t.

22. Show that if a particle moves with constant speed, then the velocity and acceleration vectors are orthogonal.

23. A projectile is fired with an initial speed of 500 m/s and angle of elevation 30°. Find (a) the range of the projectile, (b) the maximum height reached, and (c) the speed at impact.

24. Rework Exercise 23 if the projectile is fired from a position 200 m above the ground.

25. A ball is thrown at an angle of 45° to the ground. If the ball lands 90 m away, what was the initial speed of the ball?

26. A gun is fired with angle of elevation 30°. What is the muzzle speed if the maximum height of the shell is 500 m?

27. A gun has muzzle speed 150 m/s. Find two angles of elevation that can be used to hit a target 800 m away.

28. A batter hits a baseball 3 ft above the ground toward the center field fence, which is 10 ft high and 400 ft from home plate. The ball leaves the bat with speed 115 ft/s at an angle 50° above the horizontal. Is it a home run? (In other words, does the ball clear the fence?)

29. A medieval city has the shape of a square and is protected by walls with length 500 m and height 15 m. You are the commander of an attacking army and the closest you can get to the wall is 100 m. Your plan is to set fire to the city by catapulting heated rocks over the wall (with an initial speed of 80 m/s). At what range of angles should you tell your men to set the catapult? (Assume the path of the rocks is perpendicular to the wall.)

30. A ball with mass 0.8 kg is thrown southward into the air with a speed of 30 m/s at an angle of 30° to the ground. A west wind applies a steady force of 4 N to the ball in an easterly direction. Where does the ball land and with what speed?

31. Water traveling along a straight portion of a river normally flows fastest in the middle, and the speed slows to almost zero at the banks. Consider a long straight stretch of river flowing north, with parallel banks 40 m apart. If the maximum water speed is 3 m/s, we can use a quadratic function as a basic model for the rate of water flow x units from the west bank: $f(x) = \frac{3}{400} x(40 - x)$.
(a) A boat proceeds at a constant speed of 5 m/s from a point A on the west bank while maintaining a heading perpendicular to the bank. How far down the river on the opposite bank will the boat touch shore? Graph the path of the boat.
(b) Suppose we would like to pilot the boat to land at the point B on the east bank directly opposite A. If we maintain a constant speed of 5 m/s and a constant heading, find the angle at which the boat should head. Then graph the actual path the boat follows. Does the path seem realistic?

32. Another reasonable model for the water speed of the river in Exercise 31 is a sine function: $f(x) = 3 \sin(\pi x/40)$. If a boater would like to cross the river from A to B with constant heading and a constant speed of 5 m/s, determine the angle at which the boat should head.

33–38 Find the tangential and normal components of the acceleration vector.

33. $\mathbf{r}(t) = (3t - t^3) \mathbf{i} + 3t^2 \mathbf{j}$

34. $\mathbf{r}(t) = (1 + t) \mathbf{i} + (t^2 - 2t) \mathbf{j}$

35. $\mathbf{r}(t) = \cos t \, \mathbf{i} + \sin t \, \mathbf{j} + t \, \mathbf{k}$

36. $\mathbf{r}(t) = t \mathbf{i} + t^2 \mathbf{j} + 3t \, \mathbf{k}$

37. $\mathbf{r}(t) = e^t \mathbf{i} + \sqrt{2}\, t\, \mathbf{j} + e^{-t} \mathbf{k}$

38. $\mathbf{r}(t) = t\, \mathbf{i} + \cos^2 t\, \mathbf{j} + \sin^2 t\, \mathbf{k}$

---

39. The magnitude of the acceleration vector **a** is 10 cm/s^2. Use the figure to estimate the tangential and normal components of **a**.

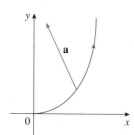

40. If a particle with mass m moves with position vector $\mathbf{r}(t)$, then its **angular momentum** is defined as $\mathbf{L}(t) = m\mathbf{r}(t) \times \mathbf{v}(t)$ and its **torque** as $\boldsymbol{\tau}(t) = m\mathbf{r}(t) \times \mathbf{a}(t)$. Show that $\mathbf{L}'(t) = \boldsymbol{\tau}(t)$. Deduce that if $\boldsymbol{\tau}(t) = \mathbf{0}$ for all t, then $\mathbf{L}(t)$ is constant. (This is the *law of conservation of angular momentum*.)

41. The position function of a spaceship is

$$\mathbf{r}(t) = (3+t)\mathbf{i} + (2 + \ln t)\mathbf{j} + \left(7 - \frac{4}{t^2 + 1}\right)\mathbf{k}$$

and the coordinates of a space station are (6, 4, 9). The captain wants the spaceship to coast into the space station. When should the engines be turned off?

42. A rocket burning its onboard fuel while moving through space has velocity $\mathbf{v}(t)$ and mass $m(t)$ at time t. If the exhaust gases escape with velocity $\mathbf{v}_e$ relative to the rocket, it can be deduced from Newton's Second Law of Motion that

$$m \frac{d\mathbf{v}}{dt} = \frac{dm}{dt}\mathbf{v}_e$$

(a) Show that $\mathbf{v}(t) = \mathbf{v}(0) - \ln \dfrac{m(0)}{m(t)} \mathbf{v}_e$.

(b) For the rocket to accelerate in a straight line from rest to twice the speed of its own exhaust gases, what fraction of its initial mass would the rocket have to burn as fuel?

APPLIED PROJECT

KEPLER'S LAWS

Johannes Kepler stated the following three laws of planetary motion on the basis of masses of data on the positions of the planets at various times.

> **KEPLER'S LAWS**
>
> **1.** A planet revolves around the sun in an elliptical orbit with the sun at one focus.
>
> **2.** The line joining the sun to a planet sweeps out equal areas in equal times.
>
> **3.** The square of the period of revolution of a planet is proportional to the cube of the length of the major axis of its orbit.

Kepler formulated these laws because they fitted the astronomical data. He wasn't able to see why they were true or how they related to each other. But Sir Isaac Newton, in his *Principia Mathematica* of 1687, showed how to deduce Kepler's three laws from two of Newton's own laws, the Second Law of Motion and the Law of Universal Gravitation. In Section 14.4 we proved Kepler's First Law using the calculus of vector functions. In this project we guide you through the proofs of Kepler's Second and Third Laws and explore some of their consequences.

1. Use the following steps to prove Kepler's Second Law. The notation is the same as in the proof of the First Law in Section 14.4. In particular, use polar coordinates so that $\mathbf{r} = (r \cos \theta)\mathbf{i} + (r \sin \theta)\mathbf{j}$.

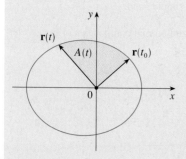

(a) Show that $\mathbf{h} = r^2 \dfrac{d\theta}{dt} \mathbf{k}$.

(b) Deduce that $r^2 \dfrac{d\theta}{dt} = h$.

(c) If $A = A(t)$ is the area swept out by the radius vector $\mathbf{r} = \mathbf{r}(t)$ in the time interval $[t_0, t]$ as in the figure, show that

$$\frac{dA}{dt} = \frac{1}{2} r^2 \frac{d\theta}{dt}$$

(d) Deduce that

$$\frac{dA}{dt} = \tfrac{1}{2}h = \text{constant}$$

This says that the rate at which A is swept out is constant and proves Kepler's Second Law.

2. Let T be the period of a planet about the sun; that is, T is the time required for it to travel once around its elliptical orbit. Suppose that the lengths of the major and minor axes of the ellipse are $2a$ and $2b$.

   (a) Use part (d) of Problem 1 to show that $T = 2\pi ab/h$.

   (b) Show that $\dfrac{h^2}{GM} = ed = \dfrac{b^2}{a}$.

   (c) Use parts (a) and (b) to show that $T^2 = \dfrac{4\pi^2}{GM}a^3$.

   This proves Kepler's Third Law. [Notice that the proportionality constant $4\pi^2/(GM)$ is independent of the planet.]

3. The period of the earth's orbit is approximately 365.25 days. Use this fact and Kepler's Third Law to find the length of the major axis of the earth's orbit. You will need the mass of the sun, $M = 1.99 \times 10^{30}$ kg, and the gravitational constant, $G = 6.67 \times 10^{-11}\ \text{N·m}^2/\text{kg}^2$.

4. It's possible to place a satellite into orbit about the earth so that it remains fixed above a given location on the equator. Compute the altitude that is needed for such a satellite. The earth's mass is 5.98×10^{24} kg; its radius is 6.37×10^6 m. (This orbit is called the Clarke Geosynchronous Orbit after Arthur C. Clarke, who first proposed the idea in 1945. The first such satellite, Syncom 2, was launched in July 1963.)

---

14 | REVIEW

CONCEPT CHECK

1. What is a vector function? How do you find its derivative and its integral?

2. What is the connection between vector functions and space curves?

3. How do you find the tangent vector to a smooth curve at a point? How do you find the tangent line? The unit tangent vector?

4. If $\mathbf{u}$ and $\mathbf{v}$ are differentiable vector functions, c is a scalar, and f is a real-valued function, write the rules for differentiating the following vector functions.
   (a) $\mathbf{u}(t) + \mathbf{v}(t)$ (b) $c\mathbf{u}(t)$ (c) $f(t)\mathbf{u}(t)$
   (d) $\mathbf{u}(t) \cdot \mathbf{v}(t)$ (e) $\mathbf{u}(t) \times \mathbf{v}(t)$ (f) $\mathbf{u}(f(t))$

5. How do you find the length of a space curve given by a vector function $\mathbf{r}(t)$?

6. (a) What is the definition of curvature?
   (b) Write a formula for curvature in terms of $\mathbf{r}'(t)$ and $\mathbf{T}'(t)$.
   (c) Write a formula for curvature in terms of $\mathbf{r}'(t)$ and $\mathbf{r}''(t)$.
   (d) Write a formula for the curvature of a plane curve with equation $y = f(x)$.

7. (a) Write formulas for the unit normal and binormal vectors of a smooth space curve $\mathbf{r}(t)$.
   (b) What is the normal plane of a curve at a point? What is the osculating plane? What is the osculating circle?

8. (a) How do you find the velocity, speed, and acceleration of a particle that moves along a space curve?
   (b) Write the acceleration in terms of its tangential and normal components.

9. State Kepler's Laws.

TRUE-FALSE QUIZ

Determine whether the statement is true or false. If it is true, explain why. If it is false, explain why or give an example that disproves the statement.

1. The curve with vector equation $\mathbf{r}(t) = t^3\mathbf{i} + 2t^3\mathbf{j} + 3t^3\mathbf{k}$ is a line.

2. The derivative of a vector function is obtained by differentiating each component function.

3. If $\mathbf{u}(t)$ and $\mathbf{v}(t)$ are differentiable vector functions, then

$$\frac{d}{dt}[\mathbf{u}(t) \times \mathbf{v}(t)] = \mathbf{u}'(t) \times \mathbf{v}'(t)$$

4. If $\mathbf{r}(t)$ is a differentiable vector function, then

$$\frac{d}{dt}|\mathbf{r}(t)| = |\mathbf{r}'(t)|$$

5. If $\mathbf{T}(t)$ is the unit tangent vector of a smooth curve, then the curvature is $\kappa = |d\mathbf{T}/dt|$.

6. The binormal vector is $\mathbf{B}(t) = \mathbf{N}(t) \times \mathbf{T}(t)$.

7. Suppose f is twice continuously differentiable. At an inflection point of the curve $y = f(x)$, the curvature is 0.

8. If $\kappa(t) = 0$ for all t, the curve is a straight line.

9. If $|\mathbf{r}(t)| = 1$ for all t, then $|\mathbf{r}'(t)|$ is a constant.

10. If $|\mathbf{r}(t)| = 1$ for all t, then $\mathbf{r}'(t)$ is orthogonal to $\mathbf{r}(t)$ for all t.

11. The osculating circle of a curve C at a point has the same tangent vector, normal vector, and curvature as C at that point.

12. Different parametrizations of the same curve result in identical tangent vectors at a given point on the curve.

EXERCISES

1. (a) Sketch the curve with vector function

$$\mathbf{r}(t) = t\mathbf{i} + \cos \pi t\,\mathbf{j} + \sin \pi t\,\mathbf{k} \qquad t \geq 0$$

(b) Find $\mathbf{r}'(t)$ and $\mathbf{r}''(t)$.

2. Let $\mathbf{r}(t) = \langle\sqrt{2 - t}, (e^t - 1)/t, \ln(t + 1)\rangle$.
(a) Find the domain of $\mathbf{r}$.
(b) Find $\lim_{t \to 0} \mathbf{r}(t)$.
(c) Find $\mathbf{r}'(t)$.

3. Find a vector function that represents the curve of intersection of the cylinder $x^2 + y^2 = 16$ and the plane $x + z = 5$.

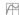 **4.** Find parametric equations for the tangent line to the curve $x = 2 \sin t$, $y = 2 \sin 2t$, $z = 2 \sin 3t$ at the point $(1, \sqrt{3}, 2)$. Graph the curve and the tangent line on a common screen.

5. If $\mathbf{r}(t) = t^2\mathbf{i} + t \cos \pi t\,\mathbf{j} + \sin \pi t\,\mathbf{k}$, evaluate $\int_0^1 \mathbf{r}(t)\,dt$.

6. Let C be the curve with equations $x = 2 - t^3$, $y = 2t - 1$, $z = \ln t$. Find (a) the point where C intersects the xz-plane, (b) parametric equations of the tangent line at $(1, 1, 0)$, and (c) an equation of the normal plane to C at $(1, 1, 0)$.

7. Use Simpson's Rule with $n = 6$ to estimate the length of the arc of the curve with equations $x = t^2$, $y = t^3$, $z = t^4$, $0 \leq t \leq 3$.

8. Find the length of the curve $\mathbf{r}(t) = \langle 2t^{3/2}, \cos 2t, \sin 2t\rangle$, $0 \leq t \leq 1$.

9. The helix $\mathbf{r}_1(t) = \cos t\,\mathbf{i} + \sin t\,\mathbf{j} + t\,\mathbf{k}$ intersects the curve $\mathbf{r}_2(t) = (1 + t)\mathbf{i} + t^2\mathbf{j} + t^3\mathbf{k}$ at the point $(1, 0, 0)$. Find the angle of intersection of these curves.

10. Reparametrize the curve $\mathbf{r}(t) = e^t\mathbf{i} + e^t \sin t\,\mathbf{j} + e^t \cos t\,\mathbf{k}$ with respect to arc length measured from the point $(1, 0, 1)$ in the direction of increasing t.

11. For the curve given by $\mathbf{r}(t) = \langle \frac{1}{3}t^3, \frac{1}{2}t^2, t\rangle$, find
(a) the unit tangent vector
(b) the unit normal vector
(c) the curvature

12. Find the curvature of the ellipse $x = 3 \cos t$, $y = 4 \sin t$ at the points $(3, 0)$ and $(0, 4)$.

13. Find the curvature of the curve $y = x^4$ at the point $(1, 1)$.

14. Find an equation of the osculating circle of the curve $y = x^4 - x^2$ at the origin. Graph both the curve and its osculating circle.

15. Find an equation of the osculating plane of the curve $x = \sin 2t$, $y = t$, $z = \cos 2t$ at the point $(0, \pi, 1)$.

16. The figure shows the curve C traced by a particle with position vector $\mathbf{r}(t)$ at time t.
(a) Draw a vector that represents the average velocity of the particle over the time interval $3 \leq t \leq 3.2$.
(b) Write an expression for the velocity $\mathbf{v}(3)$.
(c) Write an expression for the unit tangent vector $\mathbf{T}(3)$ and draw it.

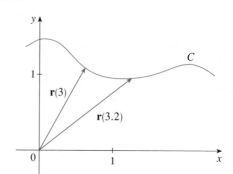

17. A particle moves with position function
$\mathbf{r}(t) = t \ln t \, \mathbf{i} + t \, \mathbf{j} + e^{-t} \mathbf{k}$. Find the velocity, speed, and acceleration of the particle.

18. A particle starts at the origin with initial velocity $\mathbf{i} - \mathbf{j} + 3\mathbf{k}$. Its acceleration is $\mathbf{a}(t) = 6t \, \mathbf{i} + 12t^2 \, \mathbf{j} - 6t \, \mathbf{k}$. Find its position function.

19. An athlete throws a shot at an angle of $45°$ to the horizontal at an initial speed of 43 ft/s. It leaves his hand 7 ft above the ground.
(a) Where is the shot 2 seconds later?
(b) How high does the shot go?
(c) Where does the shot land?

20. Find the tangential and normal components of the acceleration vector of a particle with position function
$$\mathbf{r}(t) = t \, \mathbf{i} + 2t \, \mathbf{j} + t^2 \, \mathbf{k}$$

21. A disk of radius 1 is rotating in the counterclockwise direction at a constant angular speed ω. A particle starts at the center of the disk and moves toward the edge along a fixed radius so that its position at time t, $t \geq 0$, is given by $\mathbf{r}(t) = t\mathbf{R}(t)$, where
$$\mathbf{R}(t) = \cos \omega t \, \mathbf{i} + \sin \omega t \, \mathbf{j}$$
(a) Show that the velocity $\mathbf{v}$ of the particle is
$$\mathbf{v} = \cos \omega t \, \mathbf{i} + \sin \omega t \, \mathbf{j} + t\mathbf{v}_d$$
where $\mathbf{v}_d = \mathbf{R}'(t)$ is the velocity of a point on the edge of the disk.
(b) Show that the acceleration $\mathbf{a}$ of the particle is
$$\mathbf{a} = 2\mathbf{v}_d + t\mathbf{a}_d$$
where $\mathbf{a}_d = \mathbf{R}''(t)$ is the acceleration of a point on the rim of the disk. The extra term $2\mathbf{v}_d$ is called the *Coriolis acceleration*; it is the result of the interaction of the rotation of the disk and the motion of the particle. One can obtain a physical demonstration of this acceleration by walking toward the edge of a moving merry-go-round.

(c) Determine the Coriolis acceleration of a particle that moves on a rotating disk according to the equation
$$\mathbf{r}(t) = e^{-t}\cos \omega t \, \mathbf{i} + e^{-t}\sin \omega t \, \mathbf{j}$$

22. In designing *transfer curves* to connect sections of straight railroad tracks, it's important to realize that the acceleration of the train should be continuous so that the reactive force exerted by the train on the track is also continuous. Because of the formulas for the components of acceleration in Section 14.4, this will be the case if the curvature varies continuously.
(a) A logical candidate for a transfer curve to join existing tracks given by $y = 1$ for $x \leq 0$ and $y = \sqrt{2} - x$ for $x \geq 1/\sqrt{2}$ might be the function $f(x) = \sqrt{1 - x^2}$, $0 < x < 1/\sqrt{2}$, whose graph is the arc of the circle shown in the figure. It looks reasonable at first glance. Show that the function
$$F(x) = \begin{cases} 1 & \text{if } x \leq 0 \\ \sqrt{1 - x^2} & \text{if } 0 < x < 1/\sqrt{2} \\ \sqrt{2} - x & \text{if } x \geq 1/\sqrt{2} \end{cases}$$
is continuous and has continuous slope, but does not have continuous curvature. Therefore f is not an appropriate transfer curve.
(b) Find a fifth-degree polynomial to serve as a transfer curve between the following straight line segments: $y = 0$ for $x \leq 0$ and $y = x$ for $x \geq 1$. Could this be done with a fourth-degree polynomial? Use a graphing calculator or computer to sketch the graph of the "connected" function and check to see that it looks like the one in the figure.

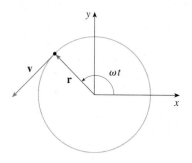

FIGURE FOR PROBLEM 1

1. A particle P moves with constant angular speed ω around a circle whose center is at the origin and whose radius is R. The particle is said to be in *uniform circular motion*. Assume that the motion is counterclockwise and that the particle is at the point $(R, 0)$ when $t = 0$. The position vector at time $t \geqslant 0$ is $\mathbf{r}(t) = R \cos \omega t\,\mathbf{i} + R \sin \omega t\,\mathbf{j}$.

(a) Find the velocity vector $\mathbf{v}$ and show that $\mathbf{v} \cdot \mathbf{r} = 0$. Conclude that $\mathbf{v}$ is tangent to the circle and points in the direction of the motion.

(b) Show that the speed $|\mathbf{v}|$ of the particle is the constant ωR. The *period* T of the particle is the time required for one complete revolution. Conclude that

$$T = \frac{2\pi R}{|\mathbf{v}|} = \frac{2\pi}{\omega}$$

(c) Find the acceleration vector $\mathbf{a}$. Show that it is proportional to $\mathbf{r}$ and that it points toward the origin. An acceleration with this property is called a *centripetal acceleration*. Show that the magnitude of the acceleration vector is $|\mathbf{a}| = R\omega^2$.

(d) Suppose that the particle has mass m. Show that the magnitude of the force $\mathbf{F}$ that is required to produce this motion, called a *centripetal force*, is

$$|\mathbf{F}| = \frac{m|\mathbf{v}|^2}{R}$$

FIGURE FOR PROBLEM 2

2. A circular curve of radius R on a highway is banked at an angle θ so that a car can safely traverse the curve without skidding when there is no friction between the road and the tires. The loss of friction could occur, for example, if the road is covered with a film of water or ice. The rated speed v_R of the curve is the maximum speed that a car can attain without skidding. Suppose a car of mass m is traversing the curve at the rated speed v_R. Two forces are acting on the car: the vertical force, mg, due to the weight of the car, and a force $\mathbf{F}$ exerted by, and normal to, the road. (See the figure.)

The vertical component of $\mathbf{F}$ balances the weight of the car, so that $|\mathbf{F}| \cos \theta = mg$. The horizontal component of $\mathbf{F}$ produces a centripetal force on the car so that, by Newton's Second Law and part (d) of Problem 1,

$$|\mathbf{F}| \sin \theta = \frac{mv_R^2}{R}$$

(a) Show that $v_R^2 = Rg \tan \theta$.

(b) Find the rated speed of a circular curve with radius 400 ft that is banked at an angle of 12°.

(c) Suppose the design engineers want to keep the banking at 12°, but wish to increase the rated speed by 50%. What should the radius of the curve be?

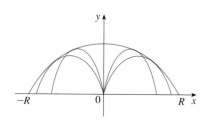

3. A projectile is fired from the origin with angle of elevation α and initial speed v_0. Assuming that air resistance is negligible and that the only force acting on the projectile is gravity, g, we showed in Example 5 in Section 14.4 that the position vector of the projectile is

$$\mathbf{r}(t) = (v_0 \cos \alpha)t\,\mathbf{i} + \left[(v_0 \sin \alpha)t - \tfrac{1}{2}gt^2\right]\mathbf{j}$$

We also showed that the maximum horizontal distance of the projectile is achieved when $\alpha = 45°$ and in this case the range is $R = v_0^2/g$.

(a) At what angle should the projectile be fired to achieve maximum height and what is the maximum height?

(b) Fix the initial speed v_0 and consider the parabola $x^2 + 2Ry - R^2 = 0$, whose graph is shown in the figure. Show that the projectile can hit any target inside or on the boundary of the region bounded by the parabola and the x-axis, and that it can't hit any target outside this region.

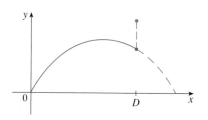

FIGURE FOR PROBLEM 3

(c) Suppose that the gun is elevated to an angle of inclination α in order to aim at a target that is suspended at a height h directly over a point D units downrange. The target is released at the instant the gun is fired. Show that the projectile always hits the target, regardless of the value v_0, provided the projectile does not hit the ground "before" D.

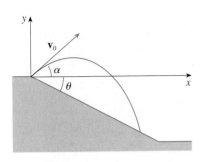

FIGURE FOR PROBLEM 4

4. (a) A projectile is fired from the origin down an inclined plane that makes an angle θ with the horizontal. The angle of elevation of the gun and the initial speed of the projectile are α and v_0, respectively. Find the position vector of the projectile and the parametric equations of the path of the projectile as functions of the time t. (Ignore air resistance.)

(b) Show that the angle of elevation α that will maximize the downhill range is the angle halfway between the plane and the vertical.

(c) Suppose the projectile is fired up an inclined plane whose angle of inclination is θ. Show that, in order to maximize the (uphill) range, the projectile should be fired in the direction halfway between the plane and the vertical.

(d) In a paper presented in 1686, Edmond Halley summarized the laws of gravity and projectile motion and applied them to gunnery. One problem he posed involved firing a projectile to hit a target a distance R up an inclined plane. Show that the angle at which the projectile should be fired to hit the target but use the least amount of energy is the same as the angle in part (c). (Use the fact that the energy needed to fire the projectile is proportional to the square of the initial speed, so minimizing the energy is equivalent to minimizing the initial speed.)

5. A ball rolls off a table with a speed of 2 ft/s. The table is 3.5 ft high.

(a) Determine the point at which the ball hits the floor and find its speed at the instant of impact.

(b) Find the angle θ between the path of the ball and the vertical line drawn through the point of impact. (See the figure.)

(c) Suppose the ball rebounds from the floor at the same angle with which it hits the floor, but loses 20% of its speed due to energy absorbed by the ball on impact. Where does the ball strike the floor on the second bounce?

FIGURE FOR PROBLEM 5

3.5 ft

6. Find the curvature of the curve with parametric equations

$$x = \int_0^t \sin\left(\tfrac{1}{2}\pi\theta^2\right) d\theta \qquad y = \int_0^t \cos\left(\tfrac{1}{2}\pi\theta^2\right) d\theta$$

7. If a projectile is fired with angle of elevation α and initial speed v, then parametric equations for its trajectory are

$$x = (v\cos\alpha)t \qquad y = (v\sin\alpha)t - \tfrac{1}{2}gt^2$$

(See Example 5 in Section 14.4.) We know that the range (horizontal distance traveled) is maximized when $\alpha = 45°$. What value of α maximizes the total distance traveled by the projectile? (State your answer correct to the nearest degree.)

8. A cable has radius r and length L and is wound around a spool with radius R without overlapping. What is the shortest length along the spool that is covered by the cable?

15

PARTIAL DERIVATIVES

Functions of two variables can be visualized by means of level curves, which connect points where the function takes on a given value. Atmospheric pressure at a given time is a function of longitude and latitude and is measured in millibars. Here the level curves are called isobars and those pictured join locations that had the same pressure on March 7, 2007. (The curves labeled 1028, for instance, connect points with pressure 1028 mb.) Surface winds tend to flow from areas of high pressure across the isobars toward areas of low pressure, and are strongest where the isobars are tightly packed.

So far we have dealt with the calculus of functions of a single variable. But, in the real world, physical quantities often depend on two or more variables, so in this chapter we turn our attention to functions of several variables and extend the basic ideas of differential calculus to such functions.

In this section we study functions of two or more variables from four points of view:

- verbally   (by a description in words)
- numerically   (by a table of values)
- algebraically   (by an explicit formula)
- visually   (by a graph or level curves)

FUNCTIONS OF TWO VARIABLES

The temperature T at a point on the surface of the earth at any given time depends on the longitude x and latitude y of the point. We can think of T as being a function of the two variables x and y, or as a function of the pair (x, y). We indicate this functional dependence by writing $T = f(x, y)$.

The volume V of a circular cylinder depends on its radius r and its height h. In fact, we know that $V = \pi r^2 h$. We say that V is a function of r and h, and we write $V(r, h) = \pi r^2 h$.

DEFINITION A **function f of two variables** is a rule that assigns to each ordered pair of real numbers (x, y) in a set D a unique real number denoted by $f(x, y)$. The set D is the **domain** of f and its **range** is the set of values that f takes on, that is, $\{f(x, y) \mid (x, y) \in D\}$.

We often write $z = f(x, y)$ to make explicit the value taken on by f at the general point (x, y). The variables x and y are **independent variables** and z is the **dependent variable**. [Compare this with the notation $y = f(x)$ for functions of a single variable.]

A function of two variables is just a function whose domain is a subset of $\mathbb{R}^2$ and whose range is a subset of $\mathbb{R}$. One way of visualizing such a function is by means of an arrow diagram (see Figure 1), where the domain D is represented as a subset of the xy-plane.

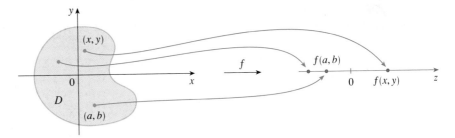

FIGURE 1

If a function f is given by a formula and no domain is specified, then the domain of f is understood to be the set of all pairs (x, y) for which the given expression is a well-defined real number.

EXAMPLE 1 For each of the following functions, evaluate $f(3, 2)$ and find the domain.

(a) $f(x, y) = \dfrac{\sqrt{x + y + 1}}{x - 1}$ (b) $f(x, y) = x \ln(y^2 - x)$

SOLUTION

(a) $$f(3, 2) = \frac{\sqrt{3 + 2 + 1}}{3 - 1} = \frac{\sqrt{6}}{2}$$

$x + y + 1 = 0$

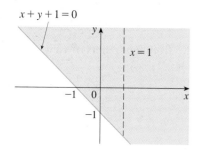

FIGURE 2

Domain of $f(x, y) = \dfrac{\sqrt{x + y + 1}}{x - 1}$

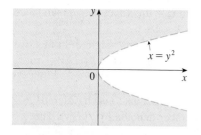

FIGURE 3

Domain of $f(x, y) = x \ln(y^2 - x)$

The expression for f makes sense if the denominator is not 0 and the quantity under the square root sign is nonnegative. So the domain of f is

$$D = \{(x, y) \mid x + y + 1 \geq 0, \ x \neq 1\}$$

The inequality $x + y + 1 \geq 0$, or $y \geq -x - 1$, describes the points that lie on or above the line $y = -x - 1$, while $x \neq 1$ means that the points on the line $x = 1$ must be excluded from the domain. (See Figure 2.)

(b) $\qquad\qquad\qquad\qquad f(3, 2) = 3 \ln(2^2 - 3) = 3 \ln 1 = 0$

Since $\ln(y^2 - x)$ is defined only when $y^2 - x > 0$, that is, $x < y^2$, the domain of f is $D = \{(x, y) \mid x < y^2\}$. This is the set of points to the left of the parabola $x = y^2$. (See Figure 3.)

Not all functions are given by explicit formulas. The function in the next example is described verbally and by numerical estimates of its values.

EXAMPLE 2 In regions with severe winter weather, the *wind-chill index* is often used to describe the apparent severity of the cold. This index W is a subjective temperature that depends on the actual temperature T and the wind speed v. So W is a function of T and v, and we can write $W = f(T, v)$. Table 1 records values of W compiled by the NOAA National Weather Service of the US and the Meteorological Service of Canada.

TABLE 1

Wind-chill index as a function of air temperature and wind speed

■ THE NEW WIND-CHILL INDEX

A new wind-chill index was introduced in November of 2001 and is more accurate than the old index at measuring how cold it feels when it's windy. The new index is based on a model of how fast a human face loses heat. It was developed through clinical trials in which volunteers were exposed to a variety of temperatures and wind speeds in a refrigerated wind tunnel.

Wind speed (km/h)

T＼v	5	10	15	20	25	30	40	50	60	70	80
5	4	3	2	1	1	0	−1	−1	−2	−2	−3
0	−2	−3	−4	−5	−6	−6	−7	−8	−9	−9	−10
−5	−7	−9	−11	−12	−12	−13	−14	−15	−16	−16	−17
−10	−13	−15	−17	−18	−19	−20	−21	−22	−23	−23	−24
−15	−19	−21	−23	−24	−25	−26	−27	−29	−30	−30	−31
−20	−24	−27	−29	−30	−32	−33	−34	−35	−36	−37	−38
−25	−30	−33	−35	−37	−38	−39	−41	−42	−43	−44	−45
−30	−36	−39	−41	−43	−44	−46	−48	−49	−50	−51	−52
−35	−41	−45	−48	−49	−51	−52	−54	−56	−57	−58	−60
−40	−47	−51	−54	−56	−57	−59	−61	−63	−64	−65	−67

Actual temperature (°C)

For instance, the table shows that if the temperature is $-5°$C and the wind speed is 50 km/h, then subjectively it would feel as cold as a temperature of about $-15°$C with no wind. So

$$f(-5, 50) = -15$$

EXAMPLE 3 In 1928 Charles Cobb and Paul Douglas published a study in which they modeled the growth of the American economy during the period 1899–1922. They con-

TABLE 2

Year	P	L	K
1899	100	100	100
1900	101	105	107
1901	112	110	114
1902	122	117	122
1903	124	122	131
1904	122	121	138
1905	143	125	149
1906	152	134	163
1907	151	140	176
1908	126	123	185
1909	155	143	198
1910	159	147	208
1911	153	148	216
1912	177	155	226
1913	184	156	236
1914	169	152	244
1915	189	156	266
1916	225	183	298
1917	227	198	335
1918	223	201	366
1919	218	196	387
1920	231	194	407
1921	179	146	417
1922	240	161	431

sidered a simplified view of the economy in which production output is determined by the amount of labor involved and the amount of capital invested. While there are many other factors affecting economic performance, their model proved to be remarkably accurate. The function they used to model production was of the form

$$\boxed{1} \qquad P(L, K) = bL^{\alpha}K^{1-\alpha}$$

where P is the total production (the monetary value of all goods produced in a year), L is the amount of labor (the total number of person-hours worked in a year), and K is the amount of capital invested (the monetary worth of all machinery, equipment, and buildings). In Section 15.3 we will show how the form of Equation 1 follows from certain economic assumptions.

Cobb and Douglas used economic data published by the government to obtain Table 2. They took the year 1899 as a baseline, and P, L, and K for 1899 were each assigned the value 100. The values for other years were expressed as percentages of the 1899 figures.

Cobb and Douglas used the method of least squares to fit the data of Table 2 to the function

$$\boxed{2} \qquad P(L, K) = 1.01L^{0.75}K^{0.25}$$

(See Exercise 75 for the details.)

If we use the model given by the function in Equation 2 to compute the production in the years 1910 and 1920, we get the values

$$P(147, 208) = 1.01(147)^{0.75}(208)^{0.25} \approx 161.9$$

$$P(194, 407) = 1.01(194)^{0.75}(407)^{0.25} \approx 235.8$$

which are quite close to the actual values, 159 and 231.

The production function (1) has subsequently been used in many settings, ranging from individual firms to global economic questions. It has become known as the **Cobb-Douglas production function**. Its domain is $\{(L, K) \mid L \geq 0, K \geq 0\}$ because L and K represent labor and capital and are therefore never negative. ☐

EXAMPLE 4 Find the domain and range of $g(x, y) = \sqrt{9 - x^2 - y^2}$.

SOLUTION The domain of g is

$$D = \{(x, y) \mid 9 - x^2 - y^2 \geq 0\} = \{(x, y) \mid x^2 + y^2 \leq 9\}$$

which is the disk with center $(0, 0)$ and radius 3. (See Figure 4.) The range of g is

$$\left\{z \mid z = \sqrt{9 - x^2 - y^2}, (x, y) \in D\right\}$$

Since z is a positive square root, $z \geq 0$. Also

$$9 - x^2 - y^2 \leq 9 \quad \Rightarrow \quad \sqrt{9 - x^2 - y^2} \leq 3$$

So the range is

$$\{z \mid 0 \leq z \leq 3\} = [0, 3]$$ ☐

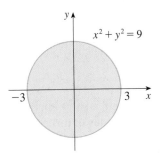

FIGURE 4
Domain of $g(x, y) = \sqrt{9 - x^2 - y^2}$

GRAPHS

Another way of visualizing the behavior of a function of two variables is to consider its graph.

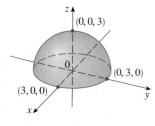

FIGURE 5

> **DEFINITION** If f is a function of two variables with domain D, then the **graph** of f is the set of all points (x, y, z) in $\mathbb{R}^3$ such that $z = f(x, y)$ and (x, y) is in D.

Just as the graph of a function f of one variable is a curve C with equation $y = f(x)$, so the graph of a function f of two variables is a surface S with equation $z = f(x, y)$. We can visualize the graph S of f as lying directly above or below its domain D in the xy-plane. (See Figure 5.)

EXAMPLE 5 Sketch the graph of the function $f(x, y) = 6 - 3x - 2y$.

SOLUTION The graph of f has the equation $z = 6 - 3x - 2y$, or $3x + 2y + z = 6$, which represents a plane. To graph the plane we first find the intercepts. Putting $y = z = 0$ in the equation, we get $x = 2$ as the x-intercept. Similarly, the y-intercept is 3 and the z-intercept is 6. This helps us sketch the portion of the graph that lies in the first octant. (See Figure 6.)

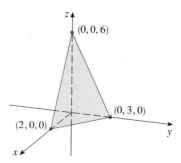

FIGURE 6

The function in Example 5 is a special case of the function

$$f(x, y) = ax + by + c$$

which is called a **linear function**. The graph of such a function has the equation

$$z = ax + by + c \qquad \text{or} \qquad ax + by - z + c = 0$$

so it is a plane. In much the same way that linear functions of one variable are important in single-variable calculus, we will see that linear functions of two variables play a central role in multivariable calculus.

V EXAMPLE 6 Sketch the graph of $g(x, y) = \sqrt{9 - x^2 - y^2}$.

SOLUTION The graph has equation $z = \sqrt{9 - x^2 - y^2}$. We square both sides of this equation to obtain $z^2 = 9 - x^2 - y^2$, or $x^2 + y^2 + z^2 = 9$, which we recognize as an equation of the sphere with center the origin and radius 3. But, since $z \geqslant 0$, the graph of g is just the top half of this sphere (see Figure 7).

FIGURE 7
Graph of $g(x, y) = \sqrt{9 - x^2 - y^2}$

NOTE An entire sphere can't be represented by a single function of x and y. As we saw in Example 6, the upper hemisphere of the sphere $x^2 + y^2 + z^2 = 9$ is represented by the function $g(x, y) = \sqrt{9 - x^2 - y^2}$. The lower hemisphere is represented by the function $h(x, y) = -\sqrt{9 - x^2 - y^2}$.

EXAMPLE 7 Use a computer to draw the graph of the Cobb-Douglas production function $P(L, K) = 1.01L^{0.75}K^{0.25}$.

SOLUTION Figure 8 shows the graph of P for values of the labor L and capital K that lie between 0 and 300. The computer has drawn the surface by plotting vertical traces. We see from these traces that the value of the production P increases as either L or K increases, as is to be expected.

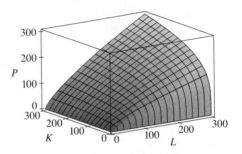

FIGURE 8

▼ EXAMPLE 8 Find the domain and range and sketch the graph of $h(x, y) = 4x^2 + y^2$.

SOLUTION Notice that $h(x, y)$ is defined for all possible ordered pairs of real numbers (x, y), so the domain is $\mathbb{R}^2$, the entire xy-plane. The range of h is the set $[0, \infty)$ of all nonnegative real numbers. [Notice that $x^2 \geqslant 0$ and $y^2 \geqslant 0$, so $h(x, y) \geqslant 0$ for all x and y.]

The graph of h has the equation $z = 4x^2 + y^2$, which is the elliptic paraboloid that we sketched in Example 4 in Section 13.6. Horizontal traces are ellipses and vertical traces are parabolas (see Figure 9).

FIGURE 9
Graph of $h(x, y) = 4x^2 + y^2$

Computer programs are readily available for graphing functions of two variables. In most such programs, traces in the vertical planes $x = k$ and $y = k$ are drawn for equally spaced values of k and parts of the graph are eliminated using hidden line removal.

Figure 10 shows computer-generated graphs of several functions. Notice that we get an especially good picture of a function when rotation is used to give views from different vantage points. In parts (a) and (b) the graph of f is very flat and close to the xy-plane except near the origin; this is because $e^{-x^2-y^2}$ is very small when x or y is large.

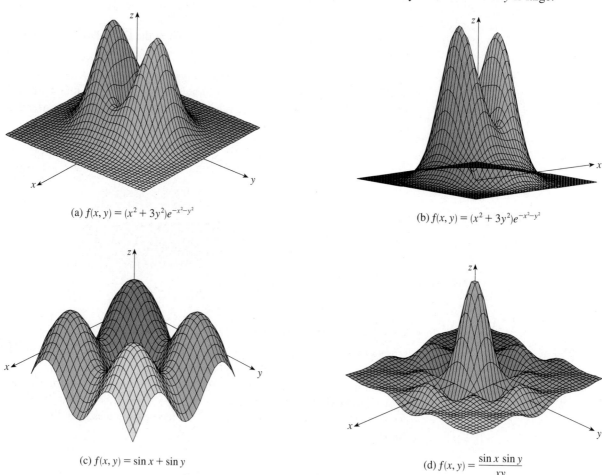

(a) $f(x, y) = (x^2 + 3y^2)e^{-x^2-y^2}$

(b) $f(x, y) = (x^2 + 3y^2)e^{-x^2-y^2}$

(c) $f(x, y) = \sin x + \sin y$

(d) $f(x, y) = \dfrac{\sin x \sin y}{xy}$

FIGURE 10

LEVEL CURVES

So far we have two methods for visualizing functions: arrow diagrams and graphs. A third method, borrowed from mapmakers, is a contour map on which points of constant elevation are joined to form *contour curves,* or *level curves.*

> **DEFINITION** The **level curves** of a function f of two variables are the curves with equations $f(x, y) = k$, where k is a constant (in the range of f).

A level curve $f(x, y) = k$ is the set of all points in the domain of f at which f takes on a given value k. In other words, it shows where the graph of f has height k.

You can see from Figure 11 the relation between level curves and horizontal traces. The level curves $f(x, y) = k$ are just the traces of the graph of f in the horizontal plane $z = k$ projected down to the xy-plane. So if you draw the level curves of a function and visualize them being lifted up to the surface at the indicated height, then you can mentally piece

FIGURE 11

FIGURE 12

TEC Visual 15.1A animates Figure 11 by showing level curves being lifted up to graphs of functions.

together a picture of the graph. The surface is steep where the level curves are close together. It is somewhat flatter where they are farther apart.

One common example of level curves occurs in topographic maps of mountainous regions, such as the map in Figure 12. The level curves are curves of constant elevation above sea level. If you walk along one of these contour lines, you neither ascend nor descend. Another common example is the temperature function introduced in the opening paragraph of this section. Here the level curves are called **isothermals** and join locations with the same temperature. Figure 13 shows a weather map of the world indicating the average January temperatures. The isothermals are the curves that separate the colored bands. The **isobars** in the atmospheric pressure map on page 890 provide another example of level curves.

FIGURE 13

World mean sea-level temperatures in January in degrees Celsius

Tarbuck, *Atmosphere: Introduction to Meteorology*, 4th Edition, © 1989. Reprinted by permission of Pearson Education, Inc., Upper Saddle River, NJ.

FIGURE 14

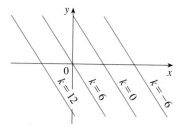

FIGURE 15
Contour map of
$f(x, y) = 6 - 3x - 2y$

EXAMPLE 9 A contour map for a function f is shown in Figure 14. Use it to estimate the values of $f(1, 3)$ and $f(4, 5)$.

SOLUTION The point $(1, 3)$ lies partway between the level curves with z-values 70 and 80. We estimate that

$$f(1, 3) \approx 73$$

Similarly, we estimate that

$$f(4, 5) \approx 56$$

EXAMPLE 10 Sketch the level curves of the function $f(x, y) = 6 - 3x - 2y$ for the values $k = -6, 0, 6, 12$.

SOLUTION The level curves are

$$6 - 3x - 2y = k \qquad \text{or} \qquad 3x + 2y + (k - 6) = 0$$

This is a family of lines with slope $-\frac{3}{2}$. The four particular level curves with $k = -6, 0, 6$, and 12 are $3x + 2y - 12 = 0$, $3x + 2y - 6 = 0$, $3x + 2y = 0$, and $3x + 2y + 6 = 0$. They are sketched in Figure 15. The level curves are equally spaced parallel lines because the graph of f is a plane (see Figure 6).

☑ EXAMPLE 11 Sketch the level curves of the function

$$g(x, y) = \sqrt{9 - x^2 - y^2} \qquad \text{for} \quad k = 0, 1, 2, 3$$

SOLUTION The level curves are

$$\sqrt{9 - x^2 - y^2} = k \qquad \text{or} \qquad x^2 + y^2 = 9 - k^2$$

This is a family of concentric circles with center $(0, 0)$ and radius $\sqrt{9 - k^2}$. The cases $k = 0, 1, 2, 3$ are shown in Figure 16. Try to visualize these level curves lifted up to form a surface and compare with the graph of g (a hemisphere) in Figure 7. (See TEC Visual 15.1A.)

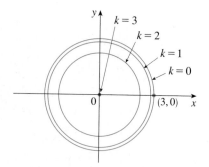

FIGURE 16
Contour map of $g(x, y) = \sqrt{9 - x^2 - y^2}$

EXAMPLE 12 Sketch some level curves of the function $h(x, y) = 4x^2 + y^2$.

SOLUTION The level curves are

$$4x^2 + y^2 = k \qquad \text{or} \qquad \frac{x^2}{k/4} + \frac{y^2}{k} = 1$$

which, for $k > 0$, describes a family of ellipses with semiaxes $\sqrt{k}/2$ and $\sqrt{k}$. Figure 17(a) shows a contour map of h drawn by a computer with level curves corresponding to $k = 0.25, 0.5, 0.75, \ldots, 4$. Figure 17(b) shows these level curves lifted up to the graph of h (an elliptic paraboloid) where they become horizontal traces. We see from Figure 17 how the graph of h is put together from the level curves.

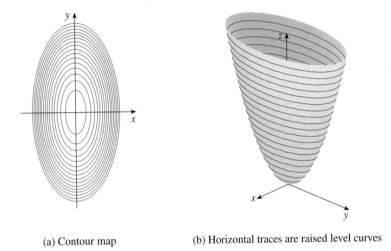

FIGURE 17
The graph of $h(x, y) = 4x^2 + y^2$ is formed by lifting the level curves.

(a) Contour map   (b) Horizontal traces are raised level curves

EXAMPLE 13 Plot level curves for the Cobb-Douglas production function of Example 3.

SOLUTION In Figure 18 we use a computer to draw a contour plot for the Cobb-Douglas production function

$$P(L, K) = 1.01 L^{0.75} K^{0.25}$$

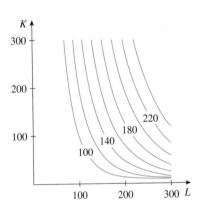

FIGURE 18

Level curves are labeled with the value of the production P. For instance, the level curve labeled 140 shows all values of the labor L and capital investment K that result in a production of $P = 140$. We see that, for a fixed value of P, as L increases K decreases, and vice versa.

For some purposes, a contour map is more useful than a graph. That is certainly true in Example 13. (Compare Figure 18 with Figure 8.) It is also true in estimating function values, as in Example 9.

Figure 19 shows some computer-generated level curves together with the corresponding computer-generated graphs. Notice that the level curves in part (c) crowd together near the origin. That corresponds to the fact that the graph in part (d) is very steep near the origin.

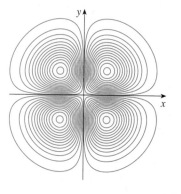

(a) Level curves of $f(x, y) = -xye^{-x^2-y^2}$

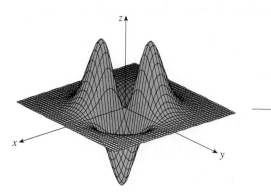

(b) Two views of $f(x, y) = -xye^{-x^2-y^2}$

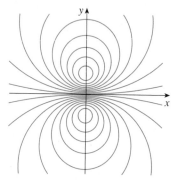

(c) Level curves of $f(x, y) = \dfrac{-3y}{x^2 + y^2 + 1}$

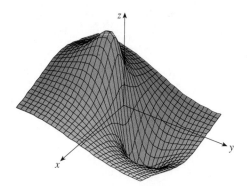

(d) $f(x, y) = \dfrac{-3y}{x^2 + y^2 + 1}$

FIGURE 19

FUNCTIONS OF THREE OR MORE VARIABLES

A **function of three variables**, f, is a rule that assigns to each ordered triple (x, y, z) in a domain $D \subset \mathbb{R}^3$ a unique real number denoted by $f(x, y, z)$. For instance, the temperature T at a point on the surface of the earth depends on the longitude x and latitude y of the point and on the time t, so we could write $T = f(x, y, t)$.

EXAMPLE 14 Find the domain of f if

$$f(x, y, z) = \ln(z - y) + xy \sin z$$

SOLUTION The expression for $f(x, y, z)$ is defined as long as $z - y > 0$, so the domain of f is

$$D = \{(x, y, z) \in \mathbb{R}^3 \mid z > y\}$$

This is a **half-space** consisting of all points that lie above the plane $z = y$. ☐

It's very difficult to visualize a function f of three variables by its graph, since that would lie in a four-dimensional space. However, we do gain some insight into f by examining its **level surfaces**, which are the surfaces with equations $f(x, y, z) = k$, where k is a constant. If the point (x, y, z) moves along a level surface, the value of $f(x, y, z)$ remains fixed.

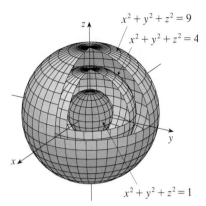

$x^2 + y^2 + z^2 = 9$

$x^2 + y^2 + z^2 = 4$

$x^2 + y^2 + z^2 = 1$

FIGURE 20

EXAMPLE 15 Find the level surfaces of the function

$$f(x, y, z) = x^2 + y^2 + z^2$$

SOLUTION The level surfaces are $x^2 + y^2 + z^2 = k$, where $k \geqslant 0$. These form a family of concentric spheres with radius $\sqrt{k}$. (See Figure 20.) Thus, as (x, y, z) varies over any sphere with center O, the value of $f(x, y, z)$ remains fixed. □

Functions of any number of variables can be considered. A **function of n variables** is a rule that assigns a number $z = f(x_1, x_2, \ldots, x_n)$ to an n-tuple $(x_1, x_2, \ldots, x_n)$ of real numbers. We denote by $\mathbb{R}^n$ the set of all such n-tuples. For example, if a company uses n different ingredients in making a food product, c_i is the cost per unit of the ith ingredient, and x_i units of the ith ingredient are used, then the total cost C of the ingredients is a function of the n variables $x_1, x_2, \ldots, x_n$:

$$\boxed{3} \qquad C = f(x_1, x_2, \ldots, x_n) = c_1 x_1 + c_2 x_2 + \cdots + c_n x_n$$

The function f is a real-valued function whose domain is a subset of $\mathbb{R}^n$. Sometimes we will use vector notation to write such functions more compactly: If $\mathbf{x} = \langle x_1, x_2, \ldots, x_n \rangle$, we often write $f(\mathbf{x})$ in place of $f(x_1, x_2, \ldots, x_n)$. With this notation we can rewrite the function defined in Equation 3 as

$$f(\mathbf{x}) = \mathbf{c} \cdot \mathbf{x}$$

where $\mathbf{c} = \langle c_1, c_2, \ldots, c_n \rangle$ and $\mathbf{c} \cdot \mathbf{x}$ denotes the dot product of the vectors $\mathbf{c}$ and $\mathbf{x}$ in V_n.

In view of the one-to-one correspondence between points $(x_1, x_2, \ldots, x_n)$ in $\mathbb{R}^n$ and their position vectors $\mathbf{x} = \langle x_1, x_2, \ldots, x_n \rangle$ in V_n, we have three ways of looking at a function f defined on a subset of $\mathbb{R}^n$:

1. As a function of n real variables $x_1, x_2, \ldots, x_n$

2. As a function of a single point variable $(x_1, x_2, \ldots, x_n)$

3. As a function of a single vector variable $\mathbf{x} = \langle x_1, x_2, \ldots, x_n \rangle$

We will see that all three points of view are useful.

15.1 EXERCISES

1. In Example 2 we considered the function $W = f(T, v)$, where W is the wind-chill index, T is the actual temperature, and v is the wind speed. A numerical representation is given in Table 1.
(a) What is the value of $f(-15, 40)$? What is its meaning?
(b) Describe in words the meaning of the question "For what value of v is $f(-20, v) = -30$?" Then answer the question.

(c) Describe in words the meaning of the question "For what value of T is $f(T, 20) = -49$?" Then answer the question.
(d) What is the meaning of the function $W = f(-5, v)$? Describe the behavior of this function.
(e) What is the meaning of the function $W = f(T, 50)$? Describe the behavior of this function.

2. The *temperature-humidity index* I (or humidex, for short) is the perceived air temperature when the actual temperature is T and the relative humidity is h, so we can write $I = f(T, h)$. The following table of values of I is an excerpt from a table compiled by the National Oceanic & Atmospheric Administration.

TABLE 3   Apparent temperature as a function of temperature and humidity

Relative humidity (%)

T \ h	20	30	40	50	60	70
80	77	78	79	81	82	83
85	82	84	86	88	90	93
90	87	90	93	96	100	106
95	93	96	101	107	114	124
100	99	104	110	120	132	144

Actual temperature (°F)

(a) What is the value of $f(95, 70)$? What is its meaning?
(b) For what value of h is $f(90, h) = 100$?
(c) For what value of T is $f(T, 50) = 88$?
(d) What are the meanings of the functions $I = f(80, h)$ and $I = f(100, h)$? Compare the behavior of these two functions of h.

3. Verify for the Cobb-Douglas production function

$$P(L, K) = 1.01L^{0.75}K^{0.25}$$

discussed in Example 3 that the production will be doubled if both the amount of labor and the amount of capital are doubled. Determine whether this is also true for the general production function

$$P(L, K) = bL^{\alpha}K^{1-\alpha}$$

4. The wind-chill index W discussed in Example 2 has been modeled by the following function:

$$W(T, v) = 13.12 + 0.6215T - 11.37v^{0.16} + 0.3965Tv^{0.16}$$

Check to see how closely this model agrees with the values in Table 1 for a few values of T and v.

5. The wave heights h in the open sea depend on the speed v of the wind and the length of time t that the wind has been blowing at that speed. Values of the function $h = f(v, t)$ are recorded in feet in Table 4.
(a) What is the value of $f(40, 15)$? What is its meaning?
(b) What is the meaning of the function $h = f(30, t)$? Describe the behavior of this function.
(c) What is the meaning of the function $h = f(v, 30)$? Describe the behavior of this function.

TABLE 4

Duration (hours)

v \ t	5	10	15	20	30	40	50
10	2	2	2	2	2	2	2
15	4	4	5	5	5	5	5
20	5	7	8	8	9	9	9
30	9	13	16	17	18	19	19
40	14	21	25	28	31	33	33
50	19	29	36	40	45	48	50
60	24	37	47	54	62	67	69

Wind speed (knots)

6. Let $f(x, y) = \ln(x + y - 1)$.
(a) Evaluate $f(1, 1)$.   (b) Evaluate $f(e, 1)$.
(c) Find and sketch the domain of f.
(d) Find the range of f.

7. Let $f(x, y) = x^2 e^{3xy}$.
(a) Evaluate $f(2, 0)$.   (b) Find the domain of f.
(c) Find the range of f.

8. Find and sketch the domain of the function $f(x, y) = \sqrt{1 + x - y^2}$. What is the range of f?

9. Let $f(x, y, z) = e^{\sqrt{z - x^2 - y^2}}$.
(a) Evaluate $f(2, -1, 6)$.   (b) Find the domain of f.
(c) Find the range of f.

10. Let $g(x, y, z) = \ln(25 - x^2 - y^2 - z^2)$.
(a) Evaluate $g(2, -2, 4)$.   (b) Find the domain of g.
(c) Find the range of g.

11–20 Find and sketch the domain of the function.

11. $f(x, y) = \sqrt{x + y}$

12. $f(x, y) = \sqrt{xy}$

13. $f(x, y) = \ln(9 - x^2 - 9y^2)$

14. $f(x, y) = \sqrt{y - x} \, \ln(y + x)$

15. $f(x, y) = \sqrt{1 - x^2} - \sqrt{1 - y^2}$

16. $f(x, y) = \sqrt{y} + \sqrt{25 - x^2 - y^2}$

17. $f(x, y) = \dfrac{\sqrt{y - x^2}}{1 - x^2}$

18. $f(x, y) = \arcsin(x^2 + y^2 - 2)$

19. $f(x, y, z) = \sqrt{1 - x^2 - y^2 - z^2}$

20. $f(x, y, z) = \ln(16 - 4x^2 - 4y^2 - z^2)$

21–29 Sketch the graph of the function.

21. $f(x, y) = 3$

22. $f(x, y) = y$

23. $f(x, y) = 10 - 4x - 5y$

24. $f(x, y) = \cos x$

25. $f(x, y) = y^2 + 1$

26. $f(x, y) = 3 - x^2 - y^2$

27. $f(x, y) = 4x^2 + y^2 + 1$

28. $f(x, y) = \sqrt{16 - x^2 - 16y^2}$

29. $f(x, y) = \sqrt{x^2 + y^2}$

---

30. Match the function with its graph (labeled I–VI). Give reasons for your choices.

(a) $f(x, y) = |x| + |y|$

(b) $f(x, y) = |xy|$

(c) $f(x, y) = \dfrac{1}{1 + x^2 + y^2}$

(d) $f(x, y) = (x^2 - y^2)^2$

(e) $f(x, y) = (x - y)^2$

(f) $f(x, y) = \sin(|x| + |y|)$

I

II

III

IV

V

VI
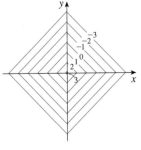

31. A contour map for a function f is shown. Use it to estimate the values of $f(-3, 3)$ and $f(3, -2)$. What can you say about the shape of the graph?

32. Two contour maps are shown. One is for a function f whose graph is a cone. The other is for a function g whose graph is a paraboloid. Which is which, and why?

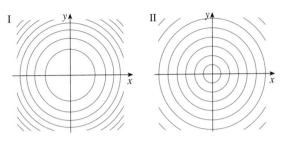

33. Locate the points A and B in the map of Lonesome Mountain (Figure 12). How would you describe the terrain near A? Near B?

34. Make a rough sketch of a contour map for the function whose graph is shown.

35–38 A contour map of a function is shown. Use it to make a rough sketch of the graph of f.

35.

36.

37.

38.

39–46 Draw a contour map of the function showing several level curves.

39. $f(x, y) = (y - 2x)^2$ 　　　　**40.** $f(x, y) = x^3 - y$

41. $f(x, y) = y - \ln x$ 　　　　**42.** $f(x, y) = e^{y/x}$

43. $f(x, y) = ye^x$ 　　　　**44.** $f(x, y) = y \sec x$

45. $f(x, y) = \sqrt{y^2 - x^2}$ 　　　**46.** $f(x, y) = y/(x^2 + y^2)$

47–48 Sketch both a contour map and a graph of the function and compare them.

47. $f(x, y) = x^2 + 9y^2$

48. $f(x, y) = \sqrt{36 - 9x^2 - 4y^2}$

---

49. A thin metal plate, located in the xy-plane, has temperature $T(x, y)$ at the point (x, y). The level curves of T are called *isothermals* because at all points on an isothermal the temperature is the same. Sketch some isothermals if the temperature function is given by
$$T(x, y) = 100/(1 + x^2 + 2y^2)$$

50. If $V(x, y)$ is the electric potential at a point (x, y) in the xy-plane, then the level curves of V are called *equipotential curves* because at all points on such a curve the electric potential is the same. Sketch some equipotential curves if $V(x, y) = c/\sqrt{r^2 - x^2 - y^2}$, where c is a positive constant.

51–54 Use a computer to graph the function using various domains and viewpoints. Get a printout of one that, in your opinion, gives a good view. If your software also produces level curves, then plot some contour lines of the same function and compare with the graph.

51. $f(x, y) = e^{-x^2} + e^{-2y^2}$

52. $f(x, y) = (1 - 3x^2 + y^2)e^{1-x^2-y^2}$

53. $f(x, y) = xy^2 - x^3$ (monkey saddle)

54. $f(x, y) = xy^3 - yx^3$ (dog saddle)

55–60 Match the function (a) with its graph (labeled A–F on page 905) and (b) with its contour map (labeled I–VI). Give reasons for your choices.

55. $z = \sin(xy)$ 　　　　**56.** $z = e^x \cos y$

57. $z = \sin(x - y)$ 　　　　**58.** $z = \sin x - \sin y$

59. $z = (1 - x^2)(1 - y^2)$ 　　**60.** $z = \dfrac{x - y}{1 + x^2 + y^2}$

61–64 Describe the level surfaces of the function.

61. $f(x, y, z) = x + 3y + 5z$

62. $f(x, y, z) = x^2 + 3y^2 + 5z^2$

63. $f(x, y, z) = x^2 - y^2 + z^2$

64. $f(x, y, z) = x^2 - y^2$

65–66 Describe how the graph of g is obtained from the graph of f.

65. (a) $g(x, y) = f(x, y) + 2$ 　　(b) $g(x, y) = 2f(x, y)$
　　(c) $g(x, y) = -f(x, y)$ 　　(d) $g(x, y) = 2 - f(x, y)$

66. (a) $g(x, y) = f(x - 2, y)$ 　　(b) $g(x, y) = f(x, y + 2)$
　　(c) $g(x, y) = f(x + 3, y - 4)$

67–68 Use a computer to graph the function using various domains and viewpoints. Get a printout that gives a good view of the "peaks and valleys." Would you say the function has a maximum value? Can you identify any points on the graph that you might consider to be "local maximum points"? What about "local minimum points"?

67. $f(x, y) = 3x - x^4 - 4y^2 - 10xy$

68. $f(x, y) = xye^{-x^2-y^2}$

69–70 Use a computer to graph the function using various domains and viewpoints. Comment on the limiting behavior of the function. What happens as both x and y become large? What happens as (x, y) approaches the origin?

69. $f(x, y) = \dfrac{x + y}{x^2 + y^2}$ 　　**70.** $f(x, y) = \dfrac{xy}{x^2 + y^2}$

---

71. Use a computer to investigate the family of functions $f(x, y) = e^{cx^2+y^2}$. How does the shape of the graph depend on c?

72. Use a computer to investigate the family of surfaces
$$z = (ax^2 + by^2)e^{-x^2-y^2}$$
How does the shape of the graph depend on the numbers a and b?

73. Use a computer to investigate the family of surfaces $z = x^2 + y^2 + cxy$. In particular, you should determine the transitional values of c for which the surface changes from one type of quadric surface to another.

Graphs and Contour Maps for Exercises 55–60

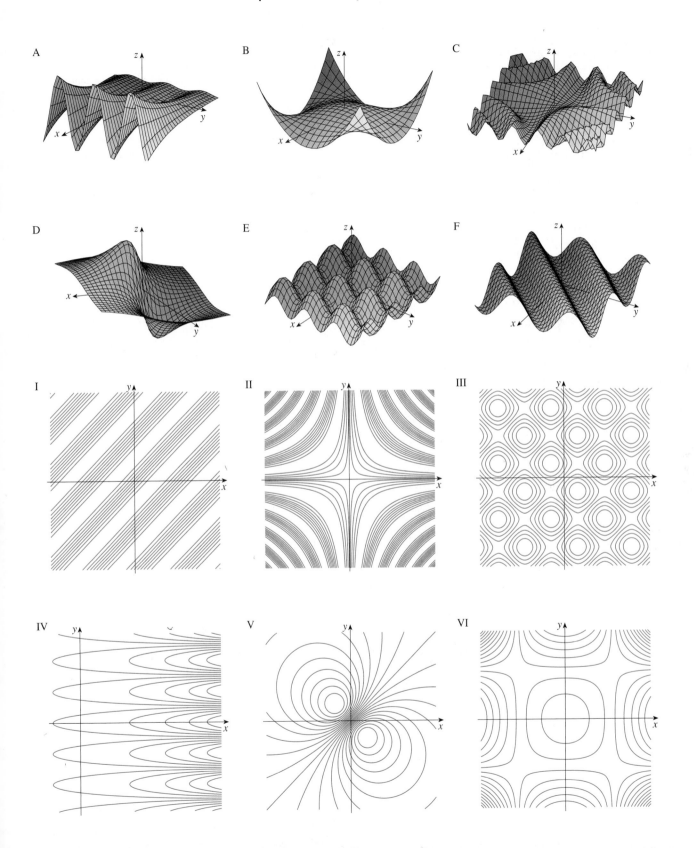

74. Graph the functions

$$f(x, y) = \sqrt{x^2 + y^2} \qquad f(x, y) = e^{\sqrt{x^2+y^2}}$$

$$f(x, y) = \ln\sqrt{x^2 + y^2} \qquad f(x, y) = \sin(\sqrt{x^2 + y^2})$$

and

$$f(x, y) = \frac{1}{\sqrt{x^2 + y^2}}$$

In general, if g is a function of one variable, how is the graph of

$$f(x, y) = g(\sqrt{x^2 + y^2})$$

obtained from the graph of g?

75. (a) Show that, by taking logarithms, the general Cobb-Douglas function $P = bL^\alpha K^{1-\alpha}$ can be expressed as

$$\ln \frac{P}{K} = \ln b + \alpha \ln \frac{L}{K}$$

(b) If we let $x = \ln(L/K)$ and $y = \ln(P/K)$, the equation in part (a) becomes the linear equation $y = \alpha x + \ln b$. Use Table 2 (in Example 3) to make a table of values of $\ln(L/K)$ and $\ln(P/K)$ for the years 1899–1922. Then use a graphing calculator or computer to find the least squares regression line through the points $(\ln(L/K), \ln(P/K))$.

(c) Deduce that the Cobb-Douglas production function is $P = 1.01L^{0.75}K^{0.25}$.

15.2 LIMITS AND CONTINUITY

Let's compare the behavior of the functions

$$f(x, y) = \frac{\sin(x^2 + y^2)}{x^2 + y^2} \qquad \text{and} \qquad g(x, y) = \frac{x^2 - y^2}{x^2 + y^2}$$

as x and y both approach 0 [and therefore the point (x, y) approaches the origin].

TABLE 1 Values of $f(x, y)$

x \ y	−1.0	−0.5	−0.2	0	0.2	0.5	1.0
−1.0	0.455	0.759	0.829	0.841	0.829	0.759	0.455
−0.5	0.759	0.959	0.986	0.990	0.986	0.959	0.759
−0.2	0.829	0.986	0.999	1.000	0.999	0.986	0.829
0	0.841	0.990	1.000		1.000	0.990	0.841
0.2	0.829	0.986	0.999	1.000	0.999	0.986	0.829
0.5	0.759	0.959	0.986	0.990	0.986	0.959	0.759
1.0	0.455	0.759	0.829	0.841	0.829	0.759	0.455

TABLE 2 Values of $g(x, y)$

x \ y	−1.0	−0.5	−0.2	0	0.2	0.5	1.0
−1.0	0.000	0.600	0.923	1.000	0.923	0.600	0.000
−0.5	−0.600	0.000	0.724	1.000	0.724	0.000	−0.600
−0.2	−0.923	−0.724	0.000	1.000	0.000	−0.724	−0.923
0	−1.000	−1.000	−1.000		−1.000	−1.000	−1.000
0.2	−0.923	−0.724	0.000	1.000	0.000	−0.724	−0.923
0.5	−0.600	0.000	0.724	1.000	0.724	0.000	−0.600
1.0	0.000	0.600	0.923	1.000	0.923	0.600	0.000

Tables 1 and 2 show values of $f(x, y)$ and $g(x, y)$, correct to three decimal places, for points (x, y) near the origin. (Notice that neither function is defined at the origin.) It appears that as (x, y) approaches $(0, 0)$, the values of $f(x, y)$ are approaching 1 whereas the values of $g(x, y)$ aren't approaching any number. It turns out that these guesses based on numerical evidence are correct, and we write

$$\lim_{(x, y) \to (0, 0)} \frac{\sin(x^2 + y^2)}{x^2 + y^2} = 1 \qquad \text{and} \qquad \lim_{(x, y) \to (0, 0)} \frac{x^2 - y^2}{x^2 + y^2} \quad \text{does not exist}$$

In general, we use the notation

$$\lim_{(x, y) \to (a, b)} f(x, y) = L$$

to indicate that the values of $f(x, y)$ approach the number L as the point (x, y) approaches the point (a, b) along any path that stays within the domain of f. In other words, we can make the values of $f(x, y)$ as close to L as we like by taking the point (x, y) sufficiently close to the point (a, b), but not equal to (a, b). A more precise definition follows.

□ **DEFINITION** Let f be a function of two variables whose domain D includes points arbitrarily close to (a, b). Then we say that the **limit of $f(x, y)$ as (x, y) approaches (a, b)** is L and we write

$$\lim_{(x, y) \to (a, b)} f(x, y) = L$$

if for every number $\varepsilon > 0$ there is a corresponding number $\delta > 0$ such that

$$\text{if} \quad (x, y) \in D \quad \text{and} \quad 0 < \sqrt{(x - a)^2 + (y - b)^2} < \delta \quad \text{then} \quad |f(x, y) - L| < \varepsilon$$

Other notations for the limit in Definition 1 are

$$\lim_{\substack{x \to a \\ y \to b}} f(x, y) = L \qquad \text{and} \qquad f(x, y) \to L \text{ as } (x, y) \to (a, b)$$

Notice that $|f(x, y) - L|$ is the distance between the numbers $f(x, y)$ and L, and $\sqrt{(x - a)^2 + (y - b)^2}$ is the distance between the point (x, y) and the point (a, b). Thus Definition 1 says that the distance between $f(x, y)$ and L can be made arbitrarily small by making the distance from (x, y) to (a, b) sufficiently small (but not 0). Figure 1 illustrates Definition 1 by means of an arrow diagram. If any small interval $(L - \varepsilon, L + \varepsilon)$ is given around L, then we can find a disk D_δ with center (a, b) and radius $\delta > 0$ such that f maps all the points in D_δ [except possibly (a, b)] into the interval $(L - \varepsilon, L + \varepsilon)$.

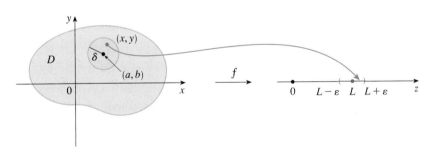

FIGURE 1

FIGURE 2

Another illustration of Definition 1 is given in Figure 2 where the surface S is the graph of f. If $\varepsilon > 0$ is given, we can find $\delta > 0$ such that if (x, y) is restricted to lie in the disk D_δ and $(x, y) \neq (a, b)$, then the corresponding part of S lies between the horizontal planes $z = L - \varepsilon$ and $z = L + \varepsilon$.

For functions of a single variable, when we let x approach a, there are only two possible directions of approach, from the left or from the right. We recall from Chapter 2 that if $\lim_{x \to a^-} f(x) \neq \lim_{x \to a^+} f(x)$, then $\lim_{x \to a} f(x)$ does not exist.

For functions of two variables the situation is not as simple because we can let (x, y) approach (a, b) from an infinite number of directions in any manner whatsoever (see Figure 3) as long as (x, y) stays within the domain of f.

FIGURE 3

Definition 1 says that the distance between $f(x, y)$ and L can be made arbitrarily small by making the distance from (x, y) to (a, b) sufficiently small (but not 0). The definition refers only to the *distance* between (x, y) and (a, b). It does not refer to the direction of approach. Therefore, if the limit exists, then $f(x, y)$ must approach the same limit no matter how (x, y) approaches (a, b). Thus if we can find two different paths of approach along which the function $f(x, y)$ has different limits, then it follows that $\lim_{(x, y) \to (a, b)} f(x, y)$ does not exist.

> If $f(x, y) \to L_1$ as $(x, y) \to (a, b)$ along a path C_1 and $f(x, y) \to L_2$ as $(x, y) \to (a, b)$ along a path C_2, where $L_1 \neq L_2$, then $\lim_{(x, y) \to (a, b)} f(x, y)$ does not exist.

☑ **EXAMPLE 1** Show that $\displaystyle\lim_{(x, y) \to (0, 0)} \frac{x^2 - y^2}{x^2 + y^2}$ does not exist.

SOLUTION Let $f(x, y) = (x^2 - y^2)/(x^2 + y^2)$. First let's approach $(0, 0)$ along the x-axis. Then $y = 0$ gives $f(x, 0) = x^2/x^2 = 1$ for all $x \neq 0$, so

$$f(x, y) \to 1 \qquad \text{as} \qquad (x, y) \to (0, 0) \text{ along the } x\text{-axis}$$

We now approach along the y-axis by putting $x = 0$. Then $f(0, y) = \dfrac{-y^2}{y^2} = -1$ for all $y \neq 0$, so

$$f(x, y) \to -1 \qquad \text{as} \qquad (x, y) \to (0, 0) \text{ along the } y\text{-axis}$$

(See Figure 4.) Since f has two different limits along two different lines, the given limit does not exist. (This confirms the conjecture we made on the basis of numerical evidence at the beginning of this section.) □

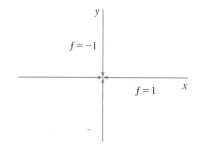

FIGURE 4

EXAMPLE 2 If $f(x, y) = \dfrac{xy}{x^2 + y^2}$, does $\displaystyle\lim_{(x, y) \to (0, 0)} f(x, y)$ exist?

SOLUTION If $y = 0$, then $f(x, 0) = 0/x^2 = 0$. Therefore

$$f(x, y) \to 0 \qquad \text{as} \qquad (x, y) \to (0, 0) \text{ along the } x\text{-axis}$$

If $x = 0$, then $f(0, y) = 0/y^2 = 0$, so

$$f(x, y) \to 0 \qquad \text{as} \qquad (x, y) \to (0, 0) \text{ along the } y\text{-axis}$$

Although we have obtained identical limits along the axes, that does not show that the given limit is 0. Let's now approach $(0, 0)$ along another line, say $y = x$. For all $x \neq 0$,

$$f(x, x) = \frac{x^2}{x^2 + x^2} = \frac{1}{2}$$

Therefore $\qquad f(x, y) \to \frac{1}{2} \qquad \text{as} \qquad (x, y) \to (0, 0) \text{ along } y = x$

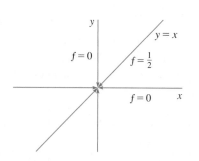

FIGURE 5

(See Figure 5.) Since we have obtained different limits along different paths, the given limit does not exist. □

Figure 6 sheds some light on Example 2. The ridge that occurs above the line $y = x$ corresponds to the fact that $f(x, y) = \frac{1}{2}$ for all points (x, y) on that line except the origin.

TEC In Visual 15.2 a rotating line on the surface in Figure 6 shows different limits at the origin from different directions.

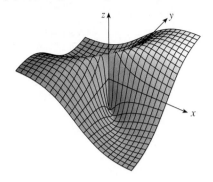

FIGURE 6

$$f(x, y) = \frac{xy}{x^2 + y^2}$$

V EXAMPLE 3 If $f(x, y) = \dfrac{xy^2}{x^2 + y^4}$, does $\displaystyle\lim_{(x, y) \to (0, 0)} f(x, y)$ exist?

SOLUTION With the solution of Example 2 in mind, let's try to save time by letting $(x, y) \to (0, 0)$ along any nonvertical line through the origin. Then $y = mx$, where m is the slope, and

$$f(x, y) = f(x, mx) = \frac{x(mx)^2}{x^2 + (mx)^4} = \frac{m^2 x^3}{x^2 + m^4 x^4} = \frac{m^2 x}{1 + m^4 x^2}$$

So $\qquad\qquad f(x, y) \to 0 \qquad$ as $\qquad (x, y) \to (0, 0)$ along $y = mx$

■ Figure 7 shows the graph of the function in Example 3. Notice the ridge above the parabola $x = y^2$.

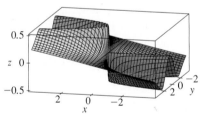

FIGURE 7

Thus f has the same limiting value along every nonvertical line through the origin. But that does not show that the given limit is 0, for if we now let $(x, y) \to (0, 0)$ along the parabola $x = y^2$, we have

$$f(x, y) = f(y^2, y) = \frac{y^2 \cdot y^2}{(y^2)^2 + y^4} = \frac{y^4}{2y^4} = \frac{1}{2}$$

so $\qquad\qquad f(x, y) \to \frac{1}{2} \qquad$ as $\qquad (x, y) \to (0, 0)$ along $x = y^2$

Since different paths lead to different limiting values, the given limit does not exist. $\qquad\square$

Now let's look at limits that *do* exist. Just as for functions of one variable, the calculation of limits for functions of two variables can be greatly simplified by the use of properties of limits. The Limit Laws listed in Section 2.3 can be extended to functions of two variables: The limit of a sum is the sum of the limits, the limit of a product is the product of the limits, and so on. In particular, the following equations are true.

$$\boxed{2} \qquad \lim_{(x, y) \to (a, b)} x = a \qquad \lim_{(x, y) \to (a, b)} y = b \qquad \lim_{(x, y) \to (a, b)} c = c$$

The Squeeze Theorem also holds.

EXAMPLE 4 Find $\displaystyle\lim_{(x, y) \to (0, 0)} \frac{3x^2 y}{x^2 + y^2}$ if it exists.

SOLUTION As in Example 3, we could show that the limit along any line through the origin is 0. This doesn't prove that the given limit is 0, but the limits along the parabolas

910 |||| CHAPTER 15 PARTIAL DERIVATIVES

$y = x^2$ and $x = y^2$ also turn out to be 0, so we begin to suspect that the limit does exist and is equal to 0.

Let $\varepsilon > 0$. We want to find $\delta > 0$ such that

$$\text{if} \quad 0 < \sqrt{x^2 + y^2} < \delta \quad \text{then} \quad \left| \frac{3x^2y}{x^2 + y^2} - 0 \right| < \varepsilon$$

that is, $\qquad\qquad \text{if} \quad 0 < \sqrt{x^2 + y^2} < \delta \quad \text{then} \quad \dfrac{3x^2|y|}{x^2 + y^2} < \varepsilon$

But $x^2 \leqslant x^2 + y^2$ since $y^2 \geqslant 0$, so $x^2/(x^2 + y^2) \leqslant 1$ and therefore

$$\boxed{3} \qquad\qquad \frac{3x^2|y|}{x^2 + y^2} \leqslant 3|y| = 3\sqrt{y^2} \leqslant 3\sqrt{x^2 + y^2}$$

Thus if we choose $\delta = \varepsilon/3$ and let $0 < \sqrt{x^2 + y^2} < \delta$, then

$$\left| \frac{3x^2y}{x^2 + y^2} - 0 \right| \leqslant 3\sqrt{x^2 + y^2} < 3\delta = 3\left(\frac{\varepsilon}{3}\right) = \varepsilon$$

Hence, by Definition 1,

$$\lim_{(x, y) \to (0, 0)} \frac{3x^2y}{x^2 + y^2} = 0 \qquad\qquad\qquad \square$$

■ Another way to do Example 4 is to use the Squeeze Theorem instead of Definition 1. From (2) it follows that

$$\lim_{(x, y) \to (0, 0)} 3|y| = 0$$

and so the first inequality in (3) shows that the given limit is 0.

CONTINUITY

Recall that evaluating limits of *continuous* functions of a single variable is easy. It can be accomplished by direct substitution because the defining property of a continuous function is $\lim_{x \to a} f(x) = f(a)$. Continuous functions of two variables are also defined by the direct substitution property.

---

4 DEFINITION A function f of two variables is called **continuous at** (a, b) if

$$\lim_{(x, y) \to (a, b)} f(x, y) = f(a, b)$$

We say f is **continuous on** D if f is continuous at every point (a, b) in D.

The intuitive meaning of continuity is that if the point (x, y) changes by a small amount, then the value of $f(x, y)$ changes by a small amount. This means that a surface that is the graph of a continuous function has no hole or break.

Using the properties of limits, you can see that sums, differences, products, and quotients of continuous functions are continuous on their domains. Let's use this fact to give examples of continuous functions.

A **polynomial function of two variables** (or polynomial, for short) is a sum of terms of the form $cx^m y^n$, where c is a constant and m and n are nonnegative integers. A **rational function** is a ratio of polynomials. For instance,

$$f(x, y) = x^4 + 5x^3y^2 + 6xy^4 - 7y + 6$$

is a polynomial, whereas

$$g(x, y) = \frac{2xy + 1}{x^2 + y^2}$$

is a rational function.

The limits in (2) show that the functions $f(x, y) = x$, $g(x, y) = y$, and $h(x, y) = c$ are continuous. Since any polynomial can be built up out of the simple functions f, g, and h by multiplication and addition, it follows that *all polynomials are continuous on* $\mathbb{R}^2$. Likewise, any rational function is continuous on its domain because it is a quotient of continuous functions.

V EXAMPLE 5 Evaluate $\lim\limits_{(x, y) \to (1, 2)} (x^2y^3 - x^3y^2 + 3x + 2y)$.

SOLUTION Since $f(x, y) = x^2y^3 - x^3y^2 + 3x + 2y$ is a polynomial, it is continuous everywhere, so we can find the limit by direct substitution:

$$\lim_{(x, y) \to (1, 2)} (x^2y^3 - x^3y^2 + 3x + 2y) = 1^2 \cdot 2^3 - 1^3 \cdot 2^2 + 3 \cdot 1 + 2 \cdot 2 = 11 \qquad \square$$

EXAMPLE 6 Where is the function $f(x, y) = \dfrac{x^2 - y^2}{x^2 + y^2}$ continuous?

SOLUTION The function f is discontinuous at $(0, 0)$ because it is not defined there. Since f is a rational function, it is continuous on its domain, which is the set $D = \{(x, y) \mid (x, y) \neq (0, 0)\}$. $\qquad \square$

EXAMPLE 7 Let

$$g(x, y) = \begin{cases} \dfrac{x^2 - y^2}{x^2 + y^2} & \text{if } (x, y) \neq (0, 0) \\ 0 & \text{if } (x, y) = (0, 0) \end{cases}$$

Here g is defined at $(0, 0)$ but g is still discontinuous there because $\lim_{(x, y) \to (0, 0)} g(x, y)$ does not exist (see Example 1). $\qquad \square$

EXAMPLE 8 Let

$$f(x, y) = \begin{cases} \dfrac{3x^2y}{x^2 + y^2} & \text{if } (x, y) \neq (0, 0) \\ 0 & \text{if } (x, y) = (0, 0) \end{cases}$$

We know f is continuous for $(x, y) \neq (0, 0)$ since it is equal to a rational function there. Also, from Example 4, we have

$$\lim_{(x, y) \to (0, 0)} f(x, y) = \lim_{(x, y) \to (0, 0)} \frac{3x^2y}{x^2 + y^2} = 0 = f(0, 0)$$

Therefore f is continuous at $(0, 0)$, and so it is continuous on $\mathbb{R}^2$. $\qquad \square$

■ Figure 8 shows the graph of the continuous function in Example 8.

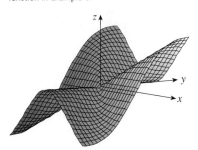

FIGURE 8

Just as for functions of one variable, composition is another way of combining two continuous functions to get a third. In fact, it can be shown that if f is a continuous function of two variables and g is a continuous function of a single variable that is defined on the range of f, then the composite function $h = g \circ f$ defined by $h(x, y) = g(f(x, y))$ is also a continuous function.

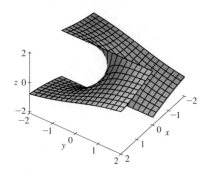

FIGURE 9

The function $h(x, y) = \arctan(y/x)$
is discontinuous where $x = 0$.

EXAMPLE 9 Where is the function $h(x, y) = \arctan(y/x)$ continuous?

SOLUTION The function $f(x, y) = y/x$ is a rational function and therefore continuous except on the line $x = 0$. The function $g(t) = \arctan t$ is continuous everywhere. So the composite function

$$g(f(x, y)) = \arctan(y/x) = h(x, y)$$

is continuous except where $x = 0$. The graph in Figure 9 shows the break in the graph of h above the y-axis. □

FUNCTIONS OF THREE OR MORE VARIABLES

Everything that we have done in this section can be extended to functions of three or more variables. The notation

$$\lim_{(x, y, z) \to (a, b, c)} f(x, y, z) = L$$

means that the values of $f(x, y, z)$ approach the number L as the point (x, y, z) approaches the point (a, b, c) along any path in the domain of f. Because the distance between two points (x, y, z) and (a, b, c) in $\mathbb{R}^3$ is given by $\sqrt{(x - a)^2 + (y - b)^2 + (z - c)^2}$, we can write the precise definition as follows: For every number $\varepsilon > 0$ there is a corresponding number $\delta > 0$ such that

if (x, y, z) is in the domain of f and $0 < \sqrt{(x - a)^2 + (y - b)^2 + (z - c)^2} < \delta$

then $|f(x, y, z) - L| < \varepsilon$

The function f is **continuous** at (a, b, c) if

$$\lim_{(x, y, z) \to (a, b, c)} f(x, y, z) = f(a, b, c)$$

For instance, the function

$$f(x, y, z) = \frac{1}{x^2 + y^2 + z^2 - 1}$$

is a rational function of three variables and so is continuous at every point in $\mathbb{R}^3$ except where $x^2 + y^2 + z^2 = 1$. In other words, it is discontinuous on the sphere with center the origin and radius 1.

If we use the vector notation introduced at the end of Section 15.1, then we can write the definitions of a limit for functions of two or three variables in a single compact form as follows.

> **5** If f is defined on a subset D of $\mathbb{R}^n$, then $\lim_{x \to a} f(x) = L$ means that for every number $\varepsilon > 0$ there is a corresponding number $\delta > 0$ such that
>
> if $x \in D$ and $0 < |x - a| < \delta$ then $|f(x) - L| < \varepsilon$

Notice that if $n = 1$, then $\mathbf{x} = x$ and $\mathbf{a} = a$, and (5) is just the definition of a limit for functions of a single variable. For the case $n = 2$, we have $\mathbf{x} = \langle x, y \rangle$, $\mathbf{a} = \langle a, b \rangle$, and $|\mathbf{x} - \mathbf{a}| = \sqrt{(x - a)^2 + (y - b)^2}$, so (5) becomes Definition 1. If $n = 3$, then $\mathbf{x} = \langle x, y, z \rangle$, $\mathbf{a} = \langle a, b, c \rangle$, and (5) becomes the definition of a limit of a function of three variables. In each case the definition of continuity can be written as

$$\lim_{\mathbf{x} \to \mathbf{a}} f(\mathbf{x}) = f(\mathbf{a})$$

15.2 EXERCISES

1. Suppose that $\lim_{(x, y) \to (3, 1)} f(x, y) = 6$. What can you say about the value of $f(3, 1)$? What if f is continuous?

2. Explain why each function is continuous or discontinuous.
(a) The outdoor temperature as a function of longitude, latitude, and time
(b) Elevation (height above sea level) as a function of longitude, latitude, and time
(c) The cost of a taxi ride as a function of distance traveled and time

3–4 Use a table of numerical values of $f(x, y)$ for (x, y) near the origin to make a conjecture about the value of the limit of $f(x, y)$ as $(x, y) \to (0, 0)$. Then explain why your guess is correct.

3. $f(x, y) = \dfrac{x^2 y^3 + x^3 y^2 - 5}{2 - xy}$ **4.** $f(x, y) = \dfrac{2xy}{x^2 + 2y^2}$

5–22 Find the limit, if it exists, or show that the limit does not exist.

5. $\lim_{(x, y) \to (1, 2)} (5x^3 - x^2 y^2)$ **6.** $\lim_{(x, y) \to (1, -1)} e^{-xy} \cos(x + y)$

7. $\lim_{(x, y) \to (2, 1)} \dfrac{4 - xy}{x^2 + 3y^2}$ **8.** $\lim_{(x, y) \to (1, 0)} \ln\left(\dfrac{1 + y^2}{x^2 + xy}\right)$

9. $\lim_{(x, y) \to (0, 0)} \dfrac{y^4}{x^4 + 3y^4}$ **10.** $\lim_{(x, y) \to (0, 0)} \dfrac{x^2 + \sin^2 y}{2x^2 + y^2}$

11. $\lim_{(x, y) \to (0, 0)} \dfrac{xy \cos y}{3x^2 + y^2}$ **12.** $\lim_{(x, y) \to (0, 0)} \dfrac{6x^3 y}{2x^4 + y^4}$

13. $\lim_{(x, y) \to (0, 0)} \dfrac{xy}{\sqrt{x^2 + y^2}}$ **14.** $\lim_{(x, y) \to (0, 0)} \dfrac{x^4 - y^4}{x^2 + y^2}$

15. $\lim_{(x, y) \to (0, 0)} \dfrac{x^2 y e^y}{x^4 + 4y^2}$ **16.** $\lim_{(x, y) \to (0, 0)} \dfrac{x^2 \sin^2 y}{x^2 + 2y^2}$

17. $\lim_{(x, y) \to (0, 0)} \dfrac{x^2 + y^2}{\sqrt{x^2 + y^2 + 1} - 1}$ **18.** $\lim_{(x, y) \to (0, 0)} \dfrac{xy^4}{x^2 + y^8}$

19. $\lim_{(x, y, z) \to (3, 0, 1)} e^{-xy} \sin(\pi z / 2)$

20. $\lim_{(x, y, z) \to (0, 0, 0)} \dfrac{x^2 + 2y^2 + 3z^2}{x^2 + y^2 + z^2}$

21. $\lim_{(x, y, z) \to (0, 0, 0)} \dfrac{xy + yz^2 + xz^2}{x^2 + y^2 + z^4}$

22. $\lim_{(x, y, z) \to (0, 0, 0)} \dfrac{yz}{x^2 + 4y^2 + 9z^2}$

23–24 Use a computer graph of the function to explain why the limit does not exist.

23. $\lim_{(x, y) \to (0, 0)} \dfrac{2x^2 + 3xy + 4y^2}{3x^2 + 5y^2}$

24. $\lim_{(x, y) \to (0, 0)} \dfrac{xy^3}{x^2 + y^6}$

25–26 Find $h(x, y) = g(f(x, y))$ and the set on which h is continuous.

25. $g(t) = t^2 + \sqrt{t}$, $f(x, y) = 2x + 3y - 6$

26. $g(t) = t + \ln t$, $f(x, y) = \dfrac{1 - xy}{1 + x^2 y^2}$

27–28 Graph the function and observe where it is discontinuous. Then use the formula to explain what you have observed.

27. $f(x, y) = e^{1/(x-y)}$ **28.** $f(x, y) = \dfrac{1}{1 - x^2 - y^2}$

29–38 Determine the set of points at which the function is continuous.

29. $F(x, y) = \dfrac{\sin(xy)}{e^x - y^2}$ **30.** $F(x, y) = \dfrac{x - y}{1 + x^2 + y^2}$

31. $F(x, y) = \arctan(x + \sqrt{y})$ **32.** $F(x, y) = e^{x^2 y} + \sqrt{x + y^2}$

33. $G(x, y) = \ln(x^2 + y^2 - 4)$ **34.** $G(x, y) = \tan^{-1}((x + y)^{-2})$

35. $f(x, y, z) = \dfrac{\sqrt{y}}{x^2 - y^2 + z^2}$

36. $f(x, y, z) = \sqrt{x + y + z}$

37. $f(x, y) = \begin{cases} \dfrac{x^2 y^3}{2x^2 + y^2} & \text{if } (x, y) \neq (0, 0) \\ 1 & \text{if } (x, y) = (0, 0) \end{cases}$

38. $f(x, y) = \begin{cases} \dfrac{xy}{x^2 + xy + y^2} & \text{if } (x, y) \neq (0, 0) \\ 0 & \text{if } (x, y) = (0, 0) \end{cases}$

39–41 Use polar coordinates to find the limit. [If (r, θ) are polar coordinates of the point (x, y) with $r \geq 0$, note that $r \to 0^+$ as $(x, y) \to (0, 0)$.]

39. $\lim_{(x, y) \to (0, 0)} \dfrac{x^3 + y^3}{x^2 + y^2}$

40. $\lim_{(x, y) \to (0, 0)} (x^2 + y^2) \ln(x^2 + y^2)$

41. $\lim_{(x, y) \to (0, 0)} \dfrac{e^{-x^2 - y^2} - 1}{x^2 + y^2}$

42. At the beginning of this section we considered the function

$$f(x, y) = \frac{\sin(x^2 + y^2)}{x^2 + y^2}$$

and guessed that $f(x, y) \to 1$ as $(x, y) \to (0, 0)$ on the basis of numerical evidence. Use polar coordinates to confirm the value of the limit. Then graph the function.

43. Graph and discuss the continuity of the function

$$f(x, y) = \begin{cases} \dfrac{\sin xy}{xy} & \text{if } xy \neq 0 \\ 1 & \text{if } xy = 0 \end{cases}$$

44. Let

$$f(x, y) = \begin{cases} 0 & \text{if } y \leq 0 \quad \text{or} \quad y \geq x^4 \\ 1 & \text{if } 0 < y < x^4 \end{cases}$$

(a) Show that $f(x, y) \to 0$ as $(x, y) \to (0, 0)$ along any path through $(0, 0)$ of the form $y = mx^a$ with $a < 4$.

(b) Despite part (a), show that f is discontinuous at $(0, 0)$.

(c) Show that f is discontinuous on two entire curves.

45. Show that the function f given by $f(\mathbf{x}) = |\mathbf{x}|$ is continuous on $\mathbb{R}^n$. [*Hint:* Consider $|\mathbf{x} - \mathbf{a}|^2 = (\mathbf{x} - \mathbf{a}) \cdot (\mathbf{x} - \mathbf{a})$.]

46. If $\mathbf{c} \in V_n$, show that the function f given by $f(\mathbf{x}) = \mathbf{c} \cdot \mathbf{x}$ is continuous on $\mathbb{R}^n$.

15.3 PARTIAL DERIVATIVES

On a hot day, extreme humidity makes us think the temperature is higher than it really is, whereas in very dry air we perceive the temperature to be lower than the thermometer indicates. The National Weather Service has devised the *heat index* (also called the temperature-humidity index, or humidex, in some countries) to describe the combined effects of temperature and humidity. The heat index I is the perceived air temperature when the actual temperature is T and the relative humidity is H. So I is a function of T and H and we can write $I = f(T, H)$. The following table of values of I is an excerpt from a table compiled by the National Weather Service.

TABLE 1

Heat index I as a function of temperature and humidity

					Relative humidity (%)				
T \ H	50	55	60	65	70	75	80	85	90
90	96	98	100	103	106	109	112	115	119
92	100	103	105	108	112	115	119	123	128
94	104	107	111	114	118	122	127	132	137
96	109	113	116	121	125	130	135	141	146
98	114	118	123	127	133	138	144	150	157
100	119	124	129	135	141	147	154	161	168

Actual temperature (°F)

If we concentrate on the highlighted column of the table, which corresponds to a relative humidity of $H = 70\%$, we are considering the heat index as a function of the single variable T for a fixed value of H. Let's write $g(T) = f(T, 70)$. Then $g(T)$ describes how the heat index I increases as the actual temperature T increases when the relative humidity is 70%. The derivative of g when $T = 96°F$ is the rate of change of I with respect to T when $T = 96°F$:

$$g'(96) = \lim_{h \to 0} \frac{g(96 + h) - g(96)}{h} = \lim_{h \to 0} \frac{f(96 + h, 70) - f(96, 70)}{h}$$

We can approximate $g'(96)$ using the values in Table 1 by taking $h = 2$ and -2:

$$g'(96) \approx \frac{g(98) - g(96)}{2} = \frac{f(98, 70) - f(96, 70)}{2} = \frac{133 - 125}{2} = 4$$

$$g'(96) \approx \frac{g(94) - g(96)}{-2} = \frac{f(94, 70) - f(96, 70)}{-2} = \frac{118 - 125}{-2} = 3.5$$

Averaging these values, we can say that the derivative $g'(96)$ is approximately 3.75. This means that, when the actual temperature is 96°F and the relative humidity is 70%, the apparent temperature (heat index) rises by about 3.75°F for every degree that the actual temperature rises!

Now let's look at the highlighted row in Table 1, which corresponds to a fixed temperature of $T = 96°$F. The numbers in this row are values of the function $G(H) = f(96, H)$, which describes how the heat index increases as the relative humidity H increases when the actual temperature is $T = 96°$F. The derivative of this function when $H = 70\%$ is the rate of change of I with respect to H when $H = 70\%$:

$$G'(70) = \lim_{h \to 0} \frac{G(70 + h) - G(70)}{h} = \lim_{h \to 0} \frac{f(96, 70 + h) - f(96, 70)}{h}$$

By taking $h = 5$ and -5, we approximate $G'(70)$ using the tabular values:

$$G'(70) \approx \frac{G(75) - G(70)}{5} = \frac{f(96, 75) - f(96, 70)}{5} = \frac{130 - 125}{5} = 1$$

$$G'(70) \approx \frac{G(65) - G(70)}{-5} = \frac{f(96, 65) - f(96, 70)}{-5} = \frac{121 - 125}{-5} = 0.8$$

By averaging these values we get the estimate $G'(70) \approx 0.9$. This says that, when the temperature is 96°F and the relative humidity is 70%, the heat index rises about 0.9°F for every percent that the relative humidity rises.

In general, if f is a function of two variables x and y, suppose we let only x vary while keeping y fixed, say $y = b$, where b is a constant. Then we are really considering a function of a single variable x, namely, $g(x) = f(x, b)$. If g has a derivative at a, then we call it the **partial derivative of f with respect to x at (a, b)** and denote it by $f_x(a, b)$. Thus

1

$$f_x(a, b) = g'(a) \qquad \text{where} \qquad g(x) = f(x, b)$$

By the definition of a derivative, we have

$$g'(a) = \lim_{h \to 0} \frac{g(a + h) - g(a)}{h}$$

and so Equation 1 becomes

2

$$f_x(a, b) = \lim_{h \to 0} \frac{f(a + h, b) - f(a, b)}{h}$$

Similarly, the **partial derivative of f with respect to y at (a, b)**, denoted by $f_y(a, b)$, is obtained by keeping x fixed ($x = a$) and finding the ordinary derivative at b of the function $G(y) = f(a, y)$:

$$\boxed{3} \qquad f_y(a, b) = \lim_{h \to 0} \frac{f(a, b + h) - f(a, b)}{h}$$

With this notation for partial derivatives, we can write the rates of change of the heat index I with respect to the actual temperature T and relative humidity H when $T = 96°F$ and $H = 70\%$ as follows:

$$f_T(96, 70) \approx 3.75 \qquad f_H(96, 70) \approx 0.9$$

If we now let the point (a, b) vary in Equations 2 and 3, f_x and f_y become functions of two variables.

> $\boxed{4}$ If f is a function of two variables, its **partial derivatives** are the functions f_x and f_y defined by
>
> $$f_x(x, y) = \lim_{h \to 0} \frac{f(x + h, y) - f(x, y)}{h}$$
>
> $$f_y(x, y) = \lim_{h \to 0} \frac{f(x, y + h) - f(x, y)}{h}$$

There are many alternative notations for partial derivatives. For instance, instead of f_x we can write f_1 or $D_1 f$ (to indicate differentiation with respect to the *first* variable) or $\partial f / \partial x$. But here $\partial f / \partial x$ can't be interpreted as a ratio of differentials.

> **NOTATIONS FOR PARTIAL DERIVATIVES** If $z = f(x, y)$, we write
>
> $$f_x(x, y) = f_x = \frac{\partial f}{\partial x} = \frac{\partial}{\partial x} f(x, y) = \frac{\partial z}{\partial x} = f_1 = D_1 f = D_x f$$
>
> $$f_y(x, y) = f_y = \frac{\partial f}{\partial y} = \frac{\partial}{\partial y} f(x, y) = \frac{\partial z}{\partial y} = f_2 = D_2 f = D_y f$$

To compute partial derivatives, all we have to do is remember from Equation 1 that the partial derivative with respect to x is just the *ordinary* derivative of the function g of a single variable that we get by keeping y fixed. Thus we have the following rule.

> **RULE FOR FINDING PARTIAL DERIVATIVES OF $z = f(x, y)$**
> **1.** To find f_x, regard y as a constant and differentiate $f(x, y)$ with respect to x.
> **2.** To find f_y, regard x as a constant and differentiate $f(x, y)$ with respect to y.

EXAMPLE 1 If $f(x, y) = x^3 + x^2y^3 - 2y^2$, find $f_x(2, 1)$ and $f_y(2, 1)$.

SOLUTION Holding y constant and differentiating with respect to x, we get

$$f_x(x, y) = 3x^2 + 2xy^3$$

and so

$$f_x(2, 1) = 3 \cdot 2^2 + 2 \cdot 2 \cdot 1^3 = 16$$

Holding x constant and differentiating with respect to y, we get

$$f_y(x, y) = 3x^2y^2 - 4y$$

$$f_y(2, 1) = 3 \cdot 2^2 \cdot 1^2 - 4 \cdot 1 = 8 \qquad \square$$

INTERPRETATIONS OF PARTIAL DERIVATIVES

To give a geometric interpretation of partial derivatives, we recall that the equation $z = f(x, y)$ represents a surface S (the graph of f). If $f(a, b) = c$, then the point $P(a, b, c)$ lies on S. By fixing $y = b$, we are restricting our attention to the curve C_1 in which the vertical plane $y = b$ intersects S. (In other words, C_1 is the trace of S in the plane $y = b$.) Likewise, the vertical plane $x = a$ intersects S in a curve C_2. Both of the curves C_1 and C_2 pass through the point P. (See Figure 1.)

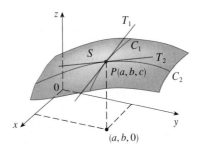

FIGURE 1

The partial derivatives of f at (a, b) are the slopes of the tangents to C_1 and C_2.

Notice that the curve C_1 is the graph of the function $g(x) = f(x, b)$, so the slope of its tangent T_1 at P is $g'(a) = f_x(a, b)$. The curve C_2 is the graph of the function $G(y) = f(a, y)$, so the slope of its tangent T_2 at P is $G'(b) = f_y(a, b)$.

Thus the partial derivatives $f_x(a, b)$ and $f_y(a, b)$ can be interpreted geometrically as the slopes of the tangent lines at $P(a, b, c)$ to the traces C_1 and C_2 of S in the planes $y = b$ and $x = a$.

As we have seen in the case of the heat index function, partial derivatives can also be interpreted as *rates of change*. If $z = f(x, y)$, then $\partial z/\partial x$ represents the rate of change of z with respect to x when y is fixed. Similarly, $\partial z/\partial y$ represents the rate of change of z with respect to y when x is fixed.

EXAMPLE 2 If $f(x, y) = 4 - x^2 - 2y^2$, find $f_x(1, 1)$ and $f_y(1, 1)$ and interpret these numbers as slopes.

SOLUTION We have

$$f_x(x, y) = -2x \qquad f_y(x, y) = -4y$$

$$f_x(1, 1) = -2 \qquad f_y(1, 1) = -4$$

The graph of f is the paraboloid $z = 4 - x^2 - 2y^2$ and the vertical plane $y = 1$ intersects it in the parabola $z = 2 - x^2$, $y = 1$. (As in the preceding discussion, we label it C_1 in Figure 2.) The slope of the tangent line to this parabola at the point $(1, 1, 1)$ is $f_x(1, 1) = -2$. Similarly, the curve C_2 in which the plane $x = 1$ intersects the paraboloid is the parabola $z = 3 - 2y^2$, $x = 1$, and the slope of the tangent line at $(1, 1, 1)$ is $f_y(1, 1) = -4$. (See Figure 3.)

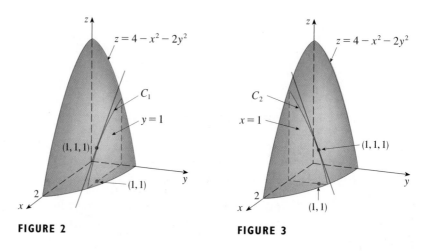

FIGURE 2

FIGURE 3

Figure 4 is a computer-drawn counterpart to Figure 2. Part (a) shows the plane $y = 1$ intersecting the surface to form the curve C_1 and part (b) shows C_1 and T_1. [We have used the vector equations $\mathbf{r}(t) = \langle t, 1, 2 - t^2 \rangle$ for C_1 and $\mathbf{r}(t) = \langle 1 + t, 1, 1 - 2t \rangle$ for T_1.] Similarly, Figure 5 corresponds to Figure 3.

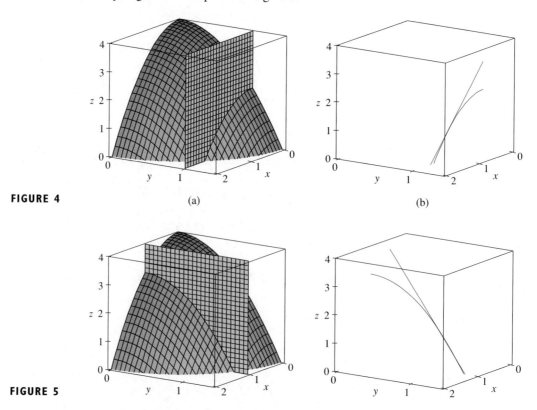

FIGURE 4

(a)

(b)

FIGURE 5

V EXAMPLE 3 If $f(x, y) = \sin\left(\dfrac{x}{1 + y}\right)$, calculate $\dfrac{\partial f}{\partial x}$ and $\dfrac{\partial f}{\partial y}$.

SOLUTION Using the Chain Rule for functions of one variable, we have

$$\frac{\partial f}{\partial x} = \cos\left(\frac{x}{1 + y}\right) \cdot \frac{\partial}{\partial x}\left(\frac{x}{1 + y}\right) = \cos\left(\frac{x}{1 + y}\right) \cdot \frac{1}{1 + y}$$

$$\frac{\partial f}{\partial y} = \cos\left(\frac{x}{1 + y}\right) \cdot \frac{\partial}{\partial y}\left(\frac{x}{1 + y}\right) = -\cos\left(\frac{x}{1 + y}\right) \cdot \frac{x}{(1 + y)^2} \qquad \square$$

■ Some computer algebra systems can plot surfaces defined by implicit equations in three variables. Figure 6 shows such a plot of the surface defined by the equation in Example 4.

FIGURE 6

V EXAMPLE 4 Find $\partial z/\partial x$ and $\partial z/\partial y$ if z is defined implicitly as a function of x and y by the equation

$$x^3 + y^3 + z^3 + 6xyz = 1$$

SOLUTION To find $\partial z/\partial x$, we differentiate implicitly with respect to x, being careful to treat y as a constant:

$$3x^2 + 3z^2 \frac{\partial z}{\partial x} + 6yz + 6xy \frac{\partial z}{\partial x} = 0$$

Solving this equation for $\partial z/\partial x$, we obtain

$$\frac{\partial z}{\partial x} = -\frac{x^2 + 2yz}{z^2 + 2xy}$$

Similarly, implicit differentiation with respect to y gives

$$\frac{\partial z}{\partial y} = -\frac{y^2 + 2xz}{z^2 + 2xy} \qquad \square$$

FUNCTIONS OF MORE THAN TWO VARIABLES

Partial derivatives can also be defined for functions of three or more variables. For example, if f is a function of three variables x, y, and z, then its partial derivative with respect to x is defined as

$$f_x(x, y, z) = \lim_{h \to 0} \frac{f(x + h, y, z) - f(x, y, z)}{h}$$

and it is found by regarding y and z as constants and differentiating $f(x, y, z)$ with respect to x. If $w = f(x, y, z)$, then $f_x = \partial w/\partial x$ can be interpreted as the rate of change of w with respect to x when y and z are held fixed. But we can't interpret it geometrically because the graph of f lies in four-dimensional space.

In general, if u is a function of n variables, $u = f(x_1, x_2, \ldots, x_n)$, its partial derivative with respect to the ith variable x_i is

$$\frac{\partial u}{\partial x_i} = \lim_{h \to 0} \frac{f(x_1, \ldots, x_{i-1}, x_i + h, x_{i+1}, \ldots, x_n) - f(x_1, \ldots, x_i, \ldots, x_n)}{h}$$

and we also write

$$\frac{\partial u}{\partial x_i} = \frac{\partial f}{\partial x_i} = f_{x_i} = f_i = D_i f$$

EXAMPLE 5 Find f_x, f_y, and f_z if $f(x, y, z) = e^{xy} \ln z$.

SOLUTION Holding y and z constant and differentiating with respect to x, we have

$$f_x = ye^{xy} \ln z$$

Similarly,
$$f_y = xe^{xy} \ln z \quad \text{and} \quad f_z = \frac{e^{xy}}{z} \qquad \square$$

HIGHER DERIVATIVES

If f is a function of two variables, then its partial derivatives f_x and f_y are also functions of two variables, so we can consider their partial derivatives $(f_x)_x$, $(f_x)_y$, $(f_y)_x$, and $(f_y)_y$, which are called the **second partial derivatives** of f. If $z = f(x, y)$, we use the following notation:

$$(f_x)_x = f_{xx} = f_{11} = \frac{\partial}{\partial x}\left(\frac{\partial f}{\partial x}\right) = \frac{\partial^2 f}{\partial x^2} = \frac{\partial^2 z}{\partial x^2}$$

$$(f_x)_y = f_{xy} = f_{12} = \frac{\partial}{\partial y}\left(\frac{\partial f}{\partial x}\right) = \frac{\partial^2 f}{\partial y\, \partial x} = \frac{\partial^2 z}{\partial y\, \partial x}$$

$$(f_y)_x = f_{yx} = f_{21} = \frac{\partial}{\partial x}\left(\frac{\partial f}{\partial y}\right) = \frac{\partial^2 f}{\partial x\, \partial y} = \frac{\partial^2 z}{\partial x\, \partial y}$$

$$(f_y)_y = f_{yy} = f_{22} = \frac{\partial}{\partial y}\left(\frac{\partial f}{\partial y}\right) = \frac{\partial^2 f}{\partial y^2} = \frac{\partial^2 z}{\partial y^2}$$

Thus the notation f_{xy} (or $\partial^2 f/\partial y\, \partial x$) means that we first differentiate with respect to x and then with respect to y, whereas in computing f_{yx} the order is reversed.

EXAMPLE 6 Find the second partial derivatives of

$$f(x, y) = x^3 + x^2 y^3 - 2y^2$$

SOLUTION In Example 1 we found that

$$f_x(x, y) = 3x^2 + 2xy^3 \qquad f_y(x, y) = 3x^2 y^2 - 4y$$

Therefore

$$f_{xx} = \frac{\partial}{\partial x}(3x^2 + 2xy^3) = 6x + 2y^3 \qquad f_{xy} = \frac{\partial}{\partial y}(3x^2 + 2xy^3) = 6xy^2$$

$$f_{yx} = \frac{\partial}{\partial x}(3x^2 y^2 - 4y) = 6xy^2 \qquad f_{yy} = \frac{\partial}{\partial y}(3x^2 y^2 - 4y) = 6x^2 y - 4 \qquad \square$$

■ Figure 7 shows the graph of the function f in Example 6 and the graphs of its first- and second-order partial derivatives for $-2 \leqslant x \leqslant 2$, $-2 \leqslant y \leqslant 2$. Notice that these graphs are consistent with our interpretations of f_x and f_y as slopes of tangent lines to traces of the graph of f. For instance, the graph of f decreases if we start at $(0, -2)$ and move in the positive x-direction. This is reflected in the negative values of f_x. You should compare the graphs of f_{yx} and f_{yy} with the graph of f_y to see the relationships.

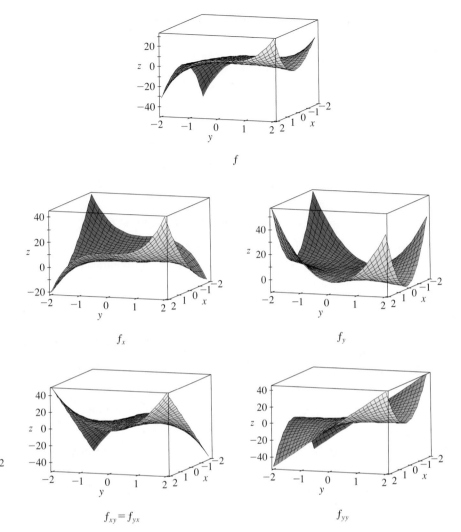

$$f$$

$$f_x$$

$$f_y$$

$$f_{xx}$$

$$f_{xy} = f_{yx}$$

$$f_{yy}$$

FIGURE 7

■ Alexis Clairaut was a child prodigy in mathematics: he read l'Hospital's textbook on calculus when he was ten and presented a paper on geometry to the French Academy of Sciences when he was 13. At the age of 18, Clairaut published *Recherches sur les courbes à double courbure*, which was the first systematic treatise on three-dimensional analytic geometry and included the calculus of space curves.

Notice that $f_{xy} = f_{yx}$ in Example 6. This is not just a coincidence. It turns out that the mixed partial derivatives f_{xy} and f_{yx} are equal for most functions that one meets in practice. The following theorem, which was discovered by the French mathematician Alexis Clairaut (1713–1765), gives conditions under which we can assert that $f_{xy} = f_{yx}$. The proof is given in Appendix F.

CLAIRAUT'S THEOREM Suppose f is defined on a disk D that contains the point (a, b). If the functions f_{xy} and f_{yx} are both continuous on D, then

$$f_{xy}(a, b) = f_{yx}(a, b)$$

Partial derivatives of order 3 or higher can also be defined. For instance,

$$f_{xyy} = (f_{xy})_y = \frac{\partial}{\partial y}\left(\frac{\partial^2 f}{\partial y\, \partial x}\right) = \frac{\partial^3 f}{\partial y^2\, \partial x}$$

and using Clairaut's Theorem it can be shown that $f_{xyy} = f_{yxy} = f_{yyx}$ if these functions are continuous.

☑ EXAMPLE 7 Calculate f_{xxyz} if $f(x, y, z) = \sin(3x + yz)$.

SOLUTION
$$f_x = 3\cos(3x + yz)$$
$$f_{xx} = -9\sin(3x + yz)$$
$$f_{xxy} = -9z\cos(3x + yz)$$
$$f_{xxyz} = -9\cos(3x + yz) + 9yz\sin(3x + yz) \qquad \square$$

PARTIAL DIFFERENTIAL EQUATIONS

Partial derivatives occur in *partial differential equations* that express certain physical laws. For instance, the partial differential equation

$$\frac{\partial^2 u}{\partial x^2} + \frac{\partial^2 u}{\partial y^2} = 0$$

is called **Laplace's equation** after Pierre Laplace (1749–1827). Solutions of this equation are called **harmonic functions**; they play a role in problems of heat conduction, fluid flow, and electric potential.

EXAMPLE 8 Show that the function $u(x, y) = e^x \sin y$ is a solution of Laplace's equation.

SOLUTION
$$u_x = e^x \sin y \qquad\qquad u_y = e^x \cos y$$
$$u_{xx} = e^x \sin y \qquad\qquad u_{yy} = -e^x \sin y$$
$$u_{xx} + u_{yy} = e^x \sin y - e^x \sin y = 0$$

Therefore u satisfies Laplace's equation. $\qquad \square$

The **wave equation**

$$\frac{\partial^2 u}{\partial t^2} = a^2 \frac{\partial^2 u}{\partial x^2}$$

describes the motion of a waveform, which could be an ocean wave, a sound wave, a light wave, or a wave traveling along a vibrating string. For instance, if $u(x, t)$ represents the displacement of a vibrating violin string at time t and at a distance x from one end of the string (as in Figure 8), then $u(x, t)$ satisfies the wave equation. Here the constant a depends on the density of the string and on the tension in the string.

FIGURE 8

EXAMPLE 9 Verify that the function $u(x, t) = \sin(x - at)$ satisfies the wave equation.

SOLUTION
$$u_x = \cos(x - at) \qquad\qquad u_{xx} = -\sin(x - at)$$
$$u_t = -a\cos(x - at) \qquad\qquad u_{tt} = -a^2 \sin(x - at) = a^2 u_{xx}$$

So u satisfies the wave equation. $\qquad \square$

THE COBB-DOUGLAS PRODUCTION FUNCTION

In Example 3 in Section 15.1 we described the work of Cobb and Douglas in modeling the total production P of an economic system as a function of the amount of labor L and the capital investment K. Here we use partial derivatives to show how the particular form of their model follows from certain assumptions they made about the economy.

If the production function is denoted by $P = P(L, K)$, then the partial derivative $\partial P/\partial L$ is the rate at which production changes with respect to the amount of labor. Economists call it the marginal production with respect to labor or the *marginal productivity of labor.* Likewise, the partial derivative $\partial P/\partial K$ is the rate of change of production with respect to capital and is called the *marginal productivity of capital.* In these terms, the assumptions made by Cobb and Douglas can be stated as follows.

(i) If either labor or capital vanishes, then so will production.

(ii) The marginal productivity of labor is proportional to the amount of production per unit of labor.

(iii) The marginal productivity of capital is proportional to the amount of production per unit of capital.

Because the production per unit of labor is P/L, assumption (ii) says that

$$\frac{\partial P}{\partial L} = \alpha \frac{P}{L}$$

for some constant α. If we keep K constant ($K = K_0$), then this partial differential equation becomes an ordinary differential equation:

$$\boxed{5} \qquad \frac{dP}{dL} = \alpha \frac{P}{L}$$

If we solve this separable differential equation by the methods of Section 10.3 (see also Exercise 79), we get

$$\boxed{6} \qquad P(L, K_0) = C_1(K_0)L^\alpha$$

Notice that we have written the constant C_1 as a function of K_0 because it could depend on the value of K_0.

Similarly, assumption (iii) says that

$$\frac{\partial P}{\partial K} = \beta \frac{P}{K}$$

and we can solve this differential equation to get

$$\boxed{7} \qquad P(L_0, K) = C_2(L_0)K^\beta$$

Comparing Equations 6 and 7, we have

$$\boxed{8} \qquad P(L, K) = bL^\alpha K^\beta$$

where b is a constant that is independent of both L and K. Assumption (i) shows that $\alpha > 0$ and $\beta > 0$.

Notice from Equation 8 that if labor and capital are both increased by a factor m, then

$$P(mL, mK) = b(mL)^{\alpha}(mK)^{\beta} = m^{\alpha+\beta}bL^{\alpha}K^{\beta} = m^{\alpha+\beta}P(L, K)$$

If $\alpha + \beta = 1$, then $P(mL, mK) = mP(L, K)$, which means that production is also increased by a factor of m. That is why Cobb and Douglas assumed that $\alpha + \beta = 1$ and therefore

$$P(L, K) = bL^{\alpha}K^{1-\alpha}$$

This is the Cobb-Douglas production function that we discussed in Section 15.1.

15.3 EXERCISES

1. The temperature T at a location in the Northern Hemisphere depends on the longitude x, latitude y, and time t, so we can write $T = f(x, y, t)$. Let's measure time in hours from the beginning of January.
   (a) What are the meanings of the partial derivatives $\partial T/\partial x$, $\partial T/\partial y$, and $\partial T/\partial t$?
   (b) Honolulu has longitude $158°$ W and latitude $21°$ N. Suppose that at 9:00 AM on January 1 the wind is blowing hot air to the northeast, so the air to the west and south is warm and the air to the north and east is cooler. Would you expect $f_x(158, 21, 9)$, $f_y(158, 21, 9)$, and $f_t(158, 21, 9)$ to be positive or negative? Explain.

2. At the beginning of this section we discussed the function $I = f(T, H)$, where I is the heat index, T is the temperature, and H is the relative humidity. Use Table 1 to estimate $f_T(92, 60)$ and $f_H(92, 60)$. What are the practical interpretations of these values?

3. The wind-chill index W is the perceived temperature when the actual temperature is T and the wind speed is v, so we can write $W = f(T, v)$. The following table of values is an excerpt from Table 1 in Section 15.1.

Wind speed (km/h)

T＼v	20	30	40	50	60	70
-10	-18	-20	-21	-22	-23	-23
-15	-24	-26	-27	-29	-30	-30
-20	-30	-33	-34	-35	-36	-37
-25	-37	-39	-41	-42	-43	-44

Actual temperature (°C) *(row label, left axis)*

(a) Estimate the values of $f_T(-15, 30)$ and $f_v(-15, 30)$. What are the practical interpretations of these values?

(b) In general, what can you say about the signs of $\partial W/\partial T$ and $\partial W/\partial v$?
(c) What appears to be the value of the following limit?

$$\lim_{v \to \infty} \frac{\partial W}{\partial v}$$

4. The wave heights h in the open sea depend on the speed v of the wind and the length of time t that the wind has been blowing at that speed. Values of the function $h = f(v, t)$ are recorded in feet in the following table.

Duration (hours)

v＼t	5	10	15	20	30	40	50
10	2	2	2	2	2	2	2
15	4	4	5	5	5	5	5
20	5	7	8	8	9	9	9
30	9	13	16	17	18	19	19
40	14	21	25	28	31	33	33
50	19	29	36	40	45	48	50
60	24	37	47	54	62	67	69

Wind speed (knots) *(row label, left axis)*

(a) What are the meanings of the partial derivatives $\partial h/\partial v$ and $\partial h/\partial t$?
(b) Estimate the values of $f_v(40, 15)$ and $f_t(40, 15)$. What are the practical interpretations of these values?
(c) What appears to be the value of the following limit?

$$\lim_{t \to \infty} \frac{\partial h}{\partial t}$$

5–8 Determine the signs of the partial derivatives for the function f whose graph is shown.

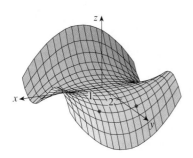

5. (a) $f_x(1, 2)$ (b) $f_y(1, 2)$

6. (a) $f_x(-1, 2)$ (b) $f_y(-1, 2)$

7. (a) $f_{xx}(-1, 2)$ (b) $f_{yy}(-1, 2)$

8. (a) $f_{xy}(1, 2)$ (b) $f_{xy}(-1, 2)$

9. The following surfaces, labeled a, b, and c, are graphs of a function f and its partial derivatives f_x and f_y. Identify each surface and give reasons for your choices.

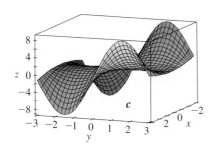

10. A contour map is given for a function f. Use it to estimate $f_x(2, 1)$ and $f_y(2, 1)$.

11. If $f(x, y) = 16 - 4x^2 - y^2$, find $f_x(1, 2)$ and $f_y(1, 2)$ and interpret these numbers as slopes. Illustrate with either hand-drawn sketches or computer plots.

12. If $f(x, y) = \sqrt{4 - x^2 - 4y^2}$, find $f_x(1, 0)$ and $f_y(1, 0)$ and interpret these numbers as slopes. Illustrate with either hand-drawn sketches or computer plots.

13–14 Find f_x and f_y and graph f, f_x, and f_y with domains and viewpoints that enable you to see the relationships between them.

13. $f(x, y) = x^2 + y^2 + x^2 y$ **14.** $f(x, y) = xe^{-x^2-y^2}$

15–38 Find the first partial derivatives of the function.

15. $f(x, y) = y^5 - 3xy$ **16.** $f(x, y) = x^4 y^3 + 8x^2 y$

17. $f(x, t) = e^{-t} \cos \pi x$ **18.** $f(x, t) = \sqrt{x} \ln t$

19. $z = (2x + 3y)^{10}$ **20.** $z = \tan xy$

21. $f(x, y) = \dfrac{x - y}{x + y}$ **22.** $f(x, y) = x^y$

23. $w = \sin \alpha \cos \beta$ **24.** $w = e^v/(u + v^2)$

25. $f(r, s) = r \ln(r^2 + s^2)$ **26.** $f(x, t) = \arctan(x\sqrt{t})$

27. $u = te^{w/t}$ **28.** $f(x, y) = \displaystyle\int_y^x \cos(t^2)\, dt$

29. $f(x, y, z) = xz - 5x^2 y^3 z^4$ **30.** $f(x, y, z) = x \sin(y - z)$

31. $w = \ln(x + 2y + 3z)$ **32.** $w = ze^{xyz}$

33. $u = xy \sin^{-1}(yz)$ **34.** $u = x^{y/z}$

35. $f(x, y, z, t) = xyz^2 \tan(yt)$ **36.** $f(x, y, z, t) = \dfrac{xy^2}{t + 2z}$

37. $u = \sqrt{x_1^2 + x_2^2 + \cdots + x_n^2}$

38. $u = \sin(x_1 + 2x_2 + \cdots + nx_n)$

39–42 Find the indicated partial derivatives.

39. $f(x, y) = \ln(x + \sqrt{x^2 + y^2}\,)$; $f_x(3, 4)$

40. $f(x, y) = \arctan(y/x)$; $f_x(2, 3)$

41. $f(x, y, z) = \dfrac{y}{x + y + z}$; $f_y(2, 1, -1)$

42. $f(x, y, z) = \sqrt{\sin^2 x + \sin^2 y + \sin^2 z}$; $\quad f_z(0, 0, \pi/4)$

43–44 Use the definition of partial derivatives as limits (4) to find $f_x(x, y)$ and $f_y(x, y)$.

43. $f(x, y) = xy^2 - x^3 y$

44. $f(x, y) = \dfrac{x}{x + y^2}$

45–48 Use implicit differentiation to find $\partial z/\partial x$ and $\partial z/\partial y$.

45. $x^2 + y^2 + z^2 = 3xyz$

46. $yz = \ln(x + z)$

47. $x - z = \arctan(yz)$

48. $\sin(xyz) = x + 2y + 3z$

49–50 Find $\partial z/\partial x$ and $\partial z/\partial y$.

49. (a) $z = f(x) + g(y)$ 　　　(b) $z = f(x + y)$

50. (a) $z = f(x)g(y)$ 　　　(b) $z = f(xy)$
　　　(c) $z = f(x/y)$

51–56 Find all the second partial derivatives.

51. $f(x, y) = x^3 y^5 + 2x^4 y$

52. $f(x, y) = \sin^2(mx + ny)$

53. $w = \sqrt{u^2 + v^2}$

54. $v = \dfrac{xy}{x - y}$

55. $z = \arctan \dfrac{x + y}{1 - xy}$

56. $v = e^{xe^y}$

57–60 Verify that the conclusion of Clairaut's Theorem holds, that is, $u_{xy} = u_{yx}$.

57. $u = x \sin(x + 2y)$

58. $u = x^4 y^2 - 2xy^5$

59. $u = \ln \sqrt{x^2 + y^2}$

60. $u = xye^y$

61–68 Find the indicated partial derivative.

61. $f(x, y) = 3xy^4 + x^3 y^2$; $\quad f_{xxy}, \; f_{yyy}$

62. $f(x, t) = x^2 e^{-ct}$; $\quad f_{ttt}, \; f_{txx}$

63. $f(x, y, z) = \cos(4x + 3y + 2z)$; $\quad f_{xyz}, \; f_{yzz}$

64. $f(r, s, t) = r \ln(rs^2 t^3)$; $\quad f_{rss}, \; f_{rst}$

65. $u = e^{r\theta} \sin \theta$; $\quad \dfrac{\partial^3 u}{\partial r^2 \, \partial \theta}$

66. $z = u\sqrt{v - w}$; $\quad \dfrac{\partial^3 z}{\partial u \, \partial v \, \partial w}$

67. $w = \dfrac{x}{y + 2z}$; $\quad \dfrac{\partial^3 w}{\partial z \, \partial y \, \partial x}, \; \dfrac{\partial^3 w}{\partial x^2 \, \partial y}$

68. $u = x^a y^b z^c$; $\quad \dfrac{\partial^6 u}{\partial x \, \partial y^2 \, \partial z^3}$

69. Use the table of values of $f(x, y)$ to estimate the values of $f_x(3, 2)$, $f_x(3, 2.2)$, and $f_{xy}(3, 2)$.

x \ y	1.8	2.0	2.2
2.5	12.5	10.2	9.3
3.0	18.1	17.5	15.9
3.5	20.0	22.4	26.1

70. Level curves are shown for a function f. Determine whether the following partial derivatives are positive or negative at the point P.

(a) f_x 　　　(b) f_y 　　　(c) f_{xx}
(d) f_{xy} 　　(e) f_{yy}

71. Verify that the function $u = e^{-\alpha^2 k^2 t} \sin kx$ is a solution of the *heat conduction equation* $u_t = \alpha^2 u_{xx}$.

72. Determine whether each of the following functions is a solution of Laplace's equation $u_{xx} + u_{yy} = 0$.
(a) $u = x^2 + y^2$ 　　　　(b) $u = x^2 - y^2$
(c) $u = x^3 + 3xy^2$ 　　　(d) $u = \ln \sqrt{x^2 + y^2}$
(e) $u = \sin x \cosh y + \cos x \sinh y$
(f) $u = e^{-x} \cos y - e^{-y} \cos x$

73. Verify that the function $u = 1/\sqrt{x^2 + y^2 + z^2}$ is a solution of the three-dimensional Laplace equation $u_{xx} + u_{yy} + u_{zz} = 0$.

74. Show that each of the following functions is a solution of the wave equation $u_{tt} = a^2 u_{xx}$.
(a) $u = \sin(kx) \sin(akt)$ 　　(b) $u = t/(a^2 t^2 - x^2)$
(c) $u = (x - at)^6 + (x + at)^6$
(d) $u = \sin(x - at) + \ln(x + at)$

75. If f and g are twice differentiable functions of a single variable, show that the function

$$u(x, t) = f(x + at) + g(x - at)$$

is a solution of the wave equation given in Exercise 74.

76. If $u = e^{a_1 x_1 + a_2 x_2 + \cdots + a_n x_n}$, where $a_1^2 + a_2^2 + \cdots + a_n^2 = 1$, show that

$$\frac{\partial^2 u}{\partial x_1^2} + \frac{\partial^2 u}{\partial x_2^2} + \cdots + \frac{\partial^2 u}{\partial x_n^2} = u$$

77. Verify that the function $z = \ln(e^x + e^y)$ is a solution of the differential equations

$$\frac{\partial z}{\partial x} + \frac{\partial z}{\partial y} = 1$$

and

$$\frac{\partial^2 z}{\partial x^2} \frac{\partial^2 z}{\partial y^2} - \left(\frac{\partial^2 z}{\partial x \, \partial y}\right)^2 = 0$$

78. Show that the Cobb-Douglas production function $P = bL^\alpha K^\beta$ satisfies the equation

$$L\frac{\partial P}{\partial L} + K\frac{\partial P}{\partial K} = (\alpha + \beta)P$$

79. Show that the Cobb-Douglas production function satisfies $P(L, K_0) = C_1(K_0)L^\alpha$ by solving the differential equation

$$\frac{dP}{dL} = \alpha \frac{P}{L}$$

(See Equation 5.)

80. The temperature at a point (x, y) on a flat metal plate is given by $T(x, y) = 60/(1 + x^2 + y^2)$, where T is measured in °C and x, y in meters. Find the rate of change of temperature with respect to distance at the point $(2, 1)$ in (a) the x-direction and (b) the y-direction.

81. The total resistance R produced by three conductors with resistances R_1, R_2, R_3 connected in a parallel electrical circuit is given by the formula

$$\frac{1}{R} = \frac{1}{R_1} + \frac{1}{R_2} + \frac{1}{R_3}$$

Find $\partial R/\partial R_1$.

82. The gas law for a fixed mass m of an ideal gas at absolute temperature T, pressure P, and volume V is $PV = mRT$, where R is the gas constant. Show that

$$\frac{\partial P}{\partial V} \frac{\partial V}{\partial T} \frac{\partial T}{\partial P} = -1$$

83. For the ideal gas of Exercise 82, show that

$$T\frac{\partial P}{\partial T} \frac{\partial V}{\partial T} = mR$$

84. The wind-chill index is modeled by the function

$$W = 13.12 + 0.6215T - 11.37v^{0.16} + 0.3965Tv^{0.16}$$

where T is the temperature (°C) and v is the wind speed (km/h). When $T = -15°$C and $v = 30$ km/h, by how much would you expect the apparent temperature W to drop if the actual temperature decreases by 1°C? What if the wind speed increases by 1 km/h?

85. The kinetic energy of a body with mass m and velocity v is $K = \frac{1}{2}mv^2$. Show that

$$\frac{\partial K}{\partial m} \frac{\partial^2 K}{\partial v^2} = K$$

86. If a, b, c are the sides of a triangle and A, B, C are the opposite angles, find $\partial A/\partial a$, $\partial A/\partial b$, $\partial A/\partial c$ by implicit differentiation of the Law of Cosines.

87. You are told that there is a function f whose partial derivatives are $f_x(x, y) = x + 4y$ and $f_y(x, y) = 3x - y$. Should you believe it?

88. The paraboloid $z = 6 - x - x^2 - 2y^2$ intersects the plane $x = 1$ in a parabola. Find parametric equations for the tangent line to this parabola at the point $(1, 2, -4)$. Use a computer to graph the paraboloid, the parabola, and the tangent line on the same screen.

89. The ellipsoid $4x^2 + 2y^2 + z^2 = 16$ intersects the plane $y = 2$ in an ellipse. Find parametric equations for the tangent line to this ellipse at the point $(1, 2, 2)$.

90. In a study of frost penetration it was found that the temperature T at time t (measured in days) at a depth x (measured in feet) can be modeled by the function

$$T(x, t) = T_0 + T_1 e^{-\lambda x} \sin(\omega t - \lambda x)$$

where $\omega = 2\pi/365$ and λ is a positive constant.
(a) Find $\partial T/\partial x$. What is its physical significance?
(b) Find $\partial T/\partial t$. What is its physical significance?
(c) Show that T satisfies the heat equation $T_t = kT_{xx}$ for a certain constant k.
(d) If $\lambda = 0.2$, $T_0 = 0$, and $T_1 = 10$, use a computer to graph $T(x, t)$.
(e) What is the physical significance of the term $-\lambda x$ in the expression $\sin(\omega t - \lambda x)$?

91. Use Clairaut's Theorem to show that if the third-order partial derivatives of f are continuous, then

$$f_{xyy} = f_{yxy} = f_{yyx}$$

92. (a) How many nth-order partial derivatives does a function of two variables have?
(b) If these partial derivatives are all continuous, how many of them can be distinct?
(c) Answer the question in part (a) for a function of three variables.

93. If $f(x, y) = x(x^2 + y^2)^{-3/2}e^{\sin(x^2 y)}$, find $f_x(1, 0)$. [*Hint:* Instead of finding $f_x(x, y)$ first, note that it's easier to use Equation 1 or Equation 2.]

94. If $f(x, y) = \sqrt[3]{x^3 + y^3}$, find $f_x(0, 0)$.

95. Let

$$f(x, y) = \begin{cases} \dfrac{x^3y - xy^3}{x^2 + y^2} & \text{if } (x, y) \neq (0, 0) \\ 0 & \text{if } (x, y) = (0, 0) \end{cases}$$

(a) Use a computer to graph f.
(b) Find $f_x(x, y)$ and $f_y(x, y)$ when $(x, y) \neq (0, 0)$.
(c) Find $f_x(0, 0)$ and $f_y(0, 0)$ using Equations 2 and 3.
(d) Show that $f_{xy}(0, 0) = -1$ and $f_{yx}(0, 0) = 1$.
(e) Does the result of part (d) contradict Clairaut's Theorem? Use graphs of f_{xy} and f_{yx} to illustrate your answer.

15.4 TANGENT PLANES AND LINEAR APPROXIMATIONS

One of the most important ideas in single-variable calculus is that as we zoom in toward a point on the graph of a differentiable function, the graph becomes indistinguishable from its tangent line and we can approximate the function by a linear function. (See Section 3.9.) Here we develop similar ideas in three dimensions. As we zoom in toward a point on a surface that is the graph of a differentiable function of two variables, the surface looks more and more like a plane (its tangent plane) and we can approximate the function by a linear function of two variables. We also extend the idea of a differential to functions of two or more variables.

TANGENT PLANES

Suppose a surface S has equation $z = f(x, y)$, where f has continuous first partial derivatives, and let $P(x_0, y_0, z_0)$ be a point on S. As in the preceding section, let C_1 and C_2 be the curves obtained by intersecting the vertical planes $y = y_0$ and $x = x_0$ with the surface S. Then the point P lies on both C_1 and C_2. Let T_1 and T_2 be the tangent lines to the curves C_1 and C_2 at the point P. Then the **tangent plane** to the surface S at the point P is defined to be the plane that contains both tangent lines T_1 and T_2. (See Figure 1.)

We will see in Section 15.6 that if C is any other curve that lies on the surface S and passes through P, then its tangent line at P also lies in the tangent plane. Therefore you can think of the tangent plane to S at P as consisting of all possible tangent lines at P to curves that lie on S and pass through P. The tangent plane at P is the plane that most closely approximates the surface S near the point P.

We know from Equation 13.5.7 that any plane passing through the point $P(x_0, y_0, z_0)$ has an equation of the form

$$A(x - x_0) + B(y - y_0) + C(z - z_0) = 0$$

By dividing this equation by C and letting $a = -A/C$ and $b = -B/C$, we can write it in the form

$$\boxed{1} \qquad z - z_0 = a(x - x_0) + b(y - y_0)$$

If Equation 1 represents the tangent plane at P, then its intersection with the plane $y = y_0$ must be the tangent line T_1. Setting $y = y_0$ in Equation 1 gives

$$z - z_0 = a(x - x_0) \qquad y = y_0$$

and we recognize these as the equations (in point-slope form) of a line with slope a. But from Section 15.3 we know that the slope of the tangent T_1 is $f_x(x_0, y_0)$. Therefore $a = f_x(x_0, y_0)$.

Similarly, putting $x = x_0$ in Equation 1, we get $z - z_0 = b(y - y_0)$, which must represent the tangent line T_2, so $b = f_y(x_0, y_0)$.

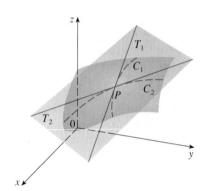

FIGURE 1
The tangent plane contains the tangent lines T_1 and T_2.

▪ Note the similarity between the equation of a tangent plane and the equation of a tangent line:
$$y - y_0 = f'(x_0)(x - x_0)$$

$\boxed{2}$ Suppose f has continuous partial derivatives. An equation of the tangent plane to the surface $z = f(x, y)$ at the point $P(x_0, y_0, z_0)$ is

$$z - z_0 = f_x(x_0, y_0)(x - x_0) + f_y(x_0, y_0)(y - y_0)$$

▼ EXAMPLE 1 Find the tangent plane to the elliptic paraboloid $z = 2x^2 + y^2$ at the point $(1, 1, 3)$.

SOLUTION Let $f(x, y) = 2x^2 + y^2$. Then

$$f_x(x, y) = 4x \qquad f_y(x, y) = 2y$$

$$f_x(1, 1) = 4 \qquad f_y(1, 1) = 2$$

Then (2) gives the equation of the tangent plane at $(1, 1, 3)$ as

$$z - 3 = 4(x - 1) + 2(y - 1)$$

or
$$z = 4x + 2y - 3 \qquad\qquad\qquad \square$$

TEC Visual 15.4 shows an animation of Figures 2 and 3.

Figure 2(a) shows the elliptic paraboloid and its tangent plane at $(1, 1, 3)$ that we found in Example 1. In parts (b) and (c) we zoom in toward the point $(1, 1, 3)$ by restricting the domain of the function $f(x, y) = 2x^2 + y^2$. Notice that the more we zoom in, the flatter the graph appears and the more it resembles its tangent plane.

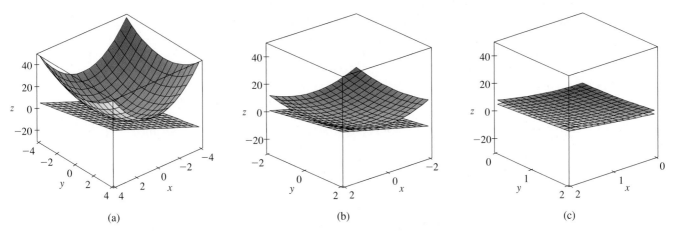

(a)   (b)   (c)

FIGURE 2 The elliptic paraboloid $z = 2x^2 + y^2$ appears to coincide with its tangent plane as we zoom in toward $(1, 1, 3)$.

In Figure 3 we corroborate this impression by zooming in toward the point $(1, 1)$ on a contour map of the function $f(x, y) = 2x^2 + y^2$. Notice that the more we zoom in, the more the level curves look like equally spaced parallel lines, which is characteristic of a plane.

FIGURE 3
Zooming in toward $(1, 1)$
on a contour map of
$f(x, y) = 2x^2 + y^2$

LINEAR APPROXIMATIONS

In Example 1 we found that an equation of the tangent plane to the graph of the function $f(x, y) = 2x^2 + y^2$ at the point $(1, 1, 3)$ is $z = 4x + 2y - 3$. Therefore, in view of the visual evidence in Figures 2 and 3, the linear function of two variables

$$L(x, y) = 4x + 2y - 3$$

is a good approximation to $f(x, y)$ when (x, y) is near $(1, 1)$. The function L is called the *linearization* of f at $(1, 1)$ and the approximation

$$f(x, y) \approx 4x + 2y - 3$$

is called the *linear approximation* or *tangent plane approximation* of f at $(1, 1)$.

For instance, at the point $(1.1, 0.95)$ the linear approximation gives

$$f(1.1, 0.95) \approx 4(1.1) + 2(0.95) - 3 = 3.3$$

which is quite close to the true value of $f(1.1, 0.95) = 2(1.1)^2 + (0.95)^2 = 3.3225$. But if we take a point farther away from $(1, 1)$, such as $(2, 3)$, we no longer get a good approximation. In fact, $L(2, 3) = 11$ whereas $f(2, 3) = 17$.

In general, we know from (2) that an equation of the tangent plane to the graph of a function f of two variables at the point $(a, b, f(a, b))$ is

$$z = f(a, b) + f_x(a, b)(x - a) + f_y(a, b)(y - b)$$

The linear function whose graph is this tangent plane, namely

$$\boxed{3} \qquad L(x, y) = f(a, b) + f_x(a, b)(x - a) + f_y(a, b)(y - b)$$

is called the **linearization** of f at (a, b) and the approximation

$$\boxed{4} \qquad f(x, y) \approx f(a, b) + f_x(a, b)(x - a) + f_y(a, b)(y - b)$$

is called the **linear approximation** or the **tangent plane approximation** of f at (a, b).

We have defined tangent planes for surfaces $z = f(x, y)$, where f has continuous first partial derivatives. What happens if f_x and f_y are not continuous? Figure 4 pictures such a function; its equation is

$$f(x, y) = \begin{cases} \dfrac{xy}{x^2 + y^2} & \text{if } (x, y) \neq (0, 0) \\ 0 & \text{if } (x, y) = (0, 0) \end{cases}$$

You can verify (see Exercise 46) that its partial derivatives exist at the origin and, in fact, $f_x(0, 0) = 0$ and $f_y(0, 0) = 0$, but f_x and f_y are not continuous. The linear approximation would be $f(x, y) \approx 0$, but $f(x, y) = \frac{1}{2}$ at all points on the line $y = x$. So a function of two variables can behave badly even though both of its partial derivatives exist. To rule out such behavior, we formulate the idea of a differentiable function of two variables.

Recall that for a function of one variable, $y = f(x)$, if x changes from a to $a + \Delta x$, we defined the increment of y as

$$\Delta y = f(a + \Delta x) - f(a)$$

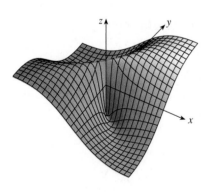

FIGURE 4

$f(x, y) = \dfrac{xy}{x^2 + y^2}$ if $(x, y) \neq (0, 0)$,

$f(0, 0) = 0$

In Chapter 3 we showed that if f is differentiable at a, then

■ This is Equation 3.5.5.

$$\boxed{5} \qquad \Delta y = f'(a)\,\Delta x + \varepsilon\,\Delta x \qquad \text{where } \varepsilon \to 0 \text{ as } \Delta x \to 0$$

Now consider a function of two variables, $z = f(x, y)$, and suppose x changes from a to $a + \Delta x$ and y changes from b to $b + \Delta y$. Then the corresponding **increment** of z is

$$\boxed{6} \qquad \Delta z = f(a + \Delta x, b + \Delta y) - f(a, b)$$

Thus the increment Δz represents the change in the value of f when (x, y) changes from (a, b) to $(a + \Delta x, b + \Delta y)$. By analogy with (5) we define the differentiability of a function of two variables as follows.

> $\boxed{7}$ **DEFINITION** If $z = f(x, y)$, then f is **differentiable** at (a, b) if Δz can be expressed in the form
>
> $$\Delta z = f_x(a, b)\,\Delta x + f_y(a, b)\,\Delta y + \varepsilon_1\,\Delta x + \varepsilon_2\,\Delta y$$
>
> where ε_1 and $\varepsilon_2 \to 0$ as $(\Delta x, \Delta y) \to (0, 0)$.

Definition 7 says that a differentiable function is one for which the linear approximation (4) is a good approximation when (x, y) is near (a, b). In other words, the tangent plane approximates the graph of f well near the point of tangency.

It's sometimes hard to use Definition 7 directly to check the differentiability of a function, but the next theorem provides a convenient sufficient condition for differentiability.

■ Theorem 8 is proved in Appendix F.

> $\boxed{8}$ **THEOREM** If the partial derivatives f_x and f_y exist near (a, b) and are continuous at (a, b), then f is differentiable at (a, b).

V EXAMPLE 2 Show that $f(x, y) = xe^{xy}$ is differentiable at $(1, 0)$ and find its linearization there. Then use it to approximate $f(1.1, -0.1)$.

SOLUTION The partial derivatives are

$$f_x(x, y) = e^{xy} + xye^{xy} \qquad\qquad f_y(x, y) = x^2 e^{xy}$$

$$f_x(1, 0) = 1 \qquad\qquad f_y(1, 0) = 1$$

Both f_x and f_y are continuous functions, so f is differentiable by Theorem 8. The linearization is

$$L(x, y) = f(1, 0) + f_x(1, 0)(x - 1) + f_y(1, 0)(y - 0)$$

$$= 1 + 1(x - 1) + 1 \cdot y = x + y$$

The corresponding linear approximation is

$$xe^{xy} \approx x + y$$

so

$$f(1.1, -0.1) \approx 1.1 - 0.1 = 1$$

Compare this with the actual value of $f(1.1, -0.1) = 1.1e^{-0.11} \approx 0.98542$. $\qquad\square$

■ Figure 5 shows the graphs of the function f and its linearization L in Example 2.

FIGURE 5

EXAMPLE 3 At the beginning of Section 15.3 we discussed the heat index (perceived temperature) I as a function of the actual temperature T and the relative humidity H and gave the following table of values from the National Weather Service.

		Relative humidity (%)							
	$\frac{\quad H}{T\quad}$	50	55	60	65	70	75	80	85	90
	90	96	98	100	103	106	109	112	115	119
	92	100	103	105	108	112	115	119	123	128
Actual temperature (°F)	94	104	107	111	114	118	122	127	132	137
	96	109	113	116	121	125	130	135	141	146
	98	114	118	123	127	133	138	144	150	157
	100	119	124	129	135	141	147	154	161	168

Find a linear approximation for the heat index $I = f(T, H)$ when T is near 96°F and H is near 70%. Use it to estimate the heat index when the temperature is 97°F and the relative humidity is 72%.

SOLUTION We read from the table that $f(96, 70) = 125$. In Section 15.3 we used the tabular values to estimate that $f_T(96, 70) \approx 3.75$ and $f_H(96, 70) \approx 0.9$. (See pages 914–15.) So the linear approximation is

$$f(T, H) \approx f(96, 70) + f_T(96, 70)(T - 96) + f_H(96, 70)(H - 70)$$

$$\approx 125 + 3.75(T - 96) + 0.9(H - 70)$$

In particular,

$$f(97, 72) \approx 125 + 3.75(1) + 0.9(2) = 130.55$$

Therefore, when $T = 97$°F and $H = 72\%$, the heat index is

$$I \approx 131°\text{F}$$ ☐

DIFFERENTIALS

For a differentiable function of one variable, $y = f(x)$, we define the differential dx to be an independent variable; that is, dx can be given the value of any real number. The differential of y is then defined as

$$\boxed{9}\qquad dy = f'(x)\, dx$$

(See Section 3.9.) Figure 6 shows the relationship between the increment Δy and the differential dy: Δy represents the change in height of the curve $y = f(x)$ and dy represents the change in height of the tangent line when x changes by an amount $dx = \Delta x$.

For a differentiable function of two variables, $z = f(x, y)$, we define the **differentials** dx and dy to be independent variables; that is, they can be given any values. Then the **differential** dz, also called the **total differential**, is defined by

$$\boxed{10}\qquad dz = f_x(x, y)\, dx + f_y(x, y)\, dy = \frac{\partial z}{\partial x}\, dx + \frac{\partial z}{\partial y}\, dy$$

$$y = f(a) + f'(a)(x - a)$$

FIGURE 6

(Compare with Equation 9.) Sometimes the notation df is used in place of dz.

If we take $dx = \Delta x = x - a$ and $dy = \Delta y = y - b$ in Equation 10, then the differential of z is

$$dz = f_x(a, b)(x - a) + f_y(a, b)(y - b)$$

So, in the notation of differentials, the linear approximation (4) can be written as

$$f(x, y) \approx f(a, b) + dz$$

Figure 7 is the three-dimensional counterpart of Figure 6 and shows the geometric interpretation of the differential dz and the increment Δz: dz represents the change in height of the tangent plane, whereas Δz represents the change in height of the surface $z = f(x, y)$ when (x, y) changes from (a, b) to $(a + \Delta x, b + \Delta y)$.

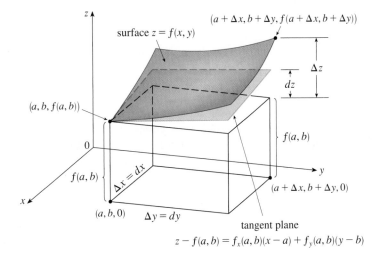

surface $z = f(x, y)$

$(a + \Delta x, b + \Delta y, f(a + \Delta x, b + \Delta y))$

Δz

dz

$(a, b, f(a, b))$

$f(a, b)$

0

$f(a, b)$

$\Delta x = dx$

$(a + \Delta x, b + \Delta y, 0)$

$(a, b, 0)$ $\Delta y = dy$

tangent plane

$z - f(a, b) = f_x(a, b)(x - a) + f_y(a, b)(y - b)$

FIGURE 7

◤ EXAMPLE 4
(a) If $z = f(x, y) = x^2 + 3xy - y^2$, find the differential dz.
(b) If x changes from 2 to 2.05 and y changes from 3 to 2.96, compare the values of Δz and dz.

SOLUTION
(a) Definition 10 gives

$$dz = \frac{\partial z}{\partial x} \, dx + \frac{\partial z}{\partial y} \, dy = (2x + 3y) \, dx + (3x - 2y) \, dy$$

■ In Example 4, dz is close to Δz because the tangent plane is a good approximation to the surface $z = x^2 + 3xy - y^2$ near (2, 3, 13). (See Figure 8.)

(b) Putting $x = 2$, $dx = \Delta x = 0.05$, $y = 3$, and $dy = \Delta y = -0.04$, we get

$$dz = [2(2) + 3(3)]0.05 + [3(2) - 2(3)](-0.04) = 0.65$$

The increment of z is

$$\Delta z = f(2.05, 2.96) - f(2, 3)$$
$$= [(2.05)^2 + 3(2.05)(2.96) - (2.96)^2] - [2^2 + 3(2)(3) - 3^2]$$
$$= 0.6449$$

Notice that $\Delta z \approx dz$ but dz is easier to compute.

FIGURE 8

EXAMPLE 5 The base radius and height of a right circular cone are measured as 10 cm and 25 cm, respectively, with a possible error in measurement of as much as 0.1 cm in each. Use differentials to estimate the maximum error in the calculated volume of the cone.

SOLUTION The volume V of a cone with base radius r and height h is $V = \pi r^2 h/3$. So the differential of V is

$$dV = \frac{\partial V}{\partial r}\, dr + \frac{\partial V}{\partial h}\, dh = \frac{2\pi rh}{3}\, dr + \frac{\pi r^2}{3}\, dh$$

Since each error is at most 0.1 cm, we have $|\Delta r| \leq 0.1$, $|\Delta h| \leq 0.1$. To find the largest error in the volume we take the largest error in the measurement of r and of h. Therefore we take $dr = 0.1$ and $dh = 0.1$ along with $r = 10$, $h = 25$. This gives

$$dV = \frac{500\pi}{3}(0.1) + \frac{100\pi}{3}(0.1) = 20\pi$$

Thus the maximum error in the calculated volume is about 20π cm³ ≈ 63 cm³. ☐

FUNCTIONS OF THREE OR MORE VARIABLES

Linear approximations, differentiability, and differentials can be defined in a similar manner for functions of more than two variables. A differentiable function is defined by an expression similar to the one in Definition 7. For such functions the **linear approximation** is

$$f(x, y, z) \approx f(a, b, c) + f_x(a, b, c)(x - a) + f_y(a, b, c)(y - b) + f_z(a, b, c)(z - c)$$

and the linearization $L(x, y, z)$ is the right side of this expression.

If $w = f(x, y, z)$, then the **increment** of w is

$$\Delta w = f(x + \Delta x, y + \Delta y, z + \Delta z) - f(x, y, z)$$

The **differential** dw is defined in terms of the differentials dx, dy, and dz of the independent variables by

$$dw = \frac{\partial w}{\partial x}\, dx + \frac{\partial w}{\partial y}\, dy + \frac{\partial w}{\partial z}\, dz$$

EXAMPLE 6 The dimensions of a rectangular box are measured to be 75 cm, 60 cm, and 40 cm, and each measurement is correct to within 0.2 cm. Use differentials to estimate the largest possible error when the volume of the box is calculated from these measurements.

SOLUTION If the dimensions of the box are x, y, and z, its volume is $V = xyz$ and so

$$dV = \frac{\partial V}{\partial x}\, dx + \frac{\partial V}{\partial y}\, dy + \frac{\partial V}{\partial z}\, dz = yz\, dx + xz\, dy + xy\, dz$$

We are given that $|\Delta x| \leq 0.2$, $|\Delta y| \leq 0.2$, and $|\Delta z| \leq 0.2$. To find the largest error in the volume, we therefore use $dx = 0.2$, $dy = 0.2$, and $dz = 0.2$ together with $x = 75$, $y = 60$, and $z = 40$:

$$\Delta V \approx dV = (60)(40)(0.2) + (75)(40)(0.2) + (75)(60)(0.2) = 1980$$

Thus an error of only 0.2 cm in measuring each dimension could lead to an error of as much as 1980 cm³ in the calculated volume! This may seem like a large error, but it's only about 1% of the volume of the box. ☐

15.4 EXERCISES

1–6 Find an equation of the tangent plane to the given surface at the specified point.

1. $z = 4x^2 - y^2 + 2y$, $(-1, 2, 4)$

2. $z = 3(x - 1)^2 + 2(y + 3)^2 + 7$, $(2, -2, 12)$

3. $z = \sqrt{xy}$, $(1, 1, 1)$

4. $z = y \ln x$, $(1, 4, 0)$

5. $z = y \cos(x - y)$, $(2, 2, 2)$

6. $z = e^{x^2 - y^2}$, $(1, -1, 1)$

7–8 Graph the surface and the tangent plane at the given point. (Choose the domain and viewpoint so that you get a good view of both the surface and the tangent plane.) Then zoom in until the surface and the tangent plane become indistinguishable.

7. $z = x^2 + xy + 3y^2$, $(1, 1, 5)$

8. $z = \arctan(xy^2)$, $(1, 1, \pi/4)$

CAS **9–10** Draw the graph of f and its tangent plane at the given point. (Use your computer algebra system both to compute the partial derivatives and to graph the surface and its tangent plane.) Then zoom in until the surface and the tangent plane become indistinguishable.

9. $f(x, y) = \dfrac{xy \sin(x - y)}{1 + x^2 + y^2}$, $(1, 1, 0)$

10. $f(x, y) = e^{-xy/10}(\sqrt{x} + \sqrt{y} + \sqrt{xy})$, $(1, 1, 3e^{-0.1})$

11–16 Explain why the function is differentiable at the given point. Then find the linearization $L(x, y)$ of the function at that point.

11. $f(x, y) = x\sqrt{y}$, $(1, 4)$

12. $f(x, y) = x^3 y^4$, $(1, 1)$

13. $f(x, y) = \dfrac{x}{x + y}$, $(2, 1)$

14. $f(x, y) = \sqrt{x + e^{4y}}$, $(3, 0)$

15. $f(x, y) = e^{-xy} \cos y$, $(\pi, 0)$

16. $f(x, y) = \sin(2x + 3y)$, $(-3, 2)$

17–18 Verify the linear approximation at $(0, 0)$.

17. $\dfrac{2x + 3}{4y + 1} \approx 3 + 2x - 12y$ **18.** $\sqrt{y + \cos^2 x} \approx 1 + \frac{1}{2}y$

19. Find the linear approximation of the function $f(x, y) = \sqrt{20 - x^2 - 7y^2}$ at $(2, 1)$ and use it to approximate $f(1.95, 1.08)$.

20. Find the linear approximation of the function $f(x, y) = \ln(x - 3y)$ at $(7, 2)$ and use it to approximate $f(6.9, 2.06)$. Illustrate by graphing f and the tangent plane.

21. Find the linear approximation of the function $f(x, y, z) = \sqrt{x^2 + y^2 + z^2}$ at $(3, 2, 6)$ and use it to approximate the number $\sqrt{(3.02)^2 + (1.97)^2 + (5.99)^2}$.

22. The wave heights h in the open sea depend on the speed v of the wind and the length of time t that the wind has been blowing at that speed. Values of the function $h = f(v, t)$ are recorded in feet in the following table.

Duration (hours)

v \ t	5	10	15	20	30	40	50
20	5	7	8	8	9	9	9
30	9	13	16	17	18	19	19
40	14	21	25	28	31	33	33
50	19	29	36	40	45	48	50
60	24	37	47	54	62	67	69

Wind speed (knots)

Use the table to find a linear approximation to the wave height function when v is near 40 knots and t is near 20 hours. Then estimate the wave heights when the wind has been blowing for 24 hours at 43 knots.

23. Use the table in Example 3 to find a linear approximation to the heat index function when the temperature is near 94°F and the relative humidity is near 80%. Then estimate the heat index when the temperature is 95°F and the relative humidity is 78%.

24. The wind-chill index W is the perceived temperature when the actual temperature is T and the wind speed is v, so we can write $W = f(T, v)$. The following table of values is an excerpt from Table 1 in Section 15.1.

Wind speed (km/h)

T \ v	20	30	40	50	60	70
−10	−18	−20	−21	−22	−23	−23
−15	−24	−26	−27	−29	−30	−30
−20	−30	−33	−34	−35	−36	−37
−25	−37	−39	−41	−42	−43	−44

Actual temperature (°C)

Use the table to find a linear approximation to the wind-chill index function when T is near $-15°C$ and v is near 50 km/h. Then estimate the wind-chill index when the temperature is $-17°C$ and the wind speed is 55 km/h.

25–30 Find the differential of the function.

25. $z = x^3 \ln(y^2)$

26. $v = y \cos xy$

27. $m = p^5 q^3$

28. $T = \dfrac{v}{1 + uvw}$

29. $R = \alpha\beta^2 \cos \gamma$

30. $w = xye^{xz}$

31. If $z = 5x^2 + y^2$ and (x, y) changes from $(1, 2)$ to $(1.05, 2.1)$, compare the values of Δz and dz.

32. If $z = x^2 - xy + 3y^2$ and (x, y) changes from $(3, -1)$ to $(2.96, -0.95)$, compare the values of Δz and dz.

33. The length and width of a rectangle are measured as 30 cm and 24 cm, respectively, with an error in measurement of at most 0.1 cm in each. Use differentials to estimate the maximum error in the calculated area of the rectangle.

34. The dimensions of a closed rectangular box are measured as 80 cm, 60 cm, and 50 cm, respectively, with a possible error of 0.2 cm in each dimension. Use differentials to estimate the maximum error in calculating the surface area of the box.

35. Use differentials to estimate the amount of tin in a closed tin can with diameter 8 cm and height 12 cm if the tin is 0.04 cm thick.

36. Use differentials to estimate the amount of metal in a closed cylindrical can that is 10 cm high and 4 cm in diameter if the metal in the top and bottom is 0.1 cm thick and the metal in the sides is 0.05 cm thick.

37. A boundary stripe 3 in. wide is painted around a rectangle whose dimensions are 100 ft by 200 ft. Use differentials to approximate the number of square feet of paint in the stripe.

38. The pressure, volume, and temperature of a mole of an ideal gas are related by the equation $PV = 8.31T$, where P is measured in kilopascals, V in liters, and T in kelvins. Use differentials to find the approximate change in the pressure if the volume increases from 12 L to 12.3 L and the temperature decreases from 310 K to 305 K.

39. If R is the total resistance of three resistors, connected in parallel, with resistances R_1, R_2, R_3, then

$$\frac{1}{R} = \frac{1}{R_1} + \frac{1}{R_2} + \frac{1}{R_3}$$

If the resistances are measured in ohms as $R_1 = 25 \, \Omega$, $R_2 = 40 \, \Omega$, and $R_3 = 50 \, \Omega$, with a possible error of 0.5% in each case, estimate the maximum error in the calculated value of R.

40. Four positive numbers, each less than 50, are rounded to the first decimal place and then multiplied together. Use differentials to estimate the maximum possible error in the computed product that might result from the rounding.

41. A model for the surface area of a human body is given by $S = 0.1091w^{0.425}h^{0.725}$, where w is the weight (in pounds), h is the height (in inches), and S is measured in square feet. If the errors in measurement of w and h are at most 2%, use differentials to estimate the maximum percentage error in the calculated surface area.

42. Suppose you need to know an equation of the tangent plane to a surface S at the point $P(2, 1, 3)$. You don't have an equation for S but you know that the curves

$$\mathbf{r}_1(t) = \langle 2 + 3t, 1 - t^2, 3 - 4t + t^2 \rangle$$

$$\mathbf{r}_2(u) = \langle 1 + u^2, 2u^3 - 1, 2u + 1 \rangle$$

both lie on S. Find an equation of the tangent plane at P.

43–44 Show that the function is differentiable by finding values of ε_1 and ε_2 that satisfy Definition 7.

43. $f(x, y) = x^2 + y^2$

44. $f(x, y) = xy - 5y^2$

45. Prove that if f is a function of two variables that is differentiable at (a, b), then f is continuous at (a, b).
   Hint: Show that

$$\lim_{(\Delta x, \Delta y) \to (0, 0)} f(a + \Delta x, b + \Delta y) = f(a, b)$$

46. (a) The function

$$f(x, y) = \begin{cases} \dfrac{xy}{x^2 + y^2} & \text{if } (x, y) \neq (0, 0) \\ 0 & \text{if } (x, y) = (0, 0) \end{cases}$$

was graphed in Figure 4. Show that $f_x(0, 0)$ and $f_y(0, 0)$ both exist but f is not differentiable at $(0, 0)$. [*Hint:* Use the result of Exercise 45.]
   (b) Explain why f_x and f_y are not continuous at $(0, 0)$.

15.5 THE CHAIN RULE

Recall that the Chain Rule for functions of a single variable gives the rule for differentiating a composite function: If $y = f(x)$ and $x = g(t)$, where f and g are differentiable functions, then y is indirectly a differentiable function of t and

$$\boxed{1} \qquad \frac{dy}{dt} = \frac{dy}{dx}\frac{dx}{dt}$$

For functions of more than one variable, the Chain Rule has several versions, each of them giving a rule for differentiating a composite function. The first version (Theorem 2) deals with the case where $z = f(x, y)$ and each of the variables x and y is, in turn, a function of a variable t. This means that z is indirectly a function of t, $z = f(g(t), h(t))$, and the Chain Rule gives a formula for differentiating z as a function of t. We assume that f is differentiable (Definition 15.4.7). Recall that this is the case when f_x and f_y are continuous (Theorem 15.4.8).

$\boxed{2}$ **THE CHAIN RULE (CASE 1)** Suppose that $z = f(x, y)$ is a differentiable function of x and y, where $x = g(t)$ and $y = h(t)$ are both differentiable functions of t. Then z is a differentiable function of t and

$$\frac{dz}{dt} = \frac{\partial f}{\partial x}\frac{dx}{dt} + \frac{\partial f}{\partial y}\frac{dy}{dt}$$

PROOF A change of Δt in t produces changes of Δx in x and Δy in y. These, in turn, produce a change of Δz in z, and from Definition 15.4.7 we have

$$\Delta z = \frac{\partial f}{\partial x}\Delta x + \frac{\partial f}{\partial y}\Delta y + \varepsilon_1 \Delta x + \varepsilon_2 \Delta y$$

where $\varepsilon_1 \to 0$ and $\varepsilon_2 \to 0$ as $(\Delta x, \Delta y) \to (0, 0)$. [If the functions ε_1 and ε_2 are not defined at $(0, 0)$, we can define them to be 0 there.] Dividing both sides of this equation by Δt, we have

$$\frac{\Delta z}{\Delta t} = \frac{\partial f}{\partial x}\frac{\Delta x}{\Delta t} + \frac{\partial f}{\partial y}\frac{\Delta y}{\Delta t} + \varepsilon_1 \frac{\Delta x}{\Delta t} + \varepsilon_2 \frac{\Delta y}{\Delta t}$$

If we now let $\Delta t \to 0$, then $\Delta x = g(t + \Delta t) - g(t) \to 0$ because g is differentiable and therefore continuous. Similarly, $\Delta y \to 0$. This, in turn, means that $\varepsilon_1 \to 0$ and $\varepsilon_2 \to 0$, so

$$\frac{dz}{dt} = \lim_{\Delta t \to 0} \frac{\Delta z}{\Delta t}$$

$$= \frac{\partial f}{\partial x}\lim_{\Delta t \to 0}\frac{\Delta x}{\Delta t} + \frac{\partial f}{\partial y}\lim_{\Delta t \to 0}\frac{\Delta y}{\Delta t} + \left(\lim_{\Delta t \to 0}\varepsilon_1\right)\lim_{\Delta t \to 0}\frac{\Delta x}{\Delta t} + \left(\lim_{\Delta t \to 0}\varepsilon_2\right)\lim_{\Delta t \to 0}\frac{\Delta y}{\Delta t}$$

$$= \frac{\partial f}{\partial x}\frac{dx}{dt} + \frac{\partial f}{\partial y}\frac{dy}{dt} + 0 \cdot \frac{dx}{dt} + 0 \cdot \frac{dy}{dt}$$

$$= \frac{\partial f}{\partial x}\frac{dx}{dt} + \frac{\partial f}{\partial y}\frac{dy}{dt} \qquad \qquad \square$$

Since we often write $\partial z/\partial x$ in place of $\partial f/\partial x$, we can rewrite the Chain Rule in the form

■ Notice the similarity to the definition of the differential:

$$dz = \frac{\partial z}{\partial x}\,dx + \frac{\partial z}{\partial y}\,dy$$

$$\frac{dz}{dt} = \frac{\partial z}{\partial x}\frac{dx}{dt} + \frac{\partial z}{\partial y}\frac{dy}{dt}$$

EXAMPLE 1 If $z = x^2 y + 3xy^4$, where $x = \sin 2t$ and $y = \cos t$, find dz/dt when $t = 0$.

SOLUTION The Chain Rule gives

$$\frac{dz}{dt} = \frac{\partial z}{\partial x}\frac{dx}{dt} + \frac{\partial z}{\partial y}\frac{dy}{dt}$$

$$= (2xy + 3y^4)(2\cos 2t) + (x^2 + 12xy^3)(-\sin t)$$

It's not necessary to substitute the expressions for x and y in terms of t. We simply observe that when $t = 0$, we have $x = \sin 0 = 0$ and $y = \cos 0 = 1$. Therefore

$$\left.\frac{dz}{dt}\right|_{t=0} = (0 + 3)(2\cos 0) + (0 + 0)(-\sin 0) = 6 \qquad \square$$

The derivative in Example 1 can be interpreted as the rate of change of z with respect to t as the point (x, y) moves along the curve C with parametric equations $x = \sin 2t$, $y = \cos t$. (See Figure 1.) In particular, when $t = 0$, the point (x, y) is $(0, 1)$ and $dz/dt = 6$ is the rate of increase as we move along the curve C through $(0, 1)$. If, for instance, $z = T(x, y) = x^2 y + 3xy^4$ represents the temperature at the point (x, y), then the composite function $z = T(\sin 2t, \cos t)$ represents the temperature at points on C and the derivative dz/dt represents the rate at which the temperature changes along C.

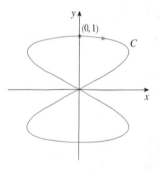

FIGURE 1
The curve $x = \sin 2t$, $y = \cos t$

▼ EXAMPLE 2 The pressure P (in kilopascals), volume V (in liters), and temperature T (in kelvins) of a mole of an ideal gas are related by the equation $PV = 8.31T$. Find the rate at which the pressure is changing when the temperature is 300 K and increasing at a rate of 0.1 K/s and the volume is 100 L and increasing at a rate of 0.2 L/s.

SOLUTION If t represents the time elapsed in seconds, then at the given instant we have $T = 300$, $dT/dt = 0.1$, $V = 100$, $dV/dt = 0.2$. Since

$$P = 8.31\frac{T}{V}$$

the Chain Rule gives

$$\frac{dP}{dt} = \frac{\partial P}{\partial T}\frac{dT}{dt} + \frac{\partial P}{\partial V}\frac{dV}{dt} = \frac{8.31}{V}\frac{dT}{dt} - \frac{8.31T}{V^2}\frac{dV}{dt}$$

$$= \frac{8.31}{100}(0.1) - \frac{8.31(300)}{100^2}(0.2) = -0.04155$$

The pressure is decreasing at a rate of about 0.042 kPa/s. $\qquad \square$

We now consider the situation where $z = f(x, y)$ but each of x and y is a function of two variables s and t: $x = g(s, t)$, $y = h(s, t)$. Then z is indirectly a function of s and t and we wish to find $\partial z/\partial s$ and $\partial z/\partial t$. Recall that in computing $\partial z/\partial t$ we hold s fixed and compute the ordinary derivative of z with respect to t. Therefore we can apply Theorem 2 to obtain

$$\frac{\partial z}{\partial t} = \frac{\partial z}{\partial x}\frac{\partial x}{\partial t} + \frac{\partial z}{\partial y}\frac{\partial y}{\partial t}$$

A similar argument holds for $\partial z/\partial s$ and so we have proved the following version of the Chain Rule.

---

3 **THE CHAIN RULE (CASE 2)** Suppose that $z = f(x, y)$ is a differentiable function of x and y, where $x = g(s, t)$ and $y = h(s, t)$ are differentiable functions of s and t. Then

$$\frac{\partial z}{\partial s} = \frac{\partial z}{\partial x}\frac{\partial x}{\partial s} + \frac{\partial z}{\partial y}\frac{\partial y}{\partial s} \qquad \frac{\partial z}{\partial t} = \frac{\partial z}{\partial x}\frac{\partial x}{\partial t} + \frac{\partial z}{\partial y}\frac{\partial y}{\partial t}$$

EXAMPLE 3 If $z = e^x \sin y$, where $x = st^2$ and $y = s^2t$, find $\partial z/\partial s$ and $\partial z/\partial t$.

SOLUTION Applying Case 2 of the Chain Rule, we get

$$\frac{\partial z}{\partial s} = \frac{\partial z}{\partial x}\frac{\partial x}{\partial s} + \frac{\partial z}{\partial y}\frac{\partial y}{\partial s} = (e^x \sin y)(t^2) + (e^x \cos y)(2st)$$

$$= t^2 e^{st^2} \sin(s^2t) + 2ste^{st^2}\cos(s^2t)$$

$$\frac{\partial z}{\partial t} = \frac{\partial z}{\partial x}\frac{\partial x}{\partial t} + \frac{\partial z}{\partial y}\frac{\partial y}{\partial t} = (e^x \sin y)(2st) + (e^x \cos y)(s^2)$$

$$= 2ste^{st^2} \sin(s^2t) + s^2 e^{st^2}\cos(s^2t) \qquad \square$$

Case 2 of the Chain Rule contains three types of variables: s and t are **independent** variables, x and y are called **intermediate** variables, and z is the **dependent** variable. Notice that Theorem 3 has one term for each intermediate variable and each of these terms resembles the one-dimensional Chain Rule in Equation 1.

To remember the Chain Rule, it's helpful to draw the **tree diagram** in Figure 2. We draw branches from the dependent variable z to the intermediate variables x and y to indicate that z is a function of x and y. Then we draw branches from x and y to the independent variables s and t. On each branch we write the corresponding partial derivative. To find $\partial z/\partial s$, we find the product of the partial derivatives along each path from z to s and then add these products:

$$\frac{\partial z}{\partial s} = \frac{\partial z}{\partial x}\frac{\partial x}{\partial s} + \frac{\partial z}{\partial y}\frac{\partial y}{\partial s}$$

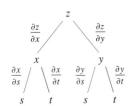

FIGURE 2

Similarly, we find $\partial z/\partial t$ by using the paths from z to t.

Now we consider the general situation in which a dependent variable u is a function of n intermediate variables $x_1, \ldots, x_n$, each of which is, in turn, a function of m independent variables $t_1, \ldots, t_m$. Notice that there are n terms, one for each intermediate variable. The proof is similar to that of Case 1.

4 **THE CHAIN RULE (GENERAL VERSION)** Suppose that u is a differentiable function of the n variables $x_1, x_2, \ldots, x_n$ and each x_j is a differentiable function of the m variables $t_1, t_2, \ldots, t_m$. Then u is a function of $t_1, t_2, \ldots, t_m$ and

$$\frac{\partial u}{\partial t_i} = \frac{\partial u}{\partial x_1}\frac{\partial x_1}{\partial t_i} + \frac{\partial u}{\partial x_2}\frac{\partial x_2}{\partial t_i} + \cdots + \frac{\partial u}{\partial x_n}\frac{\partial x_n}{\partial t_i}$$

for each $i = 1, 2, \ldots, m$.

▼ EXAMPLE 4 Write out the Chain Rule for the case where $w = f(x, y, z, t)$ and $x = x(u, v)$, $y = y(u, v)$, $z = z(u, v)$, and $t = t(u, v)$.

SOLUTION We apply Theorem 4 with $n = 4$ and $m = 2$. Figure 3 shows the tree diagram. Although we haven't written the derivatives on the branches, it's understood that if a branch leads from y to u, then the partial derivative for that branch is $\partial y/\partial u$. With the aid of the tree diagram, we can now write the required expressions:

$$\frac{\partial w}{\partial u} = \frac{\partial w}{\partial x}\frac{\partial x}{\partial u} + \frac{\partial w}{\partial y}\frac{\partial y}{\partial u} + \frac{\partial w}{\partial z}\frac{\partial z}{\partial u} + \frac{\partial w}{\partial t}\frac{\partial t}{\partial u}$$

$$\frac{\partial w}{\partial v} = \frac{\partial w}{\partial x}\frac{\partial x}{\partial v} + \frac{\partial w}{\partial y}\frac{\partial y}{\partial v} + \frac{\partial w}{\partial z}\frac{\partial z}{\partial v} + \frac{\partial w}{\partial t}\frac{\partial t}{\partial v}$$

FIGURE 3

▼ EXAMPLE 5 If $u = x^4 y + y^2 z^3$, where $x = rse^t$, $y = rs^2 e^{-t}$, and $z = r^2 s \sin t$, find the value of $\partial u/\partial s$ when $r = 2, s = 1, t = 0$.

SOLUTION With the help of the tree diagram in Figure 4, we have

$$\frac{\partial u}{\partial s} = \frac{\partial u}{\partial x}\frac{\partial x}{\partial s} + \frac{\partial u}{\partial y}\frac{\partial y}{\partial s} + \frac{\partial u}{\partial z}\frac{\partial z}{\partial s}$$

$$= (4x^3 y)(re^t) + (x^4 + 2yz^3)(2rse^{-t}) + (3y^2 z^2)(r^2 \sin t)$$

FIGURE 4

When $r = 2, s = 1$, and $t = 0$, we have $x = 2, y = 2$, and $z = 0$, so

$$\frac{\partial u}{\partial s} = (64)(2) + (16)(4) + (0)(0) = 192$$

EXAMPLE 6 If $g(s, t) = f(s^2 - t^2, t^2 - s^2)$ and f is differentiable, show that g satisfies the equation

$$t\frac{\partial g}{\partial s} + s\frac{\partial g}{\partial t} = 0$$

SOLUTION Let $x = s^2 - t^2$ and $y = t^2 - s^2$. Then $g(s, t) = f(x, y)$ and the Chain Rule gives

$$\frac{\partial g}{\partial s} = \frac{\partial f}{\partial x}\frac{\partial x}{\partial s} + \frac{\partial f}{\partial y}\frac{\partial y}{\partial s} = \frac{\partial f}{\partial x}(2s) + \frac{\partial f}{\partial y}(-2s)$$

$$\frac{\partial g}{\partial t} = \frac{\partial f}{\partial x}\frac{\partial x}{\partial t} + \frac{\partial f}{\partial y}\frac{\partial y}{\partial t} = \frac{\partial f}{\partial x}(-2t) + \frac{\partial f}{\partial y}(2t)$$

Therefore

$$t\frac{\partial g}{\partial s} + s\frac{\partial g}{\partial t} = \left(2st\frac{\partial f}{\partial x} - 2st\frac{\partial f}{\partial y}\right) + \left(-2st\frac{\partial f}{\partial x} + 2st\frac{\partial f}{\partial y}\right) = 0$$

EXAMPLE 7 If $z = f(x, y)$ has continuous second-order partial derivatives and $x = r^2 + s^2$ and $y = 2rs$, find (a) $\partial z/\partial r$ and (b) $\partial^2 z/\partial r^2$.

SOLUTION

(a) The Chain Rule gives

$$\frac{\partial z}{\partial r} = \frac{\partial z}{\partial x}\frac{\partial x}{\partial r} + \frac{\partial z}{\partial y}\frac{\partial y}{\partial r} = \frac{\partial z}{\partial x}(2r) + \frac{\partial z}{\partial y}(2s)$$

(b) Applying the Product Rule to the expression in part (a), we get

$$\frac{\partial^2 z}{\partial r^2} = \frac{\partial}{\partial r}\left(2r\frac{\partial z}{\partial x} + 2s\frac{\partial z}{\partial y}\right)$$

5

$$= 2\frac{\partial z}{\partial x} + 2r\frac{\partial}{\partial r}\left(\frac{\partial z}{\partial x}\right) + 2s\frac{\partial}{\partial r}\left(\frac{\partial z}{\partial y}\right)$$

But, using the Chain Rule again (see Figure 5), we have

$$\frac{\partial}{\partial r}\left(\frac{\partial z}{\partial x}\right) = \frac{\partial}{\partial x}\left(\frac{\partial z}{\partial x}\right)\frac{\partial x}{\partial r} + \frac{\partial}{\partial y}\left(\frac{\partial z}{\partial x}\right)\frac{\partial y}{\partial r} = \frac{\partial^2 z}{\partial x^2}(2r) + \frac{\partial^2 z}{\partial y\,\partial x}(2s)$$

$$\frac{\partial}{\partial r}\left(\frac{\partial z}{\partial y}\right) = \frac{\partial}{\partial x}\left(\frac{\partial z}{\partial y}\right)\frac{\partial x}{\partial r} + \frac{\partial}{\partial y}\left(\frac{\partial z}{\partial y}\right)\frac{\partial y}{\partial r} = \frac{\partial^2 z}{\partial x\,\partial y}(2r) + \frac{\partial^2 z}{\partial y^2}(2s)$$

FIGURE 5

Putting these expressions into Equation 5 and using the equality of the mixed second-order derivatives, we obtain

$$\frac{\partial^2 z}{\partial r^2} = 2\frac{\partial z}{\partial x} + 2r\left(2r\frac{\partial^2 z}{\partial x^2} + 2s\frac{\partial^2 z}{\partial y\,\partial x}\right) + 2s\left(2r\frac{\partial^2 z}{\partial x\,\partial y} + 2s\frac{\partial^2 z}{\partial y^2}\right)$$

$$= 2\frac{\partial z}{\partial x} + 4r^2\frac{\partial^2 z}{\partial x^2} + 8rs\frac{\partial^2 z}{\partial x\,\partial y} + 4s^2\frac{\partial^2 z}{\partial y^2} \qquad\square$$

IMPLICIT DIFFERENTIATION

The Chain Rule can be used to give a more complete description of the process of implicit differentiation that was introduced in Sections 3.6 and 15.3. We suppose that an equation of the form $F(x, y) = 0$ defines y implicitly as a differentiable function of x, that is, $y = f(x)$, where $F(x, f(x)) = 0$ for all x in the domain of f. If F is differentiable, we can apply Case 1 of the Chain Rule to differentiate both sides of the equation $F(x, y) = 0$ with respect to x. Since both x and y are functions of x, we obtain

$$\frac{\partial F}{\partial x}\frac{dx}{dx} + \frac{\partial F}{\partial y}\frac{dy}{dx} = 0$$

But $dx/dx = 1$, so if $\partial F/\partial y \neq 0$ we solve for dy/dx and obtain

6

$$\frac{dy}{dx} = -\frac{\dfrac{\partial F}{\partial x}}{\dfrac{\partial F}{\partial y}} = -\frac{F_x}{F_y}$$

To derive this equation we assumed that $F(x, y) = 0$ defines y implicitly as a function of x. The **Implicit Function Theorem**, proved in advanced calculus, gives conditions under which this assumption is valid: It states that if F is defined on a disk containing (a, b), where $F(a, b) = 0$, $F_y(a, b) \neq 0$, and F_x and F_y are continuous on the disk, then the equation $F(x, y) = 0$ defines y as a function of x near the point (a, b) and the derivative of this function is given by Equation 6.

EXAMPLE 8 Find y' if $x^3 + y^3 = 6xy$.

SOLUTION The given equation can be written as

$$F(x, y) = x^3 + y^3 - 6xy = 0$$

so Equation 6 gives

- The solution to Example 8 should be compared to the one in Example 2 in Section 3.6.

$$\frac{dy}{dx} = -\frac{F_x}{F_y} = -\frac{3x^2 - 6y}{3y^2 - 6x} = -\frac{x^2 - 2y}{y^2 - 2x}$$

Now we suppose that z is given implicitly as a function $z = f(x, y)$ by an equation of the form $F(x, y, z) = 0$. This means that $F(x, y, f(x, y)) = 0$ for all (x, y) in the domain of f. If F and f are differentiable, then we can use the Chain Rule to differentiate the equation $F(x, y, z) = 0$ as follows:

$$\frac{\partial F}{\partial x}\frac{\partial x}{\partial x} + \frac{\partial F}{\partial y}\frac{\partial y}{\partial x} + \frac{\partial F}{\partial z}\frac{\partial z}{\partial x} = 0$$

But

$$\frac{\partial}{\partial x}(x) = 1 \quad \text{and} \quad \frac{\partial}{\partial x}(y) = 0$$

so this equation becomes

$$\frac{\partial F}{\partial x} + \frac{\partial F}{\partial z}\frac{\partial z}{\partial x} = 0$$

If $\partial F/\partial z \neq 0$, we solve for $\partial z/\partial x$ and obtain the first formula in Equations 7. The formula for $\partial z/\partial y$ is obtained in a similar manner.

[7]
$$\frac{\partial z}{\partial x} = -\frac{\dfrac{\partial F}{\partial x}}{\dfrac{\partial F}{\partial z}} \qquad \frac{\partial z}{\partial y} = -\frac{\dfrac{\partial F}{\partial y}}{\dfrac{\partial F}{\partial z}}$$

Again, a version of the **Implicit Function Theorem** gives conditions under which our assumption is valid: If F is defined within a sphere containing (a, b, c), where $F(a, b, c) = 0$, $F_z(a, b, c) \neq 0$, and F_x, F_y, and F_z are continuous inside the sphere, then the equation $F(x, y, z) = 0$ defines z as a function of x and y near the point (a, b, c) and this function is differentiable, with partial derivatives given by (7).

EXAMPLE 9 Find $\dfrac{\partial z}{\partial x}$ and $\dfrac{\partial z}{\partial y}$ if $x^3 + y^3 + z^3 + 6xyz = 1$.

SOLUTION Let $F(x, y, z) = x^3 + y^3 + z^3 + 6xyz - 1$. Then, from Equations 7, we have

$$\frac{\partial z}{\partial x} = -\frac{F_x}{F_z} = -\frac{3x^2 + 6yz}{3z^2 + 6xy} = -\frac{x^2 + 2yz}{z^2 + 2xy}$$

■ The solution to Example 9 should be
compared to the one in Example 4 in
Section 15.3.

$$\frac{\partial z}{\partial y} = -\frac{F_y}{F_z} = -\frac{3y^2 + 6xz}{3z^2 + 6xy} = -\frac{y^2 + 2xz}{z^2 + 2xy}$$

15.5 EXERCISES

1–6 Use the Chain Rule to find dz/dt or dw/dt.

1. $z = x^2 + y^2 + xy$, $x = \sin t$, $y = e^t$

2. $z = \cos(x + 4y)$, $x = 5t^4$, $y = 1/t$

3. $z = \sqrt{1 + x^2 + y^2}$, $x = \ln t$, $y = \cos t$

4. $z = \tan^{-1}(y/x)$, $x = e^t$, $y = 1 - e^{-t}$

5. $w = xe^{y/z}$, $x = t^2$, $y = 1 - t$, $z = 1 + 2t$

6. $w = \ln\sqrt{x^2 + y^2 + z^2}$, $x = \sin t$, $y = \cos t$, $z = \tan t$

7–12 Use the Chain Rule to find $\partial z/\partial s$ and $\partial z/\partial t$.

7. $z = x^2 y^3$, $x = s \cos t$, $y = s \sin t$

8. $z = \arcsin(x - y)$, $x = s^2 + t^2$, $y = 1 - 2st$

9. $z = \sin\theta \cos\phi$, $\theta = st^2$, $\phi = s^2 t$

10. $z = e^{x+2y}$, $x = s/t$, $y = t/s$

11. $z = e^r \cos\theta$, $r = st$, $\theta = \sqrt{s^2 + t^2}$

12. $z = \tan(u/v)$, $u = 2s + 3t$, $v = 3s - 2t$

---

13. If $z = f(x, y)$, where f is differentiable, and

$$x = g(t) \qquad\qquad y = h(t)$$
$$g(3) = 2 \qquad\qquad h(3) = 7$$
$$g'(3) = 5 \qquad\qquad h'(3) = -4$$
$$f_x(2, 7) = 6 \qquad\quad f_y(2, 7) = -8$$

find dz/dt when $t = 3$.

14. Let $W(s, t) = F(u(s, t), v(s, t))$, where F, u, and v are
differentiable, and

$$u(1, 0) = 2 \qquad\qquad v(1, 0) = 3$$
$$u_s(1, 0) = -2 \qquad\quad v_s(1, 0) = 5$$
$$u_t(1, 0) = 6 \qquad\qquad v_t(1, 0) = 4$$
$$F_u(2, 3) = -1 \qquad\quad F_v(2, 3) = 10$$

Find $W_s(1, 0)$ and $W_t(1, 0)$.

15. Suppose f is a differentiable function of x and y, and
$g(u, v) = f(e^u + \sin v, e^u + \cos v)$. Use the table of values
to calculate $g_u(0, 0)$ and $g_v(0, 0)$.

	f	g	f_x	f_y
(0, 0)	3	6	4	8
(1, 2)	6	3	2	5

16. Suppose f is a differentiable function of x and y, and
$g(r, s) = f(2r - s, s^2 - 4r)$. Use the table of values in
Exercise 15 to calculate $g_r(1, 2)$ and $g_s(1, 2)$.

17–20 Use a tree diagram to write out the Chain Rule for the given
case. Assume all functions are differentiable.

17. $u = f(x, y)$, where $x = x(r, s, t)$, $y = y(r, s, t)$

18. $R = f(x, y, z, t)$, where $x = x(u, v, w)$, $y = y(u, v, w)$,
$z = z(u, v, w)$, $t = t(u, v, w)$

19. $w = f(r, s, t)$, where $r = r(x, y)$, $s = s(x, y)$, $t = t(x, y)$

20. $t = f(u, v, w)$, where $u = u(p, q, r, s)$, $v = v(p, q, r, s)$,
$w = w(p, q, r, s)$

21–26 Use the Chain Rule to find the indicated partial derivatives.

21. $z = x^2 + xy^3$, $\quad x = uv^2 + w^3$, $\quad y = u + ve^w$;

$\dfrac{\partial z}{\partial u}$, $\dfrac{\partial z}{\partial v}$, $\dfrac{\partial z}{\partial w}$ $\quad$ when $u = 2$, $v = 1$, $w = 0$

22. $u = \sqrt{r^2 + s^2}$, $\quad r = y + x \cos t$, $\quad s = x + y \sin t$;

$\dfrac{\partial u}{\partial x}$, $\dfrac{\partial u}{\partial y}$, $\dfrac{\partial u}{\partial t}$ $\quad$ when $x = 1$, $y = 2$, $t = 0$

23. $R = \ln(u^2 + v^2 + w^2)$,

$u = x + 2y$, $\quad v = 2x - y$, $\quad w = 2xy$;

$\dfrac{\partial R}{\partial x}$, $\dfrac{\partial R}{\partial y}$ $\quad$ when $x = y = 1$

24. $M = xe^{y-z^2}$, $\quad x = 2uv$, $\quad y = u - v$, $\quad z = u + v$;

$\dfrac{\partial M}{\partial u}$, $\dfrac{\partial M}{\partial v}$ $\quad$ when $u = 3$, $v = -1$

25. $u = x^2 + yz$, $\quad x = pr \cos \theta$, $\quad y = pr \sin \theta$, $\quad z = p + r$;

$\dfrac{\partial u}{\partial p}$, $\dfrac{\partial u}{\partial r}$, $\dfrac{\partial u}{\partial \theta}$ $\quad$ when $p = 2$, $r = 3$, $\theta = 0$

26. $Y = w \tan^{-1}(uv)$, $\quad u = r + s$, $\quad v = s + t$, $\quad w = t + r$;

$\dfrac{\partial Y}{\partial r}$, $\dfrac{\partial Y}{\partial s}$, $\dfrac{\partial Y}{\partial t}$ $\quad$ when $r = 1$, $s = 0$, $t = 1$

27–30 Use Equation 6 to find dy/dx.

27. $\sqrt{xy} = 1 + x^2y$

28. $y^5 + x^2y^3 = 1 + ye^{x^2}$

29. $\cos(x - y) = xe^y$

30. $\sin x + \cos y = \sin x \cos y$

31–34 Use Equations 7 to find $\partial z/\partial x$ and $\partial z/\partial y$.

31. $x^2 + y^2 + z^2 = 3xyz$

32. $xyz = \cos(x + y + z)$

33. $x - z = \arctan(yz)$

34. $yz = \ln(x + z)$

---

35. The temperature at a point (x, y) is $T(x, y)$, measured in degrees Celsius. A bug crawls so that its position after t seconds is given by $x = \sqrt{1 + t}$, $y = 2 + \frac{1}{3}t$, where x and y are measured in centimeters. The temperature function satisfies $T_x(2, 3) = 4$ and $T_y(2, 3) = 3$. How fast is the temperature rising on the bug's path after 3 seconds?

36. Wheat production W in a given year depends on the average temperature T and the annual rainfall R. Scientists estimate that the average temperature is rising at a rate of $0.15°C/year$ and rainfall is decreasing at a rate of 0.1 cm/year. They also estimate that, at current production levels, $\partial W/\partial T = -2$ and $\partial W/\partial R = 8$.
(a) What is the significance of the signs of these partial derivatives?
(b) Estimate the current rate of change of wheat production, dW/dt.

37. The speed of sound traveling through ocean water with salinity 35 parts per thousand has been modeled by the equation

$$C = 1449.2 + 4.6T - 0.055T^2 + 0.00029T^3 + 0.016D$$

where C is the speed of sound (in meters per second), T is the temperature (in degrees Celsius), and D is the depth below the ocean surface (in meters). A scuba diver began a leisurely dive into the ocean water; the diver's depth and the surrounding water temperature over time are recorded in the following graphs. Estimate the rate of change (with respect to time) of the speed of sound through the ocean water experienced by the diver 20 minutes into the dive. What are the units?

38. The radius of a right circular cone is increasing at a rate of 1.8 in/s while its height is decreasing at a rate of 2.5 in/s. At what rate is the volume of the cone changing when the radius is 120 in. and the height is 140 in.?

39. The length ℓ, width w, and height h of a box change with time. At a certain instant the dimensions are $\ell = 1$ m and $w = h = 2$ m, and ℓ and w are increasing at a rate of 2 m/s while h is decreasing at a rate of 3 m/s. At that instant find the rates at which the following quantities are changing.
(a) The volume
(b) The surface area
(c) The length of a diagonal

40. The voltage V in a simple electrical circuit is slowly decreasing as the battery wears out. The resistance R is slowly increasing as the resistor heats up. Use Ohm's Law, $V = IR$, to find how the current I is changing at the moment when $R = 400\ \Omega$, $I = 0.08$ A, $dV/dt = -0.01$ V/s, and $dR/dt = 0.03\ \Omega/s$.

41. The pressure of 1 mole of an ideal gas is increasing at a rate of 0.05 kPa/s and the temperature is increasing at a rate of 0.15 K/s. Use the equation in Example 2 to find the rate of change of the volume when the pressure is 20 kPa and the temperature is 320 K.

42. Car A is traveling north on Highway 16 and car B is traveling west on Highway 83. Each car is approaching the intersection of these highways. At a certain moment, car A is 0.3 km from the intersection and traveling at 90 km/h while car B is 0.4 km from the intersection and traveling at 80 km/h. How fast is the distance between the cars changing at that moment?

43. One side of a triangle is increasing at a rate of 3 cm/s and a second side is decreasing at a rate of 2 cm/s. If the area of the triangle remains constant, at what rate does the angle between the sides change when the first side is 20 cm long, the second side is 30 cm, and the angle is $\pi/6$?

44. If a sound with frequency f_s is produced by a source traveling along a line with speed v_s and an observer is traveling with speed v_o along the same line from the opposite direction toward the source, then the frequency of the sound heard by the observer is

$$f_o = \left(\frac{c + v_o}{c - v_s}\right) f_s$$

where c is the speed of sound, about 332 m/s. (This is the **Doppler effect**.) Suppose that, at a particular moment, you are in a train traveling at 34 m/s and accelerating at 1.2 m/s^2. A train is approaching you from the opposite direction on the other track at 40 m/s, accelerating at 1.4 m/s^2, and sounds its whistle, which has a frequency of 460 Hz. At that instant, what is the perceived frequency that you hear and how fast is it changing?

45–48 Assume that all the given functions are differentiable.

45. If $z = f(x, y)$, where $x = r \cos \theta$ and $y = r \sin \theta$, (a) find $\partial z/\partial r$ and $\partial z/\partial \theta$ and (b) show that

$$\left(\frac{\partial z}{\partial x}\right)^2 + \left(\frac{\partial z}{\partial y}\right)^2 = \left(\frac{\partial z}{\partial r}\right)^2 + \frac{1}{r^2}\left(\frac{\partial z}{\partial \theta}\right)^2$$

46. If $u = f(x, y)$, where $x = e^s \cos t$ and $y = e^s \sin t$, show that

$$\left(\frac{\partial u}{\partial x}\right)^2 + \left(\frac{\partial u}{\partial y}\right)^2 = e^{-2s}\left[\left(\frac{\partial u}{\partial s}\right)^2 + \left(\frac{\partial u}{\partial t}\right)^2\right]$$

47. If $z = f(x - y)$, show that $\dfrac{\partial z}{\partial x} + \dfrac{\partial z}{\partial y} = 0$.

48. If $z = f(x, y)$, where $x = s + t$ and $y = s - t$, show that

$$\left(\frac{\partial z}{\partial x}\right)^2 - \left(\frac{\partial z}{\partial y}\right)^2 = \frac{\partial z}{\partial s}\frac{\partial z}{\partial t}$$

49–54 Assume that all the given functions have continuous second-order partial derivatives.

49. Show that any function of the form

$$z = f(x + at) + g(x - at)$$

is a solution of the wave equation

$$\frac{\partial^2 z}{\partial t^2} = a^2 \frac{\partial^2 z}{\partial x^2}$$

[*Hint:* Let $u = x + at$, $v = x - at$.]

50. If $u = f(x, y)$, where $x = e^s \cos t$ and $y = e^s \sin t$, show that

$$\frac{\partial^2 u}{\partial x^2} + \frac{\partial^2 u}{\partial y^2} = e^{-2s}\left[\frac{\partial^2 u}{\partial s^2} + \frac{\partial^2 u}{\partial t^2}\right]$$

51. If $z = f(x, y)$, where $x = r^2 + s^2$ and $y = 2rs$, find $\partial^2 z/\partial r\, \partial s$. (Compare with Example 7.)

52. If $z = f(x, y)$, where $x = r \cos \theta$ and $y = r \sin \theta$, find (a) $\partial z/\partial r$, (b) $\partial z/\partial \theta$, and (c) $\partial^2 z/\partial r\, \partial \theta$.

53. If $z = f(x, y)$, where $x = r \cos \theta$ and $y = r \sin \theta$, show that

$$\frac{\partial^2 z}{\partial x^2} + \frac{\partial^2 z}{\partial y^2} = \frac{\partial^2 z}{\partial r^2} + \frac{1}{r^2}\frac{\partial^2 z}{\partial \theta^2} + \frac{1}{r}\frac{\partial z}{\partial r}$$

54. Suppose $z = f(x, y)$, where $x = g(s, t)$ and $y = h(s, t)$.
(a) Show that

$$\frac{\partial^2 z}{\partial t^2} = \frac{\partial^2 z}{\partial x^2}\left(\frac{\partial x}{\partial t}\right)^2 + 2\frac{\partial^2 z}{\partial x\, \partial y}\frac{\partial x}{\partial t}\frac{\partial y}{\partial t} + \frac{\partial^2 z}{\partial y^2}\left(\frac{\partial y}{\partial t}\right)^2$$
$$+ \frac{\partial z}{\partial x}\frac{\partial^2 x}{\partial t^2} + \frac{\partial z}{\partial y}\frac{\partial^2 y}{\partial t^2}$$

(b) Find a similar formula for $\partial^2 z/\partial s\, \partial t$.

55. A function f is called **homogeneous of degree n** if it satisfies the equation $f(tx, ty) = t^n f(x, y)$ for all t, where n is a positive integer and f has continuous second-order partial derivatives.
(a) Verify that $f(x, y) = x^2 y + 2xy^2 + 5y^3$ is homogeneous of degree 3.
(b) Show that if f is homogeneous of degree n, then

$$x\frac{\partial f}{\partial x} + y\frac{\partial f}{\partial y} = nf(x, y)$$

[*Hint:* Use the Chain Rule to differentiate $f(tx, ty)$ with respect to t.]

56. If f is homogeneous of degree n, show that

$$x^2\frac{\partial^2 f}{\partial x^2} + 2xy\frac{\partial^2 f}{\partial x\, \partial y} + y^2\frac{\partial^2 f}{\partial y^2} = n(n - 1)f(x, y)$$

57. If f is homogeneous of degree n, show that

$$f_x(tx, ty) = t^{n-1}f_x(x, y)$$

58. Suppose that the equation $F(x, y, z) = 0$ implicitly defines each of the three variables x, y, and z as functions of the other two: $z = f(x, y)$, $y = g(x, z)$, $x = h(y, z)$. If F is differentiable and F_x, F_y, and F_z are all nonzero, show that

$$\frac{\partial z}{\partial x}\frac{\partial x}{\partial y}\frac{\partial y}{\partial z} = -1$$

15.6 DIRECTIONAL DERIVATIVES AND THE GRADIENT VECTOR

FIGURE 1

The weather map in Figure 1 shows a contour map of the temperature function $T(x, y)$ for the states of California and Nevada at 3:00 PM on a day in October. The level curves, or isothermals, join locations with the same temperature. The partial derivative T_x at a location such as Reno is the rate of change of temperature with respect to distance if we travel east from Reno; T_y is the rate of change of temperature if we travel north. But what if we want to know the rate of change of temperature when we travel southeast (toward Las Vegas), or in some other direction? In this section we introduce a type of derivative, called a *directional derivative,* that enables us to find the rate of change of a function of two or more variables in any direction.

DIRECTIONAL DERIVATIVES

Recall that if $z = f(x, y)$, then the partial derivatives f_x and f_y are defined as

$$\boxed{1} \qquad \begin{aligned} f_x(x_0, y_0) &= \lim_{h \to 0} \frac{f(x_0 + h, y_0) - f(x_0, y_0)}{h} \\ f_y(x_0, y_0) &= \lim_{h \to 0} \frac{f(x_0, y_0 + h) - f(x_0, y_0)}{h} \end{aligned}$$

and represent the rates of change of z in the x- and y-directions, that is, in the directions of the unit vectors $\mathbf{i}$ and $\mathbf{j}$.

Suppose that we now wish to find the rate of change of z at (x_0, y_0) in the direction of an arbitrary unit vector $\mathbf{u} = \langle a, b \rangle$. (See Figure 2.) To do this we consider the surface S with equation $z = f(x, y)$ (the graph of f) and we let $z_0 = f(x_0, y_0)$. Then the point $P(x_0, y_0, z_0)$ lies on S. The vertical plane that passes through P in the direction of $\mathbf{u}$ intersects S in a curve C. (See Figure 3.) The slope of the tangent line T to C at the point P is the rate of change of z in the direction of $\mathbf{u}$.

FIGURE 2

A unit vector $\mathbf{u} = \langle a, b \rangle = \langle \cos\theta, \sin\theta \rangle$

TEC Visual 15.6A animates Figure 3 by rotating $\mathbf{u}$ and therefore T.

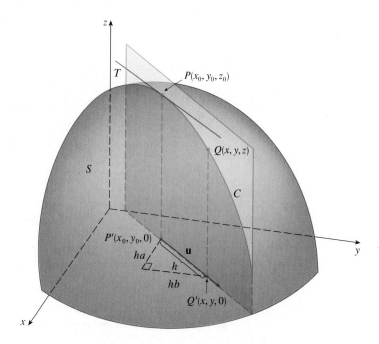

FIGURE 3

If $Q(x, y, z)$ is another point on C and P', Q' are the projections of P, Q on the xy-plane, then the vector $\overrightarrow{P'Q'}$ is parallel to $\mathbf{u}$ and so

$$\overrightarrow{P'Q'} = h\mathbf{u} = \langle ha, hb \rangle$$

for some scalar h. Therefore $x - x_0 = ha$, $y - y_0 = hb$, so $x = x_0 + ha$, $y = y_0 + hb$, and

$$\frac{\Delta z}{h} = \frac{z - z_0}{h} = \frac{f(x_0 + ha, y_0 + hb) - f(x_0, y_0)}{h}$$

If we take the limit as $h \to 0$, we obtain the rate of change of z (with respect to distance) in the direction of $\mathbf{u}$, which is called the directional derivative of f in the direction of $\mathbf{u}$.

---

2 **DEFINITION** The **directional derivative** of f at (x_0, y_0) in the direction of a unit vector $\mathbf{u} = \langle a, b \rangle$ is

$$D_{\mathbf{u}} f(x_0, y_0) = \lim_{h \to 0} \frac{f(x_0 + ha, y_0 + hb) - f(x_0, y_0)}{h}$$

if this limit exists.

By comparing Definition 2 with Equations (1), we see that if $\mathbf{u} = \mathbf{i} = \langle 1, 0 \rangle$, then $D_{\mathbf{i}} f = f_x$ and if $\mathbf{u} = \mathbf{j} = \langle 0, 1 \rangle$, then $D_{\mathbf{j}} f = f_y$. In other words, the partial derivatives of f with respect to x and y are just special cases of the directional derivative.

EXAMPLE 1 Use the weather map in Figure 1 to estimate the value of the directional derivative of the temperature function at Reno in the southeasterly direction.

SOLUTION The unit vector directed toward the southeast is $\mathbf{u} = (\mathbf{i} - \mathbf{j})/\sqrt{2}$, but we won't need to use this expression. We start by drawing a line through Reno toward the southeast. (See Figure 4.)

FIGURE 4

We approximate the directional derivative $D_{\mathbf{u}} T$ by the average rate of change of the temperature between the points where this line intersects the isothermals $T = 50$ and

$T = 60$. The temperature at the point southeast of Reno is $T = 60°F$ and the temperature at the point northwest of Reno is $T = 50°F$. The distance between these points looks to be about 75 miles. So the rate of change of the temperature in the southeasterly direction is

$$D_{\mathbf{u}} T \approx \frac{60 - 50}{75} = \frac{10}{75} \approx 0.13°F/\text{mi} \qquad \square$$

When we compute the directional derivative of a function defined by a formula, we generally use the following theorem.

> **3 THEOREM** If f is a differentiable function of x and y, then f has a directional derivative in the direction of any unit vector $\mathbf{u} = \langle a, b \rangle$ and
>
> $$D_{\mathbf{u}} f(x, y) = f_x(x, y)\, a + f_y(x, y)\, b$$

PROOF If we define a function g of the single variable h by

$$g(h) = f(x_0 + ha, y_0 + hb)$$

then, by the definition of a derivative, we have

$$
\boxed{4} \qquad g'(0) = \lim_{h \to 0} \frac{g(h) - g(0)}{h} = \lim_{h \to 0} \frac{f(x_0 + ha, y_0 + hb) - f(x_0, y_0)}{h}
$$

$$= D_{\mathbf{u}} f(x_0, y_0)$$

On the other hand, we can write $g(h) = f(x, y)$, where $x = x_0 + ha$, $y = y_0 + hb$, so the Chain Rule (Theorem 15.5.2) gives

$$g'(h) = \frac{\partial f}{\partial x} \frac{dx}{dh} + \frac{\partial f}{\partial y} \frac{dy}{dh} = f_x(x, y)\, a + f_y(x, y)\, b$$

If we now put $h = 0$, then $x = x_0$, $y = y_0$, and

$$\boxed{5} \qquad g'(0) = f_x(x_0, y_0)\, a + f_y(x_0, y_0)\, b$$

Comparing Equations 4 and 5, we see that

$$D_{\mathbf{u}} f(x_0, y_0) = f_x(x_0, y_0)\, a + f_y(x_0, y_0)\, b \qquad \square$$

If the unit vector $\mathbf{u}$ makes an angle θ with the positive x-axis (as in Figure 2), then we can write $\mathbf{u} = \langle \cos\theta, \sin\theta \rangle$ and the formula in Theorem 3 becomes

$$\boxed{6} \qquad D_{\mathbf{u}} f(x, y) = f_x(x, y)\, \cos\theta + f_y(x, y)\, \sin\theta$$

EXAMPLE 2 Find the directional derivative $D_{\mathbf{u}} f(x, y)$ if

$$f(x, y) = x^3 - 3xy + 4y^2$$

and $\mathbf{u}$ is the unit vector given by angle $\theta = \pi/6$. What is $D_{\mathbf{u}} f(1, 2)$?

■ The directional derivative $D_u f(1, 2)$ in Example 2 represents the rate of change of z in the direction of $\mathbf{u}$. This is the slope of the tangent line to the curve of intersection of the surface $z = x^3 - 3xy + 4y^2$ and the vertical plane through $(1, 2, 0)$ in the direction of $\mathbf{u}$ shown in Figure 5.

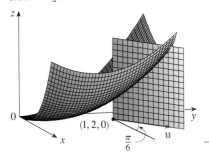

FIGURE 5

SOLUTION Formula 6 gives

$$D_u f(x, y) = f_x(x, y) \cos \frac{\pi}{6} + f_y(x, y) \sin \frac{\pi}{6}$$

$$= (3x^2 - 3y) \frac{\sqrt{3}}{2} + (-3x + 8y) \frac{1}{2}$$

$$= \tfrac{1}{2} \left[3\sqrt{3}\, x^2 - 3x + \left(8 - 3\sqrt{3} \right) y \right]$$

Therefore

$$D_u f(1, 2) = \tfrac{1}{2} \left[3\sqrt{3}\,(1)^2 - 3(1) + \left(8 - 3\sqrt{3} \right)(2) \right] = \frac{13 - 3\sqrt{3}}{2} \qquad \square$$

THE GRADIENT VECTOR

Notice from Theorem 3 that the directional derivative can be written as the dot product of two vectors:

$$\boxed{7}$$

$$D_u f(x, y) = f_x(x, y)\, a + f_y(x, y)\, b$$

$$= \langle f_x(x, y), f_y(x, y) \rangle \cdot \langle a, b \rangle$$

$$= \langle f_x(x, y), f_y(x, y) \rangle \cdot \mathbf{u}$$

The first vector in this dot product occurs not only in computing directional derivatives but in many other contexts as well. So we give it a special name (the *gradient* of f) and a special notation (**grad** f or ∇f, which is read "del f").

---

8 DEFINITION If f is a function of two variables x and y, then the **gradient** of f is the vector function ∇f defined by

$$\nabla f(x, y) = \langle f_x(x, y), f_y(x, y) \rangle = \frac{\partial f}{\partial x} \mathbf{i} + \frac{\partial f}{\partial y} \mathbf{j}$$

EXAMPLE 3 If $f(x, y) = \sin x + e^{xy}$, then

$$\nabla f(x, y) = \langle f_x, f_y \rangle = \langle \cos x + ye^{xy}, xe^{xy} \rangle$$

and

$$\nabla f(0, 1) = \langle 2, 0 \rangle \qquad \square$$

With this notation for the gradient vector, we can rewrite the expression (7) for the directional derivative as

$$\boxed{9} \qquad \boxed{D_u f(x, y) = \nabla f(x, y) \cdot \mathbf{u}}$$

This expresses the directional derivative in the direction of $\mathbf{u}$ as the scalar projection of the gradient vector onto $\mathbf{u}$.

■ The gradient vector $\nabla f(2, -1)$ in Example 4 is shown in Figure 6 with initial point $(2, -1)$. Also shown is the vector $\mathbf{v}$ that gives the direction of the directional derivative. Both of these vectors are superimposed on a contour plot of the graph of f.

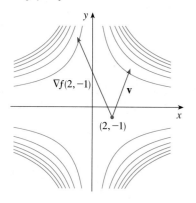

FIGURE 6

◥ **EXAMPLE 4** Find the directional derivative of the function $f(x, y) = x^2y^3 - 4y$ at the point $(2, -1)$ in the direction of the vector $\mathbf{v} = 2\mathbf{i} + 5\mathbf{j}$.

SOLUTION We first compute the gradient vector at $(2, -1)$:

$$\nabla f(x, y) = 2xy^3\mathbf{i} + (3x^2y^2 - 4)\mathbf{j}$$

$$\nabla f(2, -1) = -4\mathbf{i} + 8\mathbf{j}$$

Note that $\mathbf{v}$ is not a unit vector, but since $|\mathbf{v}| = \sqrt{29}$, the unit vector in the direction of $\mathbf{v}$ is

$$\mathbf{u} = \frac{\mathbf{v}}{|\mathbf{v}|} = \frac{2}{\sqrt{29}}\mathbf{i} + \frac{5}{\sqrt{29}}\mathbf{j}$$

Therefore, by Equation 9, we have

$$D_\mathbf{u} f(2, -1) = \nabla f(2, -1) \cdot \mathbf{u} = (-4\mathbf{i} + 8\mathbf{j}) \cdot \left(\frac{2}{\sqrt{29}}\mathbf{i} + \frac{5}{\sqrt{29}}\mathbf{j}\right)$$

$$= \frac{-4 \cdot 2 + 8 \cdot 5}{\sqrt{29}} = \frac{32}{\sqrt{29}} \qquad \square$$

FUNCTIONS OF THREE VARIABLES

For functions of three variables we can define directional derivatives in a similar manner. Again $D_\mathbf{u} f(x, y, z)$ can be interpreted as the rate of change of the function in the direction of a unit vector $\mathbf{u}$.

|10| **DEFINITION** The **directional derivative** of f at (x_0, y_0, z_0) in the direction of a unit vector $\mathbf{u} = \langle a, b, c \rangle$ is

$$D_\mathbf{u} f(x_0, y_0, z_0) = \lim_{h \to 0} \frac{f(x_0 + ha, y_0 + hb, z_0 + hc) - f(x_0, y_0, z_0)}{h}$$

if this limit exists.

If we use vector notation, then we can write both definitions (2 and 10) of the directional derivative in the compact form

|11|

$$D_\mathbf{u} f(\mathbf{x}_0) = \lim_{h \to 0} \frac{f(\mathbf{x}_0 + h\mathbf{u}) - f(\mathbf{x}_0)}{h}$$

where $\mathbf{x}_0 = \langle x_0, y_0 \rangle$ if $n = 2$ and $\mathbf{x}_0 = \langle x_0, y_0, z_0 \rangle$ if $n = 3$. This is reasonable because the vector equation of the line through $\mathbf{x}_0$ in the direction of the vector $\mathbf{u}$ is given by $\mathbf{x} = \mathbf{x}_0 + t\mathbf{u}$ (Equation 13.5.1) and so $f(\mathbf{x}_0 + h\mathbf{u})$ represents the value of f at a point on this line.

If $f(x, y, z)$ is differentiable and $\mathbf{u} = \langle a, b, c \rangle$, then the same method that was used to prove Theorem 3 can be used to show that

$$\boxed{12} \qquad D_{\mathbf{u}} f(x, y, z) = f_x(x, y, z) \, a + f_y(x, y, z) \, b + f_z(x, y, z) \, c$$

For a function f of three variables, the **gradient vector**, denoted by ∇f or **grad** f, is

$$\nabla f(x, y, z) = \langle f_x(x, y, z), f_y(x, y, z), f_z(x, y, z) \rangle$$

or, for short,

$$\boxed{13} \qquad \nabla f = \langle f_x, f_y, f_z \rangle = \frac{\partial f}{\partial x} \mathbf{i} + \frac{\partial f}{\partial y} \mathbf{j} + \frac{\partial f}{\partial z} \mathbf{k}$$

Then, just as with functions of two variables, Formula 12 for the directional derivative can be rewritten as

$$\boxed{14} \qquad D_{\mathbf{u}} f(x, y, z) = \nabla f(x, y, z) \cdot \mathbf{u}$$

☑ EXAMPLE 5 If $f(x, y, z) = x \sin yz$, (a) find the gradient of f and (b) find the directional derivative of f at $(1, 3, 0)$ in the direction of $\mathbf{v} = \mathbf{i} + 2\mathbf{j} - \mathbf{k}$.

SOLUTION

(a) The gradient of f is

$$\nabla f(x, y, z) = \langle f_x(x, y, z), f_y(x, y, z), f_z(x, y, z) \rangle$$

$$= \langle \sin yz, xz \cos yz, xy \cos yz \rangle$$

(b) At $(1, 3, 0)$ we have $\nabla f(1, 3, 0) = \langle 0, 0, 3 \rangle$. The unit vector in the direction of $\mathbf{v} = \mathbf{i} + 2\mathbf{j} - \mathbf{k}$ is

$$\mathbf{u} = \frac{1}{\sqrt{6}} \mathbf{i} + \frac{2}{\sqrt{6}} \mathbf{j} - \frac{1}{\sqrt{6}} \mathbf{k}$$

Therefore Equation 14 gives

$$D_{\mathbf{u}} f(1, 3, 0) = \nabla f(1, 3, 0) \cdot \mathbf{u}$$

$$= 3\mathbf{k} \cdot \left(\frac{1}{\sqrt{6}} \mathbf{i} + \frac{2}{\sqrt{6}} \mathbf{j} - \frac{1}{\sqrt{6}} \mathbf{k} \right)$$

$$= 3 \left(-\frac{1}{\sqrt{6}} \right) = -\sqrt{\frac{3}{2}} \qquad \square$$

MAXIMIZING THE DIRECTIONAL DERIVATIVE

Suppose we have a function f of two or three variables and we consider all possible directional derivatives of f at a given point. These give the rates of change of f in all possible directions. We can then ask the questions: In which of these directions does f change fastest and what is the maximum rate of change? The answers are provided by the following theorem.

TEC Visual 15.6B provides visual confirmation of Theorem 15.

[15] **THEOREM** Suppose f is a differentiable function of two or three variables. The maximum value of the directional derivative $D_{\mathbf{u}} f(\mathbf{x})$ is $|\nabla f(\mathbf{x})|$ and it occurs when $\mathbf{u}$ has the same direction as the gradient vector $\nabla f(\mathbf{x})$.

PROOF From Equation 9 or 14 we have

$$D_{\mathbf{u}} f = \nabla f \cdot \mathbf{u} = |\nabla f| |\mathbf{u}| \cos \theta = |\nabla f| \cos \theta$$

where θ is the angle between ∇f and $\mathbf{u}$. The maximum value of $\cos \theta$ is 1 and this occurs when $\theta = 0$. Therefore the maximum value of $D_{\mathbf{u}} f$ is $|\nabla f|$ and it occurs when $\theta = 0$, that is, when $\mathbf{u}$ has the same direction as ∇f. ☐

EXAMPLE 6
(a) If $f(x, y) = xe^y$, find the rate of change of f at the point $P(2, 0)$ in the direction from P to $Q(\frac{1}{2}, 2)$.
(b) In what direction does f have the maximum rate of change? What is this maximum rate of change?

SOLUTION
(a) We first compute the gradient vector:

$$\nabla f(x, y) = \langle f_x, f_y \rangle = \langle e^y, xe^y \rangle$$

$$\nabla f(2, 0) = \langle 1, 2 \rangle$$

FIGURE 7

■ At $(2, 0)$ the function in Example 6 increases fastest in the direction of the gradient vector $\nabla f(2, 0) = \langle 1, 2 \rangle$. Notice from Figure 7 that this vector appears to be perpendicular to the level curve through $(2, 0)$. Figure 8 shows the graph of f and the gradient vector.

The unit vector in the direction of $\overrightarrow{PQ} = \langle -1.5, 2 \rangle$ is $\mathbf{u} = \langle -\frac{3}{5}, \frac{4}{5} \rangle$, so the rate of change of f in the direction from P to Q is

$$D_{\mathbf{u}} f(2, 0) = \nabla f(2, 0) \cdot \mathbf{u} = \langle 1, 2 \rangle \cdot \langle -\frac{3}{5}, \frac{4}{5} \rangle$$

$$= 1\left(-\frac{3}{5}\right) + 2\left(\frac{4}{5}\right) = 1$$

(b) According to Theorem 15, f increases fastest in the direction of the gradient vector $\nabla f(2, 0) = \langle 1, 2 \rangle$. The maximum rate of change is

$$|\nabla f(2, 0)| = |\langle 1, 2 \rangle| = \sqrt{5}$$ ☐

FIGURE 8

EXAMPLE 7 Suppose that the temperature at a point (x, y, z) in space is given by $T(x, y, z) = 80/(1 + x^2 + 2y^2 + 3z^2)$, where T is measured in degrees Celsius and x, y, z in meters. In which direction does the temperature increase fastest at the point $(1, 1, -2)$? What is the maximum rate of increase?

SOLUTION The gradient of T is

$$\nabla T = \frac{\partial T}{\partial x} \mathbf{i} + \frac{\partial T}{\partial y} \mathbf{j} + \frac{\partial T}{\partial z} \mathbf{k}$$

$$= -\frac{160x}{(1 + x^2 + 2y^2 + 3z^2)^2} \mathbf{i} - \frac{320y}{(1 + x^2 + 2y^2 + 3z^2)^2} \mathbf{j} - \frac{480z}{(1 + x^2 + 2y^2 + 3z^2)^2} \mathbf{k}$$

$$= \frac{160}{(1 + x^2 + 2y^2 + 3z^2)^2} (-x\mathbf{i} - 2y\mathbf{j} - 3z\mathbf{k})$$

At the point $(1, 1, -2)$ the gradient vector is

$$\nabla T(1, 1, -2) = \tfrac{160}{256}(-\mathbf{i} - 2\mathbf{j} + 6\mathbf{k}) = \tfrac{5}{8}(-\mathbf{i} - 2\mathbf{j} + 6\mathbf{k})$$

By Theorem 15 the temperature increases fastest in the direction of the gradient vector $\nabla T(1, 1, -2) = \tfrac{5}{8}(-\mathbf{i} - 2\mathbf{j} + 6\mathbf{k})$ or, equivalently, in the direction of $-\mathbf{i} - 2\mathbf{j} + 6\mathbf{k}$ or the unit vector $(-\mathbf{i} - 2\mathbf{j} + 6\mathbf{k})/\sqrt{41}$. The maximum rate of increase is the length of the gradient vector:

$$|\nabla T(1, 1, -2)| = \tfrac{5}{8}|-\mathbf{i} - 2\mathbf{j} + 6\mathbf{k}| = \tfrac{5}{8}\sqrt{41}$$

Therefore the maximum rate of increase of temperature is $\tfrac{5}{8}\sqrt{41} \approx 4°\text{C}/\text{m}$. $\square$

TANGENT PLANES TO LEVEL SURFACES

Suppose S is a surface with equation $F(x, y, z) = k$, that is, it is a level surface of a function F of three variables, and let $P(x_0, y_0, z_0)$ be a point on S. Let C be any curve that lies on the surface S and passes through the point P. Recall from Section 14.1 that the curve C is described by a continuous vector function $\mathbf{r}(t) = \langle x(t), y(t), z(t) \rangle$. Let t_0 be the parameter value corresponding to P; that is, $\mathbf{r}(t_0) = \langle x_0, y_0, z_0 \rangle$. Since C lies on S, any point $(x(t), y(t), z(t))$ must satisfy the equation of S, that is,

$$\boxed{16} \qquad F(x(t), y(t), z(t)) = k$$

If x, y, and z are differentiable functions of t and F is also differentiable, then we can use the Chain Rule to differentiate both sides of Equation 16 as follows:

$$\boxed{17} \qquad \frac{\partial F}{\partial x}\frac{dx}{dt} + \frac{\partial F}{\partial y}\frac{dy}{dt} + \frac{\partial F}{\partial z}\frac{dz}{dt} = 0$$

But, since $\nabla F = \langle F_x, F_y, F_z \rangle$ and $\mathbf{r}'(t) = \langle x'(t), y'(t), z'(t) \rangle$, Equation 17 can be written in terms of a dot product as

$$\nabla F \cdot \mathbf{r}'(t) = 0$$

In particular, when $t = t_0$ we have $\mathbf{r}(t_0) = \langle x_0, y_0, z_0 \rangle$, so

$$\boxed{18} \qquad \nabla F(x_0, y_0, z_0) \cdot \mathbf{r}'(t_0) = 0$$

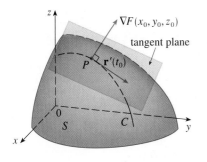

FIGURE 9

Equation 18 says that *the gradient vector at* P, $\nabla F(x_0, y_0, z_0)$, *is perpendicular to the tangent vector* $\mathbf{r}'(t_0)$ *to any curve* C *on* S *that passes through* P. (See Figure 9.) If $\nabla F(x_0, y_0, z_0) \neq \mathbf{0}$, it is therefore natural to define the **tangent plane to the level surface** $F(x, y, z) = k$ **at** $P(x_0, y_0, z_0)$ as the plane that passes through P and has normal vector $\nabla F(x_0, y_0, z_0)$. Using the standard equation of a plane (Equation 13.5.7), we can write the equation of this tangent plane as

$$\boxed{19} \qquad F_x(x_0, y_0, z_0)(x - x_0) + F_y(x_0, y_0, z_0)(y - y_0) + F_z(x_0, y_0, z_0)(z - z_0) = 0$$

The **normal line** to S at P is the line passing through P and perpendicular to the tangent plane. The direction of the normal line is therefore given by the gradient vector $\nabla F(x_0, y_0, z_0)$ and so, by Equation 13.5.3, its symmetric equations are

$$\boxed{20} \qquad \frac{x - x_0}{F_x(x_0, y_0, z_0)} = \frac{y - y_0}{F_y(x_0, y_0, z_0)} = \frac{z - z_0}{F_z(x_0, y_0, z_0)}$$

In the special case in which the equation of a surface S is of the form $z = f(x, y)$ (that is, S is the graph of a function f of two variables), we can rewrite the equation as

$$F(x, y, z) = f(x, y) - z = 0$$

and regard S as a level surface (with $k = 0$) of F. Then

$$F_x(x_0, y_0, z_0) = f_x(x_0, y_0)$$

$$F_y(x_0, y_0, z_0) = f_y(x_0, y_0)$$

$$F_z(x_0, y_0, z_0) = -1$$

so Equation 19 becomes

$$f_x(x_0, y_0)(x - x_0) + f_y(x_0, y_0)(y - y_0) - (z - z_0) = 0$$

which is equivalent to Equation 15.4.2. Thus our new, more general, definition of a tangent plane is consistent with the definition that was given for the special case of Section 15.4.

◩ **EXAMPLE 8** Find the equations of the tangent plane and normal line at the point $(-2, 1, -3)$ to the ellipsoid

$$\frac{x^2}{4} + y^2 + \frac{z^2}{9} = 3$$

SOLUTION The ellipsoid is the level surface (with $k = 3$) of the function

$$F(x, y, z) = \frac{x^2}{4} + y^2 + \frac{z^2}{9}$$

Therefore we have

$$F_x(x, y, z) = \frac{x}{2} \qquad\qquad F_y(x, y, z) = 2y \qquad\qquad F_z(x, y, z) = \frac{2z}{9}$$

$$F_x(-2, 1, -3) = -1 \qquad F_y(-2, 1, -3) = 2 \qquad F_z(-2, 1, -3) = -\tfrac{2}{3}$$

Then Equation 19 gives the equation of the tangent plane at $(-2, 1, -3)$ as

$$-1(x + 2) + 2(y - 1) - \tfrac{2}{3}(z + 3) = 0$$

which simplifies to $3x - 6y + 2z + 18 = 0$.

By Equation 20, symmetric equations of the normal line are

$$\frac{x + 2}{-1} = \frac{y - 1}{2} = \frac{z + 3}{-\tfrac{2}{3}} \qquad\qquad\qquad\qquad\qquad \square$$

◼ Figure 10 shows the ellipsoid, tangent plane, and normal line in Example 8.

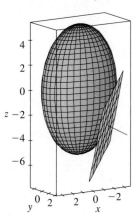

FIGURE 10

SIGNIFICANCE OF THE GRADIENT VECTOR

We now summarize the ways in which the gradient vector is significant. We first consider a function f of three variables and a point $P(x_0, y_0, z_0)$ in its domain. On the one hand, we know from Theorem 15 that the gradient vector $\nabla f(x_0, y_0, z_0)$ gives the direction of fastest increase of f. On the other hand, we know that $\nabla f(x_0, y_0, z_0)$ is orthogonal to the level surface S of f through P. (Refer to Figure 9.) These two properties are quite compatible intuitively because as we move away from P on the level surface S, the value of f does not change at all. So it seems reasonable that if we move in the perpendicular direction, we get the maximum increase.

In like manner we consider a function f of two variables and a point $P(x_0, y_0)$ in its domain. Again the gradient vector $\nabla f(x_0, y_0)$ gives the direction of fastest increase of f. Also, by considerations similar to our discussion of tangent planes, it can be shown that $\nabla f(x_0, y_0)$ is perpendicular to the level curve $f(x, y) = k$ that passes through P. Again this is intuitively plausible because the values of f remain constant as we move along the curve. (See Figure 11.)

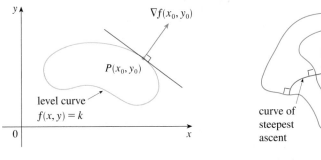

FIGURE 11   **FIGURE 12**

If we consider a topographical map of a hill and let $f(x, y)$ represent the height above sea level at a point with coordinates (x, y), then a curve of steepest ascent can be drawn as in Figure 12 by making it perpendicular to all of the contour lines. This phenomenon can also be noticed in Figure 12 in Section 15.1, where Lonesome Creek follows a curve of steepest descent.

Computer algebra systems have commands that plot sample gradient vectors. Each gradient vector $\nabla f(a, b)$ is plotted starting at the point (a, b). Figure 13 shows such a plot (called a *gradient vector field*) for the function $f(x, y) = x^2 - y^2$ superimposed on a contour map of f. As expected, the gradient vectors point "uphill" and are perpendicular to the level curves.

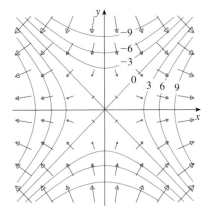

FIGURE 13

15.6 EXERCISES

1. Level curves for barometric pressure (in millibars) are shown for 6:00 AM on November 10, 1998. A deep low with pressure 972 mb is moving over northeast Iowa. The distance along the red line from K (Kearney, Nebraska) to S (Sioux City, Iowa) is 300 km. Estimate the value of the directional derivative of the pressure function at Kearney in the direction of Sioux City. What are the units of the directional derivative?

From *Meteorology Today*, 8E by C. Donald Ahrens (2007 Thomson Brooks/Cole).

2. The contour map shows the average maximum temperature for November 2004 (in °C). Estimate the value of the directional derivative of this temperature function at Dubbo, New South Wales, in the direction of Sydney. What are the units?

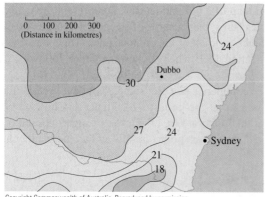

Copyright Commonwealth of Australia. Reproduced by permission.

3. A table of values for the wind-chill index $W = f(T, v)$ is given in Exercise 3 on page 924. Use the table to estimate the value of $D_{\mathbf{u}} f(-20, 30)$, where $\mathbf{u} = (\mathbf{i} + \mathbf{j})/\sqrt{2}$.

4–6 Find the directional derivative of f at the given point in the direction indicated by the angle θ.

4. $f(x, y) = x^2 y^3 - y^4$, $(2, 1)$, $\theta = \pi/4$

5. $f(x, y) = ye^{-x}$, $(0, 4)$, $\theta = 2\pi/3$

6. $f(x, y) = x \sin(xy)$, $(2, 0)$, $\theta = \pi/3$

7–10
(a) Find the gradient of f.
(b) Evaluate the gradient at the point P.
(c) Find the rate of change of f at P in the direction of the vector $\mathbf{u}$.

7. $f(x, y) = \sin(2x + 3y)$, $P(-6, 4)$, $\mathbf{u} = \frac{1}{2}(\sqrt{3}\,\mathbf{i} - \mathbf{j})$

8. $f(x, y) = y^2/x$, $P(1, 2)$, $\mathbf{u} = \frac{1}{3}(2\mathbf{i} + \sqrt{5}\,\mathbf{j})$

9. $f(x, y, z) = xe^{2yz}$, $P(3, 0, 2)$, $\mathbf{u} = \langle \frac{2}{3}, -\frac{2}{3}, \frac{1}{3} \rangle$

10. $f(x, y, z) = \sqrt{x + yz}$, $P(1, 3, 1)$, $\mathbf{u} = \langle \frac{2}{7}, \frac{3}{7}, \frac{6}{7} \rangle$

11–17 Find the directional derivative of the function at the given point in the direction of the vector $\mathbf{v}$.

11. $f(x, y) = 1 + 2x\sqrt{y}$, $(3, 4)$, $\mathbf{v} = \langle 4, -3 \rangle$

12. $f(x, y) = \ln(x^2 + y^2)$, $(2, 1)$, $\mathbf{v} = \langle -1, 2 \rangle$

13. $g(p, q) = p^4 - p^2 q^3$, $(2, 1)$, $\mathbf{v} = \mathbf{i} + 3\mathbf{j}$

14. $g(r, s) = \tan^{-1}(rs)$, $(1, 2)$, $\mathbf{v} = 5\mathbf{i} + 10\mathbf{j}$

15. $f(x, y, z) = xe^y + ye^z + ze^x$, $(0, 0, 0)$, $\mathbf{v} = \langle 5, 1, -2 \rangle$

16. $f(x, y, z) = \sqrt{xyz}$, $(3, 2, 6)$, $\mathbf{v} = \langle -1, -2, 2 \rangle$

17. $g(x, y, z) = (x + 2y + 3z)^{3/2}$, $(1, 1, 2)$, $\mathbf{v} = 2\mathbf{j} - \mathbf{k}$

18. Use the figure to estimate $D_{\mathbf{u}} f(2, 2)$.

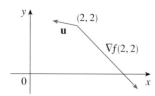

19. Find the directional derivative of $f(x, y) = \sqrt{xy}$ at $P(2, 8)$ in the direction of $Q(5, 4)$.

20. Find the directional derivative of $f(x, y, z) = xy + yz + zx$ at $P(1, -1, 3)$ in the direction of $Q(2, 4, 5)$.

21–26 Find the maximum rate of change of f at the given point and the direction in which it occurs.

21. $f(x, y) = y^2/x$, $(2, 4)$

22. $f(p, q) = qe^{-p} + pe^{-q}$, $(0, 0)$

23. $f(x, y) = \sin(xy)$, $(1, 0)$

24. $f(x, y, z) = (x + y)/z$, $(1, 1, -1)$

25. $f(x, y, z) = \sqrt{x^2 + y^2 + z^2}$, $(3, 6, -2)$

26. $f(x, y, z) = \tan(x + 2y + 3z)$, $(-5, 1, 1)$

27. (a) Show that a differentiable function f decreases most rapidly at $\mathbf{x}$ in the direction opposite to the gradient vector, that is, in the direction of $-\nabla f(\mathbf{x})$.
(b) Use the result of part (a) to find the direction in which the function $f(x, y) = x^4y - x^2y^3$ decreases fastest at the point $(2, -3)$.

28. Find the directions in which the directional derivative of $f(x, y) = ye^{-xy}$ at the point $(0, 2)$ has the value 1.

29. Find all points at which the direction of fastest change of the function $f(x, y) = x^2 + y^2 - 2x - 4y$ is $\mathbf{i} + \mathbf{j}$.

30. Near a buoy, the depth of a lake at the point with coordinates (x, y) is $z = 200 + 0.02x^2 - 0.001y^3$, where x, y, and z are measured in meters. A fisherman in a small boat starts at the point $(80, 60)$ and moves toward the buoy, which is located at $(0, 0)$. Is the water under the boat getting deeper or shallower when he departs? Explain.

31. The temperature T in a metal ball is inversely proportional to the distance from the center of the ball, which we take to be the origin. The temperature at the point $(1, 2, 2)$ is $120°$.
(a) Find the rate of change of T at $(1, 2, 2)$ in the direction toward the point $(2, 1, 3)$.
(b) Show that at any point in the ball the direction of greatest increase in temperature is given by a vector that points toward the origin.

32. The temperature at a point (x, y, z) is given by

$$T(x, y, z) = 200e^{-x^2-3y^2-9z^2}$$

where T is measured in $°C$ and x, y, z in meters.
(a) Find the rate of change of temperature at the point $P(2, -1, 2)$ in the direction toward the point $(3, -3, 3)$.
(b) In which direction does the temperature increase fastest at P?
(c) Find the maximum rate of increase at P.

33. Suppose that over a certain region of space the electrical potential V is given by $V(x, y, z) = 5x^2 - 3xy + xyz$.
(a) Find the rate of change of the potential at $P(3, 4, 5)$ in the direction of the vector $\mathbf{v} = \mathbf{i} + \mathbf{j} - \mathbf{k}$.
(b) In which direction does V change most rapidly at P?
(c) What is the maximum rate of change at P?

34. Suppose you are climbing a hill whose shape is given by the equation $z = 1000 - 0.005x^2 - 0.01y^2$, where x, y, and z are measured in meters, and you are standing at a point with coordinates $(60, 40, 966)$. The positive x-axis points east and the positive y-axis points north.
(a) If you walk due south, will you start to ascend or descend? At what rate?
(b) If you walk northwest, will you start to ascend or descend? At what rate?
(c) In which direction is the slope largest? What is the rate of ascent in that direction? At what angle above the horizontal does the path in that direction begin?

35. Let f be a function of two variables that has continuous partial derivatives and consider the points $A(1, 3)$, $B(3, 3)$, $C(1, 7)$, and $D(6, 15)$. The directional derivative of f at A in the direction of the vector $\overrightarrow{AB}$ is 3 and the directional derivative at A in the direction of $\overrightarrow{AC}$ is 26. Find the directional derivative of f at A in the direction of the vector $\overrightarrow{AD}$.

36. For the given contour map draw the curves of steepest ascent starting at P and at Q.

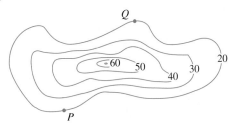

37. Show that the operation of taking the gradient of a function has the given property. Assume that u and v are differentiable functions of x and y and that a, b are constants.
(a) $\nabla(au + bv) = a\,\nabla u + b\,\nabla v$ (b) $\nabla(uv) = u\,\nabla v + v\,\nabla u$
(c) $\nabla\left(\dfrac{u}{v}\right) = \dfrac{v\,\nabla u - u\,\nabla v}{v^2}$ (d) $\nabla u^n = nu^{n-1}\,\nabla u$

38. Sketch the gradient vector $\nabla f(4, 6)$ for the function f whose level curves are shown. Explain how you chose the direction and length of this vector.

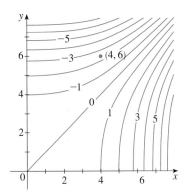

39–44 Find equations of (a) the tangent plane and (b) the normal line to the given surface at the specified point.

39. $2(x - 2)^2 + (y - 1)^2 + (z - 3)^2 = 10$, $(3, 3, 5)$

40. $y = x^2 - z^2$, $(4, 7, 3)$

41. $x^2 - 2y^2 + z^2 + yz = 2$, $(2, 1, -1)$

42. $x - z = 4\arctan(yz)$, $(1 + \pi, 1, 1)$

43. $z + 1 = xe^y \cos z$, $(1, 0, 0)$

44. $yz = \ln(x + z)$, $(0, 0, 1)$

45–46 Use a computer to graph the surface, the tangent plane, and the normal line on the same screen. Choose the domain carefully so that you avoid extraneous vertical planes. Choose the viewpoint so that you get a good view of all three objects.

45. $xy + yz + zx = 3$, $(1, 1, 1)$

46. $xyz = 6$, $(1, 2, 3)$

---

47. If $f(x, y) = xy$, find the gradient vector $\nabla f(3, 2)$ and use it to find the tangent line to the level curve $f(x, y) = 6$ at the point $(3, 2)$. Sketch the level curve, the tangent line, and the gradient vector.

48. If $g(x, y) = x^2 + y^2 - 4x$, find the gradient vector $\nabla g(1, 2)$ and use it to find the tangent line to the level curve $g(x, y) = 1$ at the point $(1, 2)$. Sketch the level curve, the tangent line, and the gradient vector.

49. Show that the equation of the tangent plane to the ellipsoid $x^2/a^2 + y^2/b^2 + z^2/c^2 = 1$ at the point (x_0, y_0, z_0) can be written as

$$\frac{xx_0}{a^2} + \frac{yy_0}{b^2} + \frac{zz_0}{c^2} = 1$$

50. Find the equation of the tangent plane to the hyperboloid $x^2/a^2 + y^2/b^2 - z^2/c^2 = 1$ at (x_0, y_0, z_0) and express it in a form similar to the one in Exercise 49.

51. Show that the equation of the tangent plane to the elliptic paraboloid $z/c = x^2/a^2 + y^2/b^2$ at the point (x_0, y_0, z_0) can be written as

$$\frac{2xx_0}{a^2} + \frac{2yy_0}{b^2} = \frac{z + z_0}{c}$$

52. At what point on the paraboloid $y = x^2 + z^2$ is the tangent plane parallel to the plane $x + 2y + 3z = 1$?

53. Are there any points on the hyperboloid $x^2 - y^2 - z^2 = 1$ where the tangent plane is parallel to the plane $z = x + y$?

54. Show that the ellipsoid $3x^2 + 2y^2 + z^2 = 9$ and the sphere $x^2 + y^2 + z^2 - 8x - 6y - 8z + 24 = 0$ are tangent to each other at the point $(1, 1, 2)$. (This means that they have a common tangent plane at the point.)

55. Show that every plane that is tangent to the cone $x^2 + y^2 = z^2$ passes through the origin.

56. Show that every normal line to the sphere $x^2 + y^2 + z^2 = r^2$ passes through the center of the sphere.

57. Show that the sum of the x-, y-, and z-intercepts of any tangent plane to the surface $\sqrt{x} + \sqrt{y} + \sqrt{z} = \sqrt{c}$ is a constant.

58. Show that the pyramids cut off from the first octant by any tangent planes to the surface $xyz = 1$ at points in the first octant must all have the same volume.

59. Find parametric equations for the tangent line to the curve of intersection of the paraboloid $z = x^2 + y^2$ and the ellipsoid $4x^2 + y^2 + z^2 = 9$ at the point $(-1, 1, 2)$.

60. (a) The plane $y + z = 3$ intersects the cylinder $x^2 + y^2 = 5$ in an ellipse. Find parametric equations for the tangent line to this ellipse at the point $(1, 2, 1)$.
    (b) Graph the cylinder, the plane, and the tangent line on the same screen.

61. (a) Two surfaces are called **orthogonal** at a point of intersection if their normal lines are perpendicular at that point. Show that surfaces with equations $F(x, y, z) = 0$ and $G(x, y, z) = 0$ are orthogonal at a point P where $\nabla F \neq \mathbf{0}$ and $\nabla G \neq \mathbf{0}$ if and only if

$$F_x G_x + F_y G_y + F_z G_z = 0 \quad \text{at } P$$

    (b) Use part (a) to show that the surfaces $z^2 = x^2 + y^2$ and $x^2 + y^2 + z^2 = r^2$ are orthogonal at every point of intersection. Can you see why this is true without using calculus?

62. (a) Show that the function $f(x, y) = \sqrt[3]{xy}$ is continuous and the partial derivatives f_x and f_y exist at the origin but the directional derivatives in all other directions do not exist.
    (b) Graph f near the origin and comment on how the graph confirms part (a).

63. Suppose that the directional derivatives of $f(x, y)$ are known at a given point in two nonparallel directions given by unit vectors $\mathbf{u}$ and $\mathbf{v}$. Is it possible to find ∇f at this point? If so, how would you do it?

64. Show that if $z = f(x, y)$ is differentiable at $\mathbf{x}_0 = \langle x_0, y_0 \rangle$, then

$$\lim_{\mathbf{x} \to \mathbf{x}_0} \frac{f(\mathbf{x}) - f(\mathbf{x}_0) - \nabla f(\mathbf{x}_0) \cdot (\mathbf{x} - \mathbf{x}_0)}{|\mathbf{x} - \mathbf{x}_0|} = 0$$

[*Hint:* Use Definition 15.4.7 directly.]

15.7 MAXIMUM AND MINIMUM VALUES

As we saw in Chapter 4, one of the main uses of ordinary derivatives is in finding maximum and minimum values. In this section we see how to use partial derivatives to locate maxima and minima of functions of two variables. In particular, in Example 6 we will see how to maximize the volume of a box without a lid if we have a fixed amount of cardboard to work with.

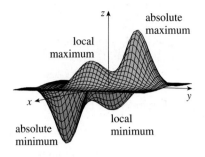

FIGURE 1

Look at the hills and valleys in the graph of f shown in Figure 1. There are two points (a, b) where f has a *local maximum*, that is, where $f(a, b)$ is larger than nearby values of $f(x, y)$. The larger of these two values is the *absolute maximum*. Likewise, f has two *local minima*, where $f(a, b)$ is smaller than nearby values. The smaller of these two values is the *absolute minimum*.

> **1** **DEFINITION** A function of two variables has a **local maximum** at (a, b) if $f(x, y) \leq f(a, b)$ when (x, y) is near (a, b). [This means that $f(x, y) \leq f(a, b)$ for all points (x, y) in some disk with center (a, b).] The number $f(a, b)$ is called a **local maximum value**. If $f(x, y) \geq f(a, b)$ when (x, y) is near (a, b), then f has a **local minimum** at (a, b) and $f(a, b)$ is a **local minimum value**.

If the inequalities in Definition 1 hold for *all* points (x, y) in the domain of f, then f has an **absolute maximum** (or **absolute minimum**) at (a, b).

■ Notice that the conclusion of Theorem 2 can be stated in the notation of gradient vectors as $\nabla f(a, b) = \mathbf{0}$.

> **2** **THEOREM** If f has a local maximum or minimum at (a, b) and the first-order partial derivatives of f exist there, then $f_x(a, b) = 0$ and $f_y(a, b) = 0$.

PROOF   Let $g(x) = f(x, b)$. If f has a local maximum (or minimum) at (a, b), then g has a local maximum (or minimum) at a, so $g'(a) = 0$ by Fermat's Theorem (see Theorem 4.1.4). But $g'(a) = f_x(a, b)$ (see Equation 15.3.1) and so $f_x(a, b) = 0$. Similarly, by applying Fermat's Theorem to the function $G(y) = f(a, y)$, we obtain $f_y(a, b) = 0$.   □

If we put $f_x(a, b) = 0$ and $f_y(a, b) = 0$ in the equation of a tangent plane (Equation 15.4.2), we get $z = z_0$. Thus the geometric interpretation of Theorem 2 is that if the graph of f has a tangent plane at a local maximum or minimum, then the tangent plane must be horizontal.

A point (a, b) is called a **critical point** (or *stationary point*) of f if $f_x(a, b) = 0$ and $f_y(a, b) = 0$, or if one of these partial derivatives does not exist. Theorem 2 says that if f has a local maximum or minimum at (a, b), then (a, b) is a critical point of f. However, as in single-variable calculus, not all critical points give rise to maxima or minima. At a critical point, a function could have a local maximum or a local minimum or neither.

EXAMPLE 1 Let $f(x, y) = x^2 + y^2 - 2x - 6y + 14$. Then

$$f_x(x, y) = 2x - 2 \qquad f_y(x, y) = 2y - 6$$

These partial derivatives are equal to 0 when $x = 1$ and $y = 3$, so the only critical point is $(1, 3)$. By completing the square, we find that

$$f(x, y) = 4 + (x - 1)^2 + (y - 3)^2$$

Since $(x - 1)^2 \geq 0$ and $(y - 3)^2 \geq 0$, we have $f(x, y) \geq 4$ for all values of x and y. Therefore $f(1, 3) = 4$ is a local minimum, and in fact it is the absolute minimum of f. This can be confirmed geometrically from the graph of f, which is the elliptic paraboloid with vertex $(1, 3, 4)$ shown in Figure 2.   □

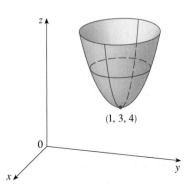

FIGURE 2
$z = x^2 + y^2 - 2x - 6y + 14$

EXAMPLE 2 Find the extreme values of $f(x, y) = y^2 - x^2$.

SOLUTION Since $f_x = -2x$ and $f_y = 2y$, the only critical point is $(0, 0)$. Notice that for points on the x-axis we have $y = 0$, so $f(x, y) = -x^2 < 0$ (if $x \neq 0$). However, for points on the y-axis we have $x = 0$, so $f(x, y) = y^2 > 0$ (if $y \neq 0$). Thus every disk with center $(0, 0)$ contains points where f takes positive values as well as points where f takes negative values. Therefore $f(0, 0) = 0$ can't be an extreme value for f, so f has no extreme value. ☐

Example 2 illustrates the fact that a function need not have a maximum or minimum value at a critical point. Figure 3 shows how this is possible. The graph of f is the hyperbolic paraboloid $z = y^2 - x^2$, which has a horizontal tangent plane ($z = 0$) at the origin. You can see that $f(0, 0) = 0$ is a maximum in the direction of the x-axis but a minimum in the direction of the y-axis. Near the origin the graph has the shape of a saddle and so $(0, 0)$ is called a *saddle point* of f.

We need to be able to determine whether or not a function has an extreme value at a critical point. The following test, which is proved at the end of this section, is analogous to the Second Derivative Test for functions of one variable.

FIGURE 3
$z = y^2 - x^2$

---

3 **SECOND DERIVATIVES TEST** Suppose the second partial derivatives of f are continuous on a disk with center (a, b), and suppose that $f_x(a, b) = 0$ and $f_y(a, b) = 0$ [that is, (a, b) is a critical point of f]. Let

$$D = D(a, b) = f_{xx}(a, b)f_{yy}(a, b) - [f_{xy}(a, b)]^2$$

(a) If $D > 0$ and $f_{xx}(a, b) > 0$, then $f(a, b)$ is a local minimum.

(b) If $D > 0$ and $f_{xx}(a, b) < 0$, then $f(a, b)$ is a local maximum.

(c) If $D < 0$, then $f(a, b)$ is not a local maximum or minimum.

NOTE 1 In case (c) the point (a, b) is called a **saddle point** of f and the graph of f crosses its tangent plane at (a, b).

NOTE 2 If $D = 0$, the test gives no information: f could have a local maximum or local minimum at (a, b), or (a, b) could be a saddle point of f.

NOTE 3 To remember the formula for D, it's helpful to write it as a determinant:

$$D = \begin{vmatrix} f_{xx} & f_{xy} \\ f_{yx} & f_{yy} \end{vmatrix} = f_{xx}f_{yy} - (f_{xy})^2$$

▼ **EXAMPLE 3** Find the local maximum and minimum values and saddle points of $f(x, y) = x^4 + y^4 - 4xy + 1$.

SOLUTION We first locate the critical points:

$$f_x = 4x^3 - 4y \qquad f_y = 4y^3 - 4x$$

Setting these partial derivatives equal to 0, we obtain the equations

$$x^3 - y = 0 \quad \text{and} \quad y^3 - x = 0$$

To solve these equations we substitute $y = x^3$ from the first equation into the second one. This gives

$$0 = x^9 - x = x(x^8 - 1) = x(x^4 - 1)(x^4 + 1) = x(x^2 - 1)(x^2 + 1)(x^4 + 1)$$

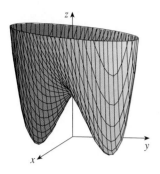

FIGURE 4
$z = x^4 + y^4 - 4xy + 1$

so there are three real roots: $x = 0, 1, -1$. The three critical points are $(0, 0)$, $(1, 1)$, and $(-1, -1)$.

Next we calculate the second partial derivatives and $D(x, y)$:

$$f_{xx} = 12x^2 \qquad f_{xy} = -4 \qquad f_{yy} = 12y^2$$

$$D(x, y) = f_{xx}f_{yy} - (f_{xy})^2 = 144x^2y^2 - 16$$

Since $D(0, 0) = -16 < 0$, it follows from case (c) of the Second Derivatives Test that the origin is a saddle point; that is, f has no local maximum or minimum at $(0, 0)$. Since $D(1, 1) = 128 > 0$ and $f_{xx}(1, 1) = 12 > 0$, we see from case (a) of the test that $f(1, 1) = -1$ is a local minimum. Similarly, we have $D(-1, -1) = 128 > 0$ and $f_{xx}(-1, -1) = 12 > 0$, so $f(-1, -1) = -1$ is also a local minimum.

The graph of f is shown in Figure 4.   ☐

■ A contour map of the function f in Example 3 is shown in Figure 5. The level curves near $(1, 1)$ and $(-1, -1)$ are oval in shape and indicate that as we move away from $(1, 1)$ or $(-1, -1)$ in any direction the values of f are increasing. The level curves near $(0, 0)$, on the other hand, resemble hyperbolas. They reveal that as we move away from the origin (where the value of f is 1), the values of f decrease in some directions but increase in other directions. Thus the contour map suggests the presence of the minima and saddle point that we found in Example 3.

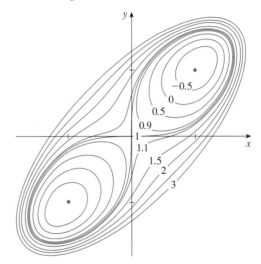

FIGURE 5

TEC In Module 15.7 you can use contour maps to estimate the locations of critical points.

EXAMPLE 4 Find and classify the critical points of the function

$$f(x, y) = 10x^2y - 5x^2 - 4y^2 - x^4 - 2y^4$$

Also find the highest point on the graph of f.

SOLUTION The first-order partial derivatives are

$$f_x = 20xy - 10x - 4x^3 \qquad f_y = 10x^2 - 8y - 8y^3$$

So to find the critical points we need to solve the equations

4     $$2x(10y - 5 - 2x^2) = 0$$

5     $$5x^2 - 4y - 4y^3 = 0$$

From Equation 4 we see that either

$$x = 0 \qquad \text{or} \qquad 10y - 5 - 2x^2 = 0$$

In the first case ($x = 0$), Equation 5 becomes $-4y(1 + y^2) = 0$, so $y = 0$ and we have the critical point $(0, 0)$.

In the second case $(10y - 5 - 2x^2 = 0)$, we get

$$\boxed{6} \qquad\qquad x^2 = 5y - 2.5$$

and, putting this in Equation 5, we have $25y - 12.5 - 4y - 4y^3 = 0$. So we have to solve the cubic equation

$$\boxed{7} \qquad\qquad 4y^3 - 21y + 12.5 = 0$$

Using a graphing calculator or computer to graph the function

$$g(y) = 4y^3 - 21y + 12.5$$

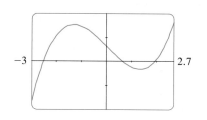

FIGURE 6

as in Figure 6, we see that Equation 7 has three real roots. By zooming in, we can find the roots to four decimal places:

$$y \approx -2.5452 \qquad y \approx 0.6468 \qquad y \approx 1.8984$$

(Alternatively, we could have used Newton's method or a rootfinder to locate these roots.) From Equation 6, the corresponding x-values are given by

$$x = \pm\sqrt{5y - 2.5}$$

If $y \approx -2.5452$, then x has no corresponding real values. If $y \approx 0.6468$, then $x \approx \pm 0.8567$. If $y \approx 1.8984$, then $x \approx \pm 2.6442$. So we have a total of five critical points, which are analyzed in the following chart. All quantities are rounded to two decimal places.

Critical point	Value of f	f_{xx}	D	Conclusion
$(0, 0)$	0.00	-10.00	80.00	local maximum
$(\pm 2.64, 1.90)$	8.50	-55.93	2488.72	local maximum
$(\pm 0.86, 0.65)$	-1.48	-5.87	-187.64	saddle point

Figures 7 and 8 give two views of the graph of f and we see that the surface opens downward. [This can also be seen from the expression for $f(x, y)$: The dominant terms are $-x^4 - 2y^4$ when $|x|$ and $|y|$ are large.] Comparing the values of f at its local maximum points, we see that the absolute maximum value of f is $f(\pm 2.64, 1.90) \approx 8.50$. In other words, the highest points on the graph of f are $(\pm 2.64, 1.90, 8.50)$.

FIGURE 7

FIGURE 8

■ The five critical points of the function f in Example 4 are shown in red in the contour map of f in Figure 9.

FIGURE 9

☑ EXAMPLE 5 Find the shortest distance from the point $(1, 0, -2)$ to the plane $x + 2y + z = 4$.

SOLUTION The distance from any point (x, y, z) to the point $(1, 0, -2)$ is

$$d = \sqrt{(x - 1)^2 + y^2 + (z + 2)^2}$$

but if (x, y, z) lies on the plane $x + 2y + z = 4$, then $z = 4 - x - 2y$ and so we have $d = \sqrt{(x - 1)^2 + y^2 + (6 - x - 2y)^2}$. We can minimize d by minimizing the simpler expression

$$d^2 = f(x, y) = (x - 1)^2 + y^2 + (6 - x - 2y)^2$$

By solving the equations

$$f_x = 2(x - 1) - 2(6 - x - 2y) = 4x + 4y - 14 = 0$$

$$f_y = 2y - 4(6 - x - 2y) = 4x + 10y - 24 = 0$$

we find that the only critical point is $\left(\frac{11}{6}, \frac{5}{3}\right)$. Since $f_{xx} = 4$, $f_{xy} = 4$, and $f_{yy} = 10$, we have $D(x, y) = f_{xx} f_{yy} - (f_{xy})^2 = 24 > 0$ and $f_{xx} > 0$, so by the Second Derivatives Test f has a local minimum at $\left(\frac{11}{6}, \frac{5}{3}\right)$. Intuitively, we can see that this local minimum is actually an absolute minimum because there must be a point on the given plane that is closest to $(1, 0, -2)$. If $x = \frac{11}{6}$ and $y = \frac{5}{3}$, then

$$d = \sqrt{(x - 1)^2 + y^2 + (6 - x - 2y)^2} = \sqrt{\left(\frac{5}{6}\right)^2 + \left(\frac{5}{3}\right)^2 + \left(\frac{5}{6}\right)^2} = \frac{5}{6}\sqrt{6}$$

■ Example 5 could also be solved using vectors. Compare with the methods of Section 13.5.

The shortest distance from $(1, 0, -2)$ to the plane $x + 2y + z = 4$ is $\frac{5}{6}\sqrt{6}$. ☐

☑ EXAMPLE 6 A rectangular box without a lid is to be made from 12 m² of cardboard. Find the maximum volume of such a box.

SOLUTION Let the length, width, and height of the box (in meters) be x, y, and z, as shown in Figure 10. Then the volume of the box is

$$V = xyz$$

We can express V as a function of just two variables x and y by using the fact that the area of the four sides and the bottom of the box is

$$2xz + 2yz + xy = 12$$

FIGURE 10

Solving this equation for z, we get $z = (12 - xy)/[2(x + y)]$, so the expression for V becomes

$$V = xy\frac{12 - xy}{2(x + y)} = \frac{12xy - x^2y^2}{2(x + y)}$$

We compute the partial derivatives:

$$\frac{\partial V}{\partial x} = \frac{y^2(12 - 2xy - x^2)}{2(x + y)^2} \qquad \frac{\partial V}{\partial y} = \frac{x^2(12 - 2xy - y^2)}{2(x + y)^2}$$

If V is a maximum, then $\partial V/\partial x = \partial V/\partial y = 0$, but $x = 0$ or $y = 0$ gives $V = 0$, so we must solve the equations

$$12 - 2xy - x^2 = 0 \qquad 12 - 2xy - y^2 = 0$$

These imply that $x^2 = y^2$ and so $x = y$. (Note that x and y must both be positive in this problem.) If we put $x = y$ in either equation we get $12 - 3x^2 = 0$, which gives $x = 2$, $y = 2$, and $z = (12 - 2 \cdot 2)/[2(2 + 2)] = 1$.

We could use the Second Derivatives Test to show that this gives a local maximum of V, or we could simply argue from the physical nature of this problem that there must be an absolute maximum volume, which has to occur at a critical point of V, so it must occur when $x = 2$, $y = 2$, $z = 1$. Then $V = 2 \cdot 2 \cdot 1 = 4$, so the maximum volume of the box is 4 m^3. ☐

ABSOLUTE MAXIMUM AND MINIMUM VALUES

For a function f of one variable the Extreme Value Theorem says that if f is continuous on a closed interval $[a, b]$, then f has an absolute minimum value and an absolute maximum value. According to the Closed Interval Method in Section 4.1, we found these by evaluating f not only at the critical numbers but also at the endpoints a and b.

There is a similar situation for functions of two variables. Just as a closed interval contains its endpoints, a **closed set** in $\mathbb{R}^2$ is one that contains all its boundary points. [A boundary point of D is a point (a, b) such that every disk with center (a, b) contains points in D and also points not in D.] For instance, the disk

$$D = \{(x, y) \mid x^2 + y^2 \leq 1\}$$

which consists of all points on and inside the circle $x^2 + y^2 = 1$, is a closed set because it contains all of its boundary points (which are the points on the circle $x^2 + y^2 = 1$). But if even one point on the boundary curve were omitted, the set would not be closed. (See Figure 11.)

A **bounded set** in $\mathbb{R}^2$ is one that is contained within some disk. In other words, it is finite in extent. Then, in terms of closed and bounded sets, we can state the following counterpart of the Extreme Value Theorem in two dimensions.

(a) Closed sets

(b) Sets that are not closed

FIGURE 11

8 EXTREME VALUE THEOREM FOR FUNCTIONS OF TWO VARIABLES If f is continuous on a closed, bounded set D in $\mathbb{R}^2$, then f attains an absolute maximum value $f(x_1, y_1)$ and an absolute minimum value $f(x_2, y_2)$ at some points (x_1, y_1) and (x_2, y_2) in D.

To find the extreme values guaranteed by Theorem 8, we note that, by Theorem 2, if f has an extreme value at (x_1, y_1), then (x_1, y_1) is either a critical point of f or a boundary point of D. Thus we have the following extension of the Closed Interval Method.

---

9 To find the absolute maximum and minimum values of a continuous function f on a closed, bounded set D:

1. Find the values of f at the critical points of f in D.

2. Find the extreme values of f on the boundary of D.

3. The largest of the values from steps 1 and 2 is the absolute maximum value; the smallest of these values is the absolute minimum value.

EXAMPLE 7 Find the absolute maximum and minimum values of the function $f(x, y) = x^2 - 2xy + 2y$ on the rectangle $D = \{(x, y) \mid 0 \leqslant x \leqslant 3, 0 \leqslant y \leqslant 2\}$.

SOLUTION Since f is a polynomial, it is continuous on the closed, bounded rectangle D, so Theorem 8 tells us there is both an absolute maximum and an absolute minimum. According to step 1 in (9), we first find the critical points. These occur when

$$f_x = 2x - 2y = 0 \qquad f_y = -2x + 2 = 0$$

so the only critical point is $(1, 1)$, and the value of f there is $f(1, 1) = 1$.

In step 2 we look at the values of f on the boundary of D, which consists of the four line segments L_1, L_2, L_3, L_4 shown in Figure 12. On L_1 we have $y = 0$ and

$$f(x, 0) = x^2 \qquad 0 \leqslant x \leqslant 3$$

This is an increasing function of x, so its minimum value is $f(0, 0) = 0$ and its maximum value is $f(3, 0) = 9$. On L_2 we have $x = 3$ and

$$f(3, y) = 9 - 4y \qquad 0 \leqslant y \leqslant 2$$

This is a decreasing function of y, so its maximum value is $f(3, 0) = 9$ and its minimum value is $f(3, 2) = 1$. On L_3 we have $y = 2$ and

$$f(x, 2) = x^2 - 4x + 4 \qquad 0 \leqslant x \leqslant 3$$

By the methods of Chapter 4, or simply by observing that $f(x, 2) = (x - 2)^2$, we see that the minimum value of this function is $f(2, 2) = 0$ and the maximum value is $f(0, 2) = 4$. Finally, on L_4 we have $x = 0$ and

$$f(0, y) = 2y \qquad 0 \leqslant y \leqslant 2$$

with maximum value $f(0, 2) = 4$ and minimum value $f(0, 0) = 0$. Thus, on the boundary, the minimum value of f is 0 and the maximum is 9.

In step 3 we compare these values with the value $f(1, 1) = 1$ at the critical point and conclude that the absolute maximum value of f on D is $f(3, 0) = 9$ and the absolute minimum value is $f(0, 0) = f(2, 2) = 0$. Figure 13 shows the graph of f. $\square$

FIGURE 12

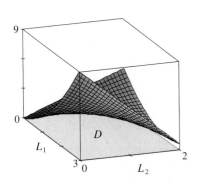

FIGURE 13

$f(x, y) = x^2 - 2xy + 2y$

We close this section by giving a proof of the first part of the Second Derivatives Test. Part (b) has a similar proof.

PROOF OF THEOREM 3, PART (A) We compute the second-order directional derivative of f in the direction of $\mathbf{u} = \langle h, k \rangle$. The first-order derivative is given by Theorem 15.6.3:

$$D_{\mathbf{u}} f = f_x h + f_y k$$

Applying this theorem a second time, we have

$$D_{\mathbf{u}}^2 f = D_{\mathbf{u}}(D_{\mathbf{u}} f) = \frac{\partial}{\partial x}(D_{\mathbf{u}} f)h + \frac{\partial}{\partial y}(D_{\mathbf{u}} f)k$$

$$= (f_{xx}h + f_{yx}k)h + (f_{xy}h + f_{yy}k)k$$

$$= f_{xx}h^2 + 2f_{xy}hk + f_{yy}k^2 \qquad \text{(by Clairaut's Theorem)}$$

If we complete the square in this expression, we obtain

$$\boxed{10} \qquad D_{\mathbf{u}}^2 f = f_{xx}\left(h + \frac{f_{xy}}{f_{xx}}k\right)^2 + \frac{k^2}{f_{xx}}(f_{xx}f_{yy} - f_{xy}^2)$$

We are given that $f_{xx}(a, b) > 0$ and $D(a, b) > 0$. But f_{xx} and $D = f_{xx}f_{yy} - f_{xy}^2$ are continuous functions, so there is a disk B with center (a, b) and radius $\delta > 0$ such that $f_{xx}(x, y) > 0$ and $D(x, y) > 0$ whenever (x, y) is in B. Therefore, by looking at Equation 10, we see that $D_{\mathbf{u}}^2 f(x, y) > 0$ whenever (x, y) is in B. This means that if C is the curve obtained by intersecting the graph of f with the vertical plane through $P(a, b, f(a, b))$ in the direction of $\mathbf{u}$, then C is concave upward on an interval of length 2δ. This is true in the direction of every vector $\mathbf{u}$, so if we restrict (x, y) to lie in B, the graph of f lies above its horizontal tangent plane at P. Thus $f(x, y) \geq f(a, b)$ whenever (x, y) is in B. This shows that $f(a, b)$ is a local minimum. $\square$

15.7 EXERCISES

1. Suppose $(1, 1)$ is a critical point of a function f with continuous second derivatives. In each case, what can you say about f?
   (a) $f_{xx}(1, 1) = 4$, $f_{xy}(1, 1) = 1$, $f_{yy}(1, 1) = 2$
   (b) $f_{xx}(1, 1) = 4$, $f_{xy}(1, 1) = 3$, $f_{yy}(1, 1) = 2$

2. Suppose $(0, 2)$ is a critical point of a function g with continuous second derivatives. In each case, what can you say about g?
   (a) $g_{xx}(0, 2) = -1$, $g_{xy}(0, 2) = 6$, $g_{yy}(0, 2) = 1$
   (b) $g_{xx}(0, 2) = -1$, $g_{xy}(0, 2) = 2$, $g_{yy}(0, 2) = -8$
   (c) $g_{xx}(0, 2) = 4$, $g_{xy}(0, 2) = 6$, $g_{yy}(0, 2) = 9$

3–4 Use the level curves in the figure to predict the location of the critical points of f and whether f has a saddle point or a local maximum or minimum at each critical point. Explain your reasoning. Then use the Second Derivatives Test to confirm your predictions.

3. $f(x, y) = 4 + x^3 + y^3 - 3xy$

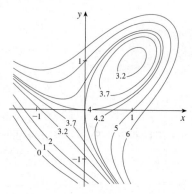

4. $f(x, y) = 3x - x^3 - 2y^2 + y^4$

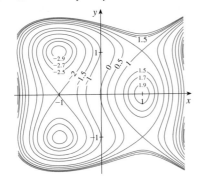

5–18 Find the local maximum and minimum values and saddle point(s) of the function. If you have three-dimensional graphing software, graph the function with a domain and viewpoint that reveal all the important aspects of the function.

5. $f(x, y) = 9 - 2x + 4y - x^2 - 4y^2$

6. $f(x, y) = x^3 y + 12x^2 - 8y$

7. $f(x, y) = x^4 + y^4 - 4xy + 2$

8. $f(x, y) = e^{4y - x^2 - y^2}$

9. $f(x, y) = (1 + xy)(x + y)$

10. $f(x, y) = 2x^3 + xy^2 + 5x^2 + y^2$

11. $f(x, y) = x^3 - 12xy + 8y^3$

12. $f(x, y) = xy + \dfrac{1}{x} + \dfrac{1}{y}$

13. $f(x, y) = e^x \cos y$

14. $f(x, y) = y \cos x$

15. $f(x, y) = (x^2 + y^2)e^{y^2 - x^2}$

16. $f(x, y) = e^y(y^2 - x^2)$

17. $f(x, y) = y^2 - 2y \cos x, \quad 1 \le x \le 7$

18. $f(x, y) = \sin x \sin y, \quad -\pi < x < \pi, \quad -\pi < y < \pi$

19. Show that $f(x, y) = x^2 + 4y^2 - 4xy + 2$ has an infinite number of critical points and that $D = 0$ at each one. Then show that f has a local (and absolute) minimum at each critical point.

20. Show that $f(x, y) = x^2 y e^{-x^2 - y^2}$ has maximum values at $(\pm 1, 1/\sqrt{2})$ and minimum values at $(\pm 1, -1/\sqrt{2})$. Show also that f has infinitely many other critical points and $D = 0$ at each of them. Which of them give rise to maximum values? Minimum values? Saddle points?

21–24 Use a graph and/or level curves to estimate the local maximum and minimum values and saddle point(s) of the function. Then use calculus to find these values precisely.

21. $f(x, y) = x^2 + y^2 + x^{-2}y^{-2}$

22. $f(x, y) = xye^{-x^2 - y^2}$

23. $f(x, y) = \sin x + \sin y + \sin(x + y),$
$0 \le x \le 2\pi, \ 0 \le y \le 2\pi$

24. $f(x, y) = \sin x + \sin y + \cos(x + y),$
$0 \le x \le \pi/4, \ 0 \le y \le \pi/4$

25–28 Use a graphing device as in Example 4 (or Newton's method or a rootfinder) to find the critical points of f correct to three decimal places. Then classify the critical points and find the highest or lowest points on the graph.

25. $f(x, y) = x^4 - 5x^2 + y^2 + 3x + 2$

26. $f(x, y) = 5 - 10xy - 4x^2 + 3y - y^4$

27. $f(x, y) = 2x + 4x^2 - y^2 + 2xy^2 - x^4 - y^4$

28. $f(x, y) = e^x + y^4 - x^3 + 4 \cos y$

29–36 Find the absolute maximum and minimum values of f on the set D.

29. $f(x, y) = 1 + 4x - 5y,$ D is the closed triangular region with vertices $(0, 0)$, $(2, 0)$, and $(0, 3)$

30. $f(x, y) = 3 + xy - x - 2y,$ D is the closed triangular region with vertices $(1, 0)$, $(5, 0)$, and $(1, 4)$

31. $f(x, y) = x^2 + y^2 + x^2y + 4,$
$D = \{(x, y) \mid |x| \le 1, |y| \le 1\}$

32. $f(x, y) = 4x + 6y - x^2 - y^2,$
$D = \{(x, y) \mid 0 \le x \le 4, 0 \le y \le 5\}$

33. $f(x, y) = x^4 + y^4 - 4xy + 2,$
$D = \{(x, y) \mid 0 \le x \le 3, 0 \le y \le 2\}$

34. $f(x, y) = xy^2, \quad D = \{(x, y) \mid x \ge 0, y \ge 0, x^2 + y^2 \le 3\}$

35. $f(x, y) = 2x^3 + y^4, \quad D = \{(x, y) \mid x^2 + y^2 \le 1\}$

36. $f(x, y) = x^3 - 3x - y^3 + 12y,$ D is the quadrilateral whose vertices are $(-2, 3)$, $(2, 3)$, $(2, 2)$, and $(-2, -2)$.

37. For functions of one variable it is impossible for a continuous function to have two local maxima and no local minimum. But for functions of two variables such functions exist. Show that the function

$$f(x, y) = -(x^2 - 1)^2 - (x^2 y - x - 1)^2$$

has only two critical points, but has local maxima at both of them. Then use a computer to produce a graph with a carefully chosen domain and viewpoint to see how this is possible.

38. If a function of one variable is continuous on an interval and has only one critical number, then a local maximum has to be an absolute maximum. But this is not true for functions of two variables. Show that the function

$$f(x, y) = 3xe^y - x^3 - e^{3y}$$

has exactly one critical point, and that f has a local maximum there that is not an absolute maximum. Then use a computer to produce a graph with a carefully chosen domain and viewpoint to see how this is possible.

39. Find the shortest distance from the point $(2, 1, -1)$ to the plane $x + y - z = 1$.

40. Find the point on the plane $x - y + z = 4$ that is closest to the point $(1, 2, 3)$.

41. Find the points on the cone $z^2 = x^2 + y^2$ that are closest to the point $(4, 2, 0)$.

42. Find the points on the surface $y^2 = 9 + xz$ that are closest to the origin.

43. Find three positive numbers whose sum is 100 and whose product is a maximum.

44. Find three positive numbers whose sum is 12 and the sum of whose squares is as small as possible.

45. Find the maximum volume of a rectangular box that is inscribed in a sphere of radius r.

46. Find the dimensions of the box with volume 1000 cm³ that has minimal surface area.

47. Find the volume of the largest rectangular box in the first octant with three faces in the coordinate planes and one vertex in the plane $x + 2y + 3z = 6$.

48. Find the dimensions of the rectangular box with largest volume if the total surface area is given as 64 cm².

49. Find the dimensions of a rectangular box of maximum volume such that the sum of the lengths of its 12 edges is a constant c.

50. The base of an aquarium with given volume V is made of slate and the sides are made of glass. If slate costs five times as much (per unit area) as glass, find the dimensions of the aquarium that minimize the cost of the materials.

51. A cardboard box without a lid is to have a volume of 32,000 cm³. Find the dimensions that minimize the amount of cardboard used.

52. A rectangular building is being designed to minimize heat loss. The east and west walls lose heat at a rate of 10 units/m² per day, the north and south walls at a rate of 8 units/m² per day, the floor at a rate of 1 unit/m² per day, and the roof at a rate of 5 units/m² per day. Each wall must be at least 30 m long, the height must be at least 4 m, and the volume must be exactly 4000 m³.
(a) Find and sketch the domain of the heat loss as a function of the lengths of the sides.

(b) Find the dimensions that minimize heat loss. (Check both the critical points and the points on the boundary of the domain.)
(c) Could you design a building with even less heat loss if the restrictions on the lengths of the walls were removed?

53. If the length of the diagonal of a rectangular box must be L, what is the largest possible volume?

54. Three alleles (alternative versions of a gene) A, B, and O determine the four blood types A (AA or AO), B (BB or BO), O (OO), and AB. The Hardy-Weinberg Law states that the proportion of individuals in a population who carry two different alleles is

$$P = 2pq + 2pr + 2rq$$

where p, q, and r are the proportions of A, B, and O in the population. Use the fact that $p + q + r = 1$ to show that P is at most $\frac{2}{3}$.

55. Suppose that a scientist has reason to believe that two quantities x and y are related linearly, that is, $y = mx + b$, at least approximately, for some values of m and b. The scientist performs an experiment and collects data in the form of points (x_1, y_1), (x_2, y_2), . . . , (x_n, y_n), and then plots these points. The points don't lie exactly on a straight line, so the scientist wants to find constants m and b so that the line $y = mx + b$ "fits" the points as well as possible. (See the figure.)

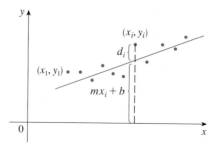

Let $d_i = y_i - (mx_i + b)$ be the vertical deviation of the point (x_i, y_i) from the line. The **method of least squares** determines m and b so as to minimize $\sum_{i=1}^{n} d_i^2$, the sum of the squares of these deviations. Show that, according to this method, the line of best fit is obtained when

$$m \sum_{i=1}^{n} x_i + bn = \sum_{i=1}^{n} y_i$$

$$m \sum_{i=1}^{n} x_i^2 + b \sum_{i=1}^{n} x_i = \sum_{i=1}^{n} x_i y_i$$

Thus the line is found by solving these two equations in the two unknowns m and b. (See Section 1.2 for a further discussion and applications of the method of least squares.)

56. Find an equation of the plane that passes through the point $(1, 2, 3)$ and cuts off the smallest volume in the first octant.

<table>
<tr><td>

**APPLIED
PROJECT**

</td><td>

DESIGNING A DUMPSTER

For this project we locate a trash dumpster in order to study its shape and construction. We then attempt to determine the dimensions of a container of similar design that minimize construction cost.

1. First locate a trash dumpster in your area. Carefully study and describe all details of its construction, and determine its volume. Include a sketch of the container.

2. While maintaining the general shape and method of construction, determine the dimensions such a container of the same volume should have in order to minimize the cost of construction. Use the following assumptions in your analysis:

   ▪ The sides, back, and front are to be made from 12-gauge (0.1046 inch thick) steel sheets, which cost $0.70 per square foot (including any required cuts or bends).

   ▪ The base is to be made from a 10-gauge (0.1345 inch thick) steel sheet, which costs $0.90 per square foot.

   ▪ Lids cost approximately $50.00 each, regardless of dimensions.

   ▪ Welding costs approximately $0.18 per foot for material and labor combined.

   Give justification of any further assumptions or simplifications made of the details of construction.

3. Describe how any of your assumptions or simplifications may affect the final result.

4. If you were hired as a consultant on this investigation, what would your conclusions be? Would you recommend altering the design of the dumpster? If so, describe the savings that would result.

</td></tr>
</table>

<table>
<tr><td>

**DISCOVERY
PROJECT**

</td><td>

QUADRATIC APPROXIMATIONS AND CRITICAL POINTS

The Taylor polynomial approximation to functions of one variable that we discussed in Chapter 12 can be extended to functions of two or more variables. Here we investigate quadratic approximations to functions of two variables and use them to give insight into the Second Derivatives Test for classifying critical points.

In Section 15.4 we discussed the linearization of a function f of two variables at a point (a, b):

$$L(x, y) = f(a, b) + f_x(a, b)(x - a) + f_y(a, b)(y - b)$$

Recall that the graph of L is the tangent plane to the surface $z = f(x, y)$ at $(a, b, f(a, b))$ and the corresponding linear approximation is $f(x, y) \approx L(x, y)$. The linearization L is also called the **first-degree Taylor polynomial** of f at (a, b).

1. If f has continuous second-order partial derivatives at (a, b), then the **second-degree Taylor polynomial** of f at (a, b) is

$$Q(x, y) = f(a, b) + f_x(a, b)(x - a) + f_y(a, b)(y - b)$$
$$+ \tfrac{1}{2}f_{xx}(a, b)(x - a)^2 + f_{xy}(a, b)(x - a)(y - b) + \tfrac{1}{2}f_{yy}(a, b)(y - b)^2$$

and the approximation $f(x, y) \approx Q(x, y)$ is called the **quadratic approximation** to f at (a, b). Verify that Q has the same first- and second-order partial derivatives as f at (a, b).

</td></tr>
</table>

2. (a) Find the first- and second-degree Taylor polynomials L and Q of $f(x, y) = e^{-x^2-y^2}$ at $(0, 0)$.

  (b) Graph f, L, and Q. Comment on how well L and Q approximate f.

3. (a) Find the first- and second-degree Taylor polynomials L and Q for $f(x, y) = xe^y$ at $(1, 0)$.
  (b) Compare the values of L, Q, and f at $(0.9, 0.1)$.
  (c) Graph f, L, and Q. Comment on how well L and Q approximate f.

4. In this problem we analyze the behavior of the polynomial $f(x, y) = ax^2 + bxy + cy^2$ (without using the Second Derivatives Test) by identifying the graph as a paraboloid.
  (a) By completing the square, show that if $a \neq 0$, then

$$f(x, y) = ax^2 + bxy + cy^2 = a\left[\left(x + \frac{b}{2a}y \right)^2 + \left(\frac{4ac - b^2}{4a^2} \right)y^2 \right]$$

  (b) Let $D = 4ac - b^2$. Show that if $D > 0$ and $a > 0$, then f has a local minimum at $(0, 0)$.
  (c) Show that if $D > 0$ and $a < 0$, then f has a local maximum at $(0, 0)$.
  (d) Show that if $D < 0$, then $(0, 0)$ is a saddle point.

5. (a) Suppose f is any function with continuous second-order partial derivatives such that $f(0, 0) = 0$ and $(0, 0)$ is a critical point of f. Write an expression for the second-degree Taylor polynomial, Q, of f at $(0, 0)$.
  (b) What can you conclude about Q from Problem 4?
  (c) In view of the quadratic approximation $f(x, y) \approx Q(x, y)$, what does part (b) suggest about f?

15.8 LAGRANGE MULTIPLIERS

In Example 6 in Section 15.7 we maximized a volume function $V = xyz$ subject to the constraint $2xz + 2yz + xy = 12$, which expressed the side condition that the surface area was 12 m². In this section we present Lagrange's method for maximizing or minimizing a general function $f(x, y, z)$ subject to a constraint (or side condition) of the form $g(x, y, z) = k$.

It's easier to explain the geometric basis of Lagrange's method for functions of two variables. So we start by trying to find the extreme values of $f(x, y)$ subject to a constraint of the form $g(x, y) = k$. In other words, we seek the extreme values of $f(x, y)$ when the point (x, y) is restricted to lie on the level curve $g(x, y) = k$. Figure 1 shows this curve together with several level curves of f. These have the equations $f(x, y) = c$, where $c = 7$, 8, 9, 10, 11. To maximize $f(x, y)$ subject to $g(x, y) = k$ is to find the largest value of c such that the level curve $f(x, y) = c$ intersects $g(x, y) = k$. It appears from Figure 1 that this happens when these curves just touch each other, that is, when they have a common tangent line. (Otherwise, the value of c could be increased further.) This means that the normal lines at the point (x_0, y_0) where they touch are identical. So the gradient vectors are parallel; that is, $\nabla f(x_0, y_0) = \lambda \nabla g(x_0, y_0)$ for some scalar λ.

This kind of argument also applies to the problem of finding the extreme values of $f(x, y, z)$ subject to the constraint $g(x, y, z) = k$. Thus the point (x, y, z) is restricted to lie on the level surface S with equation $g(x, y, z) = k$. Instead of the level curves in Figure 1, we consider the level surfaces $f(x, y, z) = c$ and argue that if the maximum value of f is $f(x_0, y_0, z_0) = c$, then the level surface $f(x, y, z) = c$ is tangent to the level surface $g(x, y, z) = k$ and so the corresponding gradient vectors are parallel.

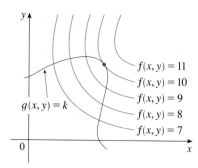

FIGURE 1

TEC Visual 15.8 animates Figure 1 for both level curves and level surfaces.

This intuitive argument can be made precise as follows. Suppose that a function f has an extreme value at a point $P(x_0, y_0, z_0)$ on the surface S and let C be a curve with vector equation $\mathbf{r}(t) = \langle x(t), y(t), z(t) \rangle$ that lies on S and passes through P. If t_0 is the parameter value corresponding to the point P, then $\mathbf{r}(t_0) = \langle x_0, y_0, z_0 \rangle$. The composite function $h(t) = f(x(t), y(t), z(t))$ represents the values that f takes on the curve C. Since f has an extreme value at (x_0, y_0, z_0), it follows that h has an extreme value at t_0, so $h'(t_0) = 0$. But if f is differentiable, we can use the Chain Rule to write

$$
\begin{aligned}
0 &= h'(t_0) \\
&= f_x(x_0, y_0, z_0)x'(t_0) + f_y(x_0, y_0, z_0)y'(t_0) + f_z(x_0, y_0, z_0)z'(t_0) \\
&= \nabla f(x_0, y_0, z_0) \cdot \mathbf{r}'(t_0)
\end{aligned}
$$

This shows that the gradient vector $\nabla f(x_0, y_0, z_0)$ is orthogonal to the tangent vector $\mathbf{r}'(t_0)$ to every such curve C. But we already know from Section 15.6 that the gradient vector of g, $\nabla g(x_0, y_0, z_0)$, is also orthogonal to $\mathbf{r}'(t_0)$ for every such curve. (See Equation 15.6.18.) This means that the gradient vectors $\nabla f(x_0, y_0, z_0)$ and $\nabla g(x_0, y_0, z_0)$ must be parallel. Therefore, if $\nabla g(x_0, y_0, z_0) \neq \mathbf{0}$, there is a number λ such that

> ■ Lagrange multipliers are named after the French-Italian mathematician Joseph-Louis Lagrange (1736–1813). See page 217 for a biographical sketch of Lagrange.

$$\boxed{1} \qquad \boxed{\nabla f(x_0, y_0, z_0) = \lambda \, \nabla g(x_0, y_0, z_0)}$$

The number λ in Equation 1 is called a **Lagrange multiplier**. The procedure based on Equation 1 is as follows.

> ■ In deriving Lagrange's method we assumed that $\nabla g \neq \mathbf{0}$. In each of our examples you can check that $\nabla g \neq \mathbf{0}$ at all points where $g(x, y, z) = k$. See Exercise 21 for what can go wrong if $\nabla g = \mathbf{0}$.

METHOD OF LAGRANGE MULTIPLIERS To find the maximum and minimum values of $f(x, y, z)$ subject to the constraint $g(x, y, z) = k$ [assuming that these extreme values exist and $\nabla g \neq \mathbf{0}$ on the surface $g(x, y, z) = k$]:

(a) Find all values of x, y, z, and λ such that

$$\nabla f(x, y, z) = \lambda \, \nabla g(x, y, z)$$

and $\qquad\qquad g(x, y, z) = k$

(b) Evaluate f at all the points (x, y, z) that result from step (a). The largest of these values is the maximum value of f; the smallest is the minimum value of f.

If we write the vector equation $\nabla f = \lambda \, \nabla g$ in terms of its components, then the equations in step (a) become

$$f_x = \lambda g_x \qquad f_y = \lambda g_y \qquad f_z = \lambda g_z \qquad g(x, y, z) = k$$

This is a system of four equations in the four unknowns x, y, z, and λ, but it is not necessary to find explicit values for λ.

For functions of two variables the method of Lagrange multipliers is similar to the method just described. To find the extreme values of $f(x, y)$ subject to the constraint $g(x, y) = k$, we look for values of x, y, and λ such that

$$\nabla f(x, y) = \lambda \, \nabla g(x, y) \qquad \text{and} \qquad g(x, y) = k$$

This amounts to solving three equations in three unknowns:

$$f_x = \lambda g_x \qquad f_y = \lambda g_y \qquad g(x, y) = k$$

Our first illustration of Lagrange's method is to reconsider the problem given in Example 6 in Section 15.7.

V EXAMPLE 1 A rectangular box without a lid is to be made from 12 m^2 of cardboard. Find the maximum volume of such a box.

SOLUTION As in Example 6 in Section 15.7, we let x, y, and z be the length, width, and height, respectively, of the box in meters. Then we wish to maximize

$$V = xyz$$

subject to the constraint

$$g(x, y, z) = 2xz + 2yz + xy = 12$$

Using the method of Lagrange multipliers, we look for values of x, y, z, and λ such that $\nabla V = \lambda \, \nabla g$ and $g(x, y, z) = 12$. This gives the equations

$$V_x = \lambda g_x \qquad V_y = \lambda g_y \qquad V_z = \lambda g_z \qquad 2xz + 2yz + xy = 12$$

which become

2
$$yz = \lambda(2z + y)$$

3
$$xz = \lambda(2z + x)$$

4
$$xy = \lambda(2x + 2y)$$

5
$$2xz + 2yz + xy = 12$$

There are no general rules for solving systems of equations. Sometimes some ingenuity is required. In the present example you might notice that if we multiply (2) by x, (3) by y, and (4) by z, then the left sides of these equations will be identical. Doing this, we have

■ Another method for solving the system of equations (2–5) is to solve each of Equations 2, 3, and 4 for λ and then to equate the resulting expressions.

6
$$xyz = \lambda(2xz + xy)$$

7
$$xyz = \lambda(2yz + xy)$$

8
$$xyz = \lambda(2xz + 2yz)$$

We observe that $\lambda \neq 0$ because $\lambda = 0$ would imply $yz = xz = xy = 0$ from (2), (3), and (4) and this would contradict (5). Therefore, from (6) and (7), we have

$$2xz + xy = 2yz + xy$$

which gives $xz = yz$. But $z \neq 0$ (since $z = 0$ would give $V = 0$), so $x = y$. From (7) and (8) we have

$$2yz + xy = 2xz + 2yz$$

which gives $2xz = xy$ and so (since $x \neq 0$) $y = 2z$. If we now put $x = y = 2z$ in (5), we get

$$4z^2 + 4z^2 + 4z^2 = 12$$

Since x, y, and z are all positive, we therefore have $z = 1$ and so $x = 2$ and $y = 2$. This agrees with our answer in Section 15.7. □

■ In geometric terms, Example 2 asks for the highest and lowest points on the curve C in Figure 2 that lies on the paraboloid $z = x^2 + 2y^2$ and directly above the constraint circle $x^2 + y^2 = 1$.

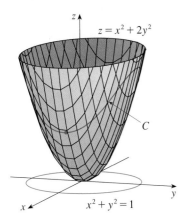

FIGURE 2

■ The geometry behind the use of Lagrange multipliers in Example 2 is shown in Figure 3. The extreme values of $f(x, y) = x^2 + 2y^2$ correspond to the level curves that touch the circle $x^2 + y^2 = 1$.

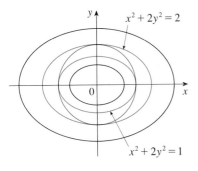

FIGURE 3

☑ EXAMPLE 2 Find the extreme values of the function $f(x, y) = x^2 + 2y^2$ on the circle $x^2 + y^2 = 1$.

SOLUTION We are asked for the extreme values of f subject to the constraint $g(x, y) = x^2 + y^2 = 1$. Using Lagrange multipliers, we solve the equations $\nabla f = \lambda \nabla g$ and $g(x, y) = 1$, which can be written as

$$f_x = \lambda g_x \qquad f_y = \lambda g_y \qquad g(x, y) = 1$$

or as

$$\boxed{9} \qquad\qquad 2x = 2x\lambda$$

$$\boxed{10} \qquad\qquad 4y = 2y\lambda$$

$$\boxed{11} \qquad\qquad x^2 + y^2 = 1$$

From (9) we have $x = 0$ or $\lambda = 1$. If $x = 0$, then (11) gives $y = \pm 1$. If $\lambda = 1$, then $y = 0$ from (10), so then (11) gives $x = \pm 1$. Therefore f has possible extreme values at the points $(0, 1)$, $(0, -1)$, $(1, 0)$, and $(-1, 0)$. Evaluating f at these four points, we find that

$$f(0, 1) = 2 \qquad f(0, -1) = 2 \qquad f(1, 0) = 1 \qquad f(-1, 0) = 1$$

Therefore the maximum value of f on the circle $x^2 + y^2 = 1$ is $f(0, \pm 1) = 2$ and the minimum value is $f(\pm 1, 0) = 1$. Checking with Figure 2, we see that these values look reasonable. ☐

EXAMPLE 3 Find the extreme values of $f(x, y) = x^2 + 2y^2$ on the disk $x^2 + y^2 \leq 1$.

SOLUTION According to the procedure in (15.7.9), we compare the values of f at the critical points with values at the points on the boundary. Since $f_x = 2x$ and $f_y = 4y$, the only critical point is $(0, 0)$. We compare the value of f at that point with the extreme values on the boundary from Example 2:

$$f(0, 0) = 0 \qquad f(\pm 1, 0) = 1 \qquad f(0, \pm 1) = 2$$

Therefore the maximum value of f on the disk $x^2 + y^2 \leq 1$ is $f(0, \pm 1) = 2$ and the minimum value is $f(0, 0) = 0$. ☐

EXAMPLE 4 Find the points on the sphere $x^2 + y^2 + z^2 = 4$ that are closest to and farthest from the point $(3, 1, -1)$.

SOLUTION The distance from a point (x, y, z) to the point $(3, 1, -1)$ is

$$d = \sqrt{(x - 3)^2 + (y - 1)^2 + (z + 1)^2}$$

but the algebra is simpler if we instead maximize and minimize the square of the distance:

$$d^2 = f(x, y, z) = (x - 3)^2 + (y - 1)^2 + (z + 1)^2$$

The constraint is that the point (x, y, z) lies on the sphere, that is,

$$g(x, y, z) = x^2 + y^2 + z^2 = 4$$

According to the method of Lagrange multipliers, we solve $\nabla f = \lambda \nabla g$, $g = 4$. This gives

$\boxed{12}$ $$2(x - 3) = 2x\lambda$$

$\boxed{13}$ $$2(y - 1) = 2y\lambda$$

$\boxed{14}$ $$2(z + 1) = 2z\lambda$$

$\boxed{15}$ $$x^2 + y^2 + z^2 = 4$$

The simplest way to solve these equations is to solve for x, y, and z in terms of λ from (12), (13), and (14), and then substitute these values into (15). From (12) we have

$$x - 3 = x\lambda \quad \text{or} \quad x(1 - \lambda) = 3 \quad \text{or} \quad x = \frac{3}{1 - \lambda}$$

[Note that $1 - \lambda \neq 0$ because $\lambda = 1$ is impossible from (12).] Similarly, (13) and (14) give

$$y = \frac{1}{1 - \lambda} \qquad z = -\frac{1}{1 - \lambda}$$

Therefore, from (15), we have

$$\frac{3^2}{(1 - \lambda)^2} + \frac{1^2}{(1 - \lambda)^2} + \frac{(-1)^2}{(1 - \lambda)^2} = 4$$

which gives $(1 - \lambda)^2 = \frac{11}{4}$, $1 - \lambda = \pm\sqrt{11}/2$, so

$$\lambda = 1 \pm \frac{\sqrt{11}}{2}$$

These values of λ then give the corresponding points (x, y, z):

$$\left(\frac{6}{\sqrt{11}}, \frac{2}{\sqrt{11}}, -\frac{2}{\sqrt{11}}\right) \quad \text{and} \quad \left(-\frac{6}{\sqrt{11}}, -\frac{2}{\sqrt{11}}, \frac{2}{\sqrt{11}}\right)$$

It's easy to see that f has a smaller value at the first of these points, so the closest point is $\left(6/\sqrt{11}, 2/\sqrt{11}, -2/\sqrt{11}\right)$ and the farthest is $\left(-6/\sqrt{11}, -2/\sqrt{11}, 2/\sqrt{11}\right)$. ☐

■ Figure 4 shows the sphere and the nearest point P in Example 4. Can you see how to find the coordinates of P without using calculus?

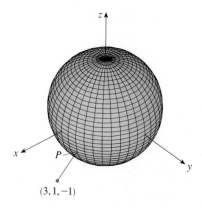

(3, 1, −1)

FIGURE 4

TWO CONSTRAINTS

Suppose now that we want to find the maximum and minimum values of a function $f(x, y, z)$ subject to two constraints (side conditions) of the form $g(x, y, z) = k$ and $h(x, y, z) = c$. Geometrically, this means that we are looking for the extreme values of f when (x, y, z) is restricted to lie on the curve of intersection C of the level surfaces $g(x, y, z) = k$ and $h(x, y, z) = c$. (See Figure 5.) Suppose f has such an extreme value at a point $P(x_0, y_0, z_0)$. We know from the beginning of this section that ∇f is orthogonal to C at P. But we also know that ∇g is orthogonal to $g(x, y, z) = k$ and ∇h is orthogonal to $h(x, y, z) = c$, so ∇g and ∇h are both orthogonal to C. This means that the gradient vector $\nabla f(x_0, y_0, z_0)$ is in the plane determined by $\nabla g(x_0, y_0, z_0)$ and $\nabla h(x_0, y_0, z_0)$. (We assume that these gradient vectors are not zero and not parallel.) So there are numbers λ and μ

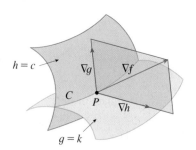

FIGURE 5

(called Lagrange multipliers) such that

$$\boxed{16} \qquad \nabla f(x_0, y_0, z_0) = \lambda \nabla g(x_0, y_0, z_0) + \mu \nabla h(x_0, y_0, z_0)$$

In this case Lagrange's method is to look for extreme values by solving five equations in the five unknowns x, y, z, λ, and μ. These equations are obtained by writing Equation 16 in terms of its components and using the constraint equations:

$$f_x = \lambda g_x + \mu h_x$$
$$f_y = \lambda g_y + \mu h_y$$
$$f_z = \lambda g_z + \mu h_z$$
$$g(x, y, z) = k$$
$$h(x, y, z) = c$$

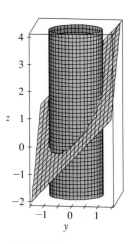

■ The cylinder $x^2 + y^2 = 1$ intersects the plane $x - y + z = 1$ in an ellipse (Figure 6). Example 5 asks for the maximum value of f when (x, y, z) is restricted to lie on the ellipse.

FIGURE 6

▼ EXAMPLE 5 Find the maximum value of the function $f(x, y, z) = x + 2y + 3z$ on the curve of intersection of the plane $x - y + z = 1$ and the cylinder $x^2 + y^2 = 1$.

SOLUTION We maximize the function $f(x, y, z) = x + 2y + 3z$ subject to the constraints $g(x, y, z) = x - y + z = 1$ and $h(x, y, z) = x^2 + y^2 = 1$. The Lagrange condition is $\nabla f = \lambda \nabla g + \mu \nabla h$, so we solve the equations

$$\boxed{17} \qquad 1 = \lambda + 2x\mu$$
$$\boxed{18} \qquad 2 = -\lambda + 2y\mu$$
$$\boxed{19} \qquad 3 = \lambda$$
$$\boxed{20} \qquad x - y + z = 1$$
$$\boxed{21} \qquad x^2 + y^2 = 1$$

Putting $\lambda = 3$ [from (19)] in (17), we get $2x\mu = -2$, so $x = -1/\mu$. Similarly, (18) gives $y = 5/(2\mu)$. Substitution in (21) then gives

$$\frac{1}{\mu^2} + \frac{25}{4\mu^2} = 1$$

and so $\mu^2 = \frac{29}{4}$, $\mu = \pm\sqrt{29}/2$. Then $x = \mp 2/\sqrt{29}$, $y = \pm 5/\sqrt{29}$, and, from (20), $z = 1 - x + y = 1 \pm 7/\sqrt{29}$. The corresponding values of f are

$$\mp \frac{2}{\sqrt{29}} + 2\left(\pm\frac{5}{\sqrt{29}}\right) + 3\left(1 \pm \frac{7}{\sqrt{29}}\right) = 3 \pm \sqrt{29}$$

Therefore the maximum value of f on the given curve is $3 + \sqrt{29}$. ☐

15.8 | EXERCISES

1. Pictured are a contour map of f and a curve with equation $g(x, y) = 8$. Estimate the maximum and minimum values of f subject to the constraint that $g(x, y) = 8$. Explain your reasoning.

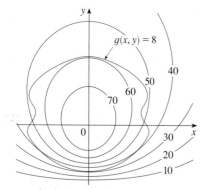

2. (a) Use a graphing calculator or computer to graph the circle $x^2 + y^2 = 1$. On the same screen, graph several curves of the form $x^2 + y = c$ until you find two that just touch the circle. What is the significance of the values of c for these two curves?

(b) Use Lagrange multipliers to find the extreme values of $f(x, y) = x^2 + y$ subject to the constraint $x^2 + y^2 = 1$. Compare your answers with those in part (a).

3–17 Use Lagrange multipliers to find the maximum and minimum values of the function subject to the given constraint(s).

3. $f(x, y) = x^2 + y^2$; $xy = 1$

4. $f(x, y) = 4x + 6y$; $x^2 + y^2 = 13$

5. $f(x, y) = x^2y$; $x^2 + 2y^2 = 6$

6. $f(x, y) = e^{xy}$; $x^3 + y^3 = 16$

7. $f(x, y, z) = 2x + 6y + 10z$; $x^2 + y^2 + z^2 = 35$

8. $f(x, y, z) = 8x - 4z$; $x^2 + 10y^2 + z^2 = 5$

9. $f(x, y, z) = xyz$; $x^2 + 2y^2 + 3z^2 = 6$

10. $f(x, y, z) = x^2y^2z^2$; $x^2 + y^2 + z^2 = 1$

11. $f(x, y, z) = x^2 + y^2 + z^2$; $x^4 + y^4 + z^4 = 1$

12. $f(x, y, z) = x^4 + y^4 + z^4$; $x^2 + y^2 + z^2 = 1$

13. $f(x, y, z, t) = x + y + z + t$; $x^2 + y^2 + z^2 + t^2 = 1$

14. $f(x_1, x_2, \ldots, x_n) = x_1 + x_2 + \cdots + x_n$;
$x_1^2 + x_2^2 + \cdots + x_n^2 = 1$

15. $f(x, y, z) = x + 2y$; $x + y + z = 1$, $y^2 + z^2 = 4$

16. $f(x, y, z) = 3x - y - 3z$;
$x + y - z = 0$, $x^2 + 2z^2 = 1$

17. $f(x, y, z) = yz + xy$; $xy = 1$, $y^2 + z^2 = 1$

18–19 Find the extreme values of f on the region described by the inequality.

18. $f(x, y) = 2x^2 + 3y^2 - 4x - 5$, $x^2 + y^2 \leqslant 16$

19. $f(x, y) = e^{-xy}$, $x^2 + 4y^2 \leqslant 1$

20. Consider the problem of maximizing the function $f(x, y) = 2x + 3y$ subject to the constraint $\sqrt{x} + \sqrt{y} = 5$.
(a) Try using Lagrange multipliers to solve the problem.
(b) Does $f(25, 0)$ give a larger value than the one in part (a)?
(c) Solve the problem by graphing the constraint equation and several level curves of f.
(d) Explain why the method of Lagrange multipliers fails to solve the problem.
(e) What is the significance of $f(9, 4)$?

21. Consider the problem of minimizing the function $f(x, y) = x$ on the curve $y^2 + x^4 - x^3 = 0$ (a piriform).
(a) Try using Lagrange multipliers to solve the problem.
(b) Show that the minimum value is $f(0, 0) = 0$ but the Lagrange condition $\nabla f(0, 0) = \lambda \nabla g(0, 0)$ is not satisfied for any value of λ.
(c) Explain why Lagrange multipliers fail to find the minimum value in this case.

CAS 22. (a) If your computer algebra system plots implicitly defined curves, use it to estimate the minimum and maximum values of $f(x, y) = x^3 + y^3 + 3xy$ subject to the constraint $(x - 3)^2 + (y - 3)^2 = 9$ by graphical methods.
(b) Solve the problem in part (a) with the aid of Lagrange multipliers. Use your CAS to solve the equations numerically. Compare your answers with those in part (a).

23. The total production P of a certain product depends on the amount L of labor used and the amount K of capital investment. In Sections 15.1 and 15.3 we discussed how the Cobb-Douglas model $P = bL^\alpha K^{1-\alpha}$ follows from certain economic assumptions, where b and α are positive constants and $\alpha < 1$. If the cost of a unit of labor is m and the cost of a unit of capital is n, and the company can spend only p dollars as its total budget, then maximizing the production P is subject to the constraint $mL + nK = p$. Show that the maximum production occurs when

$$L = \frac{\alpha p}{m} \quad \text{and} \quad K = \frac{(1 - \alpha)p}{n}$$

24. Referring to Exercise 23, we now suppose that the production is fixed at $bL^\alpha K^{1-\alpha} = Q$, where Q is a constant. What values of L and K minimize the cost function $C(L, K) = mL + nK$?

25. Use Lagrange multipliers to prove that the rectangle with maximum area that has a given perimeter p is a square.

26. Use Lagrange multipliers to prove that the triangle with maximum area that has a given perimeter p is equilateral.
Hint: Use Heron's formula for the area:
$$A = \sqrt{s(s-x)(s-y)(s-z)}$$
where $s = p/2$ and x, y, z are the lengths of the sides.

27–39 Use Lagrange multipliers to give an alternate solution to the indicated exercise in Section 15.7.

27. Exercise 39   **28.** Exercise 40

29. Exercise 41   **30.** Exercise 42

31. Exercise 43   **32.** Exercise 44

33. Exercise 45   **34.** Exercise 46

35. Exercise 47   **36.** Exercise 48

37. Exercise 49   **38.** Exercise 50

39. Exercise 53

40. Find the maximum and minimum volumes of a rectangular box whose surface area is 1500 cm^2 and whose total edge length is 200 cm.

41. The plane $x + y + 2z = 2$ intersects the paraboloid $z = x^2 + y^2$ in an ellipse. Find the points on this ellipse that are nearest to and farthest from the origin.

42. The plane $4x - 3y + 8z = 5$ intersects the cone $z^2 = x^2 + y^2$ in an ellipse.
(a) Graph the cone, the plane, and the ellipse.
(b) Use Lagrange multipliers to find the highest and lowest points on the ellipse.

CAS 43–44 Find the maximum and minimum values of f subject to the given constraints. Use a computer algebra system to solve the system of equations that arises in using Lagrange multipliers. (If your CAS finds only one solution, you may need to use additional commands.)

43. $f(x, y, z) = ye^{x-z}$; $9x^2 + 4y^2 + 36z^2 = 36$, $xy + yz = 1$

44. $f(x, y, z) = x + y + z$; $x^2 - y^2 = z$, $x^2 + z^2 = 4$

45. (a) Find the maximum value of
$$f(x_1, x_2, \ldots, x_n) = \sqrt[n]{x_1 x_2 \cdots x_n}$$
given that $x_1, x_2, \ldots, x_n$ are positive numbers and $x_1 + x_2 + \cdots + x_n = c$, where c is a constant.
(b) Deduce from part (a) that if $x_1, x_2, \ldots, x_n$ are positive numbers, then
$$\sqrt[n]{x_1 x_2 \cdots x_n} \le \frac{x_1 + x_2 + \cdots + x_n}{n}$$
This inequality says that the geometric mean of n numbers is no larger than the arithmetic mean of the numbers. Under what circumstances are these two means equal?

46. (a) Maximize $\sum_{i=1}^{n} x_i y_i$ subject to the constraints $\sum_{i=1}^{n} x_i^2 = 1$ and $\sum_{i=1}^{n} y_i^2 = 1$.
(b) Put
$$x_i = \frac{a_i}{\sqrt{\sum a_j^2}} \qquad \text{and} \qquad y_i = \frac{b_i}{\sqrt{\sum b_j^2}}$$
to show that
$$\sum a_i b_i \le \sqrt{\sum a_j^2} \sqrt{\sum b_j^2}$$
for any numbers $a_1, \ldots, a_n, b_1, \ldots, b_n$. This inequality is known as the Cauchy-Schwarz Inequality.

APPLIED PROJECT

ROCKET SCIENCE

Many rockets, such as the Pegasus XL currently used to launch satellites and the Saturn V that first put men on the moon, are designed to use three stages in their ascent into space. A large first stage initially propels the rocket until its fuel is consumed, at which point the stage is jettisoned to reduce the mass of the rocket. The smaller second and third stages function similarly in order to place the rocket's payload into orbit about the earth. (With this design, at least two stages are required in order to reach the necessary velocities, and using three stages has proven to be a good compromise between cost and performance.) Our goal here is to determine the individual masses of the three stages, which are to be designed in such a way as to minimize the total mass of the rocket while enabling it to reach a desired velocity.

For a single-stage rocket consuming fuel at a constant rate, the change in velocity resulting from the acceleration of the rocket vehicle has been modeled by

$$\Delta V = -c \ln\left(1 - \frac{(1-S)M_r}{P + M_r}\right)$$

where M_r is the mass of the rocket engine including initial fuel, P is the mass of the payload, S is a *structural factor* determined by the design of the rocket (specifically, it is the ratio of the mass of the rocket vehicle without fuel to the total mass of the rocket with payload), and c is the (constant) speed of exhaust relative to the rocket.

Now consider a rocket with three stages and a payload of mass A. Assume that outside forces are negligible and that c and S remain constant for each stage. If M_i is the mass of the ith stage, we can initially consider the rocket engine to have mass M_1 and its payload to have mass $M_2 + M_3 + A$; the second and third stages can be handled similarly.

1. Show that the velocity attained after all three stages have been jettisoned is given by

$$v_f = c\left[\ln\left(\frac{M_1 + M_2 + M_3 + A}{SM_1 + M_2 + M_3 + A}\right) + \ln\left(\frac{M_2 + M_3 + A}{SM_2 + M_3 + A}\right) + \ln\left(\frac{M_3 + A}{SM_3 + A}\right)\right]$$

2. We wish to minimize the total mass $M = M_1 + M_2 + M_3$ of the rocket engine subject to the constraint that the desired velocity v_f from Problem 1 is attained. The method of Lagrange multipliers is appropriate here, but difficult to implement using the current expressions. To simplify, we define variables N_i so that the constraint equation may be expressed as $v_f = c(\ln N_1 + \ln N_2 + \ln N_3)$. Since M is now difficult to express in terms of the N_i's, we wish to use a simpler function that will be minimized at the same place as M. Show that

$$\frac{M_1 + M_2 + M_3 + A}{M_2 + M_3 + A} = \frac{(1-S)N_1}{1 - SN_1}$$

$$\frac{M_2 + M_3 + A}{M_3 + A} = \frac{(1-S)N_2}{1 - SN_2}$$

$$\frac{M_3 + A}{A} = \frac{(1-S)N_3}{1 - SN_3}$$

and conclude that

$$\frac{M + A}{A} = \frac{(1-S)^3 N_1 N_2 N_3}{(1 - SN_1)(1 - SN_2)(1 - SN_3)}$$

3. Verify that $\ln((M + A)/A)$ is minimized at the same location as M; use Lagrange multipliers and the results of Problem 2 to find expressions for the values of N_i where the minimum occurs subject to the constraint $v_f = c(\ln N_1 + \ln N_2 + \ln N_3)$. [*Hint:* Use properties of logarithms to help simplify the expressions.]

4. Find an expression for the minimum value of M as a function of v_f.

5. If we want to put a three-stage rocket into orbit 100 miles above the earth's surface, a final velocity of approximately 17,500 mi/h is required. Suppose that each stage is built with a structural factor $S = 0.2$ and an exhaust speed of $c = 6000$ mi/h.
   (a) Find the minimum total mass M of the rocket engines as a function of A.
   (b) Find the mass of each individual stage as a function of A. (They are not equally sized!)

6. The same rocket would require a final velocity of approximately 24,700 mi/h in order to escape earth's gravity. Find the mass of each individual stage that would minimize the total mass of the rocket engines and allow the rocket to propel a 500-pound probe into deep space.

HYDRO-TURBINE OPTIMIZATION

The Katahdin Paper Company in Millinocket, Maine, operates a hydroelectric generating station on the Penobscot River. Water is piped from a dam to the power station. The rate at which the water flows through the pipe varies, depending on external conditions.

The power station has three different hydroelectric turbines, each with a known (and unique) power function that gives the amount of electric power generated as a function of the water flow arriving at the turbine. The incoming water can be apportioned in different volumes to each turbine, so the goal is to determine how to distribute water among the turbines to give the maximum total energy production for any rate of flow.

Using experimental evidence and *Bernoulli's equation*, the following quadratic models were determined for the power output of each turbine, along with the allowable flows of operation:

$$KW_1 = (-18.89 + 0.1277Q_1 - 4.08 \cdot 10^{-5}Q_1^2)(170 - 1.6 \cdot 10^{-6}Q_T^2)$$

$$KW_2 = (-24.51 + 0.1358Q_2 - 4.69 \cdot 10^{-5}Q_2^2)(170 - 1.6 \cdot 10^{-6}Q_T^2)$$

$$KW_3 = (-27.02 + 0.1380Q_3 - 3.84 \cdot 10^{-5}Q_3^2)(170 - 1.6 \cdot 10^{-6}Q_T^2)$$

$$250 \leqslant Q_1 \leqslant 1110, \quad 250 \leqslant Q_2 \leqslant 1110, \quad 250 \leqslant Q_3 \leqslant 1225$$

where

$$Q_i = \text{flow through turbine } i \text{ in cubic feet per second}$$

$$KW_i = \text{power generated by turbine } i \text{ in kilowatts}$$

$$Q_T = \text{total flow through the station in cubic feet per second}$$

1. If all three turbines are being used, we wish to determine the flow Q_i to each turbine that will give the maximum total energy production. Our limitations are that the flows must sum to the total incoming flow and the given domain restrictions must be observed. Consequently, use Lagrange multipliers to find the values for the individual flows (as functions of Q_T) that maximize the total energy production $KW_1 + KW_2 + KW_3$ subject to the constraints $Q_1 + Q_2 + Q_3 = Q_T$ and the domain restrictions on each Q_i.

2. For which values of Q_T is your result valid?

3. For an incoming flow of 2500 ft³/s, determine the distribution to the turbines and verify (by trying some nearby distributions) that your result is indeed a maximum.

4. Until now we have assumed that all three turbines are operating; is it possible in some situations that more power could be produced by using only one turbine? Make a graph of the three power functions and use it to help decide if an incoming flow of 1000 ft³/s should be distributed to all three turbines or routed to just one. (If you determine that only one turbine should be used, which one would it be?) What if the flow is only 600 ft³/s?

5. Perhaps for some flow levels it would be advantageous to use two turbines. If the incoming flow is 1500 ft³/s, which two turbines would you recommend using? Use Lagrange multipliers to determine how the flow should be distributed between the two turbines to maximize the energy produced. For this flow, is using two turbines more efficient than using all three?

6. If the incoming flow is 3400 ft³/s, what would you recommend to the company?

$$\boxed{15} \quad \text{REVIEW}$$

CONCEPT CHECK

1. (a) What is a function of two variables?
   (b) Describe three methods for visualizing a function of two variables.

2. What is a function of three variables? How can you visualize such a function?

3. What does
$$\lim_{(x,\,y)\to(a,\,b)} f(x, y) = L$$
mean? How can you show that such a limit does not exist?

4. (a) What does it mean to say that f is continuous at (a, b)?
   (b) If f is continuous on $\mathbb{R}^2$, what can you say about its graph?

5. (a) Write expressions for the partial derivatives $f_x(a, b)$ and $f_y(a, b)$ as limits.
   (b) How do you interpret $f_x(a, b)$ and $f_y(a, b)$ geometrically? How do you interpret them as rates of change?
   (c) If $f(x, y)$ is given by a formula, how do you calculate f_x and f_y?

6. What does Clairaut's Theorem say?

7. How do you find a tangent plane to each of the following types of surfaces?
   (a) A graph of a function of two variables, $z = f(x, y)$
   (b) A level surface of a function of three variables, $F(x, y, z) = k$

8. Define the linearization of f at (a, b). What is the corresponding linear approximation? What is the geometric interpretation of the linear approximation?

9. (a) What does it mean to say that f is differentiable at (a, b)?
   (b) How do you usually verify that f is differentiable?

10. If $z = f(x, y)$, what are the differentials dx, dy, and dz?

11. State the Chain Rule for the case where $z = f(x, y)$ and x and y are functions of one variable. What if x and y are functions of two variables?

12. If z is defined implicitly as a function of x and y by an equation of the form $F(x, y, z) = 0$, how do you find $\partial z/\partial x$ and $\partial z/\partial y$?

13. (a) Write an expression as a limit for the directional derivative of f at (x_0, y_0) in the direction of a unit vector $\mathbf{u} = \langle a, b \rangle$. How do you interpret it as a rate? How do you interpret it geometrically?
   (b) If f is differentiable, write an expression for $D_\mathbf{u} f(x_0, y_0)$ in terms of f_x and f_y.

14. (a) Define the gradient vector ∇f for a function f of two or three variables.
   (b) Express $D_\mathbf{u} f$ in terms of ∇f.
   (c) Explain the geometric significance of the gradient.

15. What do the following statements mean?
   (a) f has a local maximum at (a, b).
   (b) f has an absolute maximum at (a, b).
   (c) f has a local minimum at (a, b).
   (d) f has an absolute minimum at (a, b).
   (e) f has a saddle point at (a, b).

16. (a) If f has a local maximum at (a, b), what can you say about its partial derivatives at (a, b)?
   (b) What is a critical point of f?

17. State the Second Derivatives Test.

18. (a) What is a closed set in $\mathbb{R}^2$? What is a bounded set?
   (b) State the Extreme Value Theorem for functions of two variables.
   (c) How do you find the values that the Extreme Value Theorem guarantees?

19. Explain how the method of Lagrange multipliers works in finding the extreme values of $f(x, y, z)$ subject to the constraint $g(x, y, z) = k$. What if there is a second constraint $h(x, y, z) = c$?

TRUE-FALSE QUIZ

Determine whether the statement is true or false. If it is true, explain why. If it is false, explain why or give an example that disproves the statement.

1. $f_y(a, b) = \lim\limits_{y \to b} \dfrac{f(a, y) - f(a, b)}{y - b}$

2. There exists a function f with continuous second-order partial derivatives such that $f_x(x, y) = x + y^2$ and $f_y(x, y) = x - y^2$.

3. $f_{xy} = \dfrac{\partial^2 f}{\partial x \, \partial y}$

4. $D_\mathbf{k} f(x, y, z) = f_z(x, y, z)$

5. If $f(x, y) \to L$ as $(x, y) \to (a, b)$ along every straight line through (a, b), then $\lim\limits_{(x,\,y)\to(a,\,b)} f(x, y) = L$.

6. If $f_x(a, b)$ and $f_y(a, b)$ both exist, then f is differentiable at (a, b).

7. If f has a local minimum at (a, b) and f is differentiable at (a, b), then $\nabla f(a, b) = \mathbf{0}$.

8. If f is a function, then
$$\lim_{(x, y) \to (2, 5)} f(x, y) = f(2, 5)$$

9. If $f(x, y) = \ln y$, then $\nabla f(x, y) = 1/y$.

10. If $(2, 1)$ is a critical point of f and
$$f_{xx}(2, 1)f_{yy}(2, 1) < [f_{xy}(2, 1)]^2$$
then f has a saddle point at $(2, 1)$.

11. If $f(x, y) = \sin x + \sin y$, then $-\sqrt{2} \leq D_{\mathbf{u}} f(x, y) \leq \sqrt{2}$.

12. If $f(x, y)$ has two local maxima, then f must have a local minimum.

EXERCISES

1–2 Find and sketch the domain of the function.

1. $f(x, y) = \ln(x + y + 1)$

2. $f(x, y) = \sqrt{4 - x^2 - y^2} + \sqrt{1 - x^2}$

3–4 Sketch the graph of the function.

3. $f(x, y) = 1 - y^2$

4. $f(x, y) = x^2 + (y - 2)^2$

5–6 Sketch several level curves of the function.

5. $f(x, y) = \sqrt{4x^2 + y^2}$

6. $f(x, y) = e^x + y$

7. Make a rough sketch of a contour map for the function whose graph is shown.

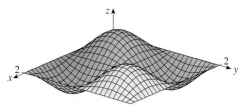

8. A contour map of a function f is shown. Use it to make a rough sketch of the graph of f.

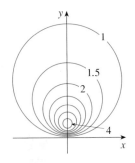

9–10 Evaluate the limit or show that it does not exist.

9. $\displaystyle\lim_{(x, y) \to (1, 1)} \frac{2xy}{x^2 + 2y^2}$

10. $\displaystyle\lim_{(x, y) \to (0, 0)} \frac{2xy}{x^2 + 2y^2}$

11. A metal plate is situated in the xy-plane and occupies the rectangle $0 \leq x \leq 10$, $0 \leq y \leq 8$, where x and y are measured in meters. The temperature at the point (x, y) in the plate is $T(x, y)$, where T is measured in degrees Celsius. Temperatures at equally spaced points were measured and recorded in the table.
(a) Estimate the values of the partial derivatives $T_x(6, 4)$ and $T_y(6, 4)$. What are the units?
(b) Estimate the value of $D_{\mathbf{u}} T(6, 4)$, where $\mathbf{u} = (\mathbf{i} + \mathbf{j})/\sqrt{2}$. Interpret your result.
(c) Estimate the value of $T_{xy}(6, 4)$.

x \ y	0	2	4	6	8
0	30	38	45	51	55
2	52	56	60	62	61
4	78	74	72	68	66
6	98	87	80	75	71
8	96	90	86	80	75
10	92	92	91	87	78

12. Find a linear approximation to the temperature function $T(x, y)$ in Exercise 11 near the point $(6, 4)$. Then use it to estimate the temperature at the point $(5, 3.8)$.

13–17 Find the first partial derivatives.

13. $f(x, y) = \sqrt{2x + y^2}$

14. $u = e^{-r} \sin 2\theta$

15. $g(u, v) = u \tan^{-1} v$

16. $w = \dfrac{x}{y - z}$

17. $T(p, q, r) = p \ln(q + e^r)$

18. The speed of sound traveling through ocean water is a function of temperature, salinity, and pressure. It has been modeled by the function

$$C = 1449.2 + 4.6T - 0.055T^2 + 0.00029T^3$$
$$+ (1.34 - 0.01T)(S - 35) + 0.016D$$

where C is the speed of sound (in meters per second), T is the temperature (in degrees Celsius), S is the salinity (the concentration of salts in parts per thousand, which means the number of grams of dissolved solids per 1000 g of water), and D is the depth below the ocean surface (in meters). Compute $\partial C/\partial T$, $\partial C/\partial S$, and $\partial C/\partial D$ when $T = 10°C$, $S = 35$ parts per thousand, and $D = 100$ m. Explain the physical significance of these partial derivatives.

19–22 Find all second partial derivatives of f.

19. $f(x, y) = 4x^3 - xy^2$

20. $z = xe^{-2y}$

21. $f(x, y, z) = x^k y^l z^m$

22. $v = r\cos(s + 2t)$

23. If $z = xy + xe^{y/x}$, show that $x\dfrac{\partial z}{\partial x} + y\dfrac{\partial z}{\partial y} = xy + z$.

24. If $z = \sin(x + \sin t)$, show that

$$\frac{\partial z}{\partial x}\frac{\partial^2 z}{\partial x\,\partial t} = \frac{\partial z}{\partial t}\frac{\partial^2 z}{\partial x^2}$$

25–29 Find equations of (a) the tangent plane and (b) the normal line to the given surface at the specified point.

25. $z = 3x^2 - y^2 + 2x$, $(1, -2, 1)$

26. $z = e^x\cos y$, $(0, 0, 1)$

27. $x^2 + 2y^2 - 3z^2 = 3$, $(2, -1, 1)$

28. $xy + yz + zx = 3$, $(1, 1, 1)$

29. $\sin(xyz) = x + 2y + 3z$, $(2, -1, 0)$

30. Use a computer to graph the surface $z = x^2 + y^4$ and its tangent plane and normal line at $(1, 1, 2)$ on the same screen. Choose the domain and viewpoint so that you get a good view of all three objects.

31. Find the points on the hyperboloid $x^2 + 4y^2 - z^2 = 4$ where the tangent plane is parallel to the plane $2x + 2y + z = 5$.

32. Find du if $u = \ln(1 + se^{2t})$.

33. Find the linear approximation of the function $f(x, y, z) = x^3\sqrt{y^2 + z^2}$ at the point $(2, 3, 4)$ and use it to estimate the number $(1.98)^3\sqrt{(3.01)^2 + (3.97)^2}$.

34. The two legs of a right triangle are measured as 5 m and 12 m with a possible error in measurement of at most 0.2 cm in each. Use differentials to estimate the maximum error in the calculated value of (a) the area of the triangle and (b) the length of the hypotenuse.

35. If $u = x^2y^3 + z^4$, where $x = p + 3p^2$, $y = pe^p$, and $z = p\sin p$, use the Chain Rule to find du/dp.

36. If $v = x^2\sin y + ye^{xy}$, where $x = s + 2t$ and $y = st$, use the Chain Rule to find $\partial v/\partial s$ and $\partial v/\partial t$ when $s = 0$ and $t = 1$.

37. Suppose $z = f(x, y)$, where $x = g(s, t)$, $y = h(s, t)$, $g(1, 2) = 3$, $g_s(1, 2) = -1$, $g_t(1, 2) = 4$, $h(1, 2) = 6$, $h_s(1, 2) = -5$, $h_t(1, 2) = 10$, $f_x(3, 6) = 7$, and $f_y(3, 6) = 8$. Find $\partial z/\partial s$ and $\partial z/\partial t$ when $s = 1$ and $t = 2$.

38. Use a tree diagram to write out the Chain Rule for the case where $w = f(t, u, v)$, $t = t(p, q, r, s)$, $u = u(p, q, r, s)$, and $v = v(p, q, r, s)$ are all differentiable functions.

39. If $z = y + f(x^2 - y^2)$, where f is differentiable, show that

$$y\frac{\partial z}{\partial x} + x\frac{\partial z}{\partial y} = x$$

40. The length x of a side of a triangle is increasing at a rate of 3 in/s, the length y of another side is decreasing at a rate of 2 in/s, and the contained angle θ is increasing at a rate of 0.05 radian/s. How fast is the area of the triangle changing when $x = 40$ in, $y = 50$ in, and $\theta = \pi/6$?

41. If $z = f(u, v)$, where $u = xy$, $v = y/x$, and f has continuous second partial derivatives, show that

$$x^2\frac{\partial^2 z}{\partial x^2} - y^2\frac{\partial^2 z}{\partial y^2} = -4uv\frac{\partial^2 z}{\partial u\,\partial v} + 2v\frac{\partial z}{\partial v}$$

42. If $yz^4 + x^2z^3 = e^{xyz}$, find $\dfrac{\partial z}{\partial x}$ and $\dfrac{\partial z}{\partial y}$.

43. Find the gradient of the function $f(x, y, z) = z^2e^{x\sqrt{y}}$.

44. (a) When is the directional derivative of f a maximum?
(b) When is it a minimum?
(c) When is it 0?
(d) When is it half of its maximum value?

45–46 Find the directional derivative of f at the given point in the indicated direction.

45. $f(x, y) = 2\sqrt{x} - y^2$, $(1, 5)$, in the direction toward the point $(4, 1)$

46. $f(x, y, z) = x^2y + x\sqrt{1 + z}$, $(1, 2, 3)$, in the direction of $\mathbf{v} = 2\mathbf{i} + \mathbf{j} - 2\mathbf{k}$

47. Find the maximum rate of change of $f(x, y) = x^2y + \sqrt{y}$ at the point $(2, 1)$. In which direction does it occur?

48. Find the direction in which $f(x, y, z) = ze^{xy}$ increases most rapidly at the point $(0, 1, 2)$. What is the maximum rate of increase?

49. The contour map shows wind speed in knots during Hurricane Andrew on August 24, 1992. Use it to estimate the value of the directional derivative of the wind speed at Homestead, Florida, in the direction of the eye of the hurricane.

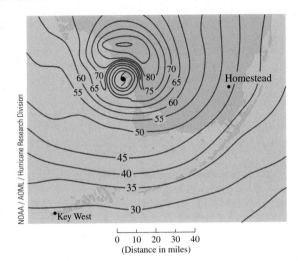

50. Find parametric equations of the tangent line at the point $(-2, 2, 4)$ to the curve of intersection of the surface $z = 2x^2 - y^2$ and the plane $z = 4$.

51–54 Find the local maximum and minimum values and saddle points of the function. If you have three-dimensional graphing software, graph the function with a domain and viewpoint that reveal all the important aspects of the function.

51. $f(x, y) = x^2 - xy + y^2 + 9x - 6y + 10$

52. $f(x, y) = x^3 - 6xy + 8y^3$

53. $f(x, y) = 3xy - x^2y - xy^2$

54. $f(x, y) = (x^2 + y)e^{y/2}$

55–56 Find the absolute maximum and minimum values of f on the set D.

55. $f(x, y) = 4xy^2 - x^2y^2 - xy^3$; D is the closed triangular region in the xy-plane with vertices $(0, 0)$, $(0, 6)$, and $(6, 0)$

56. $f(x, y) = e^{-x^2-y^2}(x^2 + 2y^2)$; D is the disk $x^2 + y^2 \leq 4$

57. Use a graph and/or level curves to estimate the local maximum and minimum values and saddle points of $f(x, y) = x^3 - 3x + y^4 - 2y^2$. Then use calculus to find these values precisely.

58. Use a graphing calculator or computer (or Newton's method or a computer algebra system) to find the critical points of $f(x, y) = 12 + 10y - 2x^2 - 8xy - y^4$ correct to three decimal places. Then classify the critical points and find the highest point on the graph.

59–62 Use Lagrange multipliers to find the maximum and minimum values of f subject to the given constraint(s).

59. $f(x, y) = x^2y$; $x^2 + y^2 = 1$

60. $f(x, y) = \dfrac{1}{x} + \dfrac{1}{y}$; $\dfrac{1}{x^2} + \dfrac{1}{y^2} = 1$

61. $f(x, y, z) = xyz$; $x^2 + y^2 + z^2 = 3$

62. $f(x, y, z) = x^2 + 2y^2 + 3z^2$;
  $x + y + z = 1$, $x - y + 2z = 2$

63. Find the points on the surface $xy^2z^3 = 2$ that are closest to the origin.

64. A package in the shape of a rectangular box can be mailed by the US Postal Service if the sum of its length and girth (the perimeter of a cross-section perpendicular to the length) is at most 108 in. Find the dimensions of the package with largest volume that can be mailed.

65. A pentagon is formed by placing an isosceles triangle on a rectangle, as shown in the figure. If the pentagon has fixed perimeter P, find the lengths of the sides of the pentagon that maximize the area of the pentagon.

66. A particle of mass m moves on the surface $z = f(x, y)$. Let $x = x(t)$ and $y = y(t)$ be the x- and y-coordinates of the particle at time t.
  (a) Find the velocity vector $\mathbf{v}$ and the kinetic energy $K = \frac{1}{2}m |\mathbf{v}|^2$ of the particle.
  (b) Determine the acceleration vector $\mathbf{a}$.
  (c) Let $z = x^2 + y^2$ and $x(t) = t \cos t$, $y(t) = t \sin t$. Find the velocity vector, the kinetic energy, and the acceleration vector.

1. A rectangle with length L and width W is cut into four smaller rectangles by two lines parallel to the sides. Find the maximum and minimum values of the sum of the squares of the areas of the smaller rectangles.

2. Marine biologists have determined that when a shark detects the presence of blood in the water, it will swim in the direction in which the concentration of the blood increases most rapidly. Based on certain tests, the concentration of blood (in parts per million) at a point $P(x, y)$ on the surface of seawater is approximated by

$$C(x, y) = e^{-(x^2 + 2y^2)/10^4}$$

where x and y are measured in meters in a rectangular coordinate system with the blood source at the origin.
(a) Identify the level curves of the concentration function and sketch several members of this family together with a path that a shark will follow to the source.
(b) Suppose a shark is at the point (x_0, y_0) when it first detects the presence of blood in the water. Find an equation of the shark's path by setting up and solving a differential equation.

3. A long piece of galvanized sheet metal with width w is to be bent into a symmetric form with three straight sides to make a rain gutter. A cross-section is shown in the figure.
(a) Determine the dimensions that allow the maximum possible flow; that is, find the dimensions that give the maximum possible cross-sectional area.
(b) Would it be better to bend the metal into a gutter with a semicircular cross-section?

$w - 2x$

4. For what values of the number r is the function

$$f(x, y, z) = \begin{cases} \dfrac{(x + y + z)^r}{x^2 + y^2 + z^2} & \text{if } (x, y, z) \neq 0 \\ 0 & \text{if } (x, y, z) = 0 \end{cases}$$

continuous on $\mathbb{R}^3$?

5. Suppose f is a differentiable function of one variable. Show that all tangent planes to the surface $z = xf(y/x)$ intersect in a common point.

6. (a) Newton's method for approximating a root of an equation $f(x) = 0$ (see Section 4.8) can be adapted to approximating a solution of a system of equations $f(x, y) = 0$ and $g(x, y) = 0$. The surfaces $z = f(x, y)$ and $z = g(x, y)$ intersect in a curve that intersects the

xy-plane at the point (r, s), which is the solution of the system. If an initial approximation (x_1, y_1) is close to this point, then the tangent planes to the surfaces at (x_1, y_1) intersect in a straight line that intersects the xy-plane in a point (x_2, y_2), which should be closer to (r, s). (Compare with Figure 2 in Section 4.8.) Show that

$$x_2 = x_1 - \frac{fg_y - f_y g}{f_x g_y - f_y g_x} \qquad \text{and} \qquad y_2 = y_1 - \frac{f_x g - fg_x}{f_x g_y - f_y g_x}$$

where f, g, and their partial derivatives are evaluated at (x_1, y_1). If we continue this procedure, we obtain successive approximations (x_n, y_n).

(b) It was Thomas Simpson (1710–1761) who formulated Newton's method as we know it today and who extended it to functions of two variables as in part (a). (See the biography of Simpson on page 538.) The example that he gave to illustrate the method was to solve the system of equations

$$x^x + y^y = 1000 \qquad x^y + y^x = 100$$

In other words, he found the points of intersection of the curves in the figure. Use the method of part (a) to find the coordinates of the points of intersection correct to six decimal places.

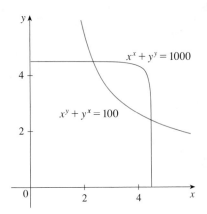

7. If the ellipse $x^2/a^2 + y^2/b^2 = 1$ is to enclose the circle $x^2 + y^2 = 2y$, what values of a and b minimize the area of the ellipse?

8. Among all planes that are tangent to the surface $xy^2 z^2 = 1$, find the ones that are farthest from the origin.

16

MULTIPLE INTEGRALS

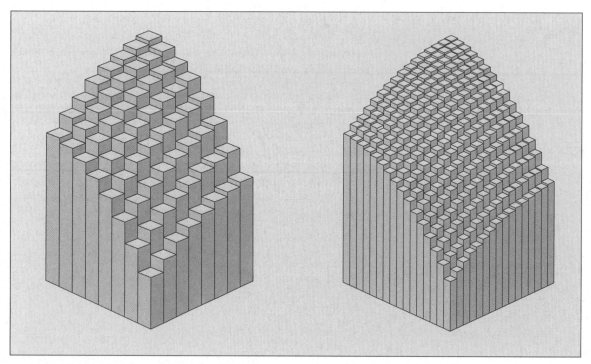

A double integral of a positive function is a volume, which
is the limit of sums of volumes of rectangular columns.

In this chapter we extend the idea of a definite integral to double and triple integrals
of functions of two or three variables. These ideas are then used to compute volumes,
masses, and centroids of more general regions than we were able to consider in
Chapters 6 and 8. We also use double integrals to calculate probabilities when two
random variables are involved.

We will see that polar coordinates are useful in computing double integrals over some
types of regions. In a similar way, we will introduce two new coordinate systems in
three-dimensional space—cylindrical coordinates and spherical coordinates—that
greatly simplify the computation of triple integrals over certain commonly occurring
solid regions.

In much the same way that our attempt to solve the area problem led to the definition of a definite integral, we now seek to find the volume of a solid and in the process we arrive at the definition of a double integral.

REVIEW OF THE DEFINITE INTEGRAL

First let's recall the basic facts concerning definite integrals of functions of a single variable. If $f(x)$ is defined for $a \leqslant x \leqslant b$, we start by dividing the interval $[a, b]$ into n subintervals $[x_{i-1}, x_i]$ of equal width $\Delta x = (b - a)/n$ and we choose sample points x_i^* in these subintervals. Then we form the Riemann sum

$$\boxed{1} \qquad \sum_{i=1}^{n} f(x_i^*) \, \Delta x$$

and take the limit of such sums as $n \to \infty$ to obtain the definite integral of f from a to b:

$$\boxed{2} \qquad \int_a^b f(x) \, dx = \lim_{n \to \infty} \sum_{i=1}^{n} f(x_i^*) \, \Delta x$$

In the special case where $f(x) \geqslant 0$, the Riemann sum can be interpreted as the sum of the areas of the approximating rectangles in Figure 1, and $\int_a^b f(x) \, dx$ represents the area under the curve $y = f(x)$ from a to b.

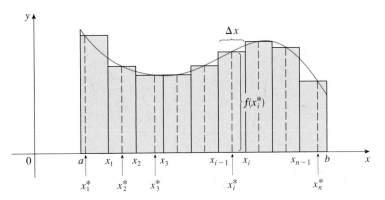

FIGURE 1

VOLUMES AND DOUBLE INTEGRALS

In a similar manner we consider a function f of two variables defined on a closed rectangle

$$R = [a, b] \times [c, d] = \{(x, y) \in \mathbb{R}^2 \mid a \leqslant x \leqslant b, \ c \leqslant y \leqslant d\}$$

and we first suppose that $f(x, y) \geqslant 0$. The graph of f is a surface with equation $z = f(x, y)$. Let S be the solid that lies above R and under the graph of f, that is,

$$S = \{(x, y, z) \in \mathbb{R}^3 \mid 0 \leqslant z \leqslant f(x, y), \ (x, y) \in R\}$$

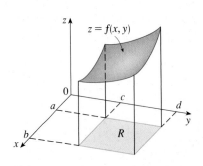

FIGURE 2

(See Figure 2.) Our goal is to find the volume of S.

The first step is to divide the rectangle R into subrectangles. We accomplish this by dividing the interval $[a, b]$ into m subintervals $[x_{i-1}, x_i]$ of equal width $\Delta x = (b - a)/m$ and dividing $[c, d]$ into n subintervals $[y_{j-1}, y_j]$ of equal width $\Delta y = (d - c)/n$. By drawing lines parallel to the coordinate axes through the endpoints of these subintervals, as in Figure 3, we form the subrectangles

$$R_{ij} = [x_{i-1}, x_i] \times [y_{j-1}, y_j] = \{(x, y) \mid x_{i-1} \leqslant x \leqslant x_i, \ y_{j-1} \leqslant y \leqslant y_j\}$$

each with area $\Delta A = \Delta x \, \Delta y$.

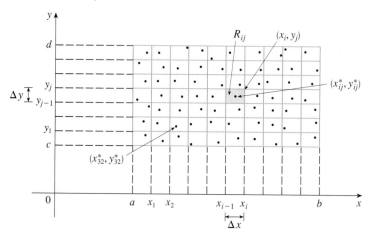

FIGURE 3
Dividing R into subrectangles

If we choose a **sample point** (x_{ij}^*, y_{ij}^*) in each R_{ij}, then we can approximate the part of S that lies above each R_{ij} by a thin rectangular box (or "column") with base R_{ij} and height $f(x_{ij}^*, y_{ij}^*)$ as shown in Figure 4. (Compare with Figure 1.) The volume of this box is the height of the box times the area of the base rectangle:

$$f(x_{ij}^*, y_{ij}^*) \, \Delta A$$

If we follow this procedure for all the rectangles and add the volumes of the corresponding boxes, we get an approximation to the total volume of S:

$$\boxed{3} \qquad\qquad V \approx \sum_{i=1}^{m} \sum_{j=1}^{n} f(x_{ij}^*, y_{ij}^*) \, \Delta A$$

(See Figure 5.) This double sum means that for each subrectangle we evaluate f at the chosen point and multiply by the area of the subrectangle, and then we add the results.

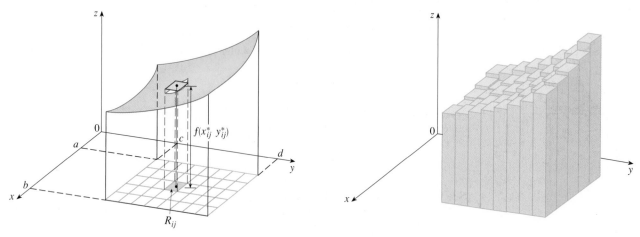

FIGURE 4

FIGURE 5

Our intuition tells us that the approximation given in (3) becomes better as m and n become larger and so we would expect that

> ■ The meaning of the double limit in Equation 4 is that we can make the double sum as close as we like to the number V [for any choice of (x_{ij}^*, y_{ij}^*) in R_{ij}] by taking m and n sufficiently large.

$$\boxed{4} \qquad V = \lim_{m, n \to \infty} \sum_{i=1}^{m} \sum_{j=1}^{n} f(x_{ij}^*, y_{ij}^*) \, \Delta A$$

We use the expression in Equation 4 to define the **volume** of the solid S that lies under the graph of f and above the rectangle R. (It can be shown that this definition is consistent with our formula for volume in Section 6.2.)

Limits of the type that appear in Equation 4 occur frequently, not just in finding volumes but in a variety of other situations as well—as we will see in Section 16.5—even when f is not a positive function. So we make the following definition.

---

5 **DEFINITION** The **double integral** of f over the rectangle R is

> ■ Notice the similarity between Definition 5 and the definition of a single integral in Equation 2.

$$\iint_R f(x, y) \, dA = \lim_{m, n \to \infty} \sum_{i=1}^{m} \sum_{j=1}^{n} f(x_{ij}^*, y_{ij}^*) \, \Delta A$$

if this limit exists.

The precise meaning of the limit in Definition 5 is that for every number $\varepsilon > 0$ there is an integer N such that

> ■ Although we have defined the double integral by dividing R into equal-sized subrectangles, we could have used subrectangles R_{ij} of unequal size. But then we would have to ensure that all of their dimensions approach 0 in the limiting process.

$$\left| \iint_R f(x, y) \, dA - \sum_{i=1}^{m} \sum_{j=1}^{n} f(x_{ij}^*, y_{ij}^*) \, \Delta A \right| < \varepsilon$$

for all integers m and n greater than N and for any choice of sample points (x_{ij}^*, y_{ij}^*) in R_{ij}.

A function f is called **integrable** if the limit in Definition 5 exists. It is shown in courses on advanced calculus that all continuous functions are integrable. In fact, the double integral of f exists provided that f is "not too discontinuous." In particular, if f is bounded [that is, there is a constant M such that $|f(x, y)| \leq M$ for all (x, y) in R], and f is continuous there, except on a finite number of smooth curves, then f is integrable over R.

The sample point (x_{ij}^*, y_{ij}^*) can be chosen to be any point in the subrectangle R_{ij}, but if we choose it to be the upper right-hand corner of R_{ij} [namely (x_i, y_j), see Figure 3], then the expression for the double integral looks simpler:

$$\boxed{6} \qquad \iint_R f(x, y) \, dA = \lim_{m, n \to \infty} \sum_{i=1}^{m} \sum_{j=1}^{n} f(x_i, y_j) \, \Delta A$$

By comparing Definitions 4 and 5, we see that a volume can be written as a double integral:

If $f(x, y) \geq 0$, then the volume V of the solid that lies above the rectangle R and below the surface $z = f(x, y)$ is

$$V = \iint_R f(x, y) \, dA$$

The sum in Definition 5,

$$\sum_{i=1}^{m} \sum_{j=1}^{n} f(x_{ij}^{*}, y_{ij}^{*}) \, \Delta A$$

is called a **double Riemann sum** and is used as an approximation to the value of the double integral. [Notice how similar it is to the Riemann sum in (1) for a function of a single variable.] If f happens to be a *positive* function, then the double Riemann sum represents the sum of volumes of columns, as in Figure 5, and is an approximation to the volume under the graph of f and above the rectangle R.

▼ EXAMPLE 1 Estimate the volume of the solid that lies above the square $R = [0, 2] \times [0, 2]$ and below the elliptic paraboloid $z = 16 - x^2 - 2y^2$. Divide R into four equal squares and choose the sample point to be the upper right corner of each square R_{ij}. Sketch the solid and the approximating rectangular boxes.

SOLUTION The squares are shown in Figure 6. The paraboloid is the graph of $f(x, y) = 16 - x^2 - 2y^2$ and the area of each square is 1. Approximating the volume by the Riemann sum with $m = n = 2$, we have

$$V \approx \sum_{i=1}^{2} \sum_{j=1}^{2} f(x_i, y_j) \, \Delta A$$

$$= f(1, 1) \, \Delta A + f(1, 2) \, \Delta A + f(2, 1) \, \Delta A + f(2, 2) \, \Delta A$$

$$= 13(1) + 7(1) + 10(1) + 4(1) = 34$$

This is the volume of the approximating rectangular boxes shown in Figure 7. ☐

We get better approximations to the volume in Example 1 if we increase the number of squares. Figure 8 shows how the columns start to look more like the actual solid and the corresponding approximations become more accurate when we use 16, 64, and 256 squares. In the next section we will be able to show that the exact volume is 48.

FIGURE 6

FIGURE 7

FIGURE 8
The Riemann sum approximations to the volume under $z = 16 - x^2 - 2y^2$ become more accurate as m and n increase.

(a) $m = n = 4$, $V \approx 41.5$

(b) $m = n = 8$, $V \approx 44.875$

(c) $m = n = 16$, $V \approx 46.46875$

▼ EXAMPLE 2 If $R = \{(x, y) \mid -1 \leq x \leq 1, -2 \leq y \leq 2\}$, evaluate the integral

$$\iint_R \sqrt{1 - x^2} \, dA$$

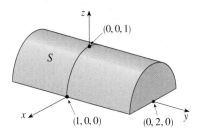

FIGURE 9

SOLUTION It would be very difficult to evaluate this integral directly from Definition 5 but, because $\sqrt{1 - x^2} \geqslant 0$, we can compute the integral by interpreting it as a volume. If $z = \sqrt{1 - x^2}$, then $x^2 + z^2 = 1$ and $z \geqslant 0$, so the given double integral represents the volume of the solid S that lies below the circular cylinder $x^2 + z^2 = 1$ and above the rectangle R. (See Figure 9.) The volume of S is the area of a semicircle with radius 1 times the length of the cylinder. Thus

$$\iint\limits_R \sqrt{1 - x^2}\, dA = \tfrac{1}{2}\pi(1)^2 \times 4 = 2\pi$$ ☐

THE MIDPOINT RULE

The methods that we used for approximating single integrals (the Midpoint Rule, the Trapezoidal Rule, Simpson's Rule) all have counterparts for double integrals. Here we consider only the Midpoint Rule for double integrals. This means that we use a double Riemann sum to approximate the double integral, where the sample point (x_{ij}^*, y_{ij}^*) in R_{ij} is chosen to be the center $(\bar{x}_i, \bar{y}_j)$ of R_{ij}. In other words, $\bar{x}_i$ is the midpoint of $[x_{i-1}, x_i]$ and $\bar{y}_j$ is the midpoint of $[y_{j-1}, y_j]$.

MIDPOINT RULE FOR DOUBLE INTEGRALS

$$\iint\limits_R f(x, y)\, dA \approx \sum_{i=1}^{m} \sum_{j=1}^{n} f(\bar{x}_i, \bar{y}_j)\, \Delta A$$

where $\bar{x}_i$ is the midpoint of $[x_{i-1}, x_i]$ and $\bar{y}_j$ is the midpoint of $[y_{j-1}, y_j]$.

☑ **EXAMPLE 3** Use the Midpoint Rule with $m = n = 2$ to estimate the value of the integral $\iint_R (x - 3y^2)\, dA$, where $R = \{(x, y) \mid 0 \leqslant x \leqslant 2, 1 \leqslant y \leqslant 2\}$.

SOLUTION In using the Midpoint Rule with $m = n = 2$, we evaluate $f(x, y) = x - 3y^2$ at the centers of the four subrectangles shown in Figure 10. So $\bar{x}_1 = \tfrac{1}{2}$, $\bar{x}_2 = \tfrac{3}{2}$, $\bar{y}_1 = \tfrac{5}{4}$, and $\bar{y}_2 = \tfrac{7}{4}$. The area of each subrectangle is $\Delta A = \tfrac{1}{2}$. Thus

$$
\begin{aligned}
\iint\limits_R (x - 3y^2)\, dA &\approx \sum_{i=1}^{2} \sum_{j=1}^{2} f(\bar{x}_i, \bar{y}_j)\, \Delta A \\
&= f(\bar{x}_1, \bar{y}_1)\, \Delta A + f(\bar{x}_1, \bar{y}_2)\, \Delta A + f(\bar{x}_2, \bar{y}_1)\, \Delta A + f(\bar{x}_2, \bar{y}_2)\, \Delta A \\
&= f\!\left(\tfrac{1}{2}, \tfrac{5}{4}\right) \Delta A + f\!\left(\tfrac{1}{2}, \tfrac{7}{4}\right) \Delta A + f\!\left(\tfrac{3}{2}, \tfrac{5}{4}\right) \Delta A + f\!\left(\tfrac{3}{2}, \tfrac{7}{4}\right) \Delta A \\
&= \left(-\tfrac{67}{16}\right)\tfrac{1}{2} + \left(-\tfrac{139}{16}\right)\tfrac{1}{2} + \left(-\tfrac{51}{16}\right)\tfrac{1}{2} + \left(-\tfrac{123}{16}\right)\tfrac{1}{2} \\
&= -\tfrac{95}{8} = -11.875
\end{aligned}
$$

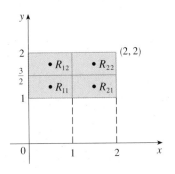

FIGURE 10

Thus we have $$\iint\limits_R (x - 3y^2)\, dA \approx -11.875$$ ☐

NOTE In the next section we will develop an efficient method for computing double integrals and then we will see that the exact value of the double integral in Example 3 is -12. (Remember that the interpretation of a double integral as a volume is valid only when the integrand f is a *positive* function. The integrand in Example 3 is not a positive function, so its integral is not a volume. In Examples 2 and 3 in Section 16.2 we will discuss how to interpret integrals of functions that are not always positive in terms of volumes.) If we keep dividing each subrectangle in Figure 10 into four smaller ones with

Number of subrectangles	Midpoint Rule approximations
1	−11.5000
4	−11.8750
16	−11.9687
64	−11.9922
256	−11.9980
1024	−11.9995

similar shape, we get the Midpoint Rule approximations displayed in the chart in the margin. Notice how these approximations approach the exact value of the double integral, −12.

AVERAGE VALUE

Recall from Section 6.5 that the average value of a function f of one variable defined on an interval $[a, b]$ is

$$f_{\text{ave}} = \frac{1}{b - a} \int_a^b f(x)\, dx$$

In a similar fashion we define the **average value** of a function f of two variables defined on a rectangle R to be

$$f_{\text{ave}} = \frac{1}{A(R)} \iint_R f(x, y)\, dA$$

where $A(R)$ is the area of R.
    If $f(x, y) \geqslant 0$, the equation

$$A(R) \times f_{\text{ave}} = \iint_R f(x, y)\, dA$$

says that the box with base R and height f_{ave} has the same volume as the solid that lies under the graph of f. [If $z = f(x, y)$ describes a mountainous region and you chop off the tops of the mountains at height f_{ave}, then you can use them to fill in the valleys so that the region becomes completely flat. See Figure 11.]

FIGURE 11

EXAMPLE 4 The contour map in Figure 12 shows the snowfall, in inches, that fell on the state of Colorado on December 20 and 21, 2006. (The state is in the shape of a rectangle that measures 388 mi west to east and 276 mi south to north.) Use the contour map to estimate the average snowfall for the entire state of Colorado on those days.

FIGURE 12

SOLUTION Let's place the origin at the southwest corner of the state. Then $0 \leqslant x \leqslant 388$, $0 \leqslant y \leqslant 276$, and $f(x, y)$ is the snowfall, in inches, at a location x miles to the east and y miles to the north of the origin. If R is the rectangle that represents Colorado, then the average snowfall for the state on December 20–21 was

$$f_{\text{ave}} = \frac{1}{A(R)} \iint\limits_{R} f(x, y) \, dA$$

where $A(R) = 388 \cdot 276$. To estimate the value of this double integral, let's use the Midpoint Rule with $m = n = 4$. In other words, we divide R into 16 subrectangles of equal size, as in Figure 13. The area of each subrectangle is

$$\Delta A = \tfrac{1}{16}(388)(276) = 6693 \text{ mi}^2$$

FIGURE 13

Using the contour map to estimate the value of f at the center of each subrectangle, we get

$$\iint\limits_{R} f(x, y) \, dA \approx \sum_{i=1}^{4} \sum_{j=1}^{4} f(\bar{x}_i, \bar{y}_j) \, \Delta A$$

$$\approx \Delta A[0 + 15 + 8 + 7 + 2 + 25 + 18.5 + 11$$
$$+ 4.5 + 28 + 17 + 13.5 + 12 + 15 + 17.5 + 13]$$
$$= (6693)(207)$$

Therefore

$$f_{\text{ave}} \approx \frac{(6693)(207)}{(388)(276)} \approx 12.9$$

On December 20–21, 2006, Colorado received an average of approximately 13 inches of snow. □

PROPERTIES OF DOUBLE INTEGRALS

We list here three properties of double integrals that can be proved in the same manner as in Section 5.2. We assume that all of the integrals exist. Properties 7 and 8 are referred to as the *linearity* of the integral.

■ Double integrals behave this way because the double sums that define them behave this way.

$$\boxed{7} \qquad \iint_R [f(x, y) + g(x, y)]\, dA = \iint_R f(x, y)\, dA + \iint_R g(x, y)\, dA$$

$$\boxed{8} \qquad \iint_R cf(x, y)\, dA = c \iint_R f(x, y)\, dA \qquad \text{where } c \text{ is a constant}$$

If $f(x, y) \geq g(x, y)$ for all (x, y) in R, then

$$\boxed{9} \qquad \iint_R f(x, y)\, dA \geq \iint_R g(x, y)\, dA$$

16.1 EXERCISES

1. (a) Estimate the volume of the solid that lies below the surface $z = xy$ and above the rectangle

$$R = \{(x, y) \mid 0 \leq x \leq 6, 0 \leq y \leq 4\}$$

Use a Riemann sum with $m = 3$, $n = 2$, and take the sample point to be the upper right corner of each square.
(b) Use the Midpoint Rule to estimate the volume of the solid in part (a).

2. If $R = [-1, 3] \times [0, 2]$, use a Riemann sum with $m = 4$, $n = 2$ to estimate the value of $\iint_R (y^2 - 2x^2)\, dA$. Take the sample points to be the upper left corners of the squares.

3. (a) Use a Riemann sum with $m = n = 2$ to estimate the value of $\iint_R \sin(x + y)\, dA$, where $R = [0, \pi] \times [0, \pi]$. Take the sample points to be lower left corners.
(b) Use the Midpoint Rule to estimate the integral in part (a).

4. (a) Estimate the volume of the solid that lies below the surface $z = x + 2y^2$ and above the rectangle $R = [0, 2] \times [0, 4]$.
Use a Riemann sum with $m = n = 2$ and choose the sample points to be lower right corners.
(b) Use the Midpoint Rule to estimate the volume in part (a).

5. A table of values is given for a function $f(x, y)$ defined on $R = [1, 3] \times [0, 4]$.
(a) Estimate $\iint_R f(x, y)\, dA$ using the Midpoint Rule with $m = n = 2$.

(b) Estimate the double integral with $m = n = 4$ by choosing the sample points to be the points farthest from the origin.

y \ x	0	1	2	3	4
1.0	2	0	−3	−6	−5
1.5	3	1	−4	−8	−6
2.0	4	3	0	−5	−8
2.5	5	5	3	−1	−4
3.0	7	8	6	3	0

6. A 20-ft-by-30-ft swimming pool is filled with water. The depth is measured at 5-ft intervals, starting at one corner of the pool, and the values are recorded in the table. Estimate the volume of water in the pool.

	0	5	10	15	20	25	30
0	2	3	4	6	7	8	8
5	2	3	4	7	8	10	8
10	2	4	6	8	10	12	10
15	2	3	4	5	6	8	7
20	2	2	2	2	3	4	4

7. Let V be the volume of the solid that lies under the graph of $f(x, y) = \sqrt{52 - x^2 - y^2}$ and above the rectangle given by $2 \leq x \leq 4$, $2 \leq y \leq 6$. We use the lines $x = 3$ and $y = 4$ to divide R into subrectangles. Let L and U be the Riemann sums computed using lower left corners and upper right corners, respectively. Without calculating the numbers V, L, and U, arrange them in increasing order and explain your reasoning.

8. The figure shows level curves of a function f in the square $R = [0, 2] \times [0, 2]$. Use the Midpoint Rule with $m = n = 2$ to estimate $\iint_R f(x, y)\, dA$. How could you improve your estimate?

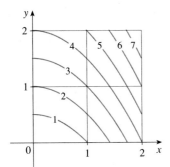

9. A contour map is shown for a function f on the square $R = [0, 4] \times [0, 4]$.
(a) Use the Midpoint Rule with $m = n = 2$ to estimate the value of $\iint_R f(x, y)\, dA$.
(b) Estimate the average value of f.

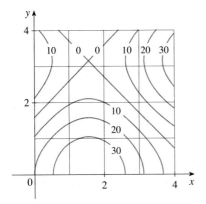

10. The contour map shows the temperature, in degrees Fahrenheit, at 4:00 PM on February 26, 2007, in Colorado. (The state measures 388 mi east to west and 276 mi north to south.) Use the Midpoint Rule with $m = n = 4$ to estimate the average temperature in Colorado at that time.

11–13 Evaluate the double integral by first identifying it as the volume of a solid.

11. $\iint_R 3\, dA$, $R = \{(x, y) \mid -2 \le x \le 2, 1 \le y \le 6\}$

12. $\iint_R (5 - x)\, dA$, $R = \{(x, y) \mid 0 \le x \le 5, 0 \le y \le 3\}$

13. $\iint_R (4 - 2y)\, dA$, $R = [0, 1] \times [0, 1]$

14. The integral $\iint_R \sqrt{9 - y^2}\, dA$, where $R = [0, 4] \times [0, 2]$, represents the volume of a solid. Sketch the solid.

15. Use a programmable calculator or computer (or the sum command on a CAS) to estimate

$$\iint_R \sqrt{1 + xe^{-y}}\, dA$$

where $R = [0, 1] \times [0, 1]$. Use the Midpoint Rule with the following numbers of squares of equal size: 1, 4, 16, 64, 256, and 1024.

16. Repeat Exercise 15 for the integral $\iint_R \sin\left(x + \sqrt{y}\right) dA$.

17. If f is a constant function, $f(x, y) = k$, and $R = [a, b] \times [c, d]$, show that $\iint_R k\, dA = k(b - a)(d - c)$.

18. Use the result of Exercise 17 to show that

$$0 \le \iint_R \sin \pi x \cos \pi y\, dA \le \frac{1}{32}$$

where $R = \left[0, \frac{1}{4}\right] \times \left[\frac{1}{4}, \frac{1}{2}\right]$.

| 16.2 | ITERATED INTEGRALS |

Recall that it is usually difficult to evaluate single integrals directly from the definition of an integral, but the Fundamental Theorem of Calculus provides a much easier method. The evaluation of double integrals from first principles is even more difficult, but in this section we see how to express a double integral as an iterated integral, which can then be evaluated by calculating two single integrals.

Suppose that f is a function of two variables that is integrable on the rectangle $R = [a, b] \times [c, d]$. We use the notation $\int_c^d f(x, y)\, dy$ to mean that x is held fixed and $f(x, y)$ is integrated with respect to y from $y = c$ to $y = d$. This procedure is called *partial integration with respect to y*. (Notice its similarity to partial differentiation.) Now $\int_c^d f(x, y)\, dy$ is a number that depends on the value of x, so it defines a function of x:

$$A(x) = \int_c^d f(x, y)\, dy$$

If we now integrate the function A with respect to x from $x = a$ to $x = b$, we get

$$\boxed{1} \qquad \int_a^b A(x)\, dx = \int_a^b \left[\int_c^d f(x, y)\, dy \right] dx$$

The integral on the right side of Equation 1 is called an **iterated integral**. Usually the brackets are omitted. Thus

$$\boxed{2} \qquad \int_a^b \int_c^d f(x, y)\, dy\, dx = \int_a^b \left[\int_c^d f(x, y)\, dy \right] dx$$

means that we first integrate with respect to y from c to d and then with respect to x from a to b.

Similarly, the iterated integral

$$\boxed{3} \qquad \int_c^d \int_a^b f(x, y)\, dx\, dy = \int_c^d \left[\int_a^b f(x, y)\, dx \right] dy$$

means that we first integrate with respect to x (holding y fixed) from $x = a$ to $x = b$ and then we integrate the resulting function of y with respect to y from $y = c$ to $y = d$. Notice that in both Equations 2 and 3 we work *from the inside out*.

EXAMPLE 1 Evaluate the iterated integrals.

(a) $\int_0^3 \int_1^2 x^2 y\, dy\, dx$
(b) $\int_1^2 \int_0^3 x^2 y\, dx\, dy$

SOLUTION
(a) Regarding x as a constant, we obtain

$$\int_1^2 x^2 y\, dy = \left[x^2 \frac{y^2}{2} \right]_{y=1}^{y=2} = x^2\left(\frac{2^2}{2}\right) - x^2\left(\frac{1^2}{2}\right) = \tfrac{3}{2}x^2$$

Thus the function A in the preceding discussion is given by $A(x) = \frac{3}{2}x^2$ in this example. We now integrate this function of x from 0 to 3:

$$\int_0^3 \int_1^2 x^2 y\, dy\, dx = \int_0^3 \left[\int_1^2 x^2 y\, dy \right] dx$$
$$= \int_0^3 \tfrac{3}{2}x^2\, dx = \frac{x^3}{2}\Big]_0^3 = \frac{27}{2}$$

(b) Here we first integrate with respect to x:

$$\int_1^2 \int_0^3 x^2 y \, dx \, dy = \int_1^2 \left[\int_0^3 x^2 y \, dx \right] dy = \int_1^2 \left[\frac{x^3}{3} y \right]_{x=0}^{x=3} dy$$

$$= \int_1^2 9y \, dy = 9 \frac{y^2}{2} \bigg]_1^2 = \frac{27}{2} \qquad \square$$

Notice that in Example 1 we obtained the same answer whether we integrated with respect to y or x first. In general, it turns out (see Theorem 4) that the two iterated integrals in Equations 2 and 3 are always equal; that is, the order of integration does not matter. (This is similar to Clairaut's Theorem on the equality of the mixed partial derivatives.)

The following theorem gives a practical method for evaluating a double integral by expressing it as an iterated integral (in either order).

■ Theorem 4 is named after the Italian mathematician Guido Fubini (1879–1943), who proved a very general version of this theorem in 1907. But the version for continuous functions was known to the French mathematician Augustin-Louis Cauchy almost a century earlier.

> **4** **FUBINI'S THEOREM** If f is continuous on the rectangle
> $R = \{(x, y) \mid a \leq x \leq b, c \leq y \leq d\}$, then
>
> $$\iint_R f(x, y) \, dA = \int_a^b \int_c^d f(x, y) \, dy \, dx = \int_c^d \int_a^b f(x, y) \, dx \, dy$$
>
> More generally, this is true if we assume that f is bounded on R, f is discontinuous only on a finite number of smooth curves, and the iterated integrals exist.

The proof of Fubini's Theorem is too difficult to include in this book, but we can at least give an intuitive indication of why it is true for the case where $f(x, y) \geq 0$. Recall that if f is positive, then we can interpret the double integral $\iint_R f(x, y) \, dA$ as the volume V of the solid S that lies above R and under the surface $z = f(x, y)$. But we have another formula that we used for volume in Chapter 6, namely,

$$V = \int_a^b A(x) \, dx$$

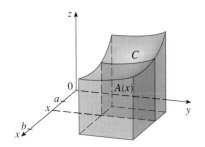

FIGURE 1

TEC Visual 16.2 illustrates Fubini's Theorem by showing an animation of Figures 1 and 2.

where $A(x)$ is the area of a cross-section of S in the plane through x perpendicular to the x-axis. From Figure 1 you can see that $A(x)$ is the area under the curve C whose equation is $z = f(x, y)$, where x is held constant and $c \leq y \leq d$. Therefore

$$A(x) = \int_c^d f(x, y) \, dy$$

and we have

$$\iint_R f(x, y) \, dA = V = \int_a^b A(x) \, dx = \int_a^b \int_c^d f(x, y) \, dy \, dx$$

A similar argument, using cross-sections perpendicular to the y-axis as in Figure 2, shows that

$$\iint_R f(x, y) \, dA = \int_c^d \int_a^b f(x, y) \, dx \, dy$$

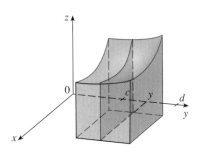

FIGURE 2

■ Notice the negative answer in Example 2; nothing is wrong with that. The function f in that example is not a positive function, so its integral doesn't represent a volume. From Figure 3 we see that f is always negative on R, so the value of the integral is the *negative* of the volume that lies *above* the graph of f and *below* R.

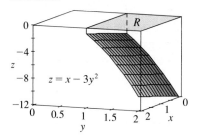

FIGURE 3

✓ EXAMPLE 2 Evaluate the double integral $\iint_R (x - 3y^2)\, dA$, where $R = \{(x, y) \mid 0 \le x \le 2,\, 1 \le y \le 2\}$. (Compare with Example 3 in Section 16.1.)

SOLUTION 1 Fubini's Theorem gives

$$\iint_R (x - 3y^2)\, dA = \int_0^2 \int_1^2 (x - 3y^2)\, dy\, dx = \int_0^2 \left[xy - y^3 \right]_{y=1}^{y=2} dx$$

$$= \int_0^2 (x - 7)\, dx = \frac{x^2}{2} - 7x \Big]_0^2 = -12$$

SOLUTION 2 Again applying Fubini's Theorem, but this time integrating with respect to x first, we have

$$\iint_R (x - 3y^2)\, dA = \int_1^2 \int_0^2 (x - 3y^2)\, dx\, dy$$

$$= \int_1^2 \left[\frac{x^2}{2} - 3xy^2 \right]_{x=0}^{x=2} dy$$

$$= \int_1^2 (2 - 6y^2)\, dy = 2y - 2y^3 \Big]_1^2 = -12 \qquad \square$$

✓ EXAMPLE 3 Evaluate $\iint_R y \sin(xy)\, dA$, where $R = [1, 2] \times [0, \pi]$.

SOLUTION 1 If we first integrate with respect to x, we get

$$\iint_R y \sin(xy)\, dA = \int_0^\pi \int_1^2 y \sin(xy)\, dx\, dy = \int_0^\pi \left[-\cos(xy) \right]_{x=1}^{x=2} dy$$

$$= \int_0^\pi (-\cos 2y + \cos y)\, dy$$

$$= -\tfrac{1}{2} \sin 2y + \sin y \Big]_0^\pi = 0$$

SOLUTION 2 If we reverse the order of integration, we get

$$\iint_R y \sin(xy)\, dA = \int_1^2 \int_0^\pi y \sin(xy)\, dy\, dx$$

■ For a function f that takes on both positive and negative values, $\iint_R f(x, y)\, dA$ is a difference of volumes: $V_1 - V_2$, where V_1 is the volume above R and below the graph of f and V_2 is the volume below R and above the graph. The fact that the integral in Example 3 is 0 means that these two volumes V_1 and V_2 are equal. (See Figure 4.)

To evaluate the inner integral, we use integration by parts with

$$u = y \qquad\qquad dv = \sin(xy)\, dy$$

$$du = dy \qquad\qquad v = -\frac{\cos(xy)}{x}$$

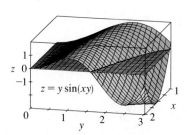

FIGURE 4

and so

$$\int_0^\pi y \sin(xy)\, dy = -\frac{y \cos(xy)}{x} \Big]_{y=0}^{y=\pi} + \frac{1}{x} \int_0^\pi \cos(xy)\, dy$$

$$= -\frac{\pi \cos \pi x}{x} + \frac{1}{x^2} \left[\sin(xy) \right]_{y=0}^{y=\pi}$$

$$= -\frac{\pi \cos \pi x}{x} + \frac{\sin \pi x}{x^2}$$

If we now integrate the first term by parts with $u = -1/x$ and $dv = \pi \cos \pi x \, dx$, we get $du = dx/x^2$, $v = \sin \pi x$, and

$$\int \left(-\frac{\pi \cos \pi x}{x} \right) dx = -\frac{\sin \pi x}{x} - \int \frac{\sin \pi x}{x^2} \, dx$$

Therefore

$$\int \left(-\frac{\pi \cos \pi x}{x} + \frac{\sin \pi x}{x^2} \right) dx = -\frac{\sin \pi x}{x}$$

and so

$$\int_1^2 \int_0^\pi y \sin(xy) \, dy \, dx = \left[-\frac{\sin \pi x}{x} \right]_1^2$$

$$= -\frac{\sin 2\pi}{2} + \sin \pi = 0 \qquad \square$$

■ In Example 2, Solutions 1 and 2 are equally straightforward, but in Example 3 the first solution is much easier than the second one. Therefore, when we evaluate double integrals, it is wise to choose the order of integration that gives simpler integrals.

▼ EXAMPLE 4 Find the volume of the solid S that is bounded by the elliptic paraboloid $x^2 + 2y^2 + z = 16$, the planes $x = 2$ and $y = 2$, and the three coordinate planes.

SOLUTION We first observe that S is the solid that lies under the surface $z = 16 - x^2 - 2y^2$ and above the square $R = [0, 2] \times [0, 2]$. (See Figure 5.) This solid was considered in Example 1 in Section 16.1, but we are now in a position to evaluate the double integral using Fubini's Theorem. Therefore

$$V = \iint\limits_R (16 - x^2 - 2y^2) \, dA = \int_0^2 \int_0^2 (16 - x^2 - 2y^2) \, dx \, dy$$

$$= \int_0^2 \left[16x - \tfrac{1}{3}x^3 - 2y^2 x \right]_{x=0}^{x=2} dy$$

$$= \int_0^2 \left(\tfrac{88}{3} - 4y^2 \right) dy = \left[\tfrac{88}{3} y - \tfrac{4}{3} y^3 \right]_0^2 = 48 \qquad \square$$

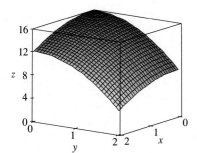

FIGURE 5

In the special case where $f(x, y)$ can be factored as the product of a function of x only and a function of y only, the double integral of f can be written in a particularly simple form. To be specific, suppose that $f(x, y) = g(x)h(y)$ and $R = [a, b] \times [c, d]$. Then Fubini's Theorem gives

$$\iint\limits_R f(x, y) \, dA = \int_c^d \int_a^b g(x)h(y) \, dx \, dy = \int_c^d \left[\int_a^b g(x)h(y) \, dx \right] dy$$

In the inner integral, y is a constant, so $h(y)$ is a constant and we can write

$$\int_c^d \left[\int_a^b g(x)h(y) \, dx \right] dy = \int_c^d \left[h(y) \left(\int_a^b g(x) \, dx \right) \right] dy = \int_a^b g(x) \, dx \int_c^d h(y) \, dy$$

since $\int_a^b g(x) \, dx$ is a constant. Therefore, in this case, the double integral of f can be written as the product of two single integrals:

$$\boxed{5} \qquad \iint\limits_R g(x) h(y) \, dA = \int_a^b g(x) \, dx \int_c^d h(y) \, dy \qquad \text{where } R = [a, b] \times [c, d]$$

EXAMPLE 5 If $R = [0, \pi/2] \times [0, \pi/2]$, then, by Equation 5,

$$\iint\limits_R \sin x \cos y \, dA = \int_0^{\pi/2} \sin x \, dx \int_0^{\pi/2} \cos y \, dy$$

$$= \left[-\cos x\right]_0^{\pi/2} \left[\sin y\right]_0^{\pi/2} = 1 \cdot 1 = 1 \qquad \square$$

■ The function $f(x, y) = \sin x \cos y$ in Example 5 is positive on R, so the integral represents the volume of the solid that lies above R and below the graph of f shown in Figure 6.

FIGURE 6

16.2 EXERCISES

1–2 Find $\int_0^5 f(x, y) \, dx$ and $\int_0^1 f(x, y) \, dy$.

1. $f(x, y) = 12x^2 y^3$

2. $f(x, y) = y + xe^y$

3–14 Calculate the iterated integral.

3. $\int_1^3 \int_0^1 (1 + 4xy) \, dx \, dy$

4. $\int_0^1 \int_1^2 (4x^3 - 9x^2 y^2) \, dy \, dx$

5. $\int_0^2 \int_0^{\pi/2} x \sin y \, dy \, dx$

6. $\int_{\pi/6}^{\pi/2} \int_{-1}^5 \cos y \, dx \, dy$

7. $\int_0^2 \int_0^1 (2x + y)^8 \, dx \, dy$

8. $\int_0^1 \int_1^2 \frac{xe^x}{y} \, dy \, dx$

9. $\int_1^4 \int_1^2 \left(\frac{x}{y} + \frac{y}{x}\right) dy \, dx$

10. $\int_0^1 \int_0^3 e^{x+3y} \, dx \, dy$

11. $\int_0^1 \int_0^1 (u - v)^5 \, du \, dv$

12. $\int_0^1 \int_0^1 xy\sqrt{x^2 + y^2} \, dy \, dx$

13. $\int_0^2 \int_0^{\pi} r \sin^2\theta \, d\theta \, dr$

14. $\int_0^1 \int_0^1 \sqrt{s + t} \, ds \, dt$

15–22 Calculate the double integral.

15. $\iint\limits_R (6x^2 y^3 - 5y^4) \, dA, \quad R = \{(x, y) \mid 0 \le x \le 3, \ 0 \le y \le 1\}$

16. $\iint\limits_R \cos(x + 2y) \, dA, \quad R = \{(x, y) \mid 0 \le x \le \pi, \ 0 \le y \le \pi/2\}$

17. $\iint\limits_R \frac{xy^2}{x^2 + 1} \, dA, \quad R = \{(x, y) \mid 0 \le x \le 1, \ -3 \le y \le 3\}$

18. $\iint\limits_R \frac{1 + x^2}{1 + y^2} \, dA, \quad R = \{(x, y) \mid 0 \le x \le 1, \ 0 \le y \le 1\}$

19. $\iint\limits_R x \sin(x + y) \, dA, \quad R = [0, \pi/6] \times [0, \pi/3]$

20. $\iint\limits_R \frac{x}{1 + xy} \, dA, \quad R = [0, 1] \times [0, 1]$

21. $\iint\limits_R xye^{x^2 y} \, dA, \quad R = [0, 1] \times [0, 2]$

22. $\iint\limits_R \frac{x}{x^2 + y^2} \, dA, \quad R = [1, 2] \times [0, 1]$

23–24 Sketch the solid whose volume is given by the iterated integral.

23. $\int_0^1 \int_0^1 (4 - x - 2y) \, dx \, dy$

24. $\int_0^1 \int_0^1 (2 - x^2 - y^2) \, dy \, dx$

25. Find the volume of the solid that lies under the plane $3x + 2y + z = 12$ and above the rectangle $R = \{(x, y) \mid 0 \le x \le 1, \ -2 \le y \le 3\}$.

26. Find the volume of the solid that lies under the hyperbolic paraboloid $z = 4 + x^2 - y^2$ and above the square $R = [-1, 1] \times [0, 2]$.

27. Find the volume of the solid lying under the elliptic paraboloid $x^2/4 + y^2/9 + z = 1$ and above the rectangle $R = [-1, 1] \times [-2, 2]$.

28. Find the volume of the solid enclosed by the surface $z = 1 + e^x \sin y$ and the planes $x = \pm 1$, $y = 0$, $y = \pi$, and $z = 0$.

29. Find the volume of the solid enclosed by the surface $z = x \sec^2 y$ and the planes $z = 0$, $x = 0$, $x = 2$, $y = 0$, and $y = \pi/4$.

30. Find the volume of the solid in the first octant bounded by the cylinder $z = 16 - x^2$ and the plane $y = 5$.

31. Find the volume of the solid enclosed by the paraboloid $z = 2 + x^2 + (y - 2)^2$ and the planes $z = 1$, $x = 1$, $x = -1$, $y = 0$, and $y = 4$.

32. Graph the solid that lies between the surface $z = 2xy/(x^2 + 1)$ and the plane $z = x + 2y$ and is bounded by the planes $x = 0$, $x = 2$, $y = 0$, and $y = 4$. Then find its volume.

[CAS] **33.** Use a computer algebra system to find the exact value of the integral $\iint_R x^5 y^3 e^{xy} \, dA$, where $R = [0, 1] \times [0, 1]$. Then use the CAS to draw the solid whose volume is given by the integral.

[CAS] **34.** Graph the solid that lies between the surfaces $z = e^{-x^2} \cos(x^2 + y^2)$ and $z = 2 - x^2 - y^2$ for $|x| \leq 1$, $|y| \leq 1$. Use a computer algebra system to approximate the volume of this solid correct to four decimal places.

35–36 Find the average value of f over the given rectangle.

35. $f(x, y) = x^2 y$, R has vertices $(-1, 0)$, $(-1, 5)$, $(1, 5)$, $(1, 0)$

36. $f(x, y) = e^y \sqrt{x + e^y}$, $R = [0, 4] \times [0, 1]$

[CAS] **37.** Use your CAS to compute the iterated integrals

$$\int_0^1 \int_0^1 \frac{x - y}{(x + y)^3} \, dy \, dx \qquad \text{and} \qquad \int_0^1 \int_0^1 \frac{x - y}{(x + y)^3} \, dx \, dy$$

Do the answers contradict Fubini's Theorem? Explain what is happening.

38. (a) In what way are the theorems of Fubini and Clairaut similar?
(b) If $f(x, y)$ is continuous on $[a, b] \times [c, d]$ and

$$g(x, y) = \int_a^x \int_c^y f(s, t) \, dt \, ds$$

for $a < x < b$, $c < y < d$, show that $g_{xy} = g_{yx} = f(x, y)$.

16.3 DOUBLE INTEGRALS OVER GENERAL REGIONS

For single integrals, the region over which we integrate is always an interval. But for double integrals, we want to be able to integrate a function f not just over rectangles but also over regions D of more general shape, such as the one illustrated in Figure 1. We suppose that D is a bounded region, which means that D can be enclosed in a rectangular region R as in Figure 2. Then we define a new function F with domain R by

$$\boxed{1} \qquad F(x, y) = \begin{cases} f(x, y) & \text{if } (x, y) \text{ is in } D \\ 0 & \text{if } (x, y) \text{ is in } R \text{ but not in } D \end{cases}$$

FIGURE 1

FIGURE 2

FIGURE 3

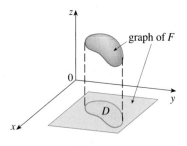

FIGURE 4

If F is integrable over R, then we define the **double integral of f over D** by

$$\boxed{2} \qquad \iint_D f(x, y)\, dA = \iint_R F(x, y)\, dA \qquad \text{where } F \text{ is given by Equation 1}$$

Definition 2 makes sense because R is a rectangle and so $\iint_R F(x, y)\, dA$ has been previously defined in Section 16.1. The procedure that we have used is reasonable because the values of $F(x, y)$ are 0 when (x, y) lies outside D and so they contribute nothing to the integral. This means that it doesn't matter what rectangle R we use as long as it contains D.

In the case where $f(x, y) \geqslant 0$, we can still interpret $\iint_D f(x, y)\, dA$ as the volume of the solid that lies above D and under the surface $z = f(x, y)$ (the graph of f). You can see that this is reasonable by comparing the graphs of f and F in Figures 3 and 4 and remembering that $\iint_R F(x, y)\, dA$ is the volume under the graph of F.

Figure 4 also shows that F is likely to have discontinuities at the boundary points of D. Nonetheless, if f is continuous on D and the boundary curve of D is "well behaved" (in a sense outside the scope of this book), then it can be shown that $\iint_R F(x, y)\, dA$ exists and therefore $\iint_D f(x, y)\, dA$ exists. In particular, this is the case for the following types of regions.

A plane region D is said to be of **type I** if it lies between the graphs of two continuous functions of x, that is,

$$D = \{(x, y) \mid a \leqslant x \leqslant b,\ g_1(x) \leqslant y \leqslant g_2(x)\}$$

where g_1 and g_2 are continuous on $[a, b]$. Some examples of type I regions are shown in Figure 5.

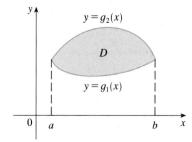

FIGURE 5 Some type I regions

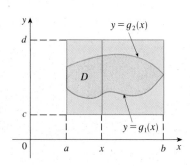

FIGURE 6

In order to evaluate $\iint_D f(x, y)\, dA$ when D is a region of type I, we choose a rectangle $R = [a, b] \times [c, d]$ that contains D, as in Figure 6, and we let F be the function given by Equation 1; that is, F agrees with f on D and F is 0 outside D. Then, by Fubini's Theorem,

$$\iint_D f(x, y)\, dA = \iint_R F(x, y)\, dA = \int_a^b \int_c^d F(x, y)\, dy\, dx$$

Observe that $F(x, y) = 0$ if $y < g_1(x)$ or $y > g_2(x)$ because (x, y) then lies outside D. Therefore

$$\int_c^d F(x, y)\, dy = \int_{g_1(x)}^{g_2(x)} F(x, y)\, dy = \int_{g_1(x)}^{g_2(x)} f(x, y)\, dy$$

because $F(x, y) = f(x, y)$ when $g_1(x) \leqslant y \leqslant g_2(x)$. Thus we have the following formula that enables us to evaluate the double integral as an iterated integral.

---

3 If f is continuous on a type I region D such that

$$D = \{(x, y) \mid a \leqslant x \leqslant b, \ g_1(x) \leqslant y \leqslant g_2(x)\}$$

then

$$\iint_D f(x, y) \, dA = \int_a^b \int_{g_1(x)}^{g_2(x)} f(x, y) \, dy \, dx$$

The integral on the right side of (3) is an iterated integral that is similar to the ones we considered in the preceding section, except that in the inner integral we regard x as being constant not only in $f(x, y)$ but also in the limits of integration, $g_1(x)$ and $g_2(x)$.

We also consider plane regions of **type II**, which can be expressed as

4 $$D = \{(x, y) \mid c \leqslant y \leqslant d, \ h_1(y) \leqslant x \leqslant h_2(y)\}$$

where h_1 and h_2 are continuous. Two such regions are illustrated in Figure 7.

Using the same methods that were used in establishing (3), we can show that

---

5 $$\iint_D f(x, y) \, dA = \int_c^d \int_{h_1(y)}^{h_2(y)} f(x, y) \, dx \, dy$$

where D is a type II region given by Equation 4.

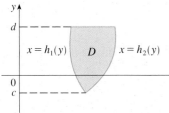

FIGURE 7

Some type II regions

☑ EXAMPLE 1 Evaluate $\iint_D (x + 2y) \, dA$, where D is the region bounded by the parabolas $y = 2x^2$ and $y = 1 + x^2$.

SOLUTION The parabolas intersect when $2x^2 = 1 + x^2$, that is, $x^2 = 1$, so $x = \pm 1$. We note that the region D, sketched in Figure 8, is a type I region but not a type II region and we can write

$$D = \{(x, y) \mid -1 \leqslant x \leqslant 1, \ 2x^2 \leqslant y \leqslant 1 + x^2\}$$

Since the lower boundary is $y = 2x^2$ and the upper boundary is $y = 1 + x^2$, Equation 3 gives

$$\iint_D (x + 2y) \, dA = \int_{-1}^1 \int_{2x^2}^{1+x^2} (x + 2y) \, dy \, dx$$

$$= \int_{-1}^1 \left[xy + y^2 \right]_{y=2x^2}^{y=1+x^2} dx$$

$$= \int_{-1}^1 \left[x(1 + x^2) + (1 + x^2)^2 - x(2x^2) - (2x^2)^2 \right] dx$$

$$= \int_{-1}^1 (-3x^4 - x^3 + 2x^2 + x + 1) \, dx$$

$$= -3\frac{x^5}{5} - \frac{x^4}{4} + 2\frac{x^3}{3} + \frac{x^2}{2} + x \Bigg]_{-1}^1 = \frac{32}{15}$$

FIGURE 8

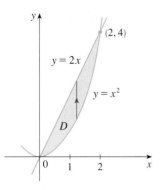

FIGURE 9

D as a type I region

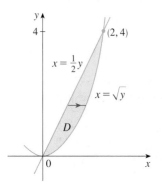

FIGURE 10

D as a type II region

■ Figure 11 shows the solid whose volume is calculated in Example 2. It lies above the xy-plane, below the paraboloid $z = x^2 + y^2$, and between the plane $y = 2x$ and the parabolic cylinder $y = x^2$.

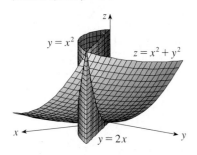

FIGURE 11

NOTE When we set up a double integral as in Example 1, it is essential to draw a diagram. Often it is helpful to draw a vertical arrow as in Figure 8. Then the limits of integration for the *inner* integral can be read from the diagram as follows: The arrow starts at the lower boundary $y = g_1(x)$, which gives the lower limit in the integral, and the arrow ends at the upper boundary $y = g_2(x)$, which gives the upper limit of integration. For a type II region the arrow is drawn horizontally from the left boundary to the right boundary.

EXAMPLE 2 Find the volume of the solid that lies under the paraboloid $z = x^2 + y^2$ and above the region D in the xy-plane bounded by the line $y = 2x$ and the parabola $y = x^2$.

SOLUTION I From Figure 9 we see that D is a type I region and

$$D = \{(x, y) \mid 0 \leq x \leq 2,\ x^2 \leq y \leq 2x\}$$

Therefore the volume under $z = x^2 + y^2$ and above D is

$$V = \iint_D (x^2 + y^2)\, dA = \int_0^2 \int_{x^2}^{2x} (x^2 + y^2)\, dy\, dx$$

$$= \int_0^2 \left[x^2 y + \frac{y^3}{3} \right]_{y=x^2}^{y=2x} dx = \int_0^2 \left[x^2(2x) + \frac{(2x)^3}{3} - x^2 x^2 - \frac{(x^2)^3}{3} \right] dx$$

$$= \int_0^2 \left(-\frac{x^6}{3} - x^4 + \frac{14x^3}{3} \right) dx = -\frac{x^7}{21} - \frac{x^5}{5} + \frac{7x^4}{6} \Bigg]_0^2 = \frac{216}{35}$$

SOLUTION 2 From Figure 10 we see that D can also be written as a type II region:

$$D = \{(x, y) \mid 0 \leq y \leq 4,\ \tfrac{1}{2}y \leq x \leq \sqrt{y}\}$$

Therefore another expression for V is

$$V = \iint_D (x^2 + y^2)\, dA = \int_0^4 \int_{\frac{1}{2}y}^{\sqrt{y}} (x^2 + y^2)\, dx\, dy$$

$$= \int_0^4 \left[\frac{x^3}{3} + y^2 x \right]_{x=\frac{1}{2}y}^{x=\sqrt{y}} dy = \int_0^4 \left(\frac{y^{3/2}}{3} + y^{5/2} - \frac{y^3}{24} - \frac{y^3}{2} \right) dy$$

$$= \tfrac{2}{15} y^{5/2} + \tfrac{2}{7} y^{7/2} - \tfrac{13}{96} y^4 \Big]_0^4 = \tfrac{216}{35} \qquad \square$$

◩ EXAMPLE 3 Evaluate $\iint_D xy\, dA$, where D is the region bounded by the line $y = x - 1$ and the parabola $y^2 = 2x + 6$.

SOLUTION The region D is shown in Figure 12. Again D is both type I and type II, but the description of D as a type I region is more complicated because the lower boundary consists of two parts. Therefore we prefer to express D as a type II region:

$$D = \{(x, y) \mid -2 \leq y \leq 4,\ \tfrac{1}{2}y^2 - 3 \leq x \leq y + 1\}$$

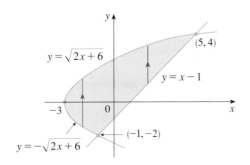

(a) D as a type I region

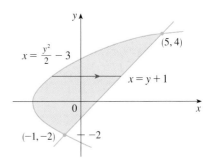

(b) D as a type II region

FIGURE 12

Then (5) gives

$$\iint_D xy \, dA = \int_{-2}^{4} \int_{\frac{1}{2}y^2-3}^{y+1} xy \, dx \, dy = \int_{-2}^{4} \left[\frac{x^2}{2} y \right]_{x=\frac{1}{2}y^2-3}^{x=y+1} dy$$

$$= \frac{1}{2} \int_{-2}^{4} y \left[(y+1)^2 - \left(\tfrac{1}{2}y^2 - 3 \right)^2 \right] dy$$

$$= \frac{1}{2} \int_{-2}^{4} \left(-\frac{y^5}{4} + 4y^3 + 2y^2 - 8y \right) dy$$

$$= \frac{1}{2} \left[-\frac{y^6}{24} + y^4 + 2\frac{y^3}{3} - 4y^2 \right]_{-2}^{4} = 36$$

If we had expressed D as a type I region using Figure 12(a), then we would have obtained

$$\iint_D xy \, dA = \int_{-3}^{-1} \int_{-\sqrt{2x+6}}^{\sqrt{2x+6}} xy \, dy \, dx + \int_{-1}^{5} \int_{x-1}^{\sqrt{2x+6}} xy \, dy \, dx$$

but this would have involved more work than the other method. □

FIGURE 13

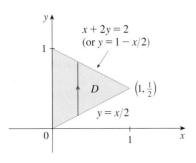

FIGURE 14

EXAMPLE 4 Find the volume of the tetrahedron bounded by the planes $x + 2y + z = 2$, $x = 2y$, $x = 0$, and $z = 0$.

SOLUTION In a question such as this, it's wise to draw two diagrams: one of the three-dimensional solid and another of the plane region D over which it lies. Figure 13 shows the tetrahedron T bounded by the coordinate planes $x = 0$, $z = 0$, the vertical plane $x = 2y$, and the plane $x + 2y + z = 2$. Since the plane $x + 2y + z = 2$ intersects the xy-plane (whose equation is $z = 0$) in the line $x + 2y = 2$, we see that T lies above the triangular region D in the xy-plane bounded by the lines $x = 2y$, $x + 2y = 2$, and $x = 0$. (See Figure 14.)

The plane $x + 2y + z = 2$ can be written as $z = 2 - x - 2y$, so the required volume lies under the graph of the function $z = 2 - x - 2y$ and above

$$D = \left\{ (x, y) \mid 0 \leqslant x \leqslant 1, \ x/2 \leqslant y \leqslant 1 - x/2 \right\}$$

Therefore

$$V = \iint_D (2 - x - 2y)\,dA = \int_0^1 \int_{x/2}^{1-x/2} (2 - x - 2y)\,dy\,dx$$

$$= \int_0^1 \left[2y - xy - y^2 \right]_{y=x/2}^{y=1-x/2} dx$$

$$= \int_0^1 \left[2 - x - x\left(1 - \frac{x}{2}\right) - \left(1 - \frac{x}{2}\right)^2 - x + \frac{x^2}{2} + \frac{x^2}{4} \right] dx$$

$$= \int_0^1 (x^2 - 2x + 1)\,dx = \frac{x^3}{3} - x^2 + x \Big]_0^1 = \frac{1}{3} \qquad \square$$

V EXAMPLE 5 Evaluate the iterated integral $\int_0^1 \int_x^1 \sin(y^2)\,dy\,dx$.

SOLUTION If we try to evaluate the integral as it stands, we are faced with the task of first evaluating $\int \sin(y^2)\,dy$. But it's impossible to do so in finite terms since $\int \sin(y^2)\,dy$ is not an elementary function. (See the end of Section 8.5.) So we must change the order of integration. This is accomplished by first expressing the given iterated integral as a double integral. Using (3) backward, we have

$$\int_0^1 \int_x^1 \sin(y^2)\,dy\,dx = \iint_D \sin(y^2)\,dA$$

where

$$D = \{(x, y) \mid 0 \le x \le 1,\ x \le y \le 1\}$$

We sketch this region D in Figure 15. Then from Figure 16 we see that an alternative description of D is

$$D = \{(x, y) \mid 0 \le y \le 1,\ 0 \le x \le y\}$$

This enables us to use (5) to express the double integral as an iterated integral in the reverse order:

$$\int_0^1 \int_x^1 \sin(y^2)\,dy\,dx = \iint_D \sin(y^2)\,dA$$

$$= \int_0^1 \int_0^y \sin(y^2)\,dx\,dy = \int_0^1 \left[x \sin(y^2) \right]_{x=0}^{x=y} dy$$

$$= \int_0^1 y \sin(y^2)\,dy = -\tfrac{1}{2}\cos(y^2) \Big]_0^1$$

$$= \tfrac{1}{2}(1 - \cos 1) \qquad \square$$

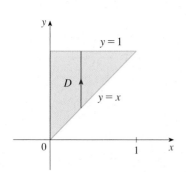

FIGURE 15
D as a type I region

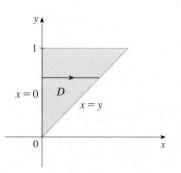

FIGURE 16
D as a type II region

PROPERTIES OF DOUBLE INTEGRALS

We assume that all of the following integrals exist. The first three properties of double integrals over a region D follow immediately from Definition 2 and Properties 7, 8, and 9 in Section 16.1.

[6]
$$\iint_D [f(x, y) + g(x, y)]\,dA = \iint_D f(x, y)\,dA + \iint_D g(x, y)\,dA$$

[7]
$$\iint_D c f(x, y)\,dA = c \iint_D f(x, y)\,dA$$

If $f(x, y) \geq g(x, y)$ for all (x, y) in D, then

$$\boxed{8} \qquad \iint\limits_{D} f(x, y)\, dA \geq \iint\limits_{D} g(x, y)\, dA$$

The next property of double integrals is similar to the property of single integrals given by the equation $\int_a^b f(x)\, dx = \int_a^c f(x)\, dx + \int_c^b f(x)\, dx$.

If $D = D_1 \cup D_2$, where D_1 and D_2 don't overlap except perhaps on their boundaries (see Figure 17), then

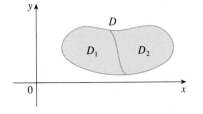

$$\boxed{9} \qquad \boxed{\iint\limits_{D} f(x, y)\, dA = \iint\limits_{D_1} f(x, y)\, dA + \iint\limits_{D_2} f(x, y)\, dA}$$

FIGURE 17

Property 9 can be used to evaluate double integrals over regions D that are neither type I nor type II but can be expressed as a union of regions of type I or type II. Figure 18 illustrates this procedure. (See Exercises 51 and 52.)

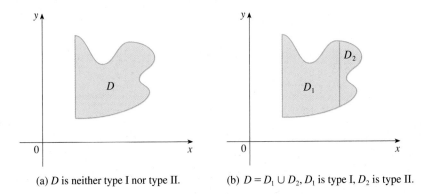

FIGURE 18

(a) D is neither type I nor type II.

(b) $D = D_1 \cup D_2$, D_1 is type I, D_2 is type II.

The next property of integrals says that if we integrate the constant function $f(x, y) = 1$ over a region D, we get the area of D:

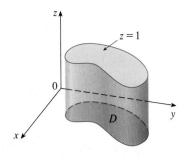

$$\boxed{10} \qquad \boxed{\iint\limits_{D} 1\, dA = A(D)}$$

Figure 19 illustrates why Equation 10 is true: A solid cylinder whose base is D and whose height is 1 has volume $A(D) \cdot 1 = A(D)$, but we know that we can also write its volume as $\iint_D 1\, dA$.

Finally, we can combine Properties 7, 8, and 10 to prove the following property. (See Exercise 57.)

FIGURE 19
Cylinder with base D and height 1

$\boxed{11}$ If $m \leq f(x, y) \leq M$ for all (x, y) in D, then

$$mA(D) \leq \iint\limits_{D} f(x, y)\, dA \leq MA(D)$$

EXAMPLE 6 Use Property 11 to estimate the integral $\iint_D e^{\sin x \cos y} \, dA$, where D is the disk with center the origin and radius 2.

SOLUTION Since $-1 \leqslant \sin x \leqslant 1$ and $-1 \leqslant \cos y \leqslant 1$, we have $-1 \leqslant \sin x \cos y \leqslant 1$ and therefore

$$e^{-1} \leqslant e^{\sin x \cos y} \leqslant e^1 = e$$

Thus, using $m = e^{-1} = 1/e$, $M = e$, and $A(D) = \pi(2)^2$ in Property 11, we obtain

$$\frac{4\pi}{e} \leqslant \iint_D e^{\sin x \cos y} \, dA \leqslant 4\pi e \qquad \square$$

16.3 EXERCISES

1–6 Evaluate the iterated integral.

1. $\int_0^4 \int_0^{\sqrt{y}} xy^2 \, dx \, dy$

2. $\int_0^1 \int_{2x}^2 (x - y) \, dy \, dx$

3. $\int_0^1 \int_{x^2}^x (1 + 2y) \, dy \, dx$

4. $\int_0^2 \int_y^{2y} xy \, dx \, dy$

5. $\int_0^{\pi/2} \int_0^{\cos \theta} e^{\sin \theta} \, dr \, d\theta$

6. $\int_0^1 \int_0^v \sqrt{1 - v^2} \, du \, dv$

7–18 Evaluate the double integral.

7. $\iint_D y^2 \, dA$, $D = \{(x, y) \mid -1 \leqslant y \leqslant 1, -y - 2 \leqslant x \leqslant y\}$

8. $\iint_D \dfrac{y}{x^5 + 1} \, dA$, $D = \{(x, y) \mid 0 \leqslant x \leqslant 1, 0 \leqslant y \leqslant x^2\}$

9. $\iint_D x \, dA$, $D = \{(x, y) \mid 0 \leqslant x \leqslant \pi, 0 \leqslant y \leqslant \sin x\}$

10. $\iint_D x^3 \, dA$, $D = \{(x, y) \mid 1 \leqslant x \leqslant e, 0 \leqslant y \leqslant \ln x\}$

11. $\iint_D y^2 e^{xy} \, dA$, $D = \{(x, y) \mid 0 \leqslant y \leqslant 4, 0 \leqslant x \leqslant y\}$

12. $\iint_D x\sqrt{y^2 - x^2} \, dA$, $D = \{(x, y) \mid 0 \leqslant y \leqslant 1, 0 \leqslant x \leqslant y\}$

13. $\iint_D x \cos y \, dA$, D is bounded by $y = 0$, $y = x^2$, $x = 1$

14. $\iint_D (x + y) \, dA$, D is bounded by $y = \sqrt{x}$ and $y = x^2$

15. $\iint_D y^3 \, dA$,

D is the triangular region with vertices $(0, 2)$, $(1, 1)$, $(3, 2)$

16. $\iint_D xy^2 \, dA$, D is enclosed by $x = 0$ and $x = \sqrt{1 - y^2}$

17. $\iint_D (2x - y) \, dA$,

D is bounded by the circle with center the origin and radius 2

18. $\iint_D 2xy \, dA$, D is the triangular region with vertices $(0, 0)$, $(1, 2)$, and $(0, 3)$

19–28 Find the volume of the given solid.

19. Under the plane $x + 2y - z = 0$ and above the region bounded by $y = x$ and $y = x^4$

20. Under the surface $z = 2x + y^2$ and above the region bounded by $x = y^2$ and $x = y^3$

21. Under the surface $z = xy$ and above the triangle with vertices $(1, 1)$, $(4, 1)$, and $(1, 2)$

22. Enclosed by the paraboloid $z = x^2 + 3y^2$ and the planes $x = 0$, $y = 1$, $y = x$, $z = 0$

23. Bounded by the coordinate planes and the plane $3x + 2y + z = 6$

24. Bounded by the planes $z = x$, $y = x$, $x + y = 2$, and $z = 0$

25. Enclosed by the cylinders $z = x^2$, $y = x^2$ and the planes $z = 0$, $y = 4$

26. Bounded by the cylinder $y^2 + z^2 = 4$ and the planes $x = 2y$, $x = 0$, $z = 0$ in the first octant

27. Bounded by the cylinder $x^2 + y^2 = 1$ and the planes $y = z$, $x = 0$, $z = 0$ in the first octant

28. Bounded by the cylinders $x^2 + y^2 = r^2$ and $y^2 + z^2 = r^2$

29. Use a graphing calculator or computer to estimate the x-coordinates of the points of intersection of the curves $y = x^4$ and $y = 3x - x^2$. If D is the region bounded by these curves, estimate $\iint_D x \, dA$.

30. Find the approximate volume of the solid in the first octant that is bounded by the planes $y = x$, $z = 0$, and $z = x$ and the cylinder $y = \cos x$. (Use a graphing device to estimate the points of intersection.)

31–32 Find the volume of the solid by subtracting two volumes.

31. The solid enclosed by the parabolic cylinders $y = 1 - x^2$, $y = x^2 - 1$ and the planes $x + y + z = 2$, $2x + 2y - z + 10 = 0$

32. The solid enclosed by the parabolic cylinder $y = x^2$ and the planes $z = 3y$, $z = 2 + y$

33–34 Sketch the solid whose volume is given by the iterated integral.

33. $\int_0^1 \int_0^{1-x} (1 - x - y) \, dy \, dx$ **34.** $\int_0^1 \int_0^{1-x^2} (1 - x) \, dy \, dx$

[CAS] **35–38** Use a computer algebra system to find the exact volume of the solid.

35. Under the surface $z = x^3 y^4 + x y^2$ and above the region bounded by the curves $y = x^3 - x$ and $y = x^2 + x$ for $x \geq 0$

36. Between the paraboloids $z = 2x^2 + y^2$ and $z = 8 - x^2 - 2y^2$ and inside the cylinder $x^2 + y^2 = 1$

37. Enclosed by $z = 1 - x^2 - y^2$ and $z = 0$

38. Enclosed by $z = x^2 + y^2$ and $z = 2y$

39–44 Sketch the region of integration and change the order of integration.

39. $\int_0^4 \int_0^{\sqrt{x}} f(x, y) \, dy \, dx$ **40.** $\int_0^1 \int_{4x}^4 f(x, y) \, dy \, dx$

41. $\int_0^3 \int_{-\sqrt{9-y^2}}^{\sqrt{9-y^2}} f(x, y) \, dx \, dy$ **42.** $\int_0^3 \int_0^{\sqrt{9-y}} f(x, y) \, dx \, dy$

[43.] $\int_1^2 \int_0^{\ln x} f(x, y) \, dy \, dx$ **44.** $\int_0^1 \int_{\arctan x}^{\pi/4} f(x, y) \, dy \, dx$

45–50 Evaluate the integral by reversing the order of integration.

[45.] $\int_0^1 \int_{3y}^3 e^{x^2} \, dx \, dy$ **46.** $\int_0^{\sqrt{\pi}} \int_y^{\sqrt{\pi}} \cos(x^2) \, dx \, dy$

47. $\int_0^4 \int_{\sqrt{x}}^2 \dfrac{1}{y^3 + 1} \, dy \, dx$ **48.** $\int_0^1 \int_x^1 e^{x/y} \, dy \, dx$

49. $\int_0^1 \int_{\arcsin y}^{\pi/2} \cos x \sqrt{1 + \cos^2 x} \, dx \, dy$

50. $\int_0^8 \int_{\sqrt[3]{y}}^2 e^{x^4} \, dx \, dy$

51–52 Express D as a union of regions of type I or type II and evaluate the integral.

[51.] $\displaystyle\iint_D x^2 \, dA$ **52.** $\displaystyle\iint_D y \, dA$

 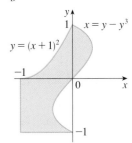

53–54 Use Property 11 to estimate the value of the integral.

53. $\displaystyle\iint_Q e^{-(x^2+y^2)^2} \, dA$, Q is the quarter-circle with center the origin and radius $\frac{1}{2}$ in the first quadrant

54. $\displaystyle\iint_T \sin^4(x + y) \, dA$, T is the triangle enclosed by the lines $y = 0$, $y = 2x$, and $x = 1$

55–56 Find the average value of f over region D.

55. $f(x, y) = xy$, D is the triangle with vertices $(0, 0)$, $(1, 0)$, and $(1, 3)$

56. $f(x, y) = x \sin y$, D is enclosed by the curves $y = 0$, $y = x^2$, and $x = 1$

---

57. Prove Property 11.

[58.] In evaluating a double integral over a region D, a sum of iterated integrals was obtained as follows:

$$\iint_D f(x, y) \, dA = \int_0^1 \int_0^{2y} f(x, y) \, dx \, dy + \int_1^3 \int_0^{3-y} f(x, y) \, dx \, dy$$

Sketch the region D and express the double integral as an iterated integral with reversed order of integration.

59. Evaluate $\iint_D (x^2 \tan x + y^3 + 4) \, dA$, where $D = \{(x, y) \mid x^2 + y^2 \leq 2\}$. [*Hint:* Exploit the fact that D is symmetric with respect to both axes.]

60. Use symmetry to evaluate $\iint_D (2 - 3x + 4y) \, dA$, where D is the region bounded by the square with vertices $(\pm 5, 0)$ and $(0, \pm 5)$.

61. Compute $\iint_D \sqrt{1 - x^2 - y^2} \, dA$, where D is the disk $x^2 + y^2 \leq 1$, by first identifying the integral as the volume of a solid.

[CAS] **62.** Graph the solid bounded by the plane $x + y + z = 1$ and the paraboloid $z = 4 - x^2 - y^2$ and find its exact volume. (Use your CAS to do the graphing, to find the equations of the boundary curves of the region of integration, and to evaluate the double integral.)

16.4 DOUBLE INTEGRALS IN POLAR COORDINATES

Suppose that we want to evaluate a double integral $\iint_R f(x, y)\, dA$, where R is one of the regions shown in Figure 1. In either case the description of R in terms of rectangular coordinates is rather complicated but R is easily described using polar coordinates.

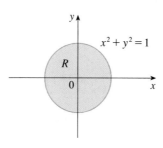

FIGURE 1

(a) $R = \{(r, \theta) \mid 0 \leq r \leq 1, 0 \leq \theta \leq 2\pi\}$

(b) $R = \{(r, \theta) \mid 1 \leq r \leq 2, 0 \leq \theta \leq \pi\}$

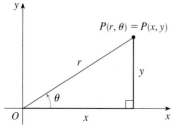

FIGURE 2

Recall from Figure 2 that the polar coordinates (r, θ) of a point are related to the rectangular coordinates (x, y) by the equations

$$r^2 = x^2 + y^2 \qquad x = r\cos\theta \qquad y = r\sin\theta$$

(See Section 11.3.)

The regions in Figure 1 are special cases of a **polar rectangle**

$$R = \{(r, \theta) \mid a \leq r \leq b, \alpha \leq \theta \leq \beta\}$$

which is shown in Figure 3. In order to compute the double integral $\iint_R f(x, y)\, dA$, where R is a polar rectangle, we divide the interval $[a, b]$ into m subintervals $[r_{i-1}, r_i]$ of equal width $\Delta r = (b - a)/m$ and we divide the interval $[\alpha, \beta]$ into n subintervals $[\theta_{j-1}, \theta_j]$ of equal width $\Delta\theta = (\beta - \alpha)/n$. Then the circles $r = r_i$ and the rays $\theta = \theta_j$ divide the polar rectangle R into the small polar rectangles shown in Figure 4.

FIGURE 3 Polar rectangle

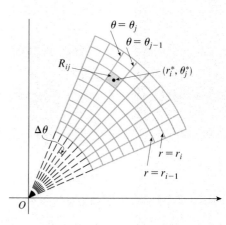

FIGURE 4 Dividing R into polar subrectangles

The "center" of the polar subrectangle

$$R_{ij} = \{(r, \theta) \mid r_{i-1} \leqslant r \leqslant r_i, \theta_{j-1} \leqslant \theta \leqslant \theta_j\}$$

has polar coordinates

$$r_i^* = \tfrac{1}{2}(r_{i-1} + r_i) \qquad \theta_j^* = \tfrac{1}{2}(\theta_{j-1} + \theta_j)$$

We compute the area of R_{ij} using the fact that the area of a sector of a circle with radius r and central angle θ is $\frac{1}{2}r^2\theta$. Subtracting the areas of two such sectors, each of which has central angle $\Delta\theta = \theta_j - \theta_{j-1}$, we find that the area of R_{ij} is

$$\Delta A_i = \tfrac{1}{2}r_i^2 \Delta\theta - \tfrac{1}{2}r_{i-1}^2 \Delta\theta = \tfrac{1}{2}(r_i^2 - r_{i-1}^2) \Delta\theta$$

$$= \tfrac{1}{2}(r_i + r_{i-1})(r_i - r_{i-1}) \Delta\theta = r_i^* \Delta r \Delta\theta$$

Although we have defined the double integral $\iint_R f(x, y) \, dA$ in terms of ordinary rectangles, it can be shown that, for continuous functions f, we always obtain the same answer using polar rectangles. The rectangular coordinates of the center of R_{ij} are $(r_i^* \cos \theta_j^*, r_i^* \sin \theta_j^*)$, so a typical Riemann sum is

$$\boxed{1} \quad \sum_{i=1}^{m} \sum_{j=1}^{n} f(r_i^* \cos \theta_j^*, r_i^* \sin \theta_j^*) \Delta A_i = \sum_{i=1}^{m} \sum_{j=1}^{n} f(r_i^* \cos \theta_j^*, r_i^* \sin \theta_j^*) r_i^* \Delta r \Delta\theta$$

If we write $g(r, \theta) = rf(r \cos \theta, r \sin \theta)$, then the Riemann sum in Equation 1 can be written as

$$\sum_{i=1}^{m} \sum_{j=1}^{n} g(r_i^*, \theta_j^*) \Delta r \Delta\theta$$

which is a Riemann sum for the double integral

$$\int_{\alpha}^{\beta} \int_{a}^{b} g(r, \theta) \, dr \, d\theta$$

Therefore we have

$$\iint_R f(x, y) \, dA = \lim_{m, n \to \infty} \sum_{i=1}^{m} \sum_{j=1}^{n} f(r_i^* \cos \theta_j^*, r_i^* \sin \theta_j^*) \Delta A_i$$

$$= \lim_{m, n \to \infty} \sum_{i=1}^{m} \sum_{j=1}^{n} g(r_i^*, \theta_j^*) \Delta r \Delta\theta = \int_{\alpha}^{\beta} \int_{a}^{b} g(r, \theta) \, dr \, d\theta$$

$$= \int_{\alpha}^{\beta} \int_{a}^{b} f(r \cos \theta, r \sin \theta) \, r \, dr \, d\theta$$

---

2 CHANGE TO POLAR COORDINATES IN A DOUBLE INTEGRAL If f is continuous on a polar rectangle R given by $0 \leqslant a \leqslant r \leqslant b$, $\alpha \leqslant \theta \leqslant \beta$, where $0 \leqslant \beta - \alpha \leqslant 2\pi$, then

$$\iint_R f(x, y) \, dA = \int_{\alpha}^{\beta} \int_{a}^{b} f(r \cos \theta, r \sin \theta) \, r \, dr \, d\theta$$

The formula in (2) says that we convert from rectangular to polar coordinates in a double integral by writing $x = r\cos\theta$ and $y = r\sin\theta$, using the appropriate limits of integration for r and θ, and replacing dA by $r\,dr\,d\theta$. Be careful not to forget the additional factor r on the right side of Formula 2. A classical method for remembering this is shown in Figure 5, where the "infinitesimal" polar rectangle can be thought of as an ordinary rectangle with dimensions $r\,d\theta$ and dr and therefore has "area" $dA = r\,dr\,d\theta$.

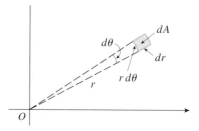

FIGURE 5

EXAMPLE I Evaluate $\iint_R (3x + 4y^2)\,dA$, where R is the region in the upper half-plane bounded by the circles $x^2 + y^2 = 1$ and $x^2 + y^2 = 4$.

SOLUTION The region R can be described as

$$R = \{(x, y) \mid y \geq 0,\ 1 \leq x^2 + y^2 \leq 4\}$$

It is the half-ring shown in Figure 1(b), and in polar coordinates it is given by $1 \leq r \leq 2$, $0 \leq \theta \leq \pi$. Therefore, by Formula 2,

$$\iint_R (3x + 4y^2)\,dA = \int_0^\pi \int_1^2 (3r\cos\theta + 4r^2\sin^2\theta)\,r\,dr\,d\theta$$

$$= \int_0^\pi \int_1^2 (3r^2\cos\theta + 4r^3\sin^2\theta)\,dr\,d\theta$$

$$= \int_0^\pi \left[r^3\cos\theta + r^4\sin^2\theta\right]_{r=1}^{r=2}\,d\theta = \int_0^\pi (7\cos\theta + 15\sin^2\theta)\,d\theta$$

$$= \int_0^\pi \left[7\cos\theta + \tfrac{15}{2}(1 - \cos 2\theta)\right]\,d\theta$$

$$= 7\sin\theta + \frac{15\theta}{2} - \frac{15}{4}\sin 2\theta\Big]_0^\pi = \frac{15\pi}{2} \qquad \square$$

■ Here we use the trigonometric identity

$$\sin^2\theta = \tfrac{1}{2}(1 - \cos 2\theta)$$

See Section 8.2 for advice on integrating trigonometric functions.

✔ EXAMPLE 2 Find the volume of the solid bounded by the plane $z = 0$ and the paraboloid $z = 1 - x^2 - y^2$.

SOLUTION If we put $z = 0$ in the equation of the paraboloid, we get $x^2 + y^2 = 1$. This means that the plane intersects the paraboloid in the circle $x^2 + y^2 = 1$, so the solid lies under the paraboloid and above the circular disk D given by $x^2 + y^2 \leq 1$ [see Figures 6 and 1(a)]. In polar coordinates D is given by $0 \leq r \leq 1$, $0 \leq \theta \leq 2\pi$. Since $1 - x^2 - y^2 = 1 - r^2$, the volume is

$$V = \iint_D (1 - x^2 - y^2)\,dA = \int_0^{2\pi} \int_0^1 (1 - r^2)\,r\,dr\,d\theta$$

$$= \int_0^{2\pi} d\theta \int_0^1 (r - r^3)\,dr = 2\pi \left[\frac{r^2}{2} - \frac{r^4}{4}\right]_0^1 = \frac{\pi}{2}$$

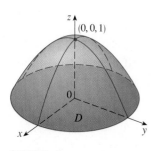

FIGURE 6

If we had used rectangular coordinates instead of polar coordinates, then we would have obtained

$$V = \iint_D (1 - x^2 - y^2) \, dA = \int_{-1}^{1} \int_{-\sqrt{1-x^2}}^{\sqrt{1-x^2}} (1 - x^2 - y^2) \, dy \, dx$$

which is not easy to evaluate because it involves finding $\int (1 - x^2)^{3/2} \, dx$. ☐

What we have done so far can be extended to the more complicated type of region shown in Figure 7. It's similar to the type II rectangular regions considered in Section 16.3. In fact, by combining Formula 2 in this section with Formula 16.3.5, we obtain the following formula.

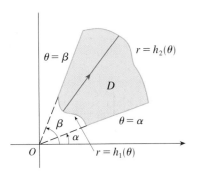

FIGURE 7
$D = \{(r, \theta) \mid \alpha \leqslant \theta \leqslant \beta, h_1(\theta) \leqslant r \leqslant h_2(\theta)\}$

3   If f is continuous on a polar region of the form

$$D = \{(r, \theta) \mid \alpha \leqslant \theta \leqslant \beta, \ h_1(\theta) \leqslant r \leqslant h_2(\theta)\}$$

then

$$\iint_D f(x, y) \, dA = \int_{\alpha}^{\beta} \int_{h_1(\theta)}^{h_2(\theta)} f(r \cos \theta, r \sin \theta) \, r \, dr \, d\theta$$

In particular, taking $f(x, y) = 1$, $h_1(\theta) = 0$, and $h_2(\theta) = h(\theta)$ in this formula, we see that the area of the region D bounded by $\theta = \alpha$, $\theta = \beta$, and $r = h(\theta)$ is

$$A(D) = \iint_D 1 \, dA = \int_{\alpha}^{\beta} \int_{0}^{h(\theta)} r \, dr \, d\theta$$

$$= \int_{\alpha}^{\beta} \left[\frac{r^2}{2} \right]_{0}^{h(\theta)} d\theta = \int_{\alpha}^{\beta} \tfrac{1}{2} [h(\theta)]^2 \, d\theta$$

and this agrees with Formula 11.4.3.

▼ **EXAMPLE 3** Use a double integral to find the area enclosed by one loop of the four-leaved rose $r = \cos 2\theta$.

SOLUTION From the sketch of the curve in Figure 8, we see that a loop is given by the region

$$D = \{(r, \theta) \mid -\pi/4 \leqslant \theta \leqslant \pi/4, \ 0 \leqslant r \leqslant \cos 2\theta\}$$

So the area is

$$A(D) = \iint_D dA = \int_{-\pi/4}^{\pi/4} \int_{0}^{\cos 2\theta} r \, dr \, d\theta$$

$$= \int_{-\pi/4}^{\pi/4} \left[\tfrac{1}{2} r^2 \right]_{0}^{\cos 2\theta} d\theta = \tfrac{1}{2} \int_{-\pi/4}^{\pi/4} \cos^2 2\theta \, d\theta$$

$$= \tfrac{1}{4} \int_{-\pi/4}^{\pi/4} (1 + \cos 4\theta) \, d\theta = \tfrac{1}{4} \left[\theta + \tfrac{1}{4} \sin 4\theta \right]_{-\pi/4}^{\pi/4} = \frac{\pi}{8}$$ ☐

FIGURE 8

FIGURE 9

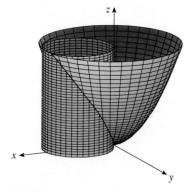

FIGURE 10

☑ EXAMPLE 4 Find the volume of the solid that lies under the paraboloid $z = x^2 + y^2$, above the xy-plane, and inside the cylinder $x^2 + y^2 = 2x$.

SOLUTION The solid lies above the disk D whose boundary circle has equation $x^2 + y^2 = 2x$ or, after completing the square,

$$(x - 1)^2 + y^2 = 1$$

(See Figures 9 and 10.) In polar coordinates we have $x^2 + y^2 = r^2$ and $x = r \cos \theta$, so the boundary circle becomes $r^2 = 2r \cos \theta$, or $r = 2 \cos \theta$. Thus the disk D is given by

$$D = \{(r, \theta) \mid -\pi/2 \leqslant \theta \leqslant \pi/2, \ 0 \leqslant r \leqslant 2 \cos \theta\}$$

and, by Formula 3, we have

$$V = \iint_D (x^2 + y^2) \, dA = \int_{-\pi/2}^{\pi/2} \int_0^{2 \cos \theta} r^2 \, r \, dr \, d\theta = \int_{-\pi/2}^{\pi/2} \left[\frac{r^4}{4}\right]_0^{2 \cos \theta} d\theta$$

$$= 4 \int_{-\pi/2}^{\pi/2} \cos^4\theta \, d\theta = 8 \int_0^{\pi/2} \cos^4\theta \, d\theta = 8 \int_0^{\pi/2} \left(\frac{1 + \cos 2\theta}{2}\right)^2 d\theta$$

$$= 2 \int_0^{\pi/2} \left[1 + 2 \cos 2\theta + \tfrac{1}{2}(1 + \cos 4\theta)\right] d\theta$$

$$= 2\left[\tfrac{3}{2}\theta + \sin 2\theta + \tfrac{1}{8} \sin 4\theta\right]_0^{\pi/2} = 2\left(\frac{3}{2}\right)\left(\frac{\pi}{2}\right) = \frac{3\pi}{2} \qquad \square$$

16.4 EXERCISES

1–4 A region R is shown. Decide whether to use polar coordinates or rectangular coordinates and write $\iint_R f(x, y) \, dA$ as an iterated integral, where f is an arbitrary continuous function on R.

1.

2.

$y = 1 - x^2$

3.

4.

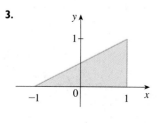

5–6 Sketch the region whose area is given by the integral and evaluate the integral.

5. $\int_\pi^{2\pi} \int_4^7 r \, dr \, d\theta$

6. $\int_0^{\pi/2} \int_0^{4 \cos \theta} r \, dr \, d\theta$

7–14 Evaluate the given integral by changing to polar coordinates.

7. $\iint_D xy \, dA$,
where D is the disk with center the origin and radius 3

8. $\iint_R (x + y) \, dA$, where R is the region that lies to the left of the y-axis between the circles $x^2 + y^2 = 1$ and $x^2 + y^2 = 4$

9. $\iint_R \cos(x^2 + y^2) \, dA$, where R is the region that lies above the x-axis within the circle $x^2 + y^2 = 9$

10. $\iint_R \sqrt{4 - x^2 - y^2} \, dA$,
where $R = \{(x, y) \mid x^2 + y^2 \leqslant 4, \ x \geqslant 0\}$

11. $\iint_D e^{-x^2 - y^2} \, dA$, where D is the region bounded by the semicircle $x = \sqrt{4 - y^2}$ and the y-axis

12. $\iint_R ye^x \, dA$, where R is the region in the first quadrant enclosed by the circle $x^2 + y^2 = 25$

13. $\iint_R \arctan(y/x) \, dA$,
where $R = \{(x, y) \mid 1 \le x^2 + y^2 \le 4, \ 0 \le y \le x\}$

14. $\iint_D x \, dA$, where D is the region in the first quadrant that lies between the circles $x^2 + y^2 = 4$ and $x^2 + y^2 = 2x$

15–18 Use a double integral to find the area of the region.

15. One loop of the rose $r = \cos 3\theta$

16. The region enclosed by the curve $r = 4 + 3\cos\theta$

17. The region within both of the circles $r = \cos\theta$ and $r = \sin\theta$

18. The region inside the cardioid $r = 1 + \cos\theta$ and outside the circle $r = 3\cos\theta$

19–27 Use polar coordinates to find the volume of the given solid.

19. Under the cone $z = \sqrt{x^2 + y^2}$ and above the disk $x^2 + y^2 \le 4$

20. Below the paraboloid $z = 18 - 2x^2 - 2y^2$ and above the xy-plane

21. Enclosed by the hyperboloid $-x^2 - y^2 + z^2 = 1$ and the plane $z = 2$

22. Inside the sphere $x^2 + y^2 + z^2 = 16$ and outside the cylinder $x^2 + y^2 = 4$

23. A sphere of radius a

24. Bounded by the paraboloid $z = 1 + 2x^2 + 2y^2$ and the plane $z = 7$ in the first octant

25. Above the cone $z = \sqrt{x^2 + y^2}$ and below the sphere $x^2 + y^2 + z^2 = 1$

26. Bounded by the paraboloids $z = 3x^2 + 3y^2$ and $z = 4 - x^2 - y^2$

27. Inside both the cylinder $x^2 + y^2 = 4$ and the ellipsoid $4x^2 + 4y^2 + z^2 = 64$

---

28. (a) A cylindrical drill with radius r_1 is used to bore a hole through the center of a sphere of radius r_2. Find the volume of the ring-shaped solid that remains.
(b) Express the volume in part (a) in terms of the height h of the ring. Notice that the volume depends only on h, not on r_1 or r_2.

29–32 Evaluate the iterated integral by converting to polar coordinates.

29. $\displaystyle\int_{-3}^{3} \int_{0}^{\sqrt{9-x^2}} \sin(x^2 + y^2) \, dy \, dx$
30. $\displaystyle\int_{0}^{a} \int_{-\sqrt{a^2-y^2}}^{0} x^2 y \, dx \, dy$

31. $\displaystyle\int_{0}^{1} \int_{y}^{\sqrt{2-y^2}} (x + y) \, dx \, dy$
32. $\displaystyle\int_{0}^{2} \int_{0}^{\sqrt{2x-x^2}} \sqrt{x^2 + y^2} \, dy \, dx$

33. A swimming pool is circular with a 40-ft diameter. The depth is constant along east-west lines and increases linearly from 2 ft at the south end to 7 ft at the north end. Find the volume of water in the pool.

34. An agricultural sprinkler distributes water in a circular pattern of radius 100 ft. It supplies water to a depth of e^{-r} feet per hour at a distance of r feet from the sprinkler.
(a) If $0 < R \le 100$, what is the total amount of water supplied per hour to the region inside the circle of radius R centered at the sprinkler?
(b) Determine an expression for the average amount of water per hour per square foot supplied to the region inside the circle of radius R.

35. Use polar coordinates to combine the sum

$$\int_{1/\sqrt{2}}^{1} \int_{\sqrt{1-x^2}}^{x} xy \, dy \, dx + \int_{1}^{\sqrt{2}} \int_{0}^{x} xy \, dy \, dx + \int_{\sqrt{2}}^{2} \int_{0}^{\sqrt{4-x^2}} xy \, dy \, dx$$

into one double integral. Then evaluate the double integral.

36. (a) We define the improper integral (over the entire plane $\mathbb{R}^2$)

$$I = \iint_{\mathbb{R}^2} e^{-(x^2+y^2)} \, dA = \int_{-\infty}^{\infty} \int_{-\infty}^{\infty} e^{-(x^2+y^2)} \, dy \, dx$$
$$= \lim_{a \to \infty} \iint_{D_a} e^{-(x^2+y^2)} \, dA$$

where D_a is the disk with radius a and center the origin. Show that

$$\int_{-\infty}^{\infty} \int_{-\infty}^{\infty} e^{-(x^2+y^2)} \, dA = \pi$$

(b) An equivalent definition of the improper integral in part (a) is

$$\iint_{\mathbb{R}^2} e^{-(x^2+y^2)} \, dA = \lim_{a \to \infty} \iint_{S_a} e^{-(x^2+y^2)} \, dA$$

where S_a is the square with vertices $(\pm a, \pm a)$. Use this to show that

$$\int_{-\infty}^{\infty} e^{-x^2} \, dx \int_{-\infty}^{\infty} e^{-y^2} \, dy = \pi$$

(c) Deduce that

$$\int_{-\infty}^{\infty} e^{-x^2} \, dx = \sqrt{\pi}$$

(d) By making the change of variable $t = \sqrt{2}\, x$, show that

$$\int_{-\infty}^{\infty} e^{-x^2/2} \, dx = \sqrt{2\pi}$$

(This is a fundamental result for probability and statistics.)

37. Use the result of Exercise 36 part (c) to evaluate the following integrals.

(a) $\displaystyle\int_{0}^{\infty} x^2 e^{-x^2} \, dx$
(b) $\displaystyle\int_{0}^{\infty} \sqrt{x}\, e^{-x} \, dx$

16.5 APPLICATIONS OF DOUBLE INTEGRALS

We have already seen one application of double integrals: computing volumes. Another geometric application is finding areas of surfaces and this will be done in Section 17.6. In this section we explore physical applications such as computing mass, electric charge, center of mass, and moment of inertia. We will see that these physical ideas are also important when applied to probability density functions of two random variables.

DENSITY AND MASS

In Section 9.3 we were able to use single integrals to compute moments and the center of mass of a thin plate or lamina with constant density. But now, equipped with the double integral, we can consider a lamina with variable density. Suppose the lamina occupies a region D of the xy-plane and its **density** (in units of mass per unit area) at a point (x, y) in D is given by $\rho(x, y)$, where ρ is a continuous function on D. This means that

$$\rho(x, y) = \lim \frac{\Delta m}{\Delta A}$$

where Δm and ΔA are the mass and area of a small rectangle that contains (x, y) and the limit is taken as the dimensions of the rectangle approach 0. (See Figure 1.)

To find the total mass m of the lamina, we divide a rectangle R containing D into subrectangles R_{ij} of equal size (as in Figure 2) and consider $\rho(x, y)$ to be 0 outside D. If we choose a point (x_{ij}^*, y_{ij}^*) in R_{ij}, then the mass of the part of the lamina that occupies R_{ij} is approximately $\rho(x_{ij}^*, y_{ij}^*) \Delta A$, where ΔA is the area of R_{ij}. If we add all such masses, we get an approximation to the total mass:

$$m \approx \sum_{i=1}^{k} \sum_{j=1}^{l} \rho(x_{ij}^*, y_{ij}^*) \Delta A$$

If we now increase the number of subrectangles, we obtain the total mass m of the lamina as the limiting value of the approximations:

FIGURE 1

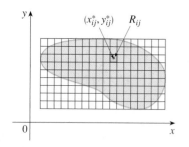

FIGURE 2

$$\boxed{1} \qquad m = \lim_{k, l \to \infty} \sum_{i=1}^{k} \sum_{j=1}^{l} \rho(x_{ij}^*, y_{ij}^*) \Delta A = \iint_D \rho(x, y)\, dA$$

Physicists also consider other types of density that can be treated in the same manner. For example, if an electric charge is distributed over a region D and the charge density (in units of charge per unit area) is given by $\sigma(x, y)$ at a point (x, y) in D, then the **total charge** Q is given by

$$\boxed{2} \qquad Q = \iint_D \sigma(x, y)\, dA$$

EXAMPLE 1 Charge is distributed over the triangular region D in Figure 3 so that the charge density at (x, y) is $\sigma(x, y) = xy$, measured in coulombs per square meter (C/m^2). Find the total charge.

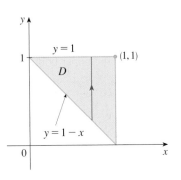

FIGURE 3

SOLUTION From Equation 2 and Figure 3 we have

$$Q = \iint_D \sigma(x, y)\, dA = \int_0^1 \int_{1-x}^1 xy\, dy\, dx$$

$$= \int_0^1 \left[x\frac{y^2}{2} \right]_{y=1-x}^{y=1} dx = \int_0^1 \frac{x}{2}[1^2 - (1-x)^2]\, dx$$

$$= \tfrac{1}{2}\int_0^1 (2x^2 - x^3)\, dx = \frac{1}{2}\left[\frac{2x^3}{3} - \frac{x^4}{4} \right]_0^1 = \frac{5}{24}$$

Thus the total charge is $\frac{5}{24}$ C. □

MOMENTS AND CENTERS OF MASS

In Section 9.3 we found the center of mass of a lamina with constant density; here we consider a lamina with variable density. Suppose the lamina occupies a region D and has density function $\rho(x, y)$. Recall from Chapter 9 that we defined the moment of a particle about an axis as the product of its mass and its directed distance from the axis. We divide D into small rectangles as in Figure 2. Then the mass of R_{ij} is approximately $\rho(x_{ij}^*, y_{ij}^*)\,\Delta A$, so we can approximate the moment of R_{ij} with respect to the x-axis by

$$[\rho(x_{ij}^*, y_{ij}^*)\,\Delta A]\, y_{ij}^*$$

If we now add these quantities and take the limit as the number of subrectangles becomes large, we obtain the **moment** of the entire lamina **about the x-axis**:

$$\boxed{3} \qquad M_x = \lim_{m,\,n \to \infty} \sum_{i=1}^m \sum_{j=1}^n y_{ij}^*\, \rho(x_{ij}^*, y_{ij}^*)\,\Delta A = \iint_D y\,\rho(x, y)\, dA$$

Similarly, the **moment about the y-axis** is

$$\boxed{4} \qquad M_y = \lim_{m,\,n \to \infty} \sum_{i=1}^m \sum_{j=1}^n x_{ij}^*\, \rho(x_{ij}^*, y_{ij}^*)\,\Delta A = \iint_D x\,\rho(x, y)\, dA$$

As before, we define the center of mass $(\bar{x}, \bar{y})$ so that $m\bar{x} = M_y$ and $m\bar{y} = M_x$. The physical significance is that the lamina behaves as if its entire mass is concentrated at its center of mass. Thus the lamina balances horizontally when supported at its center of mass (see Figure 4).

FIGURE 4

> **5** The coordinates $(\bar{x}, \bar{y})$ of the center of mass of a lamina occupying the region D and having density function $\rho(x, y)$ are
>
> $$\bar{x} = \frac{M_y}{m} = \frac{1}{m}\iint_D x\,\rho(x, y)\, dA \qquad \bar{y} = \frac{M_x}{m} = \frac{1}{m}\iint_D y\,\rho(x, y)\, dA$$
>
> where the mass m is given by
>
> $$m = \iint_D \rho(x, y)\, dA$$

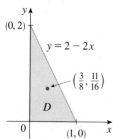

FIGURE 5

EXAMPLE 2 Find the mass and center of mass of a triangular lamina with vertices $(0, 0)$, $(1, 0)$, and $(0, 2)$ if the density function is $\rho(x, y) = 1 + 3x + y$.

SOLUTION The triangle is shown in Figure 5. (Note that the equation of the upper boundary is $y = 2 - 2x$.) The mass of the lamina is

$$m = \iint_D \rho(x, y) \, dA = \int_0^1 \int_0^{2-2x} (1 + 3x + y) \, dy \, dx$$

$$= \int_0^1 \left[y + 3xy + \frac{y^2}{2} \right]_{y=0}^{y=2-2x} dx = 4 \int_0^1 (1 - x^2) \, dx = 4 \left[x - \frac{x^3}{3} \right]_0^1 = \frac{8}{3}$$

Then the formulas in (5) give

$$\bar{x} = \frac{1}{m} \iint_D x \rho(x, y) \, dA = \frac{3}{8} \int_0^1 \int_0^{2-2x} (x + 3x^2 + xy) \, dy \, dx$$

$$= \frac{3}{8} \int_0^1 \left[xy + 3x^2 y + x \frac{y^2}{2} \right]_{y=0}^{y=2-2x} dx = \frac{3}{2} \int_0^1 (x - x^3) \, dx$$

$$= \frac{3}{2} \left[\frac{x^2}{2} - \frac{x^4}{4} \right]_0^1 = \frac{3}{8}$$

$$\bar{y} = \frac{1}{m} \iint_D y \rho(x, y) \, dA = \frac{3}{8} \int_0^1 \int_0^{2-2x} (y + 3xy + y^2) \, dy \, dx$$

$$= \frac{3}{8} \int_0^1 \left[\frac{y^2}{2} + 3x \frac{y^2}{2} + \frac{y^3}{3} \right]_{y=0}^{y=2-2x} dx = \frac{1}{4} \int_0^1 (7 - 9x - 3x^2 + 5x^3) \, dx$$

$$= \frac{1}{4} \left[7x - 9 \frac{x^2}{2} - x^3 + 5 \frac{x^4}{4} \right]_0^1 = \frac{11}{16}$$

The center of mass is at the point $\left(\frac{3}{8}, \frac{11}{16} \right)$. ☐

EXAMPLE 3 The density at any point on a semicircular lamina is proportional to the distance from the center of the circle. Find the center of mass of the lamina.

SOLUTION Let's place the lamina as the upper half of the circle $x^2 + y^2 = a^2$. (See Figure 6.) Then the distance from a point (x, y) to the center of the circle (the origin) is $\sqrt{x^2 + y^2}$. Therefore the density function is

$$\rho(x, y) = K\sqrt{x^2 + y^2}$$

where K is some constant. Both the density function and the shape of the lamina suggest that we convert to polar coordinates. Then $\sqrt{x^2 + y^2} = r$ and the region D is given by $0 \le r \le a$, $0 \le \theta \le \pi$. Thus the mass of the lamina is

$$m = \iint_D \rho(x, y) \, dA = \iint_D K\sqrt{x^2 + y^2} \, dA = \int_0^\pi \int_0^a (Kr) \, r \, dr \, d\theta$$

$$= K \int_0^\pi d\theta \int_0^a r^2 \, dr = K\pi \frac{r^3}{3} \bigg]_0^a = \frac{K\pi a^3}{3}$$

Both the lamina and the density function are symmetric with respect to the y-axis, so the

FIGURE 6

center of mass must lie on the y-axis, that is, $\bar{x} = 0$. The y-coordinate is given by

$$\bar{y} = \frac{1}{m} \iint_D y \rho(x, y) \, dA = \frac{3}{K\pi a^3} \int_0^\pi \int_0^a r \sin \theta \, (Kr) \, r \, dr \, d\theta$$

$$= \frac{3}{\pi a^3} \int_0^\pi \sin \theta \, d\theta \int_0^a r^3 \, dr = \frac{3}{\pi a^3} \left[-\cos \theta \right]_0^\pi \left[\frac{r^4}{4} \right]_0^a$$

$$= \frac{3}{\pi a^3} \frac{2a^4}{4} = \frac{3a}{2\pi}$$

■ Compare the location of the center of mass in Example 3 with Example 4 in Section 9.3, where we found that the center of mass of a lamina with the same shape but uniform density is located at the point $(0, 4a/(3\pi))$.

Therefore the center of mass is located at the point $(0, 3a/(2\pi))$. □

MOMENT OF INERTIA

The **moment of inertia** (also called the **second moment**) of a particle of mass m about an axis is defined to be mr^2, where r is the distance from the particle to the axis. We extend this concept to a lamina with density function $\rho(x, y)$ and occupying a region D by proceeding as we did for ordinary moments. We divide D into small rectangles, approximate the moment of inertia of each subrectangle about the x-axis, and take the limit of the sum as the number of subrectangles becomes large. The result is the **moment of inertia** of the lamina **about the x-axis**:

$$\boxed{6} \qquad I_x = \lim_{m, n \to \infty} \sum_{i=1}^m \sum_{j=1}^n (y_{ij}^*)^2 \rho(x_{ij}^*, y_{ij}^*) \, \Delta A = \iint_D y^2 \rho(x, y) \, dA$$

Similarly, the **moment of inertia about the y-axis** is

$$\boxed{7} \qquad I_y = \lim_{m, n \to \infty} \sum_{i=1}^m \sum_{j=1}^n (x_{ij}^*)^2 \rho(x_{ij}^*, y_{ij}^*) \, \Delta A = \iint_D x^2 \rho(x, y) \, dA$$

It is also of interest to consider the **moment of inertia about the origin**, also called the **polar moment of inertia**:

$$\boxed{8} \qquad I_0 = \lim_{m, n \to \infty} \sum_{i=1}^m \sum_{j=1}^n \left[(x_{ij}^*)^2 + (y_{ij}^*)^2 \right] \rho(x_{ij}^*, y_{ij}^*) \, \Delta A = \iint_D (x^2 + y^2) \rho(x, y) \, dA$$

Note that $I_0 = I_x + I_y$.

☑ EXAMPLE 4 Find the moments of inertia I_x, I_y, and I_0 of a homogeneous disk D with density $\rho(x, y) = \rho$, center the origin, and radius a.

SOLUTION The boundary of D is the circle $x^2 + y^2 = a^2$ and in polar coordinates D is described by $0 \leqslant \theta \leqslant 2\pi, 0 \leqslant r \leqslant a$. Let's compute I_0 first:

$$I_0 = \iint\limits_D (x^2 + y^2)\rho \, dA = \rho \int_0^{2\pi} \int_0^a r^2 r \, dr \, d\theta$$

$$= \rho \int_0^{2\pi} d\theta \int_0^a r^3 \, dr = 2\pi\rho \left[\frac{r^4}{4}\right]_0^a = \frac{\pi\rho a^4}{2}$$

Instead of computing I_x and I_y directly, we use the facts that $I_x + I_y = I_0$ and $I_x = I_y$ (from the symmetry of the problem). Thus

$$I_x = I_y = \frac{I_0}{2} = \frac{\pi\rho a^4}{4}$$

In Example 4 notice that the mass of the disk is

$$m = \text{density} \times \text{area} = \rho(\pi a^2)$$

so the moment of inertia of the disk about the origin (like a wheel about its axle) can be written as

$$I_0 = \frac{\pi\rho a^4}{2} = \tfrac{1}{2}(\rho\pi a^2)a^2 = \tfrac{1}{2}ma^2$$

Thus if we increase the mass or the radius of the disk, we thereby increase the moment of inertia. In general, the moment of inertia plays much the same role in rotational motion that mass plays in linear motion. The moment of inertia of a wheel is what makes it difficult to start or stop the rotation of the wheel, just as the mass of a car is what makes it difficult to start or stop the motion of the car.

The **radius of gyration of a lamina about an axis** is the number R such that

$$\boxed{9} \qquad\qquad\qquad mR^2 = I$$

where m is the mass of the lamina and I is the moment of inertia about the given axis. Equation 9 says that if the mass of the lamina were concentrated at a distance R from the axis, then the moment of inertia of this "point mass" would be the same as the moment of inertia of the lamina.

In particular, the radius of gyration $\overline{\overline{y}}$ with respect to the x-axis and the radius of gyration $\overline{\overline{x}}$ with respect to the y-axis are given by the equations

$$\boxed{10} \qquad\qquad m\overline{\overline{y}}^2 = I_x \qquad\qquad m\overline{\overline{x}}^2 = I_y$$

Thus $(\overline{\overline{x}}, \overline{\overline{y}})$ is the point at which the mass of the lamina can be concentrated without changing the moments of inertia with respect to the coordinate axes. (Note the analogy with the center of mass.)

☑ **EXAMPLE 5** Find the radius of gyration about the x-axis of the disk in Example 4.

SOLUTION As noted, the mass of the disk is $m = \rho\pi a^2$, so from Equations 10 we have

$$\overline{\overline{y}}^2 = \frac{I_x}{m} = \frac{\tfrac{1}{4}\pi\rho a^4}{\rho\pi a^2} = \frac{a^2}{4}$$

Therefore the radius of gyration about the x-axis is $\overline{\overline{y}} = \tfrac{1}{2}a$, which is half the radius of the disk.

PROBABILITY

In Section 9.5 we considered the *probability density function* f of a continuous random variable X. This means that $f(x) \geqslant 0$ for all x, $\int_{-\infty}^{\infty} f(x)\, dx = 1$, and the probability that X lies between a and b is found by integrating f from a to b:

$$P(a \leqslant X \leqslant b) = \int_a^b f(x)\, dx$$

Now we consider a pair of continuous random variables X and Y, such as the lifetimes of two components of a machine or the height and weight of an adult female chosen at random. The **joint density function** of X and Y is a function f of two variables such that the probability that (X, Y) lies in a region D is

$$P((X, Y) \in D) = \iint_D f(x, y)\, dA$$

In particular, if the region is a rectangle, the probability that X lies between a and b and Y lies between c and d is

$$P(a \leqslant X \leqslant b,\ c \leqslant Y \leqslant d) = \int_a^b \int_c^d f(x, y)\, dy\, dx$$

(See Figure 7.)

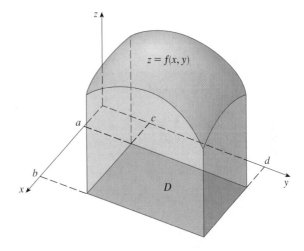

FIGURE 7

The probability that X lies between a and b and Y lies between c and d is the volume that lies above the rectangle $D = [a, b] \times [c, d]$ and below the graph of the joint density function.

Because probabilities aren't negative and are measured on a scale from 0 to 1, the joint density function has the following properties:

$$f(x, y) \geqslant 0 \qquad \iint_{\mathbb{R}^2} f(x, y)\, dA = 1$$

As in Exercise 36 in Section 16.4, the double integral over $\mathbb{R}^2$ is an improper integral defined as the limit of double integrals over expanding circles or squares and we can write

$$\iint_{\mathbb{R}^2} f(x, y)\, dA = \int_{-\infty}^{\infty} \int_{-\infty}^{\infty} f(x, y)\, dx\, dy = 1$$

EXAMPLE 6 If the joint density function for X and Y is given by

$$f(x, y) = \begin{cases} C(x + 2y) & \text{if } 0 \leqslant x \leqslant 10, \ 0 \leqslant y \leqslant 10 \\ 0 & \text{otherwise} \end{cases}$$

find the value of the constant C. Then find $P(X \leqslant 7, Y \geqslant 2)$.

SOLUTION We find the value of C by ensuring that the double integral of f is equal to 1. Because $f(x, y) = 0$ outside the rectangle $[0, 10] \times [0, 10]$, we have

$$\int_{-\infty}^{\infty} \int_{-\infty}^{\infty} f(x, y) \, dy \, dx = \int_{0}^{10} \int_{0}^{10} C(x + 2y) \, dy \, dx = C \int_{0}^{10} \left[xy + y^2 \right]_{y=0}^{y=10} dx$$

$$= C \int_{0}^{10} (10x + 100) \, dx = 1500C$$

Therefore $1500C = 1$ and so $C = \frac{1}{1500}$.

Now we can compute the probability that X is at most 7 and Y is at least 2:

$$P(X \leqslant 7, Y \geqslant 2) = \int_{-\infty}^{7} \int_{2}^{\infty} f(x, y) \, dy \, dx = \int_{0}^{7} \int_{2}^{10} \tfrac{1}{1500} (x + 2y) \, dy \, dx$$

$$= \tfrac{1}{1500} \int_{0}^{7} \left[xy + y^2 \right]_{y=2}^{y=10} dx = \tfrac{1}{1500} \int_{0}^{7} (8x + 96) \, dx$$

$$= \tfrac{868}{1500} \approx 0.5787 \qquad\qquad \square$$

Suppose X is a random variable with probability density function $f_1(x)$ and Y is a random variable with density function $f_2(y)$. Then X and Y are called **independent random variables** if their joint density function is the product of their individual density functions:

$$f(x, y) = f_1(x) f_2(y)$$

In Section 9.5 we modeled waiting times by using exponential density functions

$$f(t) = \begin{cases} 0 & \text{if } t < 0 \\ \mu^{-1} e^{-t/\mu} & \text{if } t \geqslant 0 \end{cases}$$

where μ is the mean waiting time. In the next example we consider a situation with two independent waiting times.

EXAMPLE 7 The manager of a movie theater determines that the average time movie-goers wait in line to buy a ticket for this week's film is 10 minutes and the average time they wait to buy popcorn is 5 minutes. Assuming that the waiting times are independent, find the probability that a moviegoer waits a total of less than 20 minutes before taking his or her seat.

SOLUTION Assuming that both the waiting time X for the ticket purchase and the waiting time Y in the refreshment line are modeled by exponential probability density functions, we can write the individual density functions as

$$f_1(x) = \begin{cases} 0 & \text{if } x < 0 \\ \tfrac{1}{10} e^{-x/10} & \text{if } x \geqslant 0 \end{cases} \qquad f_2(y) = \begin{cases} 0 & \text{if } y < 0 \\ \tfrac{1}{5} e^{-y/5} & \text{if } y \geqslant 0 \end{cases}$$

Since X and Y are independent, the joint density function is the product:

$$f(x, y) = f_1(x)f_2(y) = \begin{cases} \frac{1}{50}e^{-x/10}e^{-y/5} & \text{if } x \geq 0, \ y \geq 0 \\ 0 & \text{otherwise} \end{cases}$$

We are asked for the probability that $X + Y < 20$:

$$P(X + Y < 20) = P((X, Y) \in D)$$

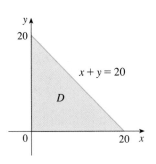

FIGURE 8

where D is the triangular region shown in Figure 8. Thus

$$P(X + Y < 20) = \iint_D f(x, y)\, dA = \int_0^{20}\int_0^{20-x} \frac{1}{50}e^{-x/10}e^{-y/5}\, dy\, dx$$

$$= \frac{1}{50}\int_0^{20}\left[e^{-x/10}(-5)e^{-y/5}\right]_{y=0}^{y=20-x}\, dx$$

$$= \frac{1}{10}\int_0^{20} e^{-x/10}(1 - e^{(x-20)/5})\, dx$$

$$= \frac{1}{10}\int_0^{20} (e^{-x/10} - e^{-4}e^{x/10})\, dx$$

$$= 1 + e^{-4} - 2e^{-2} \approx 0.7476$$

This means that about 75% of the moviegoers wait less than 20 minutes before taking their seats. □

EXPECTED VALUES

Recall from Section 9.5 that if X is a random variable with probability density function f, then its *mean* is

$$\mu = \int_{-\infty}^{\infty} xf(x)\, dx$$

Now if X and Y are random variables with joint density function f, we define the **X-mean** and **Y-mean**, also called the **expected values** of X and Y, to be

$$\boxed{11} \qquad \mu_1 = \iint_{\mathbb{R}^2} xf(x, y)\, dA \qquad \mu_2 = \iint_{\mathbb{R}^2} yf(x, y)\, dA$$

Notice how closely the expressions for μ_1 and μ_2 in (11) resemble the moments M_x and M_y of a lamina with density function ρ in Equations 3 and 4. In fact, we can think of probability as being like continuously distributed mass. We calculate probability the way we calculate mass—by integrating a density function. And because the total "probability mass" is 1, the expressions for $\bar{x}$ and $\bar{y}$ in (5) show that we can think of the expected values of X and Y, μ_1 and μ_2, as the coordinates of the "center of mass" of the probability distribution.

In the next example we deal with normal distributions. As in Section 9.5, a single random variable is *normally distributed* if its probability density function is of the form

$$f(x) = \frac{1}{\sigma\sqrt{2\pi}}\, e^{-(x-\mu)^2/(2\sigma^2)}$$

where μ is the mean and σ is the standard deviation.

EXAMPLE 8 A factory produces (cylindrically shaped) roller bearings that are sold as having diameter 4.0 cm and length 6.0 cm. In fact, the diameters X are normally distributed with mean 4.0 cm and standard deviation 0.01 cm while the lengths Y are normally distributed with mean 6.0 cm and standard deviation 0.01 cm. Assuming that X and Y are independent, write the joint density function and graph it. Find the probability that a bearing randomly chosen from the production line has either length or diameter that differs from the mean by more than 0.02 cm.

SOLUTION We are given that X and Y are normally distributed with $\mu_1 = 4.0$, $\mu_2 = 6.0$, and $\sigma_1 = \sigma_2 = 0.01$. So the individual density functions for X and Y are

$$f_1(x) = \frac{1}{0.01\sqrt{2\pi}}\, e^{-(x-4)^2/0.0002} \qquad f_2(y) = \frac{1}{0.01\sqrt{2\pi}}\, e^{-(y-6)^2/0.0002}$$

Since X and Y are independent, the joint density function is the product:

$$f(x, y) = f_1(x)f_2(y) = \frac{1}{0.0002\pi}\, e^{-(x-4)^2/0.0002}e^{-(y-6)^2/0.0002}$$

$$= \frac{5000}{\pi}\, e^{-5000[(x-4)^2+(y-6)^2]}$$

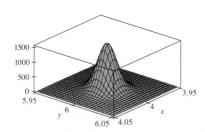

FIGURE 9
Graph of the bivariate normal joint density function in Example 8

A graph of this function is shown in Figure 9.

Let's first calculate the probability that both X and Y differ from their means by less than 0.02 cm. Using a calculator or computer to estimate the integral, we have

$$P(3.98 < X < 4.02,\ 5.98 < Y < 6.02) = \int_{3.98}^{4.02}\int_{5.98}^{6.02} f(x, y)\, dy\, dx$$

$$= \frac{5000}{\pi}\int_{3.98}^{4.02}\int_{5.98}^{6.02} e^{-5000[(x-4)^2+(y-6)^2]}\, dy\, dx$$

$$\approx 0.91$$

Then the probability that either X or Y differs from its mean by more than 0.02 cm is approximately

$$1 - 0.91 = 0.09 \qquad \square$$

16.5 EXERCISES

1. Electric charge is distributed over the rectangle $1 \le x \le 3$, $0 \le y \le 2$ so that the charge density at (x, y) is $\sigma(x, y) = 2xy + y^2$ (measured in coulombs per square meter). Find the total charge on the rectangle.

2. Electric charge is distributed over the disk $x^2 + y^2 \le 4$ so that the charge density at (x, y) is $\sigma(x, y) = x + y + x^2 + y^2$ (measured in coulombs per square meter). Find the total charge on the disk.

3–10 Find the mass and center of mass of the lamina that occupies the region D and has the given density function ρ.

3. $D = \{(x, y) \mid 0 \le x \le 2,\ -1 \le y \le 1\}$; $\rho(x, y) = xy^2$

4. $D = \{(x, y) \mid 0 \le x \le a,\ 0 \le y \le b\}$; $\rho(x, y) = cxy$

5. D is the triangular region with vertices $(0, 0)$, $(2, 1)$, $(0, 3)$; $\rho(x, y) = x + y$

6. D is the triangular region enclosed by the lines $x = 0$, $y = x$, and $2x + y = 6$; $\rho(x, y) = x^2$

7. D is bounded by $y = e^x$, $y = 0$, $x = 0$, and $x = 1$; $\rho(x, y) = y$

8. D is bounded by $y = \sqrt{x}$, $y = 0$, and $x = 1$; $\rho(x, y) = x$

9. $D = \{(x, y) \mid 0 \le y \le \sin(\pi x/L),\ 0 \le x \le L\}$; $\rho(x, y) = y$

10. D is bounded by the parabolas $y = x^2$ and $x = y^2$; $\rho(x, y) = \sqrt{x}$

11. A lamina occupies the part of the disk $x^2 + y^2 \leqslant 1$ in the first quadrant. Find its center of mass if the density at any point is proportional to its distance from the x-axis.

12. Find the center of mass of the lamina in Exercise 11 if the density at any point is proportional to the square of its distance from the origin.

13. The boundary of a lamina consists of the semicircles $y = \sqrt{1 - x^2}$ and $y = \sqrt{4 - x^2}$ together with the portions of the x-axis that join them. Find the center of mass of the lamina if the density at any point is proportional to its distance from the origin.

14. Find the center of mass of the lamina in Exercise 13 if the density at any point is inversely proportional to its distance from the origin.

15. Find the center of mass of a lamina in the shape of an isosceles right triangle with equal sides of length a if the density at any point is proportional to the square of the distance from the vertex opposite the hypotenuse.

16. A lamina occupies the region inside the circle $x^2 + y^2 = 2y$ but outside the circle $x^2 + y^2 = 1$. Find the center of mass if the density at any point is inversely proportional to its distance from the origin.

17. Find the moments of inertia I_x, I_y, I_0 for the lamina of Exercise 7.

18. Find the moments of inertia I_x, I_y, I_0 for the lamina of Exercise 12.

19. Find the moments of inertia I_x, I_y, I_0 for the lamina of Exercise 15.

20. Consider a square fan blade with sides of length 2 and the lower left corner placed at the origin. If the density of the blade is $\rho(x, y) = 1 + 0.1x$, is it more difficult to rotate the blade about the x-axis or the y-axis?

CAS 21–22 Use a computer algebra system to find the mass, center of mass, and moments of inertia of the lamina that occupies the region D and has the given density function.

21. $D = \{(x, y) \mid 0 \leqslant y \leqslant \sin x, \ 0 \leqslant x \leqslant \pi\}$; $\rho(x, y) = xy$

22. D is enclosed by the cardioid $r = 1 + \cos \theta$; $\rho(x, y) = \sqrt{x^2 + y^2}$

CAS 23–26 A lamina with constant density $\rho(x, y) = \rho$ occupies the given region. Find the moments of inertia I_x and I_y and the radii of gyration $\bar{\bar{x}}$ and $\bar{\bar{y}}$.

23. The rectangle $0 \leqslant x \leqslant b, 0 \leqslant y \leqslant h$

24. The triangle with vertices $(0, 0)$, $(b, 0)$, and $(0, h)$

25. The part of the disk $x^2 + y^2 \leqslant a^2$ in the first quadrant

26. The region under the curve $y = \sin x$ from $x = 0$ to $x = \pi$

27. The joint density function for a pair of random variables X and Y is
$$f(x, y) = \begin{cases} Cx(1 + y) & \text{if } 0 \leqslant x \leqslant 1, \ 0 \leqslant y \leqslant 2 \\ 0 & \text{otherwise} \end{cases}$$
(a) Find the value of the constant C.
(b) Find $P(X \leqslant 1, Y \leqslant 1)$.
(c) Find $P(X + Y \leqslant 1)$.

28. (a) Verify that
$$f(x, y) = \begin{cases} 4xy & \text{if } 0 \leqslant x \leqslant 1, \ 0 \leqslant y \leqslant 1 \\ 0 & \text{otherwise} \end{cases}$$
is a joint density function.
(b) If X and Y are random variables whose joint density function is the function f in part (a), find
(i) $P(X \geqslant \frac{1}{2})$ (ii) $P(X \geqslant \frac{1}{2}, Y \leqslant \frac{1}{2})$
(c) Find the expected values of X and Y.

29. Suppose X and Y are random variables with joint density function
$$f(x, y) = \begin{cases} 0.1e^{-(0.5x+0.2y)} & \text{if } x \geqslant 0, \ y \geqslant 0 \\ 0 & \text{otherwise} \end{cases}$$
(a) Verify that f is indeed a joint density function.
(b) Find the following probabilities.
(i) $P(Y \geqslant 1)$ (ii) $P(X \leqslant 2, Y \leqslant 4)$
(c) Find the expected values of X and Y.

30. (a) A lamp has two bulbs of a type with an average lifetime of 1000 hours. Assuming that we can model the probability of failure of these bulbs by an exponential density function with mean $\mu = 1000$, find the probability that both of the lamp's bulbs fail within 1000 hours.
(b) Another lamp has just one bulb of the same type as in part (a). If one bulb burns out and is replaced by a bulb of the same type, find the probability that the two bulbs fail within a total of 1000 hours.

CAS 31. Suppose that X and Y are independent random variables, where X is normally distributed with mean 45 and standard deviation 0.5 and Y is normally distributed with mean 20 and standard deviation 0.1.
(a) Find $P(40 \leqslant X \leqslant 50, 20 \leqslant Y \leqslant 25)$.
(b) Find $P(4(X - 45)^2 + 100(Y - 20)^2 \leqslant 2)$.

32. Xavier and Yolanda both have classes that end at noon and they agree to meet every day after class. They arrive at the coffee shop independently. Xavier's arrival time is X and Yolanda's arrival time is Y, where X and Y are measured in minutes after noon. The individual density functions are
$$f_1(x) = \begin{cases} e^{-x} & \text{if } x \geqslant 0 \\ 0 & \text{if } x < 0 \end{cases} \quad f_2(y) = \begin{cases} \frac{1}{50}y & \text{if } 0 \leqslant y \leqslant 10 \\ 0 & \text{otherwise} \end{cases}$$
(Xavier arrives sometime after noon and is more likely to arrive promptly than late. Yolanda always arrives by 12:10 PM and is more likely to arrive late than promptly.) After Yolanda arrives, she'll wait for up to half an hour for Xavier, but he won't wait for her. Find the probability that they meet.

33. When studying the spread of an epidemic, we assume that the probability that an infected individual will spread the disease to an uninfected individual is a function of the distance between them. Consider a circular city of radius 10 mi in which the population is uniformly distributed. For an uninfected individual at a fixed point $A(x_0, y_0)$, assume that the probability function is given by

$$f(P) = \tfrac{1}{20}[20 - d(P, A)]$$

where $d(P, A)$ denotes the distance between P and A.

(a) Suppose the exposure of a person to the disease is the sum of the probabilities of catching the disease from all members of the population. Assume that the infected people are uniformly distributed throughout the city, with k infected individuals per square mile. Find a double integral that represents the exposure of a person residing at A.

(b) Evaluate the integral for the case in which A is the center of the city and for the case in which A is located on the edge of the city. Where would you prefer to live?

16.6 TRIPLE INTEGRALS

Just as we defined single integrals for functions of one variable and double integrals for functions of two variables, so we can define triple integrals for functions of three variables. Let's first deal with the simplest case where f is defined on a rectangular box:

$$\boxed{1} \qquad B = \{(x, y, z) \mid a \leqslant x \leqslant b, \ c \leqslant y \leqslant d, \ r \leqslant z \leqslant s\}$$

The first step is to divide B into sub-boxes. We do this by dividing the interval $[a, b]$ into l subintervals $[x_{i-1}, x_i]$ of equal width Δx, dividing $[c, d]$ into m subintervals of width Δy, and dividing $[r, s]$ into n subintervals of width Δz. The planes through the endpoints of these subintervals parallel to the coordinate planes divide the box B into lmn sub-boxes

$$B_{ijk} = [x_{i-1}, x_i] \times [y_{j-1}, y_j] \times [z_{k-1}, z_k]$$

which are shown in Figure 1. Each sub-box has volume $\Delta V = \Delta x \, \Delta y \, \Delta z$.

Then we form the **triple Riemann sum**

$$\boxed{2} \qquad \sum_{i=1}^{l} \sum_{j=1}^{m} \sum_{k=1}^{n} f(x_{ijk}^*, y_{ijk}^*, z_{ijk}^*) \, \Delta V$$

where the sample point $(x_{ijk}^*, y_{ijk}^*, z_{ijk}^*)$ is in B_{ijk}. By analogy with the definition of a double integral (16.1.5), we define the triple integral as the limit of the triple Riemann sums in (2).

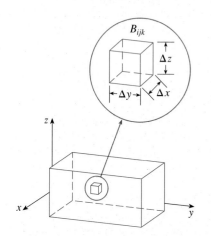

> **3 DEFINITION** The **triple integral** of f over the box B is
>
> $$\iiint\limits_{B} f(x, y, z) \, dV = \lim_{l, m, n \to \infty} \sum_{i=1}^{l} \sum_{j=1}^{m} \sum_{k=1}^{n} f(x_{ijk}^*, y_{ijk}^*, z_{ijk}^*) \, \Delta V$$
>
> if this limit exists.

FIGURE 1

Again, the triple integral always exists if f is continuous. We can choose the sample point to be any point in the sub-box, but if we choose it to be the point (x_i, y_j, z_k) we get a simpler-looking expression for the triple integral:

$$\iiint\limits_{B} f(x, y, z) \, dV = \lim_{l, m, n \to \infty} \sum_{i=1}^{l} \sum_{j=1}^{m} \sum_{k=1}^{n} f(x_i, y_j, z_k) \, \Delta V$$

Just as for double integrals, the practical method for evaluating triple integrals is to express them as iterated integrals as follows.

> **4** **FUBINI'S THEOREM FOR TRIPLE INTEGRALS** If f is continuous on the rectangular box $B = [a, b] \times [c, d] \times [r, s]$, then
>
> $$\iiint_B f(x, y, z) \, dV = \int_r^s \int_c^d \int_a^b f(x, y, z) \, dx \, dy \, dz$$

The iterated integral on the right side of Fubini's Theorem means that we integrate first with respect to x (keeping y and z fixed), then we integrate with respect to y (keeping z fixed), and finally we integrate with respect to z. There are five other possible orders in which we can integrate, all of which give the same value. For instance, if we integrate with respect to y, then z, and then x, we have

$$\iiint_B f(x, y, z) \, dV = \int_a^b \int_r^s \int_c^d f(x, y, z) \, dy \, dz \, dx$$

✔ EXAMPLE 1 Evaluate the triple integral $\iiint_B xyz^2 \, dV$, where B is the rectangular box given by

$$B = \{(x, y, z) \mid 0 \leqslant x \leqslant 1, \ -1 \leqslant y \leqslant 2, \ 0 \leqslant z \leqslant 3\}$$

SOLUTION We could use any of the six possible orders of integration. If we choose to integrate with respect to x, then y, and then z, we obtain

$$\iiint_B xyz^2 \, dV = \int_0^3 \int_{-1}^2 \int_0^1 xyz^2 \, dx \, dy \, dz = \int_0^3 \int_{-1}^2 \left[\frac{x^2 yz^2}{2} \right]_{x=0}^{x=1} dy \, dz$$

$$= \int_0^3 \int_{-1}^2 \frac{yz^2}{2} \, dy \, dz = \int_0^3 \left[\frac{y^2 z^2}{4} \right]_{y=-1}^{y=2} dz$$

$$= \int_0^3 \frac{3z^2}{4} \, dz = \frac{z^3}{4} \bigg]_0^3 = \frac{27}{4} \qquad \square$$

Now we define the **triple integral over a general bounded region** E in three-dimensional space (a solid) by much the same procedure that we used for double integrals (16.3.2). We enclose E in a box B of the type given by Equation 1. Then we define a function F so that it agrees with f on E but is 0 for points in B that are outside E. By definition,

$$\iiint_E f(x, y, z) \, dV = \iiint_B F(x, y, z) \, dV$$

This integral exists if f is continuous and the boundary of E is "reasonably smooth." The triple integral has essentially the same properties as the double integral (Properties 6–9 in Section 16.3).

We restrict our attention to continuous functions f and to certain simple types of regions. A solid region E is said to be of **type 1** if it lies between the graphs of two continuous functions of x and y, that is,

> **5**
> $$E = \{(x, y, z) \mid (x, y) \in D, \ u_1(x, y) \leqslant z \leqslant u_2(x, y)\}$$

where D is the projection of E onto the xy-plane as shown in Figure 2. Notice that the upper boundary of the solid E is the surface with equation $z = u_2(x, y)$, while the lower boundary is the surface $z = u_1(x, y)$.

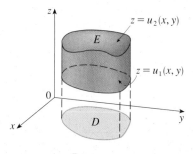

FIGURE 2
A type 1 solid region

By the same sort of argument that led to Formula 16.3.3, it can be shown that if E is a type 1 region given by Equation 5, then

$$\boxed{6} \qquad \iiint_E f(x, y, z)\, dV = \iint_D \left[\int_{u_1(x, y)}^{u_2(x, y)} f(x, y, z)\, dz \right] dA$$

The meaning of the inner integral on the right side of Equation 6 is that x and y are held fixed, and therefore $u_1(x, y)$ and $u_2(x, y)$ are regarded as constants, while $f(x, y, z)$ is integrated with respect to z.

In particular, if the projection D of E onto the xy-plane is a type I plane region (as in Figure 3), then

$$E = \{(x, y, z) \mid a \leqslant x \leqslant b,\ g_1(x) \leqslant y \leqslant g_2(x),\ u_1(x, y) \leqslant z \leqslant u_2(x, y)\}$$

and Equation 6 becomes

$$\boxed{7} \qquad \iiint_E f(x, y, z)\, dV = \int_a^b \int_{g_1(x)}^{g_2(x)} \int_{u_1(x, y)}^{u_2(x, y)} f(x, y, z)\, dz\, dy\, dx$$

FIGURE 3
A type 1 solid region where the projection D is a type I plane region

If, on the other hand, D is a type II plane region (as in Figure 4), then

$$E = \{(x, y, z) \mid c \leqslant y \leqslant d,\ h_1(y) \leqslant x \leqslant h_2(y),\ u_1(x, y) \leqslant z \leqslant u_2(x, y)\}$$

and Equation 6 becomes

$$\boxed{8} \qquad \iiint_E f(x, y, z)\, dV = \int_c^d \int_{h_1(y)}^{h_2(y)} \int_{u_1(x, y)}^{u_2(x, y)} f(x, y, z)\, dz\, dx\, dy$$

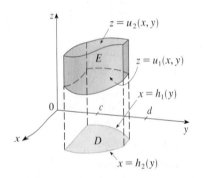

FIGURE 4
A type 1 solid region with a type II projection

EXAMPLE 2 Evaluate $\iiint_E z\, dV$, where E is the solid tetrahedron bounded by the four planes $x = 0$, $y = 0$, $z = 0$, and $x + y + z = 1$.

SOLUTION When we set up a triple integral it's wise to draw *two* diagrams: one of the solid region E (see Figure 5) and one of its projection D on the xy-plane (see Figure 6). The lower boundary of the tetrahedron is the plane $z = 0$ and the upper

FIGURE 5

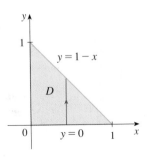

FIGURE 6

boundary is the plane $x + y + z = 1$ (or $z = 1 - x - y$), so we use $u_1(x, y) = 0$ and $u_2(x, y) = 1 - x - y$ in Formula 7. Notice that the planes $x + y + z = 1$ and $z = 0$ intersect in the line $x + y = 1$ (or $y = 1 - x$) in the xy-plane. So the projection of E is the triangular region shown in Figure 6, and we have

$$\boxed{9} \qquad E = \{(x, y, z) \mid 0 \leqslant x \leqslant 1, \ 0 \leqslant y \leqslant 1 - x, \ 0 \leqslant z \leqslant 1 - x - y\}$$

This description of E as a type 1 region enables us to evaluate the integral as follows:

$$\iiint_E z \, dV = \int_0^1 \int_0^{1-x} \int_0^{1-x-y} z \, dz \, dy \, dx = \int_0^1 \int_0^{1-x} \left[\frac{z^2}{2} \right]_{z=0}^{z=1-x-y} dy \, dx$$

$$= \frac{1}{2} \int_0^1 \int_0^{1-x} (1 - x - y)^2 \, dy \, dx = \frac{1}{2} \int_0^1 \left[-\frac{(1 - x - y)^3}{3} \right]_{y=0}^{y=1-x} dx$$

$$= \frac{1}{6} \int_0^1 (1 - x)^3 \, dx = \frac{1}{6} \left[-\frac{(1 - x)^4}{4} \right]_0^1 = \frac{1}{24} \qquad\qquad \square$$

A solid region E is of **type 2** if it is of the form

$$E = \{(x, y, z) \mid (y, z) \in D, \ u_1(y, z) \leqslant x \leqslant u_2(y, z)\}$$

where, this time, D is the projection of E onto the yz-plane (see Figure 7). The back surface is $x = u_1(y, z)$, the front surface is $x = u_2(y, z)$, and we have

$$\boxed{10} \qquad \iiint_E f(x, y, z) \, dV = \iint_D \left[\int_{u_1(y, z)}^{u_2(y, z)} f(x, y, z) \, dx \right] dA$$

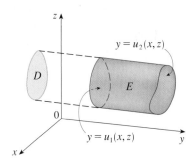

FIGURE 7 A type 2 region **FIGURE 8** A type 3 region

Finally, a **type 3** region is of the form

$$E = \{(x, y, z) \mid (x, z) \in D, \ u_1(x, z) \leqslant y \leqslant u_2(x, z)\}$$

where D is the projection of E onto the xz-plane, $y = u_1(x, z)$ is the left surface, and $y = u_2(x, z)$ is the right surface (see Figure 8). For this type of region we have

$$\boxed{11} \qquad \iiint_E f(x, y, z) \, dV = \iint_D \left[\int_{u_1(x, z)}^{u_2(x, z)} f(x, y, z) \, dy \right] dA$$

In each of Equations 10 and 11 there may be two possible expressions for the integral depending on whether D is a type I or type II plane region (and corresponding to Equations 7 and 8).

☑ **EXAMPLE 3** Evaluate $\iiint_E \sqrt{x^2 + z^2}\, dV$, where E is the region bounded by the paraboloid $y = x^2 + z^2$ and the plane $y = 4$.

SOLUTION The solid E is shown in Figure 9. If we regard it as a type 1 region, then we need to consider its projection D_1 onto the xy-plane, which is the parabolic region in Figure 10. (The trace of $y = x^2 + z^2$ in the plane $z = 0$ is the parabola $y = x^2$.)

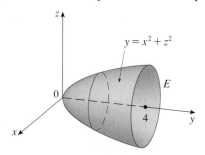

$y = x^2 + z^2$

E

0

4

y

x

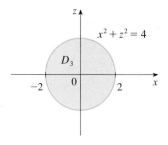

TEC Visual 16.6 illustrates how solid regions (including the one in Figure 9) project onto coordinate planes.

FIGURE 9
Region of integration

FIGURE 10
Projection on xy-plane

$y = 4$

D_1

$y = x^2$

0

x

From $y = x^2 + z^2$ we obtain $z = \pm\sqrt{y - x^2}$, so the lower boundary surface of E is $z = -\sqrt{y - x^2}$ and the upper surface is $z = \sqrt{y - x^2}$. Therefore the description of E as a type 1 region is

$$E = \left\{(x, y, z) \mid -2 \leqslant x \leqslant 2,\ x^2 \leqslant y \leqslant 4,\ -\sqrt{y - x^2} \leqslant z \leqslant \sqrt{y - x^2}\right\}$$

and so we obtain

$$\iiint_E \sqrt{x^2 + z^2}\, dV = \int_{-2}^{2} \int_{x^2}^{4} \int_{-\sqrt{y-x^2}}^{\sqrt{y-x^2}} \sqrt{x^2 + z^2}\, dz\, dy\, dx$$

Although this expression is correct, it is extremely difficult to evaluate. So let's instead consider E as a type 3 region. As such, its projection D_3 onto the xz-plane is the disk $x^2 + z^2 \leqslant 4$ shown in Figure 11.

Then the left boundary of E is the paraboloid $y = x^2 + z^2$ and the right boundary is the plane $y = 4$, so taking $u_1(x, z) = x^2 + z^2$ and $u_2(x, z) = 4$ in Equation 11, we have

$$\iiint_E \sqrt{x^2 + z^2}\, dV = \iint_{D_3} \left[\int_{x^2+z^2}^{4} \sqrt{x^2 + z^2}\, dy \right] dA = \iint_{D_3} (4 - x^2 - z^2)\sqrt{x^2 + z^2}\, dA$$

Although this integral could be written as

$$\int_{-2}^{2} \int_{-\sqrt{4-x^2}}^{\sqrt{4-x^2}} (4 - x^2 - z^2)\sqrt{x^2 + z^2}\, dz\, dx$$

FIGURE 11
Projection on xz-plane

$x^2 + z^2 = 4$

D_3

-2 0 2 x

it's easier to convert to polar coordinates in the xz-plane: $x = r\cos\theta$, $z = r\sin\theta$. This gives

$$\iiint_E \sqrt{x^2 + z^2}\, dV = \iint_{D_3} (4 - x^2 - z^2)\sqrt{x^2 + z^2}\, dA$$

$$= \int_0^{2\pi} \int_0^2 (4 - r^2)r\, r\, dr\, d\theta = \int_0^{2\pi} d\theta \int_0^2 (4r^2 - r^4)\, dr$$

$$= 2\pi \left[\frac{4r^3}{3} - \frac{r^5}{5} \right]_0^2 = \frac{128\pi}{15} \qquad \square$$

⊘ The most difficult step in evaluating a triple integral is setting up an expression for the region of integration (such as Equation 9 in Example 2). Remember that the limits of integration in the inner integral contain at most two variables, the limits of integration in the middle integral contain at most one variable, and the limits of integration in the outer integral must be constants.

APPLICATIONS OF TRIPLE INTEGRALS

Recall that if $f(x) \geqslant 0$, then the single integral $\int_a^b f(x)\,dx$ represents the area under the curve $y = f(x)$ from a to b, and if $f(x, y) \geqslant 0$, then the double integral $\iint_D f(x, y)\,dA$ represents the volume under the surface $z = f(x, y)$ and above D. The corresponding interpretation of a triple integral $\iiint_E f(x, y, z)\,dV$, where $f(x, y, z) \geqslant 0$, is not very useful because it would be the "hypervolume" of a four-dimensional object and, of course, that is very difficult to visualize. (Remember that E is just the *domain* of the function f; the graph of f lies in four-dimensional space.) Nonetheless, the triple integral $\iiint_E f(x, y, z)\,dV$ can be interpreted in different ways in different physical situations, depending on the physical interpretations of x, y, z and $f(x, y, z)$.

Let's begin with the special case where $f(x, y, z) = 1$ for all points in E. Then the triple integral does represent the volume of E:

[12]
$$V(E) = \iiint_E dV$$

For example, you can see this in the case of a type 1 region by putting $f(x, y, z) = 1$ in Formula 6:

$$\iiint_E 1\,dV = \iint_D \left[\int_{u_1(x, y)}^{u_2(x, y)} dz \right] dA = \iint_D [u_2(x, y) - u_1(x, y)]\,dA$$

and from Section 16.3 we know this represents the volume that lies between the surfaces $z = u_1(x, y)$ and $z = u_2(x, y)$.

EXAMPLE 4 Use a triple integral to find the volume of the tetrahedron T bounded by the planes $x + 2y + z = 2$, $x = 2y$, $x = 0$, and $z = 0$.

SOLUTION The tetrahedron T and its projection D on the xy-plane are shown in Figures 12 and 13. The lower boundary of T is the plane $z = 0$ and the upper boundary is the plane $x + 2y + z = 2$, that is, $z = 2 - x - 2y$.

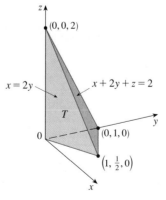

FIGURE 12   **FIGURE 13**

Therefore we have

$$V(T) = \iiint_T dV = \int_0^1 \int_{x/2}^{1-x/2} \int_0^{2-x-2y} dz\,dy\,dx$$

$$= \int_0^1 \int_{x/2}^{1-x/2} (2 - x - 2y)\,dy\,dx = \tfrac{1}{3}$$

by the same calculation as in Example 4 in Section 16.3.

(Notice that it is not necessary to use triple integrals to compute volumes. They simply give an alternative method for setting up the calculation.) ☐

All the applications of double integrals in Section 16.5 can be immediately extended to triple integrals. For example, if the density function of a solid object that occupies the region E is $\rho(x, y, z)$, in units of mass per unit volume, at any given point (x, y, z), then its **mass** is

$$\boxed{13} \qquad m = \iiint_E \rho(x, y, z)\, dV$$

and its **moments** about the three coordinate planes are

$$\boxed{14} \qquad M_{yz} = \iiint_E x\rho(x, y, z)\, dV \qquad M_{xz} = \iiint_E y\rho(x, y, z)\, dV$$

$$M_{xy} = \iiint_E z\rho(x, y, z)\, dV$$

The **center of mass** is located at the point $(\bar{x}, \bar{y}, \bar{z})$, where

$$\boxed{15} \qquad \bar{x} = \frac{M_{yz}}{m} \qquad \bar{y} = \frac{M_{xz}}{m} \qquad \bar{z} = \frac{M_{xy}}{m}$$

If the density is constant, the center of mass of the solid is called the **centroid** of E. The **moments of inertia** about the three coordinate axes are

$$\boxed{16} \qquad I_x = \iiint_E (y^2 + z^2)\rho(x, y, z)\, dV \qquad I_y = \iiint_E (x^2 + z^2)\rho(x, y, z)\, dV$$

$$I_z = \iiint_E (x^2 + y^2)\rho(x, y, z)\, dV$$

As in Section 16.5, the total **electric charge** on a solid object occupying a region E and having charge density $\sigma(x, y, z)$ is

$$Q = \iiint_E \sigma(x, y, z)\, dV$$

If we have three continuous random variables X, Y, and Z, their **joint density function** is a function of three variables such that the probability that (X, Y, Z) lies in E is

$$P((X, Y, Z) \in E) = \iiint_E f(x, y, z)\, dV$$

In particular,

$$P(a \leqslant X \leqslant b, \ c \leqslant Y \leqslant d, \ r \leqslant Z \leqslant s) = \int_a^b \int_c^d \int_r^s f(x, y, z)\, dz\, dy\, dx$$

The joint density function satisfies

$$f(x, y, z) \geqslant 0 \qquad \int_{-\infty}^{\infty} \int_{-\infty}^{\infty} \int_{-\infty}^{\infty} f(x, y, z)\, dz\, dy\, dx = 1$$

▼ EXAMPLE 5 Find the center of mass of a solid of constant density that is bounded by the parabolic cylinder $x = y^2$ and the planes $x = z$, $z = 0$, and $x = 1$.

SOLUTION The solid E and its projection onto the xy-plane are shown in Figure 14. The lower and upper surfaces of E are the planes $z = 0$ and $z = x$, so we describe E as a type 1 region:

$$E = \left\{(x, y, z) \mid -1 \leqslant y \leqslant 1, \; y^2 \leqslant x \leqslant 1, \; 0 \leqslant z \leqslant x\right\}$$

Then, if the density is $\rho(x, y, z) = \rho$, the mass is

$$m = \iiint_E \rho \, dV = \int_{-1}^{1} \int_{y^2}^{1} \int_{0}^{x} \rho \, dz \, dx \, dy$$

$$= \rho \int_{-1}^{1} \int_{y^2}^{1} x \, dx \, dy = \rho \int_{-1}^{1} \left[\frac{x^2}{2} \right]_{x=y^2}^{x=1} dy$$

$$= \frac{\rho}{2} \int_{-1}^{1} (1 - y^4) \, dy = \rho \int_{0}^{1} (1 - y^4) \, dy$$

$$= \rho \left[y - \frac{y^5}{5} \right]_0^1 = \frac{4\rho}{5}$$

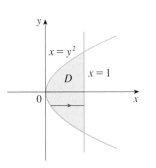

FIGURE 14

Because of the symmetry of E and ρ about the xz-plane, we can immediately say that $M_{xz} = 0$ and therefore $\bar{y} = 0$. The other moments are

$$M_{yz} = \iiint_E x\rho \, dV = \int_{-1}^{1} \int_{y^2}^{1} \int_{0}^{x} x\rho \, dz \, dx \, dy$$

$$= \rho \int_{-1}^{1} \int_{y^2}^{1} x^2 \, dx \, dy = \rho \int_{-1}^{1} \left[\frac{x^3}{3} \right]_{x=y^2}^{x=1} dy$$

$$= \frac{2\rho}{3} \int_{0}^{1} (1 - y^6) \, dy = \frac{2\rho}{3} \left[y - \frac{y^7}{7} \right]_0^1 = \frac{4\rho}{7}$$

$$M_{xy} = \iiint_E z\rho \, dV = \int_{-1}^{1} \int_{y^2}^{1} \int_{0}^{x} z\rho \, dz \, dx \, dy$$

$$= \rho \int_{-1}^{1} \int_{y^2}^{1} \left[\frac{z^2}{2} \right]_{z=0}^{z=x} dx \, dy = \frac{\rho}{2} \int_{-1}^{1} \int_{y^2}^{1} x^2 \, dx \, dy$$

$$= \frac{\rho}{3} \int_{0}^{1} (1 - y^6) \, dy = \frac{2\rho}{7}$$

Therefore the center of mass is

$$(\bar{x}, \bar{y}, \bar{z}) = \left(\frac{M_{yz}}{m}, \frac{M_{xz}}{m}, \frac{M_{xy}}{m} \right) = \left(\tfrac{5}{7}, 0, \tfrac{5}{14} \right)$$

□

16.6 EXERCISES

1. Evaluate the integral in Example 1, integrating first with respect to y, then z, and then x.

2. Evaluate the integral $\iiint_E (xz - y^3)\, dV$, where

$$E = \{(x, y, z) \mid -1 \leq x \leq 1,\ 0 \leq y \leq 2,\ 0 \leq z \leq 1\}$$

using three different orders of integration.

3–8 Evaluate the iterated integral.

3. $\displaystyle\int_0^1 \int_0^z \int_0^{x+z} 6xz\, dy\, dx\, dz$

4. $\displaystyle\int_0^1 \int_x^{2x} \int_0^y 2xyz\, dz\, dy\, dx$

5. $\displaystyle\int_0^3 \int_0^1 \int_0^{\sqrt{1-z^2}} ze^y\, dx\, dz\, dy$

6. $\displaystyle\int_0^1 \int_0^z \int_0^y ze^{-y^2}\, dx\, dy\, dz$

7. $\displaystyle\int_0^{\pi/2} \int_0^y \int_0^x \cos(x + y + z)\, dz\, dx\, dy$

8. $\displaystyle\int_0^{\sqrt{\pi}} \int_0^x \int_0^{xz} x^2 \sin y\, dy\, dz\, dx$

9–18 Evaluate the triple integral.

9. $\iiint_E 2x\, dV$, where

$$E = \{(x, y, z) \mid 0 \leq y \leq 2,\ 0 \leq x \leq \sqrt{4 - y^2},\ 0 \leq z \leq y\}$$

10. $\iiint_E yz\cos(x^5)\, dV$, where

$$E = \{(x, y, z) \mid 0 \leq x \leq 1,\ 0 \leq y \leq x,\ x \leq z \leq 2x\}$$

11. $\iiint_E 6xy\, dV$, where E lies under the plane $z = 1 + x + y$ and above the region in the xy-plane bounded by the curves $y = \sqrt{x}$, $y = 0$, and $x = 1$

12. $\iiint_E y\, dV$, where E is bounded by the planes $x = 0$, $y = 0$, $z = 0$, and $2x + 2y + z = 4$

13. $\iiint_E x^2 e^y\, dV$, where E is bounded by the parabolic cylinder $z = 1 - y^2$ and the planes $z = 0$, $x = 1$, and $x = -1$

14. $\iiint_E xy\, dV$, where E is bounded by the parabolic cylinders $y = x^2$ and $x = y^2$ and the planes $z = 0$ and $z = x + y$

15. $\iiint_T x^2\, dV$, where T is the solid tetrahedron with vertices $(0, 0, 0)$, $(1, 0, 0)$, $(0, 1, 0)$, and $(0, 0, 1)$

16. $\iiint_T xyz\, dV$, where T is the solid tetrahedron with vertices $(0, 0, 0)$, $(1, 0, 0)$, $(1, 1, 0)$, and $(1, 0, 1)$

17. $\iiint_E x\, dV$, where E is bounded by the paraboloid $x = 4y^2 + 4z^2$ and the plane $x = 4$

18. $\iiint_E z\, dV$, where E is bounded by the cylinder $y^2 + z^2 = 9$ and the planes $x = 0$, $y = 3x$, and $z = 0$ in the first octant

19–22 Use a triple integral to find the volume of the given solid.

19. The tetrahedron enclosed by the coordinate planes and the plane $2x + y + z = 4$

20. The solid bounded by the cylinder $y = x^2$ and the planes $z = 0$, $z = 4$, and $y = 9$

21. The solid enclosed by the cylinder $x^2 + y^2 = 9$ and the planes $y + z = 5$ and $z = 1$

22. The solid enclosed by the paraboloid $x = y^2 + z^2$ and the plane $x = 16$

23. (a) Express the volume of the wedge in the first octant that is cut from the cylinder $y^2 + z^2 = 1$ by the planes $y = x$ and $x = 1$ as a triple integral.
　　CAS　(b) Use either the Table of Integrals (on Reference Pages 6–10) or a computer algebra system to find the exact value of the triple integral in part (a).

24. (a) In the **Midpoint Rule for triple integrals** we use a triple Riemann sum to approximate a triple integral over a box B, where $f(x, y, z)$ is evaluated at the center $(\bar{x}_i, \bar{y}_j, \bar{z}_k)$ of the box B_{ijk}. Use the Midpoint Rule to estimate $\iiint_B \sqrt{x^2 + y^2 + z^2}\, dV$, where B is the cube defined by $0 \leq x \leq 4$, $0 \leq y \leq 4$, $0 \leq z \leq 4$. Divide B into eight cubes of equal size.
　　CAS　(b) Use a computer algebra system to approximate the integral in part (a) correct to the nearest integer. Compare with the answer to part (a).

25–26 Use the Midpoint Rule for triple integrals (Exercise 24) to estimate the value of the integral. Divide B into eight sub-boxes of equal size.

25. $\iiint_B \dfrac{1}{\ln(1 + x + y + z)}\, dV$, where
$$B = \{(x, y, z) \mid 0 \leq x \leq 4,\ 0 \leq y \leq 8,\ 0 \leq z \leq 4\}$$

26. $\iiint_B \sin(xy^2z^3)\, dV$, where
$$B = \{(x, y, z) \mid 0 \leq x \leq 4,\ 0 \leq y \leq 2,\ 0 \leq z \leq 1\}$$

27–28 Sketch the solid whose volume is given by the iterated integral.

27. $\displaystyle\int_0^1 \int_0^{1-x} \int_0^{2-2z} dy\, dz\, dx$

28. $\displaystyle\int_0^2 \int_0^{2-y} \int_0^{4-y^2} dx\, dz\, dy$

29–32 Express the integral $\iiint_E f(x, y, z)\, dV$ as an iterated integral in six different ways, where E is the solid bounded by the given surfaces.

29. $y = 4 - x^2 - 4z^2$, $\quad y = 0$

30. $y^2 + z^2 = 9$, $\quad x = -2$, $\quad x = 2$

31. $y = x^2$, $\quad z = 0$, $\quad y + 2z = 4$

32. $x = 2$, $\quad y = 2$, $\quad z = 0$, $\quad x + y - 2z = 2$

33. The figure shows the region of integration for the integral

$$\int_0^1 \int_{\sqrt{x}}^1 \int_0^{1-y} f(x, y, z) \, dz \, dy \, dx$$

Rewrite this integral as an equivalent iterated integral in the five other orders.

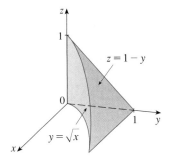

34. The figure shows the region of integration for the integral

$$\int_0^1 \int_0^{1-x^2} \int_0^{1-x} f(x, y, z) \, dy \, dz \, dx$$

Rewrite this integral as an equivalent iterated integral in the five other orders.

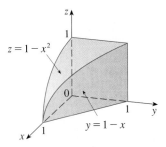

35–36 Write five other iterated integrals that are equal to the given iterated integral.

35. $\int_0^1 \int_y^1 \int_0^y f(x, y, z) \, dz \, dx \, dy$

36. $\int_0^1 \int_0^{x^2} \int_0^y f(x, y, z) \, dz \, dy \, dx$

37–40 Find the mass and center of mass of the solid E with the given density function ρ.

37. E is the solid of Exercise 11; $\rho(x, y, z) = 2$

38. E is bounded by the parabolic cylinder $z = 1 - y^2$ and the planes $x + z = 1$, $x = 0$, and $z = 0$; $\rho(x, y, z) = 4$

39. E is the cube given by $0 \le x \le a$, $0 \le y \le a$, $0 \le z \le a$; $\rho(x, y, z) = x^2 + y^2 + z^2$

40. E is the tetrahedron bounded by the planes $x = 0$, $y = 0$, $z = 0$, $x + y + z = 1$; $\rho(x, y, z) = y$

41–44 Assume that the solid has constant density k.

41. Find the moments of inertia for a cube with side length L if one vertex is located at the origin and three edges lie along the coordinate axes.

42. Find the moments of inertia for a rectangular brick with dimensions a, b, and c and mass M if the center of the brick is situated at the origin and the edges are parallel to the coordinate axes.

43. Find the moment of inertia about the z-axis of the solid cylinder $x^2 + y^2 \le a^2$, $0 \le z \le h$.

44. Find the moment of inertia about the z-axis of the solid cone $\sqrt{x^2 + y^2} \le z \le h$.

45–46 Set up, but do not evaluate, integral expressions for (a) the mass, (b) the center of mass, and (c) the moment of inertia about the z-axis.

45. The solid of Exercise 21; $\rho(x, y, z) = \sqrt{x^2 + y^2}$

46. The hemisphere $x^2 + y^2 + z^2 \le 1$, $z \ge 0$; $\rho(x, y, z) = \sqrt{x^2 + y^2 + z^2}$

CAS **47.** Let E be the solid in the first octant bounded by the cylinder $x^2 + y^2 = 1$ and the planes $y = z$, $x = 0$, and $z = 0$ with the density function $\rho(x, y, z) = 1 + x + y + z$. Use a computer algebra system to find the exact values of the following quantities for E.
(a) The mass
(b) The center of mass
(c) The moment of inertia about the z-axis

CAS **48.** If E is the solid of Exercise 18 with density function $\rho(x, y, z) = x^2 + y^2$, find the following quantities, correct to three decimal places.
(a) The mass
(b) The center of mass
(c) The moment of inertia about the z-axis

49. The joint density function for random variables X, Y, and Z is $f(x, y, z) = Cxyz$ if $0 \le x \le 2$, $0 \le y \le 2$, $0 \le z \le 2$, and $f(x, y, z) = 0$ otherwise.
(a) Find the value of the constant C.
(b) Find $P(X \le 1, Y \le 1, Z \le 1)$.
(c) Find $P(X + Y + Z \le 1)$.

50. Suppose X, Y, and Z are random variables with joint density function $f(x, y, z) = Ce^{-(0.5x+0.2y+0.1z)}$ if $x \ge 0$, $y \ge 0$, $z \ge 0$, and $f(x, y, z) = 0$ otherwise.
(a) Find the value of the constant C.
(b) Find $P(X \le 1, Y \le 1)$.
(c) Find $P(X \le 1, Y \le 1, Z \le 1)$.

51–52 The **average value** of a function $f(x, y, z)$ over a solid region E is defined to be

$$f_{\text{ave}} = \frac{1}{V(E)} \iiint_E f(x, y, z)\, dV$$

where $V(E)$ is the volume of E. For instance, if ρ is a density function, then ρ_{ave} is the average density of E.

51. Find the average value of the function $f(x, y, z) = xyz$ over the cube with side length L that lies in the first octant with one vertex at the origin and edges parallel to the coordinate axes.

52. Find the average value of the function $f(x, y, z) = x^2 z + y^2 z$ over the region enclosed by the paraboloid $z = 1 - x^2 - y^2$ and the plane $z = 0$.

53. Find the region E for which the triple integral

$$\iiint_E (1 - x^2 - 2y^2 - 3z^2)\, dV$$

is a maximum.

DISCOVERY PROJECT

VOLUMES OF HYPERSPHERES

In this project we find formulas for the volume enclosed by a hypersphere in n-dimensional space.

1. Use a double integral and trigonometric substitution, together with Formula 64 in the Table of Integrals, to find the area of a circle with radius r.

2. Use a triple integral and trigonometric substitution to find the volume of a sphere with radius r.

3. Use a quadruple integral to find the hypervolume enclosed by the hypersphere $x^2 + y^2 + z^2 + w^2 = r^2$ in $\mathbb{R}^4$. (Use only trigonometric substitution and the reduction formulas for $\int \sin^n x\, dx$ or $\int \cos^n x\, dx$.)

4. Use an n-tuple integral to find the volume enclosed by a hypersphere of radius r in n-dimensional space $\mathbb{R}^n$.   [*Hint:* The formulas are different for n even and n odd.]

16.7   TRIPLE INTEGRALS IN CYLINDRICAL COORDINATES

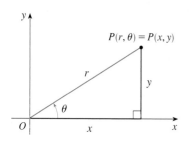

FIGURE 1

In plane geometry the polar coordinate system is used to give a convenient description of certain curves and regions. (See Section 11.3.) Figure 1 enables us to recall the connection between polar and Cartesian coordinates. If the point P has Cartesian coordinates (x, y) and polar coordinates (r, θ), then, from the figure,

$$x = r \cos \theta \qquad\qquad y = r \sin \theta$$

$$r^2 = x^2 + y^2 \qquad\qquad \tan \theta = \frac{y}{x}$$

In three dimensions there is a coordinate system, called *cylindrical coordinates*, that is similar to polar coordinates and gives convenient descriptions of some commonly occurring surfaces and solids. As we will see, some triple integrals are much easier to evaluate in cylindrical coordinates.

CYLINDRICAL COORDINATES

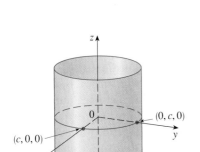

FIGURE 2
The cylindrical coordinates of a point

In the **cylindrical coordinate system**, a point P in three-dimensional space is represented by the ordered triple (r, θ, z), where r and θ are polar coordinates of the projection of P onto the xy-plane and z is the directed distance from the xy-plane to P. (See Figure 2.)

To convert from cylindrical to rectangular coordinates, we use the equations

$$\boxed{1} \qquad \boxed{\quad x = r \cos \theta \qquad y = r \sin \theta \qquad z = z \quad}$$

whereas to convert from rectangular to cylindrical coordinates, we use

$$\boxed{2} \qquad \boxed{\quad r^2 = x^2 + y^2 \qquad \tan \theta = \frac{y}{x} \qquad z = z \quad}$$

EXAMPLE 1

(a) Plot the point with cylindrical coordinates $(2, 2\pi/3, 1)$ and find its rectangular coordinates.

(b) Find cylindrical coordinates of the point with rectangular coordinates $(3, -3, -7)$.

SOLUTION

(a) The point with cylindrical coordinates $(2, 2\pi/3, 1)$ is plotted in Figure 3. From Equations 1, its rectangular coordinates are

$$x = 2 \cos \frac{2\pi}{3} = 2\left(-\frac{1}{2}\right) = -1$$

$$y = 2 \sin \frac{2\pi}{3} = 2\left(\frac{\sqrt{3}}{2}\right) = \sqrt{3}$$

$$z = 1$$

FIGURE 3

Thus the point is $\left(-1, \sqrt{3}, 1\right)$ in rectangular coordinates.

(b) From Equations 2 we have

$$r = \sqrt{3^2 + (-3)^2} = 3\sqrt{2}$$

$$\tan \theta = \frac{-3}{3} = -1 \qquad \text{so} \qquad \theta = \frac{7\pi}{4} + 2n\pi$$

$$z = -7$$

Therefore one set of cylindrical coordinates is $\left(3\sqrt{2}, 7\pi/4, -7\right)$. Another is $\left(3\sqrt{2}, -\pi/4, -7\right)$. As with polar coordinates, there are infinitely many choices. ☐

Cylindrical coordinates are useful in problems that involve symmetry about an axis, and the z-axis is chosen to coincide with this axis of symmetry. For instance, the axis of the circular cylinder with Cartesian equation $x^2 + y^2 = c^2$ is the z-axis. In cylindrical coordinates this cylinder has the very simple equation $r = c$. (See Figure 4.) This is the reason for the name "cylindrical" coordinates.

FIGURE 4
$r = c$, a cylinder

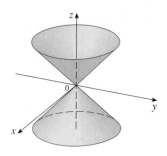

FIGURE 5

$z = r$, a cone

☑ EXAMPLE 2 Describe the surface whose equation in cylindrical coordinates is $z = r$.

SOLUTION The equation says that the z-value, or height, of each point on the surface is the same as r, the distance from the point to the z-axis. Because θ doesn't appear, it can vary. So any horizontal trace in the plane $z = k$ ($k > 0$) is a circle of radius k. These traces suggest that the surface is a cone. This prediction can be confirmed by converting the equation into rectangular coordinates. From the first equation in (2) we have

$$z^2 = r^2 = x^2 + y^2$$

We recognize the equation $z^2 = x^2 + y^2$ (by comparison with Table 1 in Section 13.6) as being a circular cone whose axis is the z-axis. (See Figure 5.) ☐

EVALUATING TRIPLE INTEGRALS WITH CYLINDRICAL COORDINATES

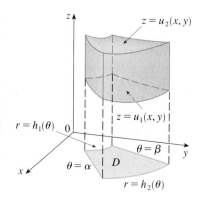

FIGURE 6

Suppose that E is a type 1 region whose projection D on the xy-plane is conveniently described in polar coordinates (see Figure 6). In particular, suppose that f is continuous and

$$E = \{(x, y, z) \mid (x, y) \in D, \ u_1(x, y) \le z \le u_2(x, y)\}$$

where D is given in polar coordinates by

$$D = \{(r, \theta) \mid \alpha \le \theta \le \beta, \ h_1(\theta) \le r \le h_2(\theta)\}$$

We know from Equation 16.6.6 that

$$\boxed{3} \qquad \iiint_E f(x, y, z)\, dV = \iint_D \left[\int_{u_1(x, y)}^{u_2(x, y)} f(x, y, z)\, dz \right] dA$$

But we also know how to evaluate double integrals in polar coordinates. In fact, combining Equation 3 with Equation 16.4.3, we obtain

$$\boxed{4} \qquad \iiint_E f(x, y, z)\, dV = \int_\alpha^\beta \int_{h_1(\theta)}^{h_2(\theta)} \int_{u_1(r\cos\theta,\, r\sin\theta)}^{u_2(r\cos\theta,\, r\sin\theta)} f(r\cos\theta, r\sin\theta, z)\, r\, dz\, dr\, d\theta$$

FIGURE 7

Volume element in cylindrical coordinates: $dV = r\, dz\, dr\, d\theta$

Formula 4 is the **formula for triple integration in cylindrical coordinates**. It says that we convert a triple integral from rectangular to cylindrical coordinates by writing $x = r\cos\theta$, $y = r\sin\theta$, leaving z as it is, using the appropriate limits of integration for z, r, and θ, and replacing dV by $r\, dz\, dr\, d\theta$. (Figure 7 shows how to remember this.) It is worthwhile to use this formula when E is a solid region easily described in cylindrical coordinates, and especially when the function $f(x, y, z)$ involves the expression $x^2 + y^2$.

☑ EXAMPLE 3 A solid E lies within the cylinder $x^2 + y^2 = 1$, below the plane $z = 4$, and above the paraboloid $z = 1 - x^2 - y^2$. (See Figure 8.) The density at any point is proportional to its distance from the axis of the cylinder. Find the mass of E.

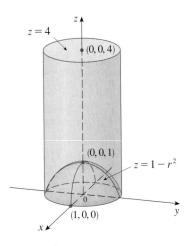

$z = 4$

$(0, 0, 4)$

$(0, 0, 1)$

$z = 1 - r^2$

$(1, 0, 0)$

FIGURE 8

SOLUTION In cylindrical coordinates the cylinder is $r = 1$ and the paraboloid is $z = 1 - r^2$, so we can write

$$E = \{(r, \theta, z) \mid 0 \leqslant \theta \leqslant 2\pi, \ 0 \leqslant r \leqslant 1, \ 1 - r^2 \leqslant z \leqslant 4\}$$

Since the density at (x, y, z) is proportional to the distance from the z-axis, the density function is

$$f(x, y, z) = K\sqrt{x^2 + y^2} = Kr$$

where K is the proportionality constant. Therefore, from Formula 16.6.13, the mass of E is

$$m = \iiint_E K\sqrt{x^2 + y^2} \, dV$$

$$= \int_0^{2\pi} \int_0^1 \int_{1-r^2}^4 (Kr) \, r \, dz \, dr \, d\theta$$

$$= \int_0^{2\pi} \int_0^1 Kr^2 [4 - (1 - r^2)] \, dr \, d\theta$$

$$= K \int_0^{2\pi} d\theta \int_0^1 (3r^2 + r^4) \, dr$$

$$= 2\pi K \left[r^3 + \frac{r^5}{5} \right]_0^1 = \frac{12\pi K}{5}$$

$\square$

EXAMPLE 4 Evaluate $\displaystyle\int_{-2}^2 \int_{-\sqrt{4-x^2}}^{\sqrt{4-x^2}} \int_{\sqrt{x^2+y^2}}^2 (x^2 + y^2) \, dz \, dy \, dx$.

SOLUTION This iterated integral is a triple integral over the solid region

$$E = \{(x, y, z) \mid -2 \leqslant x \leqslant 2, \ -\sqrt{4 - x^2} \leqslant y \leqslant \sqrt{4 - x^2}, \ \sqrt{x^2 + y^2} \leqslant z \leqslant 2\}$$

and the projection of E onto the xy-plane is the disk $x^2 + y^2 \leqslant 4$. The lower surface of E is the cone $z = \sqrt{x^2 + y^2}$ and its upper surface is the plane $z = 2$. (See Figure 9.) This region has a much simpler description in cylindrical coordinates:

$$E = \{(r, \theta, z) \mid 0 \leqslant \theta \leqslant 2\pi, \ 0 \leqslant r \leqslant 2, \ r \leqslant z \leqslant 2\}$$

Therefore, we have

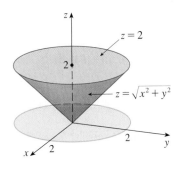

$z = 2$

$z = \sqrt{x^2 + y^2}$

FIGURE 9

$$\int_{-2}^2 \int_{-\sqrt{4-x^2}}^{\sqrt{4-x^2}} \int_{\sqrt{x^2+y^2}}^2 (x^2 + y^2) \, dz \, dy \, dx = \iiint_E (x^2 + y^2) \, dV$$

$$= \int_0^{2\pi} \int_0^2 \int_r^2 r^2 \, r \, dz \, dr \, d\theta$$

$$= \int_0^{2\pi} d\theta \int_0^2 r^3 (2 - r) \, dr$$

$$= 2\pi \left[\tfrac{1}{2} r^4 - \tfrac{1}{5} r^5 \right]_0^2 = \tfrac{16}{5}\pi$$

$\square$

16.7 EXERCISES

1–2 Plot the point whose cylindrical coordinates are given. Then find the rectangular coordinates of the point.

1. (a) $(2, \pi/4, 1)$ (b) $(4, -\pi/3, 5)$

2. (a) $(1, \pi, e)$ (b) $(1, 3\pi/2, 2)$

3–4 Change from rectangular to cylindrical coordinates.

3. (a) $(1, -1, 4)$ (b) $(-1, -\sqrt{3}, 2)$

4. (a) $(2\sqrt{3}, 2, -1)$ (b) $(4, -3, 2)$

5–6 Describe in words the surface whose equation is given.

5. $\theta = \pi/4$ 6. $r = 5$

7–8 Identify the surface whose equation is given.

7. $z = 4 - r^2$ 8. $2r^2 + z^2 = 1$

9–10 Write the equations in cylindrical coordinates.

9. (a) $z = x^2 + y^2$ (b) $x^2 + y^2 = 2y$

10. (a) $3x + 2y + z = 6$ (b) $-x^2 - y^2 + z^2 = 1$

11–12 Sketch the solid described by the given inequalities.

11. $0 \le r \le 2$, $\quad -\pi/2 \le \theta \le \pi/2$, $\quad 0 \le z \le 1$

12. $0 \le \theta \le \pi/2$, $\quad r \le z \le 2$

13. A cylindrical shell is 20 cm long, with inner radius 6 cm and outer radius 7 cm. Write inequalities that describe the shell in an appropriate coordinate system. Explain how you have positioned the coordinate system with respect to the shell.

14. Use a graphing device to draw the solid enclosed by the paraboloids $z = x^2 + y^2$ and $z = 5 - x^2 - y^2$.

15–16 Sketch the solid whose volume is given by the integral and evaluate the integral.

15. $\int_0^4 \int_0^{2\pi} \int_r^4 r \, dz \, d\theta \, dr$ 16. $\int_0^{\pi/2} \int_0^2 \int_0^{9-r^2} r \, dz \, dr \, d\theta$

17–26 Use cylindrical coordinates.

17. Evaluate $\iiint_E \sqrt{x^2 + y^2} \, dV$, where E is the region that lies inside the cylinder $x^2 + y^2 = 16$ and between the planes $z = -5$ and $z = 4$.

18. Evaluate $\iiint_E (x^3 + xy^2) \, dV$, where E is the solid in the first octant that lies beneath the paraboloid $z = 1 - x^2 - y^2$.

19. Evaluate $\iiint_E e^z \, dV$, where E is enclosed by the paraboloid $z = 1 + x^2 + y^2$, the cylinder $x^2 + y^2 = 5$, and the xy-plane.

20. Evaluate $\iiint_E x \, dV$, where E is enclosed by the planes $z = 0$ and $z = x + y + 5$ and by the cylinders $x^2 + y^2 = 4$ and $x^2 + y^2 = 9$.

21. Evaluate $\iiint_E x^2 \, dV$, where E is the solid that lies within the cylinder $x^2 + y^2 = 1$, above the plane $z = 0$, and below the cone $z^2 = 4x^2 + 4y^2$.

22. Find the volume of the solid that lies within both the cylinder $x^2 + y^2 = 1$ and the sphere $x^2 + y^2 + z^2 = 4$.

23. (a) Find the volume of the region E bounded by the paraboloids $z = x^2 + y^2$ and $z = 36 - 3x^2 - 3y^2$.
    (b) Find the centroid of E (the center of mass in the case where the density is constant).

24. (a) Find the volume of the solid that the cylinder $r = a \cos \theta$ cuts out of the sphere of radius a centered at the origin.

    (b) Illustrate the solid of part (a) by graphing the sphere and the cylinder on the same screen.

25. Find the mass and center of mass of the solid S bounded by the paraboloid $z = 4x^2 + 4y^2$ and the plane $z = a$ $(a > 0)$ if S has constant density K.

26. Find the mass of a ball B given by $x^2 + y^2 + z^2 \le a^2$ if the density at any point is proportional to its distance from the z-axis.

27–28 Evaluate the integral by changing to cylindrical coordinates.

27. $\displaystyle\int_{-2}^{2} \int_{-\sqrt{4-y^2}}^{\sqrt{4-y^2}} \int_{\sqrt{x^2+y^2}}^{2} xz \, dz \, dx \, dy$

28. $\displaystyle\int_{-3}^{3} \int_{0}^{\sqrt{9-x^2}} \int_{0}^{9-x^2-y^2} \sqrt{x^2 + y^2} \, dz \, dy \, dx$

29. When studying the formation of mountain ranges, geologists estimate the amount of work required to lift a mountain from sea level. Consider a mountain that is essentially in the shape of a right circular cone. Suppose that the weight density of the material in the vicinity of a point P is $g(P)$ and the height is $h(P)$.
    (a) Find a definite integral that represents the total work done in forming the mountain.
    (b) Assume that Mount Fuji in Japan is in the shape of a right circular cone with radius 62,000 ft, height 12,400 ft, and density a constant 200 lb/ft³. How much work was done in forming Mount Fuji if the land was initially at sea level?

THE INTERSECTION OF THREE CYLINDERS

The figure shows the solid enclosed by three circular cylinders with the same diameter that intersect at right angles. In this project we compute its volume and determine how its shape changes if
the cylinders have different diameters.

1. Sketch carefully the solid enclosed by the three cylinders $x^2 + y^2 = 1$, $x^2 + z^2 = 1$, and
   $y^2 + z^2 = 1$. Indicate the positions of the coordinate axes and label the faces with the equations of the corresponding cylinders.

2. Find the volume of the solid in Problem 1.

CAS 3. Use a computer algebra system to draw the edges of the solid.

4. What happens to the solid in Problem 1 if the radius of the first cylinder is different from 1?
   Illustrate with a hand-drawn sketch or a computer graph.

5. If the first cylinder is $x^2 + y^2 = a^2$, where $a < 1$, set up, but do not evaluate, a double integral for the volume of the solid. What if $a > 1$?

16.8 TRIPLE INTEGRALS IN SPHERICAL COORDINATES

Another useful coordinate system in three dimensions is the *spherical coordinate system*.
It simplifies the evaluation of triple integrals over regions bounded by spheres or cones.

SPHERICAL COORDINATES

The **spherical coordinates** (ρ, θ, ϕ) of a point P in space are shown in Figure 1, where
$\rho = |OP|$ is the distance from the origin to P, θ is the same angle as in cylindrical coordinates, and ϕ is the angle between the positive z-axis and the line segment OP. Note that

$$\rho \geqslant 0 \qquad 0 \leqslant \phi \leqslant \pi$$

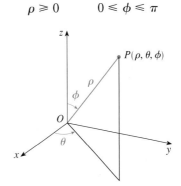

FIGURE 1
The spherical coordinates of a point

The spherical coordinate system is especially useful in problems where there is symmetry about a point, and the origin is placed at this point. For example, the sphere with center the origin and radius c has the simple equation $\rho = c$ (see Figure 2); this is the reason for the name "spherical" coordinates. The graph of the equation $\theta = c$ is a vertical half-plane (see Figure 3), and the equation $\phi = c$ represents a half-cone with the z-axis as its axis (see Figure 4).

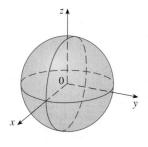

FIGURE 2 $\rho = c$, a sphere

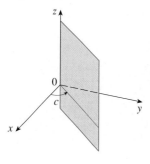

FIGURE 3 $\theta = c$, a half-plane

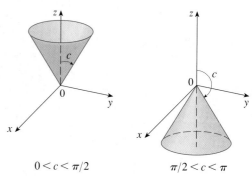

$0 < c < \pi/2$ $\pi/2 < c < \pi$

FIGURE 4 $\phi = c$, a half-cone

The relationship between rectangular and spherical coordinates can be seen from Figure 5. From triangles OPQ and OPP' we have

$$z = \rho \cos \phi \qquad r = \rho \sin \phi$$

But $x = r \cos \theta$ and $y = r \sin \theta$, so to convert from spherical to rectangular coordinates, we use the equations

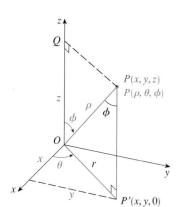

FIGURE 5

$$\boxed{1} \qquad x = \rho \sin \phi \cos \theta \qquad y = \rho \sin \phi \sin \theta \qquad z = \rho \cos \phi$$

Also, the distance formula shows that

$$\boxed{2} \qquad \rho^2 = x^2 + y^2 + z^2$$

We use this equation in converting from rectangular to spherical coordinates.

☑ **EXAMPLE 1** The point $(2, \pi/4, \pi/3)$ is given in spherical coordinates. Plot the point and find its rectangular coordinates.

SOLUTION We plot the point in Figure 6. From Equations 1 we have

$$x = \rho \sin \phi \cos \theta = 2 \sin \frac{\pi}{3} \cos \frac{\pi}{4} = 2\left(\frac{\sqrt{3}}{2}\right)\left(\frac{1}{\sqrt{2}}\right) = \sqrt{\frac{3}{2}}$$

$$y = \rho \sin \phi \sin \theta = 2 \sin \frac{\pi}{3} \sin \frac{\pi}{4} = 2\left(\frac{\sqrt{3}}{2}\right)\left(\frac{1}{\sqrt{2}}\right) = \sqrt{\frac{3}{2}}$$

$$z = \rho \cos \phi = 2 \cos \frac{\pi}{3} = 2\left(\tfrac{1}{2}\right) = 1$$

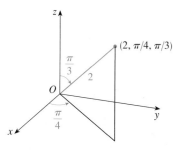

FIGURE 6

Thus the point $(2, \pi/4, \pi/3)$ is $\left(\sqrt{3/2}, \sqrt{3/2}, 1\right)$ in rectangular coordinates.   ☐

TEC In Module 16.8 you can investigate families of surfaces in cylindrical and spherical coordinates.

☑ **EXAMPLE 2** The point $(0, 2\sqrt{3}, -2)$ is given in rectangular coordinates. Find spherical coordinates for this point.

SOLUTION From Equation 2 we have

$$\rho = \sqrt{x^2 + y^2 + z^2} = \sqrt{0 + 12 + 4} = 4$$

and so Equations 1 give

$$\cos \phi = \frac{z}{\rho} = \frac{-2}{4} = -\frac{1}{2} \qquad \phi = \frac{2\pi}{3}$$

$$\cos \theta = \frac{x}{\rho \sin \phi} = 0 \qquad \theta = \frac{\pi}{2}$$

(Note that $\theta \neq 3\pi/2$ because $y = 2\sqrt{3} > 0$.) Therefore spherical coordinates of the given point are $(4, \pi/2, 2\pi/3)$. ☐

EVALUATING TRIPLE INTEGRALS WITH SPHERICAL COORDINATES

In the spherical coordinate system the counterpart of a rectangular box is a **spherical wedge**

$$E = \left\{ (\rho, \theta, \phi) \mid a \leqslant \rho \leqslant b, \ \alpha \leqslant \theta \leqslant \beta, \ c \leqslant \phi \leqslant d \right\}$$

where $a \geqslant 0$, $\beta - \alpha \leqslant 2\pi$, and $d - c \leqslant \pi$. Although we defined triple integrals by dividing solids into small boxes, it can be shown that dividing a solid into small spherical wedges always gives the same result. So we divide E into smaller spherical wedges E_{ijk} by means of equally spaced spheres $\rho = \rho_i$, half-planes $\theta = \theta_j$, and half-cones $\phi = \phi_k$. Figure 7 shows that E_{ijk} is approximately a rectangular box with dimensions $\Delta\rho$, $\rho_i \Delta\phi$ (arc of a circle with radius ρ_i, angle $\Delta\phi$), and $\rho_i \sin \phi_k \Delta\theta$ (arc of a circle with radius $\rho_i \sin \phi_k$, angle $\Delta\theta$). So an approximation to the volume of E_{ijk} is given by

$$\Delta V_{ijk} \approx (\Delta\rho)(\rho_i \Delta\phi)(\rho_i \sin \phi_k \Delta\theta) = \rho_i^2 \sin \phi_k \Delta\rho \Delta\theta \Delta\phi$$

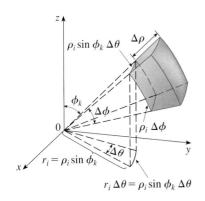

FIGURE 7

In fact, it can be shown, with the aid of the Mean Value Theorem (Exercise 45), that the volume of E_{ijk} is given exactly by

$$\Delta V_{ijk} = \tilde{\rho}_i^2 \sin \tilde{\phi}_k \Delta\rho \Delta\theta \Delta\phi$$

where $(\tilde{\rho}_i, \tilde{\theta}_j, \tilde{\phi}_k)$ is some point in E_{ijk}. Let $(x_{ijk}^*, y_{ijk}^*, z_{ijk}^*)$ be the rectangular coordinates of this point. Then

$$\iiint\limits_E f(x, y, z) \, dV = \lim_{l, m, n \to \infty} \sum_{i=1}^{l} \sum_{j=1}^{m} \sum_{k=1}^{n} f(x_{ijk}^*, y_{ijk}^*, z_{ijk}^*) \, \Delta V_{ijk}$$

$$= \lim_{l, m, n \to \infty} \sum_{i=1}^{l} \sum_{j=1}^{m} \sum_{k=1}^{n} f(\tilde{\rho}_i \sin \tilde{\phi}_k \cos \tilde{\theta}_j, \tilde{\rho}_i \sin \tilde{\phi}_k \sin \tilde{\theta}_j, \tilde{\rho}_i \cos \tilde{\phi}_k) \, \tilde{\rho}_i^2 \sin \tilde{\phi}_k \Delta\rho \Delta\theta \Delta\phi$$

But this sum is a Riemann sum for the function

$$F(\rho, \theta, \phi) = f(\rho \sin \phi \cos \theta, \rho \sin \phi \sin \theta, \rho \cos \phi) \rho^2 \sin \phi$$

Consequently, we have arrived at the following **formula for triple integration in spherical coordinates**.

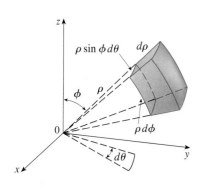

FIGURE 8
Volume element in spherical
coordinates: $dV = \rho^2 \sin \phi \, d\rho \, d\theta \, d\phi$

$$\boxed{3} \quad \iiint_E f(x, y, z) \, dV$$

$$= \int_c^d \int_\alpha^\beta \int_a^b f(\rho \sin \phi \cos \theta, \rho \sin \phi \sin \theta, \rho \cos \phi) \, \rho^2 \sin \phi \, d\rho \, d\theta \, d\phi$$

where E is a spherical wedge given by

$$E = \{(\rho, \theta, \phi) \mid a \leqslant \rho \leqslant b, \ \alpha \leqslant \theta \leqslant \beta, \ c \leqslant \phi \leqslant d\}$$

Formula 3 says that we convert a triple integral from rectangular coordinates to spherical coordinates by writing

$$x = \rho \sin \phi \cos \theta \qquad y = \rho \sin \phi \sin \theta \qquad z = \rho \cos \phi$$

using the appropriate limits of integration, and replacing dV by $\rho^2 \sin \phi \, d\rho \, d\theta \, d\phi$. This is illustrated in Figure 8.

This formula can be extended to include more general spherical regions such as

$$E = \{(\rho, \theta, \phi) \mid \alpha \leqslant \theta \leqslant \beta, \ c \leqslant \phi \leqslant d, \ g_1(\theta, \phi) \leqslant \rho \leqslant g_2(\theta, \phi)\}$$

In this case the formula is the same as in (3) except that the limits of integration for ρ are $g_1(\theta, \phi)$ and $g_2(\theta, \phi)$.

Usually, spherical coordinates are used in triple integrals when surfaces such as cones and spheres form the boundary of the region of integration.

⊽ EXAMPLE 3 Evaluate $\iiint_B e^{(x^2+y^2+z^2)^{3/2}} \, dV$, where B is the unit ball:

$$B = \{(x, y, z) \mid x^2 + y^2 + z^2 \leqslant 1\}$$

SOLUTION Since the boundary of B is a sphere, we use spherical coordinates:

$$B = \{(\rho, \theta, \phi) \mid 0 \leqslant \rho \leqslant 1, \ 0 \leqslant \theta \leqslant 2\pi, \ 0 \leqslant \phi \leqslant \pi\}$$

In addition, spherical coordinates are appropriate because

$$x^2 + y^2 + z^2 = \rho^2$$

Thus (3) gives

$$\iiint_B e^{(x^2+y^2+z^2)^{3/2}} \, dV = \int_0^\pi \int_0^{2\pi} \int_0^1 e^{(\rho^2)^{3/2}} \rho^2 \sin \phi \, d\rho \, d\theta \, d\phi$$

$$= \int_0^\pi \sin \phi \, d\phi \int_0^{2\pi} d\theta \int_0^1 \rho^2 e^{\rho^3} \, d\rho$$

$$= \left[-\cos \phi\right]_0^\pi (2\pi) \left[\tfrac{1}{3} e^{\rho^3}\right]_0^1 = \tfrac{4}{3}\pi(e - 1) \qquad \square$$

NOTE It would have been extremely awkward to evaluate the integral in Example 3 without spherical coordinates. In rectangular coordinates the iterated integral would have been

$$\int_{-1}^1 \int_{-\sqrt{1-x^2}}^{\sqrt{1-x^2}} \int_{-\sqrt{1-x^2-y^2}}^{\sqrt{1-x^2-y^2}} e^{(x^2+y^2+z^2)^{3/2}} \, dz \, dy \, dx$$

V EXAMPLE 4 Use spherical coordinates to find the volume of the solid that lies above the cone $z = \sqrt{x^2 + y^2}$ and below the sphere $x^2 + y^2 + z^2 = z$. (See Figure 9.)

FIGURE 9

■ Figure 10 gives another look (this time drawn by Maple) at the solid of Example 4.

FIGURE 10

SOLUTION Notice that the sphere passes through the origin and has center $(0, 0, \frac{1}{2})$. We write the equation of the sphere in spherical coordinates as

$$\rho^2 = \rho \cos \phi \qquad \text{or} \qquad \rho = \cos \phi$$

The equation of the cone can be written as

$$\rho \cos \phi = \sqrt{\rho^2 \sin^2\phi \, \cos^2\theta + \rho^2 \sin^2\phi \, \sin^2\theta} = \rho \sin \phi$$

This gives $\sin \phi = \cos \phi$, or $\phi = \pi/4$. Therefore the description of the solid E in spherical coordinates is

$$E = \left\{ (\rho, \theta, \phi) \mid 0 \leq \theta \leq 2\pi, \ 0 \leq \phi \leq \pi/4, \ 0 \leq \rho \leq \cos \phi \right\}$$

Figure 11 shows how E is swept out if we integrate first with respect to ρ, then ϕ, and then θ. The volume of E is

$$V(E) = \iiint_E dV = \int_0^{2\pi} \int_0^{\pi/4} \int_0^{\cos \phi} \rho^2 \sin \phi \, d\rho \, d\phi \, d\theta$$

$$= \int_0^{2\pi} d\theta \int_0^{\pi/4} \sin \phi \left[\frac{\rho^3}{3} \right]_{\rho=0}^{\rho=\cos \phi} d\phi$$

$$= \frac{2\pi}{3} \int_0^{\pi/4} \sin \phi \, \cos^3\phi \, d\phi = \frac{2\pi}{3} \left[-\frac{\cos^4\phi}{4} \right]_0^{\pi/4} = \frac{\pi}{8}$$

TEC Visual 16.8 shows an animation of Figure 11.

ρ varies from 0 to $\cos \phi$ while ϕ and θ are constant.

ϕ varies from 0 to $\pi/4$ while θ is constant.

θ varies from 0 to 2π.

FIGURE 11

16.8 EXERCISES

1–2 Plot the point whose spherical coordinates are given. Then find the rectangular coordinates of the point.

1. (a) $(1, 0, 0)$ (b) $(2, \pi/3, \pi/4)$

2. (a) $(5, \pi, \pi/2)$ (b) $(4, 3\pi/4, \pi/3)$

3–4 Change from rectangular to spherical coordinates.

3. (a) $\left(1, \sqrt{3}, 2\sqrt{3}\right)$ (b) $(0, -1, -1)$

4. (a) $\left(0, \sqrt{3}, 1\right)$ (b) $\left(-1, 1, \sqrt{6}\right)$

5–6 Describe in words the surface whose equation is given.

5. $\phi = \pi/3$ **6.** $\rho = 3$

7–8 Identify the surface whose equation is given.

7. $\rho = \sin \theta \sin \phi$ **8.** $\rho^2(\sin^2\phi \sin^2\theta + \cos^2\phi) = 9$

9–10 Write the equation in spherical coordinates.

9. (a) $z^2 = x^2 + y^2$ (b) $x^2 + z^2 = 9$

10. (a) $x^2 - 2x + y^2 + z^2 = 0$ (b) $x + 2y + 3z = 1$

11–14 Sketch the solid described by the given inequalities.

11. $\rho \leqslant 2, \quad 0 \leqslant \phi \leqslant \pi/2, \quad 0 \leqslant \theta \leqslant \pi/2$

12. $2 \leqslant \rho \leqslant 3, \quad \pi/2 \leqslant \phi \leqslant \pi$

13. $\rho \leqslant 1, \quad 3\pi/4 \leqslant \phi \leqslant \pi$

14. $\rho \leqslant 2, \quad \rho \leqslant \csc \phi$

15. A solid lies above the cone $z = \sqrt{x^2 + y^2}$ and below the sphere $x^2 + y^2 + z^2 = z$. Write a description of the solid in terms of inequalities involving spherical coordinates.

16. (a) Find inequalities that describe a hollow ball with diameter 30 cm and thickness 0.5 cm. Explain how you have positioned the coordinate system that you have chosen.
(b) Suppose the ball is cut in half. Write inequalities that describe one of the halves.

17–18 Sketch the solid whose volume is given by the integral and evaluate the integral.

17. $\int_0^{\pi/6} \int_0^{\pi/2} \int_0^3 \rho^2 \sin \phi \, d\rho \, d\theta \, d\phi$

18. $\int_0^{2\pi} \int_{\pi/2}^{\pi} \int_1^2 \rho^2 \sin \phi \, d\rho \, d\phi \, d\theta$

19–20 Set up the triple integral of an arbitrary continuous function $f(x, y, z)$ in cylindrical or spherical coordinates over the solid shown.

19.

20.

21–34 Use spherical coordinates.

21. Evaluate $\iiint_B (x^2 + y^2 + z^2)^2 \, dV$, where B is the ball with center the origin and radius 5.

22. Evaluate $\iiint_H (9 - x^2 - y^2) \, dV$, where H is the solid hemisphere $x^2 + y^2 + z^2 \leqslant 9, z \geqslant 0$.

23. Evaluate $\iiint_E z \, dV$, where E lies between the spheres $x^2 + y^2 + z^2 = 1$ and $x^2 + y^2 + z^2 = 4$ in the first octant.

24. Evaluate $\iiint_E e^{\sqrt{x^2+y^2+z^2}} \, dV$, where E is enclosed by the sphere $x^2 + y^2 + z^2 = 9$ in the first octant.

25. Evaluate $\iiint_E x^2 \, dV$, where E is bounded by the xz-plane and the hemispheres $y = \sqrt{9 - x^2 - z^2}$ and $y = \sqrt{16 - x^2 - z^2}$.

26. Evaluate $\iiint_E xyz \, dV$, where E lies between the spheres $\rho = 2$ and $\rho = 4$ and above the cone $\phi = \pi/3$.

27. Find the volume of the part of the ball $\rho \leqslant a$ that lies between the cones $\phi = \pi/6$ and $\phi = \pi/3$.

28. Find the average distance from a point in a ball of radius a to its center.

29. (a) Find the volume of the solid that lies above the cone $\phi = \pi/3$ and below the sphere $\rho = 4 \cos \phi$.
(b) Find the centroid of the solid in part (a).

30. Find the volume of the solid that lies within the sphere $x^2 + y^2 + z^2 = 4$, above the xy-plane, and below the cone $z = \sqrt{x^2 + y^2}$.

31. Find the centroid of the solid in Exercise 25.

32. Let H be a solid hemisphere of radius a whose density at any point is proportional to its distance from the center of the base.
(a) Find the mass of H.
(b) Find the center of mass of H.
(c) Find the moment of inertia of H about its axis.

33. (a) Find the centroid of a solid homogeneous hemisphere of radius a.
(b) Find the moment of inertia of the solid in part (a) about a diameter of its base.

34. Find the mass and center of mass of a solid hemisphere of radius a if the density at any point is proportional to its distance from the base.

35–38 Use cylindrical or spherical coordinates, whichever seems more appropriate.

35. Find the volume and centroid of the solid E that lies above the cone $z = \sqrt{x^2 + y^2}$ and below the sphere $x^2 + y^2 + z^2 = 1$.

36. Find the volume of the smaller wedge cut from a sphere of radius a by two planes that intersect along a diameter at an angle of $\pi/6$.

CAS 37. Evaluate $\iiint_E z \, dV$, where E lies above the paraboloid $z = x^2 + y^2$ and below the plane $z = 2y$. Use either the Table of Integrals (on Reference Pages 6–10) or a computer algebra system to evaluate the integral.

38. (a) Find the volume enclosed by the torus $\rho = \sin \phi$.
(b) Use a computer to draw the torus.

39–40 Evaluate the integral by changing to spherical coordinates.

39. $\int_0^1 \int_0^{\sqrt{1-x^2}} \int_{\sqrt{x^2+y^2}}^{\sqrt{2-x^2-y^2}} xy \, dz \, dy \, dx$

40. $\int_{-a}^a \int_{-\sqrt{a^2-y^2}}^{\sqrt{a^2-y^2}} \int_{-\sqrt{a^2-x^2-y^2}}^{\sqrt{a^2-x^2-y^2}} (x^2z + y^2z + z^3) \, dz \, dx \, dy$

41. Use a graphing device to draw a silo consisting of a cylinder with radius 3 and height 10 surmounted by a hemisphere.

42. The latitude and longitude of a point P in the Northern Hemisphere are related to spherical coordinates ρ, θ, ϕ as follows. We take the origin to be the center of the earth and the positive z-axis to pass through the North Pole. The positive x-axis passes through the point where the prime meridian (the meridian through Greenwich, England) intersects the equator. Then the latitude of P is $\alpha = 90° - \phi°$ and the longitude is $\beta = 360° - \theta°$. Find the great-circle distance from Los Angeles (lat. 34.06° N, long. 118.25° W) to Montréal (lat. 45.50° N, long. 73.60° W). Take the radius of the earth to be 3960 mi. (A *great circle* is the circle of intersection of a sphere and a plane through the center of the sphere.)

CAS 43. The surfaces $\rho = 1 + \frac{1}{5} \sin m\theta \sin n\phi$ have been used as models for tumors. The "bumpy sphere" with $m = 6$ and $n = 5$ is shown. Use a computer algebra system to find the volume it encloses.

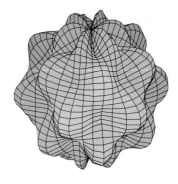

44. Show that

$$\int_{-\infty}^{\infty} \int_{-\infty}^{\infty} \int_{-\infty}^{\infty} \sqrt{x^2 + y^2 + z^2} \; e^{-(x^2+y^2+z^2)} \, dx \, dy \, dz = 2\pi$$

(The improper triple integral is defined as the limit of a triple integral over a solid sphere as the radius of the sphere increases indefinitely.)

45. (a) Use cylindrical coordinates to show that the volume of the solid bounded above by the sphere $r^2 + z^2 = a^2$ and below by the cone $z = r \cot \phi_0$ (or $\phi = \phi_0$), where $0 < \phi_0 < \pi/2$, is

$$V = \frac{2\pi a^3}{3} (1 - \cos \phi_0)$$

(b) Deduce that the volume of the spherical wedge given by $\rho_1 \leq \rho \leq \rho_2$, $\theta_1 \leq \theta \leq \theta_2$, $\phi_1 \leq \phi \leq \phi_2$ is

$$\Delta V = \frac{\rho_2^3 - \rho_1^3}{3} (\cos \phi_1 - \cos \phi_2)(\theta_2 - \theta_1)$$

(c) Use the Mean Value Theorem to show that the volume in part (b) can be written as

$$\Delta V = \tilde{\rho}^2 \sin \tilde{\phi} \, \Delta\rho \, \Delta\theta \, \Delta\phi$$

where $\tilde{\rho}$ lies between ρ_1 and ρ_2, $\tilde{\phi}$ lies between ϕ_1 and ϕ_2, $\Delta\rho = \rho_2 - \rho_1$, $\Delta\theta = \theta_2 - \theta_1$, and $\Delta\phi = \phi_2 - \phi_1$.

| APPLIED PROJECT | ROLLER DERBY |

Suppose that a solid ball (a marble), a hollow ball (a squash ball), a solid cylinder (a steel bar), and a hollow cylinder (a lead pipe) roll down a slope. Which of these objects reaches the bottom first? (Make a guess before proceeding.)

To answer this question, we consider a ball or cylinder with mass m, radius r, and moment of inertia I (about the axis of rotation). If the vertical drop is h, then the potential energy at the top is mgh. Suppose the object reaches the bottom with velocity v and angular velocity ω, so $v = \omega r$. The kinetic energy at the bottom consists of two parts: $\frac{1}{2}mv^2$ from translation (moving down the slope) and $\frac{1}{2}I\omega^2$ from rotation. If we assume that energy loss from rolling friction is negligible, then conservation of energy gives

$$mgh = \tfrac{1}{2}mv^2 + \tfrac{1}{2}I\omega^2$$

1. Show that

$$v^2 = \frac{2gh}{1 + I^*} \qquad \text{where } I^* = \frac{I}{mr^2}$$

2. If $y(t)$ is the vertical distance traveled at time t, then the same reasoning as used in Problem 1 shows that $v^2 = 2gy/(1 + I^*)$ at any time t. Use this result to show that y satisfies the differential equation

$$\frac{dy}{dt} = \sqrt{\frac{2g}{1 + I^*}} \, (\sin \alpha) \sqrt{y}$$

where α is the angle of inclination of the plane.

3. By solving the differential equation in Problem 2, show that the total travel time is

$$T = \sqrt{\frac{2h(1 + I^*)}{g \sin^2 \alpha}}$$

This shows that the object with the smallest value of I^* wins the race.

4. Show that $I^* = \frac{1}{2}$ for a solid cylinder and $I^* = 1$ for a hollow cylinder.

5. Calculate I^* for a partly hollow ball with inner radius a and outer radius r. Express your answer in terms of $b = a/r$. What happens as $a \to 0$ and as $a \to r$?

6. Show that $I^* = \frac{2}{5}$ for a solid ball and $I^* = \frac{2}{3}$ for a hollow ball. Thus the objects finish in the following order: solid ball, solid cylinder, hollow ball, hollow cylinder.

16.9 CHANGE OF VARIABLES IN MULTIPLE INTEGRALS

In one-dimensional calculus we often use a change of variable (a substitution) to simplify an integral. By reversing the roles of x and u, we can write the Substitution Rule (5.5.5) as

$$\boxed{1} \qquad \int_a^b f(x) \, dx = \int_c^d f(g(u))g'(u) \, du$$

where $x = g(u)$ and $a = g(c)$, $b = g(d)$. Another way of writing Formula 1 is as follows:

$$\boxed{2} \qquad \int_a^b f(x) \, dx = \int_c^d f(x(u)) \frac{dx}{du} \, du$$

A change of variables can also be useful in double integrals. We have already seen one example of this: conversion to polar coordinates. The new variables r and θ are related to the old variables x and y by the equations

$$x = r\cos\theta \qquad y = r\sin\theta$$

and the change of variables formula (16.4.2) can be written as

$$\iint_R f(x, y)\, dA = \iint_S f(r\cos\theta, r\sin\theta)\, r\, dr\, d\theta$$

where S is the region in the $r\theta$-plane that corresponds to the region R in the xy-plane.

More generally, we consider a change of variables that is given by a **transformation** T from the uv-plane to the xy-plane:

$$T(u, v) = (x, y)$$

where x and y are related to u and v by the equations

$$\boxed{3} \qquad\qquad x = g(u, v) \qquad y = h(u, v)$$

or, as we sometimes write,

$$x = x(u, v) \qquad y = y(u, v)$$

We usually assume that T is a C^1 **transformation**, which means that g and h have continuous first-order partial derivatives.

A transformation T is really just a function whose domain and range are both subsets of $\mathbb{R}^2$. If $T(u_1, v_1) = (x_1, y_1)$, then the point (x_1, y_1) is called the **image** of the point (u_1, v_1). If no two points have the same image, T is called **one-to-one**. Figure 1 shows the effect of a transformation T on a region S in the uv-plane. T transforms S into a region R in the xy-plane called the **image of** S, consisting of the images of all points in S.

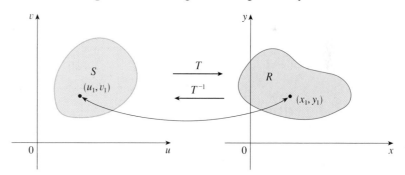

FIGURE I

If T is a one-to-one transformation, then it has an **inverse transformation** T^{-1} from the xy-plane to the uv-plane and it may be possible to solve Equations 3 for u and v in terms of x and y:

$$u = G(x, y) \qquad v = H(x, y)$$

☑ **EXAMPLE I** A transformation is defined by the equations

$$x = u^2 - v^2 \qquad y = 2uv$$

Find the image of the square $S = \{(u, v)\,|\,0 \le u \le 1,\ 0 \le v \le 1\}$.

SOLUTION The transformation maps the boundary of S into the boundary of the image. So we begin by finding the images of the sides of S. The first side, S_1, is given by $v = 0$

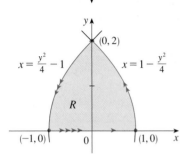

FIGURE 2

$(0 \leqslant u \leqslant 1)$. (See Figure 2.) From the given equations we have $x = u^2$, $y = 0$, and so $0 \leqslant x \leqslant 1$. Thus S_1 is mapped into the line segment from $(0, 0)$ to $(1, 0)$ in the xy-plane. The second side, S_2, is $u = 1$ $(0 \leqslant v \leqslant 1)$ and, putting $u = 1$ in the given equations, we get

$$x = 1 - v^2 \qquad y = 2v$$

Eliminating v, we obtain

$$\boxed{4} \qquad\qquad x = 1 - \frac{y^2}{4} \qquad 0 \leqslant x \leqslant 1$$

which is part of a parabola. Similarly, S_3 is given by $v = 1$ $(0 \leqslant u \leqslant 1)$, whose image is the parabolic arc

$$\boxed{5} \qquad\qquad x = \frac{y^2}{4} - 1 \qquad -1 \leqslant x \leqslant 0$$

Finally, S_4 is given by $u = 0$ $(0 \leqslant v \leqslant 1)$ whose image is $x = -v^2$, $y = 0$, that is, $-1 \leqslant x \leqslant 0$. (Notice that as we move around the square in the counterclockwise direction, we also move around the parabolic region in the counterclockwise direction.) The image of S is the region R (shown in Figure 2) bounded by the x-axis and the parabolas given by Equations 4 and 5. $\qquad\square$

Now let's see how a change of variables affects a double integral. We start with a small rectangle S in the uv-plane whose lower left corner is the point (u_0, v_0) and whose dimensions are Δu and Δv. (See Figure 3.)

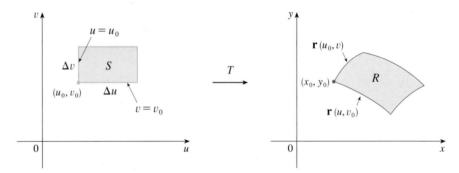

FIGURE 3

The image of S is a region R in the xy-plane, one of whose boundary points is $(x_0, y_0) = T(u_0, v_0)$. The vector

$$\mathbf{r}(u, v) = g(u, v)\,\mathbf{i} + h(u, v)\,\mathbf{j}$$

is the position vector of the image of the point (u, v). The equation of the lower side of S is $v = v_0$, whose image curve is given by the vector function $\mathbf{r}(u, v_0)$. The tangent vector at (x_0, y_0) to this image curve is

$$\mathbf{r}_u = g_u(u_0, v_0)\,\mathbf{i} + h_u(u_0, v_0)\,\mathbf{j} = \frac{\partial x}{\partial u}\,\mathbf{i} + \frac{\partial y}{\partial u}\,\mathbf{j}$$

Similarly, the tangent vector at (x_0, y_0) to the image curve of the left side of S (namely, $u = u_0$) is

$$\mathbf{r}_v = g_v(u_0, v_0)\,\mathbf{i} + h_v(u_0, v_0)\,\mathbf{j} = \frac{\partial x}{\partial v}\,\mathbf{i} + \frac{\partial y}{\partial v}\,\mathbf{j}$$

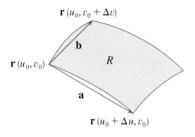

$\mathbf{r}(u_0, v_0 + \Delta v)$

$\mathbf{r}(u_0, v_0)$

b

R

a

$\mathbf{r}(u_0 + \Delta u, v_0)$

FIGURE 4

$\Delta v\, \mathbf{r}_v$

$\mathbf{r}(u_0, v_0)$

$\Delta u\, \mathbf{r}_u$

FIGURE 5

We can approximate the image region $R = T(S)$ by a parallelogram determined by the secant vectors

$$\mathbf{a} = \mathbf{r}(u_0 + \Delta u, v_0) - \mathbf{r}(u_0, v_0) \qquad \mathbf{b} = \mathbf{r}(u_0, v_0 + \Delta v) - \mathbf{r}(u_0, v_0)$$

shown in Figure 4. But

$$\mathbf{r}_u = \lim_{\Delta u \to 0} \frac{\mathbf{r}(u_0 + \Delta u, v_0) - \mathbf{r}(u_0, v_0)}{\Delta u}$$

and so

$$\mathbf{r}(u_0 + \Delta u, v_0) - \mathbf{r}(u_0, v_0) \approx \Delta u\, \mathbf{r}_u$$

Similarly

$$\mathbf{r}(u_0, v_0 + \Delta v) - \mathbf{r}(u_0, v_0) \approx \Delta v\, \mathbf{r}_v$$

This means that we can approximate R by a parallelogram determined by the vectors $\Delta u\, \mathbf{r}_u$ and $\Delta v\, \mathbf{r}_v$. (See Figure 5.) Therefore we can approximate the area of R by the area of this parallelogram, which, from Section 13.4, is

$$\boxed{6} \qquad |(\Delta u\, \mathbf{r}_u) \times (\Delta v\, \mathbf{r}_v)| = |\mathbf{r}_u \times \mathbf{r}_v|\, \Delta u\, \Delta v$$

Computing the cross product, we obtain

$$\mathbf{r}_u \times \mathbf{r}_v = \begin{vmatrix} \mathbf{i} & \mathbf{j} & \mathbf{k} \\ \dfrac{\partial x}{\partial u} & \dfrac{\partial y}{\partial u} & 0 \\ \dfrac{\partial x}{\partial v} & \dfrac{\partial y}{\partial v} & 0 \end{vmatrix} = \begin{vmatrix} \dfrac{\partial x}{\partial u} & \dfrac{\partial y}{\partial u} \\ \dfrac{\partial x}{\partial v} & \dfrac{\partial y}{\partial v} \end{vmatrix} \mathbf{k} = \begin{vmatrix} \dfrac{\partial x}{\partial u} & \dfrac{\partial x}{\partial v} \\ \dfrac{\partial y}{\partial u} & \dfrac{\partial y}{\partial v} \end{vmatrix} \mathbf{k}$$

The determinant that arises in this calculation is called the *Jacobian* of the transformation and is given a special notation.

■ The Jacobian is named after the German mathematician Carl Gustav Jacob Jacobi (1804–1851). Although the French mathematician Cauchy first used these special determinants involving partial derivatives, Jacobi developed them into a method for evaluating multiple integrals.

$\boxed{7}$ **DEFINITION** The **Jacobian** of the transformation T given by $x = g(u, v)$ and $y = h(u, v)$ is

$$\frac{\partial(x, y)}{\partial(u, v)} = \begin{vmatrix} \dfrac{\partial x}{\partial u} & \dfrac{\partial x}{\partial v} \\ \dfrac{\partial y}{\partial u} & \dfrac{\partial y}{\partial v} \end{vmatrix} = \frac{\partial x}{\partial u}\frac{\partial y}{\partial v} - \frac{\partial x}{\partial v}\frac{\partial y}{\partial u}$$

With this notation we can use Equation 6 to give an approximation to the area ΔA of R:

$$\boxed{8} \qquad \Delta A \approx \left| \frac{\partial(x, y)}{\partial(u, v)} \right| \Delta u\, \Delta v$$

where the Jacobian is evaluated at (u_0, v_0).

Next we divide a region S in the uv-plane into rectangles S_{ij} and call their images in the xy-plane R_{ij}. (See Figure 6.)

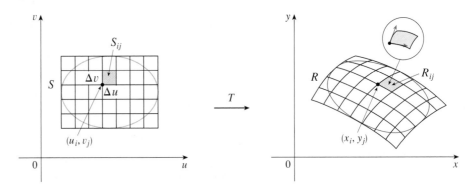

FIGURE 6

Applying the approximation (8) to each R_{ij}, we approximate the double integral of f over R as follows:

$$\iint\limits_{R} f(x, y)\, dA \approx \sum_{i=1}^{m} \sum_{j=1}^{n} f(x_i, y_j)\, \Delta A$$

$$\approx \sum_{i=1}^{m} \sum_{j=1}^{n} f\big(g(u_i, v_j), h(u_i, v_j)\big) \left| \frac{\partial(x, y)}{\partial(u, v)} \right| \Delta u\, \Delta v$$

where the Jacobian is evaluated at (u_i, v_j). Notice that this double sum is a Riemann sum for the integral

$$\iint\limits_{S} f\big(g(u, v), h(u, v)\big) \left| \frac{\partial(x, y)}{\partial(u, v)} \right| du\, dv$$

The foregoing argument suggests that the following theorem is true. (A full proof is given in books on advanced calculus.)

---

9 **CHANGE OF VARIABLES IN A DOUBLE INTEGRAL** Suppose that T is a C^1 transformation whose Jacobian is nonzero and that maps a region S in the uv-plane onto a region R in the xy-plane. Suppose that f is continuous on R and that R and S are type I or type II plane regions. Suppose also that T is one-to-one, except perhaps on the boundary of S. Then

$$\iint\limits_{R} f(x, y)\, dA = \iint\limits_{S} f\big(x(u, v), y(u, v)\big) \left| \frac{\partial(x, y)}{\partial(u, v)} \right| du\, dv$$

Theorem 9 says that we change from an integral in x and y to an integral in u and v by expressing x and y in terms of u and v and writing

$$dA = \left| \frac{\partial(x, y)}{\partial(u, v)} \right| du\, dv$$

Notice the similarity between Theorem 9 and the one-dimensional formula in Equation 2. Instead of the derivative dx/du, we have the absolute value of the Jacobian, that is, $\left| \partial(x, y)/\partial(u, v) \right|$.

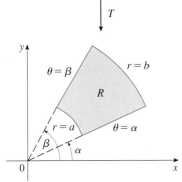

FIGURE 7

The polar coordinate transformation

As a first illustration of Theorem 9, we show that the formula for integration in polar coordinates is just a special case. Here the transformation T from the $r\theta$-plane to the xy-plane is given by

$$x = g(r, \theta) = r\cos\theta \qquad y = h(r, \theta) = r\sin\theta$$

and the geometry of the transformation is shown in Figure 7. T maps an ordinary rectangle in the $r\theta$-plane to a polar rectangle in the xy-plane. The Jacobian of T is

$$\frac{\partial(x, y)}{\partial(r, \theta)} = \begin{vmatrix} \dfrac{\partial x}{\partial r} & \dfrac{\partial x}{\partial \theta} \\ \dfrac{\partial y}{\partial r} & \dfrac{\partial y}{\partial \theta} \end{vmatrix} = \begin{vmatrix} \cos\theta & -r\sin\theta \\ \sin\theta & r\cos\theta \end{vmatrix} = r\cos^2\theta + r\sin^2\theta = r > 0$$

Thus Theorem 9 gives

$$\iint\limits_{R} f(x, y)\, dx\, dy = \iint\limits_{S} f(r\cos\theta, r\sin\theta) \left| \frac{\partial(x, y)}{\partial(r, \theta)} \right| dr\, d\theta$$

$$= \int_{\alpha}^{\beta} \int_{a}^{b} f(r\cos\theta, r\sin\theta)\, r\, dr\, d\theta$$

which is the same as Formula 16.4.2.

▼ **EXAMPLE 2** Use the change of variables $x = u^2 - v^2$, $y = 2uv$ to evaluate the integral $\iint_R y\, dA$, where R is the region bounded by the x-axis and the parabolas $y^2 = 4 - 4x$ and $y^2 = 4 + 4x$, $y \geq 0$.

SOLUTION The region R is pictured in Figure 2 (on page 1050). In Example 1 we discovered that $T(S) = R$, where S is the square $[0, 1] \times [0, 1]$. Indeed, the reason for making the change of variables to evaluate the integral is that S is a much simpler region than R. First we need to compute the Jacobian:

$$\frac{\partial(x, y)}{\partial(u, v)} = \begin{vmatrix} \dfrac{\partial x}{\partial u} & \dfrac{\partial x}{\partial v} \\ \dfrac{\partial y}{\partial u} & \dfrac{\partial y}{\partial v} \end{vmatrix} = \begin{vmatrix} 2u & -2v \\ 2v & 2u \end{vmatrix} = 4u^2 + 4v^2 > 0$$

Therefore, by Theorem 9,

$$\iint\limits_{R} y\, dA = \iint\limits_{S} 2uv \left| \frac{\partial(x, y)}{\partial(u, v)} \right| dA = \int_{0}^{1} \int_{0}^{1} (2uv)4(u^2 + v^2)\, du\, dv$$

$$= 8\int_{0}^{1} \int_{0}^{1} (u^3 v + uv^3)\, du\, dv = 8\int_{0}^{1} \left[\tfrac{1}{4}u^4 v + \tfrac{1}{2}u^2 v^3 \right]_{u=0}^{u=1} dv$$

$$= \int_{0}^{1} (2v + 4v^3)\, dv = \left[v^2 + v^4 \right]_{0}^{1} = 2 \qquad \square$$

NOTE Example 2 was not a very difficult problem to solve because we were given a suitable change of variables. If we are not supplied with a transformation, then the first step is to think of an appropriate change of variables. If $f(x, y)$ is difficult to integrate, then the form of $f(x, y)$ may suggest a transformation. If the region of integration R is awkward, then the transformation should be chosen so that the corresponding region S in the uv-plane has a convenient description.

EXAMPLE 3 Evaluate the integral $\iint_R e^{(x+y)/(x-y)}\, dA$, where R is the trapezoidal region with vertices $(1, 0)$, $(2, 0)$, $(0, -2)$, and $(0, -1)$.

SOLUTION Since it isn't easy to integrate $e^{(x+y)/(x-y)}$, we make a change of variables suggested by the form of this function:

$$\boxed{10} \qquad u = x + y \qquad v = x - y$$

These equations define a transformation T^{-1} from the xy-plane to the uv-plane. Theorem 9 talks about a transformation T from the uv-plane to the xy-plane. It is obtained by solving Equations 10 for x and y:

$$\boxed{11} \qquad x = \tfrac{1}{2}(u + v) \qquad y = \tfrac{1}{2}(u - v)$$

The Jacobian of T is

$$\frac{\partial(x, y)}{\partial(u, v)} = \begin{vmatrix} \dfrac{\partial x}{\partial u} & \dfrac{\partial x}{\partial v} \\ \dfrac{\partial y}{\partial u} & \dfrac{\partial y}{\partial v} \end{vmatrix} = \begin{vmatrix} \tfrac{1}{2} & \tfrac{1}{2} \\ \tfrac{1}{2} & -\tfrac{1}{2} \end{vmatrix} = -\tfrac{1}{2}$$

To find the region S in the uv-plane corresponding to R, we note that the sides of R lie on the lines

$$y = 0 \qquad x - y = 2 \qquad x = 0 \qquad x - y = 1$$

and, from either Equations 10 or Equations 11, the image lines in the uv-plane are

$$u = v \qquad v = 2 \qquad u = -v \qquad v = 1$$

Thus the region S is the trapezoidal region with vertices $(1, 1)$, $(2, 2)$, $(-2, 2)$, and $(-1, 1)$ shown in Figure 8. Since

$$S = \{(u, v) \mid 1 \leqslant v \leqslant 2,\ -v \leqslant u \leqslant v\}$$

Theorem 9 gives

$$\iint_R e^{(x+y)/(x-y)}\, dA = \iint_S e^{u/v} \left| \frac{\partial(x, y)}{\partial(u, v)} \right| du\, dv$$

$$= \int_1^2 \int_{-v}^v e^{u/v} \left(\tfrac{1}{2}\right) du\, dv = \tfrac{1}{2} \int_1^2 \left[v e^{u/v} \right]_{u=-v}^{u=v} dv$$

$$= \tfrac{1}{2} \int_1^2 (e - e^{-1}) v\, dv = \tfrac{3}{4}(e - e^{-1})$$

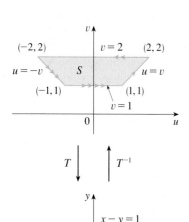

FIGURE 8

TRIPLE INTEGRALS

There is a similar change of variables formula for triple integrals. Let T be a transformation that maps a region S in uvw-space onto a region R in xyz-space by means of the equations

$$x = g(u, v, w) \qquad y = h(u, v, w) \qquad z = k(u, v, w)$$

The **Jacobian** of T is the following 3×3 determinant:

$$\boxed{12} \qquad \frac{\partial(x, y, z)}{\partial(u, v, w)} = \begin{vmatrix} \dfrac{\partial x}{\partial u} & \dfrac{\partial x}{\partial v} & \dfrac{\partial x}{\partial w} \\[2mm] \dfrac{\partial y}{\partial u} & \dfrac{\partial y}{\partial v} & \dfrac{\partial y}{\partial w} \\[2mm] \dfrac{\partial z}{\partial u} & \dfrac{\partial z}{\partial v} & \dfrac{\partial z}{\partial w} \end{vmatrix}$$

Under hypotheses similar to those in Theorem 9, we have the following formula for triple integrals:

$$\boxed{13} \qquad \iiint_R f(x, y, z)\, dV = \iiint_S f\big(x(u, v, w),\, y(u, v, w),\, z(u, v, w)\big) \left| \frac{\partial(x, y, z)}{\partial(u, v, w)} \right| du\, dv\, dw$$

▼ **EXAMPLE 4** Use Formula 13 to derive the formula for triple integration in spherical coordinates.

SOLUTION Here the change of variables is given by

$$x = \rho \sin \phi \, \cos \theta \qquad y = \rho \sin \phi \, \sin \theta \qquad z = \rho \cos \phi$$

We compute the Jacobian as follows:

$$\frac{\partial(x, y, z)}{\partial(\rho, \theta, \phi)} = \begin{vmatrix} \sin \phi \cos \theta & -\rho \sin \phi \sin \theta & \rho \cos \phi \cos \theta \\ \sin \phi \sin \theta & \rho \sin \phi \cos \theta & \rho \cos \phi \sin \theta \\ \cos \phi & 0 & -\rho \sin \phi \end{vmatrix}$$

$$= \cos \phi \begin{vmatrix} -\rho \sin \phi \sin \theta & \rho \cos \phi \cos \theta \\ \rho \sin \phi \cos \theta & \rho \cos \phi \sin \theta \end{vmatrix} - \rho \sin \phi \begin{vmatrix} \sin \phi \cos \theta & -\rho \sin \phi \sin \theta \\ \sin \phi \sin \theta & \rho \sin \phi \cos \theta \end{vmatrix}$$

$$= \cos \phi \, (-\rho^2 \sin \phi \cos \phi \sin^2\theta - \rho^2 \sin \phi \cos \phi \cos^2\theta)$$

$$\qquad - \rho \sin \phi \, (\rho \sin^2\phi \cos^2\theta + \rho \sin^2\phi \sin^2\theta)$$

$$= -\rho^2 \sin \phi \cos^2\phi - \rho^2 \sin \phi \sin^2\phi = -\rho^2 \sin \phi$$

Since $0 \leqslant \phi \leqslant \pi$, we have $\sin \phi \geqslant 0$. Therefore

$$\left| \frac{\partial(x, y, z)}{\partial(\rho, \theta, \phi)} \right| = |-\rho^2 \sin \phi| = \rho^2 \sin \phi$$

and Formula 13 gives

$$\iiint_R f(x, y, z)\, dV = \iiint_S f(\rho \sin \phi \cos \theta,\, \rho \sin \phi \sin \theta,\, \rho \cos \phi)\, \rho^2 \sin \phi \, d\rho \, d\theta \, d\phi$$

which is equivalent to Formula 16.8.3. ☐

16.9 EXERCISES

1–6 Find the Jacobian of the transformation.

1. $x = 5u - v, \quad y = u + 3v$

2. $x = uv, \quad y = u/v$

3. $x = e^{-r}\sin\theta, \quad y = e^r\cos\theta$

4. $x = e^{s+t}, \quad y = e^{s-t}$

5. $x = u/v, \quad y = v/w, \quad z = w/u$

6. $x = v + w^2, \quad y = w + u^2, \quad z = u + v^2$

7–10 Find the image of the set S under the given transformation.

7. $S = \{(u, v) \mid 0 \le u \le 3, \ 0 \le v \le 2\}$;
$x = 2u + 3v, \ y = u - v$

8. S is the square bounded by the lines $u = 0, u = 1, v = 0,$
$v = 1$; $\quad x = v, \ y = u(1 + v^2)$

9. S is the triangular region with vertices $(0, 0), (1, 1), (0, 1)$;
$x = u^2, \ y = v$

10. S is the disk given by $u^2 + v^2 \le 1$; $\quad x = au, \ y = bv$

11–16 Use the given transformation to evaluate the integral.

11. $\iint_R (x - 3y)\, dA$, where R is the triangular region with
vertices $(0, 0), (2, 1),$ and $(1, 2)$; $\quad x = 2u + v, \ y = u + 2v$

12. $\iint_R (4x + 8y)\, dA$, where R is the parallelogram with
vertices $(-1, 3), (1, -3), (3, -1),$ and $(1, 5)$;
$x = \frac{1}{4}(u + v), \ y = \frac{1}{4}(v - 3u)$

13. $\iint_R x^2\, dA$, where R is the region bounded by the ellipse
$9x^2 + 4y^2 = 36$; $\quad x = 2u, \ y = 3v$

14. $\iint_R (x^2 - xy + y^2)\, dA$, where R is the region bounded
by the ellipse $x^2 - xy + y^2 = 2$;
$x = \sqrt{2}\,u - \sqrt{2/3}\,v, \ y = \sqrt{2}\,u + \sqrt{2/3}\,v$

15. $\iint_R xy\, dA$, where R is the region in the first quadrant bounded
by the lines $y = x$ and $y = 3x$ and the hyperbolas $xy = 1,$
$xy = 3$; $\quad x = u/v, \ y = v$

16. $\iint_R y^2\, dA$, where R is the region bounded by the curves
$xy = 1, xy = 2, xy^2 = 1, xy^2 = 2$; $\quad u = xy, v = xy^2$.
Illustrate by using a graphing calculator or computer to
draw R.

17. (a) Evaluate $\iiint_E dV$, where E is the solid enclosed by the
ellipsoid $x^2/a^2 + y^2/b^2 + z^2/c^2 = 1$. Use the transformation $x = au, \ y = bv, \ z = cw$.
(b) The earth is not a perfect sphere; rotation has resulted in
flattening at the poles. So the shape can be approximated
by an ellipsoid with $a = b = 6378$ km and $c = 6356$ km.
Use part (a) to estimate the volume of the earth.

18. If the solid of Exercise 17(a) has constant density k, find its
moment of inertia about the z-axis.

19–23 Evaluate the integral by making an appropriate change of
variables.

19. $\iint_R \dfrac{x - 2y}{3x - y}\, dA$, where R is the parallelogram enclosed by
the lines $x - 2y = 0, x - 2y = 4, 3x - y = 1,$ and
$3x - y = 8$

20. $\iint_R (x + y)e^{x^2-y^2}\, dA$, where R is the rectangle enclosed by the
lines $x - y = 0, x - y = 2, x + y = 0,$ and $x + y = 3$

21. $\iint_R \cos\left(\dfrac{y - x}{y + x}\right)\, dA$, where R is the trapezoidal region
with vertices $(1, 0), (2, 0), (0, 2),$ and $(0, 1)$

22. $\iint_R \sin(9x^2 + 4y^2)\, dA$, where R is the region in the first
quadrant bounded by the ellipse $9x^2 + 4y^2 = 1$

23. $\iint_R e^{x+y}\, dA$, where R is given by the inequality $|x| + |y| \le 1$

24. Let f be continuous on $[0, 1]$ and let R be the triangular
region with vertices $(0, 0), (1, 0),$ and $(0, 1)$. Show that
$$\iint_R f(x + y)\, dA = \int_0^1 uf(u)\, du$$

16 | REVIEW

CONCEPT CHECK

1. Suppose f is a continuous function defined on a rectangle $R = [a, b] \times [c, d]$.
   (a) Write an expression for a double Riemann sum of f. If $f(x, y) \geq 0$, what does the sum represent?
   (b) Write the definition of $\iint_R f(x, y) \, dA$ as a limit.
   (c) What is the geometric interpretation of $\iint_R f(x, y) \, dA$ if $f(x, y) \geq 0$? What if f takes on both positive and negative values?
   (d) How do you evaluate $\iint_R f(x, y) \, dA$?
   (e) What does the Midpoint Rule for double integrals say?
   (f) Write an expression for the average value of f.

2. (a) How do you define $\iint_D f(x, y) \, dA$ if D is a bounded region that is not a rectangle?
   (b) What is a type I region? How do you evaluate $\iint_D f(x, y) \, dA$ if D is a type I region?
   (c) What is a type II region? How do you evaluate $\iint_D f(x, y) \, dA$ if D is a type II region?
   (d) What properties do double integrals have?

3. How do you change from rectangular coordinates to polar coordinates in a double integral? Why would you want to make the change?

4. If a lamina occupies a plane region D and has density function $\rho(x, y)$, write expressions for each of the following in terms of double integrals.
   (a) The mass
   (b) The moments about the axes
   (c) The center of mass
   (d) The moments of inertia about the axes and the origin

5. Let f be a joint density function of a pair of continuous random variables X and Y.
   (a) Write a double integral for the probability that X lies between a and b and Y lies between c and d.

   (b) What properties does f possess?
   (c) What are the expected values of X and Y?

6. (a) Write the definition of the triple integral of f over a rectangular box B.
   (b) How do you evaluate $\iiint_B f(x, y, z) \, dV$?
   (c) How do you define $\iiint_E f(x, y, z) \, dV$ if E is a bounded solid region that is not a box?
   (d) What is a type 1 solid region? How do you evaluate $\iiint_E f(x, y, z) \, dV$ if E is such a region?
   (e) What is a type 2 solid region? How do you evaluate $\iiint_E f(x, y, z) \, dV$ if E is such a region?
   (f) What is a type 3 solid region? How do you evaluate $\iiint_E f(x, y, z) \, dV$ if E is such a region?

7. Suppose a solid object occupies the region E and has density function $\rho(x, y, z)$. Write expressions for each of the following.
   (a) The mass
   (b) The moments about the coordinate planes
   (c) The coordinates of the center of mass
   (d) The moments of inertia about the axes

8. (a) How do you change from rectangular coordinates to cylindrical coordinates in a triple integral?
   (b) How do you change from rectangular coordinates to spherical coordinates in a triple integral?
   (c) In what situations would you change to cylindrical or spherical coordinates?

9. (a) If a transformation T is given by $x = g(u, v)$, $y = h(u, v)$, what is the Jacobian of T?
   (b) How do you change variables in a double integral?
   (c) How do you change variables in a triple integral?

TRUE-FALSE QUIZ

Determine whether the statement is true or false. If it is true, explain why. If it is false, explain why or give an example that disproves the statement.

1. $\displaystyle\int_{-1}^{2} \int_0^6 x^2 \sin(x - y) \, dx \, dy = \int_0^6 \int_{-1}^{2} x^2 \sin(x - y) \, dy \, dx$

2. $\displaystyle\int_0^1 \int_0^x \sqrt{x + y^2} \, dy \, dx = \int_0^x \int_0^1 \sqrt{x + y^2} \, dx \, dy$

3. $\displaystyle\int_1^2 \int_3^4 x^2 e^y \, dy \, dx = \int_1^2 x^2 \, dx \int_3^4 e^y \, dy$

4. $\displaystyle\int_{-1}^1 \int_0^1 e^{x^2 + y^2} \sin y \, dx \, dy = 0$

5. If D is the disk given by $x^2 + y^2 \leq 4$, then
$$\iint_D \sqrt{4 - x^2 - y^2} \, dA = \tfrac{16}{3}\pi$$

6. $\displaystyle\int_1^4 \int_0^1 \left(x^2 + \sqrt{y}\right) \sin(x^2 y^2) \, dx \, dy \leq 9$

7. The integral
$$\int_0^{2\pi} \int_0^2 \int_r^2 dz \, dr \, d\theta$$
represents the volume enclosed by the cone $z = \sqrt{x^2 + y^2}$ and the plane $z = 2$.

8. The integral $\iiint_E kr^3 \, dz \, dr \, d\theta$ represents the moment of inertia about the z-axis of a solid E with constant density k.

EXERCISES

1. A contour map is shown for a function f on the square $R = [0, 3] \times [0, 3]$. Use a Riemann sum with nine terms to estimate the value of $\iint_R f(x, y)\, dA$. Take the sample points to be the upper right corners of the squares.

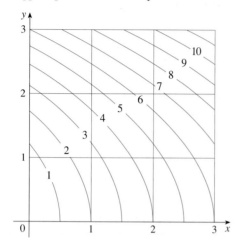

2. Use the Midpoint Rule to estimate the integral in Exercise 1.

3–8 Calculate the iterated integral.

3. $\int_1^2 \int_0^2 (y + 2xe^y)\, dx\, dy$

4. $\int_0^1 \int_0^1 ye^{xy}\, dx\, dy$

5. $\int_0^1 \int_0^x \cos(x^2)\, dy\, dx$

6. $\int_0^1 \int_x^{e^x} 3xy^2\, dy\, dx$

7. $\int_0^\pi \int_0^1 \int_0^{\sqrt{1-y^2}} y \sin x\, dz\, dy\, dx$

8. $\int_0^1 \int_0^y \int_x^1 6xyz\, dz\, dx\, dy$

9–10 Write $\iint_R f(x, y)\, dA$ as an iterated integral, where R is the region shown and f is an arbitrary continuous function on R.

9.

10.

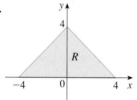

11. Describe the region whose area is given by the integral

$$\int_0^{\pi/2} \int_0^{\sin 2\theta} r\, dr\, d\theta$$

12. Describe the solid whose volume is given by the integral

$$\int_0^{\pi/2} \int_0^{\pi/2} \int_1^2 \rho^2 \sin \phi\, d\rho\, d\phi\, d\theta$$

and evaluate the integral.

13–14 Calculate the iterated integral by first reversing the order of integration.

13. $\int_0^1 \int_x^1 \cos(y^2)\, dy\, dx$

14. $\int_0^1 \int_{\sqrt{y}}^1 \frac{ye^{x^2}}{x^3}\, dx\, dy$

15–28 Calculate the value of the multiple integral.

15. $\iint_R ye^{xy}\, dA$, where $R = \{(x, y) \mid 0 \le x \le 2,\ 0 \le y \le 3\}$

16. $\iint_D xy\, dA$, where $D = \{(x, y) \mid 0 \le y \le 1,\ y^2 \le x \le y + 2\}$

17. $\iint_D \frac{y}{1 + x^2}\, dA$, where D is bounded by $y = \sqrt{x}$, $y = 0$, $x = 1$

18. $\iint_D \frac{1}{1 + x^2}\, dA$, where D is the triangular region with vertices $(0, 0)$, $(1, 1)$, and $(0, 1)$

19. $\iint_D y\, dA$, where D is the region in the first quadrant bounded by the parabolas $x = y^2$ and $x = 8 - y^2$

20. $\iint_D y\, dA$, where D is the region in the first quadrant that lies above the hyperbola $xy = 1$ and the line $y = x$ and below the line $y = 2$

21. $\iint_D (x^2 + y^2)^{3/2}\, dA$, where D is the region in the first quadrant bounded by the lines $y = 0$ and $y = \sqrt{3}\, x$ and the circle $x^2 + y^2 = 9$

22. $\iint_D x\, dA$, where D is the region in the first quadrant that lies between the circles $x^2 + y^2 = 1$ and $x^2 + y^2 = 2$

23. $\iiint_E xy\, dV$, where $E = \{(x, y, z) \mid 0 \le x \le 3,\ 0 \le y \le x,\ 0 \le z \le x + y\}$

24. $\iiint_T xy\, dV$, where T is the solid tetrahedron with vertices $(0, 0, 0)$, $(\frac{1}{3}, 0, 0)$, $(0, 1, 0)$, and $(0, 0, 1)$

25. $\iiint_E y^2z^2\, dV$, where E is bounded by the paraboloid $x = 1 - y^2 - z^2$ and the plane $x = 0$

26. $\iiint_E z\, dV$, where E is bounded by the planes $y = 0$, $z = 0$, $x + y = 2$ and the cylinder $y^2 + z^2 = 1$ in the first octant

27. $\iiint_E yz\, dV$, where E lies above the plane $z = 0$, below the plane $z = y$, and inside the cylinder $x^2 + y^2 = 4$

28. $\iiint_H z^3\sqrt{x^2 + y^2 + z^2}\, dV$, where H is the solid hemisphere that lies above the xy-plane and has center the origin and radius 1

29–34 Find the volume of the given solid.

29. Under the paraboloid $z = x^2 + 4y^2$ and above the rectangle $R = [0, 2] \times [1, 4]$

30. Under the surface $z = x^2y$ and above the triangle in the xy-plane with vertices $(1, 0)$, $(2, 1)$, and $(4, 0)$

31. The solid tetrahedron with vertices $(0, 0, 0)$, $(0, 0, 1)$, $(0, 2, 0)$, and $(2, 2, 0)$

32. Bounded by the cylinder $x^2 + y^2 = 4$ and the planes $z = 0$ and $y + z = 3$

33. One of the wedges cut from the cylinder $x^2 + 9y^2 = a^2$ by the planes $z = 0$ and $z = mx$

34. Above the paraboloid $z = x^2 + y^2$ and below the half-cone $z = \sqrt{x^2 + y^2}$

---

35. Consider a lamina that occupies the region D bounded by the parabola $x = 1 - y^2$ and the coordinate axes in the first quadrant with density function $\rho(x, y) = y$.
  (a) Find the mass of the lamina.
  (b) Find the center of mass.
  (c) Find the moments of inertia and radii of gyration about the x- and y-axes.

36. A lamina occupies the part of the disk $x^2 + y^2 \leq a^2$ that lies in the first quadrant.
  (a) Find the centroid of the lamina.
  (b) Find the center of mass of the lamina if the density function is $\rho(x, y) = xy^2$.

37. Find the centroid of a right circular cone with height h and base radius a. (Place the cone so that its base is in the xy-plane with center the origin and its axis along the positive z-axis.)

38. Find the moment of inertia of the cone in Exercise 37 about its axis (the z-axis).

39. Use polar coordinates to evaluate
$$\int_0^3 \int_{-\sqrt{9-x^2}}^{\sqrt{9-x^2}} (x^3 + xy^2) \, dy \, dx$$

40. Use spherical coordinates to evaluate
$$\int_{-2}^{2} \int_0^{\sqrt{4-y^2}} \int_{-\sqrt{4-x^2-y^2}}^{\sqrt{4-x^2-y^2}} y^2\sqrt{x^2 + y^2 + z^2} \, dz \, dx \, dy$$

41. If D is the region bounded by the curves $y = 1 - x^2$ and $y = e^x$, find the approximate value of the integral $\iint_D y^2 \, dA$. (Use a graphing device to estimate the points of intersection of the curves.)

CAS **42.** Find the center of mass of the solid tetrahedron with vertices $(0, 0, 0)$, $(1, 0, 0)$, $(0, 2, 0)$, $(0, 0, 3)$ and density function $\rho(x, y, z) = x^2 + y^2 + z^2$.

43. The joint density function for random variables X and Y is
$$f(x, y) = \begin{cases} C(x + y) & \text{if } 0 \leq x \leq 3, \ 0 \leq y \leq 2 \\ 0 & \text{otherwise} \end{cases}$$
  (a) Find the value of the constant C.
  (b) Find $P(X \leq 2, Y \geq 1)$.
  (c) Find $P(X + Y \leq 1)$.

44. A lamp has three bulbs, ea█████
800 hours. If we model the proba█████
bulbs by an exponential density functio█
find the probability that all three bulbs fail wi█
1000 hours.

45. Rewrite the integral
$$\int_{-1}^{1} \int_{x^2}^{1} \int_0^{1-y} f(x, y, z) \, dz \, dy \, dx$$
as an iterated integral in the order $dx \, dy \, dz$.

46. Give five other iterated integrals that are equal to
$$\int_0^2 \int_0^{y^3} \int_0^{y^2} f(x, y, z) \, dz \, dx \, dy$$

47. Use the transformation $u = x - y$, $v = x + y$ to evaluate $\iint_R (x - y)/(x + y) \, dA$, where R is the square with vertices $(0, 2)$, $(1, 1)$, $(2, 2)$, and $(1, 3)$.

48. Use the transformation $x = u^2$, $y = v^2$, $z = w^2$ to find the volume of the region bounded by the surface $\sqrt{x} + \sqrt{y} + \sqrt{z} = 1$ and the coordinate planes.

49. Use the change of variables formula and an appropriate transformation to evaluate $\iint_R xy \, dA$, where R is the square with vertices $(0, 0)$, $(1, 1)$, $(2, 0)$, and $(1, -1)$.

50. The **Mean Value Theorem for double integrals** says that if f is a continuous function on a plane region D that is of type I or II, then there exists a point (x_0, y_0) in D such that
$$\iint_D f(x, y) \, dA = f(x_0, y_0) A(D)$$
Use the Extreme Value Theorem (15.7.8) and Property 16.3.11 of integrals to prove this theorem. (Use the proof of the single-variable version in Section 6.5 as a guide.)

51. Suppose that f is continuous on a disk that contains the point (a, b). Let D_r be the closed disk with center (a, b) and radius r. Use the Mean Value Theorem for double integrals (see Exercise 50) to show that
$$\lim_{r \to 0} \frac{1}{\pi r^2} \iint_{D_r} f(x, y) \, dA = f(a, b)$$

52. (a) Evaluate $\iint_D \dfrac{1}{(x^2 + y^2)^{n/2}} \, dA$, where n is an integer and D is the region bounded by the circles with center the origin and radii r and R, $0 < r < R$.
  (b) For what values of n does the integral in part (a) have a limit as $r \to 0^+$?
  (c) Find $\iiint_E \dfrac{1}{(x^2 + y^2 + z^2)^{n/2}} \, dV$, where E is the region bounded by the spheres with center the origin and radii r and R, $0 < r < R$.
  (d) For what values of n does the integral in part (c) have a limit as $r \to 0^+$?

If $[\![x]\!]$ denotes the greatest integer in x, evaluate the integral

$$\iint_R [\![x + y]\!] \, dA$$

where $R = \{(x, y) \mid 1 \leqslant x \leqslant 3, \ 2 \leqslant y \leqslant 5\}$.

2. Evaluate the integral

$$\int_0^1 \int_0^1 e^{\max\{x^2, y^2\}} \, dy \, dx$$

where $\max\{x^2, y^2\}$ means the larger of the numbers x^2 and y^2.

3. Find the average value of the function $f(x) = \int_x^1 \cos(t^2) \, dt$ on the interval $[0, 1]$.

4. If $\mathbf{a}$, $\mathbf{b}$, and $\mathbf{c}$ are constant vectors, $\mathbf{r}$ is the position vector $x\mathbf{i} + y\mathbf{j} + z\mathbf{k}$, and E is given by the inequalities $0 \leqslant \mathbf{a} \cdot \mathbf{r} \leqslant \alpha$, $0 \leqslant \mathbf{b} \cdot \mathbf{r} \leqslant \beta$, $0 \leqslant \mathbf{c} \cdot \mathbf{r} \leqslant \gamma$, show that

$$\iiint_E (\mathbf{a} \cdot \mathbf{r})(\mathbf{b} \cdot \mathbf{r})(\mathbf{c} \cdot \mathbf{r}) \, dV = \frac{(\alpha\beta\gamma)^2}{8|\mathbf{a} \cdot (\mathbf{b} \times \mathbf{c})|}$$

5. The double integral $\displaystyle\int_0^1 \int_0^1 \frac{1}{1 - xy} \, dx \, dy$ is an improper integral and could be defined as the limit of double integrals over the rectangle $[0, t] \times [0, t]$ as $t \to 1^-$. But if we expand the integrand as a geometric series, we can express the integral as the sum of an infinite series. Show that

$$\int_0^1 \int_0^1 \frac{1}{1 - xy} \, dx \, dy = \sum_{n=1}^{\infty} \frac{1}{n^2}$$

6. Leonhard Euler was able to find the exact sum of the series in Problem 5. In 1736 he proved that

$$\sum_{n=1}^{\infty} \frac{1}{n^2} = \frac{\pi^2}{6}$$

In this problem we ask you to prove this fact by evaluating the double integral in Problem 5. Start by making the change of variables

$$x = \frac{u - v}{\sqrt{2}} \qquad y = \frac{u + v}{\sqrt{2}}$$

This gives a rotation about the origin through the angle $\pi/4$. You will need to sketch the corresponding region in the uv-plane.

[*Hint:* If, in evaluating the integral, you encounter either of the expressions $(1 - \sin\theta)/\cos\theta$ or $(\cos\theta)/(1 + \sin\theta)$, you might like to use the identity $\cos\theta = \sin((\pi/2) - \theta)$ and the corresponding identity for $\sin\theta$.]

7. (a) Show that

$$\int_0^1 \int_0^1 \int_0^1 \frac{1}{1 - xyz} \, dx \, dy \, dz = \sum_{n=1}^{\infty} \frac{1}{n^3}$$

(Nobody has ever been able to find the exact value of the sum of this series.)

(b) Show that

$$\int_0^1 \int_0^1 \int_0^1 \frac{1}{1 + xyz} \, dx \, dy \, dz = \sum_{n=1}^{\infty} \frac{(-1)^{n-1}}{n^3}$$

Use this equation to evaluate the triple integral correct to two decimal places.

8. Show that

$$\int_0^\infty \frac{\arctan \pi x - \arctan x}{x} \, dx = \frac{\pi}{2} \ln \pi$$

by first expressing the integral as an iterated integral.

9. (a) Show that when Laplace's equation

$$\frac{\partial^2 u}{\partial x^2} + \frac{\partial^2 u}{\partial y^2} + \frac{\partial^2 u}{\partial z^2} = 0$$

is written in cylindrical coordinates, it becomes

$$\frac{\partial^2 u}{\partial r^2} + \frac{1}{r} \frac{\partial u}{\partial r} + \frac{1}{r^2} \frac{\partial^2 u}{\partial \theta^2} + \frac{\partial^2 u}{\partial z^2} = 0$$

(b) Show that when Laplace's equation is written in spherical coordinates, it becomes

$$\frac{\partial^2 u}{\partial \rho^2} + \frac{2}{\rho} \frac{\partial u}{\partial \rho} + \frac{\cot \phi}{\rho^2} \frac{\partial u}{\partial \phi} + \frac{1}{\rho^2} \frac{\partial^2 u}{\partial \phi^2} + \frac{1}{\rho^2 \sin^2 \phi} \frac{\partial^2 u}{\partial \theta^2} = 0$$

10. (a) A lamina has constant density ρ and takes the shape of a disk with center the origin and radius R. Use Newton's Law of Gravitation (see Section 14.4) to show that the magnitude of the force of attraction that the lamina exerts on a body with mass m located at the point $(0, 0, d)$ on the positive z-axis is

$$F = 2\pi Gm\rho d \left(\frac{1}{d} - \frac{1}{\sqrt{R^2 + d^2}} \right)$$

[*Hint:* Divide the disk as in Figure 4 in Section 16.4 and first compute the vertical component of the force exerted by the polar subrectangle R_{ij}.]

(b) Show that the magnitude of the force of attraction of a lamina with density ρ that occupies an entire plane on an object with mass m located at a distance d from the plane is

$$F = 2\pi Gm\rho$$

Notice that this expression does not depend on d.

11. If f is continuous, show that

$$\int_0^x \int_0^y \int_0^z f(t) \, dt \, dz \, dy = \frac{1}{2} \int_0^x (x - t)^2 f(t) \, dt$$

17

VECTOR CALCULUS

Parametric equations enable us to plot surfaces with
strange and beautiful shapes.

In this chapter we study the calculus of vector fields. (These are functions that assign
vectors to points in space.) In particular we define line integrals (which can be used to
find the work done by a force field in moving an object along a curve). Then we define
surface integrals (which can be used to find the rate of fluid flow across a surface). The
connections between these new types of integrals and the single, double, and triple
integrals that we have already met are given by the higher-dimensional versions of the
Fundamental Theorem of Calculus: Green's Theorem, Stokes' Theorem, and the
Divergence Theorem.

The vectors in Figure 1 are air velocity vectors that indicate the wind speed and direction at points 10 m above the surface elevation in the San Francisco Bay area. (Notice that the wind patterns on consecutive days are quite different.) Associated with every point in the air we can imagine a wind velocity vector. This is an example of a *velocity vector field.*

(a) 12:00 AM, February 20, 2007

(b) 2:00 PM, February 21, 2007

FIGURE 1 Velocity vector fields showing San Francisco Bay wind patterns

Other examples of velocity vector fields are illustrated in Figure 2: ocean currents and flow past an airfoil.

(a) Ocean currents off the coast of Nova Scotia

(b) Airflow past an inclined airfoil

FIGURE 2 Velocity vector fields

Another type of vector field, called a *force field,* associates a force vector with each point in a region. An example is the gravitational force field that we will look at in Example 4.

In general, a vector field is a function whose domain is a set of points in $\mathbb{R}^2$ (or $\mathbb{R}^3$) and whose range is a set of vectors in V_2 (or V_3).

---

1 DEFINITION Let D be a set in $\mathbb{R}^2$ (a plane region). A **vector field on** $\mathbb{R}^2$ is a function $\mathbf{F}$ that assigns to each point (x, y) in D a two-dimensional vector $\mathbf{F}(x, y)$.

The best way to picture a vector field is to draw the arrow representing the vector $\mathbf{F}(x, y)$ starting at the point (x, y). Of course, it's impossible to do this for all points (x, y), but we can gain a reasonable impression of $\mathbf{F}$ by doing it for a few representative points in D as in Figure 3. Since $\mathbf{F}(x, y)$ is a two-dimensional vector, we can write it in terms of its **component functions** P and Q as follows:

$$\mathbf{F}(x, y) = P(x, y)\,\mathbf{i} + Q(x, y)\,\mathbf{j} = \langle P(x, y), Q(x, y)\rangle$$

or, for short,
$$\mathbf{F} = P\,\mathbf{i} + Q\,\mathbf{j}$$

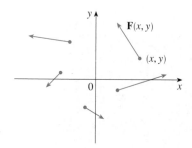

FIGURE 3
Vector field on $\mathbb{R}^2$

Notice that P and Q are scalar functions of two variables and are sometimes called **scalar fields** to distinguish them from vector fields.

---

2 DEFINITION Let E be a subset of $\mathbb{R}^3$. A **vector field on** $\mathbb{R}^3$ is a function $\mathbf{F}$ that assigns to each point (x, y, z) in E a three-dimensional vector $\mathbf{F}(x, y, z)$.

A vector field $\mathbf{F}$ on $\mathbb{R}^3$ is pictured in Figure 4. We can express it in terms of its component functions P, Q, and R as

$$\mathbf{F}(x, y, z) = P(x, y, z)\,\mathbf{i} + Q(x, y, z)\,\mathbf{j} + R(x, y, z)\,\mathbf{k}$$

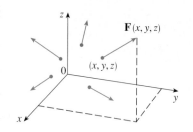

FIGURE 4
Vector field on $\mathbb{R}^3$

As with the vector functions in Section 14.1, we can define continuity of vector fields and show that $\mathbf{F}$ is continuous if and only if its component functions P, Q, and R are continuous.

We sometimes identify a point (x, y, z) with its position vector $\mathbf{x} = \langle x, y, z \rangle$ and write $\mathbf{F}(\mathbf{x})$ instead of $\mathbf{F}(x, y, z)$. Then $\mathbf{F}$ becomes a function that assigns a vector $\mathbf{F}(\mathbf{x})$ to a vector $\mathbf{x}$.

☑ EXAMPLE 1 A vector field on $\mathbb{R}^2$ is defined by $\mathbf{F}(x, y) = -y\,\mathbf{i} + x\,\mathbf{j}$. Describe $\mathbf{F}$ by sketching some of the vectors $\mathbf{F}(x, y)$ as in Figure 3.

SOLUTION Since $\mathbf{F}(1, 0) = \mathbf{j}$, we draw the vector $\mathbf{j} = \langle 0, 1 \rangle$ starting at the point $(1, 0)$ in Figure 5. Since $\mathbf{F}(0, 1) = -\mathbf{i}$, we draw the vector $\langle -1, 0 \rangle$ with starting point $(0, 1)$. Continuing in this way, we calculate several other representative values of $\mathbf{F}(x, y)$ in the table and draw the corresponding vectors to represent the vector field in Figure 5.

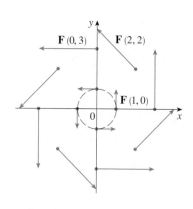

FIGURE 5
$\mathbf{F}(x, y) = -y\,\mathbf{i} + x\,\mathbf{j}$

(x, y)	$\mathbf{F}(x, y)$	(x, y)	$\mathbf{F}(x, y)$
$(1, 0)$	$\langle 0, 1 \rangle$	$(-1, 0)$	$\langle 0, -1 \rangle$
$(2, 2)$	$\langle -2, 2 \rangle$	$(-2, -2)$	$\langle 2, -2 \rangle$
$(3, 0)$	$\langle 0, 3 \rangle$	$(-3, 0)$	$\langle 0, -3 \rangle$
$(0, 1)$	$\langle -1, 0 \rangle$	$(0, -1)$	$\langle 1, 0 \rangle$
$(-2, 2)$	$\langle -2, -2 \rangle$	$(2, -2)$	$\langle 2, 2 \rangle$
$(0, 3)$	$\langle -3, 0 \rangle$	$(0, -3)$	$\langle 3, 0 \rangle$

It appears from Figure 5 that each arrow is tangent to a circle with center the origin.

To confirm this, we take the dot product of the position vector $\mathbf{x} = x\,\mathbf{i} + y\,\mathbf{j}$ with the vector $\mathbf{F}(\mathbf{x}) = \mathbf{F}(x, y)$:

$$\mathbf{x} \cdot \mathbf{F}(\mathbf{x}) = (x\,\mathbf{i} + y\,\mathbf{j}) \cdot (-y\,\mathbf{i} + x\,\mathbf{j}) = -xy + yx = 0$$

This shows that $\mathbf{F}(x, y)$ is perpendicular to the position vector $\langle x, y \rangle$ and is therefore tangent to a circle with center the origin and radius $|\mathbf{x}| = \sqrt{x^2 + y^2}$. Notice also that

$$|\mathbf{F}(x, y)| = \sqrt{(-y)^2 + x^2} = \sqrt{x^2 + y^2} = |\mathbf{x}|$$

so the magnitude of the vector $\mathbf{F}(x, y)$ is equal to the radius of the circle. ☐

Some computer algebra systems are capable of plotting vector fields in two or three dimensions. They give a better impression of the vector field than is possible by hand because the computer can plot a large number of representative vectors. Figure 6 shows a computer plot of the vector field in Example 1; Figures 7 and 8 show two other vector fields. Notice that the computer scales the lengths of the vectors so they are not too long and yet are proportional to their true lengths.

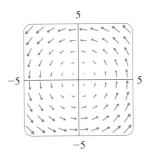

FIGURE 6
$\mathbf{F}(x, y) = \langle -y, x \rangle$

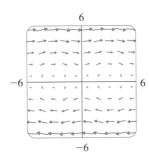

FIGURE 7
$\mathbf{F}(x, y) = \langle y, \sin x \rangle$

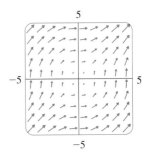

FIGURE 8
$\mathbf{F}(x, y) = \langle \ln(1 + y^2), \ln(1 + x^2) \rangle$

Ⅴ EXAMPLE 2 Sketch the vector field on $\mathbb{R}^3$ given by $\mathbf{F}(x, y, z) = z\,\mathbf{k}$.

SOLUTION The sketch is shown in Figure 9. Notice that all vectors are vertical and point upward above the xy-plane or downward below it. The magnitude increases with the distance from the xy-plane.

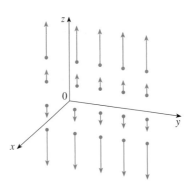

FIGURE 9
$\mathbf{F}(x, y, z) = z\,\mathbf{k}$

☐

We were able to draw the vector field in Example 2 by hand because of its particularly simple formula. Most three-dimensional vector fields, however, are virtually impossible to sketch by hand and so we need to resort to a computer algebra system. Examples are shown in Figures 10, 11, and 12. Notice that the vector fields in Figures 10 and 11 have similar formulas, but all the vectors in Figure 11 point in the general direction of the negative y-axis because their y-components are all -2. If the vector field in Figure 12 represents a velocity field, then a particle would be swept upward and would spiral around the z-axis in the clockwise direction as viewed from above.

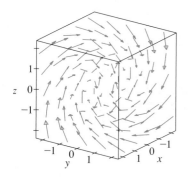

FIGURE 10
$\mathbf{F}(x, y, z) = y\,\mathbf{i} + z\,\mathbf{j} + x\,\mathbf{k}$

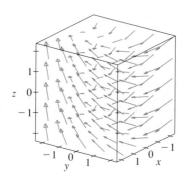

FIGURE 11
$\mathbf{F}(x, y, z) = y\,\mathbf{i} - 2\,\mathbf{j} + x\,\mathbf{k}$

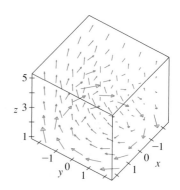

FIGURE 12
$\mathbf{F}(x, y, z) = \dfrac{y}{z}\,\mathbf{i} - \dfrac{x}{z}\,\mathbf{j} + \dfrac{z}{4}\,\mathbf{k}$

TEC In Visual 17.1 you can rotate the vector fields in Figures 10–12 as well as additional fields.

FIGURE 13
Velocity field in fluid flow

EXAMPLE 3 Imagine a fluid flowing steadily along a pipe and let $\mathbf{V}(x, y, z)$ be the velocity vector at a point (x, y, z). Then $\mathbf{V}$ assigns a vector to each point (x, y, z) in a certain domain E (the interior of the pipe) and so $\mathbf{V}$ is a vector field on $\mathbb{R}^3$ called a **velocity field**. A possible velocity field is illustrated in Figure 13. The speed at any given point is indicated by the length of the arrow.

Velocity fields also occur in other areas of physics. For instance, the vector field in Example 1 could be used as the velocity field describing the counterclockwise rotation of a wheel. We have seen other examples of velocity fields in Figures 1 and 2. ☐

EXAMPLE 4 Newton's Law of Gravitation states that the magnitude of the gravitational force between two objects with masses m and M is

$$|\mathbf{F}| = \frac{mMG}{r^2}$$

where r is the distance between the objects and G is the gravitational constant. (This is an example of an inverse square law.) Let's assume that the object with mass M is located at the origin in $\mathbb{R}^3$. (For instance, M could be the mass of the earth and the origin would be at its center.) Let the position vector of the object with mass m be $\mathbf{x} = \langle x, y, z \rangle$. Then $r = |\mathbf{x}|$, so $r^2 = |\mathbf{x}|^2$. The gravitational force exerted on this second object acts toward the origin, and the unit vector in this direction is

$$-\frac{\mathbf{x}}{|\mathbf{x}|}$$

Therefore the gravitational force acting on the object at $\mathbf{x} = \langle x, y, z \rangle$ is

$$\boxed{3} \qquad \mathbf{F}(\mathbf{x}) = -\frac{mMG}{|\mathbf{x}|^3}\,\mathbf{x}$$

[Physicists often use the notation $\mathbf{r}$ instead of $\mathbf{x}$ for the position vector, so you may see

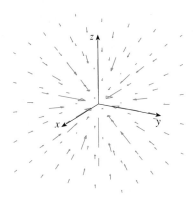

FIGURE 14
Gravitational force field

Formula 3 written in the form $\mathbf{F} = -(mMG/r^3)\mathbf{r}$.] The function given by Equation 3 is an example of a vector field, called the **gravitational field**, because it associates a vector [the force $\mathbf{F}(\mathbf{x})$] with every point $\mathbf{x}$ in space.

Formula 3 is a compact way of writing the gravitational field, but we can also write it in terms of its component functions by using the facts that $\mathbf{x} = x\,\mathbf{i} + y\,\mathbf{j} + z\,\mathbf{k}$ and $|\mathbf{x}| = \sqrt{x^2 + y^2 + z^2}$:

$$\mathbf{F}(x, y, z) = \frac{-mMGx}{(x^2 + y^2 + z^2)^{3/2}}\,\mathbf{i} + \frac{-mMGy}{(x^2 + y^2 + z^2)^{3/2}}\,\mathbf{j} + \frac{-mMGz}{(x^2 + y^2 + z^2)^{3/2}}\,\mathbf{k}$$

The gravitational field $\mathbf{F}$ is pictured in Figure 14. $\qquad\square$

EXAMPLE 5 Suppose an electric charge Q is located at the origin. According to Coulomb's Law, the electric force $\mathbf{F}(\mathbf{x})$ exerted by this charge on a charge q located at a point (x, y, z) with position vector $\mathbf{x} = \langle x, y, z \rangle$ is

$$\boxed{4} \qquad\qquad \mathbf{F}(\mathbf{x}) = \frac{\varepsilon q Q}{|\mathbf{x}|^3}\,\mathbf{x}$$

where ε is a constant (that depends on the units used). For like charges, we have $qQ > 0$ and the force is repulsive; for unlike charges, we have $qQ < 0$ and the force is attractive. Notice the similarity between Formulas 3 and 4. Both vector fields are examples of **force fields**.

Instead of considering the electric force $\mathbf{F}$, physicists often consider the force per unit charge:

$$\mathbf{E}(\mathbf{x}) = \frac{1}{q}\,\mathbf{F}(\mathbf{x}) = \frac{\varepsilon Q}{|\mathbf{x}|^3}\,\mathbf{x}$$

Then $\mathbf{E}$ is a vector field on $\mathbb{R}^3$ called the **electric field** of Q. $\qquad\square$

GRADIENT FIELDS

If f is a scalar function of two variables, recall from Section 15.6 that its gradient ∇f (or grad f) is defined by

$$\nabla f(x, y) = f_x(x, y)\,\mathbf{i} + f_y(x, y)\,\mathbf{j}$$

Therefore ∇f is really a vector field on $\mathbb{R}^2$ and is called a **gradient vector field**. Likewise, if f is a scalar function of three variables, its gradient is a vector field on $\mathbb{R}^3$ given by

$$\nabla f(x, y, z) = f_x(x, y, z)\,\mathbf{i} + f_y(x, y, z)\,\mathbf{j} + f_z(x, y, z)\,\mathbf{k}$$

▼ EXAMPLE 6 Find the gradient vector field of $f(x, y) = x^2 y - y^3$. Plot the gradient vector field together with a contour map of f. How are they related?

SOLUTION The gradient vector field is given by

$$\nabla f(x, y) = \frac{\partial f}{\partial x}\,\mathbf{i} + \frac{\partial f}{\partial y}\,\mathbf{j} = 2xy\,\mathbf{i} + (x^2 - 3y^2)\,\mathbf{j}$$

Figure 15 shows a contour map of f with the gradient vector field. Notice that the gradient vectors are perpendicular to the level curves, as we would expect from Section 15.6.

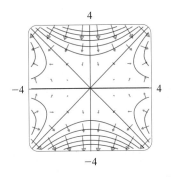

FIGURE 15

Notice also that the gradient vectors are long where the level curves are close to each other and short where the curves are farther apart. That's because the length of the gradient vector is the value of the directional derivative of f and closely spaced level curves indicate a steep graph. □

A vector field **F** is called a **conservative vector field** if it is the gradient of some scalar function, that is, if there exists a function f such that $\mathbf{F} = \nabla f$. In this situation f is called a **potential function** for **F**.

Not all vector fields are conservative, but such fields do arise frequently in physics. For example, the gravitational field **F** in Example 4 is conservative because if we define

$$f(x, y, z) = \frac{mMG}{\sqrt{x^2 + y^2 + z^2}}$$

then

$$\nabla f(x, y, z) = \frac{\partial f}{\partial x} \mathbf{i} + \frac{\partial f}{\partial y} \mathbf{j} + \frac{\partial f}{\partial z} \mathbf{k}$$

$$= \frac{-mMGx}{(x^2 + y^2 + z^2)^{3/2}} \mathbf{i} + \frac{-mMGy}{(x^2 + y^2 + z^2)^{3/2}} \mathbf{j} + \frac{-mMGz}{(x^2 + y^2 + z^2)^{3/2}} \mathbf{k}$$

$$= \mathbf{F}(x, y, z)$$

In Sections 17.3 and 17.5 we will learn how to tell whether or not a given vector field is conservative.

17.1 EXERCISES

1–10 Sketch the vector field **F** by drawing a diagram like Figure 5 or Figure 9.

1. $\mathbf{F}(x, y) = \frac{1}{2}(\mathbf{i} + \mathbf{j})$

2. $\mathbf{F}(x, y) = \mathbf{i} + x\mathbf{j}$

3. $\mathbf{F}(x, y) = y\mathbf{i} + \frac{1}{2}\mathbf{j}$

4. $\mathbf{F}(x, y) = (x - y)\mathbf{i} + x\mathbf{j}$

5. $\mathbf{F}(x, y) = \dfrac{y\mathbf{i} + x\mathbf{j}}{\sqrt{x^2 + y^2}}$

6. $\mathbf{F}(x, y) = \dfrac{y\mathbf{i} - x\mathbf{j}}{\sqrt{x^2 + y^2}}$

7. $\mathbf{F}(x, y, z) = \mathbf{k}$

8. $\mathbf{F}(x, y, z) = -y\mathbf{k}$

9. $\mathbf{F}(x, y, z) = x\mathbf{k}$

10. $\mathbf{F}(x, y, z) = \mathbf{j} - \mathbf{i}$

11–14 Match the vector fields **F** with the plots labeled I–IV. Give reasons for your choices.

11. $\mathbf{F}(x, y) = \langle y, x \rangle$

12. $\mathbf{F}(x, y) = \langle 1, \sin y \rangle$

13. $\mathbf{F}(x, y) = \langle x - 2, x + 1 \rangle$

14. $\mathbf{F}(x, y) = \langle y, 1/x \rangle$

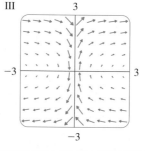

15–18 Match the vector fields **F** on $\mathbb{R}^3$ with the plots labeled I–IV. Give reasons for your choices.

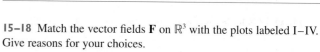

15. $\mathbf{F}(x, y, z) = \mathbf{i} + 2\mathbf{j} + 3\mathbf{k}$ **16.** $\mathbf{F}(x, y, z) = \mathbf{i} + 2\mathbf{j} + z\mathbf{k}$

17. $\mathbf{F}(x, y, z) = x\,\mathbf{i} + y\,\mathbf{j} + 3\,\mathbf{k}$

18. $\mathbf{F}(x, y, z) = x\,\mathbf{i} + y\,\mathbf{j} + z\,\mathbf{k}$

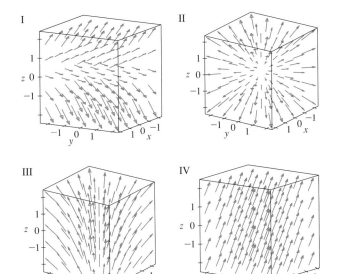

31. $f(x, y) = (x + y)^2$

32. $f(x, y) = \sin\sqrt{x^2 + y^2}$

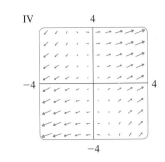

CAS 19. If you have a CAS that plots vector fields (the command is `fieldplot` in Maple and `PlotVectorField` in Mathematica), use it to plot

$$\mathbf{F}(x, y) = (y^2 - 2xy)\,\mathbf{i} + (3xy - 6x^2)\,\mathbf{j}$$

Explain the appearance by finding the set of points (x, y) such that $\mathbf{F}(x, y) = \mathbf{0}$.

CAS 20. Let $\mathbf{F}(\mathbf{x}) = (r^2 - 2r)\mathbf{x}$, where $\mathbf{x} = \langle x, y\rangle$ and $r = |\mathbf{x}|$. Use a CAS to plot this vector field in various domains until you can see what is happening. Describe the appearance of the plot and explain it by finding the points where $\mathbf{F}(\mathbf{x}) = \mathbf{0}$.

21–24 Find the gradient vector field of f.

21. $f(x, y) = xe^{xy}$

22. $f(x, y) = \tan(3x - 4y)$

23. $f(x, y, z) = \sqrt{x^2 + y^2 + z^2}$

24. $f(x, y, z) = x\cos(y/z)$

25–26 Find the gradient vector field ∇f of f and sketch it.

25. $f(x, y) = x^2 - y$

26. $f(x, y) = \sqrt{x^2 + y^2}$

CAS 27–28 Plot the gradient vector field of f together with a contour map of f. Explain how they are related to each other.

27. $f(x, y) = \sin x + \sin y$

28. $f(x, y) = \sin(x + y)$

29–32 Match the functions f with the plots of their gradient vector fields (labeled I–IV). Give reasons for your choices.

29. $f(x, y) = x^2 + y^2$

30. $f(x, y) = x(x + y)$

33. A particle moves in a velocity field $\mathbf{V}(x, y) = \langle x^2, x + y^2\rangle$. If it is at position $(2, 1)$ at time $t = 3$, estimate its location at time $t = 3.01$.

34. At time $t = 1$, a particle is located at position $(1, 3)$. If it moves in a velocity field

$$\mathbf{F}(x, y) = \langle xy - 2, y^2 - 10\rangle$$

find its approximate location at time $t = 1.05$.

35. The **flow lines** (or **streamlines**) of a vector field are the paths followed by a particle whose velocity field is the given vector field. Thus the vectors in a vector field are tangent to the flow lines.

(a) Use a sketch of the vector field $\mathbf{F}(x, y) = x\,\mathbf{i} - y\,\mathbf{j}$ to draw some flow lines. From your sketches, can you guess the equations of the flow lines?

(b) If parametric equations of a flow line are $x = x(t)$, $y = y(t)$, explain why these functions satisfy the differential equations $dx/dt = x$ and $dy/dt = -y$. Then solve the differential equations to find an equation of the flow line that passes through the point $(1, 1)$.

36. (a) Sketch the vector field $\mathbf{F}(x, y) = \mathbf{i} + x\,\mathbf{j}$ and then sketch some flow lines. What shape do these flow lines appear to have?

(b) If parametric equations of the flow lines are $x = x(t)$, $y = y(t)$, what differential equations do these functions satisfy? Deduce that $dy/dx = x$.

(c) If a particle starts at the origin in the velocity field given by $\mathbf{F}$, find an equation of the path it follows.

17.2 LINE INTEGRALS

In this section we define an integral that is similar to a single integral except that instead of integrating over an interval $[a, b]$, we integrate over a curve C. Such integrals are called *line integrals*, although "curve integrals" would be better terminology. They were invented in the early 19th century to solve problems involving fluid flow, forces, electricity, and magnetism.

We start with a plane curve C given by the parametric equations

$$\boxed{1} \qquad\qquad x = x(t) \qquad y = y(t) \qquad a \leqslant t \leqslant b$$

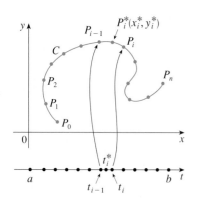

FIGURE 1

or, equivalently, by the vector equation $\mathbf{r}(t) = x(t)\,\mathbf{i} + y(t)\,\mathbf{j}$, and we assume that C is a smooth curve. [This means that $\mathbf{r}'$ is continuous and $\mathbf{r}'(t) \neq \mathbf{0}$. See Section 14.3.] If we divide the parameter interval $[a, b]$ into n subintervals $[t_{i-1}, t_i]$ of equal width and we let $x_i = x(t_i)$ and $y_i = y(t_i)$, then the corresponding points $P_i(x_i, y_i)$ divide C into n subarcs with lengths $\Delta s_1, \Delta s_2, \ldots, \Delta s_n$. (See Figure 1.) We choose any point $P_i^*(x_i^*, y_i^*)$ in the ith subarc. (This corresponds to a point t_i^* in $[t_{i-1}, t_i]$.) Now if f is any function of two variables whose domain includes the curve C, we evaluate f at the point (x_i^*, y_i^*), multiply by the length Δs_i of the subarc, and form the sum

$$\sum_{i=1}^{n} f(x_i^*, y_i^*)\,\Delta s_i$$

which is similar to a Riemann sum. Then we take the limit of these sums and make the following definition by analogy with a single integral.

$\boxed{2}$ **DEFINITION** If f is defined on a smooth curve C given by Equations 1, then the **line integral of f along C** is

$$\int_C f(x, y)\,ds = \lim_{n \to \infty} \sum_{i=1}^{n} f(x_i^*, y_i^*)\,\Delta s_i$$

if this limit exists.

In Section 11.2 we found that the length of C is

$$L = \int_a^b \sqrt{\left(\frac{dx}{dt}\right)^2 + \left(\frac{dy}{dt}\right)^2}\, dt$$

A similar type of argument can be used to show that if f is a continuous function, then the limit in Definition 2 always exists and the following formula can be used to evaluate the line integral:

$$\boxed{3} \qquad \int_C f(x, y)\,ds = \int_a^b f(x(t), y(t)) \sqrt{\left(\frac{dx}{dt}\right)^2 + \left(\frac{dy}{dt}\right)^2}\, dt$$

The value of the line integral does not depend on the parametrization of the curve, provided that the curve is traversed exactly once as t increases from a to b.

■ The arc length function s is discussed in Section 14.3.

If $s(t)$ is the length of C between $\mathbf{r}(a)$ and $\mathbf{r}(t)$, then

$$\frac{ds}{dt} = \sqrt{\left(\frac{dx}{dt}\right)^2 + \left(\frac{dy}{dt}\right)^2}$$

So the way to remember Formula 3 is to express everything in terms of the parameter t: Use the parametric equations to express x and y in terms of t and write ds as

$$ds = \sqrt{\left(\frac{dx}{dt}\right)^2 + \left(\frac{dy}{dt}\right)^2}\, dt$$

In the special case where C is the line segment that joins $(a, 0)$ to $(b, 0)$, using x as the parameter, we can write the parametric equations of C as follows: $x = x$, $y = 0$, $a \leqslant x \leqslant b$. Formula 3 then becomes

$$\int_C f(x, y)\, ds = \int_a^b f(x, 0)\, dx$$

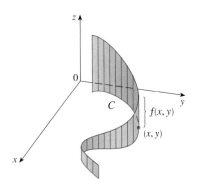

FIGURE 2

and so the line integral reduces to an ordinary single integral in this case.

Just as for an ordinary single integral, we can interpret the line integral of a *positive* function as an area. In fact, if $f(x, y) \geqslant 0$, $\int_C f(x, y)\, ds$ represents the area of one side of the "fence" or "curtain" in Figure 2, whose base is C and whose height above the point (x, y) is $f(x, y)$.

EXAMPLE 1 Evaluate $\int_C (2 + x^2 y)\, ds$, where C is the upper half of the unit circle $x^2 + y^2 = 1$.

SOLUTION In order to use Formula 3, we first need parametric equations to represent C. Recall that the unit circle can be parametrized by means of the equations

$$x = \cos t \qquad y = \sin t$$

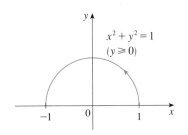

FIGURE 3

and the upper half of the circle is described by the parameter interval $0 \leqslant t \leqslant \pi$. (See Figure 3.) Therefore Formula 3 gives

$$\int_C (2 + x^2 y)\, ds = \int_0^\pi (2 + \cos^2 t \sin t) \sqrt{\left(\frac{dx}{dt}\right)^2 + \left(\frac{dy}{dt}\right)^2}\, dt$$

$$= \int_0^\pi (2 + \cos^2 t \sin t) \sqrt{\sin^2 t + \cos^2 t}\, dt$$

$$= \int_0^\pi (2 + \cos^2 t \sin t)\, dt = \left[2t - \frac{\cos^3 t}{3} \right]_0^\pi$$

$$= 2\pi + \tfrac{2}{3} \qquad \qquad \square$$

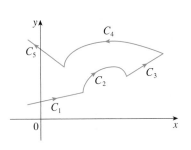

FIGURE 4
A piecewise-smooth curve

Suppose now that C is a **piecewise-smooth curve**; that is, C is a union of a finite number of smooth curves $C_1, C_2, \ldots, C_n$, where, as illustrated in Figure 4, the initial point of C_{i+1} is the terminal point of C_i. Then we define the integral of f along C as the sum of the integrals of f along each of the smooth pieces of C:

$$\int_C f(x, y)\, ds = \int_{C_1} f(x, y)\, ds + \int_{C_2} f(x, y)\, ds + \cdots + \int_{C_n} f(x, y)\, ds$$

EXAMPLE 2 Evaluate $\int_C 2x\, ds$, where C consists of the arc C_1 of the parabola $y = x^2$ from $(0, 0)$ to $(1, 1)$ followed by the vertical line segment C_2 from $(1, 1)$ to $(1, 2)$.

SOLUTION The curve C is shown in Figure 5. C_1 is the graph of a function of x, so we can choose x as the parameter and the equations for C_1 become

$$x = x \qquad y = x^2 \qquad 0 \leqslant x \leqslant 1$$

Therefore

$$\int_{C_1} 2x\, ds = \int_0^1 2x \sqrt{\left(\frac{dx}{dx}\right)^2 + \left(\frac{dy}{dx}\right)^2}\, dx = \int_0^1 2x\sqrt{1 + 4x^2}\, dx$$

$$= \tfrac{1}{4} \cdot \tfrac{2}{3}(1 + 4x^2)^{3/2}\Big]_0^1 = \frac{5\sqrt{5} - 1}{6}$$

On C_2 we choose y as the parameter, so the equations of C_2 are

$$x = 1 \qquad y = y \qquad 1 \leqslant y \leqslant 2$$

and

$$\int_{C_2} 2x\, ds = \int_1^2 2(1) \sqrt{\left(\frac{dx}{dy}\right)^2 + \left(\frac{dy}{dy}\right)^2}\, dy = \int_1^2 2\, dy = 2$$

Thus

$$\int_C 2x\, ds = \int_{C_1} 2x\, ds + \int_{C_2} 2x\, ds = \frac{5\sqrt{5} - 1}{6} + 2 \qquad \square$$

Any physical interpretation of a line integral $\int_C f(x, y)\, ds$ depends on the physical interpretation of the function f. Suppose that $\rho(x, y)$ represents the linear density at a point (x, y) of a thin wire shaped like a curve C. Then the mass of the part of the wire from P_{i-1} to P_i in Figure 1 is approximately $\rho(x_i^*, y_i^*)\, \Delta s_i$ and so the total mass of the wire is approximately $\sum \rho(x_i^*, y_i^*)\, \Delta s_i$. By taking more and more points on the curve, we obtain the **mass** m of the wire as the limiting value of these approximations:

$$m = \lim_{n \to \infty} \sum_{i=1}^n \rho(x_i^*, y_i^*)\, \Delta s_i = \int_C \rho(x, y)\, ds$$

[For example, if $f(x, y) = 2 + x^2 y$ represents the density of a semicircular wire, then the integral in Example 1 would represent the mass of the wire.] The **center of mass** of the wire with density function ρ is located at the point $(\bar{x}, \bar{y})$, where

$$\boxed{4} \qquad \bar{x} = \frac{1}{m} \int_C x \rho(x, y)\, ds \qquad \bar{y} = \frac{1}{m} \int_C y \rho(x, y)\, ds$$

Other physical interpretations of line integrals will be discussed later in this chapter.

☑ **EXAMPLE 3** A wire takes the shape of the semicircle $x^2 + y^2 = 1$, $y \geqslant 0$, and is thicker near its base than near the top. Find the center of mass of the wire if the linear density at any point is proportional to its distance from the line $y = 1$.

SOLUTION As in Example 1 we use the parametrization $x = \cos t$, $y = \sin t$, $0 \leqslant t \leqslant \pi$, and find that $ds = dt$. The linear density is

$$\rho(x, y) = k(1 - y)$$

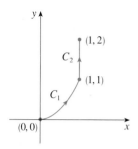

FIGURE 5
$C = C_1 \cup C_2$

where k is a constant, and so the mass of the wire is

$$m = \int_C k(1 - y)\, ds = \int_0^\pi k(1 - \sin t)\, dt = k\big[t + \cos t\big]_0^\pi = k(\pi - 2)$$

From Equations 4 we have

$$\bar{y} = \frac{1}{m} \int_C y\, \rho(x, y)\, ds = \frac{1}{k(\pi - 2)} \int_C y\, k(1 - y)\, ds$$

$$= \frac{1}{\pi - 2} \int_0^\pi (\sin t - \sin^2 t)\, dt = \frac{1}{\pi - 2}\big[-\cos t - \tfrac{1}{2}t + \tfrac{1}{4}\sin 2t\big]_0^\pi$$

$$= \frac{4 - \pi}{2(\pi - 2)}$$

By symmetry we see that $\bar{x} = 0$, so the center of mass is

$$\left(0, \frac{4 - \pi}{2(\pi - 2)}\right) \approx (0, 0.38)$$

See Figure 6. □

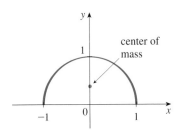

center of mass

FIGURE 6

Two other line integrals are obtained by replacing Δs_i by either $\Delta x_i = x_i - x_{i-1}$ or $\Delta y_i = y_i - y_{i-1}$ in Definition 2. They are called the **line integrals of f along C with respect to x and y**:

$$\boxed{5}\qquad \int_C f(x, y)\, dx = \lim_{n\to\infty} \sum_{i=1}^n f(x_i^*, y_i^*)\, \Delta x_i$$

$$\boxed{6}\qquad \int_C f(x, y)\, dy = \lim_{n\to\infty} \sum_{i=1}^n f(x_i^*, y_i^*)\, \Delta y_i$$

When we want to distinguish the original line integral $\int_C f(x, y)\, ds$ from those in Equations 5 and 6, we call it the **line integral with respect to arc length**.

The following formulas say that line integrals with respect to x and y can also be evaluated by expressing everything in terms of t: $x = x(t)$, $y = y(t)$, $dx = x'(t)\, dt$, $dy = y'(t)\, dt$.

$$\boxed{7}\qquad \int_C f(x, y)\, dx = \int_a^b f\big(x(t), y(t)\big)\, x'(t)\, dt$$

$$\int_C f(x, y)\, dy = \int_a^b f\big(x(t), y(t)\big)\, y'(t)\, dt$$

It frequently happens that line integrals with respect to x and y occur together. When this happens, it's customary to abbreviate by writing

$$\int_C P(x, y)\, dx + \int_C Q(x, y)\, dy = \int_C P(x, y)\, dx + Q(x, y)\, dy$$

When we are setting up a line integral, sometimes the most difficult thing is to think of a parametric representation for a curve whose geometric description is given. In particular, we often need to parametrize a line segment, so it's useful to remember that a vector representation of the line segment that starts at $\mathbf{r}_0$ and ends at $\mathbf{r}_1$ is given by

$$\boxed{8} \qquad \mathbf{r}(t) = (1 - t)\mathbf{r}_0 + t\mathbf{r}_1 \qquad 0 \leqslant t \leqslant 1}$$

(See Equation 13.5.4.)

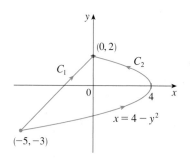

FIGURE 7

☑ **EXAMPLE 4** Evaluate $\int_C y^2 \, dx + x \, dy$, where (a) $C = C_1$ is the line segment from $(-5, -3)$ to $(0, 2)$ and (b) $C = C_2$ is the arc of the parabola $x = 4 - y^2$ from $(-5, -3)$ to $(0, 2)$. (See Figure 7.)

SOLUTION
(a) A parametric representation for the line segment is

$$x = 5t - 5 \qquad y = 5t - 3 \qquad 0 \leqslant t \leqslant 1$$

(Use Equation 8 with $\mathbf{r}_0 = \langle -5, -3 \rangle$ and $\mathbf{r}_1 = \langle 0, 2 \rangle$.) Then $dx = 5 \, dt$, $dy = 5 \, dt$, and Formulas 7 give

$$\int_{C_1} y^2 \, dx + x \, dy = \int_0^1 (5t - 3)^2 (5 \, dt) + (5t - 5)(5 \, dt)$$

$$= 5 \int_0^1 (25t^2 - 25t + 4) \, dt$$

$$= 5 \left[\frac{25t^3}{3} - \frac{25t^2}{2} + 4t \right]_0^1 = -\frac{5}{6}$$

(b) Since the parabola is given as a function of y, let's take y as the parameter and write C_2 as

$$x = 4 - y^2 \qquad y = y \qquad -3 \leqslant y \leqslant 2$$

Then $dx = -2y \, dy$ and by Formulas 7 we have

$$\int_{C_2} y^2 \, dx + x \, dy = \int_{-3}^2 y^2(-2y) \, dy + (4 - y^2) \, dy$$

$$= \int_{-3}^2 (-2y^3 - y^2 + 4) \, dy$$

$$= \left[-\frac{y^4}{2} - \frac{y^3}{3} + 4y \right]_{-3}^2 = 40\frac{5}{6} \qquad \square$$

Notice that we got different answers in parts (a) and (b) of Example 4 even though the two curves had the same endpoints. Thus, in general, the value of a line integral depends not just on the endpoints of the curve but also on the path. (But see Section 17.3 for conditions under which the integral is independent of the path.)

Notice also that the answers in Example 4 depend on the direction, or orientation, of the curve. If $-C_1$ denotes the line segment from $(0, 2)$ to $(-5, -3)$, you can verify, using the parametrization

$$x = -5t \qquad y = 2 - 5t \qquad 0 \leqslant t \leqslant 1$$

that

$$\int_{-C_1} y^2 \, dx + x \, dy = \frac{5}{6}$$

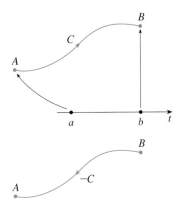

FIGURE 8

In general, a given parametrization $x = x(t)$, $y = y(t)$, $a \leqslant t \leqslant b$, determines an **orientation** of a curve C, with the positive direction corresponding to increasing values of the parameter t. (See Figure 8, where the initial point A corresponds to the parameter value a and the terminal point B corresponds to $t = b$.)

If $-C$ denotes the curve consisting of the same points as C but with the opposite orientation (from initial point B to terminal point A in Figure 8), then we have

$$\int_{-C} f(x, y)\, dx = -\int_C f(x, y)\, dx \qquad \int_{-C} f(x, y)\, dy = -\int_C f(x, y)\, dy$$

But if we integrate with respect to arc length, the value of the line integral does *not* change when we reverse the orientation of the curve:

$$\int_{-C} f(x, y)\, ds = \int_C f(x, y)\, ds$$

This is because Δs_i is always positive, whereas Δx_i and Δy_i change sign when we reverse the orientation of C.

LINE INTEGRALS IN SPACE

We now suppose that C is a smooth space curve given by the parametric equations

$$x = x(t) \qquad y = y(t) \qquad z = z(t) \qquad a \leqslant t \leqslant b$$

or by a vector equation $\mathbf{r}(t) = x(t)\,\mathbf{i} + y(t)\,\mathbf{j} + z(t)\,\mathbf{k}$. If f is a function of three variables that is continuous on some region containing C, then we define the **line integral of f along C** (with respect to arc length) in a manner similar to that for plane curves:

$$\int_C f(x, y, z)\, ds = \lim_{n \to \infty} \sum_{i=1}^{n} f(x_i^*, y_i^*, z_i^*)\, \Delta s_i$$

We evaluate it using a formula similar to Formula 3:

$$\boxed{9} \quad \int_C f(x, y, z)\, ds = \int_a^b f\big(x(t), y(t), z(t)\big) \sqrt{\left(\frac{dx}{dt}\right)^2 + \left(\frac{dy}{dt}\right)^2 + \left(\frac{dz}{dt}\right)^2}\, dt$$

Observe that the integrals in both Formulas 3 and 9 can be written in the more compact vector notation

$$\int_a^b f(\mathbf{r}(t))\, |\mathbf{r}'(t)|\, dt$$

For the special case $f(x, y, z) = 1$, we get

$$\int_C ds = \int_a^b |\mathbf{r}'(t)|\, dt = L$$

where L is the length of the curve C (see Formula 14.3.3).

Line integrals along C with respect to x, y, and z can also be defined. For example,

$$\int_C f(x, y, z)\, dz = \lim_{n \to \infty} \sum_{i=1}^{n} f(x_i^*, y_i^*, z_i^*)\, \Delta z_i$$

$$= \int_a^b f\big(x(t), y(t), z(t)\big)\, z'(t)\, dt$$

Therefore, as with line integrals in the plane, we evaluate integrals of the form

[10] $$\int_C P(x, y, z)\, dx + Q(x, y, z)\, dy + R(x, y, z)\, dz$$

by expressing everything (x, y, z, dx, dy, dz) in terms of the parameter t.

☑ **EXAMPLE 5** Evaluate $\int_C y \sin z \, ds$, where C is the circular helix given by the equations $x = \cos t$, $y = \sin t$, $z = t$, $0 \le t \le 2\pi$. (See Figure 9.)

SOLUTION Formula 9 gives

$$\int_C y \sin z \, ds = \int_0^{2\pi} (\sin t) \sin t \sqrt{\left(\frac{dx}{dt}\right)^2 + \left(\frac{dy}{dt}\right)^2 + \left(\frac{dz}{dt}\right)^2} \, dt$$

$$= \int_0^{2\pi} \sin^2 t \sqrt{\sin^2 t + \cos^2 t + 1} \, dt = \sqrt{2} \int_0^{2\pi} \tfrac{1}{2}(1 - \cos 2t)\, dt$$

$$= \frac{\sqrt{2}}{2} \left[t - \tfrac{1}{2}\sin 2t \right]_0^{2\pi} = \sqrt{2}\, \pi \qquad \square$$

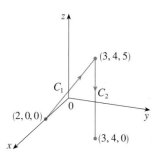

FIGURE 9

EXAMPLE 6 Evaluate $\int_C y\, dx + z\, dy + x\, dz$, where C consists of the line segment C_1 from $(2, 0, 0)$ to $(3, 4, 5)$, followed by the vertical line segment C_2 from $(3, 4, 5)$ to $(3, 4, 0)$.

SOLUTION The curve C is shown in Figure 10. Using Equation 8, we write C_1 as

$$\mathbf{r}(t) = (1 - t)\langle 2, 0, 0\rangle + t\langle 3, 4, 5\rangle = \langle 2 + t, 4t, 5t\rangle$$

or, in parametric form, as

$$x = 2 + t \qquad y = 4t \qquad z = 5t \qquad 0 \le t \le 1$$

Thus

$$\int_{C_1} y\, dx + z\, dy + x\, dz = \int_0^1 (4t)\, dt + (5t)4\, dt + (2 + t)5\, dt$$

$$= \int_0^1 (10 + 29t)\, dt = 10t + 29\frac{t^2}{2} \Bigg]_0^1 = 24.5$$

FIGURE 10

Likewise, C_2 can be written in the form

$$\mathbf{r}(t) = (1 - t)\langle 3, 4, 5\rangle + t\langle 3, 4, 0\rangle = \langle 3, 4, 5 - 5t\rangle$$

or

$$x = 3 \qquad y = 4 \qquad z = 5 - 5t \qquad 0 \le t \le 1$$

Then $dx = 0 = dy$, so

$$\int_{C_2} y\,dx + z\,dy + x\,dz = \int_0^1 3(-5)\,dt = -15$$

Adding the values of these integrals, we obtain

$$\int_C y\,dx + z\,dy + x\,dz = 24.5 - 15 = 9.5 \qquad \square$$

LINE INTEGRALS OF VECTOR FIELDS

Recall from Section 6.4 that the work done by a variable force $f(x)$ in moving a particle from a to b along the x-axis is $W = \int_a^b f(x)\,dx$. Then in Section 13.3 we found that the work done by a constant force $\mathbf{F}$ in moving an object from a point P to another point Q in space is $W = \mathbf{F} \cdot \mathbf{D}$, where $\mathbf{D} = \overrightarrow{PQ}$ is the displacement vector.

Now suppose that $\mathbf{F} = P\,\mathbf{i} + Q\,\mathbf{j} + R\,\mathbf{k}$ is a continuous force field on $\mathbb{R}^3$, such as the gravitational field of Example 4 in Section 17.1 or the electric force field of Example 5 in Section 17.1. (A force field on $\mathbb{R}^2$ could be regarded as a special case where $R = 0$ and P and Q depend only on x and y.) We wish to compute the work done by this force in moving a particle along a smooth curve C.

We divide C into subarcs $P_{i-1}P_i$ with lengths Δs_i by dividing the parameter interval $[a, b]$ into subintervals of equal width. (See Figure 1 for the two-dimensional case or Figure 11 for the three-dimensional case.) Choose a point $P_i^*(x_i^*, y_i^*, z_i^*)$ on the ith subarc corresponding to the parameter value t_i^*. If Δs_i is small, then as the particle moves from P_{i-1} to P_i along the curve, it proceeds approximately in the direction of $\mathbf{T}(t_i^*)$, the unit tangent vector at P_i^*. Thus the work done by the force $\mathbf{F}$ in moving the particle from P_{i-1} to P_i is approximately

$$\mathbf{F}(x_i^*, y_i^*, z_i^*) \cdot [\Delta s_i\,\mathbf{T}(t_i^*)] = [\mathbf{F}(x_i^*, y_i^*, z_i^*) \cdot \mathbf{T}(t_i^*)]\,\Delta s_i$$

and the total work done in moving the particle along C is approximately

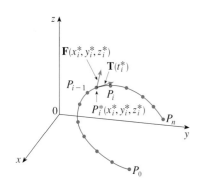

FIGURE 11

$$\boxed{11} \qquad \sum_{i=1}^n [\mathbf{F}(x_i^*, y_i^*, z_i^*) \cdot \mathbf{T}(x_i^*, y_i^*, z_i^*)]\,\Delta s_i$$

where $\mathbf{T}(x, y, z)$ is the unit tangent vector at the point (x, y, z) on C. Intuitively, we see that these approximations ought to become better as n becomes larger. Therefore we define the **work** W done by the force field $\mathbf{F}$ as the limit of the Riemann sums in (11), namely,

$$\boxed{12} \qquad W = \int_C \mathbf{F}(x, y, z) \cdot \mathbf{T}(x, y, z)\,ds = \int_C \mathbf{F} \cdot \mathbf{T}\,ds$$

Equation 12 says that *work is the line integral with respect to arc length of the tangential component of the force.*

If the curve C is given by the vector equation $\mathbf{r}(t) = x(t)\,\mathbf{i} + y(t)\,\mathbf{j} + z(t)\,\mathbf{k}$, then $\mathbf{T}(t) = \mathbf{r}'(t)/|\mathbf{r}'(t)|$, so using Equation 9 we can rewrite Equation 12 in the form

$$W = \int_a^b \left[\mathbf{F}(\mathbf{r}(t)) \cdot \frac{\mathbf{r}'(t)}{|\mathbf{r}'(t)|} \right] |\mathbf{r}'(t)|\,dt = \int_a^b \mathbf{F}(\mathbf{r}(t)) \cdot \mathbf{r}'(t)\,dt$$

This integral is often abbreviated as $\int_C \mathbf{F} \cdot d\mathbf{r}$ and occurs in other areas of physics as well. Therefore we make the following definition for the line integral of *any* continuous vector field.

---

[13] DEFINITION Let $\mathbf{F}$ be a continuous vector field defined on a smooth curve C given by a vector function $\mathbf{r}(t)$, $a \leqslant t \leqslant b$. Then the **line integral of $\mathbf{F}$ along C** is

$$\int_C \mathbf{F} \cdot d\mathbf{r} = \int_a^b \mathbf{F}(\mathbf{r}(t)) \cdot \mathbf{r}'(t)\, dt = \int_C \mathbf{F} \cdot \mathbf{T}\, ds$$

When using Definition 13, remember that $\mathbf{F}(\mathbf{r}(t))$ is just an abbreviation for $\mathbf{F}(x(t), y(t), z(t))$, so we evaluate $\mathbf{F}(\mathbf{r}(t))$ simply by putting $x = x(t)$, $y = y(t)$, and $z = z(t)$ in the expression for $\mathbf{F}(x, y, z)$. Notice also that we can formally write $d\mathbf{r} = \mathbf{r}'(t)\, dt$.

■ Figure 12 shows the force field and the curve in Example 7. The work done is negative because the field impedes movement along the curve.

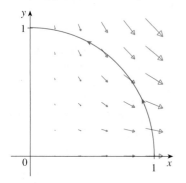

FIGURE 12

EXAMPLE 7 Find the work done by the force field $\mathbf{F}(x, y) = x^2\, \mathbf{i} - xy\, \mathbf{j}$ in moving a particle along the quarter-circle $\mathbf{r}(t) = \cos t\, \mathbf{i} + \sin t\, \mathbf{j}$, $0 \leqslant t \leqslant \pi/2$.

SOLUTION Since $x = \cos t$ and $y = \sin t$, we have

$$\mathbf{F}(\mathbf{r}(t)) = \cos^2 t\, \mathbf{i} - \cos t \sin t\, \mathbf{j}$$

and

$$\mathbf{r}'(t) = -\sin t\, \mathbf{i} + \cos t\, \mathbf{j}$$

Therefore the work done is

$$\int_C \mathbf{F} \cdot d\mathbf{r} = \int_0^{\pi/2} \mathbf{F}(\mathbf{r}(t)) \cdot \mathbf{r}'(t)\, dt = \int_0^{\pi/2} (-2\cos^2 t \sin t)\, dt$$

$$= 2\, \frac{\cos^3 t}{3} \Bigg]_0^{\pi/2} = -\frac{2}{3} \qquad \square$$

NOTE Even though $\int_C \mathbf{F} \cdot d\mathbf{r} = \int_C \mathbf{F} \cdot \mathbf{T}\, ds$ and integrals with respect to arc length are unchanged when orientation is reversed, it is still true that

$$\int_{-C} \mathbf{F} \cdot d\mathbf{r} = -\int_C \mathbf{F} \cdot d\mathbf{r}$$

because the unit tangent vector $\mathbf{T}$ is replaced by its negative when C is replaced by $-C$.

■ Figure 13 shows the twisted cubic C in Example 8 and some typical vectors acting at three points on C.

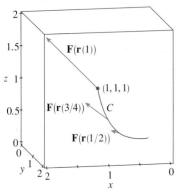

FIGURE 13

EXAMPLE 8 Evaluate $\int_C \mathbf{F} \cdot d\mathbf{r}$, where $\mathbf{F}(x, y, z) = xy\, \mathbf{i} + yz\, \mathbf{j} + zx\, \mathbf{k}$ and C is the twisted cubic given by

$$x = t \qquad y = t^2 \qquad z = t^3 \qquad 0 \leqslant t \leqslant 1$$

SOLUTION We have

$$\mathbf{r}(t) = t\, \mathbf{i} + t^2\, \mathbf{j} + t^3\, \mathbf{k}$$

$$\mathbf{r}'(t) = \mathbf{i} + 2t\, \mathbf{j} + 3t^2\, \mathbf{k}$$

$$\mathbf{F}(\mathbf{r}(t)) = t^3\, \mathbf{i} + t^5\, \mathbf{j} + t^4\, \mathbf{k}$$

Thus
$$\int_C \mathbf{F} \cdot d\mathbf{r} = \int_0^1 \mathbf{F}(\mathbf{r}(t)) \cdot \mathbf{r}'(t)\, dt$$

$$= \int_0^1 (t^3 + 5t^6)\, dt = \frac{t^4}{4} + \frac{5t^7}{7} \Bigg]_0^1 = \frac{27}{28} \qquad \square$$

Finally, we note the connection between line integrals of vector fields and line integrals of scalar fields. Suppose the vector field $\mathbf{F}$ on $\mathbb{R}^3$ is given in component form by the equation $\mathbf{F} = P\,\mathbf{i} + Q\,\mathbf{j} + R\,\mathbf{k}$. We use Definition 13 to compute its line integral along C:

$$\int_C \mathbf{F} \cdot d\mathbf{r} = \int_a^b \mathbf{F}(\mathbf{r}(t)) \cdot \mathbf{r}'(t)\, dt$$

$$= \int_a^b (P\,\mathbf{i} + Q\,\mathbf{j} + R\,\mathbf{k}) \cdot \left(x'(t)\,\mathbf{i} + y'(t)\,\mathbf{j} + z'(t)\,\mathbf{k}\right) dt$$

$$= \int_a^b \left[P\big(x(t), y(t), z(t)\big)\,x'(t) + Q\big(x(t), y(t), z(t)\big)\,y'(t) + R\big(x(t), y(t), z(t)\big)\,z'(t) \right] dt$$

But this last integral is precisely the line integral in (10). Therefore we have

$$\int_C \mathbf{F} \cdot d\mathbf{r} = \int_C P\, dx + Q\, dy + R\, dz \qquad \text{where } \mathbf{F} = P\,\mathbf{i} + Q\,\mathbf{j} + R\,\mathbf{k}$$

For example, the integral $\int_C y\, dx + z\, dy + x\, dz$ in Example 6 could be expressed as $\int_C \mathbf{F} \cdot d\mathbf{r}$ where

$$\mathbf{F}(x, y, z) = y\,\mathbf{i} + z\,\mathbf{j} + x\,\mathbf{k}$$

17.2 EXERCISES

1–16 Evaluate the line integral, where C is the given curve.

1. $\int_C y^3\, ds$, $C: x = t^3$, $y = t$, $0 \le t \le 2$

2. $\int_C xy\, ds$, $C: x = t^2$, $y = 2t$, $0 \le t \le 1$

3. $\int_C xy^4\, ds$, C is the right half of the circle $x^2 + y^2 = 16$

4. $\int_C x \sin y\, ds$, C is the line segment from $(0, 3)$ to $(4, 6)$

5. $\int_C (x^2 y^3 - \sqrt{x})\, dy$,
  C is the arc of the curve $y = \sqrt{x}$ from $(1, 1)$ to $(4, 2)$

6. $\int_C xe^y\, dx$,
  C is the arc of the curve $x = e^y$ from $(1, 0)$ to $(e, 1)$

7. $\int_C xy\, dx + (x - y)\, dy$, C consists of line segments from $(0, 0)$ to $(2, 0)$ and from $(2, 0)$ to $(3, 2)$

8. $\int_C \sin x\, dx + \cos y\, dy$, C consists of the top half of the circle $x^2 + y^2 = 1$ from $(1, 0)$ to $(-1, 0)$ and the line segment from $(-1, 0)$ to $(-2, 3)$

9. $\int_C xyz\, ds$,
  $C: x = 2 \sin t$, $y = t$, $z = -2 \cos t$, $0 \le t \le \pi$

10. $\int_C xyz^2\, ds$,
  C is the line segment from $(-1, 5, 0)$ to $(1, 6, 4)$

11. $\int_C xe^{yz}\, ds$,
  C is the line segment from $(0, 0, 0)$ to $(1, 2, 3)$

12. $\int_C (2x + 9z)\, ds$, $C: x = t$, $y = t^2$, $z = t^3$, $0 \le t \le 1$

13. $\int_C x^2 y \sqrt{z}\, dz$, $C: x = t^3$, $y = t$, $z = t^2$, $0 \le t \le 1$

14. $\int_C z\, dx + x\, dy + y\, dz$,
  $C: x = t^2$, $y = t^3$, $z = t^2$, $0 \le t \le 1$

15. $\int_C (x + yz)\, dx + 2x\, dy + xyz\, dz$, C consists of line segments from $(1, 0, 1)$ to $(2, 3, 1)$ and from $(2, 3, 1)$ to $(2, 5, 2)$

16. $\int_C x^2\, dx + y^2\, dy + z^2\, dz$, C consists of line segments from $(0, 0, 0)$ to $(1, 2, -1)$ and from $(1, 2, -1)$ to $(3, 2, 0)$

17. Let **F** be the vector field shown in the figure.
  (a) If C_1 is the vertical line segment from $(-3, -3)$ to $(-3, 3)$, determine whether $\int_{C_1} \mathbf{F} \cdot d\mathbf{r}$ is positive, negative, or zero.
  (b) If C_2 is the counterclockwise-oriented circle with radius 3 and center the origin, determine whether $\int_{C_2} \mathbf{F} \cdot d\mathbf{r}$ is positive, negative, or zero.

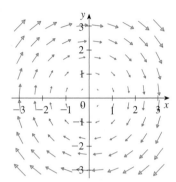

18. The figure shows a vector field **F** and two curves C_1 and C_2. Are the line integrals of **F** over C_1 and C_2 positive, negative, or zero? Explain.

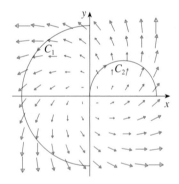

19–22 Evaluate the line integral $\int_C \mathbf{F} \cdot d\mathbf{r}$, where C is given by the vector function $\mathbf{r}(t)$.

19. $\mathbf{F}(x, y) = xy\,\mathbf{i} + 3y^2\,\mathbf{j}$,
   $\mathbf{r}(t) = 11t^4\,\mathbf{i} + t^3\,\mathbf{j}, \quad 0 \le t \le 1$

20. $\mathbf{F}(x, y, z) = (x + y)\,\mathbf{i} + (y - z)\,\mathbf{j} + z^2\,\mathbf{k}$,
   $\mathbf{r}(t) = t^2\,\mathbf{i} + t^3\,\mathbf{j} + t^2\,\mathbf{k}, \quad 0 \le t \le 1$

21. $\mathbf{F}(x, y, z) = \sin x\,\mathbf{i} + \cos y\,\mathbf{j} + xz\,\mathbf{k}$,
   $\mathbf{r}(t) = t^3\,\mathbf{i} - t^2\,\mathbf{j} + t\,\mathbf{k}, \quad 0 \le t \le 1$

22. $\mathbf{F}(x, y, z) = z\,\mathbf{i} + y\,\mathbf{j} - x\,\mathbf{k}$,
   $\mathbf{r}(t) = t\,\mathbf{i} + \sin t\,\mathbf{j} + \cos t\,\mathbf{k}, \quad 0 \le t \le \pi$

23–26 Use a calculator or CAS to evaluate the line integral correct to four decimal places.

23. $\int_C \mathbf{F} \cdot d\mathbf{r}$, where $\mathbf{F}(x, y) = xy\,\mathbf{i} + \sin y\,\mathbf{j}$ and
   $\mathbf{r}(t) = e^t\,\mathbf{i} + e^{-t^2}\,\mathbf{j}, \; 1 \le t \le 2$

24. $\int_C \mathbf{F} \cdot d\mathbf{r}$, where $\mathbf{F}(x, y, z) = y \sin z\,\mathbf{i} + z \sin x\,\mathbf{j} + x \sin y\,\mathbf{k}$ and $\mathbf{r}(t) = \cos t\,\mathbf{i} + \sin t\,\mathbf{j} + \sin 5t\,\mathbf{k}, \; 0 \le t \le \pi$

25. $\int_C x \sin(y + z)\,ds$, where C has parametric equations $x = t^2$, $y = t^3, z = t^4, \; 0 \le t \le 5$

26. $\int_C z e^{-xy}\,ds$, where C has parametric equations $x = t, y = t^2$, $z = e^{-t}, \; 0 \le t \le 1$

[CAS] **27–28** Use a graph of the vector field **F** and the curve C to guess whether the line integral of **F** over C is positive, negative, or zero. Then evaluate the line integral.

27. $\mathbf{F}(x, y) = (x - y)\,\mathbf{i} + xy\,\mathbf{j}$,
   C is the arc of the circle $x^2 + y^2 = 4$ traversed counterclockwise from $(2, 0)$ to $(0, -2)$

28. $\mathbf{F}(x, y) = \dfrac{x}{\sqrt{x^2 + y^2}}\,\mathbf{i} + \dfrac{y}{\sqrt{x^2 + y^2}}\,\mathbf{j}$,
   C is the parabola $y = 1 + x^2$ from $(-1, 2)$ to $(1, 2)$

29. (a) Evaluate the line integral $\int_C \mathbf{F} \cdot d\mathbf{r}$, where $\mathbf{F}(x, y) = e^{x-1}\,\mathbf{i} + xy\,\mathbf{j}$ and C is given by $\mathbf{r}(t) = t^2\,\mathbf{i} + t^3\,\mathbf{j}, 0 \le t \le 1$.
   (b) Illustrate part (a) by using a graphing calculator or computer to graph C and the vectors from the vector field corresponding to $t = 0, 1/\sqrt{2}$, and 1 (as in Figure 13).

30. (a) Evaluate the line integral $\int_C \mathbf{F} \cdot d\mathbf{r}$, where $\mathbf{F}(x, y, z) = x\,\mathbf{i} - z\,\mathbf{j} + y\,\mathbf{k}$ and C is given by $\mathbf{r}(t) = 2t\,\mathbf{i} + 3t\,\mathbf{j} - t^2\,\mathbf{k}, -1 \le t \le 1$.
   (b) Illustrate part (a) by using a computer to graph C and the vectors from the vector field corresponding to $t = \pm 1$ and $\pm\frac{1}{2}$ (as in Figure 13).

[CAS] **31.** Find the exact value of $\int_C x^3 y^2 z\,ds$, where C is the curve with parametric equations $x = e^{-t} \cos 4t, y = e^{-t} \sin 4t, z = e^{-t}$, $0 \le t \le 2\pi$.

32. (a) Find the work done by the force field $\mathbf{F}(x, y) = x^2\,\mathbf{i} + xy\,\mathbf{j}$ on a particle that moves once around the circle $x^2 + y^2 = 4$ oriented in the counterclockwise direction.
   [CAS] (b) Use a computer algebra system to graph the force field and circle on the same screen. Use the graph to explain your answer to part (a).

33. A thin wire is bent into the shape of a semicircle $x^2 + y^2 = 4$, $x \ge 0$. If the linear density is a constant k, find the mass and center of mass of the wire.

34. A thin wire has the shape of the first-quadrant part of the circle with center the origin and radius a. If the density function is $\rho(x, y) = kxy$, find the mass and center of mass of the wire.

35. (a) Write the formulas similar to Equations 4 for the center of mass $(\bar{x}, \bar{y}, \bar{z})$ of a thin wire in the shape of a space curve C if the wire has density function $\rho(x, y, z)$.

(b) Find the center of mass of a wire in the shape of the helix $x = 2 \sin t$, $y = 2 \cos t$, $z = 3t$, $0 \le t \le 2\pi$, if the density is a constant k.

36. Find the mass and center of mass of a wire in the shape of the helix $x = t$, $y = \cos t$, $z = \sin t$, $0 \le t \le 2\pi$, if the density at any point is equal to the square of the distance from the origin.

37. If a wire with linear density $\rho(x, y)$ lies along a plane curve C, its **moments of inertia** about the x- and y-axes are defined as

$$I_x = \int_C y^2 \rho(x, y)\, ds \qquad I_y = \int_C x^2 \rho(x, y)\, ds$$

Find the moments of inertia for the wire in Example 3.

38. If a wire with linear density $\rho(x, y, z)$ lies along a space curve C, its **moments of inertia** about the x-, y-, and z-axes are defined as

$$I_x = \int_C (y^2 + z^2)\rho(x, y, z)\, ds$$

$$I_y = \int_C (x^2 + z^2)\rho(x, y, z)\, ds$$

$$I_z = \int_C (x^2 + y^2)\rho(x, y, z)\, ds$$

Find the moments of inertia for the wire in Exercise 35.

39. Find the work done by the force field $\mathbf{F}(x, y) = x\,\mathbf{i} + (y + 2)\,\mathbf{j}$ in moving an object along an arch of the cycloid $\mathbf{r}(t) = (t - \sin t)\,\mathbf{i} + (1 - \cos t)\,\mathbf{j}$, $0 \le t \le 2\pi$.

40. Find the work done by the force field $\mathbf{F}(x, y) = x \sin y\,\mathbf{i} + y\,\mathbf{j}$ on a particle that moves along the parabola $y = x^2$ from $(-1, 1)$ to $(2, 4)$.

41. Find the work done by the force field $\mathbf{F}(x, y, z) = \langle y + z, x + z, x + y \rangle$ on a particle that moves along the line segment from $(1, 0, 0)$ to $(3, 4, 2)$.

42. The force exerted by an electric charge at the origin on a charged particle at a point (x, y, z) with position vector $\mathbf{r} = \langle x, y, z \rangle$ is $\mathbf{F}(\mathbf{r}) = K\mathbf{r}/|\mathbf{r}|^3$ where K is a constant. (See Example 5 in Section 17.1.) Find the work done as the particle moves along a straight line from $(2, 0, 0)$ to $(2, 1, 5)$.

43. A 160-lb man carries a 25-lb can of paint up a helical staircase that encircles a silo with a radius of 20 ft. If the silo is 90 ft high and the man makes exactly three complete revolutions, how much work is done by the man against gravity in climbing to the top?

44. Suppose there is a hole in the can of paint in Exercise 43 and 9 lb of paint leaks steadily out of the can during the man's ascent. How much work is done?

45. (a) Show that a constant force field does zero work on a particle that moves once uniformly around the circle $x^2 + y^2 = 1$.

(b) Is this also true for a force field $\mathbf{F}(\mathbf{x}) = k\mathbf{x}$, where k is a constant and $\mathbf{x} = \langle x, y \rangle$?

46. The base of a circular fence with radius 10 m is given by $x = 10 \cos t$, $y = 10 \sin t$. The height of the fence at position (x, y) is given by the function $h(x, y) = 4 + 0.01(x^2 - y^2)$, so the height varies from 3 m to 5 m. Suppose that 1 L of paint covers 100 m². Sketch the fence and determine how much paint you will need if you paint both sides of the fence.

47. An object moves along the curve C shown in the figure from $(1, 2)$ to $(9, 8)$. The lengths of the vectors in the force field $\mathbf{F}$ are measured in newtons by the scales on the axes. Estimate the work done by $\mathbf{F}$ on the object.

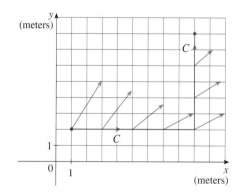

48. Experiments show that a steady current I in a long wire produces a magnetic field $\mathbf{B}$ that is tangent to any circle that lies in the plane perpendicular to the wire and whose center is the axis of the wire (as in the figure). *Ampère's Law* relates the electric current to its magnetic effects and states that

$$\int_C \mathbf{B} \cdot d\mathbf{r} = \mu_0 I$$

where I is the net current that passes through any surface bounded by a closed curve C, and μ_0 is a constant called the permeability of free space. By taking C to be a circle with radius r, show that the magnitude $B = |\mathbf{B}|$ of the magnetic field at a distance r from the center of the wire is

$$B = \frac{\mu_0 I}{2\pi r}$$

17.3 THE FUNDAMENTAL THEOREM FOR LINE INTEGRALS

Recall from Section 5.3 that Part 2 of the Fundamental Theorem of Calculus can be written as

$$\boxed{1} \qquad \int_a^b F'(x)\,dx = F(b) - F(a)$$

where F' is continuous on $[a, b]$. We also called Equation 1 the Net Change Theorem: The integral of a rate of change is the net change.

If we think of the gradient vector ∇f of a function f of two or three variables as a sort of derivative of f, then the following theorem can be regarded as a version of the Fundamental Theorem for line integrals.

> **2 THEOREM** Let C be a smooth curve given by the vector function $\mathbf{r}(t)$, $a \leq t \leq b$. Let f be a differentiable function of two or three variables whose gradient vector ∇f is continuous on C. Then
>
> $$\int_C \nabla f \cdot d\mathbf{r} = f(\mathbf{r}(b)) - f(\mathbf{r}(a))$$

NOTE Theorem 2 says that we can evaluate the line integral of a conservative vector field (the gradient vector field of the potential function f) simply by knowing the value of f at the endpoints of C. In fact, Theorem 2 says that the line integral of ∇f is the net change in f. If f is a function of two variables and C is a plane curve with initial point $A(x_1, y_1)$ and terminal point $B(x_2, y_2)$, as in Figure 1, then Theorem 2 becomes

$$\int_C \nabla f \cdot d\mathbf{r} = f(x_2, y_2) - f(x_1, y_1)$$

If f is a function of three variables and C is a space curve joining the point $A(x_1, y_1, z_1)$ to the point $B(x_2, y_2, z_2)$, then we have

$$\int_C \nabla f \cdot d\mathbf{r} = f(x_2, y_2, z_2) - f(x_1, y_1, z_1)$$

Let's prove Theorem 2 for this case.

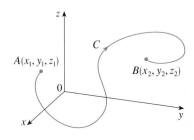

FIGURE 1

PROOF OF THEOREM 2   Using Definition 17.2.13, we have

$$\int_C \nabla f \cdot d\mathbf{r} = \int_a^b \nabla f(\mathbf{r}(t)) \cdot \mathbf{r}'(t)\, dt$$

$$= \int_a^b \left(\frac{\partial f}{\partial x} \frac{dx}{dt} + \frac{\partial f}{\partial y} \frac{dy}{dt} + \frac{\partial f}{\partial z} \frac{dz}{dt} \right) dt$$

$$= \int_a^b \frac{d}{dt} f(\mathbf{r}(t))\, dt \qquad\qquad \text{(by the Chain Rule)}$$

$$= f(\mathbf{r}(b)) - f(\mathbf{r}(a))$$

The last step follows from the Fundamental Theorem of Calculus (Equation 1). ☐

Although we have proved Theorem 2 for smooth curves, it is also true for piecewise-smooth curves. This can be seen by subdividing C into a finite number of smooth curves and adding the resulting integrals.

EXAMPLE I   Find the work done by the gravitational field

$$\mathbf{F}(\mathbf{x}) = -\frac{mMG}{|\mathbf{x}|^3} \mathbf{x}$$

in moving a particle with mass m from the point $(3, 4, 12)$ to the point $(2, 2, 0)$ along a piecewise-smooth curve C. (See Example 4 in Section 17.1.)

SOLUTION   From Section 17.1 we know that $\mathbf{F}$ is a conservative vector field and, in fact, $\mathbf{F} = \nabla f$, where

$$f(x, y, z) = \frac{mMG}{\sqrt{x^2 + y^2 + z^2}}$$

Therefore, by Theorem 2, the work done is

$$W = \int_C \mathbf{F} \cdot d\mathbf{r} = \int_C \nabla f \cdot d\mathbf{r}$$

$$= f(2, 2, 0) - f(3, 4, 12)$$

$$= \frac{mMG}{\sqrt{2^2 + 2^2}} - \frac{mMG}{\sqrt{3^2 + 4^2 + 12^2}} = mMG \left(\frac{1}{2\sqrt{2}} - \frac{1}{13} \right) \qquad ☐$$

INDEPENDENCE OF PATH

Suppose C_1 and C_2 are two piecewise-smooth curves (which are called **paths**) that have the same initial point A and terminal point B. We know from Example 4 in Section 17.2 that, in general, $\int_{C_1} \mathbf{F} \cdot d\mathbf{r} \neq \int_{C_2} \mathbf{F} \cdot d\mathbf{r}$. But one implication of Theorem 2 is that

$$\int_{C_1} \nabla f \cdot d\mathbf{r} = \int_{C_2} \nabla f \cdot d\mathbf{r}$$

whenever ∇f is continuous. In other words, the line integral of a *conservative* vector field depends only on the initial point and terminal point of a curve.

In general, if $\mathbf{F}$ is a continuous vector field with domain D, we say that the line integral $\int_C \mathbf{F} \cdot d\mathbf{r}$ is **independent of path** if $\int_{C_1} \mathbf{F} \cdot d\mathbf{r} = \int_{C_2} \mathbf{F} \cdot d\mathbf{r}$ for any two paths C_1 and C_2 in

FIGURE 2
A closed curve

FIGURE 3

D that have the same initial and terminal points. With this terminology we can say that *line integrals of conservative vector fields are independent of path.*

A curve is called **closed** if its terminal point coincides with its initial point, that is, $\mathbf{r}(b) = \mathbf{r}(a)$. (See Figure 2.) If $\int_C \mathbf{F} \cdot d\mathbf{r}$ is independent of path in D and C is any closed path in D, we can choose any two points A and B on C and regard C as being composed of the path C_1 from A to B followed by the path C_2 from B to A. (See Figure 3.) Then

$$\int_C \mathbf{F} \cdot d\mathbf{r} = \int_{C_1} \mathbf{F} \cdot d\mathbf{r} + \int_{C_2} \mathbf{F} \cdot d\mathbf{r} = \int_{C_1} \mathbf{F} \cdot d\mathbf{r} - \int_{-C_2} \mathbf{F} \cdot d\mathbf{r} = 0$$

since C_1 and $-C_2$ have the same initial and terminal points.

Conversely, if it is true that $\int_C \mathbf{F} \cdot d\mathbf{r} = 0$ whenever C is a closed path in D, then we demonstrate independence of path as follows. Take any two paths C_1 and C_2 from A to B in D and define C to be the curve consisting of C_1 followed by $-C_2$. Then

$$0 = \int_C \mathbf{F} \cdot d\mathbf{r} = \int_{C_1} \mathbf{F} \cdot d\mathbf{r} + \int_{-C_2} \mathbf{F} \cdot d\mathbf{r} = \int_{C_1} \mathbf{F} \cdot d\mathbf{r} - \int_{C_2} \mathbf{F} \cdot d\mathbf{r}$$

and so $\int_{C_1} \mathbf{F} \cdot d\mathbf{r} = \int_{C_2} \mathbf{F} \cdot d\mathbf{r}$. Thus we have proved the following theorem.

> **3** **THEOREM** $\int_C \mathbf{F} \cdot d\mathbf{r}$ is independent of path in D if and only if $\int_C \mathbf{F} \cdot d\mathbf{r} = 0$ for every closed path C in D.

Since we know that the line integral of any conservative vector field $\mathbf{F}$ is independent of path, it follows that $\int_C \mathbf{F} \cdot d\mathbf{r} = 0$ for any closed path. The physical interpretation is that the work done by a conservative force field (such as the gravitational or electric field in Section 17.1) as it moves an object around a closed path is 0.

The following theorem says that the *only* vector fields that are independent of path are conservative. It is stated and proved for plane curves, but there is a similar version for space curves. We assume that D is **open**, which means that for every point P in D there is a disk with center P that lies entirely in D. (So D doesn't contain any of its boundary points.) In addition, we assume that D is **connected**. This means that any two points in D can be joined by a path that lies in D.

> **4** **THEOREM** Suppose $\mathbf{F}$ is a vector field that is continuous on an open connected region D. If $\int_C \mathbf{F} \cdot d\mathbf{r}$ is independent of path in D, then $\mathbf{F}$ is a conservative vector field on D; that is, there exists a function f such that $\nabla f = \mathbf{F}$.

PROOF Let $A(a, b)$ be a fixed point in D. We construct the desired potential function f by defining

$$f(x, y) = \int_{(a, b)}^{(x, y)} \mathbf{F} \cdot d\mathbf{r}$$

for any point (x, y) in D. Since $\int_C \mathbf{F} \cdot d\mathbf{r}$ is independent of path, it does not matter which path C from (a, b) to (x, y) is used to evaluate $f(x, y)$. Since D is open, there exists a disk contained in D with center (x, y). Choose any point (x_1, y) in the disk with $x_1 < x$ and let C consist of any path C_1 from (a, b) to (x_1, y) followed by the horizontal line segment C_2 from (x_1, y) to (x, y). (See Figure 4.) Then

$$f(x, y) = \int_{C_1} \mathbf{F} \cdot d\mathbf{r} + \int_{C_2} \mathbf{F} \cdot d\mathbf{r} = \int_{(a, b)}^{(x_1, y)} \mathbf{F} \cdot d\mathbf{r} + \int_{C_2} \mathbf{F} \cdot d\mathbf{r}$$

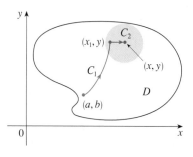

FIGURE 4

Notice that the first of these integrals does not depend on x, so

$$\frac{\partial}{\partial x} f(x, y) = 0 + \frac{\partial}{\partial x} \int_{C_2} \mathbf{F} \cdot d\mathbf{r}$$

If we write $\mathbf{F} = P\,\mathbf{i} + Q\,\mathbf{j}$, then

$$\int_{C_2} \mathbf{F} \cdot d\mathbf{r} = \int_{C_2} P\,dx + Q\,dy$$

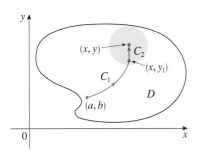

FIGURE 5

On C_2, y is constant, so $dy = 0$. Using t as the parameter, where $x_1 \leqslant t \leqslant x$, we have

$$\frac{\partial}{\partial x} f(x, y) = \frac{\partial}{\partial x} \int_{C_2} P\,dx + Q\,dy = \frac{\partial}{\partial x} \int_{x_1}^{x} P(t, y)\,dt = P(x, y)$$

by Part 1 of the Fundamental Theorem of Calculus (see Section 5.3). A similar argument, using a vertical line segment (see Figure 5), shows that

$$\frac{\partial}{\partial y} f(x, y) = \frac{\partial}{\partial y} \int_{C_2} P\,dx + Q\,dy = \frac{\partial}{\partial y} \int_{y_1}^{y} Q(x, t)\,dt = Q(x, y)$$

Thus

$$\mathbf{F} = P\,\mathbf{i} + Q\,\mathbf{j} = \frac{\partial f}{\partial x}\,\mathbf{i} + \frac{\partial f}{\partial y}\,\mathbf{j} = \nabla f$$

which says that $\mathbf{F}$ is conservative. ☐

The question remains: How is it possible to determine whether or not a vector field $\mathbf{F}$ is conservative? Suppose it is known that $\mathbf{F} = P\,\mathbf{i} + Q\,\mathbf{j}$ is conservative, where P and Q have continuous first-order partial derivatives. Then there is a function f such that $\mathbf{F} = \nabla f$, that is,

$$P = \frac{\partial f}{\partial x} \qquad \text{and} \qquad Q = \frac{\partial f}{\partial y}$$

Therefore, by Clairaut's Theorem,

$$\frac{\partial P}{\partial y} = \frac{\partial^2 f}{\partial y\,\partial x} = \frac{\partial^2 f}{\partial x\,\partial y} = \frac{\partial Q}{\partial x}$$

---

⑤ THEOREM If $\mathbf{F}(x, y) = P(x, y)\,\mathbf{i} + Q(x, y)\,\mathbf{j}$ is a conservative vector field, where P and Q have continuous first-order partial derivatives on a domain D, then throughout D we have

$$\frac{\partial P}{\partial y} = \frac{\partial Q}{\partial x}$$

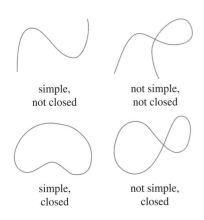

simple,
not closed

not simple,
not closed

simple,
closed

not simple,
closed

FIGURE 6

Types of curves

The converse of Theorem 5 is true only for a special type of region. To explain this, we first need the concept of a **simple curve**, which is a curve that doesn't intersect itself anywhere between its endpoints. [See Figure 6; $\mathbf{r}(a) = \mathbf{r}(b)$ for a simple closed curve, but $\mathbf{r}(t_1) \neq \mathbf{r}(t_2)$ when $a < t_1 < t_2 < b$.]

In Theorem 4 we needed an open connected region. For the next theorem we need a stronger condition. A **simply-connected region** in the plane is a connected region D such

simply-connected region

regions that are not simply-connected

FIGURE 7

that every simple closed curve in D encloses only points that are in D. Notice from Figure 7 that, intuitively speaking, a simply-connected region contains no hole and can't consist of two separate pieces.

In terms of simply-connected regions we can now state a partial converse to Theorem 5 that gives a convenient method for verifying that a vector field on $\mathbb{R}^2$ is conservative. The proof will be sketched in the next section as a consequence of Green's Theorem.

---

6 THEOREM Let $\mathbf{F} = P\,\mathbf{i} + Q\,\mathbf{j}$ be a vector field on an open simply-connected region D. Suppose that P and Q have continuous first-order derivatives and

$$\frac{\partial P}{\partial y} = \frac{\partial Q}{\partial x} \qquad \text{throughout } D$$

Then $\mathbf{F}$ is conservative.

FIGURE 8

■ Figures 8 and 9 show the vector fields in Examples 2 and 3, respectively. The vectors in Figure 8 that start on the closed curve C all appear to point in roughly the same direction as C. So it looks as if $\int_C \mathbf{F} \cdot d\mathbf{r} > 0$ and therefore $\mathbf{F}$ is not conservative. The calculation in Example 2 confirms this impression. Some of the vectors near the curves C_1 and C_2 in Figure 9 point in approximately the same direction as the curves, whereas others point in the opposite direction. So it appears plausible that line integrals around all closed paths are 0. Example 3 shows that $\mathbf{F}$ is indeed conservative.

FIGURE 9

▼ EXAMPLE 2 Determine whether or not the vector field

$$\mathbf{F}(x, y) = (x - y)\,\mathbf{i} + (x - 2)\,\mathbf{j}$$

is conservative.

SOLUTION Let $P(x, y) = x - y$ and $Q(x, y) = x - 2$. Then

$$\frac{\partial P}{\partial y} = -1 \qquad \frac{\partial Q}{\partial x} = 1$$

Since $\partial P/\partial y \neq \partial Q/\partial x$, $\mathbf{F}$ is not conservative by Theorem 5. □

▼ EXAMPLE 3 Determine whether or not the vector field

$$\mathbf{F}(x, y) = (3 + 2xy)\,\mathbf{i} + (x^2 - 3y^2)\,\mathbf{j}$$

is conservative.

SOLUTION Let $P(x, y) = 3 + 2xy$ and $Q(x, y) = x^2 - 3y^2$. Then

$$\frac{\partial P}{\partial y} = 2x = \frac{\partial Q}{\partial x}$$

Also, the domain of $\mathbf{F}$ is the entire plane $(D = \mathbb{R}^2)$, which is open and simply-connected. Therefore we can apply Theorem 6 and conclude that $\mathbf{F}$ is conservative. □

In Example 3, Theorem 6 told us that $\mathbf{F}$ is conservative, but it did not tell us how to find the (potential) function f such that $\mathbf{F} = \nabla f$. The proof of Theorem 4 gives us a clue as to how to find f. We use "partial integration" as in the following example.

EXAMPLE 4
(a) If $\mathbf{F}(x, y) = (3 + 2xy)\,\mathbf{i} + (x^2 - 3y^2)\,\mathbf{j}$, find a function f such that $\mathbf{F} = \nabla f$.
(b) Evaluate the line integral $\int_C \mathbf{F} \cdot d\mathbf{r}$, where C is the curve given by

$$\mathbf{r}(t) = e^t \sin t\,\mathbf{i} + e^t \cos t\,\mathbf{j} \qquad 0 \leqslant t \leqslant \pi.$$

SOLUTION
(a) From Example 3 we know that $\mathbf{F}$ is conservative and so there exists a function f with $\nabla f = \mathbf{F}$, that is,

$$\boxed{7} \qquad\qquad f_x(x, y) = 3 + 2xy$$

$$\boxed{8} \qquad\qquad f_y(x, y) = x^2 - 3y^2$$

Integrating (7) with respect to x, we obtain

$$\boxed{9} \qquad\qquad f(x, y) = 3x + x^2y + g(y)$$

Notice that the constant of integration is a constant with respect to x, that is, a function of y, which we have called $g(y)$. Next we differentiate both sides of (9) with respect to y:

$$\boxed{10} \qquad\qquad f_y(x, y) = x^2 + g'(y)$$

Comparing (8) and (10), we see that

$$g'(y) = -3y^2$$

Integrating with respect to y, we have

$$g(y) = -y^3 + K$$

where K is a constant. Putting this in (9), we have

$$f(x, y) = 3x + x^2y - y^3 + K$$

as the desired potential function.

(b) To use Theorem 2 all we have to know are the initial and terminal points of C, namely, $\mathbf{r}(0) = (0, 1)$ and $\mathbf{r}(\pi) = (0, -e^\pi)$. In the expression for $f(x, y)$ in part (a), any value of the constant K will do, so let's choose $K = 0$. Then we have

$$\int_C \mathbf{F} \cdot d\mathbf{r} = \int_C \nabla f \cdot d\mathbf{r} = f(0, -e^\pi) - f(0, 1) = e^{3\pi} - (-1) = e^{3\pi} + 1$$

This method is much shorter than the straightforward method for evaluating line integrals that we learned in Section 17.2. ☐

A criterion for determining whether or not a vector field $\mathbf{F}$ on $\mathbb{R}^3$ is conservative is given in Section 17.5. Meanwhile, the next example shows that the technique for finding the potential function is much the same as for vector fields on $\mathbb{R}^2$.

☑ **EXAMPLE 5** If $\mathbf{F}(x, y, z) = y^2\mathbf{i} + (2xy + e^{3z})\mathbf{j} + 3ye^{3z}\mathbf{k}$, find a function f such that $\nabla f = \mathbf{F}$.

SOLUTION If there is such a function f, then

$$\boxed{11} \qquad\qquad f_x(x, y, z) = y^2$$

$$\boxed{12} \qquad\qquad f_y(x, y, z) = 2xy + e^{3z}$$

$$\boxed{13} \qquad\qquad f_z(x, y, z) = 3ye^{3z}$$

Integrating (11) with respect to x, we get

$$\boxed{14} \qquad\qquad f(x, y, z) = xy^2 + g(y, z)$$

where $g(y, z)$ is a constant with respect to x. Then differentiating (14) with respect to y, we have

$$f_y(x, y, z) = 2xy + g_y(y, z)$$

and comparison with (12) gives

$$g_y(y, z) = e^{3z}$$

Thus $g(y, z) = ye^{3z} + h(z)$ and we rewrite (14) as

$$f(x, y, z) = xy^2 + ye^{3z} + h(z)$$

Finally, differentiating with respect to z and comparing with (13), we obtain $h'(z) = 0$ and therefore $h(z) = K$, a constant. The desired function is

$$f(x, y, z) = xy^2 + ye^{3z} + K$$

It is easily verified that $\nabla f = \mathbf{F}$. $\qquad\qquad\qquad\qquad\qquad\qquad\qquad\qquad\qquad$ $\square$

CONSERVATION OF ENERGY

Let's apply the ideas of this chapter to a continuous force field $\mathbf{F}$ that moves an object along a path C given by $\mathbf{r}(t)$, $a \leqslant t \leqslant b$, where $\mathbf{r}(a) = A$ is the initial point and $\mathbf{r}(b) = B$ is the terminal point of C. According to Newton's Second Law of Motion (see Section 14.4), the force $\mathbf{F}(\mathbf{r}(t))$ at a point on C is related to the acceleration $\mathbf{a}(t) = \mathbf{r}''(t)$ by the equation

$$\mathbf{F}(\mathbf{r}(t)) = m\mathbf{r}''(t)$$

So the work done by the force on the object is

$$W = \int_C \mathbf{F} \cdot d\mathbf{r} = \int_a^b \mathbf{F}(\mathbf{r}(t)) \cdot \mathbf{r}'(t)\, dt = \int_a^b m\mathbf{r}''(t) \cdot \mathbf{r}'(t)\, dt$$

$$= \frac{m}{2} \int_a^b \frac{d}{dt}[\mathbf{r}'(t) \cdot \mathbf{r}'(t)]\, dt \qquad\qquad \text{(Theorem 14.2.3, Formula 4)}$$

$$= \frac{m}{2} \int_a^b \frac{d}{dt}\,|\mathbf{r}'(t)|^2\, dt = \frac{m}{2}\Big[\,|\mathbf{r}'(t)|^2\Big]_a^b \qquad \text{(Fundamental Theorem of Calculus)}$$

$$= \frac{m}{2}\left(|\mathbf{r}'(b)|^2 - |\mathbf{r}'(a)|^2\right)$$

Therefore

$$\boxed{15} \qquad\qquad W = \tfrac{1}{2}m\,|\mathbf{v}(b)|^2 - \tfrac{1}{2}m\,|\mathbf{v}(a)|^2$$

where $\mathbf{v} = \mathbf{r}'$ is the velocity.

The quantity $\tfrac{1}{2}m\,|\mathbf{v}(t)|^2$, that is, half the mass times the square of the speed, is called the **kinetic energy** of the object. Therefore we can rewrite Equation 15 as

$$\boxed{16} \qquad\qquad W = K(B) - K(A)$$

which says that the work done by the force field along C is equal to the change in kinetic energy at the endpoints of C.

Now let's further assume that $\mathbf{F}$ is a conservative force field; that is, we can write $\mathbf{F} = \nabla f$. In physics, the **potential energy** of an object at the point (x, y, z) is defined as $P(x, y, z) = -f(x, y, z)$, so we have $\mathbf{F} = -\nabla P$. Then by Theorem 2 we have

$$W = \int_C \mathbf{F} \cdot d\mathbf{r} = -\int_C \nabla P \cdot d\mathbf{r} = -[P(\mathbf{r}(b)) - P(\mathbf{r}(a))] = P(A) - P(B)$$

Comparing this equation with Equation 16, we see that

$$P(A) + K(A) = P(B) + K(B)$$

which says that if an object moves from one point A to another point B under the influence of a conservative force field, then the sum of its potential energy and its kinetic energy remains constant. This is called the **Law of Conservation of Energy** and it is the reason the vector field is called *conservative*.

17.3 EXERCISES

1. The figure shows a curve C and a contour map of a function f whose gradient is continuous. Find $\int_C \nabla f \cdot d\mathbf{r}$.

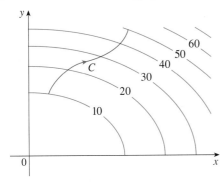

2. A table of values of a function f with continuous gradient is given. Find $\int_C \nabla f \cdot d\mathbf{r}$, where C has parametric equations

$$x = t^2 + 1 \qquad y = t^3 + t \qquad 0 \le t \le 1$$

y \ x	0	1	2
0	1	6	4
1	3	5	7
2	8	2	9

3–10 Determine whether or not $\mathbf{F}$ is a conservative vector field. If it is, find a function f such that $\mathbf{F} = \nabla f$.

3. $\mathbf{F}(x, y) = (2x - 3y)\mathbf{i} + (-3x + 4y - 8)\mathbf{j}$

4. $\mathbf{F}(x, y) = e^x \cos y\,\mathbf{i} + e^x \sin y\,\mathbf{j}$

5. $\mathbf{F}(x, y) = e^x \sin y\,\mathbf{i} + e^x \cos y\,\mathbf{j}$

6. $\mathbf{F}(x, y) = (3x^2 - 2y^2)\mathbf{i} + (4xy + 3)\mathbf{j}$

7. $\mathbf{F}(x, y) = (ye^x + \sin y)\mathbf{i} + (e^x + x \cos y)\mathbf{j}$

8. $\mathbf{F}(x, y) = (xy \cos xy + \sin xy)\mathbf{i} + (x^2 \cos xy)\mathbf{j}$

9. $\mathbf{F}(x, y) = (\ln y + 2xy^3)\mathbf{i} + (3x^2y^2 + x/y)\mathbf{j}$

10. $\mathbf{F}(x, y) = (xy \cosh xy + \sinh xy)\mathbf{i} + (x^2 \cosh xy)\mathbf{j}$

11. The figure shows the vector field $\mathbf{F}(x, y) = \langle 2xy, x^2 \rangle$ and three curves that start at $(1, 2)$ and end at $(3, 2)$.
(a) Explain why $\int_C \mathbf{F} \cdot d\mathbf{r}$ has the same value for all three curves.
(b) What is this common value?

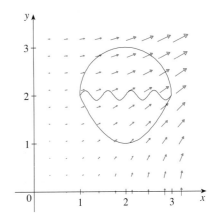

12–18 (a) Find a function f such that $\mathbf{F} = \nabla f$ and (b) use part (a) to evaluate $\int_C \mathbf{F} \cdot d\mathbf{r}$ along the given curve C.

12. $\mathbf{F}(x, y) = x^2\,\mathbf{i} + y^2\,\mathbf{j}$,
C is the arc of the parabola $y = 2x^2$ from $(-1, 2)$ to $(2, 8)$

13. $\mathbf{F}(x, y) = xy^2\,\mathbf{i} + x^2y\,\mathbf{j}$,
C: $\mathbf{r}(t) = \langle t + \sin \frac{1}{2}\pi t,\ t + \cos \frac{1}{2}\pi t \rangle$, $\ 0 \leqslant t \leqslant 1$

14. $\mathbf{F}(x, y) = \dfrac{y^2}{1 + x^2}\,\mathbf{i} + 2y \arctan x\,\mathbf{j}$,
C: $\mathbf{r}(t) = t^2\,\mathbf{i} + 2t\,\mathbf{j}$, $\ 0 \leqslant t \leqslant 1$

15. $\mathbf{F}(x, y, z) = yz\,\mathbf{i} + xz\,\mathbf{j} + (xy + 2z)\,\mathbf{k}$,
C is the line segment from $(1, 0, -2)$ to $(4, 6, 3)$

16. $\mathbf{F}(x, y, z) = (2xz + y^2)\,\mathbf{i} + 2xy\,\mathbf{j} + (x^2 + 3z^2)\,\mathbf{k}$,
C: $x = t^2$, $y = t + 1$, $z = 2t - 1$, $\ 0 \leqslant t \leqslant 1$

17. $\mathbf{F}(x, y, z) = y^2 \cos z\,\mathbf{i} + 2xy \cos z\,\mathbf{j} - xy^2 \sin z\,\mathbf{k}$,
C: $\mathbf{r}(t) = t^2\,\mathbf{i} + \sin t\,\mathbf{j} + t\,\mathbf{k}$, $\ 0 \leqslant t \leqslant \pi$

18. $\mathbf{F}(x, y, z) = e^y\,\mathbf{i} + xe^y\,\mathbf{j} + (z + 1)e^z\,\mathbf{k}$,
C: $\mathbf{r}(t) = t\,\mathbf{i} + t^2\,\mathbf{j} + t^3\,\mathbf{k}$, $\ 0 \leqslant t \leqslant 1$

19–20 Show that the line integral is independent of path and evaluate the integral.

19. $\int_C \tan y\,dx + x \sec^2 y\,dy$,
C is any path from $(1, 0)$ to $(2, \pi/4)$

20. $\int_C (1 - ye^{-x})\,dx + e^{-x}\,dy$,
C is any path from $(0, 1)$ to $(1, 2)$

21–22 Find the work done by the force field $\mathbf{F}$ in moving an object from P to Q.

21. $\mathbf{F}(x, y) = 2y^{3/2}\,\mathbf{i} + 3x\sqrt{y}\,\mathbf{j}$; $\ P(1, 1)$, $Q(2, 4)$

22. $\mathbf{F}(x, y) = e^{-y}\,\mathbf{i} - xe^{-y}\,\mathbf{j}$; $\ P(0, 1)$, $Q(2, 0)$

23–24 Is the vector field shown in the figure conservative? Explain.

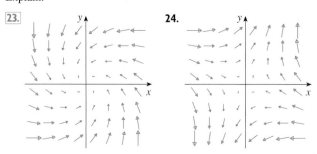

23.

24.

CAS 25. If $\mathbf{F}(x, y) = \sin y\,\mathbf{i} + (1 + x \cos y)\,\mathbf{j}$, use a plot to guess whether $\mathbf{F}$ is conservative. Then determine whether your guess is correct.

26. Let $\mathbf{F} = \nabla f$, where $f(x, y) = \sin(x - 2y)$. Find curves C_1 and C_2 that are not closed and satisfy the equation.

(a) $\displaystyle\int_{C_1} \mathbf{F} \cdot d\mathbf{r} = 0$ $\qquad$ (b) $\displaystyle\int_{C_2} \mathbf{F} \cdot d\mathbf{r} = 1$

27. Show that if the vector field $\mathbf{F} = P\,\mathbf{i} + Q\,\mathbf{j} + R\,\mathbf{k}$ is conservative and P, Q, R have continuous first-order partial derivatives, then

$$\frac{\partial P}{\partial y} = \frac{\partial Q}{\partial x} \qquad \frac{\partial P}{\partial z} = \frac{\partial R}{\partial x} \qquad \frac{\partial Q}{\partial z} = \frac{\partial R}{\partial y}$$

28. Use Exercise 27 to show that the line integral $\int_C y\,dx + x\,dy + xyz\,dz$ is not independent of path.

29–32 Determine whether or not the given set is (a) open, (b) connected, and (c) simply-connected.

29. $\{(x, y) \mid x > 0,\ y > 0\}$ $\qquad$ **30** $\{(x, y) \mid x \neq 0\}$

31. $\{(x, y) \mid 1 < x^2 + y^2 < 4\}$

32. $\{(x, y) \mid x^2 + y^2 \leqslant 1 \text{ or } 4 \leqslant x^2 + y^2 \leqslant 9\}$

---

33. Let $\mathbf{F}(x, y) = \dfrac{-y\,\mathbf{i} + x\,\mathbf{j}}{x^2 + y^2}$.

(a) Show that $\partial P/\partial y = \partial Q/\partial x$.

(b) Show that $\int_C \mathbf{F} \cdot d\mathbf{r}$ is not independent of path. [*Hint:* Compute $\int_{C_1} \mathbf{F} \cdot d\mathbf{r}$ and $\int_{C_2} \mathbf{F} \cdot d\mathbf{r}$, where C_1 and C_2 are the upper and lower halves of the circle $x^2 + y^2 = 1$ from $(1, 0)$ to $(-1, 0)$.] Does this contradict Theorem 6?

34. (a) Suppose that $\mathbf{F}$ is an inverse square force field, that is,

$$\mathbf{F}(\mathbf{r}) = \frac{c\mathbf{r}}{|\mathbf{r}|^3}$$

for some constant c, where $\mathbf{r} = x\,\mathbf{i} + y\,\mathbf{j} + z\,\mathbf{k}$. Find the work done by $\mathbf{F}$ in moving an object from a point P_1 along a path to a point P_2 in terms of the distances d_1 and d_2 from these points to the origin.

(b) An example of an inverse square field is the gravitational field $\mathbf{F} = -(mMG)\mathbf{r}/|\mathbf{r}|^3$ discussed in Example 4 in Section 17.1. Use part (a) to find the work done by the gravitational field when the earth moves from aphelion (at a maximum distance of 1.52×10^8 km from the sun) to perihelion (at a minimum distance of 1.47×10^8 km). (Use the values $m = 5.97 \times 10^{24}$ kg, $M = 1.99 \times 10^{30}$ kg, and $G = 6.67 \times 10^{-11}$ N·m²/kg².)

(c) Another example of an inverse square field is the electric force field $\mathbf{F} = \varepsilon qQ\mathbf{r}/|\mathbf{r}|^3$ discussed in Example 5 in Section 17.1. Suppose that an electron with a charge of -1.6×10^{-19} C is located at the origin. A positive unit charge is positioned a distance 10^{-12} m from the electron and moves to a position half that distance from the electron. Use part (a) to find the work done by the electric force field. (Use the value $\varepsilon = 8.985 \times 10^9$.)

17.4 GREEN'S THEOREM

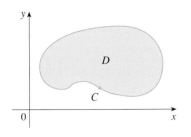

FIGURE 1

Green's Theorem gives the relationship between a line integral around a simple closed curve C and a double integral over the plane region D bounded by C. (See Figure 1. We assume that D consists of all points inside C as well as all points on C.) In stating Green's Theorem we use the convention that the **positive orientation** of a simple closed curve C refers to a single *counterclockwise* traversal of C. Thus if C is given by the vector function $\mathbf{r}(t)$, $a \le t \le b$, then the region D is always on the left as the point $\mathbf{r}(t)$ traverses C. (See Figure 2.)

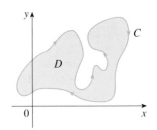

FIGURE 2

(a) Positive orientation   (b) Negative orientation

> **GREEN'S THEOREM** Let C be a positively oriented, piecewise-smooth, simple closed curve in the plane and let D be the region bounded by C. If P and Q have continuous partial derivatives on an open region that contains D, then
>
> $$\int_C P \, dx + Q \, dy = \iint_D \left(\frac{\partial Q}{\partial x} - \frac{\partial P}{\partial y} \right) dA$$

■ Recall that the left side of this equation is another way of writing $\int_C \mathbf{F} \cdot d\mathbf{r}$, where $\mathbf{F} = P\mathbf{i} + Q\mathbf{j}$.

NOTE The notation

$$\oint_C P \, dx + Q \, dy \qquad \text{or} \qquad \oint_C P \, dx + Q \, dy$$

is sometimes used to indicate that the line integral is calculated using the positive orientation of the closed curve C. Another notation for the positively oriented boundary curve of D is ∂D, so the equation in Green's Theorem can be written as

$$\boxed{1} \qquad \iint_D \left(\frac{\partial Q}{\partial x} - \frac{\partial P}{\partial y} \right) dA = \int_{\partial D} P \, dx + Q \, dy$$

Green's Theorem should be regarded as the counterpart of the Fundamental Theorem of Calculus for double integrals. Compare Equation 1 with the statement of the Fundamental Theorem of Calculus, Part 2, in the following equation:

$$\int_a^b F'(x) \, dx = F(b) - F(a)$$

In both cases there is an integral involving derivatives (F', $\partial Q/\partial x$, and $\partial P/\partial y$) on the left side of the equation. And in both cases the right side involves the values of the original functions (F, Q, and P) only on the *boundary* of the domain. (In the one-dimensional case, the domain is an interval $[a, b]$ whose boundary consists of just two points, a and b.)

Green's Theorem is not easy to prove in general, but we can give a proof for the special case where the region is both of type I and of type II (see Section 16.3). Let's call such regions **simple regions**.

■ Green's Theorem is named after the self-taught English scientist George Green (1793–1841). He worked full-time in his father's bakery from the age of nine and taught himself mathematics from library books. In 1828 he published privately *An Essay on the Application of Mathematical Analysis to the Theories of Electricity and Magnetism*, but only 100 copies were printed and most of those went to his friends. This pamphlet contained a theorem that is equivalent to what we know as Green's Theorem, but it didn't become widely known at that time. Finally, at age 40, Green entered Cambridge University as an undergraduate but died four years after graduation. In 1846 William Thomson (Lord Kelvin) located a copy of Green's essay, realized its significance, and had it reprinted. Green was the first person to try to formulate a mathematical theory of electricity and magnetism. His work was the basis for the subsequent electromagnetic theories of Thomson, Stokes, Rayleigh, and Maxwell.

PROOF OF GREEN'S THEOREM FOR THE CASE IN WHICH D IS A SIMPLE REGION Notice that Green's Theorem will be proved if we can show that

$$\boxed{2} \qquad \int_C P\,dx = -\iint_D \frac{\partial P}{\partial y}\,dA$$

and

$$\boxed{3} \qquad \int_C Q\,dy = \iint_D \frac{\partial Q}{\partial x}\,dA$$

We prove Equation 2 by expressing D as a type I region:

$$D = \{(x, y) \mid a \le x \le b,\ g_1(x) \le y \le g_2(x)\}$$

where g_1 and g_2 are continuous functions. This enables us to compute the double integral on the right side of Equation 2 as follows:

$$\boxed{4} \qquad \iint_D \frac{\partial P}{\partial y}\,dA = \int_a^b \int_{g_1(x)}^{g_2(x)} \frac{\partial P}{\partial y}(x, y)\,dy\,dx = \int_a^b [P(x, g_2(x)) - P(x, g_1(x))]\,dx$$

where the last step follows from the Fundamental Theorem of Calculus.

Now we compute the left side of Equation 2 by breaking up C as the union of the four curves $C_1, C_2, C_3,$ and C_4 shown in Figure 3. On C_1 we take x as the parameter and write the parametric equations as $x = x,\ y = g_1(x),\ a \le x \le b$. Thus

$$\int_{C_1} P(x, y)\,dx = \int_a^b P(x, g_1(x))\,dx$$

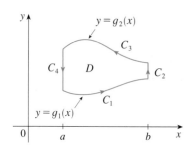

FIGURE 3

Observe that C_3 goes from right to left but $-C_3$ goes from left to right, so we can write the parametric equations of $-C_3$ as $x = x,\ y = g_2(x),\ a \le x \le b$. Therefore

$$\int_{C_3} P(x, y)\,dx = -\int_{-C_3} P(x, y)\,dx = -\int_a^b P(x, g_2(x))\,dx$$

On C_2 or C_4 (either of which might reduce to just a single point), x is constant, so $dx = 0$ and

$$\int_{C_2} P(x, y)\,dx = 0 = \int_{C_4} P(x, y)\,dx$$

Hence

$$\int_C P(x, y)\,dx = \int_{C_1} P(x, y)\,dx + \int_{C_2} P(x, y)\,dx + \int_{C_3} P(x, y)\,dx + \int_{C_4} P(x, y)\,dx$$

$$= \int_a^b P(x, g_1(x))\,dx - \int_a^b P(x, g_2(x))\,dx$$

Comparing this expression with the one in Equation 4, we see that

$$\int_C P(x, y)\, dx = -\iint_D \frac{\partial P}{\partial y}\, dA$$

Equation 3 can be proved in much the same way by expressing D as a type II region (see Exercise 28). Then, by adding Equations 2 and 3, we obtain Green's Theorem. □

EXAMPLE 1 Evaluate $\int_C x^4\, dx + xy\, dy$, where C is the triangular curve consisting of the line segments from $(0, 0)$ to $(1, 0)$, from $(1, 0)$ to $(0, 1)$, and from $(0, 1)$ to $(0, 0)$.

SOLUTION Although the given line integral could be evaluated as usual by the methods of Section 17.2, that would involve setting up three separate integrals along the three sides of the triangle, so let's use Green's Theorem instead. Notice that the region D enclosed by C is simple and C has positive orientation (see Figure 4). If we let $P(x, y) = x^4$ and $Q(x, y) = xy$, then we have

$$\int_C x^4\, dx + xy\, dy = \iint_D \left(\frac{\partial Q}{\partial x} - \frac{\partial P}{\partial y} \right) dA = \int_0^1 \int_0^{1-x} (y - 0)\, dy\, dx$$

$$= \int_0^1 \left[\tfrac{1}{2} y^2 \right]_{y=0}^{y=1-x} dx = \tfrac{1}{2} \int_0^1 (1 - x)^2\, dx$$

$$= -\tfrac{1}{6}(1 - x)^3 \Big]_0^1 = \tfrac{1}{6}$$ □

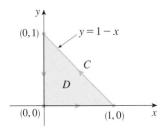

FIGURE 4

☑ EXAMPLE 2 Evaluate $\oint_C (3y - e^{\sin x})\, dx + \left(7x + \sqrt{y^4 + 1}\right) dy$, where C is the circle $x^2 + y^2 = 9$.

SOLUTION The region D bounded by C is the disk $x^2 + y^2 \le 9$, so let's change to polar coordinates after applying Green's Theorem:

$$\oint_C (3y - e^{\sin x})\, dx + \left(7x + \sqrt{y^4 + 1}\right) dy$$

$$= \iint_D \left[\frac{\partial}{\partial x} \left(7x + \sqrt{y^4 + 1}\right) - \frac{\partial}{\partial y} (3y - e^{\sin x}) \right] dA$$

$$= \int_0^{2\pi} \int_0^3 (7 - 3)\, r\, dr\, d\theta = 4 \int_0^{2\pi} d\theta \int_0^3 r\, dr = 36\pi$$ □

■ Instead of using polar coordinates, we could simply use the fact that D is a disk of radius 3 and write

$$\iint_D 4\, dA = 4 \cdot \pi(3)^2 = 36\pi$$

In Examples 1 and 2 we found that the double integral was easier to evaluate than the line integral. (Try setting up the line integral in Example 2 and you'll soon be convinced!) But sometimes it's easier to evaluate the line integral, and Green's Theorem is used in the reverse direction. For instance, if it is known that $P(x, y) = Q(x, y) = 0$ on the curve C, then Green's Theorem gives

$$\iint_D \left(\frac{\partial Q}{\partial x} - \frac{\partial P}{\partial y} \right) dA = \int_C P\, dx + Q\, dy = 0$$

no matter what values P and Q assume in the region D.

Another application of the reverse direction of Green's Theorem is in computing areas. Since the area of D is $\iint_D 1\, dA$, we wish to choose P and Q so that

$$\frac{\partial Q}{\partial x} - \frac{\partial P}{\partial y} = 1$$

There are several possibilities:

$$P(x, y) = 0 \qquad P(x, y) = -y \qquad P(x, y) = -\tfrac{1}{2}y$$

$$Q(x, y) = x \qquad Q(x, y) = 0 \qquad Q(x, y) = \tfrac{1}{2}x$$

Then Green's Theorem gives the following formulas for the area of D:

$$\boxed{5} \qquad \boxed{A = \oint_C x\, dy = -\oint_C y\, dx = \tfrac{1}{2}\oint_C x\, dy - y\, dx}$$

EXAMPLE 3 Find the area enclosed by the ellipse $\dfrac{x^2}{a^2} + \dfrac{y^2}{b^2} = 1$.

SOLUTION The ellipse has parametric equations $x = a\cos t$ and $y = b\sin t$, where $0 \leqslant t \leqslant 2\pi$. Using the third formula in Equation 5, we have

$$A = \tfrac{1}{2}\int_C x\, dy - y\, dx$$

$$= \tfrac{1}{2}\int_0^{2\pi} (a\cos t)(b\cos t)\, dt - (b\sin t)(-a\sin t)\, dt$$

$$= \frac{ab}{2}\int_0^{2\pi} dt = \pi ab \qquad \square$$

Although we have proved Green's Theorem only for the case where D is simple, we can now extend it to the case where D is a finite union of simple regions. For example, if D is the region shown in Figure 5, then we can write $D = D_1 \cup D_2$, where D_1 and D_2 are both simple. The boundary of D_1 is $C_1 \cup C_3$ and the boundary of D_2 is $C_2 \cup (-C_3)$ so, applying Green's Theorem to D_1 and D_2 separately, we get

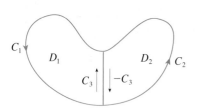

FIGURE 5

$$\int_{C_1 \cup C_3} P\, dx + Q\, dy = \iint_{D_1} \left(\frac{\partial Q}{\partial x} - \frac{\partial P}{\partial y} \right) dA$$

$$\int_{C_2 \cup (-C_3)} P\, dx + Q\, dy = \iint_{D_2} \left(\frac{\partial Q}{\partial x} - \frac{\partial P}{\partial y} \right) dA$$

If we add these two equations, the line integrals along C_3 and $-C_3$ cancel, so we get

$$\int_{C_1 \cup C_2} P\, dx + Q\, dy = \iint_{D} \left(\frac{\partial Q}{\partial x} - \frac{\partial P}{\partial y} \right) dA$$

which is Green's Theorem for $D = D_1 \cup D_2$, since its boundary is $C = C_1 \cup C_2$.

The same sort of argument allows us to establish Green's Theorem for any finite union of nonoverlapping simple regions (see Figure 6).

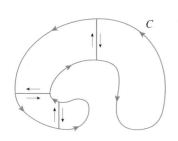

FIGURE 6

☑ EXAMPLE 4 Evaluate $\oint_C y^2\, dx + 3xy\, dy$, where C is the boundary of the semiannular region D in the upper half-plane between the circles $x^2 + y^2 = 1$ and $x^2 + y^2 = 4$.

SOLUTION Notice that although D is not simple, the y-axis divides it into two simple regions (see Figure 7). In polar coordinates we can write

$$D = \{(r, \theta)\,|\, 1 \leqslant r \leqslant 2,\ 0 \leqslant \theta \leqslant \pi\}$$

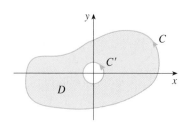

Therefore Green's Theorem gives

$$\oint_C y^2\,dx + 3xy\,dy = \iint_D \left[\frac{\partial}{\partial x}(3xy) - \frac{\partial}{\partial y}(y^2) \right] dA$$

$$= \iint_D y\,dA = \int_0^{\pi}\int_1^2 (r\sin\theta)\,r\,dr\,d\theta$$

$$= \int_0^{\pi}\sin\theta\,d\theta \int_1^2 r^2\,dr = \left[-\cos\theta\right]_0^{\pi}\left[\tfrac13 r^3\right]_1^2 = \frac{14}{3} \qquad \square$$

Green's Theorem can be extended to apply to regions with holes, that is, regions that are not simply-connected. Observe that the boundary C of the region D in Figure 8 consists of two simple closed curves C_1 and C_2. We assume that these boundary curves are oriented so that the region D is always on the left as the curve C is traversed. Thus the positive direction is counterclockwise for the outer curve C_1 but clockwise for the inner curve C_2. If we divide D into two regions D' and D'' by means of the lines shown in Figure 9 and then apply Green's Theorem to each of D' and D'', we get

$$\iint_D \left(\frac{\partial Q}{\partial x} - \frac{\partial P}{\partial y} \right) dA = \iint_{D'} \left(\frac{\partial Q}{\partial x} - \frac{\partial P}{\partial y} \right) dA + \iint_{D''} \left(\frac{\partial Q}{\partial x} - \frac{\partial P}{\partial y} \right) dA$$

$$= \int_{\partial D'} P\,dx + Q\,dy + \int_{\partial D''} P\,dx + Q\,dy$$

Since the line integrals along the common boundary lines are in opposite directions, they cancel and we get

$$\iint_D \left(\frac{\partial Q}{\partial x} - \frac{\partial P}{\partial y} \right) dA = \int_{C_1} P\,dx + Q\,dy + \int_{C_2} P\,dx + Q\,dy = \int_C P\,dx + Q\,dy$$

which is Green's Theorem for the region D.

▼ EXAMPLE 5 If $\mathbf{F}(x, y) = (-y\,\mathbf{i} + x\,\mathbf{j})/(x^2 + y^2)$, show that $\int_C \mathbf{F}\cdot d\mathbf{r} = 2\pi$ for every positively oriented simple closed path that encloses the origin.

SOLUTION Since C is an *arbitrary* closed path that encloses the origin, it's difficult to compute the given integral directly. So let's consider a counterclockwise-oriented circle C' with center the origin and radius a, where a is chosen to be small enough that C' lies inside C. (See Figure 10.) Let D be the region bounded by C and C'. Then its positively oriented boundary is $C \cup (-C')$ and so the general version of Green's Theorem gives

$$\int_C P\,dx + Q\,dy + \int_{-C'} P\,dx + Q\,dy = \iint_D \left(\frac{\partial Q}{\partial x} - \frac{\partial P}{\partial y} \right) dA$$

$$= \iint_D \left[\frac{y^2 - x^2}{(x^2 + y^2)^2} - \frac{y^2 - x^2}{(x^2 + y^2)^2} \right] dA = 0$$

Therefore

$$\int_C P\,dx + Q\,dy = \int_{C'} P\,dx + Q\,dy$$

that is,

$$\int_C \mathbf{F}\cdot d\mathbf{r} = \int_{C'} \mathbf{F}\cdot d\mathbf{r}$$

FIGURE 7

FIGURE 8

FIGURE 9

FIGURE 10

We now easily compute this last integral using the parametrization given by $\mathbf{r}(t) = a \cos t \, \mathbf{i} + a \sin t \, \mathbf{j}$, $0 \leqslant t \leqslant 2\pi$. Thus

$$\int_C \mathbf{F} \cdot d\mathbf{r} = \int_{C'} \mathbf{F} \cdot d\mathbf{r} = \int_0^{2\pi} \mathbf{F}(\mathbf{r}(t)) \cdot \mathbf{r}'(t) \, dt$$

$$= \int_0^{2\pi} \frac{(-a \sin t)(-a \sin t) + (a \cos t)(a \cos t)}{a^2 \cos^2 t + a^2 \sin^2 t} \, dt = \int_0^{2\pi} dt = 2\pi \qquad \square$$

We end this section by using Green's Theorem to discuss a result that was stated in the preceding section.

SKETCH OF PROOF OF THEOREM 17.3.6 We're assuming that $\mathbf{F} = P\mathbf{i} + Q\mathbf{j}$ is a vector field on an open simply-connected region D, that P and Q have continuous first-order partial derivatives, and that

$$\frac{\partial P}{\partial y} = \frac{\partial Q}{\partial x} \qquad \text{throughout } D$$

If C is any simple closed path in D and R is the region that C encloses, then Green's Theorem gives

$$\oint_C \mathbf{F} \cdot d\mathbf{r} = \oint_C P \, dx + Q \, dy = \iint_R \left(\frac{\partial Q}{\partial x} - \frac{\partial P}{\partial y} \right) dA = \iint_R 0 \, dA = 0$$

A curve that is not simple crosses itself at one or more points and can be broken up into a number of simple curves. We have shown that the line integrals of $\mathbf{F}$ around these simple curves are all 0 and, adding these integrals, we see that $\int_C \mathbf{F} \cdot d\mathbf{r} = 0$ for any closed curve C. Therefore $\int_C \mathbf{F} \cdot d\mathbf{r}$ is independent of path in D by Theorem 17.3.3. It follows that $\mathbf{F}$ is a conservative vector field. $\qquad \square$

17.4 EXERCISES

1–4 Evaluate the line integral by two methods: (a) directly and (b) using Green's Theorem.

1. $\oint_C (x - y) \, dx + (x + y) \, dy$,
C is the circle with center the origin and radius 2

2. $\oint_C xy \, dx + x^2 \, dy$,
C is the rectangle with vertices $(0, 0)$, $(3, 0)$, $(3, 1)$, and $(0, 1)$

3. $\oint_C xy \, dx + x^2 y^3 \, dy$,
C is the triangle with vertices $(0, 0)$, $(1, 0)$, and $(1, 2)$

4. $\oint_C x \, dx + y \, dy$, C consists of the line segments from $(0, 1)$
to $(0, 0)$ and from $(0, 0)$ to $(1, 0)$ and the parabola $y = 1 - x^2$
from $(1, 0)$ to $(0, 1)$

5–10 Use Green's Theorem to evaluate the line integral along the given positively oriented curve.

5. $\int_C xy^2 \, dx + 2x^2 y \, dy$,
C is the triangle with vertices $(0, 0)$, $(2, 2)$, and $(2, 4)$

6. $\int_C \cos y \, dx + x^2 \sin y \, dy$,
C is the rectangle with vertices $(0, 0)$, $(5, 0)$, $(5, 2)$, and $(0, 2)$

7. $\int_C (y + e^{\sqrt{x}}) \, dx + (2x + \cos y^2) \, dy$,
C is the boundary of the region enclosed by the parabolas
$y = x^2$ and $x = y^2$

8. $\int_C xe^{-2x} \, dx + (x^4 + 2x^2 y^2) \, dy$,
C is the boundary of the region between the circles
$x^2 + y^2 = 1$ and $x^2 + y^2 = 4$

9. $\int_C y^3 \, dx - x^3 \, dy$, C is the circle $x^2 + y^2 = 4$

10. $\int_C \sin y \, dx + x \cos y \, dy$, C is the ellipse $x^2 + xy + y^2 = 1$

11–14 Use Green's Theorem to evaluate $\int_C \mathbf{F} \cdot d\mathbf{r}$. (Check the orientation of the curve before applying the theorem.)

11. $\mathbf{F}(x, y) = \langle \sqrt{x} + y^3, x^2 + \sqrt{y} \rangle$,
C consists of the arc of the curve $y = \sin x$ from $(0, 0)$ to $(\pi, 0)$
and the line segment from $(\pi, 0)$ to $(0, 0)$

12. $\mathbf{F}(x, y) = \langle y^2 \cos x, x^2 + 2y \sin x \rangle$,
C is the triangle from $(0, 0)$ to $(2, 6)$ to $(2, 0)$ to $(0, 0)$

13. $\mathbf{F}(x, y) = \langle e^x + x^2 y, e^y - xy^2 \rangle$,
C is the circle $x^2 + y^2 = 25$ oriented clockwise

14. $\mathbf{F}(x, y) = \langle y - \ln(x^2 + y^2), 2 \tan^{-1}(y/x) \rangle$, C is the circle
$(x - 2)^2 + (y - 3)^2 = 1$ oriented counterclockwise

[CAS] **15–16** Verify Green's Theorem by using a computer algebra system to evaluate both the line integral and the double integral.

15. $P(x, y) = y^2 e^x$, $\quad Q(x, y) = x^2 e^y$,
C consists of the line segment from $(-1, 1)$ to $(1, 1)$ followed by the arc of the parabola $y = 2 - x^2$ from $(1, 1)$ to $(-1, 1)$

16. $P(x, y) = 2x - x^3 y^5$, $\quad Q(x, y) = x^3 y^8$,
C is the ellipse $4x^2 + y^2 = 4$

17. Use Green's Theorem to find the work done by the force $\mathbf{F}(x, y) = x(x + y)\,\mathbf{i} + xy^2\,\mathbf{j}$ in moving a particle from the origin along the x-axis to $(1, 0)$, then along the line segment to $(0, 1)$, and then back to the origin along the y-axis.

18. A particle starts at the point $(-2, 0)$, moves along the x-axis to $(2, 0)$, and then along the semicircle $y = \sqrt{4 - x^2}$ to the starting point. Use Green's Theorem to find the work done on this particle by the force field $\mathbf{F}(x, y) = \langle x, x^3 + 3xy^2 \rangle$.

19. Use one of the formulas in (5) to find the area under one arch of the cycloid $x = t - \sin t$, $y = 1 - \cos t$.

20. If a circle C with radius 1 rolls along the outside of the circle $x^2 + y^2 = 16$, a fixed point P on C traces out a curve called an *epicycloid,* with parametric equations $x = 5 \cos t - \cos 5t$, $y = 5 \sin t - \sin 5t$. Graph the epicycloid and use (5) to find the area it encloses.

21. (a) If C is the line segment connecting the point (x_1, y_1) to the point (x_2, y_2), show that

$$\int_C x\,dy - y\,dx = x_1 y_2 - x_2 y_1$$

(b) If the vertices of a polygon, in counterclockwise order, are $(x_1, y_1), (x_2, y_2), \ldots, (x_n, y_n)$, show that the area of the polygon is

$$A = \tfrac{1}{2}[(x_1 y_2 - x_2 y_1) + (x_2 y_3 - x_3 y_2) + \cdots$$
$$+ (x_{n-1} y_n - x_n y_{n-1}) + (x_n y_1 - x_1 y_n)]$$

(c) Find the area of the pentagon with vertices $(0, 0)$, $(2, 1)$, $(1, 3)$, $(0, 2)$, and $(-1, 1)$.

22. Let D be a region bounded by a simple closed path C in the xy-plane. Use Green's Theorem to prove that the coordinates of the centroid $(\bar{x}, \bar{y})$ of D are

$$\bar{x} = \frac{1}{2A} \oint_C x^2\,dy \qquad \bar{y} = -\frac{1}{2A} \oint_C y^2\,dx$$

where A is the area of D.

23. Use Exercise 22 to find the centroid of a quarter-circular region of radius a.

24. Use Exercise 22 to find the centroid of the triangle with vertices $(0, 0)$, $(a, 0)$, and (a, b), where $a > 0$ and $b > 0$.

25. A plane lamina with constant density $\rho(x, y) = \rho$ occupies a region in the xy-plane bounded by a simple closed path C. Show that its moments of inertia about the axes are

$$I_x = -\frac{\rho}{3} \oint_C y^3\,dx \qquad I_y = \frac{\rho}{3} \oint_C x^3\,dy$$

26. Use Exercise 25 to find the moment of inertia of a circular disk of radius a with constant density ρ about a diameter. (Compare with Example 4 in Section 16.5.)

27. If $\mathbf{F}$ is the vector field of Example 5, show that $\int_C \mathbf{F} \cdot d\mathbf{r} = 0$ for every simple closed path that does not pass through or enclose the origin.

28. Complete the proof of the special case of Green's Theorem by proving Equation 3.

29. Use Green's Theorem to prove the change of variables formula for a double integral (Formula 16.9.9) for the case where $f(x, y) = 1$:

$$\iint_R dx\,dy = \iint_S \left| \frac{\partial(x, y)}{\partial(u, v)} \right| du\,dv$$

Here R is the region in the xy-plane that corresponds to the region S in the uv-plane under the transformation given by $x = g(u, v)$, $y = h(u, v)$.
[*Hint:* Note that the left side is $A(R)$ and apply the first part of Equation 5. Convert the line integral over ∂R to a line integral over ∂S and apply Green's Theorem in the uv-plane.]

17.5 CURL AND DIVERGENCE

In this section we define two operations that can be performed on vector fields and that play a basic role in the applications of vector calculus to fluid flow and electricity and magnetism. Each operation resembles differentiation, but one produces a vector field whereas the other produces a scalar field.

CURL

If $\mathbf{F} = P\,\mathbf{i} + Q\,\mathbf{j} + R\,\mathbf{k}$ is a vector field on $\mathbb{R}^3$ and the partial derivatives of P, Q, and R all exist, then the **curl** of $\mathbf{F}$ is the vector field on $\mathbb{R}^3$ defined by

$$
\boxed{1} \qquad \text{curl } \mathbf{F} = \left(\frac{\partial R}{\partial y} - \frac{\partial Q}{\partial z} \right) \mathbf{i} + \left(\frac{\partial P}{\partial z} - \frac{\partial R}{\partial x} \right) \mathbf{j} + \left(\frac{\partial Q}{\partial x} - \frac{\partial P}{\partial y} \right) \mathbf{k}
$$

As an aid to our memory, let's rewrite Equation 1 using operator notation. We introduce the vector differential operator ∇ ("del") as

$$
\nabla = \mathbf{i}\,\frac{\partial}{\partial x} + \mathbf{j}\,\frac{\partial}{\partial y} + \mathbf{k}\,\frac{\partial}{\partial z}
$$

It has meaning when it operates on a scalar function to produce the gradient of f:

$$
\nabla f = \mathbf{i}\,\frac{\partial f}{\partial x} + \mathbf{j}\,\frac{\partial f}{\partial y} + \mathbf{k}\,\frac{\partial f}{\partial z} = \frac{\partial f}{\partial x}\,\mathbf{i} + \frac{\partial f}{\partial y}\,\mathbf{j} + \frac{\partial f}{\partial z}\,\mathbf{k}
$$

If we think of ∇ as a vector with components $\partial/\partial x$, $\partial/\partial y$, and $\partial/\partial z$, we can also consider the formal cross product of ∇ with the vector field $\mathbf{F}$ as follows:

$$
\nabla \times \mathbf{F} = \begin{vmatrix} \mathbf{i} & \mathbf{j} & \mathbf{k} \\ \dfrac{\partial}{\partial x} & \dfrac{\partial}{\partial y} & \dfrac{\partial}{\partial z} \\ P & Q & R \end{vmatrix}
$$

$$
= \left(\frac{\partial R}{\partial y} - \frac{\partial Q}{\partial z} \right) \mathbf{i} + \left(\frac{\partial P}{\partial z} - \frac{\partial R}{\partial x} \right) \mathbf{j} + \left(\frac{\partial Q}{\partial x} - \frac{\partial P}{\partial y} \right) \mathbf{k}
$$

$$
= \text{curl } \mathbf{F}
$$

Thus the easiest way to remember Definition 1 is by means of the symbolic expression

$$
\boxed{2} \qquad \boxed{\text{curl } \mathbf{F} = \nabla \times \mathbf{F}}
$$

EXAMPLE I If $\mathbf{F}(x, y, z) = xz\,\mathbf{i} + xyz\,\mathbf{j} - y^2\,\mathbf{k}$, find curl $\mathbf{F}$.

SOLUTION Using Equation 2, we have

$$
\text{curl } \mathbf{F} = \nabla \times \mathbf{F} = \begin{vmatrix} \mathbf{i} & \mathbf{j} & \mathbf{k} \\ \dfrac{\partial}{\partial x} & \dfrac{\partial}{\partial y} & \dfrac{\partial}{\partial z} \\ xz & xyz & -y^2 \end{vmatrix}
$$

$$
= \left[\frac{\partial}{\partial y}(-y^2) - \frac{\partial}{\partial z}(xyz) \right] \mathbf{i} - \left[\frac{\partial}{\partial x}(-y^2) - \frac{\partial}{\partial z}(xz) \right] \mathbf{j}
$$

$$
+ \left[\frac{\partial}{\partial x}(xyz) - \frac{\partial}{\partial y}(xz) \right] \mathbf{k}
$$

$$
= (-2y - xy)\,\mathbf{i} - (0 - x)\,\mathbf{j} + (yz - 0)\,\mathbf{k}
$$

$$
= -y(2 + x)\,\mathbf{i} + x\,\mathbf{j} + yz\,\mathbf{k} \qquad\qquad \square
$$

▪ Most computer algebra systems have commands that compute the curl and divergence of vector fields. If you have access to a CAS, use these commands to check the answers to the examples and exercises in this section.

Recall that the gradient of a function f of three variables is a vector field on $\mathbb{R}^3$ and so we can compute its curl. The following theorem says that the curl of a gradient vector field is $\mathbf{0}$.

---

3 THEOREM If f is a function of three variables that has continuous second-order partial derivatives, then

$$\text{curl}(\nabla f) = \mathbf{0}$$

PROOF   We have

$$\text{curl}(\nabla f) = \nabla \times (\nabla f) = \begin{vmatrix} \mathbf{i} & \mathbf{j} & \mathbf{k} \\ \dfrac{\partial}{\partial x} & \dfrac{\partial}{\partial y} & \dfrac{\partial}{\partial z} \\ \dfrac{\partial f}{\partial x} & \dfrac{\partial f}{\partial y} & \dfrac{\partial f}{\partial z} \end{vmatrix}$$

■ Notice the similarity to what we know from Section 13.4: $\mathbf{a} \times \mathbf{a} = \mathbf{0}$ for every three-dimensional vector $\mathbf{a}$.

$$= \left(\frac{\partial^2 f}{\partial y\, \partial z} - \frac{\partial^2 f}{\partial z\, \partial y} \right) \mathbf{i} + \left(\frac{\partial^2 f}{\partial z\, \partial x} - \frac{\partial^2 f}{\partial x\, \partial z} \right) \mathbf{j} + \left(\frac{\partial^2 f}{\partial x\, \partial y} - \frac{\partial^2 f}{\partial y\, \partial x} \right) \mathbf{k}$$

$$= 0\,\mathbf{i} + 0\,\mathbf{j} + 0\,\mathbf{k} = \mathbf{0}$$

by Clairaut's Theorem. □

Since a conservative vector field is one for which $\mathbf{F} = \nabla f$, Theorem 3 can be rephrased as follows:

■ Compare this with Exercise 27 in Section 17.3.

$$\text{If } \mathbf{F} \text{ is conservative, then curl } \mathbf{F} = \mathbf{0}.$$

This gives us a way of verifying that a vector field is not conservative.

▼ EXAMPLE 2 Show that the vector field $\mathbf{F}(x, y, z) = xz\,\mathbf{i} + xyz\,\mathbf{j} - y^2\,\mathbf{k}$ is not conservative.

SOLUTION   In Example 1 we showed that

$$\text{curl } \mathbf{F} = -y(2 + x)\,\mathbf{i} + x\,\mathbf{j} + yz\,\mathbf{k}$$

This shows that curl $\mathbf{F} \neq \mathbf{0}$ and so, by Theorem 3, $\mathbf{F}$ is not conservative. □

The converse of Theorem 3 is not true in general, but the following theorem says the converse is true if $\mathbf{F}$ is defined everywhere. (More generally it is true if the domain is simply-connected, that is, "has no hole.") Theorem 4 is the three-dimensional version of Theorem 17.3.6. Its proof requires Stokes' Theorem and is sketched at the end of Section 17.8.

---

4 THEOREM If $\mathbf{F}$ is a vector field defined on all of $\mathbb{R}^3$ whose component functions have continuous partial derivatives and curl $\mathbf{F} = \mathbf{0}$, then $\mathbf{F}$ is a conservative vector field.

◤ EXAMPLE 3

(a) Show that

$$\mathbf{F}(x, y, z) = y^2z^3\,\mathbf{i} + 2xyz^3\,\mathbf{j} + 3xy^2z^2\,\mathbf{k}$$

is a conservative vector field.

(b) Find a function f such that $\mathbf{F} = \nabla f$.

SOLUTION

(a) We compute the curl of $\mathbf{F}$:

$$\operatorname{curl}\mathbf{F} = \nabla \times \mathbf{F} = \begin{vmatrix} \mathbf{i} & \mathbf{j} & \mathbf{k} \\ \dfrac{\partial}{\partial x} & \dfrac{\partial}{\partial y} & \dfrac{\partial}{\partial z} \\ y^2z^3 & 2xyz^3 & 3xy^2z^2 \end{vmatrix}$$

$$= (6xyz^2 - 6xyz^2)\,\mathbf{i} - (3y^2z^2 - 3y^2z^2)\,\mathbf{j} + (2yz^3 - 2yz^3)\,\mathbf{k}$$

$$= \mathbf{0}$$

Since $\operatorname{curl}\mathbf{F} = \mathbf{0}$ and the domain of $\mathbf{F}$ is $\mathbb{R}^3$, $\mathbf{F}$ is a conservative vector field by Theorem 4.

(b) The technique for finding f was given in Section 17.3. We have

$$\boxed{5} \qquad\qquad f_x(x, y, z) = y^2z^3$$

$$\boxed{6} \qquad\qquad f_y(x, y, z) = 2xyz^3$$

$$\boxed{7} \qquad\qquad f_z(x, y, z) = 3xy^2z^2$$

Integrating (5) with respect to x, we obtain

$$\boxed{8} \qquad\qquad f(x, y, z) = xy^2z^3 + g(y, z)$$

Differentiating (8) with respect to y, we get $f_y(x, y, z) = 2xyz^3 + g_y(y, z)$, so comparison with (6) gives $g_y(y, z) = 0$. Thus $g(y, z) = h(z)$ and

$$f_z(x, y, z) = 3xy^2z^2 + h'(z)$$

Then (7) gives $h'(z) = 0$. Therefore

$$f(x, y, z) = xy^2z^3 + K \qquad\qquad\qquad \square$$

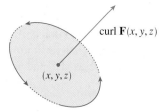

curl $\mathbf{F}(x, y, z)$

(x, y, z)

FIGURE I

The reason for the name *curl* is that the curl vector is associated with rotations. One connection is explained in Exercise 37. Another occurs when $\mathbf{F}$ represents the velocity field in fluid flow (see Example 3 in Section 17.1). Particles near (x, y, z) in the fluid tend to rotate about the axis that points in the direction of curl $\mathbf{F}(x, y, z)$ and the length of this curl vector is a measure of how quickly the particles move around the axis (see Figure 1). If curl $\mathbf{F} = \mathbf{0}$ at a point P, then the fluid is free from rotations at P and $\mathbf{F}$ is called **irrotational** at P. In other words, there is no whirlpool or eddy at P. If curl $\mathbf{F} = \mathbf{0}$, then a tiny paddle wheel moves with the fluid but doesn't rotate about its axis. If curl $\mathbf{F} \neq \mathbf{0}$, the paddle wheel rotates about its axis. We give a more detailed explanation in Section 17.8 as a consequence of Stokes' Theorem.

DIVERGENCE

If $\mathbf{F} = P\mathbf{i} + Q\mathbf{j} + R\mathbf{k}$ is a vector field on $\mathbb{R}^3$ and $\partial P/\partial x$, $\partial Q/\partial y$, and $\partial R/\partial z$ exist, then the **divergence of F** is the function of three variables defined by

$\boxed{9}$

$$\operatorname{div} \mathbf{F} = \frac{\partial P}{\partial x} + \frac{\partial Q}{\partial y} + \frac{\partial R}{\partial z}$$

Observe that curl $\mathbf{F}$ is a vector field but div $\mathbf{F}$ is a scalar field. In terms of the gradient operator $\nabla = (\partial/\partial x)\,\mathbf{i} + (\partial/\partial y)\,\mathbf{j} + (\partial/\partial z)\,\mathbf{k}$, the divergence of $\mathbf{F}$ can be written symbolically as the dot product of ∇ and $\mathbf{F}$:

$\boxed{10}$

$$\operatorname{div} \mathbf{F} = \nabla \cdot \mathbf{F}$$

EXAMPLE 4 If $\mathbf{F}(x, y, z) = xz\,\mathbf{i} + xyz\,\mathbf{j} - y^2\,\mathbf{k}$, find div $\mathbf{F}$.

SOLUTION By the definition of divergence (Equation 9 or 10) we have

$$\operatorname{div} \mathbf{F} = \nabla \cdot \mathbf{F} = \frac{\partial}{\partial x}(xz) + \frac{\partial}{\partial y}(xyz) + \frac{\partial}{\partial z}(-y^2) = z + xz \qquad \square$$

If $\mathbf{F}$ is a vector field on $\mathbb{R}^3$, then curl $\mathbf{F}$ is also a vector field on $\mathbb{R}^3$. As such, we can compute its divergence. The next theorem shows that the result is 0.

> $\boxed{11}$ **THEOREM** If $\mathbf{F} = P\mathbf{i} + Q\mathbf{j} + R\mathbf{k}$ is a vector field on $\mathbb{R}^3$ and P, Q, and R have continuous second-order partial derivatives, then
>
> $$\operatorname{div} \operatorname{curl} \mathbf{F} = 0$$

■ Note the analogy with the scalar triple product: $\mathbf{a} \cdot (\mathbf{a} \times \mathbf{b}) = 0$.

PROOF Using the definitions of divergence and curl, we have

$$\operatorname{div} \operatorname{curl} \mathbf{F} = \nabla \cdot (\nabla \times \mathbf{F})$$

$$= \frac{\partial}{\partial x}\left(\frac{\partial R}{\partial y} - \frac{\partial Q}{\partial z}\right) + \frac{\partial}{\partial y}\left(\frac{\partial P}{\partial z} - \frac{\partial R}{\partial x}\right) + \frac{\partial}{\partial z}\left(\frac{\partial Q}{\partial x} - \frac{\partial P}{\partial y}\right)$$

$$= \frac{\partial^2 R}{\partial x\,\partial y} - \frac{\partial^2 Q}{\partial x\,\partial z} + \frac{\partial^2 P}{\partial y\,\partial z} - \frac{\partial^2 R}{\partial y\,\partial x} + \frac{\partial^2 Q}{\partial z\,\partial x} - \frac{\partial^2 P}{\partial z\,\partial y}$$

$$= 0$$

because the terms cancel in pairs by Clairaut's Theorem. $\qquad \square$

▼ EXAMPLE 5 Show that the vector field $\mathbf{F}(x, y, z) = xz\,\mathbf{i} + xyz\,\mathbf{j} - y^2\,\mathbf{k}$ can't be written as the curl of another vector field, that is, $\mathbf{F} \neq \operatorname{curl} \mathbf{G}$.

SOLUTION In Example 4 we showed that

$$\operatorname{div} \mathbf{F} = z + xz$$

and therefore div $\mathbf{F} \neq 0$. If it were true that $\mathbf{F} = \text{curl } \mathbf{G}$, then Theorem 11 would give

$$\text{div } \mathbf{F} = \text{div curl } \mathbf{G} = 0$$

which contradicts div $\mathbf{F} \neq 0$. Therefore $\mathbf{F}$ is not the curl of another vector field. ☐

■ The reason for this interpretation of div $\mathbf{F}$ will be explained at the end of Section 17.9 as a consequence of the Divergence Theorem.

Again, the reason for the name *divergence* can be understood in the context of fluid flow. If $\mathbf{F}(x, y, z)$ is the velocity of a fluid (or gas), then div $\mathbf{F}(x, y, z)$ represents the net rate of change (with respect to time) of the mass of fluid (or gas) flowing from the point (x, y, z) per unit volume. In other words, div $\mathbf{F}(x, y, z)$ measures the tendency of the fluid to diverge from the point (x, y, z). If div $\mathbf{F} = 0$, then $\mathbf{F}$ is said to be **incompressible**.

Another differential operator occurs when we compute the divergence of a gradient vector field ∇f. If f is a function of three variables, we have

$$\text{div}(\nabla f) = \nabla \cdot (\nabla f) = \frac{\partial^2 f}{\partial x^2} + \frac{\partial^2 f}{\partial y^2} + \frac{\partial^2 f}{\partial z^2}$$

and this expression occurs so often that we abbreviate it as $\nabla^2 f$. The operator

$$\nabla^2 = \nabla \cdot \nabla$$

is called the **Laplace operator** because of its relation to **Laplace's equation**

$$\nabla^2 f = \frac{\partial^2 f}{\partial x^2} + \frac{\partial^2 f}{\partial y^2} + \frac{\partial^2 f}{\partial z^2} = 0$$

We can also apply the Laplace operator ∇^2 to a vector field

$$\mathbf{F} = P\mathbf{i} + Q\mathbf{j} + R\mathbf{k}$$

in terms of its components:

$$\nabla^2 \mathbf{F} = \nabla^2 P\mathbf{i} + \nabla^2 Q\mathbf{j} + \nabla^2 R\mathbf{k}$$

VECTOR FORMS OF GREEN'S THEOREM

The curl and divergence operators allow us to rewrite Green's Theorem in versions that will be useful in our later work. We suppose that the plane region D, its boundary curve C, and the functions P and Q satisfy the hypotheses of Green's Theorem. Then we consider the vector field $\mathbf{F} = P\mathbf{i} + Q\mathbf{j}$. Its line integral is

$$\oint_C \mathbf{F} \cdot d\mathbf{r} = \oint_C P\,dx + Q\,dy$$

and, regarding $\mathbf{F}$ as a vector field on $\mathbb{R}^3$ with third component 0, we have

$$\text{curl } \mathbf{F} = \begin{vmatrix} \mathbf{i} & \mathbf{j} & \mathbf{k} \\ \dfrac{\partial}{\partial x} & \dfrac{\partial}{\partial y} & \dfrac{\partial}{\partial z} \\ P(x, y) & Q(x, y) & 0 \end{vmatrix} = \left(\frac{\partial Q}{\partial x} - \frac{\partial P}{\partial y} \right) \mathbf{k}$$

Therefore

$$(\text{curl } \mathbf{F}) \cdot \mathbf{k} = \left(\frac{\partial Q}{\partial x} - \frac{\partial P}{\partial y} \right) \mathbf{k} \cdot \mathbf{k} = \frac{\partial Q}{\partial x} - \frac{\partial P}{\partial y}$$

and we can now rewrite the equation in Green's Theorem in the vector form

[12]
$$\oint_C \mathbf{F} \cdot d\mathbf{r} = \iint_D (\text{curl } \mathbf{F}) \cdot \mathbf{k} \, dA$$

Equation 12 expresses the line integral of the tangential component of $\mathbf{F}$ along C as the double integral of the vertical component of curl $\mathbf{F}$ over the region D enclosed by C. We now derive a similar formula involving the *normal* component of $\mathbf{F}$.

If C is given by the vector equation

$$\mathbf{r}(t) = x(t)\, \mathbf{i} + y(t)\, \mathbf{j} \qquad a \leqslant t \leqslant b$$

then the unit tangent vector (see Section 14.2) is

$$\mathbf{T}(t) = \frac{x'(t)}{|\mathbf{r}'(t)|} \mathbf{i} + \frac{y'(t)}{|\mathbf{r}'(t)|} \mathbf{j}$$

You can verify that the outward unit normal vector to C is given by

$$\mathbf{n}(t) = \frac{y'(t)}{|\mathbf{r}'(t)|} \mathbf{i} - \frac{x'(t)}{|\mathbf{r}'(t)|} \mathbf{j}$$

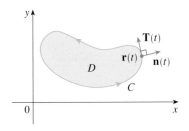

FIGURE 2

(See Figure 2.) Then, from Equation 14.2.3, we have

$$\oint_C \mathbf{F} \cdot \mathbf{n} \, ds = \int_a^b (\mathbf{F} \cdot \mathbf{n})(t) \, |\mathbf{r}'(t)| \, dt$$

$$= \int_a^b \left[\frac{P(x(t), y(t))\, y'(t)}{|\mathbf{r}'(t)|} - \frac{Q(x(t), y(t))\, x'(t)}{|\mathbf{r}'(t)|} \right] |\mathbf{r}'(t)| \, dt$$

$$= \int_a^b P(x(t), y(t))\, y'(t) \, dt - Q(x(t), y(t))\, x'(t) \, dt$$

$$= \int_C P \, dy - Q \, dx = \iint_D \left(\frac{\partial P}{\partial x} + \frac{\partial Q}{\partial y} \right) dA$$

by Green's Theorem. But the integrand in this double integral is just the divergence of $\mathbf{F}$. So we have a second vector form of Green's Theorem.

[13]
$$\oint_C \mathbf{F} \cdot \mathbf{n} \, ds = \iint_D \text{div } \mathbf{F}(x, y) \, dA$$

This version says that the line integral of the normal component of $\mathbf{F}$ along C is equal to the double integral of the divergence of $\mathbf{F}$ over the region D enclosed by C.

17.5 EXERCISES

1–8 Find (a) the curl and (b) the divergence of the vector field.

1. $\mathbf{F}(x, y, z) = xyz\,\mathbf{i} - x^2y\,\mathbf{k}$

2. $\mathbf{F}(x, y, z) = x^2yz\,\mathbf{i} + xy^2z\,\mathbf{j} + xyz^2\,\mathbf{k}$

3. $\mathbf{F}(x, y, z) = \mathbf{i} + (x + yz)\,\mathbf{j} + \left(xy - \sqrt{z}\,\right)\mathbf{k}$

4. $\mathbf{F}(x, y, z) = \cos xz\,\mathbf{j} - \sin xy\,\mathbf{k}$

5. $\mathbf{F}(x, y, z) = \dfrac{1}{\sqrt{x^2 + y^2 + z^2}}\,(x\,\mathbf{i} + y\,\mathbf{j} + z\,\mathbf{k})$

6. $\mathbf{F}(x, y, z) = e^{xy}\sin z\,\mathbf{j} + y\tan^{-1}(x/z)\,\mathbf{k}$

7. $\mathbf{F}(x, y, z) = \langle \ln x, \ln(xy), \ln(xyz)\rangle$

8. $\mathbf{F}(x, y, z) = \langle e^x, e^{xy}, e^{xyz}\rangle$

9–11 The vector field $\mathbf{F}$ is shown in the xy-plane and looks the same in all other horizontal planes. (In other words, $\mathbf{F}$ is independent of z and its z-component is 0.)
(a) Is div $\mathbf{F}$ positive, negative, or zero? Explain.
(b) Determine whether curl $\mathbf{F} = \mathbf{0}$. If not, in which direction does curl $\mathbf{F}$ point?

9.

10.

11.
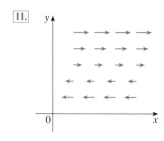

12. Let f be a scalar field and $\mathbf{F}$ a vector field. State whether each expression is meaningful. If not, explain why. If so, state whether it is a scalar field or a vector field.
 (a) curl f
 (b) grad f
 (c) div $\mathbf{F}$
 (d) curl(grad f)
 (e) grad $\mathbf{F}$
 (f) grad(div $\mathbf{F}$)
 (g) div(grad f)
 (h) grad(div f)
 (i) curl(curl $\mathbf{F}$)
 (j) div(div $\mathbf{F}$)
 (k) (grad f) × (div $\mathbf{F}$)
 (l) div(curl(grad f))

13–18 Determine whether or not the vector field is conservative. If it is conservative, find a function f such that $\mathbf{F} = \nabla f$.

13. $\mathbf{F}(x, y, z) = y^2z^3\,\mathbf{i} + 2xyz^3\,\mathbf{j} + 3xy^2z^2\,\mathbf{k}$

14. $\mathbf{F}(x, y, z) = xyz^2\,\mathbf{i} + x^2yz^2\,\mathbf{j} + x^2y^2z\,\mathbf{k}$

15. $\mathbf{F}(x, y, z) = 2xy\,\mathbf{i} + (x^2 + 2yz)\,\mathbf{j} + y^2\,\mathbf{k}$

16. $\mathbf{F}(x, y, z) = e^z\,\mathbf{i} + \mathbf{j} + xe^z\,\mathbf{k}$

17. $\mathbf{F}(x, y, z) = ye^{-x}\,\mathbf{i} + e^{-x}\,\mathbf{j} + 2z\,\mathbf{k}$

18. $\mathbf{F}(x, y, z) = y\cos xy\,\mathbf{i} + x\cos xy\,\mathbf{j} - \sin z\,\mathbf{k}$

19. Is there a vector field $\mathbf{G}$ on $\mathbb{R}^3$ such that curl $\mathbf{G} = \langle x\sin y, \cos y, z - xy\rangle$? Explain.

20. Is there a vector field $\mathbf{G}$ on $\mathbb{R}^3$ such that curl $\mathbf{G} = \langle xyz, -y^2z, yz^2\rangle$? Explain.

21. Show that any vector field of the form

$$\mathbf{F}(x, y, z) = f(x)\,\mathbf{i} + g(y)\,\mathbf{j} + h(z)\,\mathbf{k}$$

where f, g, h are differentiable functions, is irrotational.

22. Show that any vector field of the form

$$\mathbf{F}(x, y, z) = f(y, z)\,\mathbf{i} + g(x, z)\,\mathbf{j} + h(x, y)\,\mathbf{k}$$

is incompressible.

23–29 Prove the identity, assuming that the appropriate partial derivatives exist and are continuous. If f is a scalar field and $\mathbf{F}, \mathbf{G}$ are vector fields, then $f\mathbf{F}, \mathbf{F}\cdot\mathbf{G}$, and $\mathbf{F}\times\mathbf{G}$ are defined by

$$(f\mathbf{F})(x, y, z) = f(x, y, z)\,\mathbf{F}(x, y, z)$$
$$(\mathbf{F}\cdot\mathbf{G})(x, y, z) = \mathbf{F}(x, y, z)\cdot\mathbf{G}(x, y, z)$$
$$(\mathbf{F}\times\mathbf{G})(x, y, z) = \mathbf{F}(x, y, z)\times\mathbf{G}(x, y, z)$$

23. div$(\mathbf{F} + \mathbf{G}) = $ div $\mathbf{F} + $ div $\mathbf{G}$

24. curl$(\mathbf{F} + \mathbf{G}) = $ curl $\mathbf{F} + $ curl $\mathbf{G}$

25. div$(f\mathbf{F}) = f$ div $\mathbf{F} + \mathbf{F}\cdot\nabla f$

26. curl$(f\mathbf{F}) = f$ curl $\mathbf{F} + (\nabla f)\times\mathbf{F}$

27. div$(\mathbf{F}\times\mathbf{G}) = \mathbf{G}\cdot$ curl $\mathbf{F} - \mathbf{F}\cdot$ curl $\mathbf{G}$

28. div$(\nabla f\times\nabla g) = 0$

29. curl(curl $\mathbf{F}$) $= $ grad(div $\mathbf{F}$) $- \nabla^2\mathbf{F}$

30–32 Let $\mathbf{r} = x\,\mathbf{i} + y\,\mathbf{j} + z\,\mathbf{k}$ and $r = |\mathbf{r}|$.

30. Verify each identity.
 (a) $\nabla\cdot\mathbf{r} = 3$
 (b) $\nabla\cdot(r\mathbf{r}) = 4r$
 (c) $\nabla^2r^3 = 12r$

31. Verify each identity.

(a) $\nabla r = \mathbf{r}/r$ (b) $\nabla \times \mathbf{r} = \mathbf{0}$

(c) $\nabla(1/r) = -\mathbf{r}/r^3$ (d) $\nabla \ln r = \mathbf{r}/r^2$

32. If $\mathbf{F} = \mathbf{r}/r^p$, find div $\mathbf{F}$. Is there a value of p for which div $\mathbf{F} = 0$?

---

33. Use Green's Theorem in the form of Equation 13 to prove **Green's first identity**:

$$\iint_D f \nabla^2 g \, dA = \oint_C f(\nabla g) \cdot \mathbf{n} \, ds - \iint_D \nabla f \cdot \nabla g \, dA$$

where D and C satisfy the hypotheses of Green's Theorem and the appropriate partial derivatives of f and g exist and are continuous. (The quantity $\nabla g \cdot \mathbf{n} = D_\mathbf{n} g$ occurs in the line integral. This is the directional derivative in the direction of the normal vector $\mathbf{n}$ and is called the **normal derivative** of g.)

34. Use Green's first identity (Exercise 33) to prove **Green's second identity**:

$$\iint_D (f \nabla^2 g - g \nabla^2 f) \, dA = \oint_C (f \nabla g - g \nabla f) \cdot \mathbf{n} \, ds$$

where D and C satisfy the hypotheses of Green's Theorem and the appropriate partial derivatives of f and g exist and are continuous.

35. Recall from Section 15.3 that a function g is called *harmonic* on D if it satisfies Laplace's equation, that is, $\nabla^2 g = 0$ on D. Use Green's first identity (with the same hypotheses as in Exercise 33) to show that if g is harmonic on D, then $\oint_C D_\mathbf{n} g \, ds = 0$. Here $D_\mathbf{n} g$ is the normal derivative of g defined in Exercise 33.

36. Use Green's first identity to show that if f is harmonic on D, and if $f(x, y) = 0$ on the boundary curve C, then $\iint_D |\nabla f|^2 \, dA = 0$. (Assume the same hypotheses as in Exercise 33.)

37. This exercise demonstrates a connection between the curl vector and rotations. Let B be a rigid body rotating about the z-axis. The rotation can be described by the vector $\mathbf{w} = \omega \mathbf{k}$, where ω is the angular speed of B, that is, the tangential speed of any point P in B divided by the distance d from the axis of rotation. Let $\mathbf{r} = \langle x, y, z \rangle$ be the position vector of P.

(a) By considering the angle θ in the figure, show that the velocity field of B is given by $\mathbf{v} = \mathbf{w} \times \mathbf{r}$.

(b) Show that $\mathbf{v} = -\omega y \, \mathbf{i} + \omega x \, \mathbf{j}$.

(c) Show that curl $\mathbf{v} = 2\mathbf{w}$.

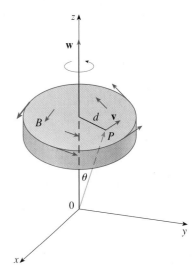

38. Maxwell's equations relating the electric field $\mathbf{E}$ and magnetic field $\mathbf{H}$ as they vary with time in a region containing no charge and no current can be stated as follows:

$$\text{div } \mathbf{E} = 0 \qquad\qquad \text{div } \mathbf{H} = 0$$

$$\text{curl } \mathbf{E} = -\frac{1}{c}\frac{\partial \mathbf{H}}{\partial t} \qquad \text{curl } \mathbf{H} = \frac{1}{c}\frac{\partial \mathbf{E}}{\partial t}$$

where c is the speed of light. Use these equations to prove the following:

(a) $\nabla \times (\nabla \times \mathbf{E}) = -\dfrac{1}{c^2}\dfrac{\partial^2 \mathbf{E}}{\partial t^2}$

(b) $\nabla \times (\nabla \times \mathbf{H}) = -\dfrac{1}{c^2}\dfrac{\partial^2 \mathbf{H}}{\partial t^2}$

(c) $\nabla^2 \mathbf{E} = \dfrac{1}{c^2}\dfrac{\partial^2 \mathbf{E}}{\partial t^2}$ [*Hint:* Use Exercise 29.]

(d) $\nabla^2 \mathbf{H} = \dfrac{1}{c^2}\dfrac{\partial^2 \mathbf{H}}{\partial t^2}$

39. We have seen that all vector fields of the form $\mathbf{F} = \nabla g$ satisfy the equation curl $\mathbf{F} = \mathbf{0}$ and that all vector fields of the form $\mathbf{F} = \text{curl } \mathbf{G}$ satisfy the equation div $\mathbf{F} = 0$ (assuming continuity of the appropriate partial derivatives). This suggests the question: Are there any equations that all functions of the form $f = \text{div } \mathbf{G}$ must satisfy? Show that the answer to this question is "No" by proving that *every* continuous function f on $\mathbb{R}^3$ is the divergence of some vector field. [*Hint:* Let $\mathbf{G}(x, y, z) = \langle g(x, y, z), 0, 0 \rangle$, where $g(x, y, z) = \int_0^x f(t, y, z) \, dt$.]

17.6 PARAMETRIC SURFACES AND THEIR AREAS

So far we have considered special types of surfaces: cylinders, quadric surfaces, graphs of functions of two variables, and level surfaces of functions of three variables. Here we use vector functions to describe more general surfaces, called *parametric surfaces*, and compute their areas. Then we take the general surface area formula and see how it applies to special surfaces.

PARAMETRIC SURFACES

In much the same way that we describe a space curve by a vector function $\mathbf{r}(t)$ of a single parameter t, we can describe a surface by a vector function $\mathbf{r}(u, v)$ of two parameters u and v. We suppose that

$$\boxed{1} \qquad \mathbf{r}(u, v) = x(u, v)\,\mathbf{i} + y(u, v)\,\mathbf{j} + z(u, v)\,\mathbf{k}$$

is a vector-valued function defined on a region D in the uv-plane. So x, y, and z, the component functions of $\mathbf{r}$, are functions of the two variables u and v with domain D. The set of all points (x, y, z) in $\mathbb{R}^3$ such that

$$\boxed{2} \qquad x = x(u, v) \qquad y = y(u, v) \qquad z = z(u, v)$$

and (u, v) varies throughout D, is called a **parametric surface** S and Equations 2 are called **parametric equations** of S. Each choice of u and v gives a point on S; by making all choices, we get all of S. In other words, the surface S is traced out by the tip of the position vector $\mathbf{r}(u, v)$ as (u, v) moves throughout the region D. (See Figure 1.)

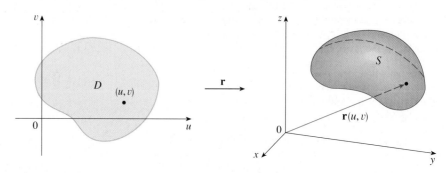

FIGURE 1
A parametric surface

EXAMPLE 1 Identify and sketch the surface with vector equation

$$\mathbf{r}(u, v) = 2\cos u\,\mathbf{i} + v\,\mathbf{j} + 2\sin u\,\mathbf{k}$$

SOLUTION The parametric equations for this surface are

$$x = 2\cos u \qquad y = v \qquad z = 2\sin u$$

So for any point (x, y, z) on the surface, we have

$$x^2 + z^2 = 4\cos^2 u + 4\sin^2 u = 4$$

This means that vertical cross-sections parallel to the xz-plane (that is, with y constant) are all circles with radius 2. Since $y = v$ and no restriction is placed on v, the surface is a circular cylinder with radius 2 whose axis is the y-axis. (See Figure 2.) ☐

FIGURE 2

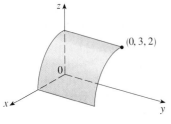

FIGURE 3

In Example 1 we placed no restrictions on the parameters u and v and so we obtained the entire cylinder. If, for instance, we restrict u and v by writing the parameter domain as

$$0 \leqslant u \leqslant \pi/2 \qquad 0 \leqslant v \leqslant 3$$

then $x \geqslant 0, z \geqslant 0, 0 \leqslant y \leqslant 3$, and we get the quarter-cylinder with length 3 illustrated in Figure 3.

If a parametric surface S is given by a vector function $\mathbf{r}(u, v)$, then there are two useful families of curves that lie on S, one family with u constant and the other with v constant. These families correspond to vertical and horizontal lines in the uv-plane. If we keep u constant by putting $u = u_0$, then $\mathbf{r}(u_0, v)$ becomes a vector function of the single parameter v and defines a curve C_1 lying on S. (See Figure 4.)

TEC Visual 17.6 shows animated versions of Figures 4 and 5, with moving grid curves, for several parametric surfaces.

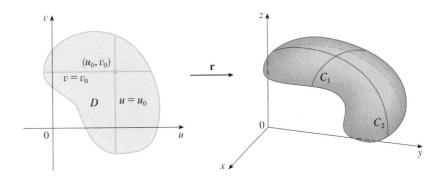

FIGURE 4

Similarly, if we keep v constant by putting $v = v_0$, we get a curve C_2 given by $\mathbf{r}(u, v_0)$ that lies on S. We call these curves **grid curves**. (In Example 1, for instance, the grid curves obtained by letting u be constant are horizontal lines whereas the grid curves with v constant are circles.) In fact, when a computer graphs a parametric surface, it usually depicts the surface by plotting these grid curves, as we see in the following example.

EXAMPLE 2 Use a computer algebra system to graph the surface

$$\mathbf{r}(u, v) = \langle (2 + \sin v) \cos u, (2 + \sin v) \sin u, u + \cos v \rangle$$

Which grid curves have u constant? Which have v constant?

SOLUTION We graph the portion of the surface with parameter domain $0 \leqslant u \leqslant 4\pi$, $0 \leqslant v \leqslant 2\pi$ in Figure 5. It has the appearance of a spiral tube. To identify the grid curves, we write the corresponding parametric equations:

$$x = (2 + \sin v) \cos u \qquad y = (2 + \sin v) \sin u \qquad z = u + \cos v$$

If v is constant, then $\sin v$ and $\cos v$ are constant, so the parametric equations resemble those of the helix in Example 4 in Section 14.1. So the grid curves with v constant are the spiral curves in Figure 5. We deduce that the grid curves with u constant must be the curves that look like circles in the figure. Further evidence for this assertion is that if u is kept constant, $u = u_0$, then the equation $z = u_0 + \cos v$ shows that the z-values vary from $u_0 - 1$ to $u_0 + 1$. ☐

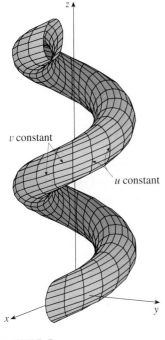

v constant

u constant

FIGURE 5

In Examples 1 and 2 we were given a vector equation and asked to graph the corresponding parametric surface. In the following examples, however, we are given the more challenging problem of finding a vector function to represent a given surface. In the rest of this chapter we will often need to do exactly that.

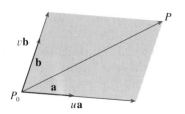

FIGURE 6

EXAMPLE 3 Find a vector function that represents the plane that passes through the point P_0 with position vector $\mathbf{r}_0$ and that contains two nonparallel vectors $\mathbf{a}$ and $\mathbf{b}$.

SOLUTION If P is any point in the plane, we can get from P_0 to P by moving a certain distance in the direction of $\mathbf{a}$ and another distance in the direction of $\mathbf{b}$. So there are scalars u and v such that $\overrightarrow{P_0P} = u\mathbf{a} + v\mathbf{b}$. (Figure 6 illustrates how this works, by means of the Parallelogram Law, for the case where u and v are positive. See also Exercise 40 in Section 13.2.) If $\mathbf{r}$ is the position vector of P, then

$$\mathbf{r} = \overrightarrow{OP_0} + \overrightarrow{P_0P} = \mathbf{r}_0 + u\mathbf{a} + v\mathbf{b}$$

So the vector equation of the plane can be written as

$$\mathbf{r}(u, v) = \mathbf{r}_0 + u\mathbf{a} + v\mathbf{b}$$

where u and v are real numbers.

If we write $\mathbf{r} = \langle x, y, z \rangle$, $\mathbf{r}_0 = \langle x_0, y_0, z_0 \rangle$, $\mathbf{a} = \langle a_1, a_2, a_3 \rangle$, and $\mathbf{b} = \langle b_1, b_2, b_3 \rangle$, then we can write the parametric equations of the plane through the point (x_0, y_0, z_0) as follows:

$$x = x_0 + ua_1 + vb_1 \qquad y = y_0 + ua_2 + vb_2 \qquad z = z_0 + ua_3 + vb_3 \qquad \square$$

☑ EXAMPLE 4 Find a parametric representation of the sphere

$$x^2 + y^2 + z^2 = a^2$$

SOLUTION The sphere has a simple representation $\rho = a$ in spherical coordinates, so let's choose the angles ϕ and θ in spherical coordinates as the parameters (see Section 16.8). Then, putting $\rho = a$ in the equations for conversion from spherical to rectangular coordinates (Equations 16.8.1), we obtain

$$x = a \sin\phi \cos\theta \qquad y = a \sin\phi \sin\theta \qquad z = a \cos\phi$$

as the parametric equations of the sphere. The corresponding vector equation is

$$\mathbf{r}(\phi, \theta) = a \sin\phi \cos\theta\, \mathbf{i} + a \sin\phi \sin\theta\, \mathbf{j} + a \cos\phi\, \mathbf{k}$$

We have $0 \leq \phi \leq \pi$ and $0 \leq \theta \leq 2\pi$, so the parameter domain is the rectangle $D = [0, \pi] \times [0, 2\pi]$. The grid curves with ϕ constant are the circles of constant latitude (including the equator). The grid curves with θ constant are the meridians (semicircles), which connect the north and south poles. $\square$

■ One of the uses of parametric surfaces is in computer graphics. Figure 7 shows the result of trying to graph the sphere $x^2 + y^2 + z^2 = 1$ by solving the equation for z and graphing the top and bottom hemispheres separately. Part of the sphere appears to be missing because of the rectangular grid system used by the computer. The much better picture in Figure 8 was produced by a computer using the parametric equations found in Example 4.

FIGURE 7

FIGURE 8

EXAMPLE 5 Find a parametric representation for the cylinder

$$x^2 + y^2 = 4 \qquad 0 \leqslant z \leqslant 1$$

SOLUTION The cylinder has a simple representation $r = 2$ in cylindrical coordinates, so we choose as parameters θ and z in cylindrical coordinates. Then the parametric equations of the cylinder are

$$x = 2 \cos \theta \qquad y = 2 \sin \theta \qquad z = z$$

where $0 \leqslant \theta \leqslant 2\pi$ and $0 \leqslant z \leqslant 1$. ☐

▼ EXAMPLE 6 Find a vector function that represents the elliptic paraboloid $z = x^2 + 2y^2$.

SOLUTION If we regard x and y as parameters, then the parametric equations are simply

$$x = x \qquad y = y \qquad z = x^2 + 2y^2$$

and the vector equation is

$$\mathbf{r}(x, y) = x\,\mathbf{i} + y\,\mathbf{j} + (x^2 + 2y^2)\,\mathbf{k}$$ ☐

TEC In Module 17.6 you can investigate several families of parametric surfaces.

In general, a surface given as the graph of a function of x and y, that is, with an equation of the form $z = f(x, y)$, can always be regarded as a parametric surface by taking x and y as parameters and writing the parametric equations as

$$x = x \qquad y = y \qquad z = f(x, y)$$

Parametric representations (also called parametrizations) of surfaces are not unique. The next example shows two ways to parametrize a cone.

EXAMPLE 7 Find a parametric representation for the surface $z = 2\sqrt{x^2 + y^2}$, that is, the top half of the cone $z^2 = 4x^2 + 4y^2$.

SOLUTION I One possible representation is obtained by choosing x and y as parameters:

$$x = x \qquad y = y \qquad z = 2\sqrt{x^2 + y^2}$$

So the vector equation is

$$\mathbf{r}(x, y) = x\,\mathbf{i} + y\,\mathbf{j} + 2\sqrt{x^2 + y^2}\,\mathbf{k}$$

■ For some purposes the parametric representations in Solutions 1 and 2 are equally good, but Solution 2 might be preferable in certain situations. If we are interested only in the part of the cone that lies below the plane $z = 1$, for instance, all we have to do in Solution 2 is change the parameter domain to

$$0 \leqslant r \leqslant \tfrac{1}{2} \qquad 0 \leqslant \theta \leqslant 2\pi$$

SOLUTION 2 Another representation results from choosing as parameters the polar coordinates r and θ. A point (x, y, z) on the cone satisfies $x = r \cos \theta$, $y = r \sin \theta$, and $z = 2\sqrt{x^2 + y^2} = 2r$. So a vector equation for the cone is

$$\mathbf{r}(r, \theta) = r \cos \theta\,\mathbf{i} + r \sin \theta\,\mathbf{j} + 2r\,\mathbf{k}$$

where $r \geqslant 0$ and $0 \leqslant \theta \leqslant 2\pi$. ☐

SURFACES OF REVOLUTION

Surfaces of revolution can be represented parametrically and thus graphed using a computer. For instance, let's consider the surface S obtained by rotating the curve $y = f(x)$, $a \leqslant x \leqslant b$, about the x-axis, where $f(x) \geqslant 0$. Let θ be the angle of rotation as shown in

FIGURE 9

FIGURE 10

Figure 9. If (x, y, z) is a point on S, then

$$\boxed{3} \qquad\qquad x = x \qquad y = f(x) \cos \theta \qquad z = f(x) \sin \theta$$

Therefore we take x and θ as parameters and regard Equations 3 as parametric equations of S. The parameter domain is given by $a \leqslant x \leqslant b, 0 \leqslant \theta \leqslant 2\pi$.

EXAMPLE 8 Find parametric equations for the surface generated by rotating the curve $y = \sin x, 0 \leqslant x \leqslant 2\pi$, about the x-axis. Use these equations to graph the surface of revolution.

SOLUTION From Equations 3, the parametric equations are

$$x = x \qquad y = \sin x \cos \theta \qquad z = \sin x \sin \theta$$

and the parameter domain is $0 \leqslant x \leqslant 2\pi, 0 \leqslant \theta \leqslant 2\pi$. Using a computer to plot these equations and rotate the image, we obtain the graph in Figure 10. ☐

We can adapt Equations 3 to represent a surface obtained through revolution about the y- or z-axis. (See Exercise 30.)

TANGENT PLANES

We now find the tangent plane to a parametric surface S traced out by a vector function

$$\mathbf{r}(u, v) = x(u, v) \, \mathbf{i} + y(u, v) \, \mathbf{j} + z(u, v) \, \mathbf{k}$$

at a point P_0 with position vector $\mathbf{r}(u_0, v_0)$. If we keep u constant by putting $u = u_0$, then $\mathbf{r}(u_0, v)$ becomes a vector function of the single parameter v and defines a grid curve C_1 lying on S. (See Figure 11.) The tangent vector to C_1 at P_0 is obtained by taking the partial derivative of $\mathbf{r}$ with respect to v:

$$\boxed{4} \qquad \mathbf{r}_v = \frac{\partial x}{\partial v}(u_0, v_0)\,\mathbf{i} + \frac{\partial y}{\partial v}(u_0, v_0)\,\mathbf{j} + \frac{\partial z}{\partial v}(u_0, v_0)\,\mathbf{k}$$

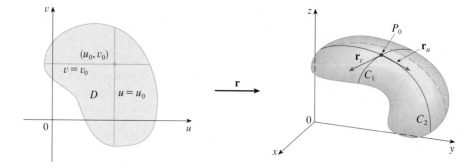

FIGURE 11

Similarly, if we keep v constant by putting $v = v_0$, we get a grid curve C_2 given by $\mathbf{r}(u, v_0)$ that lies on S, and its tangent vector at P_0 is

$$\boxed{5} \qquad \mathbf{r}_u = \frac{\partial x}{\partial u}(u_0, v_0)\,\mathbf{i} + \frac{\partial y}{\partial u}(u_0, v_0)\,\mathbf{j} + \frac{\partial z}{\partial u}(u_0, v_0)\,\mathbf{k}$$

If $\mathbf{r}_u \times \mathbf{r}_v$ is not $\mathbf{0}$, then the surface S is called **smooth** (it has no "corners"). For a smooth surface, the **tangent plane** is the plane that contains the tangent vectors $\mathbf{r}_u$ and $\mathbf{r}_v$, and the vector $\mathbf{r}_u \times \mathbf{r}_v$ is a normal vector to the tangent plane.

■ Figure 12 shows the self-intersecting surface in Example 9 and its tangent plane at $(1, 1, 3)$.

☑ EXAMPLE 9 Find the tangent plane to the surface with parametric equations $x = u^2$, $y = v^2$, $z = u + 2v$ at the point $(1, 1, 3)$.

SOLUTION We first compute the tangent vectors:

$$\mathbf{r}_u = \frac{\partial x}{\partial u}\,\mathbf{i} + \frac{\partial y}{\partial u}\,\mathbf{j} + \frac{\partial z}{\partial u}\,\mathbf{k} = 2u\,\mathbf{i} + \mathbf{k}$$

$$\mathbf{r}_v = \frac{\partial x}{\partial v}\,\mathbf{i} + \frac{\partial y}{\partial v}\,\mathbf{j} + \frac{\partial z}{\partial v}\,\mathbf{k} = 2v\,\mathbf{j} + 2\,\mathbf{k}$$

Thus a normal vector to the tangent plane is

$$\mathbf{r}_u \times \mathbf{r}_v = \begin{vmatrix} \mathbf{i} & \mathbf{j} & \mathbf{k} \\ 2u & 0 & 1 \\ 0 & 2v & 2 \end{vmatrix} = -2v\,\mathbf{i} - 4u\,\mathbf{j} + 4uv\,\mathbf{k}$$

Notice that the point $(1, 1, 3)$ corresponds to the parameter values $u = 1$ and $v = 1$, so the normal vector there is

$$-2\,\mathbf{i} - 4\,\mathbf{j} + 4\,\mathbf{k}$$

Therefore an equation of the tangent plane at $(1, 1, 3)$ is

$$-2(x - 1) - 4(y - 1) + 4(z - 3) = 0$$

or $$x + 2y - 2z + 3 = 0 \qquad \square$$

FIGURE 12

SURFACE AREA

Now we define the surface area of a general parametric surface given by Equation 1. For simplicity we start by considering a surface whose parameter domain D is a rectangle, and we divide it into subrectangles R_{ij}. Let's choose (u_i^*, v_j^*) to be the lower left corner of R_{ij}. (See Figure 13.) The part S_{ij} of the surface S that corresponds to R_{ij} is called a *patch* and has the point P_{ij} with position vector $\mathbf{r}(u_i^*, v_j^*)$ as one of its corners. Let

$$\mathbf{r}_u^* = \mathbf{r}_u(u_i^*, v_j^*) \qquad \text{and} \qquad \mathbf{r}_v^* = \mathbf{r}_v(u_i^*, v_j^*)$$

be the tangent vectors at P_{ij} as given by Equations 5 and 4.

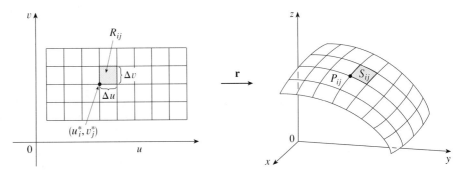

FIGURE 13
The image of the subrectangle R_{ij} is the patch S_{ij}.

S_{ij}

P_{ij}

(a)

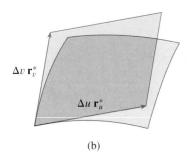

$\Delta v\, \mathbf{r}_v^*$

$\Delta u\, \mathbf{r}_u^*$

(b)

FIGURE 14
Approximating a patch
by a parallelogram

Figure 14(a) shows how the two edges of the patch that meet at P_{ij} can be approximated by vectors. These vectors, in turn, can be approximated by the vectors $\Delta u\, \mathbf{r}_u^*$ and $\Delta v\, \mathbf{r}_v^*$ because partial derivatives can be approximated by difference quotients. So we approximate S_{ij} by the parallelogram determined by the vectors $\Delta u\, \mathbf{r}_u^*$ and $\Delta v\, \mathbf{r}_v^*$. This parallelogram is shown in Figure 14(b) and lies in the tangent plane to S at P_{ij}. The area of this parallelogram is

$$\left| (\Delta u\, \mathbf{r}_u^*) \times (\Delta v\, \mathbf{r}_v^*) \right| = \left| \mathbf{r}_u^* \times \mathbf{r}_v^* \right| \Delta u\, \Delta v$$

and so an approximation to the area of S is

$$\sum_{i=1}^{m} \sum_{j=1}^{n} \left| \mathbf{r}_u^* \times \mathbf{r}_v^* \right| \Delta u\, \Delta v$$

Our intuition tells us that this approximation gets better as we increase the number of subrectangles, and we recognize the double sum as a Riemann sum for the double integral $\iint_D |\mathbf{r}_u \times \mathbf{r}_v|\, du\, dv$. This motivates the following definition.

---

6   DEFINITION If a smooth parametric surface S is given by the equation

$$\mathbf{r}(u, v) = x(u, v)\, \mathbf{i} + y(u, v)\, \mathbf{j} + z(u, v)\, \mathbf{k} \qquad (u, v) \in D$$

and S is covered just once as (u, v) ranges throughout the parameter domain D, then the **surface area** of S is

$$A(S) = \iint_D |\mathbf{r}_u \times \mathbf{r}_v|\, dA$$

where $\quad \mathbf{r}_u = \dfrac{\partial x}{\partial u}\, \mathbf{i} + \dfrac{\partial y}{\partial u}\, \mathbf{j} + \dfrac{\partial z}{\partial u}\, \mathbf{k} \qquad \mathbf{r}_v = \dfrac{\partial x}{\partial v}\, \mathbf{i} + \dfrac{\partial y}{\partial v}\, \mathbf{j} + \dfrac{\partial z}{\partial v}\, \mathbf{k}$

EXAMPLE 10 Find the surface area of a sphere of radius a.

SOLUTION In Example 4 we found the parametric representation

$$x = a \sin \phi \cos \theta \qquad y = a \sin \phi \sin \theta \qquad z = a \cos \phi$$

where the parameter domain is

$$D = \left\{ (\phi, \theta) \mid 0 \leqslant \phi \leqslant \pi,\ 0 \leqslant \theta \leqslant 2\pi \right\}$$

We first compute the cross product of the tangent vectors:

$$\mathbf{r}_\phi \times \mathbf{r}_\theta = \begin{vmatrix} \mathbf{i} & \mathbf{j} & \mathbf{k} \\[2pt] \dfrac{\partial x}{\partial \phi} & \dfrac{\partial y}{\partial \phi} & \dfrac{\partial z}{\partial \phi} \\[6pt] \dfrac{\partial x}{\partial \theta} & \dfrac{\partial y}{\partial \theta} & \dfrac{\partial z}{\partial \theta} \end{vmatrix} = \begin{vmatrix} \mathbf{i} & \mathbf{j} & \mathbf{k} \\[4pt] a \cos \phi \cos \theta & a \cos \phi \sin \theta & -a \sin \phi \\[4pt] -a \sin \phi \sin \theta & a \sin \phi \cos \theta & 0 \end{vmatrix}$$

$$= a^2 \sin^2\phi \cos \theta\, \mathbf{i} + a^2 \sin^2\phi \sin \theta\, \mathbf{j} + a^2 \sin \phi \cos \phi\, \mathbf{k}$$

Thus

$$|\mathbf{r}_\phi \times \mathbf{r}_\theta| = \sqrt{a^4 \sin^4\phi \, \cos^2\theta + a^4 \sin^4\phi \, \sin^2\theta + a^4 \sin^2\phi \, \cos^2\phi}$$

$$= \sqrt{a^4 \sin^4\phi + a^4 \sin^2\phi \, \cos^2\phi} = a^2\sqrt{\sin^2\phi} = a^2 \sin\phi$$

since $\sin\phi \geqslant 0$ for $0 \leqslant \phi \leqslant \pi$. Therefore, by Definition 6, the area of the sphere is

$$A = \iint\limits_D |\mathbf{r}_\phi \times \mathbf{r}_\theta| \, dA = \int_0^{2\pi} \int_0^\pi a^2 \sin\phi \, d\phi \, d\theta$$

$$= a^2 \int_0^{2\pi} d\theta \int_0^\pi \sin\phi \, d\phi = a^2(2\pi)2 = 4\pi a^2 \qquad \square$$

SURFACE AREA OF THE GRAPH OF A FUNCTION

For the special case of a surface S with equation $z = f(x, y)$, where (x, y) lies in D and f has continuous partial derivatives, we take x and y as parameters. The parametric equations are

$$x = x \qquad y = y \qquad z = f(x, y)$$

so

$$\mathbf{r}_x = \mathbf{i} + \left(\frac{\partial f}{\partial x}\right)\mathbf{k} \qquad \mathbf{r}_y = \mathbf{j} + \left(\frac{\partial f}{\partial y}\right)\mathbf{k}$$

and

$$\boxed{7} \qquad \mathbf{r}_x \times \mathbf{r}_y = \begin{vmatrix} \mathbf{i} & \mathbf{j} & \mathbf{k} \\ 1 & 0 & \dfrac{\partial f}{\partial x} \\ 0 & 1 & \dfrac{\partial f}{\partial y} \end{vmatrix} = -\frac{\partial f}{\partial x}\mathbf{i} - \frac{\partial f}{\partial y}\mathbf{j} + \mathbf{k}$$

Thus we have

■ Notice the similarity between the surface area formula in Equation 9 and the arc length formula

$$L = \int_a^b \sqrt{1 + \left(\frac{dy}{dx}\right)^2}\, dx$$

from Section 9.1.

$$\boxed{8} \qquad |\mathbf{r}_x \times \mathbf{r}_y| = \sqrt{\left(\frac{\partial f}{\partial x}\right)^2 + \left(\frac{\partial f}{\partial y}\right)^2 + 1} = \sqrt{1 + \left(\frac{\partial z}{\partial x}\right)^2 + \left(\frac{\partial z}{\partial y}\right)^2}$$

and the surface area formula in Definition 6 becomes

$$\boxed{9} \qquad A(S) = \iint\limits_D \sqrt{1 + \left(\frac{\partial z}{\partial x}\right)^2 + \left(\frac{\partial z}{\partial y}\right)^2}\, dA$$

▼ **EXAMPLE 11** Find the area of the part of the paraboloid $z = x^2 + y^2$ that lies under the plane $z = 9$.

SOLUTION The plane intersects the paraboloid in the circle $x^2 + y^2 = 9$, $z = 9$. Therefore the given surface lies above the disk D with center the origin and radius 3. (See Figure 15.) Using Formula 9, we have

$$A = \iint\limits_D \sqrt{1 + \left(\frac{\partial z}{\partial x}\right)^2 + \left(\frac{\partial z}{\partial y}\right)^2}\, dA = \iint\limits_D \sqrt{1 + (2x)^2 + (2y)^2}\, dA$$

$$= \iint\limits_D \sqrt{1 + 4(x^2 + y^2)}\, dA$$

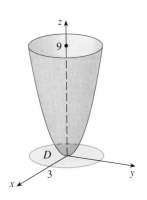

FIGURE 15

Converting to polar coordinates, we obtain

$$A = \int_0^{2\pi} \int_0^3 \sqrt{1 + 4r^2} \; r \, dr \, d\theta = \int_0^{2\pi} d\theta \int_0^3 r\sqrt{1 + 4r^2} \; dr$$

$$= 2\pi \left(\tfrac{1}{8}\right)\tfrac{2}{3}(1 + 4r^2)^{3/2}\Big]_0^3 = \frac{\pi}{6}\left(37\sqrt{37} - 1\right) \qquad \square$$

The question remains whether our definition of surface area (6) is consistent with the surface area formula from single-variable calculus (9.2.4).

We consider the surface S obtained by rotating the curve $y = f(x)$, $a \le x \le b$, about the x-axis, where $f(x) \ge 0$ and f' is continuous. From Equations 3 we know that parametric equations of S are

$$x = x \qquad y = f(x) \cos\theta \qquad z = f(x) \sin\theta \qquad a \le x \le b \qquad 0 \le \theta \le 2\pi$$

To compute the surface area of S we need the tangent vectors

$$\mathbf{r}_x = \mathbf{i} + f'(x) \cos\theta \, \mathbf{j} + f'(x) \sin\theta \, \mathbf{k}$$

$$\mathbf{r}_\theta = -f(x) \sin\theta \, \mathbf{j} + f(x) \cos\theta \, \mathbf{k}$$

Thus

$$\mathbf{r}_x \times \mathbf{r}_\theta = \begin{vmatrix} \mathbf{i} & \mathbf{j} & \mathbf{k} \\ 1 & f'(x) \cos\theta & f'(x) \sin\theta \\ 0 & -f(x) \sin\theta & f(x) \cos\theta \end{vmatrix}$$

$$= f(x)f'(x) \, \mathbf{i} - f(x) \cos\theta \, \mathbf{j} - f(x) \sin\theta \, \mathbf{k}$$

and so
$$|\mathbf{r}_x \times \mathbf{r}_\theta| = \sqrt{[f(x)]^2[f'(x)]^2 + [f(x)]^2\cos^2\theta + [f(x)]^2\sin^2\theta}$$

$$= \sqrt{[f(x)]^2[1 + [f'(x)]^2]} = f(x)\sqrt{1 + [f'(x)]^2}$$

because $f(x) \ge 0$. Therefore the area of S is

$$A = \iint_D |\mathbf{r}_x \times \mathbf{r}_\theta| \, dA = \int_0^{2\pi} \int_a^b f(x)\sqrt{1 + [f'(x)]^2} \; dx \, d\theta$$

$$= 2\pi \int_a^b f(x)\sqrt{1 + [f'(x)]^2} \; dx$$

This is precisely the formula that was used to define the area of a surface of revolution in single-variable calculus (9.2.4).

17.6 EXERCISES

1–2 Determine whether the points P and Q lie on the given surface.

1. $\mathbf{r}(u, v) = \langle 2u + 3v, 1 + 5u - v, 2 + u + v \rangle$
$P(7, 10, 4)$, $Q(5, 22, 5)$

2. $\mathbf{r}(u, v) = \langle u + v, u^2 - v, u + v^2 \rangle$
$P(3, -1, 5)$, $Q(-1, 3, 4)$

3–6 Identify the surface with the given vector equation.

3. $\mathbf{r}(u, v) = (u + v)\,\mathbf{i} + (3 - v)\,\mathbf{j} + (1 + 4u + 5v)\,\mathbf{k}$

4. $\mathbf{r}(u, v) = 2 \sin u \, \mathbf{i} + 3 \cos u \, \mathbf{j} + v \, \mathbf{k}$, $\quad 0 \le v \le 2$

5. $\mathbf{r}(s, t) = \langle s, t, t^2 - s^2 \rangle$

6. $\mathbf{r}(s, t) = \langle s \sin 2t, s^2, s \cos 2t \rangle$

7–12 Use a computer to graph the parametric surface. Get a printout and indicate on it which grid curves have u constant and which have v constant.

7. $\mathbf{r}(u, v) = \langle u^2 + 1, v^3 + 1, u + v \rangle$, $\quad -1 \le u \le 1$, $-1 \le v \le 1$

8. $\mathbf{r}(u, v) = \langle u + v, u^2, v^2 \rangle$, $\quad -1 \le u \le 1$, $-1 \le v \le 1$

9. $\mathbf{r}(u, v) = \langle u \cos v, u \sin v, u^5 \rangle$, $\quad -1 \le u \le 1$, $0 \le v \le 2\pi$

10. $\mathbf{r}(u, v) = \langle \cos u \sin v, \sin u \sin v, \cos v + \ln \tan(v/2) \rangle$,
$0 \leqslant u \leqslant 2\pi,\ 0.1 \leqslant v \leqslant 6.2$

11. $x = \sin v,\quad y = \cos u \sin 4v,\quad z = \sin 2u \sin 4v$,
$0 \leqslant u \leqslant 2\pi,\ -\pi/2 \leqslant v \leqslant \pi/2$

12. $x = u \sin u \cos v,\quad y = u \cos u \cos v,\quad z = u \sin v$

13–18 Match the equations with the graphs labeled I–VI and give reasons for your answers. Determine which families of grid curves have u constant and which have v constant.

13. $\mathbf{r}(u, v) = u \cos v\,\mathbf{i} + u \sin v\,\mathbf{j} + v\,\mathbf{k}$

14. $\mathbf{r}(u, v) = u \cos v\,\mathbf{i} + u \sin v\,\mathbf{j} + \sin u\,\mathbf{k},\quad -\pi \leqslant u \leqslant \pi$

15. $\mathbf{r}(u, v) = \sin v\,\mathbf{i} + \cos u \sin 2v\,\mathbf{j} + \sin u \sin 2v\,\mathbf{k}$

16. $x = (1 - u)(3 + \cos v) \cos 4\pi u$,
$y = (1 - u)(3 + \cos v) \sin 4\pi u$,
$z = 3u + (1 - u) \sin v$

17. $x = \cos^3 u \cos^3 v,\quad y = \sin^3 u \cos^3 v,\quad z = \sin^3 v$

18. $x = (1 - |u|) \cos v,\quad y = (1 - |u|) \sin v,\quad z = u$

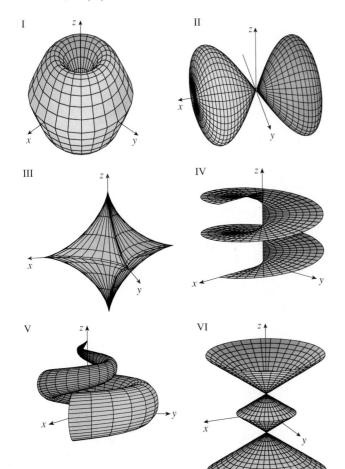

I II III IV V VI

19–26 Find a parametric representation for the surface.

19. The plane that passes through the point $(1, 2, -3)$ and contains the vectors $\mathbf{i} + \mathbf{j} - \mathbf{k}$ and $\mathbf{i} - \mathbf{j} + \mathbf{k}$

20. The lower half of the ellipsoid $2x^2 + 4y^2 + z^2 = 1$

21. The part of the hyperboloid $x^2 + y^2 - z^2 = 1$ that lies to the right of the xz-plane

22. The part of the elliptic paraboloid $x + y^2 + 2z^2 = 4$ that lies in front of the plane $x = 0$

23. The part of the sphere $x^2 + y^2 + z^2 = 4$ that lies above the cone $z = \sqrt{x^2 + y^2}$

24. The part of the sphere $x^2 + y^2 + z^2 = 16$ that lies between the planes $z = -2$ and $z = 2$

25. The part of the cylinder $y^2 + z^2 = 16$ that lies between the planes $x = 0$ and $x = 5$

26. The part of the plane $z = x + 3$ that lies inside the cylinder $x^2 + y^2 = 1$

CAS **27–28** Use a computer algebra system to produce a graph that looks like the given one.

27. **28.**

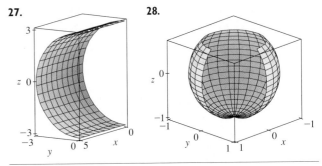

---

29. Find parametric equations for the surface obtained by rotating the curve $y = e^{-x}$, $0 \leqslant x \leqslant 3$, about the x-axis and use them to graph the surface.

30. Find parametric equations for the surface obtained by rotating the curve $x = 4y^2 - y^4$, $-2 \leqslant y \leqslant 2$, about the y-axis and use them to graph the surface.

31. (a) What happens to the spiral tube in Example 2 (see Figure 5) if we replace $\cos u$ by $\sin u$ and $\sin u$ by $\cos u$?
(b) What happens if we replace $\cos u$ by $\cos 2u$ and $\sin u$ by $\sin 2u$?

32. The surface with parametric equations

$$x = 2 \cos \theta + r \cos(\theta/2)$$
$$y = 2 \sin \theta + r \cos(\theta/2)$$
$$z = r \sin(\theta/2)$$

where $-\tfrac{1}{2} \leqslant r \leqslant \tfrac{1}{2}$ and $0 \leqslant \theta \leqslant 2\pi$, is called a **Möbius strip**. Graph this surface with several viewpoints. What is unusual about it?

33–36 Find an equation of the tangent plane to the given para-metric surface at the specified point. If you have software that graphs parametric surfaces, use a computer to graph the surface and the tangent plane.

33. $x = u + v, \quad y = 3u^2, \quad z = u - v; \qquad (2, 3, 0)$

34. $x = u^2, \quad y = v^2, \quad z = uv; \quad u = 1, v = 1$

35. $\mathbf{r}(u, v) = u^2\,\mathbf{i} + 2u \sin v\,\mathbf{j} + u \cos v\,\mathbf{k}; \quad u = 1, v = 0$

36. $\mathbf{r}(u, v) = uv\,\mathbf{i} + u \sin v\,\mathbf{j} + v \cos u\,\mathbf{k}; \quad u = 0, v = \pi$

37–47 Find the area of the surface.

37. The part of the plane $3x + 2y + z = 6$ that lies in the first octant

38. The part of the plane $2x + 5y + z = 10$ that lies inside the cylinder $x^2 + y^2 = 9$

39. The surface $z = \frac{2}{3}(x^{3/2} + y^{3/2}),\ 0 \le x \le 1,\ 0 \le y \le 1$

40. The part of the plane with vector equation
$\mathbf{r}(u, v) = \langle 1 + v, u - 2v, 3 - 5u + v \rangle$ that is given by
$0 \le u \le 1, 0 \le v \le 1$

41. The part of the surface $z = xy$ that lies within the cylinder $x^2 + y^2 = 1$

42. The part of the surface $z = 1 + 3x + 2y^2$ that lies above the triangle with vertices $(0, 0)$, $(0, 1)$, and $(2, 1)$

43. The part of the hyperbolic paraboloid $z = y^2 - x^2$ that lies between the cylinders $x^2 + y^2 = 1$ and $x^2 + y^2 = 4$

44. The part of the paraboloid $x = y^2 + z^2$ that lies inside the cylinder $y^2 + z^2 = 9$

45. The part of the surface $y = 4x + z^2$ that lies between the planes $x = 0$, $x = 1$, $z = 0$, and $z = 1$

46. The helicoid (or spiral ramp) with vector equation
$\mathbf{r}(u, v) = u \cos v\,\mathbf{i} + u \sin v\,\mathbf{j} + v\,\mathbf{k}, 0 \le u \le 1, 0 \le v \le \pi$

47. The surface with parametric equations $x = u^2,\ y = uv,$
$z = \frac{1}{2}v^2, 0 \le u \le 1, 0 \le v \le 2$

48–49 Find the area of the surface correct to four decimal places by expressing the area in terms of a single integral and using your calculator to estimate the integral.

48. The part of the surface $z = \cos(x^2 + y^2)$ that lies inside the cylinder $x^2 + y^2 = 1$

49. The part of the surface $z = e^{-x^2 - y^2}$ that lies above the disk $x^2 + y^2 \le 4$

[CAS] 50. Find, to four decimal places, the area of the part of the surface $z = (1 + x^2)/(1 + y^2)$ that lies above the square $|x| + |y| \le 1$. Illustrate by graphing this part of the surface.

51. (a) Use the Midpoint Rule for double integrals (see Section 16.1) with six squares to estimate the area of the surface $z = 1/(1 + x^2 + y^2), 0 \le x \le 6, 0 \le y \le 4$.
   [CAS] (b) Use a computer algebra system to approximate the surface area in part (a) to four decimal places. Compare with the answer to part (a).

[CAS] 52. Find the area of the surface with vector equation
$\mathbf{r}(u, v) = \langle \cos^3 u \cos^3 v, \sin^3 u \cos^3 v, \sin^3 v \rangle, 0 \le u \le \pi,$
$0 \le v \le 2\pi$. State your answer correct to four decimal places.

[CAS] 53. Find the exact area of the surface $z = 1 + 2x + 3y + 4y^2,$
$1 \le x \le 4, 0 \le y \le 1$.

54. (a) Set up, but do not evaluate, a double integral for the area of the surface with parametric equations $x = au \cos v$, $y = bu \sin v, z = u^2, 0 \le u \le 2, 0 \le v \le 2\pi$.
   (b) Eliminate the parameters to show that the surface is an elliptic paraboloid and set up another double integral for the surface area.
   (c) Use the parametric equations in part (a) with $a = 2$ and $b = 3$ to graph the surface.
   [CAS] (d) For the case $a = 2$, $b = 3$, use a computer algebra system to find the surface area correct to four decimal places.

55. (a) Show that the parametric equations $x = a \sin u \cos v$, $y = b \sin u \sin v, z = c \cos u, 0 \le u \le \pi, 0 \le v \le 2\pi$, represent an ellipsoid.
   (b) Use the parametric equations in part (a) to graph the ellipsoid for the case $a = 1, b = 2, c = 3$.
   (c) Set up, but do not evaluate, a double integral for the surface area of the ellipsoid in part (b).

56. (a) Show that the parametric equations $x = a \cosh u \cos v$, $y = b \cosh u \sin v, z = c \sinh u$, represent a hyperboloid of one sheet.
   (b) Use the parametric equations in part (a) to graph the hyperboloid for the case $a = 1, b = 2, c = 3$.
   (c) Set up, but do not evaluate, a double integral for the surface area of the part of the hyperboloid in part (b) that lies between the planes $z = -3$ and $z = 3$.

57. Find the area of the part of the sphere $x^2 + y^2 + z^2 = 4z$ that lies inside the paraboloid $z = x^2 + y^2$.

58. The figure shows the surface created when the cylinder $y^2 + z^2 = 1$ intersects the cylinder $x^2 + z^2 = 1$. Find the area of this surface.

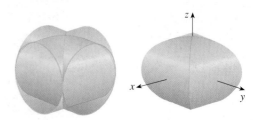

59. Find the area of the part of the sphere $x^2 + y^2 + z^2 = a^2$ that lies inside the cylinder $x^2 + y^2 = ax$.

60. (a) Find a parametric representation for the torus obtained by rotating about the z-axis the circle in the xz-plane with center $(b, 0, 0)$ and radius $a < b$. [*Hint:* Take as parameters the angles θ and α shown in the figure.]

(b) Use the parametric equations found in part (a) to graph the torus for several values of a and b.

(c) Use the parametric representation from part (a) to find the surface area of the torus.

17.7 SURFACE INTEGRALS

The relationship between surface integrals and surface area is much the same as the relationship between line integrals and arc length. Suppose f is a function of three variables whose domain includes a surface S. We will define the surface integral of f over S in such a way that, in the case where $f(x, y, z) = 1$, the value of the surface integral is equal to the surface area of S. We start with parametric surfaces and then deal with the special case where S is the graph of a function of two variables.

PARAMETRIC SURFACES

Suppose that a surface S has a vector equation

$$\mathbf{r}(u, v) = x(u, v)\, \mathbf{i} + y(u, v)\, \mathbf{j} + z(u, v)\, \mathbf{k} \qquad (u, v) \in D$$

We first assume that the parameter domain D is a rectangle and we divide it into subrectangles R_{ij} with dimensions Δu and Δv. Then the surface S is divided into corresponding patches S_{ij} as in Figure 1. We evaluate f at a point P_{ij}^* in each patch, multiply by the area ΔS_{ij} of the patch, and form the Riemann sum

$$\sum_{i=1}^{m} \sum_{j=1}^{n} f(P_{ij}^*)\, \Delta S_{ij}$$

Then we take the limit as the number of patches increases and define the **surface integral of f over the surface S** as

$$\boxed{1} \qquad \iint_S f(x, y, z)\, dS = \lim_{m, n \to \infty} \sum_{i=1}^{m} \sum_{j=1}^{n} f(P_{ij}^*)\, \Delta S_{ij}$$

Notice the analogy with the definition of a line integral (17.2.2) and also the analogy with the definition of a double integral (16.1.5).

To evaluate the surface integral in Equation 1 we approximate the patch area ΔS_{ij} by the area of an approximating parallelogram in the tangent plane. In our discussion of surface area in Section 17.6 we made the approximation

$$\Delta S_{ij} \approx |\mathbf{r}_u \times \mathbf{r}_v|\, \Delta u\, \Delta v$$

FIGURE 1

where $\qquad \mathbf{r}_u = \dfrac{\partial x}{\partial u}\,\mathbf{i} + \dfrac{\partial y}{\partial u}\,\mathbf{j} + \dfrac{\partial z}{\partial u}\,\mathbf{k} \qquad \mathbf{r}_v = \dfrac{\partial x}{\partial v}\,\mathbf{i} + \dfrac{\partial y}{\partial v}\,\mathbf{j} + \dfrac{\partial z}{\partial v}\,\mathbf{k}$

are the tangent vectors at a corner of S_{ij}. If the components are continuous and $\mathbf{r}_u$ and $\mathbf{r}_v$ are nonzero and nonparallel in the interior of D, it can be shown from Definition 1, even when D is not a rectangle, that

■ We assume that the surface is covered only once as (u, v) ranges throughout D. The value of the surface integral does not depend on the parametrization that is used.

$$\boxed{\;\;\iint_S f(x, y, z)\, dS = \iint_D f(\mathbf{r}(u, v))\,|\mathbf{r}_u \times \mathbf{r}_v|\, dA\;\;}$$

$\boxed{2}$

This should be compared with the formula for a line integral:

$$\int_C f(x, y, z)\, ds = \int_a^b f(\mathbf{r}(t))\,|\mathbf{r}'(t)|\, dt$$

Observe also that

$$\iint_S 1\, dS = \iint_D |\mathbf{r}_u \times \mathbf{r}_v|\, dA = A(S)$$

Formula 2 allows us to compute a surface integral by converting it into a double integral over the parameter domain D. When using this formula, remember that $f(\mathbf{r}(u, v))$ is evaluated by writing $x = x(u, v)$, $y = y(u, v)$, and $z = z(u, v)$ in the formula for $f(x, y, z)$.

EXAMPLE 1 Compute the surface integral $\iint_S x^2\, dS$, where S is the unit sphere $x^2 + y^2 + z^2 = 1$.

SOLUTION As in Example 4 in Section 17.6, we use the parametric representation

$$x = \sin\phi\,\cos\theta \qquad y = \sin\phi\,\sin\theta \qquad z = \cos\phi \qquad 0 \leqslant \phi \leqslant \pi \qquad 0 \leqslant \theta \leqslant 2\pi$$

that is, $\qquad \mathbf{r}(\phi, \theta) = \sin\phi\,\cos\theta\,\mathbf{i} + \sin\phi\,\sin\theta\,\mathbf{j} + \cos\phi\,\mathbf{k}$

As in Example 10 in Section 17.6, we can compute that

$$|\mathbf{r}_\phi \times \mathbf{r}_\theta| = \sin\phi$$

Therefore, by Formula 2,

$$\iint_S x^2\, dS = \iint_D (\sin\phi\,\cos\theta)^2\,|\mathbf{r}_\phi \times \mathbf{r}_\theta|\, dA$$

■ Here we use the identities

$\cos^2\theta = \tfrac{1}{2}(1 + \cos 2\theta)$

$\sin^2\phi = 1 - \cos^2\phi$

Instead, we could use Formulas 64 and 67 in the Table of Integrals.

$$= \int_0^{2\pi} \int_0^\pi \sin^2\phi\,\cos^2\theta\,\sin\phi\, d\phi\, d\theta = \int_0^{2\pi} \cos^2\theta\, d\theta \int_0^\pi \sin^3\phi\, d\phi$$

$$= \int_0^{2\pi} \tfrac{1}{2}(1 + \cos 2\theta)\, d\theta \int_0^\pi (\sin\phi - \sin\phi\,\cos^2\phi)\, d\phi$$

$$= \tfrac{1}{2}\big[\theta + \tfrac{1}{2}\sin 2\theta\big]_0^{2\pi}\,\big[-\cos\phi + \tfrac{1}{3}\cos^3\phi\big]_0^\pi = \frac{4\pi}{3} \qquad \square$$

Surface integrals have applications similar to those for the integrals we have previously considered. For example, if a thin sheet (say, of aluminum foil) has the shape of a surface

S and the density (mass per unit area) at the point (x, y, z) is $\rho(x, y, z)$, then the total **mass** of the sheet is

$$m = \iint_S \rho(x, y, z) \, dS$$

and the **center of mass** is $(\bar{x}, \bar{y}, \bar{z})$, where

$$\bar{x} = \frac{1}{m} \iint_S x\rho(x, y, z) \, dS \qquad \bar{y} = \frac{1}{m} \iint_S y\rho(x, y, z) \, dS \qquad \bar{z} = \frac{1}{m} \iint_S z\rho(x, y, z) \, dS$$

Moments of inertia can also be defined as before (see Exercise 39).

GRAPHS

Any surface S with equation $z = g(x, y)$ can be regarded as a parametric surface with parametric equations

$$x = x \qquad y = y \qquad z = g(x, y)$$

and so we have

$$\mathbf{r}_x = \mathbf{i} + \left(\frac{\partial g}{\partial x} \right) \mathbf{k} \qquad \mathbf{r}_y = \mathbf{j} + \left(\frac{\partial g}{\partial y} \right) \mathbf{k}$$

Thus

$$\boxed{3} \qquad \mathbf{r}_x \times \mathbf{r}_y = -\frac{\partial g}{\partial x} \mathbf{i} - \frac{\partial g}{\partial y} \mathbf{j} + \mathbf{k}$$

and

$$|\mathbf{r}_x \times \mathbf{r}_y| = \sqrt{\left(\frac{\partial z}{\partial x} \right)^2 + \left(\frac{\partial z}{\partial y} \right)^2 + 1}$$

Therefore, in this case, Formula 2 becomes

$$\boxed{4} \qquad \iint_S f(x, y, z) \, dS = \iint_D f(x, y, g(x, y)) \sqrt{\left(\frac{\partial z}{\partial x} \right)^2 + \left(\frac{\partial z}{\partial y} \right)^2 + 1} \, dA$$

Similar formulas apply when it is more convenient to project S onto the yz-plane or xz-plane. For instance, if S is a surface with equation $y = h(x, z)$ and D is its projection on the xz-plane, then

$$\iint_S f(x, y, z) \, dS = \iint_D f(x, h(x, z), z) \sqrt{\left(\frac{\partial y}{\partial x} \right)^2 + \left(\frac{\partial y}{\partial z} \right)^2 + 1} \, dA$$

EXAMPLE 2 Evaluate $\iint_S y \, dS$, where S is the surface $z = x + y^2$, $0 \leqslant x \leqslant 1$, $0 \leqslant y \leqslant 2$. (See Figure 2.)

SOLUTION Since

$$\frac{\partial z}{\partial x} = 1 \qquad \text{and} \qquad \frac{\partial z}{\partial y} = 2y$$

FIGURE 2

Formula 4 gives

$$\iint_S y \, dS = \iint_D y \sqrt{1 + \left(\frac{\partial z}{\partial x}\right)^2 + \left(\frac{\partial z}{\partial y}\right)^2} \, dA$$

$$= \int_0^1 \int_0^2 y \sqrt{1 + 1 + 4y^2} \, dy \, dx$$

$$= \int_0^1 dx \, \sqrt{2} \int_0^2 y \sqrt{1 + 2y^2} \, dy$$

$$= \sqrt{2} \left(\tfrac{1}{4}\right)\tfrac{2}{3}(1 + 2y^2)^{3/2}\big]_0^2 = \frac{13\sqrt{2}}{3} \qquad \square$$

If S is a piecewise-smooth surface, that is, a finite union of smooth surfaces $S_1, S_2, \ldots,$ S_n that intersect only along their boundaries, then the surface integral of f over S is defined by

$$\iint_S f(x, y, z) \, dS = \iint_{S_1} f(x, y, z) \, dS + \cdots + \iint_{S_n} f(x, y, z) \, dS$$

◢ EXAMPLE 3 Evaluate $\iint_S z \, dS$, where S is the surface whose sides S_1 are given by the cylinder $x^2 + y^2 = 1$, whose bottom S_2 is the disk $x^2 + y^2 \leq 1$ in the plane $z = 0$, and whose top S_3 is the part of the plane $z = 1 + x$ that lies above S_2.

SOLUTION The surface S is shown in Figure 3. (We have changed the usual position of the axes to get a better look at S.) For S_1 we use θ and z as parameters (see Example 5 in Section 17.6) and write its parametric equations as

$$x = \cos \theta \qquad y = \sin \theta \qquad z = z$$

where

$$0 \leq \theta \leq 2\pi \qquad \text{and} \qquad 0 \leq z \leq 1 + x = 1 + \cos \theta$$

Therefore

$$\mathbf{r}_\theta \times \mathbf{r}_z = \begin{vmatrix} \mathbf{i} & \mathbf{j} & \mathbf{k} \\ -\sin \theta & \cos \theta & 0 \\ 0 & 0 & 1 \end{vmatrix} = \cos \theta \, \mathbf{i} + \sin \theta \, \mathbf{j}$$

and

$$|\mathbf{r}_\theta \times \mathbf{r}_z| = \sqrt{\cos^2\theta + \sin^2\theta} = 1$$

Thus the surface integral over S_1 is

$$\iint_{S_1} z \, dS = \iint_D z \, |\mathbf{r}_\theta \times \mathbf{r}_z| \, dA$$

$$= \int_0^{2\pi} \int_0^{1+\cos\theta} z \, dz \, d\theta = \int_0^{2\pi} \tfrac{1}{2}(1 + \cos\theta)^2 \, d\theta$$

$$= \tfrac{1}{2} \int_0^{2\pi} \left[1 + 2\cos\theta + \tfrac{1}{2}(1 + \cos 2\theta)\right] d\theta$$

$$= \tfrac{1}{2}\left[\tfrac{3}{2}\theta + 2\sin\theta + \tfrac{1}{4}\sin 2\theta\right]_0^{2\pi} = \frac{3\pi}{2}$$

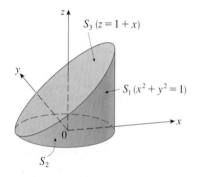

$S_3 \, (z = 1 + x)$

$S_1 \, (x^2 + y^2 = 1)$

S_2

FIGURE 3

Since S_2 lies in the plane $z = 0$, we have

$$\iint\limits_{S_2} z\, dS = \iint\limits_{S_2} 0\, dS = 0$$

The top surface S_3 lies above the unit disk D and is part of the plane $z = 1 + x$. So, taking $g(x, y) = 1 + x$ in Formula 4 and converting to polar coordinates, we have

$$\iint\limits_{S_3} z\, dS = \iint\limits_{D} (1 + x) \sqrt{1 + \left(\frac{\partial z}{\partial x}\right)^2 + \left(\frac{\partial z}{\partial y}\right)^2}\, dA$$

$$= \int_0^{2\pi} \int_0^1 (1 + r\cos\theta)\sqrt{1 + 1 + 0}\; r\, dr\, d\theta$$

$$= \sqrt{2} \int_0^{2\pi} \int_0^1 (r + r^2 \cos\theta)\, dr\, d\theta$$

$$= \sqrt{2} \int_0^{2\pi} \left(\tfrac{1}{2} + \tfrac{1}{3}\cos\theta\right) d\theta$$

$$= \sqrt{2} \left[\frac{\theta}{2} + \frac{\sin\theta}{3}\right]_0^{2\pi} = \sqrt{2}\,\pi$$

Therefore

$$\iint\limits_{S} z\, dS = \iint\limits_{S_1} z\, dS + \iint\limits_{S_2} z\, dS + \iint\limits_{S_3} z\, dS$$

$$= \frac{3\pi}{2} + 0 + \sqrt{2}\,\pi = \left(\tfrac{3}{2} + \sqrt{2}\right)\pi \qquad \square$$

ORIENTED SURFACES

To define surface integrals of vector fields, we need to rule out nonorientable surfaces such as the Möbius strip shown in Figure 4. [It is named after the German geometer August Möbius (1790–1868).] You can construct one for yourself by taking a long rectangular strip of paper, giving it a half-twist, and taping the short edges together as in Figure 5. If an ant were to crawl along the Möbius strip starting at a point P, it would end up on the "other side" of the strip (that is, with its upper side pointing in the opposite direction). Then, if the ant continued to crawl in the same direction, it would end up back at the same point P without ever having crossed an edge. (If you have constructed a Möbius strip, try drawing a pencil line down the middle.) Therefore a Möbius strip really has only one side. You can graph the Möbius strip using the parametric equations in Exercise 32 in Section 17.6.

FIGURE 4
A Möbius strip

FIGURE 5
Constructing a Möbius strip

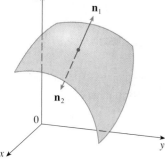

FIGURE 6

From now on we consider only orientable (two-sided) surfaces. We start with a surface S that has a tangent plane at every point (x, y, z) on S (except at any boundary point). There are two unit normal vectors $\mathbf{n}_1$ and $\mathbf{n}_2 = -\mathbf{n}_1$ at (x, y, z). (See Figure 6.)

If it is possible to choose a unit normal vector $\mathbf{n}$ at every such point (x, y, z) so that $\mathbf{n}$ varies continuously over S, then S is called an **oriented surface** and the given choice of $\mathbf{n}$ provides S with an **orientation**. There are two possible orientations for any orientable surface (see Figure 7).

FIGURE 7
The two orientations
of an orientable surface

For a surface $z = g(x, y)$ given as the graph of g, we use Equation 3 to associate with the surface a natural orientation given by the unit normal vector

$$\boxed{5} \qquad \mathbf{n} = \frac{-\dfrac{\partial g}{\partial x}\,\mathbf{i} - \dfrac{\partial g}{\partial y}\,\mathbf{j} + \mathbf{k}}{\sqrt{1 + \left(\dfrac{\partial g}{\partial x}\right)^2 + \left(\dfrac{\partial g}{\partial y}\right)^2}}$$

Since the $\mathbf{k}$-component is positive, this gives the *upward* orientation of the surface.

If S is a smooth orientable surface given in parametric form by a vector function $\mathbf{r}(u, v)$, then it is automatically supplied with the orientation of the unit normal vector

$$\boxed{6} \qquad \mathbf{n} = \frac{\mathbf{r}_u \times \mathbf{r}_v}{|\mathbf{r}_u \times \mathbf{r}_v|}$$

and the opposite orientation is given by $-\mathbf{n}$. For instance, in Example 4 in Section 17.6 we found the parametric representation

$$\mathbf{r}(\phi, \theta) = a \sin \phi \cos \theta\,\mathbf{i} + a \sin \phi \sin \theta\,\mathbf{j} + a \cos \phi\,\mathbf{k}$$

for the sphere $x^2 + y^2 + z^2 = a^2$. Then in Example 10 in Section 17.6 we found that

$$\mathbf{r}_\phi \times \mathbf{r}_\theta = a^2 \sin^2\phi \cos \theta\,\mathbf{i} + a^2 \sin^2\phi \sin \theta\,\mathbf{j} + a^2 \sin \phi \cos \phi\,\mathbf{k}$$

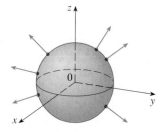

FIGURE 8
Positive orientation

and

$$|\mathbf{r}_\phi \times \mathbf{r}_\theta| = a^2 \sin \phi$$

So the orientation induced by $\mathbf{r}(\phi, \theta)$ is defined by the unit normal vector

$$\mathbf{n} = \frac{\mathbf{r}_\phi \times \mathbf{r}_\theta}{|\mathbf{r}_\phi \times \mathbf{r}_\theta|} = \sin \phi \cos \theta\,\mathbf{i} + \sin \phi \sin \theta\,\mathbf{j} + \cos \phi\,\mathbf{k} = \frac{1}{a}\,\mathbf{r}(\phi, \theta)$$

Observe that $\mathbf{n}$ points in the same direction as the position vector, that is, outward from the sphere (see Figure 8). The opposite (inward) orientation would have been obtained (see Figure 9) if we had reversed the order of the parameters because $\mathbf{r}_\theta \times \mathbf{r}_\phi = -\mathbf{r}_\phi \times \mathbf{r}_\theta$.

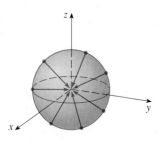

FIGURE 9
Negative orientation

For a **closed surface**, that is, a surface that is the boundary of a solid region E, the convention is that the **positive orientation** is the one for which the normal vectors point *outward* from E, and inward-pointing normals give the negative orientation (see Figures 8 and 9).

SURFACE INTEGRALS OF VECTOR FIELDS

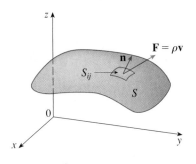

FIGURE 10

Suppose that S is an oriented surface with unit normal vector $\mathbf{n}$, and imagine a fluid with density $\rho(x, y, z)$ and velocity field $\mathbf{v}(x, y, z)$ flowing through S. (Think of S as an imaginary surface that doesn't impede the fluid flow, like a fishing net across a stream.) Then the rate of flow (mass per unit time) per unit area is $\rho\mathbf{v}$. If we divide S into small patches S_{ij}, as in Figure 10 (compare with Figure 1), then S_{ij} is nearly planar and so we can approximate the mass of fluid crossing S_{ij} in the direction of the normal $\mathbf{n}$ per unit time by the quantity

$$(\rho\mathbf{v} \cdot \mathbf{n})A(S_{ij})$$

where ρ, $\mathbf{v}$, and $\mathbf{n}$ are evaluated at some point on S_{ij}. (Recall that the component of the vector $\rho\mathbf{v}$ in the direction of the unit vector $\mathbf{n}$ is $\rho\mathbf{v} \cdot \mathbf{n}$.) By summing these quantities and taking the limit we get, according to Definition 1, the surface integral of the function $\rho\mathbf{v} \cdot \mathbf{n}$ over S:

$$\boxed{7} \qquad \iint_S \rho\mathbf{v} \cdot \mathbf{n} \, dS = \iint_S \rho(x, y, z)\mathbf{v}(x, y, z) \cdot \mathbf{n}(x, y, z) \, dS$$

and this is interpreted physically as the rate of flow through S.

If we write $\mathbf{F} = \rho\mathbf{v}$, then $\mathbf{F}$ is also a vector field on $\mathbb{R}^3$ and the integral in Equation 7 becomes

$$\iint_S \mathbf{F} \cdot \mathbf{n} \, dS$$

A surface integral of this form occurs frequently in physics, even when $\mathbf{F}$ is not $\rho\mathbf{v}$, and is called the *surface integral* (or *flux integral*) of $\mathbf{F}$ over S.

---

8 DEFINITION If $\mathbf{F}$ is a continuous vector field defined on an oriented surface S with unit normal vector $\mathbf{n}$, then the **surface integral of F over S** is

$$\iint_S \mathbf{F} \cdot d\mathbf{S} = \iint_S \mathbf{F} \cdot \mathbf{n} \, dS$$

This integral is also called the **flux** of $\mathbf{F}$ across S.

In words, Definition 8 says that the surface integral of a vector field over S is equal to the surface integral of its normal component over S (as previously defined).

If S is given by a vector function $\mathbf{r}(u, v)$, then $\mathbf{n}$ is given by Equation 6, and from Definition 8 and Equation 2 we have

$$\iint_S \mathbf{F} \cdot d\mathbf{S} = \iint_S \mathbf{F} \cdot \frac{\mathbf{r}_u \times \mathbf{r}_v}{|\mathbf{r}_u \times \mathbf{r}_v|} \, dS$$

$$= \iint_D \left[\mathbf{F}(\mathbf{r}(u, v)) \cdot \frac{\mathbf{r}_u \times \mathbf{r}_v}{|\mathbf{r}_u \times \mathbf{r}_v|} \right] |\mathbf{r}_u \times \mathbf{r}_v| \, dA$$

where D is the parameter domain. Thus we have

■ Compare Equation 9 to the similar expression for evaluating line integrals of vector fields in Definition 17.2.13:

$$\int_C \mathbf{F} \cdot d\mathbf{r} = \int_a^b \mathbf{F}(\mathbf{r}(t)) \cdot \mathbf{r}'(t) \, dt$$

$$\boxed{9} \qquad \iint_S \mathbf{F} \cdot d\mathbf{S} = \iint_D \mathbf{F} \cdot (\mathbf{r}_u \times \mathbf{r}_v) \, dA$$

EXAMPLE 4 Find the flux of the vector field $\mathbf{F}(x, y, z) = z\,\mathbf{i} + y\,\mathbf{j} + x\,\mathbf{k}$ across the unit sphere $x^2 + y^2 + z^2 = 1$.

SOLUTION Using the parametric representation

$$\mathbf{r}(\phi, \theta) = \sin\phi\cos\theta\,\mathbf{i} + \sin\phi\sin\theta\,\mathbf{j} + \cos\phi\,\mathbf{k} \qquad 0 \le \phi \le \pi \qquad 0 \le \theta \le 2\pi$$

we have

$$\mathbf{F}(\mathbf{r}(\phi, \theta)) = \cos\phi\,\mathbf{i} + \sin\phi\sin\theta\,\mathbf{j} + \sin\phi\cos\theta\,\mathbf{k}$$

and, from Example 10 in Section 17.6,

$$\mathbf{r}_\phi \times \mathbf{r}_\theta = \sin^2\phi\cos\theta\,\mathbf{i} + \sin^2\phi\sin\theta\,\mathbf{j} + \sin\phi\cos\phi\,\mathbf{k}$$

Therefore

$$\mathbf{F}(\mathbf{r}(\phi, \theta)) \cdot (\mathbf{r}_\phi \times \mathbf{r}_\theta) = \cos\phi\sin^2\phi\cos\theta + \sin^3\phi\sin^2\theta + \sin^2\phi\cos\phi\cos\theta$$

and, by Formula 9, the flux is

$$\iint_S \mathbf{F} \cdot d\mathbf{S} = \iint_D \mathbf{F} \cdot (\mathbf{r}_\phi \times \mathbf{r}_\theta)\, dA$$

$$= \int_0^{2\pi} \int_0^{\pi} (2\sin^2\phi\cos\phi\cos\theta + \sin^3\phi\sin^2\theta)\, d\phi\, d\theta$$

$$= 2\int_0^{\pi} \sin^2\phi\cos\phi\, d\phi \int_0^{2\pi} \cos\theta\, d\theta + \int_0^{\pi} \sin^3\phi\, d\phi \int_0^{2\pi} \sin^2\theta\, d\theta$$

$$= 0 + \int_0^{\pi} \sin^3\phi\, d\phi \int_0^{2\pi} \sin^2\theta\, d\theta \qquad \left(\text{since } \int_0^{2\pi} \cos\theta\, d\theta = 0\right)$$

$$= \frac{4\pi}{3}$$

by the same calculation as in Example 1. ◻

If, for instance, the vector field in Example 4 is a velocity field describing the flow of a fluid with density 1, then the answer, $4\pi/3$, represents the rate of flow through the unit sphere in units of mass per unit time.

In the case of a surface S given by a graph $z = g(x, y)$, we can think of x and y as parameters and use Equation 3 to write

$$\mathbf{F} \cdot (\mathbf{r}_x \times \mathbf{r}_y) = (P\,\mathbf{i} + Q\,\mathbf{j} + R\,\mathbf{k}) \cdot \left(-\frac{\partial g}{\partial x}\,\mathbf{i} - \frac{\partial g}{\partial y}\,\mathbf{j} + \mathbf{k}\right)$$

Thus Formula 9 becomes

[10]
$$\iint_S \mathbf{F} \cdot d\mathbf{S} = \iint_D \left(-P\frac{\partial g}{\partial x} - Q\frac{\partial g}{\partial y} + R\right) dA$$

This formula assumes the upward orientation of S; for a downward orientation we multiply by -1. Similar formulas can be worked out if S is given by $y = h(x, z)$ or $x = k(y, z)$. (See Exercises 35 and 36.)

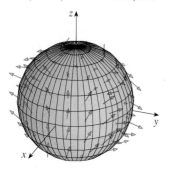

■ Figure 11 shows the vector field $\mathbf{F}$ in Example 4 at points on the unit sphere.

FIGURE 11

◩ EXAMPLE 5 Evaluate $\iint_S \mathbf{F} \cdot d\mathbf{S}$, where $\mathbf{F}(x, y, z) = y\,\mathbf{i} + x\,\mathbf{j} + z\,\mathbf{k}$ and S is the boundary of the solid region E enclosed by the paraboloid $z = 1 - x^2 - y^2$ and the plane $z = 0$.

SOLUTION S consists of a parabolic top surface S_1 and a circular bottom surface S_2. (See Figure 12.) Since S is a closed surface, we use the convention of positive (outward) orientation. This means that S_1 is oriented upward and we can use Equation 10 with D being the projection of S_1 on the xy-plane, namely, the disk $x^2 + y^2 \leqslant 1$. Since

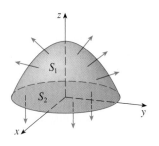

FIGURE 12

$$P(x, y, z) = y \qquad Q(x, y, z) = x \qquad R(x, y, z) = z = 1 - x^2 - y^2$$

on S_1 and

$$\frac{\partial g}{\partial x} = -2x \qquad \frac{\partial g}{\partial y} = -2y$$

we have

$$\iint_{S_1} \mathbf{F} \cdot d\mathbf{S} = \iint_D \left(-P\frac{\partial g}{\partial x} - Q\frac{\partial g}{\partial y} + R \right) dA$$

$$= \iint_D [-y(-2x) - x(-2y) + 1 - x^2 - y^2]\,dA$$

$$= \iint_D (1 + 4xy - x^2 - y^2)\,dA$$

$$= \int_0^{2\pi} \int_0^1 (1 + 4r^2 \cos\theta \sin\theta - r^2)\,r\,dr\,d\theta$$

$$= \int_0^{2\pi} \int_0^1 (r - r^3 + 4r^3 \cos\theta \sin\theta)\,dr\,d\theta$$

$$= \int_0^{2\pi} \left(\tfrac{1}{4} + \cos\theta \sin\theta \right) d\theta = \tfrac{1}{4}(2\pi) + 0 = \frac{\pi}{2}$$

The disk S_2 is oriented downward, so its unit normal vector is $\mathbf{n} = -\mathbf{k}$ and we have

$$\iint_{S_2} \mathbf{F} \cdot d\mathbf{S} = \iint_{S_2} \mathbf{F} \cdot (-\mathbf{k})\,dS = \iint_D (-z)\,dA = \iint_D 0\,dA = 0$$

since $z = 0$ on S_2. Finally, we compute, by definition, $\iint_S \mathbf{F} \cdot d\mathbf{S}$ as the sum of the surface integrals of $\mathbf{F}$ over the pieces S_1 and S_2:

$$\iint_S \mathbf{F} \cdot d\mathbf{S} = \iint_{S_1} \mathbf{F} \cdot d\mathbf{S} + \iint_{S_2} \mathbf{F} \cdot d\mathbf{S} = \frac{\pi}{2} + 0 = \frac{\pi}{2} \qquad \square$$

Although we motivated the surface integral of a vector field using the example of fluid flow, this concept also arises in other physical situations. For instance, if $\mathbf{E}$ is an electric field (see Example 5 in Section 17.1), then the surface integral

$$\iint_S \mathbf{E} \cdot d\mathbf{S}$$

is called the **electric flux** of $\mathbf{E}$ through the surface S. One of the important laws of electrostatics is **Gauss's Law**, which says that the net charge enclosed by a closed surface S is

$$\boxed{11} \qquad Q = \varepsilon_0 \iint\limits_{S} \mathbf{E} \cdot d\mathbf{S}$$

where ε_0 is a constant (called the permittivity of free space) that depends on the units used. (In the SI system, $\varepsilon_0 \approx 8.8542 \times 10^{-12} \text{ C}^2/\text{N}\cdot\text{m}^2$.) Therefore, if the vector field $\mathbf{F}$ in Example 4 represents an electric field, we can conclude that the charge enclosed by S is $Q = 4\pi\varepsilon_0/3$.

Another application of surface integrals occurs in the study of heat flow. Suppose the temperature at a point (x, y, z) in a body is $u(x, y, z)$. Then the **heat flow** is defined as the vector field

$$\mathbf{F} = -K \nabla u$$

where K is an experimentally determined constant called the **conductivity** of the substance. The rate of heat flow across the surface S in the body is then given by the surface integral

$$\iint\limits_{S} \mathbf{F} \cdot d\mathbf{S} = -K \iint\limits_{S} \nabla u \cdot d\mathbf{S}$$

▼ EXAMPLE 6 The temperature u in a metal ball is proportional to the square of the distance from the center of the ball. Find the rate of heat flow across a sphere S of radius a with center at the center of the ball.

SOLUTION Taking the center of the ball to be at the origin, we have

$$u(x, y, z) = C(x^2 + y^2 + z^2)$$

where C is the proportionality constant. Then the heat flow is

$$\mathbf{F}(x, y, z) = -K \nabla u = -KC(2x\,\mathbf{i} + 2y\,\mathbf{j} + 2z\,\mathbf{k})$$

where K is the conductivity of the metal. Instead of using the usual parametrization of the sphere as in Example 4, we observe that the outward unit normal to the sphere $x^2 + y^2 + z^2 = a^2$ at the point (x, y, z) is

$$\mathbf{n} = \frac{1}{a}(x\,\mathbf{i} + y\,\mathbf{j} + z\,\mathbf{k})$$

and so

$$\mathbf{F} \cdot \mathbf{n} = -\frac{2KC}{a}(x^2 + y^2 + z^2)$$

But on S we have $x^2 + y^2 + z^2 = a^2$, so $\mathbf{F} \cdot \mathbf{n} = -2aKC$. Therefore the rate of heat flow across S is

$$\iint\limits_{S} \mathbf{F} \cdot d\mathbf{S} = \iint\limits_{S} \mathbf{F} \cdot \mathbf{n}\, dS = -2aKC \iint\limits_{S} dS$$

$$= -2aKCA(S) = -2aKC(4\pi a^2) = -8KC\pi a^3 \qquad \square$$

17.7 EXERCISES

1. Let S be the boundary surface of the box enclosed by the planes $x = 0$, $x = 2$, $y = 0$, $y = 4$, $z = 0$, and $z = 6$. Approximate $\iint_S e^{-0.1(x+y+z)} \, dS$ by using a Riemann sum as in Definition 1, taking the patches S_{ij} to be the rectangles that are the faces of the box S and the points P_{ij}^* to be the centers of the rectangles.

2. A surface S consists of the cylinder $x^2 + y^2 = 1$, $-1 \leqslant z \leqslant 1$, together with its top and bottom disks. Suppose you know that f is a continuous function with

$$f(\pm 1, 0, 0) = 2 \qquad f(0, \pm 1, 0) = 3 \qquad f(0, 0, \pm 1) = 4$$

Estimate the value of $\iint_S f(x, y, z) \, dS$ by using a Riemann sum, taking the patches S_{ij} to be four quarter-cylinders and the top and bottom disks.

3. Let H be the hemisphere $x^2 + y^2 + z^2 = 50$, $z \geqslant 0$, and suppose f is a continuous function with $f(3, 4, 5) = 7$, $f(3, -4, 5) = 8$, $f(-3, 4, 5) = 9$, and $f(-3, -4, 5) = 12$. By dividing H into four patches, estimate the value of $\iint_H f(x, y, z) \, dS$.

4. Suppose that $f(x, y, z) = g(\sqrt{x^2 + y^2 + z^2})$, where g is a function of one variable such that $g(2) = -5$. Evaluate $\iint_S f(x, y, z) \, dS$, where S is the sphere $x^2 + y^2 + z^2 = 4$.

5–18 Evaluate the surface integral.

5. $\iint_S x^2 yz \, dS$,
S is the part of the plane $z = 1 + 2x + 3y$ that lies above the rectangle $[0, 3] \times [0, 2]$

6. $\iint_S xy \, dS$,
S is the triangular region with vertices $(1, 0, 0)$, $(0, 2, 0)$, and $(0, 0, 2)$

7. $\iint_S yz \, dS$,
S is the part of the plane $x + y + z = 1$ that lies in the first octant

8. $\iint_S y \, dS$,
S is the surface $z = \frac{2}{3}(x^{3/2} + y^{3/2})$, $0 \leqslant x \leqslant 1$, $0 \leqslant y \leqslant 1$

9. $\iint_S yz \, dS$,
S is the surface with parametric equations $x = u^2$, $y = u \sin v$, $z = u \cos v$, $0 \leqslant u \leqslant 1$, $0 \leqslant v \leqslant \pi/2$

10. $\iint_S \sqrt{1 + x^2 + y^2} \, dS$,
S is the helicoid with vector equation $\mathbf{r}(u, v) = u \cos v \, \mathbf{i} + u \sin v \, \mathbf{j} + v \, \mathbf{k}$, $0 \leqslant u \leqslant 1$, $0 \leqslant v \leqslant \pi$

11. $\iint_S x^2 z^2 \, dS$,
S is the part of the cone $z^2 = x^2 + y^2$ that lies between the planes $z = 1$ and $z = 3$

12. $\iint_S z \, dS$,
S is the surface $x = y + 2z^2$, $0 \leqslant y \leqslant 1$, $0 \leqslant z \leqslant 1$

13. $\iint_S y \, dS$,
S is the part of the paraboloid $y = x^2 + z^2$ that lies inside the cylinder $x^2 + z^2 = 4$

14. $\iint_S y^2 \, dS$,
S is the part of the sphere $x^2 + y^2 + z^2 = 4$ that lies inside the cylinder $x^2 + y^2 = 1$ and above the xy-plane

15. $\iint_S (x^2 z + y^2 z) \, dS$,
S is the hemisphere $x^2 + y^2 + z^2 = 4$, $z \geqslant 0$

16. $\iint_S xz \, dS$,
S is the boundary of the region enclosed by the cylinder $y^2 + z^2 = 9$ and the planes $x = 0$ and $x + y = 5$

17. $\iint_S (z + x^2 y) \, dS$,
S is the part of the cylinder $y^2 + z^2 = 1$ that lies between the planes $x = 0$ and $x = 3$ in the first octant

18. $\iint_S (x^2 + y^2 + z^2) \, dS$,
S is the part of the cylinder $x^2 + y^2 = 9$ between the planes $z = 0$ and $z = 2$, together with its top and bottom disks

---

19–30 Evaluate the surface integral $\iint_S \mathbf{F} \cdot d\mathbf{S}$ for the given vector field $\mathbf{F}$ and the oriented surface S. In other words, find the flux of $\mathbf{F}$ across S. For closed surfaces, use the positive (outward) orientation.

19. $\mathbf{F}(x, y, z) = xy \, \mathbf{i} + yz \, \mathbf{j} + zx \, \mathbf{k}$, S is the part of the paraboloid $z = 4 - x^2 - y^2$ that lies above the square $0 \leqslant x \leqslant 1$, $0 \leqslant y \leqslant 1$, and has upward orientation

20. $\mathbf{F}(x, y, z) = y \, \mathbf{i} + x \, \mathbf{j} + z^2 \, \mathbf{k}$,
S is the helicoid of Exercise 10 with upward orientation

21. $\mathbf{F}(x, y, z) = xze^y \, \mathbf{i} - xze^y \, \mathbf{j} + z \, \mathbf{k}$,
S is the part of the plane $x + y + z = 1$ in the first octant and has downward orientation

22. $\mathbf{F}(x, y, z) = x \, \mathbf{i} + y \, \mathbf{j} + z^4 \, \mathbf{k}$,
S is the part of the cone $z = \sqrt{x^2 + y^2}$ beneath the plane $z = 1$ with downward orientation

23. $\mathbf{F}(x, y, z) = x \, \mathbf{i} - z \, \mathbf{j} + y \, \mathbf{k}$,
S is the part of the sphere $x^2 + y^2 + z^2 = 4$ in the first octant, with orientation toward the origin

24. $\mathbf{F}(x, y, z) = xz \, \mathbf{i} + x \, \mathbf{j} + y \, \mathbf{k}$,
S is the hemisphere $x^2 + y^2 + z^2 = 25$, $y \geqslant 0$, oriented in the direction of the positive y-axis

25. $\mathbf{F}(x, y, z) = y \, \mathbf{j} - z \, \mathbf{k}$,
S consists of the paraboloid $y = x^2 + z^2$, $0 \leqslant y \leqslant 1$, and the disk $x^2 + z^2 \leqslant 1$, $y = 1$

26. $\mathbf{F}(x, y, z) = xy \, \mathbf{i} + 4x^2 \, \mathbf{j} + yz \, \mathbf{k}$, S is the surface $z = xe^y$, $0 \leqslant x \leqslant 1$, $0 \leqslant y \leqslant 1$, with upward orientation

27. $\mathbf{F}(x, y, z) = x\,\mathbf{i} + 2y\,\mathbf{j} + 3z\,\mathbf{k}$,
S is the cube with vertices $(\pm 1, \pm 1, \pm 1)$

28. $\mathbf{F}(x, y, z) = x\,\mathbf{i} + y\,\mathbf{j} + 5\,\mathbf{k}$, S is the boundary of the region enclosed by the cylinder $x^2 + z^2 = 1$ and the planes $y = 0$ and $x + y = 2$

29. $\mathbf{F}(x, y, z) = x^2\,\mathbf{i} + y^2\,\mathbf{j} + z^2\,\mathbf{k}$, S is the boundary of the solid half-cylinder $0 \le z \le \sqrt{1 - y^2}$, $0 \le x \le 2$

30. $\mathbf{F}(x, y, z) = y\,\mathbf{i} + (z - y)\,\mathbf{j} + x\,\mathbf{k}$,
S is the surface of the tetrahedron with vertices $(0, 0, 0)$, $(1, 0, 0)$, $(0, 1, 0)$, and $(0, 0, 1)$

CAS 31. Evaluate $\iint_S xyz\,dS$ correct to four decimal places, where S is the surface $z = xy$, $0 \le x \le 1$, $0 \le y \le 1$.

CAS 32. Find the exact value of $\iint_S x^2 yz\,dS$, where S is the surface in Exercise 31.

CAS 33. Find the value of $\iint_S x^2 y^2 z^2\,dS$ correct to four decimal places, where S is the part of the paraboloid $z = 3 - 2x^2 - y^2$ that lies above the xy-plane.

CAS 34. Find the flux of

$$\mathbf{F}(x, y, z) = \sin(xyz)\,\mathbf{i} + x^2 y\,\mathbf{j} + z^2 e^{x/5}\,\mathbf{k}$$

across the part of the cylinder $4y^2 + z^2 = 4$ that lies above the xy-plane and between the planes $x = -2$ and $x = 2$ with upward orientation. Illustrate by using a computer algebra system to draw the cylinder and the vector field on the same screen.

35. Find a formula for $\iint_S \mathbf{F} \cdot d\mathbf{S}$ similar to Formula 10 for the case where S is given by $y = h(x, z)$ and $\mathbf{n}$ is the unit normal that points toward the left.

36. Find a formula for $\iint_S \mathbf{F} \cdot d\mathbf{S}$ similar to Formula 10 for the case where S is given by $x = k(y, z)$ and $\mathbf{n}$ is the unit normal that points forward (that is, toward the viewer when the axes are drawn in the usual way).

37. Find the center of mass of the hemisphere $x^2 + y^2 + z^2 = a^2$, $z \ge 0$, if it has constant density.

38. Find the mass of a thin funnel in the shape of a cone $z = \sqrt{x^2 + y^2}$, $1 \le z \le 4$, if its density function is $\rho(x, y, z) = 10 - z$.

39. (a) Give an integral expression for the moment of inertia I_z about the z-axis of a thin sheet in the shape of a surface S if the density function is ρ.
(b) Find the moment of inertia about the z-axis of the funnel in Exercise 38.

40. Let S be the part of the sphere $x^2 + y^2 + z^2 = 25$ that lies above the plane $z = 4$. If S has constant density k, find (a) the center of mass and (b) the moment of inertia about the z-axis.

41. A fluid has density 870 kg/m³ and flows with velocity $\mathbf{v} = z\,\mathbf{i} + y^2\,\mathbf{j} + x^2\,\mathbf{k}$, where x, y, and z are measured in meters and the components of $\mathbf{v}$ in meters per second. Find the rate of flow outward through the cylinder $x^2 + y^2 = 4$, $0 \le z \le 1$.

42. Seawater has density 1025 kg/m³ and flows in a velocity field $\mathbf{v} = y\,\mathbf{i} + x\,\mathbf{j}$, where x, y, and z are measured in meters and the components of $\mathbf{v}$ in meters per second. Find the rate of flow outward through the hemisphere $x^2 + y^2 + z^2 = 9$, $z \ge 0$.

43. Use Gauss's Law to find the charge contained in the solid hemisphere $x^2 + y^2 + z^2 \le a^2$, $z \ge 0$, if the electric field is

$$\mathbf{E}(x, y, z) = x\,\mathbf{i} + y\,\mathbf{j} + 2z\,\mathbf{k}$$

44. Use Gauss's Law to find the charge enclosed by the cube with vertices $(\pm 1, \pm 1, \pm 1)$ if the electric field is

$$\mathbf{E}(x, y, z) = x\,\mathbf{i} + y\,\mathbf{j} + z\,\mathbf{k}$$

45. The temperature at the point (x, y, z) in a substance with conductivity $K = 6.5$ is $u(x, y, z) = 2y^2 + 2z^2$. Find the rate of heat flow inward across the cylindrical surface $y^2 + z^2 = 6$, $0 \le x \le 4$.

46. The temperature at a point in a ball with conductivity K is inversely proportional to the distance from the center of the ball. Find the rate of heat flow across a sphere S of radius a with center at the center of the ball.

47. Let $\mathbf{F}$ be an inverse square field, that is, $\mathbf{F}(\mathbf{r}) = c\mathbf{r}/|\mathbf{r}|^3$ for some constant c, where $\mathbf{r} = x\,\mathbf{i} + y\,\mathbf{j} + z\,\mathbf{k}$. Show that the flux of $\mathbf{F}$ across a sphere S with center the origin is independent of the radius of S.

17.8 STOKES' THEOREM

Stokes' Theorem can be regarded as a higher-dimensional version of Green's Theorem. Whereas Green's Theorem relates a double integral over a plane region D to a line integral around its plane boundary curve, Stokes' Theorem relates a surface integral over a surface S to a line integral around the boundary curve of S (which is a space curve). Figure 1 shows

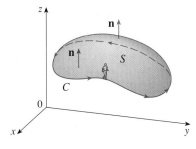

FIGURE 1

■ Stokes' Theorem is named after the Irish mathematical physicist Sir George Stokes (1819–1903). Stokes was a professor at Cambridge University (in fact he held the same position as Newton, Lucasian Professor of Mathematics) and was especially noted for his studies of fluid flow and light. What we call Stokes' Theorem was actually discovered by the Scottish physicist Sir William Thomson (1824–1907, known as Lord Kelvin). Stokes learned of this theorem in a letter from Thomson in 1850 and asked students to prove it on an examination at Cambridge University in 1854. We don't know if any of those students was able to do so.

an oriented surface with unit normal vector **n**. The orientation of S induces the **positive orientation of the boundary curve C** shown in the figure. This means that if you walk in the positive direction around C with your head pointing in the direction of **n**, then the surface will always be on your left.

STOKES' THEOREM Let S be an oriented piecewise-smooth surface that is bounded by a simple, closed, piecewise-smooth boundary curve C with positive orientation. Let **F** be a vector field whose components have continuous partial derivatives on an open region in $\mathbb{R}^3$ that contains S. Then

$$\int_C \mathbf{F} \cdot d\mathbf{r} = \iint_S \text{curl } \mathbf{F} \cdot d\mathbf{S}$$

Since

$$\int_C \mathbf{F} \cdot d\mathbf{r} = \int_C \mathbf{F} \cdot \mathbf{T} \, ds \qquad \text{and} \qquad \iint_S \text{curl } \mathbf{F} \cdot d\mathbf{S} = \iint_S \text{curl } \mathbf{F} \cdot \mathbf{n} \, dS$$

Stokes' Theorem says that the line integral around the boundary curve of S of the tangential component of **F** is equal to the surface integral of the normal component of the curl of **F**.

The positively oriented boundary curve of the oriented surface S is often written as ∂S, so Stokes' Theorem can be expressed as

$$\boxed{1} \qquad \qquad \iint_S \text{curl } \mathbf{F} \cdot d\mathbf{S} = \int_{\partial S} \mathbf{F} \cdot d\mathbf{r}$$

There is an analogy among Stokes' Theorem, Green's Theorem, and the Fundamental Theorem of Calculus. As before, there is an integral involving derivatives on the left side of Equation 1 (recall that curl **F** is a sort of derivative of **F**) and the right side involves the values of **F** only on the *boundary* of S.

In fact, in the special case where the surface S is flat and lies in the xy-plane with upward orientation, the unit normal is **k**, the surface integral becomes a double integral, and Stokes' Theorem becomes

$$\int_C \mathbf{F} \cdot d\mathbf{r} = \iint_S \text{curl } \mathbf{F} \cdot d\mathbf{S} = \iint_S (\text{curl } \mathbf{F}) \cdot \mathbf{k} \, dA$$

This is precisely the vector form of Green's Theorem given in Equation 17.5.12. Thus we see that Green's Theorem is really a special case of Stokes' Theorem.

Although Stokes' Theorem is too difficult for us to prove in its full generality, we can give a proof when S is a graph and **F**, S, and C are well behaved.

PROOF OF A SPECIAL CASE OF STOKES' THEOREM We assume that the equation of S is $z = g(x, y)$, $(x, y) \in D$, where g has continuous second-order partial derivatives and D is a simple plane region whose boundary curve C_1 corresponds to C. If the orientation of S is upward, then the positive orientation of C corresponds to the positive orientation of C_1. (See Figure 2.) We are also given that $\mathbf{F} = P \mathbf{i} + Q \mathbf{j} + R \mathbf{k}$, where the partial derivatives of P, Q, and R are continuous.

FIGURE 2

Since S is a graph of a function, we can apply Formula 17.7.10 with $\mathbf{F}$ replaced by curl $\mathbf{F}$. The result is

$$\boxed{2} \quad \iint_S \text{curl } \mathbf{F} \cdot d\mathbf{S}$$

$$= \iint_D \left[-\left(\frac{\partial R}{\partial y} - \frac{\partial Q}{\partial z}\right)\frac{\partial z}{\partial x} - \left(\frac{\partial P}{\partial z} - \frac{\partial R}{\partial x}\right)\frac{\partial z}{\partial y} + \left(\frac{\partial Q}{\partial x} - \frac{\partial P}{\partial y}\right) \right] dA$$

where the partial derivatives of P, Q, and R are evaluated at $(x, y, g(x, y))$. If

$$x = x(t) \qquad y = y(t) \qquad a \leqslant t \leqslant b$$

is a parametric representation of C_1, then a parametric representation of C is

$$x = x(t) \qquad y = y(t) \qquad z = g(x(t), y(t)) \qquad a \leqslant t \leqslant b$$

This allows us, with the aid of the Chain Rule, to evaluate the line integral as follows:

$$\int_C \mathbf{F} \cdot d\mathbf{r} = \int_a^b \left(P\frac{dx}{dt} + Q\frac{dy}{dt} + R\frac{dz}{dt} \right) dt$$

$$= \int_a^b \left[P\frac{dx}{dt} + Q\frac{dy}{dt} + R\left(\frac{\partial z}{\partial x}\frac{dx}{dt} + \frac{\partial z}{\partial y}\frac{dy}{dt}\right) \right] dt$$

$$= \int_a^b \left[\left(P + R\frac{\partial z}{\partial x}\right)\frac{dx}{dt} + \left(Q + R\frac{\partial z}{\partial y}\right)\frac{dy}{dt} \right] dt$$

$$= \int_{C_1} \left(P + R\frac{\partial z}{\partial x}\right) dx + \left(Q + R\frac{\partial z}{\partial y}\right) dy$$

$$= \iint_D \left[\frac{\partial}{\partial x}\left(Q + R\frac{\partial z}{\partial y}\right) - \frac{\partial}{\partial y}\left(P + R\frac{\partial z}{\partial x}\right) \right] dA$$

where we have used Green's Theorem in the last step. Then, using the Chain Rule again and remembering that P, Q, and R are functions of x, y, and z and that z is itself a function of x and y, we get

$$\int_C \mathbf{F} \cdot d\mathbf{r} = \iint_D \left[\left(\frac{\partial Q}{\partial x} + \frac{\partial Q}{\partial z}\frac{\partial z}{\partial x} + \frac{\partial R}{\partial x}\frac{\partial z}{\partial y} + \frac{\partial R}{\partial z}\frac{\partial z}{\partial x}\frac{\partial z}{\partial y} + R\frac{\partial^2 z}{\partial x \partial y}\right) \right.$$

$$\left. - \left(\frac{\partial P}{\partial y} + \frac{\partial P}{\partial z}\frac{\partial z}{\partial y} + \frac{\partial R}{\partial y}\frac{\partial z}{\partial x} + \frac{\partial R}{\partial z}\frac{\partial z}{\partial y}\frac{\partial z}{\partial x} + R\frac{\partial^2 z}{\partial y \partial x}\right) \right] dA$$

Four of the terms in this double integral cancel and the remaining six terms can be arranged to coincide with the right side of Equation 2. Therefore

$$\int_C \mathbf{F} \cdot d\mathbf{r} = \iint_S \text{curl } \mathbf{F} \cdot d\mathbf{S} \qquad \qquad \square$$

▼ EXAMPLE 1 Evaluate $\int_C \mathbf{F} \cdot d\mathbf{r}$, where $\mathbf{F}(x, y, z) = -y^2\,\mathbf{i} + x\,\mathbf{j} + z^2\,\mathbf{k}$ and C is the curve of intersection of the plane $y + z = 2$ and the cylinder $x^2 + y^2 = 1$. (Orient C to be counterclockwise when viewed from above.)

SOLUTION The curve C (an ellipse) is shown in Figure 3. Although $\int_C \mathbf{F} \cdot d\mathbf{r}$ could be evaluated directly, it's easier to use Stokes' Theorem. We first compute

$$\operatorname{curl} \mathbf{F} = \begin{vmatrix} \mathbf{i} & \mathbf{j} & \mathbf{k} \\ \dfrac{\partial}{\partial x} & \dfrac{\partial}{\partial y} & \dfrac{\partial}{\partial z} \\ -y^2 & x & z^2 \end{vmatrix} = (1 + 2y)\,\mathbf{k}$$

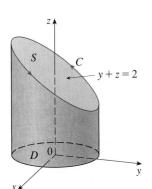

FIGURE 3

Although there are many surfaces with boundary C, the most convenient choice is the elliptical region S in the plane $y + z = 2$ that is bounded by C. If we orient S upward, then C has the induced positive orientation. The projection D of S on the xy-plane is the disk $x^2 + y^2 \leqslant 1$ and so using Equation 17.7.10 with $z = g(x, y) = 2 - y$, we have

$$\int_C \mathbf{F} \cdot d\mathbf{r} = \iint_S \operatorname{curl} \mathbf{F} \cdot d\mathbf{S} = \iint_D (1 + 2y)\,dA$$

$$= \int_0^{2\pi} \int_0^1 (1 + 2r\sin\theta)\, r\, dr\, d\theta$$

$$= \int_0^{2\pi} \left[\frac{r^2}{2} + 2\frac{r^3}{3}\sin\theta \right]_0^1 d\theta = \int_0^{2\pi} \left(\tfrac{1}{2} + \tfrac{2}{3}\sin\theta \right) d\theta$$

$$= \tfrac{1}{2}(2\pi) + 0 = \pi \qquad \square$$

▼ EXAMPLE 2 Use Stokes' Theorem to compute the integral $\iint_S \operatorname{curl} \mathbf{F} \cdot d\mathbf{S}$, where $\mathbf{F}(x, y, z) = xz\,\mathbf{i} + yz\,\mathbf{j} + xy\,\mathbf{k}$ and S is the part of the sphere $x^2 + y^2 + z^2 = 4$ that lies inside the cylinder $x^2 + y^2 = 1$ and above the xy-plane. (See Figure 4.)

SOLUTION To find the boundary curve C we solve the equations $x^2 + y^2 + z^2 = 4$ and $x^2 + y^2 = 1$. Subtracting, we get $z^2 = 3$ and so $z = \sqrt{3}$ (since $z > 0$). Thus C is the circle given by the equations $x^2 + y^2 = 1$, $z = \sqrt{3}$. A vector equation of C is

$$\mathbf{r}(t) = \cos t\,\mathbf{i} + \sin t\,\mathbf{j} + \sqrt{3}\,\mathbf{k} \qquad 0 \leqslant t \leqslant 2\pi$$

so

$$\mathbf{r}'(t) = -\sin t\,\mathbf{i} + \cos t\,\mathbf{j}$$

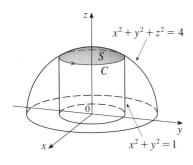

FIGURE 4

Also, we have

$$\mathbf{F}(\mathbf{r}(t)) = \sqrt{3}\,\cos t\,\mathbf{i} + \sqrt{3}\,\sin t\,\mathbf{j} + \cos t\,\sin t\,\mathbf{k}$$

Therefore, by Stokes' Theorem,

$$\iint_S \operatorname{curl} \mathbf{F} \cdot d\mathbf{S} = \int_C \mathbf{F} \cdot d\mathbf{r} = \int_0^{2\pi} \mathbf{F}(\mathbf{r}(t)) \cdot \mathbf{r}'(t)\, dt$$

$$= \int_0^{2\pi} \left(-\sqrt{3}\,\cos t\,\sin t + \sqrt{3}\,\sin t\,\cos t \right) dt$$

$$= \sqrt{3} \int_0^{2\pi} 0\, dt = 0 \qquad \square$$

Note that in Example 2 we computed a surface integral simply by knowing the values of **F** on the boundary curve C. This means that if we have another oriented surface with the same boundary curve C, then we get exactly the same value for the surface integral!

In general, if S_1 and S_2 are oriented surfaces with the same oriented boundary curve C and both satisfy the hypotheses of Stokes' Theorem, then

$$\boxed{3} \qquad \iint_{S_1} \text{curl } \mathbf{F} \cdot d\mathbf{S} = \int_C \mathbf{F} \cdot d\mathbf{r} = \iint_{S_2} \text{curl } \mathbf{F} \cdot d\mathbf{S}$$

This fact is useful when it is difficult to integrate over one surface but easy to integrate over the other.

We now use Stokes' Theorem to throw some light on the meaning of the curl vector. Suppose that C is an oriented closed curve and $\mathbf{v}$ represents the velocity field in fluid flow. Consider the line integral

$$\int_C \mathbf{v} \cdot d\mathbf{r} = \int_C \mathbf{v} \cdot \mathbf{T} \, ds$$

and recall that $\mathbf{v} \cdot \mathbf{T}$ is the component of $\mathbf{v}$ in the direction of the unit tangent vector $\mathbf{T}$. This means that the closer the direction of $\mathbf{v}$ is to the direction of $\mathbf{T}$, the larger the value of $\mathbf{v} \cdot \mathbf{T}$. Thus $\int_C \mathbf{v} \cdot d\mathbf{r}$ is a measure of the tendency of the fluid to move around C and is called the **circulation** of $\mathbf{v}$ around C. (See Figure 5.)

Now let $P_0(x_0, y_0, z_0)$ be a point in the fluid and let S_a be a small disk with radius a and center P_0. Then $(\text{curl } \mathbf{F})(P) \approx (\text{curl } \mathbf{F})(P_0)$ for all points P on S_a because curl $\mathbf{F}$ is continuous. Thus, by Stokes' Theorem, we get the following approximation to the circulation around the boundary circle C_a:

$$\int_{C_a} \mathbf{v} \cdot d\mathbf{r} = \iint_{S_a} \text{curl } \mathbf{v} \cdot d\mathbf{S} = \iint_{S_a} \text{curl } \mathbf{v} \cdot \mathbf{n} \, dS$$

$$\approx \iint_{S_a} \text{curl } \mathbf{v}(P_0) \cdot \mathbf{n}(P_0) \, dS = \text{curl } \mathbf{v}(P_0) \cdot \mathbf{n}(P_0) \pi a^2$$

This approximation becomes better as $a \to 0$ and we have

$$\boxed{4} \qquad \text{curl } \mathbf{v}(P_0) \cdot \mathbf{n}(P_0) = \lim_{a \to 0} \frac{1}{\pi a^2} \int_{C_a} \mathbf{v} \cdot d\mathbf{r}$$

Equation 4 gives the relationship between the curl and the circulation. It shows that curl $\mathbf{v} \cdot \mathbf{n}$ is a measure of the rotating effect of the fluid about the axis $\mathbf{n}$. The curling effect is greatest about the axis parallel to curl $\mathbf{v}$.

Finally, we mention that Stokes' Theorem can be used to prove Theorem 17.5.4 (which states that if curl $\mathbf{F} = \mathbf{0}$ on all of $\mathbb{R}^3$, then $\mathbf{F}$ is conservative). From our previous work (Theorems 17.3.3 and 17.3.4), we know that $\mathbf{F}$ is conservative if $\int_C \mathbf{F} \cdot d\mathbf{r} = 0$ for every closed path C. Given C, suppose we can find an orientable surface S whose boundary is C. (This can be done, but the proof requires advanced techniques.) Then Stokes' Theorem gives

$$\int_C \mathbf{F} \cdot d\mathbf{r} = \iint_S \text{curl } \mathbf{F} \cdot d\mathbf{S} = \iint_S \mathbf{0} \cdot d\mathbf{S} = 0$$

A curve that is not simple can be broken into a number of simple curves, and the integrals around these simple curves are all 0. Adding these integrals, we obtain $\int_C \mathbf{F} \cdot d\mathbf{r} = 0$ for any closed curve C.

(a) $\int_C \mathbf{v} \cdot d\mathbf{r} > 0$, positive circulation

(b) $\int_C \mathbf{v} \cdot d\mathbf{r} < 0$, negative circulation

FIGURE 5

■ Imagine a tiny paddle wheel placed in the fluid at a point P, as in Figure 6; the paddle wheel rotates fastest when its axis is parallel to curl $\mathbf{v}$.

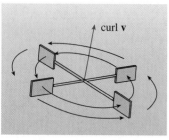

FIGURE 6

17.8 EXERCISES

1. A hemisphere H and a portion P of a paraboloid are shown. Suppose $\mathbf{F}$ is a vector field on $\mathbb{R}^3$ whose components have continuous partial derivatives. Explain why

$$\iint_H \operatorname{curl} \mathbf{F} \cdot d\mathbf{S} = \iint_P \operatorname{curl} \mathbf{F} \cdot d\mathbf{S}$$

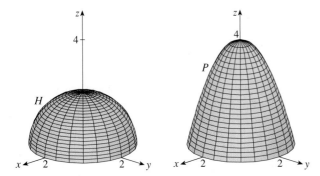

2–6 Use Stokes' Theorem to evaluate $\iint_S \operatorname{curl} \mathbf{F} \cdot d\mathbf{S}$.

2. $\mathbf{F}(x, y, z) = 2y \cos z\, \mathbf{i} + e^x \sin z\, \mathbf{j} + x e^y\, \mathbf{k}$,
S is the hemisphere $x^2 + y^2 + z^2 = 9$, $z \geqslant 0$, oriented upward

3. $\mathbf{F}(x, y, z) = x^2 z^2\, \mathbf{i} + y^2 z^2\, \mathbf{j} + xyz\, \mathbf{k}$,
S is the part of the paraboloid $z = x^2 + y^2$ that lies inside the cylinder $x^2 + y^2 = 4$, oriented upward

4. $\mathbf{F}(x, y, z) = x^2 y^3 z\, \mathbf{i} + \sin(xyz)\, \mathbf{j} + xyz\, \mathbf{k}$,
S is the part of the cone $y^2 = x^2 + z^2$ that lies between the planes $y = 0$ and $y = 3$, oriented in the direction of the positive y-axis

5. $\mathbf{F}(x, y, z) = xyz\, \mathbf{i} + xy\, \mathbf{j} + x^2 yz\, \mathbf{k}$,
S consists of the top and the four sides (but not the bottom) of the cube with vertices $(\pm 1, \pm 1, \pm 1)$, oriented outward
[*Hint:* Use Equation 3.]

6. $\mathbf{F}(x, y, z) = e^{xy} \cos z\, \mathbf{i} + x^2 z\, \mathbf{j} + xy\, \mathbf{k}$,
S is the hemisphere $x = \sqrt{1 - y^2 - z^2}$, oriented in the direction of the positive x-axis   [*Hint:* Use Equation 3.]

7–10 Use Stokes' Theorem to evaluate $\int_C \mathbf{F} \cdot d\mathbf{r}$. In each case C is oriented counterclockwise as viewed from above.

7. $\mathbf{F}(x, y, z) = (x + y^2)\, \mathbf{i} + (y + z^2)\, \mathbf{j} + (z + x^2)\, \mathbf{k}$,
C is the triangle with vertices $(1, 0, 0)$, $(0, 1, 0)$, and $(0, 0, 1)$

8. $\mathbf{F}(x, y, z) = e^{-x}\, \mathbf{i} + e^x\, \mathbf{j} + e^z\, \mathbf{k}$,
C is the boundary of the part of the plane $2x + y + 2z = 2$ in the first octant

9. $\mathbf{F}(x, y, z) = yz\, \mathbf{i} + 2xz\, \mathbf{j} + e^{xy}\, \mathbf{k}$,
C is the circle $x^2 + y^2 = 16$, $z = 5$

10. $\mathbf{F}(x, y, z) = xy\, \mathbf{i} + 2z\, \mathbf{j} + 3y\, \mathbf{k}$, C is the curve of intersection of the plane $x + z = 5$ and the cylinder $x^2 + y^2 = 9$

11. (a) Use Stokes' Theorem to evaluate $\int_C \mathbf{F} \cdot d\mathbf{r}$, where

$$\mathbf{F}(x, y, z) = x^2 z\, \mathbf{i} + xy^2\, \mathbf{j} + z^2\, \mathbf{k}$$

and C is the curve of intersection of the plane $x + y + z = 1$ and the cylinder $x^2 + y^2 = 9$ oriented counterclockwise as viewed from above.

(b) Graph both the plane and the cylinder with domains chosen so that you can see the curve C and the surface that you used in part (a).

(c) Find parametric equations for C and use them to graph C.

12. (a) Use Stokes' Theorem to evaluate $\int_C \mathbf{F} \cdot d\mathbf{r}$, where $\mathbf{F}(x, y, z) = x^2 y\, \mathbf{i} + \frac{1}{3}x^3\, \mathbf{j} + xy\, \mathbf{k}$ and C is the curve of intersection of the hyperbolic paraboloid $z = y^2 - x^2$ and the cylinder $x^2 + y^2 = 1$ oriented counterclockwise as viewed from above.

(b) Graph both the hyperbolic paraboloid and the cylinder with domains chosen so that you can see the curve C and the surface that you used in part (a).

(c) Find parametric equations for C and use them to graph C.

13–15 Verify that Stokes' Theorem is true for the given vector field $\mathbf{F}$ and surface S.

13. $\mathbf{F}(x, y, z) = y^2\, \mathbf{i} + x\, \mathbf{j} + z^2\, \mathbf{k}$,
S is the part of the paraboloid $z = x^2 + y^2$ that lies below the plane $z = 1$, oriented upward

14. $\mathbf{F}(x, y, z) = x\, \mathbf{i} + y\, \mathbf{j} + xyz\, \mathbf{k}$,
S is the part of the plane $2x + y + z = 2$ that lies in the first octant, oriented upward

15. $\mathbf{F}(x, y, z) = y\, \mathbf{i} + z\, \mathbf{j} + x\, \mathbf{k}$,
S is the hemisphere $x^2 + y^2 + z^2 = 1$, $y \geqslant 0$, oriented in the direction of the positive y-axis

16. Let C be a simple closed smooth curve that lies in the plane $x + y + z = 1$. Show that the line integral

$$\int_C z\, dx - 2x\, dy + 3y\, dz$$

depends only on the area of the region enclosed by C and not on the shape of C or its location in the plane.

17. A particle moves along line segments from the origin to the points $(1, 0, 0)$, $(1, 2, 1)$, $(0, 2, 1)$, and back to the origin under the influence of the force field

$$\mathbf{F}(x, y, z) = z^2\, \mathbf{i} + 2xy\, \mathbf{j} + 4y^2\, \mathbf{k}$$

Find the work done.

18. Evaluate

$$\int_C (y + \sin x) \, dx + (z^2 + \cos y) \, dy + x^3 \, dz$$

where C is the curve $\mathbf{r}(t) = \langle \sin t, \cos t, \sin 2t \rangle$, $0 \le t \le 2\pi$.
[*Hint:* Observe that C lies on the surface $z = 2xy$.]

19. If S is a sphere and $\mathbf{F}$ satisfies the hypotheses of Stokes'
Theorem, show that $\iint_S \text{curl } \mathbf{F} \cdot d\mathbf{S} = 0$.

20. Suppose S and C satisfy the hypotheses of Stokes' Theorem
and f, g have continuous second-order partial derivatives. Use
Exercises 24 and 26 in Section 16.5 to show the following.

(a) $\int_C (f \, \nabla g) \cdot d\mathbf{r} = \iint_S (\nabla f \times \nabla g) \cdot d\mathbf{S}$

(b) $\int_C (f \, \nabla f) \cdot d\mathbf{r} = 0$

(c) $\int_C (f \, \nabla g + g \, \nabla f) \cdot d\mathbf{r} = 0$

WRITING PROJECT

■ The photograph shows a stained-glass window at Cambridge University in honor of George Green.

Courtesy of the Masters and Fellows of Gonville and Caius College, University of Cambridge, England

www.stewartcalculus.com
The Internet is another source of information for this project. Click on *History of Mathematics*. Follow the links to the St. Andrew's site and that of the British Society for the History of Mathematics.

THREE MEN AND TWO THEOREMS

Although two of the most important theorems in vector calculus are named after George Green and George Stokes, a third man, William Thomson (also known as Lord Kelvin), played a large role in the formulation, dissemination, and application of both of these results. All three men were interested in how the two theorems could help to explain and predict physical phenomena in electricity and magnetism and fluid flow. The basic facts of the story are given in the margin notes on pages 1092 and 1129.

Write a report on the historical origins of Green's Theorem and Stokes' Theorem. Explain the similarities and relationship between the theorems. Discuss the roles that Green, Thomson, and Stokes played in discovering these theorems and making them widely known. Show how both theorems arose from the investigation of electricity and magnetism and were later used to study a variety of physical problems.

The dictionary edited by Gillispie [2] is a good source for both biographical and scientific information. The book by Hutchinson [5] gives an account of Stokes' life and the book by Thompson [8] is a biography of Lord Kelvin. The articles by Grattan-Guinness [3] and Gray [4] and the book by Cannell [1] give background on the extraordinary life and works of Green. Additional historical and mathematical information is found in the books by Katz [6] and Kline [7].

1. D. M. Cannell, *George Green, Mathematician and Physicist 1793–1841: The Background to His Life and Work* (Philadelphia: Society for Industrial and Applied Mathematics, 2001).

2. C. C. Gillispie, ed., *Dictionary of Scientific Biography* (New York: Scribner's, 1974). See the article on Green by P. J. Wallis in Volume XV and the articles on Thomson by Jed Buchwald and on Stokes by E. M. Parkinson in Volume XIII.

3. I. Grattan-Guinness, "Why did George Green write his essay of 1828 on electricity and magnetism?" *Amer. Math. Monthly*, Vol. 102 (1995), pp. 387–396.

4. J. Gray, "There was a jolly miller." *The New Scientist*, Vol. 139 (1993), pp. 24–27.

5. G. E. Hutchinson, *The Enchanted Voyage and Other Studies* (Westport, CT: Greenwood Press, 1978).

6. Victor Katz, *A History of Mathematics: An Introduction* (New York: HarperCollins, 1993), pp. 678–680.

7. Morris Kline, *Mathematical Thought from Ancient to Modern Times* (New York: Oxford University Press, 1972), pp. 683–685.

8. Sylvanus P. Thompson, *The Life of Lord Kelvin* (New York: Chelsea, 1976).

17.9 | THE DIVERGENCE THEOREM

In Section 17.5 we rewrote Green's Theorem in a vector version as

$$\int_C \mathbf{F} \cdot \mathbf{n} \, ds = \iint_D \operatorname{div} \mathbf{F}(x, y) \, dA$$

where C is the positively oriented boundary curve of the plane region D. If we were seeking to extend this theorem to vector fields on $\mathbb{R}^3$, we might make the guess that

$$\boxed{1} \qquad \qquad \iint_S \mathbf{F} \cdot \mathbf{n} \, dS = \iiint_E \operatorname{div} \mathbf{F}(x, y, z) \, dV$$

where S is the boundary surface of the solid region E. It turns out that Equation 1 is true, under appropriate hypotheses, and is called the Divergence Theorem. Notice its similarity to Green's Theorem and Stokes' Theorem in that it relates the integral of a derivative of a function (div $\mathbf{F}$ in this case) over a region to the integral of the original function $\mathbf{F}$ over the boundary of the region.

At this stage you may wish to review the various types of regions over which we were able to evaluate triple integrals in Section 16.6. We state and prove the Divergence Theorem for regions E that are simultaneously of types 1, 2, and 3 and we call such regions **simple solid regions**. (For instance, regions bounded by ellipsoids or rectangular boxes are simple solid regions.) The boundary of E is a closed surface, and we use the convention, introduced in Section 17.7, that the positive orientation is outward; that is, the unit normal vector $\mathbf{n}$ is directed outward from E.

■ The Divergence Theorem is sometimes called Gauss's Theorem after the great German mathematician Karl Friedrich Gauss (1777–1855), who discovered this theorem during his investigation of electrostatics. In Eastern Europe the Divergence Theorem is known as Ostrogradsky's Theorem after the Russian mathematician Mikhail Ostrogradsky (1801–1862), who published this result in 1826.

THE DIVERGENCE THEOREM Let E be a simple solid region and let S be the boundary surface of E, given with positive (outward) orientation. Let $\mathbf{F}$ be a vector field whose component functions have continuous partial derivatives on an open region that contains E. Then

$$\iint_S \mathbf{F} \cdot d\mathbf{S} = \iiint_E \operatorname{div} \mathbf{F} \, dV$$

Thus the Divergence Theorem states that, under the given conditions, the flux of $\mathbf{F}$ across the boundary surface of E is equal to the triple integral of the divergence of $\mathbf{F}$ over E.

PROOF Let $\mathbf{F} = P\,\mathbf{i} + Q\,\mathbf{j} + R\,\mathbf{k}$. Then

$$\operatorname{div} \mathbf{F} = \frac{\partial P}{\partial x} + \frac{\partial Q}{\partial y} + \frac{\partial R}{\partial z}$$

so

$$\iiint_E \operatorname{div} \mathbf{F} \, dV = \iiint_E \frac{\partial P}{\partial x} \, dV + \iiint_E \frac{\partial Q}{\partial y} \, dV + \iiint_E \frac{\partial R}{\partial z} \, dV$$

If $\mathbf{n}$ is the unit outward normal of S, then the surface integral on the left side of the

Divergence Theorem is

$$\iint_S \mathbf{F} \cdot d\mathbf{S} = \iint_S \mathbf{F} \cdot \mathbf{n}\, dS = \iint_S (P\mathbf{i} + Q\mathbf{j} + R\mathbf{k}) \cdot \mathbf{n}\, dS$$

$$= \iint_S P\mathbf{i} \cdot \mathbf{n}\, dS + \iint_S Q\mathbf{j} \cdot \mathbf{n}\, dS + \iint_S R\mathbf{k} \cdot \mathbf{n}\, dS$$

Therefore, to prove the Divergence Theorem, it suffices to prove the following three equations:

2
$$\iint_S P\mathbf{i} \cdot \mathbf{n}\, dS = \iiint_E \frac{\partial P}{\partial x}\, dV$$

3
$$\iint_S Q\mathbf{j} \cdot \mathbf{n}\, dS = \iiint_E \frac{\partial Q}{\partial y}\, dV$$

4
$$\iint_S R\mathbf{k} \cdot \mathbf{n}\, dS = \iiint_E \frac{\partial R}{\partial z}\, dV$$

To prove Equation 4 we use the fact that E is a type 1 region:

$$E = \{(x, y, z) \mid (x, y) \in D, u_1(x, y) \le z \le u_2(x, y)\}$$

where D is the projection of E onto the xy-plane. By Equation 16.6.6, we have

$$\iiint_E \frac{\partial R}{\partial z}\, dV = \iint_D \left[\int_{u_1(x, y)}^{u_2(x, y)} \frac{\partial R}{\partial z}(x, y, z)\, dz \right] dA$$

and therefore, by the Fundamental Theorem of Calculus,

5
$$\iiint_E \frac{\partial R}{\partial z}\, dV = \iint_D \left[R(x, y, u_2(x, y)) - R(x, y, u_1(x, y)) \right] dA$$

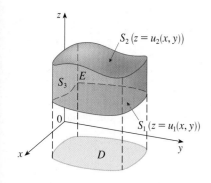

FIGURE 1

The boundary surface S consists of three pieces: the bottom surface S_1, the top surface S_2, and possibly a vertical surface S_3, which lies above the boundary curve of D. (See Figure 1. It might happen that S_3 doesn't appear, as in the case of a sphere.) Notice that on S_3 we have $\mathbf{k} \cdot \mathbf{n} = 0$, because $\mathbf{k}$ is vertical and $\mathbf{n}$ is horizontal, and so

$$\iint_{S_3} R\mathbf{k} \cdot \mathbf{n}\, dS = \iint_{S_3} 0\, dS = 0$$

Thus, regardless of whether there is a vertical surface, we can write

6
$$\iint_S R\mathbf{k} \cdot \mathbf{n}\, dS = \iint_{S_1} R\mathbf{k} \cdot \mathbf{n}\, dS + \iint_{S_2} R\mathbf{k} \cdot \mathbf{n}\, dS$$

The equation of S_2 is $z = u_2(x, y)$, $(x, y) \in D$, and the outward normal $\mathbf{n}$ points upward, so from Equation 17.7.10 (with $\mathbf{F}$ replaced by $R\mathbf{k}$) we have

$$\iint_{S_2} R\mathbf{k} \cdot \mathbf{n}\, dS = \iint_D R(x, y, u_2(x, y))\, dA$$

On S_1 we have $z = u_1(x, y)$, but here the outward normal $\mathbf{n}$ points downward, so we multiply by -1:

$$\iint\limits_{S_1} R\,\mathbf{k}\cdot\mathbf{n}\,dS = -\iint\limits_{D} R(x, y, u_1(x, y))\,dA$$

Therefore Equation 6 gives

$$\iint\limits_{S} R\,\mathbf{k}\cdot\mathbf{n}\,dS = \iint\limits_{D} \left[R(x, y, u_2(x, y)) - R(x, y, u_1(x, y))\right]dA$$

Comparison with Equation 5 shows that

$$\iint\limits_{S} R\,\mathbf{k}\cdot\mathbf{n}\,dS = \iiint\limits_{E} \frac{\partial R}{\partial z}\,dV$$

■ Notice that the method of proof of the Divergence Theorem is very similar to that of Green's Theorem.

Equations 2 and 3 are proved in a similar manner using the expressions for E as a type 2 or type 3 region, respectively. ☐

◨ EXAMPLE 1 Find the flux of the vector field $\mathbf{F}(x, y, z) = z\,\mathbf{i} + y\,\mathbf{j} + x\,\mathbf{k}$ over the unit sphere $x^2 + y^2 + z^2 = 1$.

SOLUTION First we compute the divergence of $\mathbf{F}$:

$$\text{div}\,\mathbf{F} = \frac{\partial}{\partial x}(z) + \frac{\partial}{\partial y}(y) + \frac{\partial}{\partial z}(x) = 1$$

The unit sphere S is the boundary of the unit ball B given by $x^2 + y^2 + z^2 \leqslant 1$. Thus the Divergence Theorem gives the flux as

■ The solution in Example 1 should be compared with the solution in Example 4 in Section 17.7.

$$\iint\limits_{S} \mathbf{F}\cdot d\mathbf{S} = \iiint\limits_{B} \text{div}\,\mathbf{F}\,dV = \iiint\limits_{B} 1\,dV = V(B) = \tfrac{4}{3}\pi(1)^3 = \frac{4\pi}{3}$$ ☐

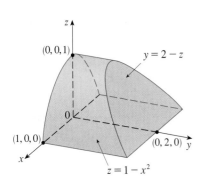

FIGURE 2

◨ EXAMPLE 2 Evaluate $\iint\limits_{S} \mathbf{F}\cdot d\mathbf{S}$, where

$$\mathbf{F}(x, y, z) = xy\,\mathbf{i} + \left(y^2 + e^{xz^2}\right)\mathbf{j} + \sin(xy)\,\mathbf{k}$$

and S is the surface of the region E bounded by the parabolic cylinder $z = 1 - x^2$ and the planes $z = 0$, $y = 0$, and $y + z = 2$. (See Figure 2.)

SOLUTION It would be extremely difficult to evaluate the given surface integral directly. (We would have to evaluate four surface integrals corresponding to the four pieces of S.) Furthermore, the divergence of $\mathbf{F}$ is much less complicated than $\mathbf{F}$ itself:

$$\text{div}\,\mathbf{F} = \frac{\partial}{\partial x}(xy) + \frac{\partial}{\partial y}\left(y^2 + e^{xz^2}\right) + \frac{\partial}{\partial z}(\sin xy) = y + 2y = 3y$$

Therefore we use the Divergence Theorem to transform the given surface integral into a triple integral. The easiest way to evaluate the triple integral is to express E as a type 3 region:

$$E = \left\{(x, y, z) \mid -1 \leqslant x \leqslant 1,\ 0 \leqslant z \leqslant 1 - x^2,\ 0 \leqslant y \leqslant 2 - z\right\}$$

Then we have

$$\iint_S \mathbf{F} \cdot d\mathbf{S} = \iiint_E \operatorname{div} \mathbf{F} \, dV = \iiint_E 3y \, dV$$

$$= 3 \int_{-1}^{1} \int_0^{1-x^2} \int_0^{2-z} y \, dy \, dz \, dx = 3 \int_{-1}^{1} \int_0^{1-x^2} \frac{(2-z)^2}{2} \, dz \, dx$$

$$= \frac{3}{2} \int_{-1}^{1} \left[-\frac{(2-z)^3}{3} \right]_0^{1-x^2} dx = -\frac{1}{2} \int_{-1}^{1} \left[(x^2+1)^3 - 8 \right] dx$$

$$= -\int_0^1 (x^6 + 3x^4 + 3x^2 - 7) \, dx = \tfrac{184}{35} \qquad \square$$

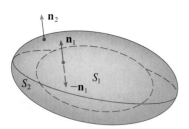

FIGURE 3

Although we have proved the Divergence Theorem only for simple solid regions, it can be proved for regions that are finite unions of simple solid regions. (The procedure is similar to the one we used in Section 17.4 to extend Green's Theorem.)

For example, let's consider the region E that lies between the closed surfaces S_1 and S_2, where S_1 lies inside S_2. Let $\mathbf{n}_1$ and $\mathbf{n}_2$ be outward normals of S_1 and S_2. Then the boundary surface of E is $S = S_1 \cup S_2$ and its normal $\mathbf{n}$ is given by $\mathbf{n} = -\mathbf{n}_1$ on S_1 and $\mathbf{n} = \mathbf{n}_2$ on S_2. (See Figure 3.) Applying the Divergence Theorem to S, we get

$$\boxed{7} \qquad \iiint_E \operatorname{div} \mathbf{F} \, dV = \iint_S \mathbf{F} \cdot d\mathbf{S} = \iint_S \mathbf{F} \cdot \mathbf{n} \, dS$$

$$= \iint_{S_1} \mathbf{F} \cdot (-\mathbf{n}_1) \, dS + \iint_{S_2} \mathbf{F} \cdot \mathbf{n}_2 \, dS$$

$$= -\iint_{S_1} \mathbf{F} \cdot d\mathbf{S} + \iint_{S_2} \mathbf{F} \cdot d\mathbf{S}$$

Let's apply this to the electric field (see Example 5 in Section 17.1):

$$\mathbf{E}(\mathbf{x}) = \frac{\varepsilon Q}{|\mathbf{x}|^3} \mathbf{x}$$

where S_1 is a small sphere with radius a and center the origin. You can verify that $\operatorname{div} \mathbf{E} = 0$. (See Exercise 23.) Therefore Equation 7 gives

$$\iint_{S_2} \mathbf{E} \cdot d\mathbf{S} = \iint_{S_1} \mathbf{E} \cdot d\mathbf{S} + \iiint_E \operatorname{div} \mathbf{E} \, dV = \iint_{S_1} \mathbf{E} \cdot d\mathbf{S} = \iint_{S_1} \mathbf{E} \cdot \mathbf{n} \, dS$$

The point of this calculation is that we can compute the surface integral over S_1 because S_1 is a sphere. The normal vector at $\mathbf{x}$ is $\mathbf{x}/|\mathbf{x}|$. Therefore

$$\mathbf{E} \cdot \mathbf{n} = \frac{\varepsilon Q}{|\mathbf{x}|^3} \mathbf{x} \cdot \left(\frac{\mathbf{x}}{|\mathbf{x}|} \right) = \frac{\varepsilon Q}{|\mathbf{x}|^4} \mathbf{x} \cdot \mathbf{x} = \frac{\varepsilon Q}{|\mathbf{x}|^2} = \frac{\varepsilon Q}{a^2}$$

since the equation of S_1 is $|\mathbf{x}| = a$. Thus we have

$$\iint_{S_2} \mathbf{E} \cdot d\mathbf{S} = \iint_{S_1} \mathbf{E} \cdot \mathbf{n} \, dS = \frac{\varepsilon Q}{a^2} \iint_{S_1} dS$$

$$= \frac{\varepsilon Q}{a^2} A(S_1) = \frac{\varepsilon Q}{a^2} 4\pi a^2 = 4\pi \varepsilon Q$$

This shows that the electric flux of $\mathbf{E}$ is $4\pi\varepsilon Q$ through *any* closed surface S_2 that contains the origin. [This is a special case of Gauss's Law (Equation 17.7.11) for a single charge. The relationship between ε and ε_0 is $\varepsilon = 1/(4\pi\varepsilon_0)$.]

Another application of the Divergence Theorem occurs in fluid flow. Let $\mathbf{v}(x, y, z)$ be the velocity field of a fluid with constant density ρ. Then $\mathbf{F} = \rho\mathbf{v}$ is the rate of flow per unit area. If $P_0(x_0, y_0, z_0)$ is a point in the fluid and B_a is a ball with center P_0 and very small radius a, then div $\mathbf{F}(P) \approx$ div $\mathbf{F}(P_0)$ for all points in B_a since div $\mathbf{F}$ is continuous. We approximate the flux over the boundary sphere S_a as follows:

$$\iint_{S_a} \mathbf{F} \cdot d\mathbf{S} = \iiint_{B_a} \text{div } \mathbf{F} \, dV = \iiint_{B_a} \text{div } \mathbf{F}(P_0) \, dV = \text{div } \mathbf{F}(P_0)V(B_a)$$

This approximation becomes better as $a \to 0$ and suggests that

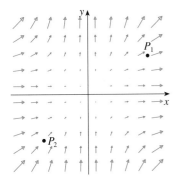

FIGURE 4
The vector field $\mathbf{F} = x^2\mathbf{i} + y^2\mathbf{j}$

$$\boxed{8} \qquad \text{div } \mathbf{F}(P_0) = \lim_{a \to 0} \frac{1}{V(B_a)} \iint_{S_a} \mathbf{F} \cdot d\mathbf{S}$$

Equation 8 says that div $\mathbf{F}(P_0)$ is the net rate of outward flux per unit volume at P_0. (This is the reason for the name *divergence*.) If div $\mathbf{F}(P) > 0$, the net flow is outward near P and P is called a **source**. If div $\mathbf{F}(P) < 0$, the net flow is inward near P and P is called a **sink**.

For the vector field in Figure 4, it appears that the vectors that end near P_1 are shorter than the vectors that start near P_1. Thus the net flow is outward near P_1, so div $\mathbf{F}(P_1) > 0$ and P_1 is a source. Near P_2, on the other hand, the incoming arrows are longer than the outgoing arrows. Here the net flow is inward, so div $\mathbf{F}(P_2) < 0$ and P_2 is a sink. We can use the formula for $\mathbf{F}$ to confirm this impression. Since $\mathbf{F} = x^2\mathbf{i} + y^2\mathbf{j}$, we have div $\mathbf{F} = 2x + 2y$, which is positive when $y > -x$. So the points above the line $y = -x$ are sources and those below are sinks.

17.9 EXERCISES

1–4 Verify that the Divergence Theorem is true for the vector field $\mathbf{F}$ on the region E.

1. $\mathbf{F}(x, y, z) = 3x\mathbf{i} + xy\mathbf{j} + 2xz\mathbf{k}$,
E is the cube bounded by the planes $x = 0$, $x = 1$, $y = 0$, $y = 1$, $z = 0$, and $z = 1$.

2. $\mathbf{F}(x, y, z) = x^2\mathbf{i} + xy\mathbf{j} + z\mathbf{k}$,
E is the solid bounded by the paraboloid $z = 4 - x^2 - y^2$ and the xy-plane

3. $\mathbf{F}(x, y, z) = xy\mathbf{i} + yz\mathbf{j} + zx\mathbf{k}$,
E is the solid cylinder $x^2 + y^2 \leq 1$, $0 \leq z \leq 1$

4. $\mathbf{F}(x, y, z) = x\mathbf{i} + y\mathbf{j} + z\mathbf{k}$,
E is the unit ball $x^2 + y^2 + z^2 \leq 1$

5–15 Use the Divergence Theorem to calculate the surface integral $\iint_S \mathbf{F} \cdot d\mathbf{S}$; that is, calculate the flux of $\mathbf{F}$ across S.

5. $\mathbf{F}(x, y, z) = e^x \sin y\,\mathbf{i} + e^x \cos y\,\mathbf{j} + yz^2\,\mathbf{k}$,
S is the surface of the box bounded by the planes $x = 0$, $x = 1$, $y = 0$, $y = 1$, $z = 0$, and $z = 2$

6. $\mathbf{F}(x, y, z) = x^2z^3\,\mathbf{i} + 2xyz^3\,\mathbf{j} + xz^4\,\mathbf{k}$,
S is the surface of the box with vertices $(\pm 1, \pm 2, \pm 3)$

7. $\mathbf{F}(x, y, z) = 3xy^2\,\mathbf{i} + xe^z\,\mathbf{j} + z^3\,\mathbf{k}$,
S is the surface of the solid bounded by the cylinder $y^2 + z^2 = 1$ and the planes $x = -1$ and $x = 2$

8. $\mathbf{F}(x, y, z) = x^3y\,\mathbf{i} - x^2y^2\,\mathbf{j} - x^2yz\,\mathbf{k}$,
S is the surface of the solid bounded by the hyperboloid $x^2 + y^2 - z^2 = 1$ and the planes $z = -2$ and $z = 2$

9. $\mathbf{F}(x, y, z) = xy \sin z\,\mathbf{i} + \cos(xz)\,\mathbf{j} + y \cos z\,\mathbf{k}$,
S is the ellipsoid $x^2/a^2 + y^2/b^2 + z^2/c^2 = 1$

10. $\mathbf{F}(x, y, z) = x^2y\,\mathbf{i} + xy^2\,\mathbf{j} + 2xyz\,\mathbf{k}$,
S is the surface of the tetrahedron bounded by the planes $x = 0$, $y = 0$, $z = 0$, and $x + 2y + z = 2$

11. $\mathbf{F}(x, y, z) = (\cos z + xy^2)\,\mathbf{i} + xe^{-z}\,\mathbf{j} + (\sin y + x^2z)\,\mathbf{k}$,
S is the surface of the solid bounded by the paraboloid $z = x^2 + y^2$ and the plane $z = 4$

12. $\mathbf{F}(x, y, z) = x^4\mathbf{i} - x^3z^2\,\mathbf{j} + 4xy^2z\,\mathbf{k}$,
S is the surface of the solid bounded by the cylinder $x^2 + y^2 = 1$ and the planes $z = x + 2$ and $z = 0$

13. $\mathbf{F}(x, y, z) = 4x^3z\,\mathbf{i} + 4y^3z\,\mathbf{j} + 3z^4\,\mathbf{k}$,
S is the sphere with radius R and center the origin

14. $\mathbf{F} = \mathbf{r}/|\mathbf{r}|$, where $r = x\,\mathbf{i} + y\,\mathbf{j} + z\,\mathbf{k}$,
S consists of the hemisphere $z = \sqrt{1 - x^2 - y^2}$ and the
disk $x^2 + y^2 \leqslant 1$ in the xy-plane

CAS 15. $\mathbf{F}(x, y, z) = e^y \tan z\,\mathbf{i} + y\sqrt{3 - x^2}\,\mathbf{j} + x \sin y\,\mathbf{k}$,
S is the surface of the solid that lies above the xy-plane
and below the surface $z = 2 - x^4 - y^4$, $-1 \leqslant x \leqslant 1$,
$-1 \leqslant y \leqslant 1$

CAS 16. Use a computer algebra system to plot the vector field
$\mathbf{F}(x, y, z) = \sin x \cos^2 y\,\mathbf{i} + \sin^3 y \cos^4 z\,\mathbf{j} + \sin^5 z \cos^6 x\,\mathbf{k}$
in the cube cut from the first octant by the planes $x = \pi/2$,
$y = \pi/2$, and $z = \pi/2$. Then compute the flux across the
surface of the cube.

17. Use the Divergence Theorem to evaluate $\iint_S \mathbf{F} \cdot d\mathbf{S}$, where
$\mathbf{F}(x, y, z) = z^2 x\,\mathbf{i} + \left(\frac{1}{3}y^3 + \tan z\right)\mathbf{j} + (x^2 z + y^2)\,\mathbf{k}$
and S is the top half of the sphere $x^2 + y^2 + z^2 = 1$.
[*Hint:* Note that S is not a closed surface. First compute
integrals over S_1 and S_2, where S_1 is the disk $x^2 + y^2 \leqslant 1$,
oriented downward, and $S_2 = S \cup S_1$.]

18. Let $\mathbf{F}(x, y, z) = z \tan^{-1}(y^2)\,\mathbf{i} + z^3 \ln(x^2 + 1)\,\mathbf{j} + z\,\mathbf{k}$.
Find the flux of $\mathbf{F}$ across the part of the paraboloid
$x^2 + y^2 + z = 2$ that lies above the plane $z = 1$ and is
oriented upward.

19. A vector field $\mathbf{F}$ is shown. Use the interpretation of divergence derived in this section to determine whether div $\mathbf{F}$
is positive or negative at P_1 and at P_2.

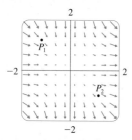

20. (a) Are the points P_1 and P_2 sources or sinks for the vector
field $\mathbf{F}$ shown in the figure? Give an explanation based
solely on the picture.
(b) Given that $\mathbf{F}(x, y) = \langle x, y^2 \rangle$, use the definition of divergence to verify your answer to part (a).

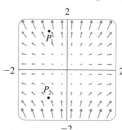

CAS 21–22 Plot the vector field and guess where div $\mathbf{F} > 0$ and
where div $\mathbf{F} < 0$. Then calculate div $\mathbf{F}$ to check your guess.

21. $\mathbf{F}(x, y) = \langle xy, x + y^2 \rangle$

22. $F(x, y) = \langle x^2, y^2 \rangle$

23. Verify that div $\mathbf{E} = 0$ for the electric field $\mathbf{E}(\mathbf{x}) = \dfrac{\varepsilon Q}{|\mathbf{x}|^3}\,\mathbf{x}$.

24. Use the Divergence Theorem to evaluate $\iint_S (2x + 2y + z^2)\,dS$
where S is the sphere $x^2 + y^2 + z^2 = 1$.

25–30 Prove each identity, assuming that S and E satisfy the conditions of the Divergence Theorem and the scalar functions and
components of the vector fields have continuous second-order
partial derivatives.

25. $\displaystyle\iint_S \mathbf{a} \cdot \mathbf{n}\, dS = 0$, where $\mathbf{a}$ is a constant vector

26. $V(E) = \frac{1}{3} \displaystyle\iint_S \mathbf{F} \cdot d\mathbf{S}$, where $\mathbf{F}(x, y, z) = x\,\mathbf{i} + y\,\mathbf{j} + z\,\mathbf{k}$

27. $\displaystyle\iint_S \text{curl } \mathbf{F} \cdot d\mathbf{S} = 0$

28. $\displaystyle\iint_S D_n f\, dS = \displaystyle\iiint_E \nabla^2 f\, dV$

29. $\displaystyle\iint_S (f \nabla g) \cdot \mathbf{n}\, dS = \displaystyle\iiint_E (f \nabla^2 g + \nabla f \cdot \nabla g)\, dV$

30. $\displaystyle\iint_S (f \nabla g - g \nabla f) \cdot \mathbf{n}\, dS = \displaystyle\iiint_E (f \nabla^2 g - g \nabla^2 f)\, dV$

31. Suppose S and E satisfy the conditions of the Divergence Theorem and f is a scalar function with continuous partial derivatives. Prove that

$$\iint_S f\mathbf{n}\, dS = \iiint_E \nabla f\, dV$$

These surface and triple integrals of vector functions are
vectors defined by integrating each component function.
[*Hint:* Start by applying the Divergence Theorem to $\mathbf{F} = f\mathbf{c}$,
where $\mathbf{c}$ is an arbitrary constant vector.]

32. A solid occupies a region E with surface S and is immersed in
a liquid with constant density ρ. We set up a coordinate
system so that the xy-plane coincides with the surface of the
liquid and positive values of z are measured downward into
the liquid. Then the pressure at depth z is $p = \rho g z$, where g is
the acceleration due to gravity (see Section 6.5). The total
buoyant force on the solid due to the pressure distribution is
given by the surface integral

$$\mathbf{F} = -\iint_S p\mathbf{n}\, dS$$

where $\mathbf{n}$ is the outer unit normal. Use the result of Exercise 31
to show that $\mathbf{F} = -W\mathbf{k}$, where W is the weight of the liquid
displaced by the solid. (Note that $\mathbf{F}$ is directed upward
because z is directed downward.) The result is *Archimedes'
principle:* The buoyant force on an object equals the weight of
the displaced liquid.

17.10 SUMMARY

The main results of this chapter are all higher-dimensional versions of the Fundamental Theorem of Calculus. To help you remember them, we collect them together here (without hypotheses) so that you can see more easily their essential similarity. Notice that in each case we have an integral of a "derivative" over a region on the left side, and the right side involves the values of the original function only on the *boundary* of the region.

Fundamental Theorem of Calculus

$$\int_a^b F'(x)\,dx = F(b) - F(a)$$

Fundamental Theorem for Line Integrals

$$\int_C \nabla f \cdot d\mathbf{r} = f(\mathbf{r}(b)) - f(\mathbf{r}(a))$$

Green's Theorem

$$\iint_D \left(\frac{\partial Q}{\partial x} - \frac{\partial P}{\partial y} \right) dA = \int_C P\,dx + Q\,dy$$

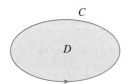

Stokes' Theorem

$$\iint_S \operatorname{curl} \mathbf{F} \cdot d\mathbf{S} = \int_C \mathbf{F} \cdot d\mathbf{r}$$

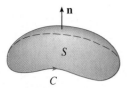

Divergence Theorem

$$\iiint_E \operatorname{div} \mathbf{F}\,dV = \iint_S \mathbf{F} \cdot d\mathbf{S}$$

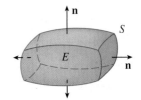

$$\boxed{17} \quad \text{REVIEW}$$

CONCEPT CHECK

1. What is a vector field? Give three examples that have physical meaning.

2. (a) What is a conservative vector field?
   (b) What is a potential function?

3. (a) Write the definition of the line integral of a scalar function f along a smooth curve C with respect to arc length.
   (b) How do you evaluate such a line integral?
   (c) Write expressions for the mass and center of mass of a thin wire shaped like a curve C if the wire has linear density function $\rho(x, y)$.
   (d) Write the definitions of the line integrals along C of a scalar function f with respect to x, y, and z.
   (e) How do you evaluate these line integrals?

4. (a) Define the line integral of a vector field $\mathbf{F}$ along a smooth curve C given by a vector function $\mathbf{r}(t)$.
   (b) If $\mathbf{F}$ is a force field, what does this line integral represent?
   (c) If $\mathbf{F} = \langle P, Q, R \rangle$, what is the connection between the line integral of $\mathbf{F}$ and the line integrals of the component functions P, Q, and R?

5. State the Fundamental Theorem for Line Integrals.

6. (a) What does it mean to say that $\int_C \mathbf{F} \cdot d\mathbf{r}$ is independent of path?
   (b) If you know that $\int_C \mathbf{F} \cdot d\mathbf{r}$ is independent of path, what can you say about $\mathbf{F}$?

7. State Green's Theorem.

8. Write expressions for the area enclosed by a curve C in terms of line integrals around C.

9. Suppose $\mathbf{F}$ is a vector field on $\mathbb{R}^3$.
   (a) Define curl $\mathbf{F}$.
   (b) Define div $\mathbf{F}$.

(c) If $\mathbf{F}$ is a velocity field in fluid flow, what are the physical interpretations of curl $\mathbf{F}$ and div $\mathbf{F}$?

10. If $\mathbf{F} = P\,\mathbf{i} + Q\,\mathbf{j}$, how do you test to determine whether $\mathbf{F}$ is conservative? What if $\mathbf{F}$ is a vector field on $\mathbb{R}^3$?

11. (a) What is a parametric surface? What are its grid curves?
    (b) Write an expression for the area of a parametric surface.
    (c) What is the area of a surface given by an equation $z = g(x, y)$?

12. (a) Write the definition of the surface integral of a scalar function f over a surface S.
    (b) How do you evaluate such an integral if S is a parametric surface given by a vector function $\mathbf{r}(u, v)$?
    (c) What if S is given by an equation $z = g(x, y)$?
    (d) If a thin sheet has the shape of a surface S, and the density at (x, y, z) is $\rho(x, y, z)$, write expressions for the mass and center of mass of the sheet.

13. (a) What is an oriented surface? Give an example of a non-orientable surface.
    (b) Define the surface integral (or flux) of a vector field $\mathbf{F}$ over an oriented surface S with unit normal vector $\mathbf{n}$.
    (c) How do you evaluate such an integral if S is a parametric surface given by a vector function $\mathbf{r}(u, v)$?
    (d) What if S is given by an equation $z = g(x, y)$?

14. State Stokes' Theorem.

15. State the Divergence Theorem.

16. In what ways are the Fundamental Theorem for Line Integrals, Green's Theorem, Stokes' Theorem, and the Divergence Theorem similar?

TRUE-FALSE QUIZ

Determine whether the statement is true or false. If it is true, explain why. If it is false, explain why or give an example that disproves the statement.

1. If $\mathbf{F}$ is a vector field, then div $\mathbf{F}$ is a vector field.

2. If $\mathbf{F}$ is a vector field, then curl $\mathbf{F}$ is a vector field.

3. If f has continuous partial derivatives of all orders on $\mathbb{R}^3$, then $\text{div}(\text{curl }\nabla f) = 0$.

4. If f has continuous partial derivatives on $\mathbb{R}^3$ and C is any circle, then $\int_C \nabla f \cdot d\mathbf{r} = 0$.

5. If $\mathbf{F} = P\,\mathbf{i} + Q\,\mathbf{j}$ and $P_y = Q_x$ in an open region D, then $\mathbf{F}$ is conservative.

6. $\int_{-C} f(x, y)\, ds = -\int_C f(x, y)\, ds$

7. If S is a sphere and $\mathbf{F}$ is a constant vector field, then $\iint_S \mathbf{F} \cdot d\mathbf{S} = 0$.

8. There is a vector field $\mathbf{F}$ such that

$$\text{curl } \mathbf{F} = x\,\mathbf{i} + y\,\mathbf{j} + z\,\mathbf{k}$$

EXERCISES

1. A vector field $\mathbf{F}$, a curve C, and a point P are shown.
  (a) Is $\int_C \mathbf{F} \cdot d\mathbf{r}$ positive, negative, or zero? Explain.
  (b) Is div $\mathbf{F}(P)$ positive, negative, or zero? Explain.

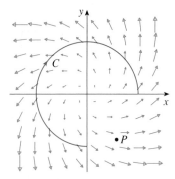

2–9 Evaluate the line integral.

2. $\int_C x\,ds$,
  C is the arc of the parabola $y = x^2$ from $(0, 0)$ to $(1, 1)$

3. $\int_C yz \cos x\,ds$,
  $C: x = t,\ y = 3 \cos t,\ z = 3 \sin t,\ 0 \le t \le \pi$

4. $\int_C y\,dx + (x + y^2)\,dy$, C is the ellipse $4x^2 + 9y^2 = 36$ with counterclockwise orientation

5. $\int_C y^3\,dx + x^2\,dy$, C is the arc of the parabola $x = 1 - y^2$
  from $(0, -1)$ to $(0, 1)$

6. $\int_C \sqrt{xy}\,dx + e^y\,dy + xz\,dz$,
  C is given by $\mathbf{r}(t) = t^4\,\mathbf{i} + t^2\,\mathbf{j} + t^3\,\mathbf{k},\ 0 \le t \le 1$

7. $\int_C xy\,dx + y^2\,dy + yz\,dz$,
  C is the line segment from $(1, 0, -1)$, to $(3, 4, 2)$

8. $\int_C \mathbf{F} \cdot d\mathbf{r}$, where $\mathbf{F}(x, y) = xy\,\mathbf{i} + x^2\,\mathbf{j}$ and C is given by
  $\mathbf{r}(t) = \sin t\,\mathbf{i} + (1 + t)\,\mathbf{j},\ 0 \le t \le \pi$

9. $\int_C \mathbf{F} \cdot d\mathbf{r}$, where $\mathbf{F}(x, y, z) = e^z\,\mathbf{i} + xz\,\mathbf{j} + (x + y)\,\mathbf{k}$ and
  C is given by $\mathbf{r}(t) = t^2\,\mathbf{i} + t^3\,\mathbf{j} - t\,\mathbf{k},\ 0 \le t \le 1$

10. Find the work done by the force field
  $\mathbf{F}(x, y, z) = z\,\mathbf{i} + x\,\mathbf{j} + y\,\mathbf{k}$ in moving a particle from the
  point $(3, 0, 0)$ to the point $(0, \pi/2, 3)$ along
  (a) a straight line
  (b) the helix $x = 3 \cos t,\ y = t,\ z = 3 \sin t$

11–12 Show that $\mathbf{F}$ is a conservative vector field. Then find a function f such that $\mathbf{F} = \nabla f$.

11. $\mathbf{F}(x, y) = (1 + xy)e^{xy}\,\mathbf{i} + (e^y + x^2 e^{xy})\,\mathbf{j}$

12. $\mathbf{F}(x, y, z) = \sin y\,\mathbf{i} + x \cos y\,\mathbf{j} - \sin z\,\mathbf{k}$

13–14 Show that $\mathbf{F}$ is conservative and use this fact to evaluate
$\int_C \mathbf{F} \cdot d\mathbf{r}$ along the given curve.

13. $\mathbf{F}(x, y) = (4x^3 y^2 - 2xy^3)\,\mathbf{i} + (2x^4 y - 3x^2 y^2 + 4y^3)\,\mathbf{j}$,
  $C: \mathbf{r}(t) = (t + \sin \pi t)\,\mathbf{i} + (2t + \cos \pi t)\,\mathbf{j},\ 0 \le t \le 1$

14. $\mathbf{F}(x, y, z) = e^y\,\mathbf{i} + (xe^y + e^z)\,\mathbf{j} + ye^z\,\mathbf{k}$,
  C is the line segment from $(0, 2, 0)$ to $(4, 0, 3)$

15. Verify that Green's Theorem is true for the line integral
  $\int_C xy^2\,dx - x^2 y\,dy$, where C consists of the parabola $y = x^2$
  from $(-1, 1)$ to $(1, 1)$ and the line segment from $(1, 1)$ to
  $(-1, 1)$.

16. Use Green's Theorem to evaluate $\int_C \sqrt{1 + x^3}\,dx + 2xy\,dy$,
  where C is the triangle with vertices $(0, 0)$, $(1, 0)$, and $(1, 3)$.

17. Use Green's Theorem to evaluate $\int_C x^2 y\,dx - xy^2\,dy$,
  where C is the circle $x^2 + y^2 = 4$ with counterclockwise
  orientation.

18. Find curl $\mathbf{F}$ and div $\mathbf{F}$ if

$$\mathbf{F}(x, y, z) = e^{-x} \sin y\,\mathbf{i} + e^{-y} \sin z\,\mathbf{j} + e^{-z} \sin x\,\mathbf{k}$$

19. Show that there is no vector field $\mathbf{G}$ such that
  curl $\mathbf{G} = 2x\,\mathbf{i} + 3yz\,\mathbf{j} - xz^2\,\mathbf{k}$.

20. Show that, under conditions to be stated on the vector fields $\mathbf{F}$
  and $\mathbf{G}$,

  curl$(\mathbf{F} \times \mathbf{G}) = \mathbf{F}$ div $\mathbf{G} - \mathbf{G}$ div $\mathbf{F} + (\mathbf{G} \cdot \nabla)\mathbf{F} - (\mathbf{F} \cdot \nabla)\mathbf{G}$

21. If C is any piecewise-smooth simple closed plane curve
  and f and g are differentiable functions, show that
  $\int_C f(x)\,dx + g(y)\,dy = 0$.

22. If f and g are twice differentiable functions, show that

$$\nabla^2(fg) = f\nabla^2 g + g\nabla^2 f + 2\nabla f \cdot \nabla g$$

23. If f is a harmonic function, that is, $\nabla^2 f = 0$, show that the line
  integral $\int f_y\,dx - f_x\,dy$ is independent of path in any simple
  region D.

24. (a) Sketch the curve C with parametric equations

  $$x = \cos t \qquad y = \sin t \qquad z = \sin t \qquad 0 \le t \le 2\pi$$

  (b) Find $\int_C 2xe^{2y}\,dx + (2x^2 e^{2y} + 2y \cot z)\,dy - y^2 \csc^2 z\,dz$.

25. Find the area of the part of the surface $z = x^2 + 2y$ that lies
  above the triangle with vertices $(0, 0)$, $(1, 0)$, and $(1, 2)$.

26. (a) Find an equation of the tangent plane at the point $(4, -2, 1)$
  to the parametric surface S given by

  $$\mathbf{r}(u, v) = v^2\,\mathbf{i} - uv\,\mathbf{j} + u^2\,\mathbf{k} \qquad 0 \le u \le 3,\ -3 \le v \le 3$$

(b) Use a computer to graph the surface S and the tangent plane found in part (a).

(c) Set up, but do not evaluate, an integral for the surface area of S.

(d) If

$$\mathbf{F}(x, y, z) = \frac{z^2}{1 + x^2}\mathbf{i} + \frac{x^2}{1 + y^2}\mathbf{j} + \frac{y^2}{1 + z^2}\mathbf{k}$$

find $\iint_S \mathbf{F} \cdot d\mathbf{S}$ correct to four decimal places.

27–30 Evaluate the surface integral.

27. $\iint_S z \, dS$, where S is the part of the paraboloid $z = x^2 + y^2$ that lies under the plane $z = 4$

28. $\iint_S (x^2 z + y^2 z) \, dS$, where S is the part of the plane $z = 4 + x + y$ that lies inside the cylinder $x^2 + y^2 = 4$

29. $\iint_S \mathbf{F} \cdot d\mathbf{S}$, where $\mathbf{F}(x, y, z) = xz\,\mathbf{i} - 2y\,\mathbf{j} + 3x\,\mathbf{k}$ and S is the sphere $x^2 + y^2 + z^2 = 4$ with outward orientation

30. $\iint_S \mathbf{F} \cdot d\mathbf{S}$, where $\mathbf{F}(x, y, z) = x^2\mathbf{i} + xy\,\mathbf{j} + z\,\mathbf{k}$ and S is the part of the paraboloid $z = x^2 + y^2$ below the plane $z = 1$ with upward orientation

---

31. Verify that Stokes' Theorem is true for the vector field $\mathbf{F}(x, y, z) = x^2\mathbf{i} + y^2\mathbf{j} + z^2\mathbf{k}$, where S is the part of the paraboloid $z = 1 - x^2 - y^2$ that lies above the xy-plane and S has upward orientation.

32. Use Stokes' Theorem to evaluate $\iint_S \text{curl } \mathbf{F} \cdot d\mathbf{S}$, where $\mathbf{F}(x, y, z) = x^2 yz\,\mathbf{i} + yz^2\mathbf{j} + z^3 e^{xy}\mathbf{k}$, S is the part of the sphere $x^2 + y^2 + z^2 = 5$ that lies above the plane $z = 1$, and S is oriented upward.

33. Use Stokes' Theorem to evaluate $\int_C \mathbf{F} \cdot d\mathbf{r}$, where $\mathbf{F}(x, y, z) = xy\,\mathbf{i} + yz\,\mathbf{j} + zx\,\mathbf{k}$, and C is the triangle with vertices $(1, 0, 0)$, $(0, 1, 0)$, and $(0, 0, 1)$, oriented counterclockwise as viewed from above.

34. Use the Divergence Theorem to calculate the surface integral $\iint_S \mathbf{F} \cdot d\mathbf{S}$, where $\mathbf{F}(x, y, z) = x^3\mathbf{i} + y^3\mathbf{j} + z^3\mathbf{k}$ and S is the surface of the solid bounded by the cylinder $x^2 + y^2 = 1$ and the planes $z = 0$ and $z = 2$.

35. Verify that the Divergence Theorem is true for the vector field $\mathbf{F}(x, y, z) = x\mathbf{i} + y\mathbf{j} + z\mathbf{k}$, where E is the unit ball $x^2 + y^2 + z^2 \leq 1$.

36. Compute the outward flux of

$$\mathbf{F}(x, y, z) = \frac{x\mathbf{i} + y\mathbf{j} + z\mathbf{k}}{(x^2 + y^2 + z^2)^{3/2}}$$

through the ellipsoid $4x^2 + 9y^2 + 6z^2 = 36$.

37. Let

$$\mathbf{F}(x, y, z) = (3x^2 yz - 3y)\mathbf{i} + (x^3 z - 3x)\mathbf{j} + (x^3 y + 2z)\mathbf{k}$$

Evaluate $\int_C \mathbf{F} \cdot d\mathbf{r}$, where C is the curve with initial point $(0, 0, 2)$ and terminal point $(0, 3, 0)$ shown in the figure.

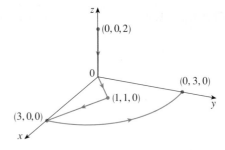

38. Let

$$\mathbf{F}(x, y) = \frac{(2x^3 + 2xy^2 - 2y)\,\mathbf{i} + (2y^3 + 2x^2 y + 2x)\,\mathbf{j}}{x^2 + y^2}$$

Evaluate $\oint_C \mathbf{F} \cdot d\mathbf{r}$, where C is shown in the figure.

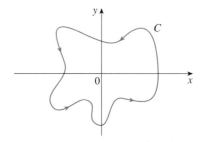

39. Find $\iint_S \mathbf{F} \cdot \mathbf{n} \, dS$, where $\mathbf{F}(x, y, z) = x\mathbf{i} + y\mathbf{j} + z\mathbf{k}$ and S is the outwardly oriented surface shown in the figure (the boundary surface of a cube with a unit corner cube removed).

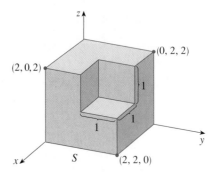

40. If the components of $\mathbf{F}$ have continuous second partial derivatives and S is the boundary surface of a simple solid region, show that $\iint_S \text{curl } \mathbf{F} \cdot d\mathbf{S} = 0$.

41. If $\mathbf{a}$ is a constant vector, $\mathbf{r} = x\mathbf{i} + y\mathbf{j} + z\mathbf{k}$, and S is an oriented, smooth surface with a simple, closed, smooth, positively oriented boundary curve C, show that

$$\iint_S 2\mathbf{a} \cdot d\mathbf{S} = \int_C (\mathbf{a} \times \mathbf{r}) \cdot d\mathbf{r}$$

PROBLEMS PLUS

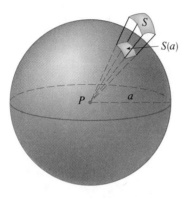

FIGURE FOR PROBLEM 1

1. Let S be a smooth parametric surface and let P be a point such that each line that starts at P intersects S at most once. The **solid angle** $\Omega(S)$ subtended by S at P is the set of lines starting at P and passing through S. Let $S(a)$ be the intersection of $\Omega(S)$ with the surface of the sphere with center P and radius a. Then the measure of the solid angle (in *steradians*) is defined to be

$$|\Omega(S)| = \frac{\text{area of } S(a)}{a^2}$$

Apply the Divergence Theorem to the part of $\Omega(S)$ between $S(a)$ and S to show that

$$|\Omega(S)| = \iint_S \frac{\mathbf{r} \cdot \mathbf{n}}{r^3} \, dS$$

where $\mathbf{r}$ is the radius vector from P to any point on S, $r = |\mathbf{r}|$, and the unit normal vector $\mathbf{n}$ is directed away from P.

This shows that the definition of the measure of a solid angle is independent of the radius a of the sphere. Thus the measure of the solid angle is equal to the area subtended on a *unit* sphere. (Note the analogy with the definition of radian measure.) The total solid angle subtended by a sphere at its center is thus 4π steradians.

2. Find the positively oriented simple closed curve C for which the value of the line integral $\int_C (y^3 - y) \, dx - 2x^3 \, dy$ is a maximum.

3. Let C be a simple closed piecewise-smooth space curve that lies in a plane with unit normal vector $\mathbf{n} = \langle a, b, c \rangle$ and has positive orientation with respect to $\mathbf{n}$. Show that the plane area enclosed by C is $\frac{1}{2} \int_C (bz - cy) \, dx + (cx - az) \, dy + (ay - bx) \, dz$.

4. Investigate the shape of the surface with parametric equations $x = \sin u$, $y = \sin v$, $z = \sin(u + v)$. Start by graphing the surface from several points of view. Explain the appearance of the graphs by determining the traces in the horizontal planes $z = 0$, $z = \pm 1$, and $z = \pm \frac{1}{2}$.

5. Prove the following identity:

$$\nabla(\mathbf{F} \cdot \mathbf{G}) = (\mathbf{F} \cdot \nabla)\mathbf{G} + (\mathbf{G} \cdot \nabla)\mathbf{F} + \mathbf{F} \times \text{curl } \mathbf{G} + \mathbf{G} \times \text{curl } \mathbf{F}$$

FIGURE FOR PROBLEM 6

6. The figure depicts the sequence of events in each cylinder of a four-cylinder internal combustion engine. Each piston moves up and down and is connected by a pivoted arm to a rotating crankshaft. Let $P(t)$ and $V(t)$ be the pressure and volume within a cylinder at time t, where $a \leq t \leq b$ gives the time required for a complete cycle. The graph shows how P and V vary through one cycle of a four-stroke engine. During the intake stroke (from ① to ②) a mixture of air and gasoline at atmospheric pressure is drawn into a cylinder through the intake valve as the piston moves downward. Then the piston rapidly compresses the mix with the valves closed in the compression stroke (from ② to ③) during which the pressure rises and the volume decreases. At ③ the sparkplug ignites the fuel, raising the temperature and pressure at almost constant volume to ④. Then, with valves closed, the rapid expansion forces the piston downward during the power stroke (from ④ to ⑤). The exhaust valve opens, temperature and pressure drop, and mechanical energy stored in a rotating flywheel pushes the piston upward, forcing the waste products out of the exhaust valve in the exhaust stroke. The exhaust valve closes and the intake valve opens. We're now back at ① and the cycle starts again.

(a) Show that the work done on the piston during one cycle of a four-stroke engine is $W = \int_C P \, dV$, where C is the curve in the PV-plane shown in the figure.

[*Hint:* Let $x(t)$ be the distance from the piston to the top of the cylinder and note that the force on the piston is $\mathbf{F} = AP(t) \, \mathbf{i}$, where A is the area of the top of the piston. Then $W = \int_{C_1} \mathbf{F} \cdot d\mathbf{r}$, where C_1 is given by $\mathbf{r}(t) = x(t) \, \mathbf{i}$, $a \leq t \leq b$. An alternative approach is to work directly with Riemann sums.]

(b) Use Formula 17.4.5 to show that the work is the difference of the areas enclosed by the two loops of C.

APPENDIXES

A **NUMBERS, INEQUALITIES, AND ABSOLUTE VALUES**

Calculus is based on the real number system. We start with the **integers**:

$$\ldots, \quad -3, \quad -2, \quad -1, \quad 0, \quad 1, \quad 2, \quad 3, \quad 4, \quad \ldots$$

Then we construct the **rational numbers**, which are ratios of integers. Thus any rational number r can be expressed as

$$r = \frac{m}{n} \qquad \text{where } m \text{ and } n \text{ are integers and } n \neq 0$$

Examples are

$$\tfrac{1}{2} \qquad -\tfrac{3}{7} \qquad 46 = \tfrac{46}{1} \qquad 0.17 = \tfrac{17}{100}$$

(Recall that division by 0 is always ruled out, so expressions like $\frac{3}{0}$ and $\frac{0}{0}$ are undefined.) Some real numbers, such as $\sqrt{2}$, can't be expressed as a ratio of integers and are therefore called **irrational numbers**. It can be shown, with varying degrees of difficulty, that the following are also irrational numbers:

$$\sqrt{3} \qquad \sqrt{5} \qquad \sqrt[3]{2} \qquad \pi \qquad \sin 1° \qquad \log_{10} 2$$

The set of all real numbers is usually denoted by the symbol $\mathbb{R}$. When we use the word *number* without qualification, we mean "real number."

Every number has a decimal representation. If the number is rational, then the corresponding decimal is repeating. For example,

$$\tfrac{1}{2} = 0.5000\ldots = 0.5\overline{0} \qquad\qquad \tfrac{2}{3} = 0.66666\ldots = 0.\overline{6}$$

$$\tfrac{157}{495} = 0.317171717\ldots = 0.3\overline{17} \qquad \tfrac{9}{7} = 1.285714285714\ldots = 1.\overline{285714}$$

(The bar indicates that the sequence of digits repeats forever.) On the other hand, if the number is irrational, the decimal is nonrepeating:

$$\sqrt{2} = 1.414213562373095\ldots \qquad \pi = 3.141592653589793\ldots$$

If we stop the decimal expansion of any number at a certain place, we get an approximation to the number. For instance, we can write

$$\pi \approx 3.14159265$$

where the symbol $\approx$ is read "is approximately equal to." The more decimal places we retain, the better the approximation we get.

The real numbers can be represented by points on a line as in Figure 1. The positive direction (to the right) is indicated by an arrow. We choose an arbitrary reference point O, called the **origin**, which corresponds to the real number 0. Given any convenient unit of measurement, each positive number x is represented by the point on the line a distance of x units to the right of the origin, and each negative number $-x$ is represented by the point x units to the left of the origin. Thus every real number is represented by a point on the line, and every point P on the line corresponds to exactly one real number. The number associated with the point P is called the **coordinate** of P and the line is then called a **coor-**

dinate line**, or a **real number line**, or simply a **real line**. Often we identify the point with its coordinate and think of a number as being a point on the real line.

FIGURE 1

The real numbers are ordered. We say *a is less than b* and write $a < b$ if $b - a$ is a positive number. Geometrically this means that a lies to the left of b on the number line. (Equivalently, we say *b is greater than a* and write $b > a$.) The symbol $a \leqslant b$ (or $b \geqslant a$) means that either $a < b$ or $a = b$ and is read "*a* is less than or equal to *b*." For instance, the following are true inequalities:

$$7 < 7.4 < 7.5 \qquad -3 > -\pi \qquad \sqrt{2} < 2 \qquad \sqrt{2} \leqslant 2 \qquad 2 \leqslant 2$$

In what follows we need to use *set notation*. A **set** is a collection of objects, and these objects are called the **elements** of the set. If S is a set, the notation $a \in S$ means that a is an element of S, and $a \notin S$ means that a is not an element of S. For example, if Z represents the set of integers, then $-3 \in Z$ but $\pi \notin Z$. If S and T are sets, then their **union** $S \cup T$ is the set consisting of all elements that are in S or T (or in both S and T). The **intersection** of S and T is the set $S \cap T$ consisting of all elements that are in both S and T. In other words, $S \cap T$ is the common part of S and T. The empty set, denoted by $\varnothing$, is the set that contains no element.

Some sets can be described by listing their elements between braces. For instance, the set A consisting of all positive integers less than 7 can be written as

$$A = \{1, 2, 3, 4, 5, 6\}$$

We could also write A in *set-builder notation* as

$$A = \{x \,|\, x \text{ is an integer and } 0 < x < 7\}$$

which is read "A is the set of x such that x is an integer and $0 < x < 7$."

INTERVALS

Certain sets of real numbers, called **intervals,** occur frequently in calculus and correspond geometrically to line segments. For example, if $a < b$, the **open interval** from a to b consists of all numbers between a and b and is denoted by the symbol (a, b). Using set-builder notation, we can write

$$(a, b) = \{x \,|\, a < x < b\}$$

FIGURE 2
Open interval (a, b)

Notice that the endpoints of the interval—namely, a and b—are excluded. This is indicated by the round brackets ( ) and by the open dots in Figure 2. The **closed interval** from a to b is the set

$$[a, b] = \{x \,|\, a \leqslant x \leqslant b\}$$

FIGURE 3
Closed interval $[a, b]$

Here the endpoints of the interval are included. This is indicated by the square brackets [ ] and by the solid dots in Figure 3. It is also possible to include only one endpoint in an interval, as shown in Table 1.

1 **TABLE OF INTERVALS**

■ Table 1 lists the nine possible types of intervals. When these intervals are discussed, it is always assumed that $a < b$.

Notation	Set description	Picture
(a, b)	$\{x \mid a < x < b\}$	
$[a, b]$	$\{x \mid a \le x \le b\}$	
$[a, b)$	$\{x \mid a \le x < b\}$	
$(a, b]$	$\{x \mid a < x \le b\}$	
(a, ∞)	$\{x \mid x > a\}$	
$[a, \infty)$	$\{x \mid x \ge a\}$	
$(-\infty, b)$	$\{x \mid x < b\}$	
$(-\infty, b]$	$\{x \mid x \le b\}$	
$(-\infty, \infty)$	$\mathbb{R}$ (set of all real numbers)	

We also need to consider infinite intervals such as

$$(a, \infty) = \{x \mid x > a\}$$

This does not mean that ∞ ("infinity") is a number. The notation (a, ∞) stands for the set of all numbers that are greater than a, so the symbol ∞ simply indicates that the interval extends indefinitely far in the positive direction.

INEQUALITIES

When working with inequalities, note the following rules.

2 **RULES FOR INEQUALITIES**

1. If $a < b$, then $a + c < b + c$.

2. If $a < b$ and $c < d$, then $a + c < b + d$.

3. If $a < b$ and $c > 0$, then $ac < bc$.

4. If $a < b$ and $c < 0$, then $ac > bc$.

5. If $0 < a < b$, then $1/a > 1/b$.

Rule 1 says that we can add any number to both sides of an inequality, and Rule 2 says that two inequalities can be added. However, we have to be careful with multiplication. Rule 3 says that we can multiply both sides of an inequality by a *positive* number, but ⊘ Rule 4 says that if we multiply both sides of an inequality by a negative number, then we reverse the direction of the inequality. For example, if we take the inequality $3 < 5$ and multiply by 2, we get $6 < 10$, but if we multiply by -2, we get $-6 > -10$. Finally, Rule 5 says that if we take reciprocals, then we reverse the direction of an inequality (provided the numbers are positive).

EXAMPLE 1 Solve the inequality $1 + x < 7x + 5$.

SOLUTION The given inequality is satisfied by some values of x but not by others. To *solve* an inequality means to determine the set of numbers x for which the inequality is true. This is called the *solution set*.

First we subtract 1 from each side of the inequality (using Rule 1 with $c = -1$):

$$x < 7x + 4$$

Then we subtract $7x$ from both sides (Rule 1 with $c = -7x$):

$$-6x < 4$$

Now we divide both sides by -6 $\left(\text{Rule 4 with } c = -\tfrac{1}{6}\right)$:

$$x > -\tfrac{4}{6} = -\tfrac{2}{3}$$

These steps can all be reversed, so the solution set consists of all numbers greater than $-\tfrac{2}{3}$. In other words, the solution of the inequality is the interval $\left(-\tfrac{2}{3}, \infty\right)$.

EXAMPLE 2 Solve the inequalities $4 \leqslant 3x - 2 < 13$.

SOLUTION Here the solution set consists of all values of x that satisfy both inequalities. Using the rules given in (2), we see that the following inequalities are equivalent:

$$4 \leqslant 3x - 2 < 13$$

$$6 \leqslant 3x < 15 \qquad \text{(add 2)}$$

$$2 \leqslant x < 5 \qquad \text{(divide by 3)}$$

Therefore the solution set is $[2, 5)$.

EXAMPLE 3 Solve the inequality $x^2 - 5x + 6 \leqslant 0$.

SOLUTION First we factor the left side:

$$(x - 2)(x - 3) \leqslant 0$$

We know that the corresponding equation $(x - 2)(x - 3) = 0$ has the solutions 2 and 3. The numbers 2 and 3 divide the real line into three intervals:

$$(-\infty, 2) \qquad (2, 3) \qquad (3, \infty)$$

On each of these intervals we determine the signs of the factors. For instance,

$$x \in (-\infty, 2) \quad \Rightarrow \quad x < 2 \quad \Rightarrow \quad x - 2 < 0$$

Then we record these signs in the following chart:

Interval	$x - 2$	$x - 3$	$(x - 2)(x - 3)$
$x < 2$	$-$	$-$	$+$
$2 < x < 3$	$+$	$-$	$-$
$x > 3$	$+$	$+$	$+$

A visual method for solving Example 3 is to use a graphing device to graph the parabola $y = x^2 - 5x + 6$ (as in Figure 4) and observe that the curve lies on or below the x-axis when $2 \leqslant x \leqslant 3$.

FIGURE 4

Another method for obtaining the information in the chart is to use *test values*. For instance, if we use the test value $x = 1$ for the interval $(-\infty, 2)$, then substitution in $x^2 - 5x + 6$ gives

$$1^2 - 5(1) + 6 = 2$$

The polynomial $x^2 - 5x + 6$ doesn't change sign inside any of the three intervals, so we conclude that it is positive on $(-\infty, 2)$.

Then we read from the chart that $(x - 2)(x - 3)$ is negative when $2 < x < 3$. Thus the solution of the inequality $(x - 2)(x - 3) \leqslant 0$ is

$$\{x \mid 2 \leqslant x \leqslant 3\} = [2, 3]$$

Notice that we have included the endpoints 2 and 3 because we are looking for values of x such that the product is either negative or zero. The solution is illustrated in Figure 5. □

EXAMPLE 4 Solve $x^3 + 3x^2 > 4x$.

SOLUTION First we take all nonzero terms to one side of the inequality sign and factor the resulting expression:

$$x^3 + 3x^2 - 4x > 0 \qquad \text{or} \qquad x(x - 1)(x + 4) > 0$$

As in Example 3 we solve the corresponding equation $x(x - 1)(x + 4) = 0$ and use the solutions $x = -4$, $x = 0$, and $x = 1$ to divide the real line into four intervals $(-\infty, -4)$, $(-4, 0)$, $(0, 1)$, and $(1, \infty)$. On each interval the product keeps a constant sign as shown in the following chart:

Interval	x	$x - 1$	$x + 4$	$x(x - 1)(x + 4)$
$x < -4$	$-$	$-$	$-$	$-$
$-4 < x < 0$	$-$	$-$	$+$	$+$
$0 < x < 1$	$+$	$-$	$+$	$-$
$x > 1$	$+$	$+$	$+$	$+$

Then we read from the chart that the solution set is

$$\{x \mid -4 < x < 0 \text{ or } x > 1\} = (-4, 0) \cup (1, \infty)$$

The solution is illustrated in Figure 6. □

FIGURE 5

FIGURE 6

ABSOLUTE VALUE

The **absolute value** of a number a, denoted by $|a|$, is the distance from a to 0 on the real number line. Distances are always positive or 0, so we have

$$|a| \geqslant 0 \qquad \text{for every number } a$$

For example,

$$|3| = 3 \qquad |-3| = 3 \qquad |0| = 0 \qquad |\sqrt{2} - 1| = \sqrt{2} - 1 \qquad |3 - \pi| = \pi - 3$$

In general, we have

■ Remember that if a is negative, then $-a$ is positive.

$\boxed{3}$

$$\boxed{\begin{aligned} |a| &= a \qquad \text{if } a \geqslant 0 \\ |a| &= -a \qquad \text{if } a < 0 \end{aligned}}$$

EXAMPLE 5 Express $|3x - 2|$ without using the absolute-value symbol.

SOLUTION

$$|3x - 2| = \begin{cases} 3x - 2 & \text{if } 3x - 2 \geq 0 \\ -(3x - 2) & \text{if } 3x - 2 < 0 \end{cases}$$

$$= \begin{cases} 3x - 2 & \text{if } x \geq \frac{2}{3} \\ 2 - 3x & \text{if } x < \frac{2}{3} \end{cases}$$

Recall that the symbol $\sqrt{}$ means "the positive square root of." Thus $\sqrt{r} = s$ means $s^2 = r$ and $s \geq 0$. Therefore, the equation $\sqrt{a^2} = a$ is not always true. It is true only when $a \geq 0$. If $a < 0$, then $-a > 0$, so we have $\sqrt{a^2} = -a$. In view of (3), we then have the equation

$$\boxed{4} \qquad \boxed{\sqrt{a^2} = |a|}$$

which is true for all values of a.

Hints for the proofs of the following properties are given in the exercises.

> **5 PROPERTIES OF ABSOLUTE VALUES** Suppose a and b are any real numbers and n is an integer. Then
>
> **1.** $|ab| = |a||b|$ **2.** $\left|\dfrac{a}{b}\right| = \dfrac{|a|}{|b|}$ $(b \neq 0)$ **3.** $|a^n| = |a|^n$

For solving equations or inequalities involving absolute values, it's often very helpful to use the following statements.

> **6** Suppose $a > 0$. Then
> **4.** $|x| = a$ if and only if $x = \pm a$
> **5.** $|x| < a$ if and only if $-a < x < a$
> **6.** $|x| > a$ if and only if $x > a$ or $x < -a$

FIGURE 7

For instance, the inequality $|x| < a$ says that the distance from x to the origin is less than a, and you can see from Figure 7 that this is true if and only if x lies between $-a$ and a.

If a and b are any real numbers, then the distance between a and b is the absolute value of the difference, namely, $|a - b|$, which is also equal to $|b - a|$. (See Figure 8.)

EXAMPLE 6 Solve $|2x - 5| = 3$.

SOLUTION By Property 4 of (6), $|2x - 5| = 3$ is equivalent to

$$2x - 5 = 3 \qquad \text{or} \qquad 2x - 5 = -3$$

FIGURE 8
Length of a line segment $= |a - b|$

So $2x = 8$ or $2x = 2$. Thus $x = 4$ or $x = 1$.

EXAMPLE 7 Solve $|x - 5| < 2$.

SOLUTION 1 By Property 5 of (6), $|x - 5| < 2$ is equivalent to

$$-2 < x - 5 < 2$$

Therefore, adding 5 to each side, we have

$$3 < x < 7$$

and the solution set is the open interval $(3, 7)$.

SOLUTION 2 Geometrically the solution set consists of all numbers x whose distance from 5 is less than 2. From Figure 9 we see that this is the interval $(3, 7)$.   □

FIGURE 9

EXAMPLE 8 Solve $|3x + 2| \geq 4$.

SOLUTION By Properties 4 and 6 of (6), $|3x + 2| \geq 4$ is equivalent to

$$3x + 2 \geq 4 \qquad \text{or} \qquad 3x + 2 \leq -4$$

In the first case $3x \geq 2$, which gives $x \geq \frac{2}{3}$. In the second case $3x \leq -6$, which gives $x \leq -2$. So the solution set is

$$\left\{ x \mid x \leq -2 \ \text{ or } \ x \geq \tfrac{2}{3} \right\} = (-\infty, -2] \cup \left[\tfrac{2}{3}, \infty\right)$$ □

Another important property of absolute value, called the Triangle Inequality, is used frequently not only in calculus but throughout mathematics in general.

---

7 **THE TRIANGLE INEQUALITY** If a and b are any real numbers, then

$$|a + b| \leq |a| + |b|$$

Observe that if the numbers a and b are both positive or both negative, then the two sides in the Triangle Inequality are actually equal. But if a and b have opposite signs, the left side involves a subtraction and the right side does not. This makes the Triangle Inequality seem reasonable, but we can prove it as follows.

Notice that

$$-|a| \leq a \leq |a|$$

is always true because a equals either $|a|$ or $-|a|$. The corresponding statement for b is

$$-|b| \leq b \leq |b|$$

Adding these inequalities, we get

$$-(|a| + |b|) \leq a + b \leq |a| + |b|$$

If we now apply Properties 4 and 5 $\big($with x replaced by $a + b$ and a by $|a| + |b|\big)$, we obtain

$$|a + b| \leq |a| + |b|$$

which is what we wanted to show.

EXAMPLE 9 If $|x - 4| < 0.1$ and $|y - 7| < 0.2$, use the Triangle Inequality to estimate $|(x + y) - 11|$.

SOLUTION In order to use the given information, we use the Triangle Inequality with $a = x - 4$ and $b = y - 7$:

$$|(x + y) - 11| = |(x - 4) + (y - 7)|$$
$$\leq |x - 4| + |y - 7|$$
$$< 0.1 + 0.2 = 0.3$$

Thus $\qquad |(x + y) - 11| < 0.3$ ☐

A EXERCISES

1–12 Rewrite the expression without using the absolute value symbol.

1. $|5 - 23|$

2. $|5| - |-23|$

3. $|-\pi|$

4. $|\pi - 2|$

5. $|\sqrt{5} - 5|$

6. $||-2| - |-3||$

7. $|x - 2|$ if $x < 2$

8. $|x - 2|$ if $x > 2$

9. $|x + 1|$

10. $|2x - 1|$

11. $|x^2 + 1|$

12. $|1 - 2x^2|$

13–38 Solve the inequality in terms of intervals and illustrate the solution set on the real number line.

13. $2x + 7 > 3$

14. $3x - 11 < 4$

15. $1 - x \leq 2$

16. $4 - 3x \geq 6$

17. $2x + 1 < 5x - 8$

18. $1 + 5x > 5 - 3x$

19. $-1 < 2x - 5 < 7$

20. $1 < 3x + 4 \leq 16$

21. $0 \leq 1 - x < 1$

22. $-5 \leq 3 - 2x \leq 9$

23. $4x < 2x + 1 \leq 3x + 2$

24. $2x - 3 < x + 4 < 3x - 2$

25. $(x - 1)(x - 2) > 0$

26. $(2x + 3)(x - 1) \leq 0$

27. $2x^2 + x \leq 1$

28. $(2x + 3)(x - 1) \geq 0$

29. $x^2 + x + 1 > 0$

30. $x^2 + x > 1$

31. $x^2 < 3$

32. $x^2 \geq 5$

33. $x^3 - x^2 \leq 0$

34. $(x + 1)(x - 2)(x + 3) \geq 0$

35. $x^3 > x$

36. $x^3 + 3x < 4x^2$

37. $\dfrac{1}{x} < 4$

38. $-3 < \dfrac{1}{x} \leq 1$

39. The relationship between the Celsius and Fahrenheit temperature scales is given by $C = \frac{5}{9}(F - 32)$, where C is the temper-

ature in degrees Celsius and F is the temperature in degrees Fahrenheit. What interval on the Celsius scale corresponds to the temperature range $50 \leq F \leq 95$?

40. Use the relationship between C and F given in Exercise 39 to find the interval on the Fahrenheit scale corresponding to the temperature range $20 \leq C \leq 30$.

41. As dry air moves upward, it expands and in so doing cools at a rate of about 1°C for each 100-m rise, up to about 12 km.
 (a) If the ground temperature is 20°C, write a formula for the temperature at height h.
 (b) What range of temperature can be expected if a plane takes off and reaches a maximum height of 5 km?

42. If a ball is thrown upward from the top of a building 128 ft high with an initial velocity of 16 ft/s, then the height h above the ground t seconds later will be

$$h = 128 + 16t - 16t^2$$

During what time interval will the ball be at least 32 ft above the ground?

43–46 Solve the equation for x.

43. $|2x| = 3$

44. $|3x + 5| = 1$

45. $|x + 3| = |2x + 1|$

46. $\left|\dfrac{2x - 1}{x + 1}\right| = 3$

47–56 Solve the inequality.

47. $|x| < 3$

48. $|x| \geq 3$

49. $|x - 4| < 1$

50. $|x - 6| < 0.1$

51. $|x + 5| \geq 2$

52. $|x + 1| \geq 3$

53. $|2x - 3| \leq 0.4$

54. $|5x - 2| < 6$

55. $1 \leq |x| \leq 4$

56. $0 < |x - 5| < \frac{1}{2}$

57–58 Solve for x, assuming a, b, and c are positive constants.

57. $a(bx - c) \geqslant bc$ **58.** $a \leqslant bx + c < 2a$

59–60 Solve for x, assuming a, b, and c are negative constants.

59. $ax + b < c$ **60.** $\dfrac{ax + b}{c} \leqslant b$

61. Suppose that $|x - 2| < 0.01$ and $|y - 3| < 0.04$. Use the Triangle Inequality to show that $|(x + y) - 5| < 0.05$.

62. Show that if $|x + 3| < \frac{1}{2}$, then $|4x + 13| < 3$.

63. Show that if $a < b$, then $a < \dfrac{a + b}{2} < b$.

64. Use Rule 3 to prove Rule 5 of (2).

65. Prove that $|ab| = |a||b|$. [*Hint:* Use Equation 4.]

66. Prove that $\left|\dfrac{a}{b}\right| = \dfrac{|a|}{|b|}$.

67. Show that if $0 < a < b$, then $a^2 < b^2$.

68. Prove that $|x - y| \geqslant |x| - |y|$. [*Hint:* Use the Triangle Inequality with $a = x - y$ and $b = y$.]

69. Show that the sum, difference, and product of rational numbers are rational numbers.

70. (a) Is the sum of two irrational numbers always an irrational number?
    (b) Is the product of two irrational numbers always an irrational number?

B   COORDINATE GEOMETRY AND LINES

Just as the points on a line can be identified with real numbers by assigning them coordinates, as described in Appendix A, so the points in a plane can be identified with ordered pairs of real numbers. We start by drawing two perpendicular coordinate lines that intersect at the origin O on each line. Usually one line is horizontal with positive direction to the right and is called the *x*-axis; the other line is vertical with positive direction upward and is called the *y*-axis.

Any point P in the plane can be located by a unique ordered pair of numbers as follows. Draw lines through P perpendicular to the *x*- and *y*-axes. These lines intersect the axes in points with coordinates a and b as shown in Figure 1. Then the point P is assigned the ordered pair (a, b). The first number a is called the **x-coordinate** of P; the second number b is called the **y-coordinate** of P. We say that P is the point with coordinates (a, b), and we denote the point by the symbol $P(a, b)$. Several points are labeled with their coordinates in Figure 2.

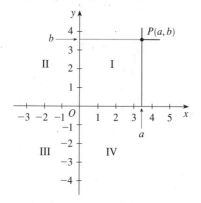

FIGURE 1   **FIGURE 2**

By reversing the preceding process we can start with an ordered pair (a, b) and arrive at the corresponding point P. Often we identify the point P with the ordered pair (a, b) and refer to "the point (a, b)." [Although the notation used for an open interval (a, b) is the same as the notation used for a point (a, b), you will be able to tell from the context which meaning is intended.]

This coordinate system is called the **rectangular coordinate system** or the **Cartesian coordinate system** in honor of the French mathematician René Descartes (1596–1650), even though another Frenchman, Pierre Fermat (1601–1665), invented the principles of analytic geometry at about the same time as Descartes. The plane supplied with this coordinate system is called the **coordinate plane** or the **Cartesian plane** and is denoted by $\mathbb{R}^2$.

The x- and y-axes are called the **coordinate axes** and divide the Cartesian plane into four quadrants, which are labeled I, II, III, and IV in Figure 1. Notice that the first quadrant consists of those points whose x- and y-coordinates are both positive.

EXAMPLE 1 Describe and sketch the regions given by the following sets.
(a) $\{(x, y) \mid x \geq 0\}$ (b) $\{(x, y) \mid y = 1\}$ (c) $\{(x, y) \mid |y| < 1\}$

SOLUTION
(a) The points whose x-coordinates are 0 or positive lie on the y-axis or to the right of it as indicated by the shaded region in Figure 3(a).

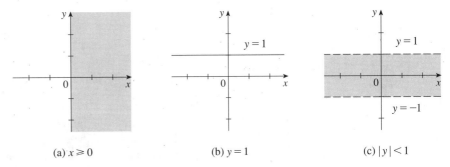

FIGURE 3   (a) $x \geq 0$ (b) $y = 1$ (c) $|y| < 1$

(b) The set of all points with y-coordinate 1 is a horizontal line one unit above the x-axis [see Figure 3(b)].

(c) Recall from Appendix A that

$$|y| < 1 \quad \text{if and only if} \quad -1 < y < 1$$

The given region consists of those points in the plane whose y-coordinates lie between -1 and 1. Thus the region consists of all points that lie between (but not on) the horizontal lines $y = 1$ and $y = -1$. [These lines are shown as dashed lines in Figure 3(c) to indicate that the points on these lines don't lie in the set.]

Recall from Appendix A that the distance between points a and b on a number line is $|a - b| = |b - a|$. Thus the distance between points $P_1(x_1, y_1)$ and $P_3(x_2, y_1)$ on a horizontal line must be $|x_2 - x_1|$ and the distance between $P_2(x_2, y_2)$ and $P_3(x_2, y_1)$ on a vertical line must be $|y_2 - y_1|$. (See Figure 4.)

To find the distance $|P_1P_2|$ between any two points $P_1(x_1, y_1)$ and $P_2(x_2, y_2)$, we note that triangle $P_1P_2P_3$ in Figure 4 is a right triangle, and so by the Pythagorean Theorem we have

$$|P_1P_2| = \sqrt{|P_1P_3|^2 + |P_2P_3|^2} = \sqrt{|x_2 - x_1|^2 + |y_2 - y_1|^2}$$
$$= \sqrt{(x_2 - x_1)^2 + (y_2 - y_1)^2}$$

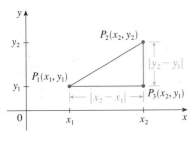

FIGURE 4

> **1** **DISTANCE FORMULA** The distance between the points $P_1(x_1, y_1)$ and $P_2(x_2, y_2)$ is
>
> $$|P_1P_2| = \sqrt{(x_2 - x_1)^2 + (y_2 - y_1)^2}$$

EXAMPLE 2 The distance between $(1, -2)$ and $(5, 3)$ is

$$\sqrt{(5 - 1)^2 + [3 - (-2)]^2} = \sqrt{4^2 + 5^2} = \sqrt{41}$$

LINES

We want to find an equation of a given line L; such an equation is satisfied by the coordinates of the points on L and by no other point. To find the equation of L we use its *slope*, which is a measure of the steepness of the line.

> **2** **DEFINITION** The **slope** of a nonvertical line that passes through the points $P_1(x_1, y_1)$ and $P_2(x_2, y_2)$ is
>
> $$m = \frac{\Delta y}{\Delta x} = \frac{y_2 - y_1}{x_2 - x_1}$$
>
> The slope of a vertical line is not defined.

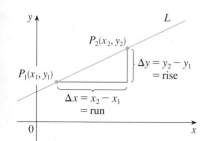

FIGURE 5

Thus the slope of a line is the ratio of the change in y, Δy, to the change in x, Δx. (See Figure 5.) The slope is therefore the rate of change of y with respect to x. The fact that the line is straight means that the rate of change is constant.

Figure 6 shows several lines labeled with their slopes. Notice that lines with positive slope slant upward to the right, whereas lines with negative slope slant downward to the right. Notice also that the steepest lines are the ones for which the absolute value of the slope is largest, and a horizontal line has slope 0.

Now let's find an equation of the line that passes through a given point $P_1(x_1, y_1)$ and has slope m. A point $P(x, y)$ with $x \neq x_1$ lies on this line if and only if the slope of the line through P_1 and P is equal to m; that is,

$$\frac{y - y_1}{x - x_1} = m$$

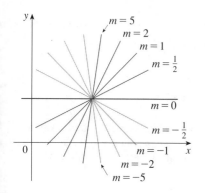

FIGURE 6

This equation can be rewritten in the form

$$y - y_1 = m(x - x_1)$$

and we observe that this equation is also satisfied when $x = x_1$ and $y = y_1$. Therefore it is an equation of the given line.

> **3** **POINT-SLOPE FORM OF THE EQUATION OF A LINE** An equation of the line passing through the point $P_1(x_1, y_1)$ and having slope m is
>
> $$y - y_1 = m(x - x_1)$$

EXAMPLE 3 Find an equation of the line through $(1, -7)$ with slope $-\frac{1}{2}$.

SOLUTION Using (3) with $m = -\frac{1}{2}$, $x_1 = 1$, and $y_1 = -7$, we obtain an equation of the line as

$$y + 7 = -\tfrac{1}{2}(x - 1)$$

which we can rewrite as

$$2y + 14 = -x + 1 \qquad \text{or} \qquad x + 2y + 13 = 0 \qquad \square$$

EXAMPLE 4 Find an equation of the line through the points $(-1, 2)$ and $(3, -4)$.

SOLUTION By Definition 2 the slope of the line is

$$m = \frac{-4 - 2}{3 - (-1)} = -\frac{3}{2}$$

Using the point-slope form with $x_1 = -1$ and $y_1 = 2$, we obtain

$$y - 2 = -\tfrac{3}{2}(x + 1)$$

which simplifies to $\qquad\qquad 3x + 2y = 1 \qquad \square$

Suppose a nonvertical line has slope m and y-intercept b. (See Figure 7.) This means it intersects the y-axis at the point $(0, b)$, so the point-slope form of the equation of the line, with $x_1 = 0$ and $y_1 = b$, becomes

$$y - b = m(x - 0)$$

This simplifies as follows.

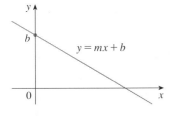

FIGURE 7

> **4** **SLOPE-INTERCEPT FORM OF THE EQUATION OF A LINE** An equation of the line with slope m and y-intercept b is
>
> $$y = mx + b$$

In particular, if a line is horizontal, its slope is $m = 0$, so its equation is $y = b$, where b is the y-intercept (see Figure 8). A vertical line does not have a slope, but we can write its equation as $x = a$, where a is the x-intercept, because the x-coordinate of every point on the line is a.

Observe that the equation of every line can be written in the form

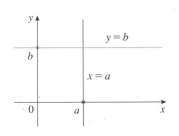

FIGURE 8

$$\boxed{5} \qquad\qquad\qquad \boxed{Ax + By + C = 0}$$

because a vertical line has the equation $x = a$ or $x - a = 0$ ($A = 1$, $B = 0$, $C = -a$) and a nonvertical line has the equation $y = mx + b$ or $-mx + y - b = 0$ ($A = -m$, $B = 1$, $C = -b$). Conversely, if we start with a general first-degree equation, that is, an equation of the form (5), where A, B, and C are constants and A and B are not both 0, then we can show that it is the equation of a line. If $B = 0$, the equation becomes $Ax + C = 0$ or $x = -C/A$, which represents a vertical line with x-intercept $-C/A$. If $B \neq 0$, the equation can be rewritten by solving for y:

$$y = -\frac{A}{B}x - \frac{C}{B}$$

and we recognize this as being the slope-intercept form of the equation of a line ($m = -A/B$, $b = -C/B$). Therefore an equation of the form (5) is called a **linear equation** or the **general equation of a line**. For brevity, we often refer to "the line $Ax + By + C = 0$" instead of "the line whose equation is $Ax + By + C = 0$."

EXAMPLE 5 Sketch the graph of the equation $3x - 5y = 15$.

SOLUTION Since the equation is linear, its graph is a line. To draw the graph, we can simply find two points on the line. It's easiest to find the intercepts. Substituting $y = 0$ (the equation of the x-axis) in the given equation, we get $3x = 15$, so $x = 5$ is the x-intercept. Substituting $x = 0$ in the equation, we see that the y-intercept is -3. This allows us to sketch the graph as in Figure 9.

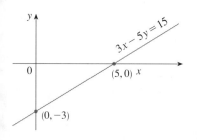

FIGURE 9

EXAMPLE 6 Graph the inequality $x + 2y > 5$.

SOLUTION We are asked to sketch the graph of the set $\{(x, y) \mid x + 2y > 5\}$ and we do so by solving the inequality for y:

$$x + 2y > 5$$

$$2y > -x + 5$$

$$y > -\tfrac{1}{2}x + \tfrac{5}{2}$$

Compare this inequality with the equation $y = -\tfrac{1}{2}x + \tfrac{5}{2}$, which represents a line with slope $-\tfrac{1}{2}$ and y-intercept $\tfrac{5}{2}$. We see that the given graph consists of points whose y-coordinates are *larger* than those on the line $y = -\tfrac{1}{2}x + \tfrac{5}{2}$. Thus the graph is the region that lies *above* the line, as illustrated in Figure 10.

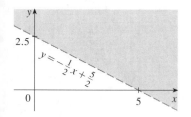

FIGURE 10

PARALLEL AND PERPENDICULAR LINES

Slopes can be used to show that lines are parallel or perpendicular. The following facts are proved, for instance, in *Precalculus: Mathematics for Calculus, Fifth Edition* by Stewart, Redlin, and Watson (Thomson Brooks/Cole, Belmont, CA, 2006).

---

6 **PARALLEL AND PERPENDICULAR LINES**

1. Two nonvertical lines are parallel if and only if they have the same slope.

2. Two lines with slopes m_1 and m_2 are perpendicular if and only if $m_1 m_2 = -1$; that is, their slopes are negative reciprocals:

$$m_2 = -\frac{1}{m_1}$$

EXAMPLE 7 Find an equation of the line through the point $(5, 2)$ that is parallel to the line $4x + 6y + 5 = 0$.

SOLUTION The given line can be written in the form

$$y = -\tfrac{2}{3}x - \tfrac{5}{6}$$

which is in slope-intercept form with $m = -\frac{2}{3}$. Parallel lines have the same slope, so the required line has slope $-\frac{2}{3}$ and its equation in point-slope form is

$$y - 2 = -\tfrac{2}{3}(x - 5)$$

We can write this equation as $2x + 3y = 16$.

EXAMPLE 8 Show that the lines $2x + 3y = 1$ and $6x - 4y - 1 = 0$ are perpendicular.

SOLUTION The equations can be written as

$$y = -\tfrac{2}{3}x + \tfrac{1}{3} \qquad \text{and} \qquad y = \tfrac{3}{2}x - \tfrac{1}{4}$$

from which we see that the slopes are

$$m_1 = -\tfrac{2}{3} \qquad \text{and} \qquad m_2 = \tfrac{3}{2}$$

Since $m_1 m_2 = -1$, the lines are perpendicular.

B EXERCISES

1–6 Find the distance between the points.

1. $(1, 1)$, $(4, 5)$

2. $(1, -3)$, $(5, 7)$

3. $(6, -2)$, $(-1, 3)$

4. $(1, -6)$, $(-1, -3)$

5. $(2, 5)$, $(4, -7)$

6. (a, b), (b, a)

7–10 Find the slope of the line through P and Q.

7. $P(1, 5)$, $Q(4, 11)$

8. $P(-1, 6)$, $Q(4, -3)$

9. $P(-3, 3)$, $Q(-1, -6)$

10. $P(-1, -4)$, $Q(6, 0)$

11. Show that the triangle with vertices $A(0, 2)$, $B(-3, -1)$, and $C(-4, 3)$ is isosceles.

12. (a) Show that the triangle with vertices $A(6, -7)$, $B(11, -3)$, and $C(2, -2)$ is a right triangle using the converse of the Pythagorean Theorem.
(b) Use slopes to show that ABC is a right triangle.
(c) Find the area of the triangle.

13. Show that the points $(-2, 9)$, $(4, 6)$, $(1, 0)$, and $(-5, 3)$ are the vertices of a square.

14. (a) Show that the points $A(-1, 3)$, $B(3, 11)$, and $C(5, 15)$ are collinear (lie on the same line) by showing that $|AB| + |BC| = |AC|$.
(b) Use slopes to show that A, B, and C are collinear.

15. Show that $A(1, 1)$, $B(7, 4)$, $C(5, 10)$, and $D(-1, 7)$ are vertices of a parallelogram.

16. Show that $A(1, 1)$, $B(11, 3)$, $C(10, 8)$, and $D(0, 6)$ are vertices of a rectangle.

17–20 Sketch the graph of the equation.

17. $x = 3$

18. $y = -2$

19. $xy = 0$

20. $|y| = 1$

21–36 Find an equation of the line that satisfies the given conditions.

21. Through $(2, -3)$, slope 6

22. Through $(-1, 4)$, slope -3

23. Through $(1, 7)$, slope $\frac{2}{3}$

24. Through $(-3, -5)$, slope $-\frac{7}{2}$

25. Through $(2, 1)$ and $(1, 6)$

26. Through $(-1, -2)$ and $(4, 3)$

27. Slope 3, y-intercept -2

28. Slope $\frac{2}{5}$, y-intercept 4

29. x-intercept 1, y-intercept -3

30. x-intercept -8, y-intercept 6

31. Through $(4, 5)$, parallel to the x-axis

32. Through $(4, 5)$, parallel to the y-axis

33. Through $(1, -6)$, parallel to the line $x + 2y = 6$

34. y-intercept 6, parallel to the line $2x + 3y + 4 = 0$

35. Through $(-1, -2)$, perpendicular to the line $2x + 5y + 8 = 0$

36. Through $\left(\frac{1}{2}, -\frac{2}{3}\right)$, perpendicular to the line $4x - 8y = 1$

37–42 Find the slope and y-intercept of the line and draw its graph.

37. $x + 3y = 0$

38. $2x - 5y = 0$

39. $y = -2$

40. $2x - 3y + 6 = 0$

41. $3x - 4y = 12$

42. $4x + 5y = 10$

43–52 Sketch the region in the xy-plane.

43. $\{(x, y) \mid x < 0\}$

44. $\{(x, y) \mid y > 0\}$

45. $\{(x, y) \mid xy < 0\}$

46. $\{(x, y) \mid x \geq 1 \text{ and } y < 3\}$

47. $\{(x, y) \mid |x| \leq 2\}$

48. $\{(x, y) \mid |x| < 3 \text{ and } |y| < 2\}$

49. $\{(x, y) \mid 0 \leq y \leq 4 \text{ and } x \leq 2\}$

50. $\{(x, y) \mid y > 2x - 1\}$

51. $\{(x, y) \mid 1 + x \leq y \leq 1 - 2x\}$

52. $\{(x, y) \mid -x \leq y < \frac{1}{2}(x + 3)\}$

53. Find a point on the y-axis that is equidistant from $(5, -5)$ and $(1, 1)$.

54. Show that the midpoint of the line segment from $P_1(x_1, y_1)$ to $P_2(x_2, y_2)$ is

$$\left(\frac{x_1 + x_2}{2}, \frac{y_1 + y_2}{2} \right)$$

55. Find the midpoint of the line segment joining the given points.
(a) $(1, 3)$ and $(7, 15)$ (b) $(-1, 6)$ and $(8, -12)$

56. Find the lengths of the medians of the triangle with vertices $A(1, 0)$, $B(3, 6)$, and $C(8, 2)$. (A median is a line segment from a vertex to the midpoint of the opposite side.)

57. Show that the lines $2x - y = 4$ and $6x - 2y = 10$ are not parallel and find their point of intersection.

58. Show that the lines $3x - 5y + 19 = 0$ and $10x + 6y - 50 = 0$ are perpendicular and find their point of intersection.

59. Find an equation of the perpendicular bisector of the line segment joining the points $A(1, 4)$ and $B(7, -2)$.

60. (a) Find equations for the sides of the triangle with vertices $P(1, 0)$, $Q(3, 4)$, and $R(-1, 6)$.
(b) Find equations for the medians of this triangle. Where do they intersect?

61. (a) Show that if the x- and y-intercepts of a line are nonzero numbers a and b, then the equation of the line can be put in the form

$$\frac{x}{a} + \frac{y}{b} = 1$$

This equation is called the **two-intercept form** of an equation of a line.
(b) Use part (a) to find an equation of the line whose x-intercept is 6 and whose y-intercept is -8.

62. A car leaves Detroit at 2:00 PM, traveling at a constant speed west along I-96. It passes Ann Arbor, 40 mi from Detroit, at 2:50 PM.
(a) Express the distance traveled in terms of the time elapsed.
(b) Draw the graph of the equation in part (a).
(c) What is the slope of this line? What does it represent?

C GRAPHS OF SECOND-DEGREE EQUATIONS

In Appendix B we saw that a first-degree, or linear, equation $Ax + By + C = 0$ represents a line. In this section we discuss second-degree equations such as

$$x^2 + y^2 = 1 \qquad y = x^2 + 1 \qquad \frac{x^2}{9} + \frac{y^2}{4} = 1 \qquad x^2 - y^2 = 1$$

which represent a circle, a parabola, an ellipse, and a hyperbola, respectively.

The graph of such an equation in x and y is the set of all points (x, y) that satisfy the equation; it gives a visual representation of the equation. Conversely, given a curve in the xy-plane, we may have to find an equation that represents it, that is, an equation satisfied by the coordinates of the points on the curve and by no other point. This is the other half of the basic principle of analytic geometry as formulated by Descartes and Fermat. The idea is that if a geometric curve can be represented by an algebraic equation, then the rules of algebra can be used to analyze the geometric problem.

CIRCLES

As an example of this type of problem, let's find an equation of the circle with radius r and center (h, k). By definition, the circle is the set of all points $P(x, y)$ whose distance from

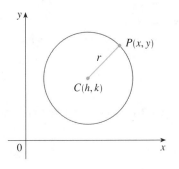

FIGURE I

the center $C(h, k)$ is r. (See Figure 1.) Thus P is on the circle if and only if $|PC| = r$. From the distance formula, we have

$$\sqrt{(x - h)^2 + (y - k)^2} = r$$

or equivalently, squaring both sides, we get

$$(x - h)^2 + (y - k)^2 = r^2$$

This is the desired equation.

$\boxed{1}$ **EQUATION OF A CIRCLE** An equation of the circle with center (h, k) and radius r is

$$(x - h)^2 + (y - k)^2 = r^2$$

In particular, if the center is the origin $(0, 0)$, the equation is

$$x^2 + y^2 = r^2$$

EXAMPLE 1 Find an equation of the circle with radius 3 and center $(2, -5)$.

SOLUTION From Equation 1 with $r = 3$, $h = 2$, and $k = -5$, we obtain

$$(x - 2)^2 + (y + 5)^2 = 9 \qquad \square$$

EXAMPLE 2 Sketch the graph of the equation $x^2 + y^2 + 2x - 6y + 7 = 0$ by first showing that it represents a circle and then finding its center and radius.

SOLUTION We first group the x-terms and y-terms as follows:

$$(x^2 + 2x) + (y^2 - 6y) = -7$$

Then we complete the square within each grouping, adding the appropriate constants to both sides of the equation:

$$(x^2 + 2x + 1) + (y^2 - 6y + 9) = -7 + 1 + 9$$

or $$(x + 1)^2 + (y - 3)^2 = 3$$

Comparing this equation with the standard equation of a circle (1), we see that $h = -1$, $k = 3$, and $r = \sqrt{3}$, so the given equation represents a circle with center $(-1, 3)$ and radius $\sqrt{3}$. It is sketched in Figure 2.

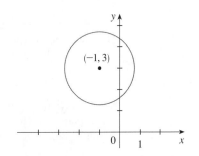

FIGURE 2
$x^2 + y^2 + 2x - 6y + 7 = 0$

PARABOLAS

The geometric properties of parabolas are reviewed in Section 10.5. Here we regard a parabola as a graph of an equation of the form $y = ax^2 + bx + c$.

EXAMPLE 3 Draw the graph of the parabola $y = x^2$.

SOLUTION We set up a table of values, plot points, and join them by a smooth curve to obtain the graph in Figure 3.

x	$y = x^2$
0	0
$\pm\frac{1}{2}$	$\frac{1}{4}$
± 1	1
± 2	4
± 3	9

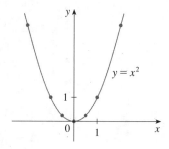

FIGURE 3

Figure 4 shows the graphs of several parabolas with equations of the form $y = ax^2$ for various values of the number a. In each case the *vertex,* the point where the parabola changes direction, is the origin. We see that the parabola $y = ax^2$ opens upward if $a > 0$ and downward if $a < 0$ (as in Figure 5).

FIGURE 4

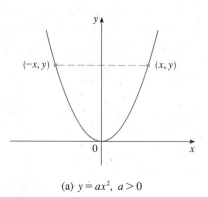

(a) $y = ax^2$, $a > 0$

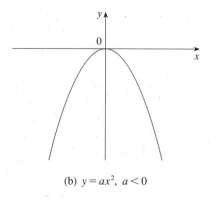

(b) $y = ax^2$, $a < 0$

FIGURE 5

Notice that if (x, y) satisfies $y = ax^2$, then so does $(-x, y)$. This corresponds to the geometric fact that if the right half of the graph is reflected about the y-axis, then the left half of the graph is obtained. We say that the graph is **symmetric with respect to the y-axis**.

> The graph of an equation is symmetric with respect to the y-axis if the equation is unchanged when x is replaced by $-x$.

If we interchange x and y in the equation $y = ax^2$, the result is $x = ay^2$, which also represents a parabola. (Interchanging x and y amounts to reflecting about the diagonal line $y = x$.) The parabola $x = ay^2$ opens to the right if $a > 0$ and to the left if $a < 0$. (See

Figure 6.) This time the parabola is symmetric with respect to the x-axis because if (x, y) satisfies $x = ay^2$, then so does $(x, -y)$.

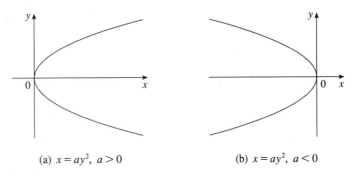

FIGURE 6

(a) $x = ay^2$, $a > 0$

(b) $x = ay^2$, $a < 0$

The graph of an equation is symmetric with respect to the x-axis if the equation is unchanged when y is replaced by $-y$.

EXAMPLE 4 Sketch the region bounded by the parabola $x = y^2$ and the line $y = x - 2$.

SOLUTION First we find the points of intersection by solving the two equations. Substituting $x = y + 2$ into the equation $x = y^2$, we get $y + 2 = y^2$, which gives

$$0 = y^2 - y - 2 = (y - 2)(y + 1)$$

so $y = 2$ or -1. Thus the points of intersection are $(4, 2)$ and $(1, -1)$, and we draw the line $y = x - 2$ passing through these points. We then sketch the parabola $x = y^2$ by referring to Figure 6(a) and having the parabola pass through $(4, 2)$ and $(1, -1)$. The region bounded by $x = y^2$ and $y = x - 2$ means the finite region whose boundaries are these curves. It is sketched in Figure 7. ☐

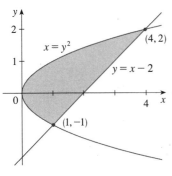

FIGURE 7

ELLIPSES

The curve with equation

$$\boxed{2} \qquad \frac{x^2}{a^2} + \frac{y^2}{b^2} = 1$$

where a and b are positive numbers, is called an **ellipse** in standard position. (Geometric properties of ellipses are discussed in Section 10.5.) Observe that Equation 2 is unchanged if x is replaced by $-x$ or y is replaced by $-y$, so the ellipse is symmetric with respect to both axes. As a further aid to sketching the ellipse, we find its intercepts.

The **x-intercepts** of a graph are the x-coordinates of the points where the graph intersects the x-axis. They are found by setting $y = 0$ in the equation of the graph.

The **y-intercepts** are the y-coordinates of the points where the graph intersects the y-axis. They are found by setting $x = 0$ in its equation.

FIGURE 8
$\dfrac{x^2}{a^2} + \dfrac{y^2}{b^2} = 1$

If we set $y = 0$ in Equation 2, we get $x^2 = a^2$ and so the x-intercepts are $\pm a$. Setting $x = 0$, we get $y^2 = b^2$, so the y-intercepts are $\pm b$. Using this information, together with symmetry, we sketch the ellipse in Figure 8. If $a = b$, the ellipse is a circle with radius a.

EXAMPLE 5 Sketch the graph of $9x^2 + 16y^2 = 144$.

SOLUTION We divide both sides of the equation by 144:

$$\frac{x^2}{16} + \frac{y^2}{9} = 1$$

The equation is now in the standard form for an ellipse (2), so we have $a^2 = 16$, $b^2 = 9$, $a = 4$, and $b = 3$. The x-intercepts are ± 4; the y-intercepts are ± 3. The graph is sketched in Figure 9.

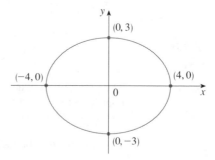

FIGURE 9

$9x^2 + 16y^2 = 144$

HYPERBOLAS

The curve with equation

3

$$\frac{x^2}{a^2} - \frac{y^2}{b^2} = 1$$

is called a **hyperbola** in standard position. Again, Equation 3 is unchanged when x is replaced by $-x$ or y is replaced by $-y$, so the hyperbola is symmetric with respect to both axes. To find the x-intercepts we set $y = 0$ and obtain $x^2 = a^2$ and $x = \pm a$. However, if we put $x = 0$ in Equation 3, we get $y^2 = -b^2$, which is impossible, so there is no y-intercept. In fact, from Equation 3 we obtain

$$\frac{x^2}{a^2} = 1 + \frac{y^2}{b^2} \geq 1$$

which shows that $x^2 \geq a^2$ and so $|x| = \sqrt{x^2} \geq a$. Therefore we have $x \geq a$ or $x \leq -a$. This means that the hyperbola consists of two parts, called its *branches*. It is sketched in Figure 10.

In drawing a hyperbola it is useful to draw first its *asymptotes*, which are the lines $y = (b/a)x$ and $y = -(b/a)x$ shown in Figure 10. Both branches of the hyperbola approach the asymptotes; that is, they come arbitrarily close to the asymptotes. This involves the idea of a limit, which is discussed in Chapter 2. (See also Exercise 55 in Section 4.5.)

By interchanging the roles of x and y we get an equation of the form

$$\frac{y^2}{a^2} - \frac{x^2}{b^2} = 1$$

which also represents a hyperbola and is sketched in Figure 11.

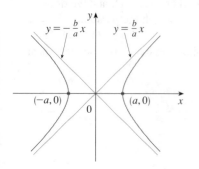

FIGURE 10

The hyperbola $\dfrac{x^2}{a^2} - \dfrac{y^2}{b^2} = 1$

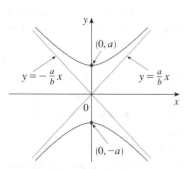

FIGURE 11

The hyperbola $\dfrac{y^2}{a^2} - \dfrac{x^2}{b^2} = 1$

EXAMPLE 6 Sketch the curve $9x^2 - 4y^2 = 36$.

SOLUTION Dividing both sides by 36, we obtain

$$\frac{x^2}{4} - \frac{y^2}{9} = 1$$

which is the standard form of the equation of a hyperbola (Equation 3). Since $a^2 = 4$, the x-intercepts are ± 2. Since $b^2 = 9$, we have $b = 3$ and the asymptotes are $y = \pm\left(\frac{3}{2}\right)x$. The hyperbola is sketched in Figure 12.

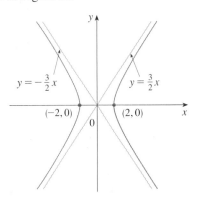

FIGURE 12
The hyperbola $9x^2 - 4y^2 = 36$

If $b = a$, a hyperbola has the equation $x^2 - y^2 = a^2$ (or $y^2 - x^2 = a^2$) and is called an *equilateral hyperbola* [see Figure 13(a)]. Its asymptotes are $y = \pm x$, which are perpendicular. If an equilateral hyperbola is rotated by $45°$, the asymptotes become the x- and y-axes, and it can be shown that the new equation of the hyperbola is $xy = k$, where k is a constant [see Figure 13(b)].

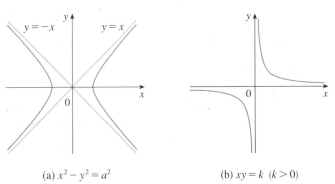

FIGURE 13
Equilateral hyperbolas

(a) $x^2 - y^2 = a^2$ (b) $xy = k$ $(k > 0)$

SHIFTED CONICS

Recall that an equation of the circle with center the origin and radius r is $x^2 + y^2 = r^2$, but if the center is the point (h, k), then the equation of the circle becomes

$$(x - h)^2 + (y - k)^2 = r^2$$

Similarly, if we take the ellipse with equation

$$\boxed{4}$$

$$\boxed{\frac{x^2}{a^2} + \frac{y^2}{b^2} = 1}$$

and translate it (shift it) so that its center is the point (h, k), then its equation becomes

$$\boxed{5} \qquad \frac{(x-h)^2}{a^2} + \frac{(y-k)^2}{b^2} = 1$$

(See Figure 14.)

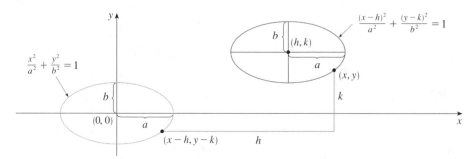

FIGURE 14

Notice that in shifting the ellipse, we replaced x by $x - h$ and y by $y - k$ in Equation 4 to obtain Equation 5. We use the same procedure to shift the parabola $y = ax^2$ so that its vertex (the origin) becomes the point (h, k) as in Figure 15. Replacing x by $x - h$ and y by $y - k$, we see that the new equation is

$$y - k = a(x - h)^2 \qquad \text{or} \qquad y = a(x - h)^2 + k$$

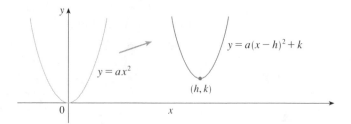

FIGURE 15

EXAMPLE 7 Sketch the graph of the equation $y = 2x^2 - 4x + 1$.

SOLUTION First we complete the square:

$$y = 2(x^2 - 2x) + 1 = 2(x - 1)^2 - 1$$

In this form we see that the equation represents the parabola obtained by shifting $y = 2x^2$ so that its vertex is at the point $(1, -1)$. The graph is sketched in Figure 16.

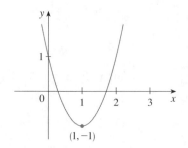

FIGURE 16
$y = 2x^2 - 4x + 1$

EXAMPLE 8 Sketch the curve $x = 1 - y^2$.

SOLUTION This time we start with the parabola $x = -y^2$ (as in Figure 6 with $a = -1$) and shift one unit to the right to get the graph of $x = 1 - y^2$. (See Figure 17.)

(a) $x = -y^2$

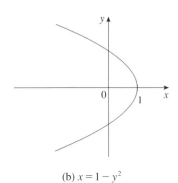

(b) $x = 1 - y^2$

FIGURE 17

C EXERCISES

1–4 Find an equation of a circle that satisfies the given conditions.

1. Center $(3, -1)$, radius 5

2. Center $(-2, -8)$, radius 10

3. Center at the origin, passes through $(4, 7)$

4. Center $(-1, 5)$, passes through $(-4, -6)$

5–9 Show that the equation represents a circle and find the center and radius.

5. $x^2 + y^2 - 4x + 10y + 13 = 0$

6. $x^2 + y^2 + 6y + 2 = 0$

7. $x^2 + y^2 + x = 0$

8. $16x^2 + 16y^2 + 8x + 32y + 1 = 0$

9. $2x^2 + 2y^2 - x + y = 1$

---

10. Under what condition on the coefficients a, b, and c does the equation $x^2 + y^2 + ax + by + c = 0$ represent a circle? When that condition is satisfied, find the center and radius of the circle.

11–32 Identify the type of curve and sketch the graph. Do not plot points. Just use the standard graphs given in Figures 5, 6, 8, 10, and 11 and shift if necessary.

11. $y = -x^2$

12. $y^2 - x^2 = 1$

13. $x^2 + 4y^2 = 16$

14. $x = -2y^2$

15. $16x^2 - 25y^2 = 400$

16. $25x^2 + 4y^2 = 100$

17. $4x^2 + y^2 = 1$

18. $y = x^2 + 2$

19. $x = y^2 - 1$

20. $9x^2 - 25y^2 = 225$

21. $9y^2 - x^2 = 9$

22. $2x^2 + 5y^2 = 10$

23. $xy = 4$

24. $y = x^2 + 2x$

25. $9(x - 1)^2 + 4(y - 2)^2 = 36$

26. $16x^2 + 9y^2 - 36y = 108$

27. $y = x^2 - 6x + 13$

28. $x^2 - y^2 - 4x + 3 = 0$

29. $x = 4 - y^2$

30. $y^2 - 2x + 6y + 5 = 0$

31. $x^2 + 4y^2 - 6x + 5 = 0$

32. $4x^2 + 9y^2 - 16x + 54y + 61 = 0$

33–34 Sketch the region bounded by the curves.

33. $y = 3x$, $\quad y = x^2$

34. $y = 4 - x^2$, $\quad x - 2y = 2$

35. Find an equation of the parabola with vertex $(1, -1)$ that passes through the points $(-1, 3)$ and $(3, 3)$.

36. Find an equation of the ellipse with center at the origin that passes through the points $\left(1, -10\sqrt{2}/3\right)$ and $\left(-2, 5\sqrt{5}/3\right)$.

37–40 Sketch the graph of the set.

37. $\{(x, y) \mid x^2 + y^2 \leqslant 1\}$

38. $\{(x, y) \mid x^2 + y^2 > 4\}$

39. $\{(x, y) \mid y \geqslant x^2 - 1\}$

40. $\{(x, y) \mid x^2 + 4y^2 \leqslant 4\}$

D | TRIGONOMETRY

ANGLES

Angles can be measured in degrees or in radians (abbreviated as rad). The angle given by a complete revolution contains 360°, which is the same as 2π rad. Therefore

$$\boxed{1} \qquad \pi \text{ rad} = 180°$$

and

$$\boxed{2} \qquad 1 \text{ rad} = \left(\frac{180}{\pi}\right)° \approx 57.3° \qquad 1° = \frac{\pi}{180} \text{ rad} \approx 0.017 \text{ rad}$$

EXAMPLE I

(a) Find the radian measure of 60°. (b) Express $5\pi/4$ rad in degrees.

SOLUTION

(a) From Equation 1 or 2 we see that to convert from degrees to radians we multiply by $\pi/180$. Therefore

$$60° = 60\left(\frac{\pi}{180}\right) = \frac{\pi}{3} \text{ rad}$$

(b) To convert from radians to degrees we multiply by $180/\pi$. Thus

$$\frac{5\pi}{4} \text{ rad} = \frac{5\pi}{4}\left(\frac{180}{\pi}\right) = 225°$$

In calculus we use radians to measure angles except when otherwise indicated. The following table gives the correspondence between degree and radian measures of some common angles.

Degrees	0°	30°	45°	60°	90°	120°	135°	150°	180°	270°	360°
Radians	0	$\frac{\pi}{6}$	$\frac{\pi}{4}$	$\frac{\pi}{3}$	$\frac{\pi}{2}$	$\frac{2\pi}{3}$	$\frac{3\pi}{4}$	$\frac{5\pi}{6}$	π	$\frac{3\pi}{2}$	2π

Figure 1 shows a sector of a circle with central angle θ and radius r subtending an arc with length a. Since the length of the arc is proportional to the size of the angle, and since the entire circle has circumference $2\pi r$ and central angle 2π, we have

$$\frac{\theta}{2\pi} = \frac{a}{2\pi r}$$

Solving this equation for θ and for a, we obtain

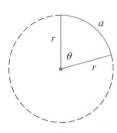

FIGURE I

$$\boxed{3} \qquad \theta = \frac{a}{r} \qquad\qquad a = r\theta$$

Remember that Equations 3 are valid only when θ is measured in radians.

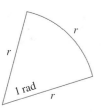

FIGURE 2

In particular, putting $a = r$ in Equation 3, we see that an angle of 1 rad is the angle subtended at the center of a circle by an arc equal in length to the radius of the circle (see Figure 2).

EXAMPLE 2

(a) If the radius of a circle is 5 cm, what angle is subtended by an arc of 6 cm?

(b) If a circle has radius 3 cm, what is the length of an arc subtended by a central angle of $3\pi/8$ rad?

SOLUTION

(a) Using Equation 3 with $a = 6$ and $r = 5$, we see that the angle is

$$\theta = \tfrac{6}{5} = 1.2 \text{ rad}$$

(b) With $r = 3$ cm and $\theta = 3\pi/8$ rad, the arc length is

$$a = r\theta = 3\left(\frac{3\pi}{8}\right) = \frac{9\pi}{8} \text{ cm}$$

The **standard position** of an angle occurs when we place its vertex at the origin of a coordinate system and its initial side on the positive x-axis as in Figure 3. A **positive** angle is obtained by rotating the initial side counterclockwise until it coincides with the terminal side. Likewise, **negative** angles are obtained by clockwise rotation as in Figure 4.

FIGURE 3 $\theta \geqslant 0$

FIGURE 4 $\theta < 0$

Figure 5 shows several examples of angles in standard position. Notice that different angles can have the same terminal side. For instance, the angles $3\pi/4$, $-5\pi/4$, and $11\pi/4$ have the same initial and terminal sides because

$$\frac{3\pi}{4} - 2\pi = -\frac{5\pi}{4} \qquad \frac{3\pi}{4} + 2\pi = \frac{11\pi}{4}$$

and 2π rad represents a complete revolution.

FIGURE 5
Angles in standard position

THE TRIGONOMETRIC FUNCTIONS

For an acute angle θ the six trigonometric functions are defined as ratios of lengths of sides of a right triangle as follows (see Figure 6).

FIGURE 6

$\boxed{4}$

$$\sin \theta = \frac{\text{opp}}{\text{hyp}} \qquad \csc \theta = \frac{\text{hyp}}{\text{opp}}$$

$$\cos \theta = \frac{\text{adj}}{\text{hyp}} \qquad \sec \theta = \frac{\text{hyp}}{\text{adj}}$$

$$\tan \theta = \frac{\text{opp}}{\text{adj}} \qquad \cot \theta = \frac{\text{adj}}{\text{opp}}$$

This definition doesn't apply to obtuse or negative angles, so for a general angle θ in standard position we let $P(x, y)$ be any point on the terminal side of θ and we let r be the distance $|OP|$ as in Figure 7. Then we define

FIGURE 7

$\boxed{5}$

$$\sin \theta = \frac{y}{r} \qquad \csc \theta = \frac{r}{y}$$

$$\cos \theta = \frac{x}{r} \qquad \sec \theta = \frac{r}{x}$$

$$\tan \theta = \frac{y}{x} \qquad \cot \theta = \frac{x}{y}$$

Since division by 0 is not defined, $\tan \theta$ and $\sec \theta$ are undefined when $x = 0$ and $\csc \theta$ and $\cot \theta$ are undefined when $y = 0$. Notice that the definitions in (4) and (5) are consistent when θ is an acute angle.

If θ is a number, the convention is that $\sin \theta$ means the sine of the angle whose *radian* measure is θ. For example, the expression $\sin 3$ implies that we are dealing with an angle of 3 rad. When finding a calculator approximation to this number, we must remember to set our calculator in radian mode, and then we obtain

$$\sin 3 \approx 0.14112$$

If we want to know the sine of the angle 3° we would write $\sin 3°$ and, with our calculator in degree mode, we find that

$$\sin 3° \approx 0.05234$$

The exact trigonometric ratios for certain angles can be read from the triangles in Figure 8. For instance,

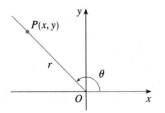

FIGURE 8

$$\sin \frac{\pi}{4} = \frac{1}{\sqrt{2}} \qquad \sin \frac{\pi}{6} = \frac{1}{2} \qquad \sin \frac{\pi}{3} = \frac{\sqrt{3}}{2}$$

$$\cos \frac{\pi}{4} = \frac{1}{\sqrt{2}} \qquad \cos \frac{\pi}{6} = \frac{\sqrt{3}}{2} \qquad \cos \frac{\pi}{3} = \frac{1}{2}$$

$$\tan \frac{\pi}{4} = 1 \qquad \tan \frac{\pi}{6} = \frac{1}{\sqrt{3}} \qquad \tan \frac{\pi}{3} = \sqrt{3}$$

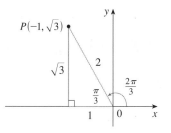

FIGURE 9

FIGURE 10

The signs of the trigonometric functions for angles in each of the four quadrants can be remembered by means of the rule "All Students Take Calculus" shown in Figure 9.

EXAMPLE 3 Find the exact trigonometric ratios for $\theta = 2\pi/3$.

SOLUTION From Figure 10 we see that a point on the terminal line for $\theta = 2\pi/3$ is $P(-1, \sqrt{3}\,)$. Therefore, taking

$$x = -1 \qquad y = \sqrt{3} \qquad r = 2$$

in the definitions of the trigonometric ratios, we have

$$\sin\frac{2\pi}{3} = \frac{\sqrt{3}}{2} \qquad \cos\frac{2\pi}{3} = -\frac{1}{2} \qquad \tan\frac{2\pi}{3} = -\sqrt{3}$$

$$\csc\frac{2\pi}{3} = \frac{2}{\sqrt{3}} \qquad \sec\frac{2\pi}{3} = -2 \qquad \cot\frac{2\pi}{3} = -\frac{1}{\sqrt{3}} \qquad \square$$

The following table gives some values of $\sin\theta$ and $\cos\theta$ found by the method of Example 3.

θ	0	$\dfrac{\pi}{6}$	$\dfrac{\pi}{4}$	$\dfrac{\pi}{3}$	$\dfrac{\pi}{2}$	$\dfrac{2\pi}{3}$	$\dfrac{3\pi}{4}$	$\dfrac{5\pi}{6}$	π	$\dfrac{3\pi}{2}$	2π
$\sin\theta$	0	$\dfrac{1}{2}$	$\dfrac{1}{\sqrt{2}}$	$\dfrac{\sqrt{3}}{2}$	1	$\dfrac{\sqrt{3}}{2}$	$\dfrac{1}{\sqrt{2}}$	$\dfrac{1}{2}$	0	-1	0
$\cos\theta$	1	$\dfrac{\sqrt{3}}{2}$	$\dfrac{1}{\sqrt{2}}$	$\dfrac{1}{2}$	0	$-\dfrac{1}{2}$	$-\dfrac{1}{\sqrt{2}}$	$-\dfrac{\sqrt{3}}{2}$	-1	0	1

EXAMPLE 4 If $\cos\theta = \frac{2}{5}$ and $0 < \theta < \pi/2$, find the other five trigonometric functions of θ.

SOLUTION Since $\cos\theta = \frac{2}{5}$, we can label the hypotenuse as having length 5 and the adjacent side as having length 2 in Figure 11. If the opposite side has length x, then the Pythagorean Theorem gives $x^2 + 4 = 25$ and so $x^2 = 21$, $x = \sqrt{21}$. We can now use the diagram to write the other five trigonometric functions:

$$\sin\theta = \frac{\sqrt{21}}{5} \qquad \tan\theta = \frac{\sqrt{21}}{2}$$

$$\csc\theta = \frac{5}{\sqrt{21}} \qquad \sec\theta = \frac{5}{2} \qquad \cot\theta = \frac{2}{\sqrt{21}} \qquad \square$$

FIGURE 11

FIGURE 12

EXAMPLE 5 Use a calculator to approximate the value of x in Figure 12.

SOLUTION From the diagram we see that

$$\tan 40° = \frac{16}{x}$$

Therefore

$$x = \frac{16}{\tan 40°} \approx 19.07 \qquad \square$$

TRIGONOMETRIC IDENTITIES

A trigonometric identity is a relationship among the trigonometric functions. The most elementary are the following, which are immediate consequences of the definitions of the trigonometric functions.

---

6 $$\csc\theta = \frac{1}{\sin\theta} \qquad \sec\theta = \frac{1}{\cos\theta} \qquad \cot\theta = \frac{1}{\tan\theta}$$

$$\tan\theta = \frac{\sin\theta}{\cos\theta} \qquad \cot\theta = \frac{\cos\theta}{\sin\theta}$$

For the next identity we refer back to Figure 7. The distance formula (or, equivalently, the Pythagorean Theorem) tells us that $x^2 + y^2 = r^2$. Therefore

$$\sin^2\theta + \cos^2\theta = \frac{y^2}{r^2} + \frac{x^2}{r^2} = \frac{x^2 + y^2}{r^2} = \frac{r^2}{r^2} = 1$$

We have therefore proved one of the most useful of all trigonometric identities:

7 $$\sin^2\theta + \cos^2\theta = 1$$

If we now divide both sides of Equation 7 by $\cos^2\theta$ and use Equations 6, we get

8 $$\tan^2\theta + 1 = \sec^2\theta$$

Similarly, if we divide both sides of Equation 7 by $\sin^2\theta$, we get

9 $$1 + \cot^2\theta = \csc^2\theta$$

The identities

10a $$\sin(-\theta) = -\sin\theta$$

10b $$\cos(-\theta) = \cos\theta$$

■ Odd functions and even functions are discussed in Section 1.1.

show that sin is an odd function and cos is an even function. They are easily proved by drawing a diagram showing θ and $-\theta$ in standard position (see Exercise 39).

Since the angles θ and $\theta + 2\pi$ have the same terminal side, we have

11 $$\sin(\theta + 2\pi) = \sin\theta \qquad \cos(\theta + 2\pi) = \cos\theta$$

These identities show that the sine and cosine functions are periodic with period 2π.

The remaining trigonometric identities are all consequences of two basic identities called the **addition formulas**:

12a	$$\sin(x + y) = \sin x \cos y + \cos x \sin y$$
12b	$$\cos(x + y) = \cos x \cos y - \sin x \sin y$$

The proofs of these addition formulas are outlined in Exercises 85, 86, and 87.

By substituting $-y$ for y in Equations 12a and 12b and using Equations 10a and 10b, we obtain the following **subtraction formulas**:

13a	$$\sin(x - y) = \sin x \cos y - \cos x \sin y$$
13b	$$\cos(x - y) = \cos x \cos y + \sin x \sin y$$

Then, by dividing the formulas in Equations 12 or Equations 13, we obtain the corresponding formulas for $\tan(x \pm y)$:

14a	$$\tan(x + y) = \frac{\tan x + \tan y}{1 - \tan x \tan y}$$
14b	$$\tan(x - y) = \frac{\tan x - \tan y}{1 + \tan x \tan y}$$

If we put $y = x$ in the addition formulas (12), we get the **double-angle formulas**:

15a	$$\sin 2x = 2 \sin x \cos x$$
15b	$$\cos 2x = \cos^2 x - \sin^2 x$$

Then, by using the identity $\sin^2 x + \cos^2 x = 1$, we obtain the following alternate forms of the double-angle formulas for $\cos 2x$:

16a	$$\cos 2x = 2 \cos^2 x - 1$$
16b	$$\cos 2x = 1 - 2 \sin^2 x$$

If we now solve these equations for $\cos^2 x$ and $\sin^2 x$, we get the following **half-angle formulas**, which are useful in integral calculus:

17a	$$\cos^2 x = \frac{1 + \cos 2x}{2}$$
17b	$$\sin^2 x = \frac{1 - \cos 2x}{2}$$

Finally, we state the **product formulas**, which can be deduced from Equations 12 and 13:

18a	$\sin x \cos y = \frac{1}{2}[\sin(x + y) + \sin(x - y)]$
18b	$\cos x \cos y = \frac{1}{2}[\cos(x + y) + \cos(x - y)]$
18c	$\sin x \sin y = \frac{1}{2}[\cos(x - y) - \cos(x + y)]$

There are many other trigonometric identities, but those we have stated are the ones used most often in calculus. If you forget any of them, remember that they can all be deduced from Equations 12a and 12b.

EXAMPLE 6 Find all values of x in the interval $[0, 2\pi]$ such that $\sin x = \sin 2x$.

SOLUTION Using the double-angle formula (15a), we rewrite the given equation as

$$\sin x = 2 \sin x \cos x \qquad \text{or} \qquad \sin x (1 - 2 \cos x) = 0$$

Therefore, there are two possibilities:

$$\sin x = 0 \qquad \text{or} \qquad 1 - 2 \cos x = 0$$

$$x = 0, \pi, 2\pi \qquad\qquad \cos x = \tfrac{1}{2}$$

$$x = \frac{\pi}{3}, \frac{5\pi}{3}$$

The given equation has five solutions: $0, \pi/3, \pi, 5\pi/3,$ and $2\pi.$ ☐

GRAPHS OF THE TRIGONOMETRIC FUNCTIONS

The graph of the function $f(x) = \sin x$, shown in Figure 13(a), is obtained by plotting points for $0 \le x \le 2\pi$ and then using the periodic nature of the function (from Equation 11) to complete the graph. Notice that the zeros of the sine function occur at the

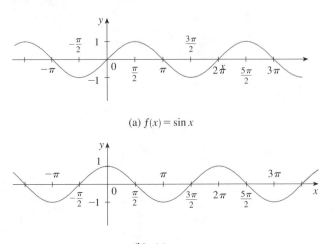

(a) $f(x) = \sin x$

(b) $g(x) = \cos x$

FIGURE 13

integer multiples of π, that is,

$$\sin x = 0 \qquad \text{whenever } x = n\pi, \quad n \text{ an integer}$$

Because of the identity

$$\cos x = \sin\left(x + \frac{\pi}{2}\right)$$

(which can be verified using Equation 12a), the graph of cosine is obtained by shifting the graph of sine by an amount $\pi/2$ to the left [see Figure 13(b)]. Note that for both the sine and cosine functions the domain is $(-\infty, \infty)$ and the range is the closed interval $[-1, 1]$. Thus, for all values of x, we have

$$-1 \leqslant \sin x \leqslant 1 \qquad -1 \leqslant \cos x \leqslant 1$$

The graphs of the remaining four trigonometric functions are shown in Figure 14 and their domains are indicated there. Notice that tangent and cotangent have range $(-\infty, \infty)$, whereas cosecant and secant have range $(-\infty, -1] \cup [1, \infty)$. All four functions are periodic: tangent and cotangent have period π, whereas cosecant and secant have period 2π.

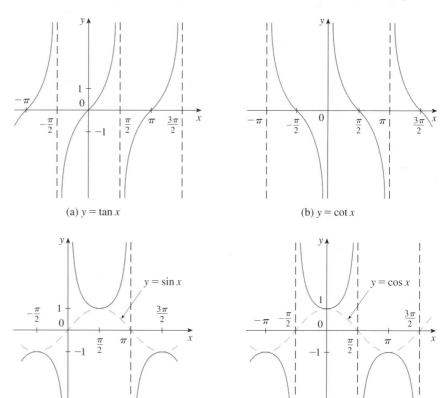

FIGURE 14

(a) $y = \tan x$

(b) $y = \cot x$

(c) $y = \csc x$

(d) $y = \sec x$

D | EXERCISES

1–6 Convert from degrees to radians.

1. $210°$

2. $300°$

3. $9°$

4. $-315°$

5. $900°$

6. $36°$

7–12 Convert from radians to degrees.

7. 4π

8. $-\dfrac{7\pi}{2}$

9. $\dfrac{5\pi}{12}$

10. $\dfrac{8\pi}{3}$

11. $-\dfrac{3\pi}{8}$

12. 5

13. Find the length of a circular arc subtended by an angle of $\pi/12$ rad if the radius of the circle is 36 cm.

14. If a circle has radius 10 cm, find the length of the arc subtended by a central angle of $72°$.

15. A circle has radius 1.5 m. What angle is subtended at the center of the circle by an arc 1 m long?

16. Find the radius of a circular sector with angle $3\pi/4$ and arc length 6 cm.

17–22 Draw, in standard position, the angle whose measure is given.

17. $315°$

18. $-150°$

19. $-\dfrac{3\pi}{4}$ rad

20. $\dfrac{7\pi}{3}$ rad

21. 2 rad

22. -3 rad

23–28 Find the exact trigonometric ratios for the angle whose radian measure is given.

23. $\dfrac{3\pi}{4}$

24. $\dfrac{4\pi}{3}$

25. $\dfrac{9\pi}{2}$

26. -5π

27. $\dfrac{5\pi}{6}$

28. $\dfrac{11\pi}{4}$

29–34 Find the remaining trigonometric ratios.

29. $\sin\theta = \dfrac{3}{5}, \quad 0 < \theta < \dfrac{\pi}{2}$

30. $\tan\alpha = 2, \quad 0 < \alpha < \dfrac{\pi}{2}$

31. $\sec\phi = -1.5, \quad \dfrac{\pi}{2} < \phi < \pi$

32. $\cos x = -\dfrac{1}{3}, \quad \pi < x < \dfrac{3\pi}{2}$

33. $\cot\beta = 3, \quad \pi < \beta < 2\pi$

34. $\csc\theta = -\dfrac{4}{3}, \quad \dfrac{3\pi}{2} < \theta < 2\pi$

35–38 Find, correct to five decimal places, the length of the side labeled x.

35.

36.

37.

38.

39–41 Prove each equation.

39. (a) Equation 10a   (b) Equation 10b

40. (a) Equation 14a   (b) Equation 14b

41. (a) Equation 18a   (b) Equation 18b
(c) Equation 18c

42–58 Prove the identity.

42. $\cos\left(\dfrac{\pi}{2} - x\right) = \sin x$

43. $\sin\left(\dfrac{\pi}{2} + x\right) = \cos x$ **44.** $\sin(\pi - x) = \sin x$

45. $\sin\theta \cot\theta = \cos\theta$ **46.** $(\sin x + \cos x)^2 = 1 + \sin 2x$

47. $\sec y - \cos y = \tan y \sin y$

48. $\tan^2\alpha - \sin^2\alpha = \tan^2\alpha \sin^2\alpha$

49. $\cot^2\theta + \sec^2\theta = \tan^2\theta + \csc^2\theta$

50. $2\csc 2t = \sec t \csc t$

51. $\tan 2\theta = \dfrac{2\tan\theta}{1 - \tan^2\theta}$

52. $\dfrac{1}{1 - \sin\theta} + \dfrac{1}{1 + \sin\theta} = 2\sec^2\theta$

53. $\sin x \sin 2x + \cos x \cos 2x = \cos x$

54. $\sin^2 x - \sin^2 y = \sin(x + y)\sin(x - y)$

55. $\dfrac{\sin\phi}{1 - \cos\phi} = \csc\phi + \cot\phi$

56. $\tan x + \tan y = \dfrac{\sin(x + y)}{\cos x \cos y}$

57. $\sin 3\theta + \sin \theta = 2 \sin 2\theta \cos \theta$

58. $\cos 3\theta = 4 \cos^3\theta - 3 \cos \theta$

59–64 If $\sin x = \frac{1}{3}$ and $\sec y = \frac{5}{4}$, where x and y lie between 0 and $\pi/2$, evaluate the expression.

59. $\sin(x + y)$ **60.** $\cos(x + y)$

61. $\cos(x - y)$ **62.** $\sin(x - y)$

63. $\sin 2y$ **64.** $\cos 2y$

65–72 Find all values of x in the interval $[0, 2\pi]$ that satisfy the equation.

65. $2 \cos x - 1 = 0$ **66.** $3 \cot^2 x = 1$

67. $2 \sin^2 x = 1$ **68.** $|\tan x| = 1$

69. $\sin 2x = \cos x$ **70.** $2 \cos x + \sin 2x = 0$

71. $\sin x = \tan x$ **72.** $2 + \cos 2x = 3 \cos x$

73–76 Find all values of x in the interval $[0, 2\pi]$ that satisfy the inequality.

73. $\sin x \leq \frac{1}{2}$ **74.** $2 \cos x + 1 > 0$

75. $-1 < \tan x < 1$ **76.** $\sin x > \cos x$

77–82 Graph the function by starting with the graphs in Figures 13 and 14 and applying the transformations of Section 1.3 where appropriate.

77. $y = \cos\left(x - \dfrac{\pi}{3}\right)$ **78.** $y = \tan 2x$

79. $y = \dfrac{1}{3} \tan\left(x - \dfrac{\pi}{2}\right)$ **80.** $y = 1 + \sec x$

81. $y = |\sin x|$ **82.** $y = 2 + \sin\left(x + \dfrac{\pi}{4}\right)$

83. Prove the **Law of Cosines**: If a triangle has sides with lengths a, b, and c, and θ is the angle between the sides with lengths a and b, then

$$c^2 = a^2 + b^2 - 2ab \cos \theta$$

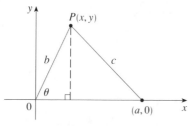

[*Hint:* Introduce a coordinate system so that θ is in standard

position as in the figure. Express x and y in terms of θ and then use the distance formula to compute c.]

84. In order to find the distance $|AB|$ across a small inlet, a point C is located as in the figure and the following measurements were recorded:

$$\angle C = 103° \qquad |AC| = 820 \text{ m} \qquad |BC| = 910 \text{ m}$$

Use the Law of Cosines from Exercise 83 to find the required distance.

85. Use the figure to prove the subtraction formula

$$\cos(\alpha - \beta) = \cos \alpha \cos \beta + \sin \alpha \sin \beta$$

[*Hint:* Compute c^2 in two ways (using the Law of Cosines from Exercise 83 and also using the distance formula) and compare the two expressions.]

86. Use the formula in Exercise 85 to prove the addition formula for cosine (12b).

87. Use the addition formula for cosine and the identities

$$\cos\left(\dfrac{\pi}{2} - \theta\right) = \sin \theta \qquad \sin\left(\dfrac{\pi}{2} - \theta\right) = \cos \theta$$

to prove the subtraction formula for the sine function.

88. Show that the area of a triangle with sides of lengths a and b and with included angle θ is

$$A = \tfrac{1}{2}ab \sin \theta$$

89. Find the area of triangle ABC, correct to five decimal places, if

$$|AB| = 10 \text{ cm} \qquad |BC| = 3 \text{ cm} \qquad \angle ABC = 107°$$

A convenient way of writing sums uses the Greek letter Σ (capital sigma, corresponding to our letter S) and is called **sigma notation**.

This tells us to end with $i = n$.

This tells us to add.

This tells us to start with $i = m$.

$$\sum_{i=m}^{n} a_i$$

---

1 DEFINITION If $a_m, a_{m+1}, \ldots, a_n$ are real numbers and m and n are integers such that $m \leq n$, then

$$\sum_{i=m}^{n} a_i = a_m + a_{m+1} + a_{m+2} + \cdots + a_{n-1} + a_n$$

With function notation, Definition 1 can be written as

$$\sum_{i=m}^{n} f(i) = f(m) + f(m + 1) + f(m + 2) + \cdots + f(n - 1) + f(n)$$

Thus the symbol $\sum_{i=m}^{n}$ indicates a summation in which the letter i (called the **index of summation**) takes on consecutive integer values beginning with m and ending with n, that is, $m, m + 1, \ldots, n$. Other letters can also be used as the index of summation.

EXAMPLE I

(a) $\displaystyle\sum_{i=1}^{4} i^2 = 1^2 + 2^2 + 3^2 + 4^2 = 30$

(b) $\displaystyle\sum_{i=3}^{n} i = 3 + 4 + 5 + \cdots + (n - 1) + n$

(c) $\displaystyle\sum_{j=0}^{5} 2^j = 2^0 + 2^1 + 2^2 + 2^3 + 2^4 + 2^5 = 63$

(d) $\displaystyle\sum_{k=1}^{n} \frac{1}{k} = 1 + \frac{1}{2} + \frac{1}{3} + \cdots + \frac{1}{n}$

(e) $\displaystyle\sum_{i=1}^{3} \frac{i-1}{i^2+3} = \frac{1-1}{1^2+3} + \frac{2-1}{2^2+3} + \frac{3-1}{3^2+3} = 0 + \frac{1}{7} + \frac{1}{6} = \frac{13}{42}$

(f) $\displaystyle\sum_{i=1}^{4} 2 = 2 + 2 + 2 + 2 = 8$

EXAMPLE 2 Write the sum $2^3 + 3^3 + \cdots + n^3$ in sigma notation.

SOLUTION There is no unique way of writing a sum in sigma notation. We could write

$$2^3 + 3^3 + \cdots + n^3 = \sum_{i=2}^{n} i^3$$

or

$$2^3 + 3^3 + \cdots + n^3 = \sum_{j=1}^{n-1} (j + 1)^3$$

or

$$2^3 + 3^3 + \cdots + n^3 = \sum_{k=0}^{n-2} (k + 2)^3$$

The following theorem gives three simple rules for working with sigma notation.

> **2** **THEOREM** If c is any constant (that is, it does not depend on i), then
>
> (a) $\displaystyle\sum_{i=m}^{n} ca_i = c \sum_{i=m}^{n} a_i$ (b) $\displaystyle\sum_{i=m}^{n} (a_i + b_i) = \sum_{i=m}^{n} a_i + \sum_{i=m}^{n} b_i$
>
> (c) $\displaystyle\sum_{i=m}^{n} (a_i - b_i) = \sum_{i=m}^{n} a_i - \sum_{i=m}^{n} b_i$

PROOF   To see why these rules are true, all we have to do is write both sides in expanded form. Rule (a) is just the distributive property of real numbers:

$$ca_m + ca_{m+1} + \cdots + ca_n = c(a_m + a_{m+1} + \cdots + a_n)$$

Rule (b) follows from the associative and commutative properties:

$$(a_m + b_m) + (a_{m+1} + b_{m+1}) + \cdots + (a_n + b_n)$$
$$= (a_m + a_{m+1} + \cdots + a_n) + (b_m + b_{m+1} + \cdots + b_n)$$

Rule (c) is proved similarly.   □

EXAMPLE 3   Find $\displaystyle\sum_{i=1}^{n} 1$.

SOLUTION
$$\sum_{i=1}^{n} 1 = \underbrace{1 + 1 + \cdots + 1}_{n \text{ terms}} = n$$

EXAMPLE 4   Prove the formula for the sum of the first n positive integers:

$$\sum_{i=1}^{n} i = 1 + 2 + 3 + \cdots + n = \frac{n(n+1)}{2}$$

SOLUTION   This formula can be proved by mathematical induction (see page 77) or by the following method used by the German mathematician Karl Friedrich Gauss (1777–1855) when he was ten years old.

Write the sum S twice, once in the usual order and once in reverse order:

$$S = 1 + \quad 2 \quad + \quad 3 \quad + \cdots + (n-1) + n$$
$$S = n + (n-1) + (n-2) + \cdots + \quad 2 \quad + 1$$

Adding all columns vertically, we get

$$2S = (n+1) + (n+1) + (n+1) + \cdots + (n+1) + (n+1)$$

On the right side there are n terms, each of which is $n+1$, so

$$2S = n(n+1) \quad \text{or} \quad S = \frac{n(n+1)}{2}$$

EXAMPLE 5   Prove the formula for the sum of the squares of the first n positive integers:

$$\sum_{i=1}^{n} i^2 = 1^2 + 2^2 + 3^2 + \cdots + n^2 = \frac{n(n+1)(2n+1)}{6}$$

SOLUTION 1 Let S be the desired sum. We start with the *telescoping sum* (or collapsing sum):

Most terms cancel in pairs.

$$\sum_{i=1}^{n} [(1+i)^3 - i^3] = (2^3 - 1^3) + (3^3 - 2^3) + (4^3 - 3^3) + \cdots + [(n+1)^3 - n^3]$$

$$= (n+1)^3 - 1^3 = n^3 + 3n^2 + 3n$$

On the other hand, using Theorem 2 and Examples 3 and 4, we have

$$\sum_{i=1}^{n} [(1+i)^3 - i^3] = \sum_{i=1}^{n} [3i^2 + 3i + 1] = 3\sum_{i=1}^{n} i^2 + 3\sum_{i=1}^{n} i + \sum_{i=1}^{n} 1$$

$$= 3S + 3\frac{n(n+1)}{2} + n = 3S + \tfrac{3}{2}n^2 + \tfrac{5}{2}n$$

Thus we have

$$n^3 + 3n^2 + 3n = 3S + \tfrac{3}{2}n^2 + \tfrac{5}{2}n$$

Solving this equation for S, we obtain

$$3S = n^3 + \tfrac{3}{2}n^2 + \tfrac{1}{2}n$$

or
$$S = \frac{2n^3 + 3n^2 + n}{6} = \frac{n(n+1)(2n+1)}{6}$$

■ PRINCIPLE OF MATHEMATICAL INDUCTION

Let S_n be a statement involving the positive integer n. Suppose that

1. S_1 is true.
2. If S_k is true, then S_{k+1} is true.

Then S_n is true for all positive integers n.

■ See pages 55 and 58 for a more thorough discussion of mathematical induction.

SOLUTION 2 Let S_n be the given formula.

1. S_1 is true because
$$1^2 = \frac{1(1+1)(2 \cdot 1 + 1)}{6}$$

2. Assume that S_k is true; that is,

$$1^2 + 2^2 + 3^2 + \cdots + k^2 = \frac{k(k+1)(2k+1)}{6}$$

Then

$$1^2 + 2^2 + 3^2 + \cdots + (k+1)^2 = (1^2 + 2^2 + 3^2 + \cdots + k^2) + (k+1)^2$$

$$= \frac{k(k+1)(2k+1)}{6} + (k+1)^2$$

$$= (k+1)\frac{k(2k+1) + 6(k+1)}{6}$$

$$= (k+1)\frac{2k^2 + 7k + 6}{6}$$

$$= \frac{(k+1)(k+2)(2k+3)}{6}$$

$$= \frac{(k+1)[(k+1)+1][2(k+1)+1]}{6}$$

So S_{k+1} is true.

By the Principle of Mathematical Induction, S_n is true for all n.

We list the results of Examples 3, 4, and 5 together with a similar result for cubes (see Exercises 37–40) as Theorem 3. These formulas are needed for finding areas and evaluating integrals in Chapter 5.

---

3 **THEOREM** Let c be a constant and n a positive integer. Then

(a) $\displaystyle\sum_{i=1}^{n} 1 = n$

(b) $\displaystyle\sum_{i=1}^{n} c = nc$

(c) $\displaystyle\sum_{i=1}^{n} i = \frac{n(n+1)}{2}$

(d) $\displaystyle\sum_{i=1}^{n} i^2 = \frac{n(n+1)(2n+1)}{6}$

(e) $\displaystyle\sum_{i=1}^{n} i^3 = \left[\frac{n(n+1)}{2}\right]^2$

EXAMPLE 6 Evaluate $\displaystyle\sum_{i=1}^{n} i(4i^2 - 3)$.

SOLUTION Using Theorems 2 and 3, we have

$$\sum_{i=1}^{n} i(4i^2 - 3) = \sum_{i=1}^{n} (4i^3 - 3i) = 4 \sum_{i=1}^{n} i^3 - 3 \sum_{i=1}^{n} i$$

$$= 4\left[\frac{n(n+1)}{2}\right]^2 - 3\frac{n(n+1)}{2}$$

$$= \frac{n(n+1)[2n(n+1) - 3]}{2}$$

$$= \frac{n(n+1)(2n^2 + 2n - 3)}{2}$$

■ The type of calculation in Example 7 arises in Chapter 5 when we compute areas.

EXAMPLE 7 Find $\displaystyle\lim_{n \to \infty} \sum_{i=1}^{n} \frac{3}{n}\left[\left(\frac{i}{n}\right)^2 + 1\right]$.

SOLUTION

$$\lim_{n \to \infty} \sum_{i=1}^{n} \frac{3}{n}\left[\left(\frac{i}{n}\right)^2 + 1\right] = \lim_{n \to \infty} \sum_{i=1}^{n} \left[\frac{3}{n^3} i^2 + \frac{3}{n}\right]$$

$$= \lim_{n \to \infty} \left[\frac{3}{n^3} \sum_{i=1}^{n} i^2 + \frac{3}{n} \sum_{i=1}^{n} 1\right]$$

$$= \lim_{n \to \infty} \left[\frac{3}{n^3} \frac{n(n+1)(2n+1)}{6} + \frac{3}{n} \cdot n\right]$$

$$= \lim_{n \to \infty} \left[\frac{1}{2} \cdot \frac{n}{n} \cdot \left(\frac{n+1}{n}\right)\left(\frac{2n+1}{n}\right) + 3\right]$$

$$= \lim_{n \to \infty} \left[\frac{1}{2} \cdot 1\left(1 + \frac{1}{n}\right)\left(2 + \frac{1}{n}\right) + 3\right]$$

$$= \tfrac{1}{2} \cdot 1 \cdot 1 \cdot 2 + 3 = 4$$

E EXERCISES

1–10 Write the sum in expanded form.

1. $\displaystyle\sum_{i=1}^{5} \sqrt{i}$

2. $\displaystyle\sum_{i=1}^{6} \frac{1}{i+1}$

3. $\displaystyle\sum_{i=4}^{6} 3^i$

4. $\displaystyle\sum_{i=4}^{6} i^3$

5. $\displaystyle\sum_{k=0}^{4} \frac{2k-1}{2k+1}$

6. $\displaystyle\sum_{k=5}^{8} x^k$

7. $\displaystyle\sum_{i=1}^{n} i^{10}$

8. $\displaystyle\sum_{j=n}^{n+3} j^2$

9. $\displaystyle\sum_{j=0}^{n-1} (-1)^j$

10. $\displaystyle\sum_{i=1}^{n} f(x_i)\,\Delta x_i$

11–20 Write the sum in sigma notation.

11. $1 + 2 + 3 + 4 + \cdots + 10$

12. $\sqrt{3} + \sqrt{4} + \sqrt{5} + \sqrt{6} + \sqrt{7}$

13. $\frac{1}{2} + \frac{2}{3} + \frac{3}{4} + \frac{4}{5} + \cdots + \frac{19}{20}$

14. $\frac{3}{7} + \frac{4}{8} + \frac{5}{9} + \frac{6}{10} + \cdots + \frac{23}{27}$

15. $2 + 4 + 6 + 8 + \cdots + 2n$

16. $1 + 3 + 5 + 7 + \cdots + (2n-1)$

17. $1 + 2 + 4 + 8 + 16 + 32$

18. $\frac{1}{1} + \frac{1}{4} + \frac{1}{9} + \frac{1}{16} + \frac{1}{25} + \frac{1}{36}$

19. $x + x^2 + x^3 + \cdots + x^n$

20. $1 - x + x^2 - x^3 + \cdots + (-1)^n x^n$

21–35 Find the value of the sum.

21. $\displaystyle\sum_{i=4}^{8} (3i-2)$

22. $\displaystyle\sum_{i=3}^{6} i(i+2)$

23. $\displaystyle\sum_{j=1}^{6} 3^{j+1}$

24. $\displaystyle\sum_{k=0}^{8} \cos k\pi$

25. $\displaystyle\sum_{n=1}^{20} (-1)^n$

26. $\displaystyle\sum_{i=1}^{100} 4$

27. $\displaystyle\sum_{i=0}^{4} (2^i + i^2)$

28. $\displaystyle\sum_{i=-2}^{4} 2^{3-i}$

29. $\displaystyle\sum_{i=1}^{n} 2i$

30. $\displaystyle\sum_{i=1}^{n} (2 - 5i)$

31. $\displaystyle\sum_{i=1}^{n} (i^2 + 3i + 4)$

32. $\displaystyle\sum_{i=1}^{n} (3 + 2i)^2$

33. $\displaystyle\sum_{i=1}^{n} (i+1)(i+2)$

34. $\displaystyle\sum_{i=1}^{n} i(i+1)(i+2)$

35. $\displaystyle\sum_{i=1}^{n} (i^3 - i - 2)$

36. Find the number n such that $\displaystyle\sum_{i=1}^{n} i = 78$.

37. Prove formula (b) of Theorem 3.

38. Prove formula (e) of Theorem 3 using mathematical induction.

39. Prove formula (e) of Theorem 3 using a method similar to that of Example 5, Solution 1 [start with $(1 + i)^4 - i^4$].

40. Prove formula (e) of Theorem 3 using the following method published by Abu Bekr Mohammed ibn Alhusain Alkarchi in about AD 1010. The figure shows a square $ABCD$ in which sides AB and AD have been divided into segments of lengths 1, 2, 3, ..., n. Thus the side of the square has length $n(n + 1)/2$ so the area is $[n(n + 1)/2]^2$. But the area is also the sum of the areas of the n "gnomons" $G_1, G_2, \ldots, G_n$ shown in the figure. Show that the area of G_i is i^3 and conclude that formula (e) is true.

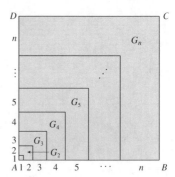

41. Evaluate each telescoping sum.

(a) $\displaystyle\sum_{i=1}^{n} [i^4 - (i-1)^4]$

(b) $\displaystyle\sum_{i=1}^{100} (5^i - 5^{i-1})$

(c) $\displaystyle\sum_{i=3}^{99} \left(\frac{1}{i} - \frac{1}{i+1} \right)$

(d) $\displaystyle\sum_{i=1}^{n} (a_i - a_{i-1})$

42. Prove the generalized triangle inequality:

$$\left| \sum_{i=1}^{n} a_i \right| \le \sum_{i=1}^{n} |a_i|$$

43–46 Find the limit.

43. $\displaystyle\lim_{n\to\infty} \sum_{i=1}^{n} \frac{1}{n} \left(\frac{i}{n} \right)^2$

44. $\displaystyle\lim_{n\to\infty} \sum_{i=1}^{n} \frac{1}{n} \left[\left(\frac{i}{n} \right)^3 + 1 \right]$

45. $\displaystyle\lim_{n\to\infty} \sum_{i=1}^{n} \frac{2}{n} \left[\left(\frac{2i}{n} \right)^3 + 5 \left(\frac{2i}{n} \right) \right]$

46. $\lim\limits_{n \to \infty} \sum\limits_{i=1}^{n} \dfrac{3}{n}\left[\left(1 + \dfrac{3i}{n}\right)^3 - 2\left(1 + \dfrac{3i}{n}\right)\right]$

48. Evaluate $\sum\limits_{i=1}^{n} \dfrac{3}{2^{i-1}}$.

47. Prove the formula for the sum of a finite geometric series with first term a and common ratio $r \neq 1$:

$$\sum_{i=1}^{n} ar^{i-1} = a + ar + ar^2 + \cdots + ar^{n-1} = \frac{a(r^n - 1)}{r - 1}$$

49. Evaluate $\sum\limits_{i=1}^{n} (2i + 2^i)$.

50. Evaluate $\sum\limits_{i=1}^{m}\left[\sum\limits_{j=1}^{n} (i + j)\right]$.

F PROOFS OF THEOREMS

In this appendix we present proofs of several theorems that are stated in the main body of the text. The sections in which they occur are indicated in the margin.

SECTION 2.3

LIMIT LAWS Suppose that c is a constant and the limits

$$\lim_{x \to a} f(x) = L \qquad \text{and} \qquad \lim_{x \to a} g(x) = M$$

exist. Then

1. $\lim\limits_{x \to a} [f(x) + g(x)] = L + M$ 　　**2.** $\lim\limits_{x \to a} [f(x) - g(x)] = L - M$

3. $\lim\limits_{x \to a} [cf(x)] = cL$ 　　**4.** $\lim\limits_{x \to a} [f(x)g(x)] = LM$

5. $\lim\limits_{x \to a} \dfrac{f(x)}{g(x)} = \dfrac{L}{M}$ 　if $M \neq 0$

PROOF OF LAW 4 Let $\varepsilon > 0$ be given. We want to find $\delta > 0$ such that

$$\text{if} \qquad 0 < |x - a| < \delta \qquad \text{then} \qquad |f(x)g(x) - LM| < \varepsilon$$

In order to get terms that contain $|f(x) - L|$ and $|g(x) - M|$, we add and subtract $Lg(x)$ as follows:

$$\begin{aligned}
|f(x)g(x) - LM| &= |f(x)g(x) - Lg(x) + Lg(x) - LM| \\
&= |[f(x) - L]g(x) + L[g(x) - M]| \\
&\leqslant |[f(x) - L]g(x)| + |L[g(x) - M]| \qquad \text{(Triangle Inequality)} \\
&= |f(x) - L||g(x)| + |L||g(x) - M|
\end{aligned}$$

We want to make each of these terms less than $\varepsilon/2$.

Since $\lim_{x \to a} g(x) = M$, there is a number $\delta_1 > 0$ such that

$$\text{if} \qquad 0 < |x - a| < \delta_1 \qquad \text{then} \qquad |g(x) - M| < \frac{\varepsilon}{2(1 + |L|)}$$

Also, there is a number $\delta_2 > 0$ such that if $0 < |x - a| < \delta_2$, then

$$|g(x) - M| < 1$$

and therefore

$$|g(x)| = |g(x) - M + M| \leqslant |g(x) - M| + |M| < 1 + |M|$$

Since $\lim_{x \to a} f(x) = L$, there is a number $\delta_3 > 0$ such that

$$\text{if} \quad 0 < |x - a| < \delta_3 \quad \text{then} \quad |f(x) - L| < \frac{\varepsilon}{2(1 + |M|)}$$

Let $\delta = \min\{\delta_1, \delta_2, \delta_3\}$. If $0 < |x - a| < \delta$, then we have $0 < |x - a| < \delta_1$, $0 < |x - a| < \delta_2$, and $0 < |x - a| < \delta_3$, so we can combine the inequalities to obtain

$$|f(x)g(x) - LM| \leq |f(x) - L||g(x)| + |L||g(x) - M|$$

$$< \frac{\varepsilon}{2(1 + |M|)}(1 + |M|) + |L|\frac{\varepsilon}{2(1 + |L|)}$$

$$< \frac{\varepsilon}{2} + \frac{\varepsilon}{2} = \varepsilon$$

This shows that $\lim_{x \to a} f(x)g(x) = LM$. $\qquad\square$

PROOF OF LAW 3   If we take $g(x) = c$ in Law 4, we get

$$\lim_{x \to a}[cf(x)] = \lim_{x \to a}[g(x)f(x)] = \lim_{x \to a} g(x) \cdot \lim_{x \to a} f(x)$$

$$= \lim_{x \to a} c \cdot \lim_{x \to a} f(x)$$

$$= c \lim_{x \to a} f(x) \qquad \text{(by Law 7)} \qquad\square$$

PROOF OF LAW 2   Using Law 1 and Law 3 with $c = -1$, we have

$$\lim_{x \to a}[f(x) - g(x)] = \lim_{x \to a}[f(x) + (-1)g(x)] = \lim_{x \to a} f(x) + \lim_{x \to a}(-1)g(x)$$

$$= \lim_{x \to a} f(x) + (-1)\lim_{x \to a} g(x) = \lim_{x \to a} f(x) - \lim_{x \to a} g(x) \qquad\square$$

PROOF OF LAW 5   First let us show that

$$\lim_{x \to a} \frac{1}{g(x)} = \frac{1}{M}$$

To do this we must show that, given $\varepsilon > 0$, there exists $\delta > 0$ such that

$$\text{if} \quad 0 < |x - a| < \delta \quad \text{then} \quad \left|\frac{1}{g(x)} - \frac{1}{M}\right| < \varepsilon$$

Observe that
$$\left|\frac{1}{g(x)} - \frac{1}{M}\right| = \frac{|M - g(x)|}{|Mg(x)|}$$

We know that we can make the numerator small. But we also need to know that the denominator is not small when x is near a. Since $\lim_{x \to a} g(x) = M$, there is a number $\delta_1 > 0$ such that, whenever $0 < |x - a| < \delta_1$, we have

$$|g(x) - M| < \frac{|M|}{2}$$

and therefore $|M| = |M - g(x) + g(x)| \leq |M - g(x)| + |g(x)|$

$$< \frac{|M|}{2} + |g(x)|$$

This shows that

$$\text{if} \qquad 0 < |x - a| < \delta_1 \qquad \text{then} \qquad |g(x)| > \frac{|M|}{2}$$

and so, for these values of x,

$$\frac{1}{|Mg(x)|} = \frac{1}{|M||g(x)|} < \frac{1}{|M|} \cdot \frac{2}{|M|} = \frac{2}{M^2}$$

Also, there exists $\delta_2 > 0$ such that

$$\text{if} \qquad 0 < |x - a| < \delta_2 \qquad \text{then} \qquad |g(x) - M| < \frac{M^2}{2} \varepsilon$$

Let $\delta = \min\{\delta_1, \delta_2\}$. Then, for $0 < |x - a| < \delta$, we have

$$\left| \frac{1}{g(x)} - \frac{1}{M} \right| = \frac{|M - g(x)|}{|Mg(x)|} < \frac{2}{M^2} \frac{M^2}{2} \varepsilon = \varepsilon$$

It follows that $\lim_{x \to a} 1/g(x) = 1/M$. Finally, using Law 4, we obtain

$$\lim_{x \to a} \frac{f(x)}{g(x)} = \lim_{x \to a} f(x) \left(\frac{1}{g(x)} \right) = \lim_{x \to a} f(x) \lim_{x \to a} \frac{1}{g(x)} = L \cdot \frac{1}{M} = \frac{L}{M} \qquad \square$$

---

2 **THEOREM** If $f(x) \leq g(x)$ for all x in an open interval that contains a (except possibly at a) and

$$\lim_{x \to a} f(x) = L \qquad \text{and} \qquad \lim_{x \to a} g(x) = M$$

then $L \leq M$.

PROOF   We use the method of proof by contradiction. Suppose, if possible, that $L > M$. Law 2 of limits says that

$$\lim_{x \to a} [g(x) - f(x)] = M - L$$

Therefore, for any $\varepsilon > 0$, there exists $\delta > 0$ such that

$$\text{if} \qquad 0 < |x - a| < \delta \qquad \text{then} \qquad |[g(x) - f(x)] - (M - L)| < \varepsilon$$

In particular, taking $\varepsilon = L - M$ (noting that $L - M > 0$ by hypothesis), we have a number $\delta > 0$ such that

$$\text{if} \qquad 0 < |x - a| < \delta \qquad \text{then} \qquad |[g(x) - f(x)] - (M - L)| < L - M$$

Since $a \leq |a|$ for any number a, we have

$$\text{if} \qquad 0 < |x - a| < \delta \qquad \text{then} \qquad [g(x) - f(x)] - (M - L) < L - M$$

which simplifies to

$$\text{if} \qquad 0 < |x - a| < \delta \qquad \text{then} \qquad g(x) < f(x)$$

But this contradicts $f(x) \leq g(x)$. Thus the inequality $L > M$ must be false. Therefore $L \leq M$. $\qquad \square$

$\boxed{3}$ **THE SQUEEZE THEOREM** If $f(x) \leq g(x) \leq h(x)$ for all x in an open interval that contains a (except possibly at a) and

$$\lim_{x \to a} f(x) = \lim_{x \to a} h(x) = L$$

then

$$\lim_{x \to a} g(x) = L$$

PROOF Let $\varepsilon > 0$ be given. Since $\lim_{x \to a} f(x) = L$, there is a number $\delta_1 > 0$ such that

$$\text{if} \quad 0 < |x - a| < \delta_1 \quad \text{then} \quad |f(x) - L| < \varepsilon$$

that is,

$$\text{if} \quad 0 < |x - a| < \delta_1 \quad \text{then} \quad L - \varepsilon < f(x) < L + \varepsilon$$

Since $\lim_{x \to a} h(x) = L$, there is a number $\delta_2 > 0$ such that

$$\text{if} \quad 0 < |x - a| < \delta_2 \quad \text{then} \quad |h(x) - L| < \varepsilon$$

that is,

$$\text{if} \quad 0 < |x - a| < \delta_2 \quad \text{then} \quad L - \varepsilon < h(x) < L + \varepsilon$$

Let $\delta = \min\{\delta_1, \delta_2\}$. If $0 < |x - a| < \delta$, then $0 < |x - a| < \delta_1$ and $0 < |x - a| < \delta_2$, so

$$L - \varepsilon < f(x) \leq g(x) \leq h(x) < L + \varepsilon$$

In particular,

$$L - \varepsilon < g(x) < L + \varepsilon$$

and so $|g(x) - L| < \varepsilon$. Therefore $\lim_{x \to a} g(x) = L$. $\qquad\square$

SECTION 2.5

$\boxed{8}$ **THEOREM** If f is continuous at b and $\lim_{x \to a} g(x) = b$, then

$$\lim_{x \to a} f(g(x)) = f(b)$$

PROOF Let $\varepsilon > 0$ be given. We want to find a number $\delta > 0$ such that

$$\text{if} \quad 0 < |x - a| < \delta \quad \text{then} \quad |f(g(x)) - f(b)| < \varepsilon$$

Since f is continuous at b, we have

$$\lim_{y \to b} f(y) = f(b)$$

and so there exists $\delta_1 > 0$ such that

$$\text{if} \quad 0 < |y - b| < \delta_1 \quad \text{then} \quad |f(y) - f(b)| < \varepsilon$$

Since $\lim_{x \to a} g(x) = b$, there exists $\delta > 0$ such that

$$\text{if} \quad 0 < |x - a| < \delta \quad \text{then} \quad |g(x) - b| < \delta_1$$

Combining these two statements, we see that whenever $0 < |x - a| < \delta$ we have $|g(x) - b| < \delta_1$, which implies that $|f(g(x)) - f(b)| < \varepsilon$. Therefore we have proved that $\lim_{x \to a} f(g(x)) = f(b)$. ☐

SECTION 3.4

The proof of the following result was promised when we proved that $\lim_{\theta \to 0} \dfrac{\sin \theta}{\theta} = 1$.

THEOREM If $0 < \theta < \pi/2$, then $\theta \leqslant \tan \theta$.

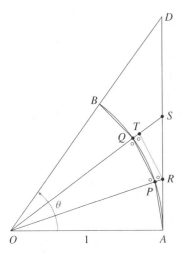

FIGURE 1

PROOF Figure 1 shows a sector of a circle with center O, central angle θ, and radius 1. Then

$$|AD| = |OA| \tan \theta = \tan \theta$$

We approximate the arc AB by an inscribed polygon consisting of n equal line segments and we look at a typical segment PQ. We extend the lines OP and OQ to meet AD in the points R and S. Then we draw $RT \| PQ$ as in Figure 1. Observe that

$$\angle RTO = \angle PQO < 90°$$

and so $\angle RTS > 90°$. Therefore we have

$$|PQ| < |RT| < |RS|$$

If we add n such inequalities, we get

$$L_n < |AD| = \tan \theta$$

where L_n is the length of the inscribed polygon. Thus, by Theorem 2.3.2, we have

$$\lim_{n \to \infty} L_n \leqslant \tan \theta$$

But the arc length is defined in Equation 9.1.1 as the limit of the lengths of inscribed polygons, so

$$\theta = \lim_{n \to \infty} L_n \leqslant \tan \theta \qquad ☐$$

SECTION 4.3

CONCAVITY TEST
(a) If $f''(x) > 0$ for all x in I, then the graph of f is concave upward on I.
(b) If $f''(x) < 0$ for all x in I, then the graph of f is concave downward on I.

FIGURE 2

PROOF OF (a) Let a be any number in I. We must show that the curve $y = f(x)$ lies above the tangent line at the point $(a, f(a))$. The equation of this tangent is

$$y = f(a) + f'(a)(x - a)$$

So we must show that

$$f(x) > f(a) + f'(a)(x - a)$$

whenever $x \in I$ $(x \neq a)$. (See Figure 2.)

First let us take the case where $x > a$. Applying the Mean Value Theorem to f on the interval $[a, x]$, we get a number c, with $a < c < x$, such that

$$\boxed{1} \qquad\qquad f(x) - f(a) = f'(c)(x - a)$$

Since $f'' > 0$ on I, we know from the Increasing/Decreasing Test that f' is increasing on I. Thus, since $a < c$, we have

$$f'(a) < f'(c)$$

and so, multiplying this inequality by the positive number $x - a$, we get

$$\boxed{2} \qquad\qquad f'(a)(x - a) < f'(c)(x - a)$$

Now we add $f(a)$ to both sides of this inequality:

$$f(a) + f'(a)(x - a) < f(a) + f'(c)(x - a)$$

But from Equation 1 we have $f(x) = f(a) + f'(c)(x - a)$. So this inequality becomes

$$\boxed{3} \qquad\qquad f(x) > f(a) + f'(a)(x - a)$$

which is what we wanted to prove.

For the case where $x < a$ we have $f'(c) < f'(a)$, but multiplication by the negative number $x - a$ reverses the inequality, so we get (2) and (3) as before. $\qquad\square$

SECTION 7.1

> $\boxed{6}$ **THEOREM** If f is a one-to-one continuous function defined on an interval (a, b), then its inverse function f^{-1} is also continuous.

PROOF First we show that if f is both one-to-one and continuous on (a, b), then it must be either increasing or decreasing on (a, b). If it were neither increasing nor decreasing, then there would exist numbers x_1, x_2, and x_3 in (a, b) with $x_1 < x_2 < x_3$ such that $f(x_2)$ does not lie between $f(x_1)$ and $f(x_3)$. There are two possibilities: either (1) $f(x_3)$ lies between $f(x_1)$ and $f(x_2)$ or (2) $f(x_1)$ lies between $f(x_2)$ and $f(x_3)$. (Draw a picture.) In case (1) we apply the Intermediate Value Theorem to the continuous function f to get a number c between x_1 and x_2 such that $f(c) = f(x_3)$. In case (2) the Intermediate Value Theorem gives a number c between x_2 and x_3 such that $f(c) = f(x_1)$. In either case we have contradicted the fact that f is one-to-one.

Let us assume, for the sake of definiteness, that f is increasing on (a, b). We take any number y_0 in the domain of f^{-1} and we let $f^{-1}(y_0) = x_0$; that is, x_0 is the number in (a, b) such that $f(x_0) = y_0$. To show that f^{-1} is continuous at y_0 we take any $\varepsilon > 0$ such that the interval $(x_0 - \varepsilon, x_0 + \varepsilon)$ is contained in the interval (a, b). Since f is increasing, it maps the numbers in the interval $(x_0 - \varepsilon, x_0 + \varepsilon)$ onto the numbers in the interval $(f(x_0 - \varepsilon), f(x_0 + \varepsilon))$ and f^{-1} reverses the correspondence. If we let δ denote the smaller of the numbers $\delta_1 = y_0 - f(x_0 - \varepsilon)$ and $\delta_2 = f(x_0 + \varepsilon) - y_0$, then the interval $(y_0 - \delta, y_0 + \delta)$ is contained in the interval $(f(x_0 - \varepsilon), f(x_0 + \varepsilon))$ and so is mapped into the interval $(x_0 - \varepsilon, x_0 + \varepsilon)$ by f^{-1}. (See the arrow diagram in Figure 3.) We have therefore found a number $\delta > 0$ such that

$$\text{if} \qquad |y - y_0| < \delta \qquad \text{then} \qquad |f^{-1}(y) - f^{-1}(y_0)| < \varepsilon$$

FIGURE 3

This shows that $\lim_{y \to y_0} f^{-1}(y) = f^{-1}(y_0)$ and so f^{-1} is continuous at any number y_0 in its domain. ☐

SECTION 12.8

In order to prove Theorem 12.8.3, we first need the following results.

THEOREM

1. If a power series $\Sigma c_n x^n$ converges when $x = b$ (where $b \neq 0$), then it converges whenever $|x| < |b|$.

2. If a power series $\Sigma c_n x^n$ diverges when $x = d$ (where $d \neq 0$), then it diverges whenever $|x| > |d|$.

PROOF OF 1 Suppose that $\Sigma c_n b^n$ converges. Then, by Theorem 12.2.6, we have $\lim_{n \to \infty} c_n b^n = 0$. According to Definition 12.1.2 with $\varepsilon = 1$, there is a positive integer N such that $|c_n b^n| < 1$ whenever $n \geq N$. Thus, for $n \geq N$, we have

$$|c_n x^n| = \left| \frac{c_n b^n x^n}{b^n} \right| = |c_n b^n| \left| \frac{x}{b} \right|^n < \left| \frac{x}{b} \right|^n$$

If $|x| < |b|$, then $|x/b| < 1$, so $\Sigma |x/b|^n$ is a convergent geometric series. Therefore, by the Comparison Test, the series $\Sigma_{n=N}^{\infty} |c_n x^n|$ is convergent. Thus the series $\Sigma c_n x^n$ is absolutely convergent and therefore convergent. ☐

PROOF OF 2 Suppose that $\Sigma c_n d^n$ diverges. If x is any number such that $|x| > |d|$, then $\Sigma c_n x^n$ cannot converge because, by part 1, the convergence of $\Sigma c_n x^n$ would imply the convergence of $\Sigma c_n d^n$. Therefore $\Sigma c_n x^n$ diverges whenever $|x| > |d|$. ☐

THEOREM For a power series $\Sigma c_n x^n$ there are only three possibilities:

1. The series converges only when $x = 0$.

2. The series converges for all x.

3. There is a positive number R such that the series converges if $|x| < R$ and diverges if $|x| > R$.

PROOF Suppose that neither case 1 nor case 2 is true. Then there are nonzero numbers b and d such that $\Sigma c_n x^n$ converges for $x = b$ and diverges for $x = d$. Therefore the set $S = \{x \mid \Sigma c_n x^n \text{ converges}\}$ is not empty. By the preceding theorem, the series diverges if $|x| > |d|$, so $|x| \leq |d|$ for all $x \in S$. This says that $|d|$ is an upper bound for the set S. Thus, by the Completeness Axiom (see Section 12.1), S has a least upper bound R. If $|x| > R$, then $x \notin S$, so $\Sigma c_n x^n$ diverges. If $|x| < R$, then $|x|$ is not an upper bound for S and so there exists $b \in S$ such that $b > |x|$. Since $b \in S$, $\Sigma c_n b^n$ converges, so by the preceding theorem $\Sigma c_n x^n$ converges. ☐

> **3** **THEOREM** For a power series $\sum c_n(x - a)^n$ there are only three possibilities:
>
> **1.** The series converges only when $x = a$.
>
> **2.** The series converges for all x.
>
> **3.** There is a positive number R such that the series converges if $|x - a| < R$ and diverges if $|x - a| > R$.

PROOF   If we make the change of variable $u = x - a$, then the power series becomes $\sum c_n u^n$ and we can apply the preceding theorem to this series. In case 3 we have convergence for $|u| < R$ and divergence for $|u| > R$. Thus we have convergence for $|x - a| < R$ and divergence for $|x - a| > R$.   □

SECTION 15.3

> **CLAIRAUT'S THEOREM** Suppose f is defined on a disk D that contains the point (a, b). If the functions f_{xy} and f_{yx} are both continuous on D, then $f_{xy}(a, b) = f_{yx}(a, b)$.

PROOF   For small values of h, $h \neq 0$, consider the difference

$$\Delta(h) = [f(a + h, b + h) - f(a + h, b)] - [f(a, b + h) - f(a, b)]$$

Notice that if we let $g(x) = f(x, b + h) - f(x, b)$, then

$$\Delta(h) = g(a + h) - g(a)$$

By the Mean Value Theorem, there is a number c between a and $a + h$ such that

$$g(a + h) - g(a) = g'(c)h = h[f_x(c, b + h) - f_x(c, b)]$$

Applying the Mean Value Theorem again, this time to f_x, we get a number d between b and $b + h$ such that

$$f_x(c, b + h) - f_x(c, b) = f_{xy}(c, d)h$$

Combining these equations, we obtain

$$\Delta(h) = h^2 f_{xy}(c, d)$$

If $h \to 0$, then $(c, d) \to (a, b)$, so the continuity of f_{xy} at (a, b) gives

$$\lim_{h \to 0} \frac{\Delta(h)}{h^2} = \lim_{(c, d) \to (a, b)} f_{xy}(c, d) = f_{xy}(a, b)$$

Similarly, by writing

$$\Delta(h) = [f(a + h, b + h) - f(a, b + h)] - [f(a + h, b) - f(a, b)]$$

and using the Mean Value Theorem twice and the continuity of f_{yx} at (a, b), we obtain

$$\lim_{h \to 0} \frac{\Delta(h)}{h^2} = f_{yx}(a, b)$$

It follows that $f_{xy}(a, b) = f_{yx}(a, b)$.   □

8 **THEOREM** If the partial derivatives f_x and f_y exist near (a, b) and are continuous at (a, b), then f is differentiable at (a, b).

PROOF Let

$$\Delta z = f(a + \Delta x, b + \Delta y) - f(a, b)$$

According to (15.4.7), to prove that f is differentiable at (a, b) we have to show that we can write Δz in the form

$$\Delta z = f_x(a, b)\,\Delta x + f_y(a, b)\,\Delta y + \varepsilon_1\,\Delta x + \varepsilon_2\,\Delta y$$

where ε_1 and $\varepsilon_2 \to 0$ as $(\Delta x, \Delta y) \to (0, 0)$.

Referring to Figure 4, we write

1   $$\Delta z = [f(a + \Delta x, b + \Delta y) - f(a, b + \Delta y)] + [f(a, b + \Delta y) - f(a, b)]$$

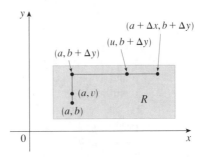

FIGURE 4

Observe that the function of a single variable

$$g(x) = f(x, b + \Delta y)$$

is defined on the interval $[a, a + \Delta x]$ and $g'(x) = f_x(x, b + \Delta y)$. If we apply the Mean Value Theorem to g, we get

$$g(a + \Delta x) - g(a) = g'(u)\,\Delta x$$

where u is some number between a and $a + \Delta x$. In terms of f, this equation becomes

$$f(a + \Delta x, b + \Delta y) - f(a, b + \Delta y) = f_x(u, b + \Delta y)\,\Delta x$$

This gives us an expression for the first part of the right side of Equation 1. For the second part we let $h(y) = f(a, y)$. Then h is a function of a single variable defined on the interval $[b, b + \Delta y]$ and $h'(y) = f_y(a, y)$. A second application of the Mean Value Theorem then gives

$$h(b + \Delta y) - h(b) = h'(v)\,\Delta y$$

where v is some number between b and $b + \Delta y$. In terms of f, this becomes

$$f(a, b + \Delta y) - f(a, b) = f_y(a, v)\,\Delta y$$

We now substitute these expressions into Equation 1 and obtain

$$\Delta z = f_x(u, b + \Delta y)\,\Delta x + f_y(a, v)\,\Delta y$$

$$= f_x(a, b)\,\Delta x + [f_x(u, b + \Delta y) - f_x(a, b)]\,\Delta x + f_y(a, b)\,\Delta y$$

$$+ [f_y(a, v) - f_y(a, b)]\,\Delta y$$

$$= f_x(a, b)\,\Delta x + f_y(a, b)\,\Delta y + \varepsilon_1\,\Delta x + \varepsilon_2\,\Delta y$$

where
$$\varepsilon_1 = f_x(u, b + \Delta y) - f_x(a, b)$$

$$\varepsilon_2 = f_y(a, v) - f_y(a, b)$$

Since $(u, b + \Delta y) \to (a, b)$ and $(a, v) \to (a, b)$ as $(\Delta x, \Delta y) \to (0, 0)$ and since f_x and f_y are continuous at (a, b), we see that $\varepsilon_1 \to 0$ and $\varepsilon_2 \to 0$ as $(\Delta x, \Delta y) \to (0, 0)$.

Therefore f is differentiable at (a, b) . $\qquad\square$

G COMPLEX NUMBERS

FIGURE 1

Complex numbers as points in the Argand plane

A **complex number** can be represented by an expression of the form $a + bi$, where a and b are real numbers and i is a symbol with the property that $i^2 = -1$. The complex number $a + bi$ can also be represented by the ordered pair (a, b) and plotted as a point in a plane (called the Argand plane) as in Figure 1. Thus the complex number $i = 0 + 1 \cdot i$ is identified with the point $(0, 1)$.

The **real part** of the complex number $a + bi$ is the real number a and the **imaginary part** is the real number b. Thus the real part of $4 - 3i$ is 4 and the imaginary part is -3. Two complex numbers $a + bi$ and $c + di$ are **equal** if $a = c$ and $b = d$; that is, their real parts are equal and their imaginary parts are equal. In the Argand plane the horizontal axis is called the real axis and the vertical axis is called the imaginary axis.

The sum and difference of two complex numbers are defined by adding or subtracting their real parts and their imaginary parts:

$$(a + bi) + (c + di) = (a + c) + (b + d)i$$

$$(a + bi) - (c + di) = (a - c) + (b - d)i$$

For instance,

$$(1 - i) + (4 + 7i) = (1 + 4) + (-1 + 7)i = 5 + 6i$$

The product of complex numbers is defined so that the usual commutative and distributive laws hold:

$$(a + bi)(c + di) = a(c + di) + (bi)(c + di)$$

$$= ac + adi + bci + bdi^2$$

Since $i^2 = -1$, this becomes

$$(a + bi)(c + di) = (ac - bd) + (ad + bc)i$$

EXAMPLE 1

$$(-1 + 3i)(2 - 5i) = (-1)(2 - 5i) + 3i(2 - 5i)$$

$$= -2 + 5i + 6i - 15(-1) = 13 + 11i \qquad\square$$

Division of complex numbers is much like rationalizing the denominator of a rational expression. For the complex number $z = a + bi$, we define its **complex conjugate** to be $\bar{z} = a - bi$. To find the quotient of two complex numbers we multiply numerator and denominator by the complex conjugate of the denominator.

EXAMPLE 2 Express the number $\dfrac{-1 + 3i}{2 + 5i}$ in the form $a + bi$.

SOLUTION We multiply numerator and denominator by the complex conjugate of $2 + 5i$, namely $2 - 5i$, and we take advantage of the result of Example 1:

$$\frac{-1 + 3i}{2 + 5i} = \frac{-1 + 3i}{2 + 5i} \cdot \frac{2 - 5i}{2 - 5i} = \frac{13 + 11i}{2^2 + 5^2} = \frac{13}{29} + \frac{11}{29}i \qquad \square$$

The geometric interpretation of the complex conjugate is shown in Figure 2: $\bar{z}$ is the reflection of z in the real axis. We list some of the properties of the complex conjugate in the following box. The proofs follow from the definition and are requested in Exercise 18.

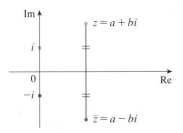

FIGURE 2

PROPERTIES OF CONJUGATES

$$\overline{z + w} = \bar{z} + \bar{w} \qquad\qquad \overline{zw} = \bar{z}\,\bar{w} \qquad\qquad \overline{z^n} = \bar{z}^n$$

The **modulus**, or **absolute value**, $|z|$ of a complex number $z = a + bi$ is its distance from the origin. From Figure 3 we see that if $z = a + bi$, then

$$\boxed{|z| = \sqrt{a^2 + b^2}}$$

Notice that

$$z\bar{z} = (a + bi)(a - bi) = a^2 + abi - abi - b^2i^2 = a^2 + b^2$$

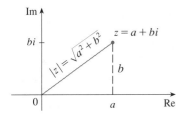

FIGURE 3

and so

$$\boxed{z\bar{z} = |z|^2}$$

This explains why the division procedure in Example 2 works in general:

$$\frac{z}{w} = \frac{z\bar{w}}{w\bar{w}} = \frac{z\bar{w}}{|w|^2}$$

Since $i^2 = -1$, we can think of i as a square root of -1. But notice that we also have $(-i)^2 = i^2 = -1$ and so $-i$ is also a square root of -1. We say that i is the **principal square root** of -1 and write $\sqrt{-1} = i$. In general, if c is any positive number, we write

$$\sqrt{-c} = \sqrt{c}\,i$$

With this convention, the usual derivation and formula for the roots of the quadratic equation $ax^2 + bx + c = 0$ are valid even when $b^2 - 4ac < 0$:

$$x = \frac{-b \pm \sqrt{b^2 - 4ac}}{2a}$$

EXAMPLE 3 Find the roots of the equation $x^2 + x + 1 = 0$.

SOLUTION Using the quadratic formula, we have

$$x = \frac{-1 \pm \sqrt{1^2 - 4 \cdot 1}}{2} = \frac{-1 \pm \sqrt{-3}}{2} = \frac{-1 \pm \sqrt{3}\, i}{2}$$

We observe that the solutions of the equation in Example 3 are complex conjugates of each other. In general, the solutions of any quadratic equation $ax^2 + bx + c = 0$ with real coefficients a, b, and c are always complex conjugates. (If z is real, $\bar{z} = z$, so z is its own conjugate.)

We have seen that if we allow complex numbers as solutions, then every quadratic equation has a solution. More generally, it is true that every polynomial equation

$$a_n x^n + a_{n-1} x^{n-1} + \cdots + a_1 x + a_0 = 0$$

of degree at least one has a solution among the complex numbers. This fact is known as the Fundamental Theorem of Algebra and was proved by Gauss.

POLAR FORM

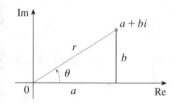

FIGURE 4

We know that any complex number $z = a + bi$ can be considered as a point (a, b) and that any such point can be represented by polar coordinates (r, θ) with $r \geqslant 0$. In fact,

$$a = r \cos \theta \qquad b = r \sin \theta$$

as in Figure 4. Therefore we have

$$z = a + bi = (r \cos \theta) + (r \sin \theta)i$$

Thus we can write any complex number z in the form

$$z = r(\cos \theta + i \sin \theta)$$

where

$$r = |z| = \sqrt{a^2 + b^2} \qquad \text{and} \qquad \tan \theta = \frac{b}{a}$$

The angle θ is called the **argument** of z and we write $\theta = \arg(z)$. Note that $\arg(z)$ is not unique; any two arguments of z differ by an integer multiple of 2π.

EXAMPLE 4 Write the following numbers in polar form.
(a) $z = 1 + i$ (b) $w = \sqrt{3} - i$

SOLUTION
(a) We have $r = |z| = \sqrt{1^2 + 1^2} = \sqrt{2}$ and $\tan \theta = 1$, so we can take $\theta = \pi/4$. Therefore the polar form is

$$z = \sqrt{2}\left(\cos \frac{\pi}{4} + i \sin \frac{\pi}{4}\right)$$

(b) Here we have $r = |w| = \sqrt{3 + 1} = 2$ and $\tan \theta = -1/\sqrt{3}$. Since w lies in the

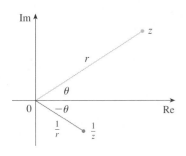

fourth quadrant, we take $\theta = -\pi/6$ and

$$w = 2\left[\cos\left(-\frac{\pi}{6}\right) + i\sin\left(-\frac{\pi}{6}\right)\right]$$

The numbers z and w are shown in Figure 5.

FIGURE 5

The polar form of complex numbers gives insight into multiplication and division. Let

$$z_1 = r_1(\cos\theta_1 + i\sin\theta_1) \qquad z_2 = r_2(\cos\theta_2 + i\sin\theta_2)$$

be two complex numbers written in polar form. Then

$$z_1 z_2 = r_1 r_2(\cos\theta_1 + i\sin\theta_1)(\cos\theta_2 + i\sin\theta_2)$$

$$= r_1 r_2[(\cos\theta_1\cos\theta_2 - \sin\theta_1\sin\theta_2) + i(\sin\theta_1\cos\theta_2 + \cos\theta_1\sin\theta_2)]$$

Therefore, using the addition formulas for cosine and sine, we have

$\boxed{1}$
$$z_1 z_2 = r_1 r_2[\cos(\theta_1 + \theta_2) + i\sin(\theta_1 + \theta_2)]$$

FIGURE 6

This formula says that *to multiply two complex numbers we multiply the moduli and add the arguments.* (See Figure 6.)

A similar argument using the subtraction formulas for sine and cosine shows that *to divide two complex numbers we divide the moduli and subtract the arguments.*

$$\frac{z_1}{z_2} = \frac{r_1}{r_2}[\cos(\theta_1 - \theta_2) + i\sin(\theta_1 - \theta_2)] \qquad z_2 \neq 0$$

In particular, taking $z_1 = 1$ and $z_2 = z$ (and therefore $\theta_1 = 0$ and $\theta_2 = \theta$), we have the following, which is illustrated in Figure 7.

$$\text{If } z = r(\cos\theta + i\sin\theta), \quad \text{then} \quad \frac{1}{z} = \frac{1}{r}(\cos\theta - i\sin\theta).$$

FIGURE 7

EXAMPLE 5 Find the product of the complex numbers $1 + i$ and $\sqrt{3} - i$ in polar form.

SOLUTION From Example 4 we have

$$1 + i = \sqrt{2}\left(\cos\frac{\pi}{4} + i\sin\frac{\pi}{4}\right)$$

and
$$\sqrt{3} - i = 2\left[\cos\left(-\frac{\pi}{6}\right) + i\sin\left(-\frac{\pi}{6}\right)\right]$$

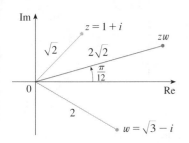

FIGURE 8

So, by Equation 1,

$$(1 + i)(\sqrt{3} - i) = 2\sqrt{2}\left[\cos\left(\frac{\pi}{4} - \frac{\pi}{6}\right) + i\sin\left(\frac{\pi}{4} - \frac{\pi}{6}\right)\right]$$

$$= 2\sqrt{2}\left(\cos\frac{\pi}{12} + i\sin\frac{\pi}{12}\right)$$

This is illustrated in Figure 8.

Repeated use of Formula 1 shows how to compute powers of a complex number. If

$$z = r(\cos\theta + i\sin\theta)$$

then

$$z^2 = r^2(\cos 2\theta + i\sin 2\theta)$$

and

$$z^3 = zz^2 = r^3(\cos 3\theta + i\sin 3\theta)$$

In general, we obtain the following result, which is named after the French mathematician Abraham De Moivre (1667–1754).

---

2 DE MOIVRE'S THEOREM If $z = r(\cos\theta + i\sin\theta)$ and n is a positive integer, then

$$z^n = [r(\cos\theta + i\sin\theta)]^n = r^n(\cos n\theta + i\sin n\theta)$$

This says that *to take the nth power of a complex number we take the nth power of the modulus and multiply the argument by n.*

EXAMPLE 6 Find $\left(\frac{1}{2} + \frac{1}{2}i\right)^{10}$.

SOLUTION Since $\frac{1}{2} + \frac{1}{2}i = \frac{1}{2}(1 + i)$, it follows from Example 4(a) that $\frac{1}{2} + \frac{1}{2}i$ has the polar form

$$\frac{1}{2} + \frac{1}{2}i = \frac{\sqrt{2}}{2}\left(\cos\frac{\pi}{4} + i\sin\frac{\pi}{4}\right)$$

So by De Moivre's Theorem,

$$\left(\frac{1}{2} + \frac{1}{2}i\right)^{10} = \left(\frac{\sqrt{2}}{2}\right)^{10}\left(\cos\frac{10\pi}{4} + i\sin\frac{10\pi}{4}\right)$$

$$= \frac{2^5}{2^{10}}\left(\cos\frac{5\pi}{2} + i\sin\frac{5\pi}{2}\right) = \frac{1}{32}i$$

De Moivre's Theorem can also be used to find the nth roots of complex numbers. An nth root of the complex number z is a complex number w such that

$$w^n = z$$

Writing these two numbers in trigonometric form as

$$w = s(\cos\phi + i\sin\phi) \qquad \text{and} \qquad z = r(\cos\theta + i\sin\theta)$$

and using De Moivre's Theorem, we get

$$s^n(\cos n\phi + i \sin n\phi) = r(\cos \theta + i \sin \theta)$$

The equality of these two complex numbers shows that

$$s^n = r \qquad \text{or} \qquad s = r^{1/n}$$

and $\qquad\qquad\qquad \cos n\phi = \cos \theta \qquad$ and $\qquad \sin n\phi = \sin \theta$

From the fact that sine and cosine have period 2π it follows that

$$n\phi = \theta + 2k\pi \qquad \text{or} \qquad \phi = \frac{\theta + 2k\pi}{n}$$

Thus $\qquad\qquad\qquad w = r^{1/n}\left[\cos\left(\frac{\theta + 2k\pi}{n}\right) + i \sin\left(\frac{\theta + 2k\pi}{n}\right)\right]$

Since this expression gives a different value of w for $k = 0, 1, 2, \ldots, n - 1$, we have the following.

---

3 **ROOTS OF A COMPLEX NUMBER** Let $z = r(\cos \theta + i \sin \theta)$ and let n be a positive integer. Then z has the n distinct nth roots

$$w_k = r^{1/n}\left[\cos\left(\frac{\theta + 2k\pi}{n}\right) + i \sin\left(\frac{\theta + 2k\pi}{n}\right)\right]$$

where $k = 0, 1, 2, \ldots, n - 1$.

Notice that each of the nth roots of z has modulus $|w_k| = r^{1/n}$. Thus all the nth roots of z lie on the circle of radius $r^{1/n}$ in the complex plane. Also, since the argument of each successive nth root exceeds the argument of the previous root by $2\pi/n$, we see that the nth roots of z are equally spaced on this circle.

EXAMPLE 7 Find the six sixth roots of $z = -8$ and graph these roots in the complex plane.

SOLUTION In trigonometric form, $z = 8(\cos \pi + i \sin \pi)$. Applying Equation 3 with $n = 6$, we get

$$w_k = 8^{1/6}\left(\cos \frac{\pi + 2k\pi}{6} + i \sin \frac{\pi + 2k\pi}{6}\right)$$

We get the six sixth roots of -8 by taking $k = 0, 1, 2, 3, 4, 5$ in this formula:

$$w_0 = 8^{1/6}\left(\cos \frac{\pi}{6} + i \sin \frac{\pi}{6}\right) = \sqrt{2}\left(\frac{\sqrt{3}}{2} + \frac{1}{2}i\right)$$

$$w_1 = 8^{1/6}\left(\cos \frac{\pi}{2} + i \sin \frac{\pi}{2}\right) = \sqrt{2}\, i$$

$$w_2 = 8^{1/6}\left(\cos \frac{5\pi}{6} + i \sin \frac{5\pi}{6}\right) = \sqrt{2}\left(-\frac{\sqrt{3}}{2} + \frac{1}{2}i\right)$$

FIGURE 9
The six sixth roots of $z = -8$

$$w_3 = 8^{1/6}\left(\cos\frac{7\pi}{6} + i\sin\frac{7\pi}{6}\right) = \sqrt{2}\left(-\frac{\sqrt{3}}{2} - \frac{1}{2}i\right)$$

$$w_4 = 8^{1/6}\left(\cos\frac{3\pi}{2} + i\sin\frac{3\pi}{2}\right) = -\sqrt{2}\,i$$

$$w_5 = 8^{1/6}\left(\cos\frac{11\pi}{6} + i\sin\frac{11\pi}{6}\right) = \sqrt{2}\left(\frac{\sqrt{3}}{2} - \frac{1}{2}i\right)$$

All these points lie on the circle of radius $\sqrt{2}$ as shown in Figure 9. ☐

COMPLEX EXPONENTIALS

We also need to give a meaning to the expression e^z when $z = x + iy$ is a complex number. The theory of infinite series as developed in Chapter 12 can be extended to the case where the terms are complex numbers. Using the Taylor series for e^x (12.10.11) as our guide, we define

$$\boxed{4} \qquad e^z = \sum_{n=0}^{\infty} \frac{z^n}{n!} = 1 + z + \frac{z^2}{2!} + \frac{z^3}{3!} + \cdots$$

and it turns out that this complex exponential function has the same properties as the real exponential function. In particular, it is true that

$$\boxed{5} \qquad e^{z_1+z_2} = e^{z_1}e^{z_2}$$

If we put $z = iy$, where y is a real number, in Equation 4, and use the facts that

$$i^2 = -1, \quad i^3 = i^2 i = -i, \quad i^4 = 1, \quad i^5 = i, \quad \ldots$$

we get
$$e^{iy} = 1 + iy + \frac{(iy)^2}{2!} + \frac{(iy)^3}{3!} + \frac{(iy)^4}{4!} + \frac{(iy)^5}{5!} + \cdots$$

$$= 1 + iy - \frac{y^2}{2!} - i\frac{y^3}{3!} + \frac{y^4}{4!} + i\frac{y^5}{5!} + \cdots$$

$$= \left(1 - \frac{y^2}{2!} + \frac{y^4}{4!} - \frac{y^6}{6!} + \cdots\right) + i\left(y - \frac{y^3}{3!} + \frac{y^5}{5!} - \cdots\right)$$

$$= \cos y + i\sin y$$

Here we have used the Taylor series for $\cos y$ and $\sin y$ (Equations 12.10.16 and 12.10.15). The result is a famous formula called **Euler's formula**:

$$\boxed{6} \qquad e^{iy} = \cos y + i\sin y$$

Combining Euler's formula with Equation 5, we get

$$\boxed{7} \qquad e^{x+iy} = e^x e^{iy} = e^x(\cos y + i\sin y)$$

EXAMPLE 8 Evaluate: (a) $e^{i\pi}$ (b) $e^{-1+i\pi/2}$

SOLUTION

■ We could write the result of Example 8(a) as

$$e^{i\pi} + 1 = 0$$

This equation relates the five most famous numbers in all of mathematics: 0, 1, e, i, and π.

(a) From Euler's equation (6) we have

$$e^{i\pi} = \cos \pi + i \sin \pi = -1 + i(0) = -1$$

(b) Using Equation 7 we get

$$e^{-1+i\pi/2} = e^{-1}\left(\cos \frac{\pi}{2} + i \sin \frac{\pi}{2}\right) = \frac{1}{e}[0 + i(1)] = \frac{i}{e}$$

Finally, we note that Euler's equation provides us with an easier method of proving De Moivre's Theorem:

$$[r(\cos \theta + i \sin \theta)]^n = (re^{i\theta})^n = r^n e^{in\theta} = r^n(\cos n\theta + i \sin n\theta)$$

G EXERCISES

1–14 Evaluate the expression and write your answer in the form $a + bi$.

1. $(5 - 6i) + (3 + 2i)$

2. $\left(4 - \frac{1}{2}i\right) - \left(9 + \frac{5}{2}i\right)$

3. $(2 + 5i)(4 - i)$

4. $(1 - 2i)(8 - 3i)$

5. $\overline{12 + 7i}$

6. $\overline{2i\left(\frac{1}{2} - i\right)}$

7. $\dfrac{1 + 4i}{3 + 2i}$

8. $\dfrac{3 + 2i}{1 - 4i}$

9. $\dfrac{1}{1 + i}$

10. $\dfrac{3}{4 - 3i}$

11. i^3

12. i^{100}

13. $\sqrt{-25}$

14. $\sqrt{-3}\,\sqrt{-12}$

15–17 Find the complex conjugate and the modulus of the number.

15. $12 - 5i$

16. $-1 + 2\sqrt{2}\,i$

17. $-4i$

18. Prove the following properties of complex numbers.
   (a) $\overline{z + w} = \bar{z} + \bar{w}$ (b) $\overline{zw} = \bar{z}\,\bar{w}$
   (c) $\overline{z^n} = \bar{z}^n$, where n is a positive integer
   [*Hint:* Write $z = a + bi$, $w = c + di$.]

19–24 Find all solutions of the equation.

19. $4x^2 + 9 = 0$

20. $x^4 = 1$

21. $x^2 + 2x + 5 = 0$

22. $2x^2 - 2x + 1 = 0$

23. $z^2 + z + 2 = 0$

24. $z^2 + \frac{1}{2}z + \frac{1}{4} = 0$

25–28 Write the number in polar form with argument between 0 and 2π.

25. $-3 + 3i$

26. $1 - \sqrt{3}\,i$

27. $3 + 4i$

28. $8i$

29–32 Find polar forms for zw, z/w, and $1/z$ by first putting z and w into polar form.

29. $z = \sqrt{3} + i$, $w = 1 + \sqrt{3}\,i$

30. $z = 4\sqrt{3} - 4i$, $w = 8i$

31. $z = 2\sqrt{3} - 2i$, $w = -1 + i$

32. $z = 4\left(\sqrt{3} + i\right)$, $w = -3 - 3i$

33–36 Find the indicated power using De Moivre's Theorem.

33. $(1 + i)^{20}$

34. $\left(1 - \sqrt{3}\,i\right)^5$

35. $\left(2\sqrt{3} + 2i\right)^5$

36. $(1 - i)^8$

37–40 Find the indicated roots. Sketch the roots in the complex plane.

37. The eighth roots of 1

38. The fifth roots of 32

39. The cube roots of i

40. The cube roots of $1 + i$

41–46 Write the number in the form $a + bi$.

41. $e^{i\pi/2}$

42. $e^{2\pi i}$

43. $e^{i\pi/3}$

44. $e^{-i\pi}$

45. $e^{2+i\pi}$

46. $e^{\pi+i}$

47. Use De Moivre's Theorem with $n = 3$ to express $\cos 3\theta$ and $\sin 3\theta$ in terms of $\cos \theta$ and $\sin \theta$.

48. Use Euler's formula to prove the following formulas for $\cos x$ and $\sin x$:

$$\cos x = \frac{e^{ix} + e^{-ix}}{2} \qquad \sin x = \frac{e^{ix} - e^{-ix}}{2i}$$

49. If $u(x) = f(x) + ig(x)$ is a complex-valued function of a real variable x and the real and imaginary parts $f(x)$ and $g(x)$ are differentiable functions of x, then the derivative of u is defined to be $u'(x) = f'(x) + ig'(x)$. Use this together with Equation 7 to prove that if $F(x) = e^{rx}$, then $F'(x) = re^{rx}$ when $r = a + bi$ is a complex number.

50. (a) If u is a complex-valued function of a real variable, its indefinite integral $\int u(x)\, dx$ is an antiderivative of u. Evaluate

$$\int e^{(1+i)x}\, dx$$

(b) By considering the real and imaginary parts of the integral in part (a), evaluate the real integrals

$$\int e^x \cos x\, dx \qquad \text{and} \qquad \int e^x \sin x\, dx$$

(c) Compare with the method used in Example 4 in Section 8.1.

H ANSWERS TO ODD-NUMBERED EXERCISES

CHAPTER 1

EXERCISES 1.1 ■ PAGE 20

1. (a) -2 (b) 2.8 (c) $-3, 1$ (d) $-2.5, 0.3$
(e) $[-3, 3], [-2, 3]$ (f) $[-1, 3]$
3. $[-85, 115]$ **5.** No
7. Yes, $[-3, 2], [-3, -2) \cup [-1, 3]$
9. Diet, exercise, or illness
11.
13.
15.
17.
19. (a) (b) In millions: 92; 485

21. $12, 16, 3a^2 - a + 2, 3a^2 + a + 2, 3a^2 + 5a + 4,$
$6a^2 - 2a + 4, 12a^2 - 2a + 2, 3a^4 - a^2 + 2,$
$9a^4 - 6a^3 + 13a^2 - 4a + 4, 3a^2 + 6ah + 3h^2 - a - h + 2$
23. $-3 - h$ **25.** $-1/(ax)$
27. $\{x \mid x \neq \frac{1}{3}\} = (-\infty, \frac{1}{3}) \cup (\frac{1}{3}, \infty)$
29. $[0, \infty)$ **31.** $(-\infty, 0) \cup (5, \infty)$

33. $(-\infty, \infty)$

35. $(-\infty, \infty)$

37. $[5, \infty)$

39. $(-\infty, 0) \cup (0, \infty)$

41. $(-\infty, \infty)$

43. $(-\infty, \infty)$

45. $f(x) = \frac{5}{2}x - \frac{11}{2}, 1 \leq x \leq 5$ **47.** $f(x) = 1 - \sqrt{-x}$

49. $f(x) = \begin{cases} -x + 3 & \text{if } 0 \leq x \leq 3 \\ 2x - 6 & \text{if } 3 < x \leq 5 \end{cases}$

51. $A(L) = 10L - L^2, 0 < L < 10$
53. $A(x) = \sqrt{3}x^2/4, x > 0$ **55.** $S(x) = x^2 + (8/x), x > 0$
57. $V(x) = 4x^3 - 64x^2 + 240x, 0 < x < 6$
59. (a) (b) $400, $1900

(c)
61. f is odd, g is even
63. (a) $(-5, 3)$ (b) $(-5, -3)$
65. Odd **67.** Neither **69.** Even

EXERCISES 1.2 ■ PAGE 34

1. (a) Root (b) Algebraic (c) Polynomial (degree 9)
(d) Rational (e) Trigonometric (f) Logarithmic
3. (a) h (b) f (c) g

5. (a) $y = 2x + b$,
where b is the y-intercept.

(b) $y = mx + 1 - 2m$,
where m is the slope.
See graph at right.
(c) $y = 2x - 3$

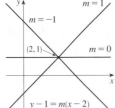

7. Their graphs have slope -1.

9. $f(x) = -3x(x + 1)(x - 2)$
11. (a) 8.34, change in mg for every 1 year change
(b) 8.34 mg

13. (a)

(b) $\frac{9}{5}$, change in °F for every
1°C change; 32, Fahrenheit
temperature corresponding
to 0°C

15. (a) $T = \frac{1}{6}N + \frac{307}{6}$ (b) $\frac{1}{6}$, change in °F for every chirp per
minute change   (c) 76°F
17. (a) $P = 0.434d + 15$ (b) 196 ft
19. (a) Cosine   (b) Linear
21. (a)

(b) $y = -0.000105x + 14.521$

Linear model is
appropriate

(c) $y = -0.00009979x + 13.951$ [See graph in (b).]
(d) About 11.5 per 100 population   (e) About 6%   (f) No
23. (a)

Linear model is appropriate
(b) $y = 0.08912x - 158.24$ (c) 20 ft   (d) No

25. $y \approx 0.0012937x^3 - 7.06142x^2 + 12{,}823x - 7{,}743{,}770$;
1914 million

EXERCISES 1.3 ■ PAGE 43

1. (a) $y = f(x) + 3$ (b) $y = f(x) - 3$ (c) $y = f(x - 3)$
(d) $y = f(x + 3)$ (e) $y = -f(x)$ (f) $y = f(-x)$
(g) $y = 3f(x)$ (h) $y = \frac{1}{3}f(x)$
3. (a) 3   (b) 1   (c) 4   (d) 5   (e) 2
5. (a)

(b)

(c)

(d)

7. $y = -\sqrt{-x^2 - 5x - 4} - 1$
9.

11.

13.

15.

$y = \sin(x/2)$

17.

$y = \sqrt{x+3}$

19.

$y = \frac{1}{2}(x^2 + 8x)$

21.

$x = -1$ $y = \dfrac{2}{x+1}$

23.

$y = |\sin x|$

25. $L(t) = 12 + 2 \sin\left[\dfrac{2\pi}{365}(t - 80)\right]$

27. (a) The portion of the graph of $y = f(x)$ to the right of the
y-axis is reflected about the y-axis.
(b)   (c)

$y = \sin|x|$

$y = \sqrt{|x|}$

29. $(f + g)(x) = x^3 + 5x^2 - 1, (-\infty, \infty)$
$(f - g)(x) = x^3 - x^2 + 1, (-\infty, \infty)$
$(fg)(x) = 3x^5 + 6x^4 - x^3 - 2x^2, (-\infty, \infty)$
$(f/g)(x) = (x^3 + 2x^2)/(3x^2 - 1), \{x \mid x \neq \pm 1/\sqrt{3}\}$

31. (a) $(f \circ g)(x) = 4x^2 + 4x, (-\infty, \infty)$
(b) $(g \circ f)(x) = 2x^2 - 1, (-\infty, \infty)$
(c) $(f \circ f)(x) = x^4 - 2x^2, (-\infty, \infty)$
(d) $(g \circ g)(x) = 4x + 3, (-\infty, \infty)$

33. (a) $(f \circ g)(x) = 1 - 3 \cos x, (-\infty, \infty)$
(b) $(g \circ f)(x) = \cos(1 - 3x), (-\infty, \infty)$
(c) $(f \circ f)(x) = 9x - 2, (-\infty, \infty)$
(d) $(g \circ g)(x) = \cos(\cos x), (-\infty, \infty)$

35. (a) $(f \circ g)(x) = (2x^2 + 6x + 5)/[(x + 2)(x + 1)],$
$\{x \mid x \neq -2, -1\}$
(b) $(g \circ f)(x) = (x^2 + x + 1)/(x + 1)^2, \{x \mid x \neq -1, 0\}$
(c) $(f \circ f)(x) = (x^4 + 3x^2 + 1)/[x(x^2 + 1)], \{x \mid x \neq 0\}$
(d) $(g \circ g)(x) = (2x + 3)/(3x + 5), \{x \mid x \neq -2, -\frac{5}{3}\}$

37. $(f \circ g \circ h)(x) = 2x - 1$

39. $(f \circ g \circ h)(x) = \sqrt{x^6 + 4x^3 + 1}$

41. $g(x) = x^2 + 1, f(x) = x^{10}$

43. $g(x) = \sqrt[3]{x}, f(x) = x/(1 + x)$

45. $g(t) = \cos t, f(t) = \sqrt{t}$

47. $h(x) = x^2, g(x) = 3^x, f(x) = 1 - x$

49. $h(x) = \sqrt{x}, g(x) = \sec x, f(x) = x^4$

51. (a) 4   (b) 3   (c) 0   (d) Does not exist; $f(6) = 6$ is not
in the domain of g.   (e) 4   (f) -2

53. (a) $r(t) = 60t$ (b) $(A \circ r)(t) = 3600\pi t^2$; the area of the
circle as a function of time

55. (a) $s = \sqrt{d^2 + 36}$ (b) $d = 30t$
(c) $s = \sqrt{900t^2 + 36}$; the distance between the lighthouse and the
ship as a function of the time elapsed since noon

57. (a)   (b)

$V(t) = 120H(t)$

(c)

$V(t) = 240H(t - 5)$

59. Yes; $m_1 m_2$

61. (a) $f(x) = x^2 + 6$ (b) $g(x) = x^2 + x - 1$

63. (a) Even; even   (b) Odd; even

65. Yes

EXERCISES 1.4 ■ **PAGE 51**

1. (c)

3.

5.

7.

9.

11.

13.

15.

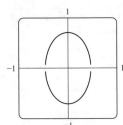

17. No   **19.** 9.05   **21.** 0, 0.88   **23.** g

25. $-0.85 < x < 0.85$

27. (a)

(b)

(c)

(d) Graphs of even roots are similar to $\sqrt{x}$, graphs of odd roots are similar to $\sqrt[3]{x}$. As n increases, the graph of $y = \sqrt[n]{x}$ becomes steeper near 0 and flatter for $x > 1$.

29.

If $c < -1.5$, the graph has three humps: two minimum points and a maximum point. These humps get flatter as c increases until at $c = -1.5$ two of the humps disappear and there is only one minimum point. This single hump then moves to the right and approaches the origin as c increases.

31. The hump gets larger and moves to the right.

33. If $c < 0$, the loop is to the right of the origin; if $c > 0$, the loop is to the left. The closer c is to 0, the larger the loop.

CHAPTER I REVIEW ▪ PAGE 52

True-False Quiz

1. False   **3.** False   **5.** True

Exercises

1. (a) 2.7   (b) 2.3, 5.6   (c) $[-6, 6]$ (d) $[-4, 4]$

(e) $[-4, 4]$ (f) Odd; its graph is symmetric about the origin.

3. $2a + h - 2$ **5.** $\left(-\infty, \frac{1}{3}\right) \cup \left(\frac{1}{3}, \infty\right)$, $(-\infty, 0) \cup (0, \infty)$

7. $\mathbb{R}, [0, 2]$

9. (a) Shift the graph 8 units upward.

(b) Shift the graph 8 units to the left.

(c) Stretch the graph vertically by a factor of 2, then shift it 1 unit upward.

(d) Shift the graph 2 units to the right and 2 units downward.

(e) Reflect the graph about the x-axis.

(f) Reflect the graph about the line x-axis, then shift it 3 units upward.

11.

13.

15.

17. (a) Neither   (b) Odd   (c) Even   (d) Neither

19. (a) $(f \circ g)(x) = \sqrt{\sin x}$, $\{x \mid x \in [2n\pi, \pi + 2n\pi], n \text{ an integer}\}$

(b) $(g \circ f)(x) = \sin \sqrt{x}$, $[0, \infty)$

(c) $(f \circ f)(x) = \sqrt[4]{x}$, $[0, \infty)$

(d) $(g \circ g)(x) = \sin(\sin x)$, $\mathbb{R}$

21. All have domain $\mathbb{R}$. The range is $[-1, 1]$ for n odd and $[0, 1]$ for n even. The spikes become sharper as $n \to \infty$.

23. $y = 0.2493x - 423.4818$; about 77.6 years

PRINCIPLES OF PROBLEM SOLVING ▪ PAGE 59

1. $a = 4\sqrt{h^2 - 16}/h$, where a is the length of the altitude and h is the length of the hypotenuse

3. $-\frac{7}{3}, 9$

5.

7.

9.

11. 40 mi/h   **15.** $f_n(x) = x^{2^{n+1}}$

CHAPTER 2

1. (a) $-44.4, -38.8, -27.8, -22.2, -16.\overline{6}$
(b) -33.3 (c) $-33\frac{1}{3}$
3. (a) (i) 0.333333   (ii) 0.263158   (iii) 0.251256
(iv) 0.250125   (v) 0.2   (vi) 0.238095   (vii) 0.248756
(viii) 0.249875   (b) $\frac{1}{4}$ (c) $y = \frac{1}{4}x + \frac{1}{4}$
5. (a) (i) -32 ft/s   (ii) -25.6 ft/s   (iii) -24.8 ft/s
(iv) -24.16 ft/s   (b) -24 ft/s
7. (a) (i) 4.65 m/s   (ii) 5.6 m/s   (iii) 7.55 m/s
(iv) 7 m/s   (b) 6.3 m/s
9. (a) $0, 1.7321, -1.0847, -2.7433, 4.3301, -2.8173, 0,$
$-2.1651, -2.6061, -5, 3.4202$; no   (c) -31.4

1. Yes
3. (a) $\lim_{x \to -3} f(x) = \infty$ means that the values of $f(x)$ can be
made arbitrarily large (as large as we please) by taking x sufficiently close to -3 (but not equal to -3).
(b) $\lim_{x \to 4^+} f(x) = -\infty$ means that the values of $f(x)$ can be made arbitrarily large negative by taking x sufficiently close to 4 through values larger than 4.
5. (a) 2   (b) 3   (c) Does not exist   (d) 4
(e) Does not exist
7. (a) -1 (b) -2 (c) Does not exist   (d) 2   (e) 0
(f) Does not exist   (g) 1   (h) 3
9. (a) $-\infty$ (b) ∞ (c) ∞ (d) $-\infty$ (e) ∞
(f) $x = -7, x = -3, x = 0, x = 6$
11. (a) 1   (b) 0   (c) Does not exist
13.   **15.**

17. $\frac{2}{3}$ **19.** $\frac{1}{2}$ **21.** $\frac{1}{4}$ **23.** $\frac{3}{5}$ **25.** $-\infty$
27. ∞ **29.** $-\infty$ **31.** $-\infty$ **33.** $-\infty; \infty$
35. (a) 2.71828   (b)

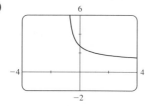

37. (a) 0.998000, 0.638259, 0.358484, 0.158680, 0.038851,
0.008928, 0.001465; 0
(b) 0.000572, $-0.000614, -0.000907, -0.000978, -0.000993,$
$-0.001000; -0.001$
39. No matter how many times we zoom in toward the origin, the graph appears to consist of almost-vertical lines. This indicates more and more frequent oscillations as $x \to 0$.
41. $x \approx \pm 0.90, \pm 2.24; x = \pm\sin^{-1}(\pi/4), \pm(\pi - \sin^{-1}(\pi/4))$

1. (a) -6 (b) -8 (c) 2   (d) -6
(e) Does not exist   (f) 0
3. 59   **5.** 390   **7.** $\frac{1}{8}$ **9.** 0   **11.** 5
13. Does not exist   **15.** $\frac{6}{5}$ **17.** 8   **19.** $\frac{1}{12}$ **21.** 6
23. $\frac{1}{6}$ **25.** $-\frac{1}{16}$ **27.** $\frac{1}{128}$ **29.** $-\frac{1}{2}$ **31.** (a), (b) $\frac{2}{3}$
35. 7   **39.** 6   **41.** -4 **43.** Does not exist
45. (a)   (b) (i) 1
(ii) -1
(iii) Does not exist
(iv) 1

47. (a) (i) 2   (ii) -2 (b) No   (c)

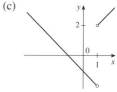

49. (a) (i) -2 (ii) Does not exist   (iii) -3
(b) (i) $n - 1$ (ii) n (c) a is not an integer.
55. 8   **61.** 15; -1

1. $\frac{4}{7}$ (or any smaller positive number)
3. 1.44 (or any smaller positive number)
5. 0.0906 (or any smaller positive number)
7. 0.11, 0.012 (or smaller positive numbers)
9. (a) 0.031   (b) 0.010
11. (a) $\sqrt{1000/\pi}$ cm   (b) Within approximately 0.0445 cm
(c) Radius; area; $\sqrt{1000/\pi}$; 1000; 5; ≈ 0.0445
13. (a) 0.025   (b) 0.0025
35. (a) 0.093   (b) $\delta = (B^{2/3} - 12)/(6B^{1/3}) - 1$, where
$B = 216 + 108\varepsilon + 12\sqrt{336 + 324\varepsilon + 81\varepsilon^2}$
41. Within 0.1

1. $\lim_{x \to 4} f(x) = f(4)$
3. (a) -4 (removable), -2 (jump), 2 (jump), 4 (infinite)
(b) -4, neither; -2, left; 2, right; 4, right
5.

7. (a)   (b) Discontinuous at $t = 1, 2, 3, 4$

9. 6

15. $f(1)$ is not defined.   **17.** $\lim\limits_{x \to 1} f(x)$ does not exist.

19. $\lim\limits_{x \to 0} f(x) \neq f(0)$

21. $\{x \mid x \neq -3, -2\}$ **23.** $\left[\frac{1}{2}, \infty\right)$
25. $\mathbb{R}$ **27.** $[0, \infty)$
29. $x = (-\pi/2) + 2n\pi$, n an integer

31. $\frac{7}{3}$ **33.** $\pi/8$
37. 0, left   **39.** 0, right; 1, left

41. $\frac{2}{3}$
43. (a) $g(x) = x^3 + x^2 + x + 1$ (b) $g(x) = x^2 + x$
51. (b) $(0.86, 0.87)$ **53.** (b) 1.434
59. None   **61.** Yes

CHAPTER 2 REVIEW ■ PAGE 108

True-False Quiz

1. False   **3.** True   **5.** False   **7.** True   **9.** False
11. True   **13.** True   **15.** True

Exercises

1. (a) (i) 3   (ii) 0   (iii) Does not exist   (iv) 2
(v) ∞ (vi) $-\infty$
(b) $x = 0$, $x = 2$ (c) $-3, 0, 2, 4$
3. 1   **5.** $\frac{3}{2}$ **7.** 3   **9.** ∞ **11.** $\frac{4}{7}$ **13.** $-\frac{1}{8}$
15. 0   **17.** 1

23. (a) (i) 3   (ii) 0   (iii) Does not exist   (iv) 0   (v) 0   (vi) 0
(b) At 0 and 3   (c)

25. $[0, \infty)$ **29.** 0

PROBLEMS PLUS ■ PAGE 110

1. $\frac{2}{3}$ **3.** -4 **5.** (a) Does not exist.   (b) 1
7. $a = \frac{1}{2} \pm \frac{1}{2}\sqrt{5}$
9. $\frac{3}{4}$ **11.** (b) Yes   (c) Yes; no

CHAPTER 3

EXERCISES 3.1 ■ PAGE 119

1. (a) $\dfrac{f(x) - f(3)}{x - 3}$ (b) $\lim\limits_{x \to 3} \dfrac{f(x) - f(3)}{x - 3}$
3. (a) 2   (b) $y = 2x + 1$ (c)

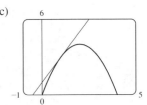

5. $y = -x + 5$ **7.** $y = \frac{1}{2}x + \frac{1}{2}$
9. (a) $8a - 6a^2$ (b) $y = 2x + 3$, $y = -8x + 19$
(c)

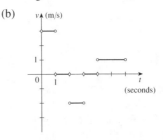

11. (a) Right: $0 < t < 1$ and $4 < t < 6$; left: $2 < t < 3$;
standing still: $1 < t < 2$ and $3 < t < 4$
(b)

13. -24 ft/s   **15.** $-2/a^3$ m/s; -2 m/s; $-\frac{1}{4}$ m/s; $-\frac{2}{27}$ m/s
17. $g'(0), 0, g'(4), g'(2), g'(-2)$

19.

21. 7; $y = 7x - 12$

23. (a) $-\frac{3}{5}$; $y = -\frac{3}{5}x + \frac{16}{5}$ (b)

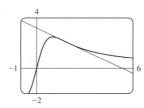

25. $-2 + 8a$ **27.** $\dfrac{5}{(a + 3)^2}$ **29.** $\dfrac{-1}{2(a + 2)^{3/2}}$

31. $f(x) = x^{10}$, $a = 1$ or $f(x) = (1 + x)^{10}$, $a = 0$

33. $f(x) = 2^x$, $a = 5$

35. $f(x) = \cos x$, $a = \pi$ or $f(x) = \cos(\pi + x)$, $a = 0$

37. 1 m/s; 1 m/s

39.

Greater (in magnitude)

41. (a) (i) 11 percent/year (ii) 13 percent/year
(iii) 16 percent/year
(b) 14.5 percent/year (c) 15 percent/year

43. (a) (i) $20.25/unit (ii) $20.05/unit (b) $20/unit

45. (a) The rate at which the cost is changing per ounce of gold produced; dollars per ounce
(b) When the 800th ounce of gold is produced, the cost of production is $17/oz.
(c) Decrease in the short term; increase in the long term

47. The rate at which the temperature is changing at 10:00 AM; $4°$F/h

49. (a) The rate at which the oxygen solubility changes with respect to the water temperature; (mg/L)/$°$C
(b) $S'(16) \approx -0.25$; as the temperature increases past $16°$C, the oxygen solubility is decreasing at a rate of 0.25 (mg/L)/$°$C.

51. Does not exist

EXERCISES 3.2 ▪ PAGE 131

1. (a) 1.5
(b) 1
(c) 0
(d) -4
(e) 0
(f) 1
(g) 1.5

3. (a) II (b) IV (c) I (d) III

5.

7.

9.

11.

13. 1963 to 1971

15. (a) 0, 1, 2, 4 (b) $-1, -2, -4$ (c) $f'(x) = 2x$

17. $f'(x) = \frac{1}{2}$, $\mathbb{R}$, $\mathbb{R}$ **19.** $f'(t) = 5 - 18t$, $\mathbb{R}$, $\mathbb{R}$

21. $f'(x) = 3x^2 - 3$, $\mathbb{R}$, $\mathbb{R}$

23. $g'(x) = 1/\sqrt{1 + 2x}$, $\left[-\frac{1}{2}, \infty\right)$, $\left(-\frac{1}{2}, \infty\right)$

25. $G'(t) = \dfrac{4}{(t + 1)^2}$, $(-\infty, -1) \cup (-1, \infty)$, $(-\infty, -1) \cup (-1, \infty)$

27. $f'(x) = 4x^3$, $\mathbb{R}$, $\mathbb{R}$ **29.** (a) $f'(x) = 4x^3 + 2$

31. (a) The rate at which the unemployment rate is changing, in percent unemployed per year
(b)

t	$U'(t)$	t	$U'(t)$
1993	-0.80	1998	-0.35
1994	-0.65	1999	-0.25
1995	-0.35	2000	0.25
1996	-0.35	2001	0.90
1997	-0.45	2002	1.10

33. -4 (corner); 0 (discontinuity)

35. -1 (vertical tangent); 4 (corner)

37.

Differentiable at -1; not differentiable at 0

39. $a = f$, $b = f'$, $c = f''$

41. $a =$ acceleration, $b =$ velocity, $c =$ position

43.

$f'(x) = 4 - 2x,$
$f''(x) = -2$

45.

$f'(x) = 4x - 3x^2,$
$f''(x) = 4 - 6x,$
$f'''(x) = -6,$
$f^{(4)}(x) = 0$

47. (a) $\frac{1}{3}a^{-2/3}$

49. $f'(x) = \begin{cases} -1 & \text{if } x < 6 \\ 1 & \text{if } x > 6 \end{cases}$

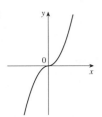

or $f'(x) = \dfrac{x - 6}{|x - 6|}$

51. (a)

(b) All x
(c) $f'(x) = 2|x|$

55. 63°

EXERCISES 3.3 ▪ PAGE 144

1. $f'(x) = 0$　　**3.** $f'(t) = -\frac{2}{3}$　　**5.** $f'(x) = 3x^2 - 4$

7. $f'(t) = t^3$　　**9.** $V'(r) = 4\pi r^2$　　**11.** $Y'(t) = -54t^{-10}$

13. $F'(x) = \frac{5}{32}x^4$　　**15.** $A'(s) = 60/s^6$　　**17.** $y' = 0$

19. $u' = \frac{1}{5}t^{-4/5} + 10t^{3/2}$　　**21.** $y' = 5x^4 + 3x^2 + 2x$

23. $V'(x) = 14x^6 - 4x^3 - 6$　　**25.** $F'(y) = 5 + 14/y^2 + 9/y^4$

27. $g'(x) = 5/(2x + 1)^2$　　**29.** $y' = \dfrac{x^2(3 - x^2)}{(1 - x^2)^2}$

31. $y' = 2v - 1/\sqrt{v}$　　**33.** $y' = \dfrac{2t(-t^4 - 4t^2 + 7)}{(t^4 - 3t^2 + 1)^2}$

35. $y' = 2ax + b$　　**37.** $y' = \dfrac{r(4 + 3\sqrt{r})}{2(1 + \sqrt{r})^2}$

39. $y' = (7t^3 + 4t^2 - 2)/(3t^{5/3})$　　**41.** $f'(x) = 2cx/(x^2 + c)^2$

43. $P'(x) = na_n x^{n-1} + (n - 1)a_{n-1}x^{n-2} + \cdots + 2a_2 x + a_1$

45. $45x^{14} - 15x^2$

47. (a)

(c) $4x^3 - 9x^2 - 12x + 7$

49. $y = \frac{1}{2}x + \frac{1}{2}$

51. (a) $y = \frac{1}{2}x + 1$　　(b)

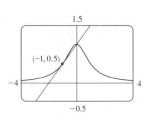

53. $y = \frac{3}{2}x + \frac{1}{2}, y = -\frac{2}{3}x + \frac{8}{3}$　　**55.** $y = -\frac{1}{2}x + \frac{5}{2}, y = 2x$

57. $f'(x) = 4x^3 - 9x^2 + 16, f''(x) = 12x^2 - 18x$

59. $\dfrac{2x^2 + 2x}{(1 + 2x)^2}, \dfrac{2}{(1 + 2x)^3}$

61. (a) $v(t) = 3t^2 - 3, a(t) = 6t$　　(b) 12 m/s^2
(c) $a(1) = 6 \text{ m/s}^2$

63. (a) -16　　(b) $-\frac{20}{9}$　　(c) 20

65. 16　　**67.** (a) 0　　(b) $-\frac{2}{3}$

69. (a) $y' = xg'(x) + g(x)$　　(b) $y' = [g(x) - xg'(x)]/[g(x)]^2$
(c) $y' = [xg'(x) - g(x)]/x^2$

71. $(-2, 21), (1, -6)$　　**75.** $y = 12x - 15, y = 12x + 17$

77. $y = \frac{1}{3}x - \frac{1}{3}$　　**79.** $(\pm 2, 4)$

81. (c) $3(x^4 + 3x^3 + 17x + 82)^2(4x^3 + 9x^2 + 17)$

83. $P(x) = x^2 - x + 3$　　**85.** $y = \frac{3}{16}x^3 - \frac{9}{4}x + 3$

87. $\$1.627 \text{ billion/year}$

89. No

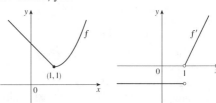

91. (a) Not differentiable at 3 or -3

$f'(x) = \begin{cases} 2x & \text{if } |x| > 3 \\ -2x & \text{if } |x| < 3 \end{cases}$

(b)

93. $a = -\frac{1}{2}, b = 2$　　**95.** 6　　**99.** 1000　　**101.** $3, 1$

EXERCISES 3.4 ▪ PAGE 154

1. $f'(x) = 6x + 2\sin x$　　**3.** $f'(x) = \cos x - \frac{1}{2}\csc^2 x$

5. $g'(t) = 3t^2 \cos t - t^3 \sin t$

7. $h'(\theta) = \csc \theta - \theta \csc \theta \cot \theta + \csc^2 \theta$

9. $y' = \dfrac{2 - \tan x + x \sec^2 x}{(2 - \tan x)^2}$　　**11.** $f'(\theta) = \dfrac{\sec \theta \tan \theta}{(1 + \sec \theta)^2}$

13. $y' = (x \cos x - 2 \sin x)/x^3$　　**15.** $y' = \sec \theta (\sec^2 \theta + \tan^2 \theta)$

21. $y = 2\sqrt{3}x - \frac{2}{3}\sqrt{3}\pi + 2$　　**23.** $y = x + 1$

25. (a) $y = 2x$ (b) $\frac{3\pi}{2}$

27. (a) $\sec x \tan x - 1$

29. $\theta \cos \theta + \sin \theta$; $2 \cos \theta - \theta \sin \theta$

31. (a) $f'(x) = (1 + \tan x)/\sec x$ (b) $f'(x) = \cos x + \sin x$

33. $(2n + 1)\pi \pm \frac{1}{3}\pi$, n an integer

35. (a) $v(t) = 8 \cos t$, $a(t) = -8 \sin t$

(b) $4\sqrt{3}, -4, -4\sqrt{3}$; to the left

37. 5 ft/rad   **39.** 3   **41.** 3   **43.** $\sin 1$

45. $\frac{1}{2}$ **47.** $-\sqrt{2}$

49. (a) $\sec^2 x = 1/\cos^2 x$ (b) $\sec x \tan x = (\sin x)/\cos^2 x$

(c) $\cos x - \sin x = (\cot x - 1)/\csc x$

51. 1

EXERCISES 3.5 ■ PAGE 161

1. $4 \cos 4x$ **3.** $-20x(1 - x^2)^9$ **5.** $\dfrac{\cos x}{2\sqrt{\sin x}}$

7. $F'(x) = 10x(x^4 + 3x^2 - 2)^4(2x^2 + 3)$

9. $F'(x) = \dfrac{2 + 3x^2}{4(1 + 2x + x^3)^{3/4}}$ **11.** $g'(t) = -\dfrac{12t^3}{(t^4 + 1)^4}$

13. $y' = -3x^2 \sin(a^3 + x^3)$ **15.** $y' = \sec kx(kx \tan kx + 1)$

17. $g'(x) = 4(1 + 4x)^4(3 + x - x^2)^7(17 + 9x - 21x^2)$

19. $y' = 8(2x - 5)^3(8x^2 - 5)^{-4}(-4x^2 + 30x - 5)$

21. $y' = \dfrac{-12x(x^2 + 1)^2}{(x^2 - 1)^4}$

23. $y' = (\cos x - x \sin x)\cos(x \cos x)$

25. $F'(z) = 1/[(z - 1)^{1/2}(z + 1)^{3/2}]$

27. $y' = (r^2 + 1)^{-3/2}$ **29.** $y' = 2 \cos(\tan 2x) \sec^2(2x)$

31. $y' = (x \cos\sqrt{1 + x^2})/\sqrt{1 + x^2}$ **33.** $y' = 4 \sec^2 x \tan x$

35. $y' = \dfrac{16 \sin 2x(1 - \cos 2x)^3}{(1 + \cos 2x)^5}$

37. $y' = -2 \cos \theta \cot(\sin \theta) \csc^2(\sin \theta)$

39. $y' = 3[x^2 + (1 - 3x)^5]^2[2x - 15(1 - 3x)^4]$

41. $y' = \dfrac{1 + 1/(2\sqrt{x})}{2\sqrt{x + \sqrt{x}}}$

43. $g'(x) = p(2r \sin rx + n)^{p-1}(2r^2 \cos rx)$

45. $y' = \dfrac{-\pi \cos(\tan \pi x) \sec^2(\pi x) \sin\sqrt{\sin(\tan \pi x)}}{2\sqrt{\sin(\tan \pi x)}}$

47. $h'(x) = x/\sqrt{x^2 + 1}$, $h''(x) = 1/(x^2 + 1)^{3/2}$

49. $H'(t) = 3 \sec^2 3t$, $H''(t) = 18 \sec^2 3t \tan 3t$

51. $y = 20x + 1$ **53.** $y = -x + \pi$

55. (a) $y = \pi x - \pi + 1$ (b)   3

57. (a) $f'(x) = (2 - 2x^2)/\sqrt{2 - x^2}$

59. $((\pi/2) + 2n\pi, 3)$, $((3\pi/2) + 2n\pi, -1)$, n an integer

61. 24

63. (a) 30   (b) 36

65. (a) $\frac{3}{4}$ (b) Does not exist   (c) -2

67. (a) $F'(x) = -\sin x f'(\cos x)$ (b) $G'(x) = -\sin(f(x))f'(x)$

69. 120   **71.** 96   **73.** $2^{103} \sin 2x$

75. $v(t) = \frac{5}{2}\pi \cos(10\pi t)$ cm/s

77. (a) $\dfrac{dB}{dt} = \dfrac{7\pi}{54} \cos \dfrac{2\pi t}{5.4}$ (b) 0.16

79. dv/dt is the rate of change of velocity with respect to time; dv/ds is the rate of change of velocity with respect to displacement

81. (b) The factored form

85. (b) $-n \cos^{n-1} x \sin[(n + 1)x]$

EXERCISES 3.6 ■ PAGE 169

1. (a) $y' = -(y + 2 + 6x)/x$

(b) $y = (4/x) - 2 - 3x$, $y' = -(4/x^2) - 3$

3. (a) $y' = -y^2/x^2$ (b) $y = x/(x - 1)$, $y' = -1/(x - 1)^2$

5. $y' = -x^2/y^2$

7. $y' = \dfrac{2x + y}{2y - x}$ **9.** $y' = \dfrac{3y^2 - 5x^4 - 4x^3 y}{x^4 + 3y^2 - 6xy}$

11. $y' = \dfrac{-2xy^2 - \sin y}{2x^2 y + x \cos y}$ **13.** $y' = \tan x \tan y$

15. $y' = \dfrac{y \sec^2(x/y) - y^2}{y^2 + x \sec^2(x/y)}$ **17.** $y' = \dfrac{4xy\sqrt{xy} - y}{x - 2x^2\sqrt{xy}}$

19. $y' = \dfrac{y \sin x + y \cos(xy)}{\cos x - x \cos(xy)}$ **21.** $-\frac{16}{13}$

23. $x' = \dfrac{-2x^4 y + x^3 - 6xy^2}{4x^3 y^2 - 3x^2 y + 2y^3}$ **25.** $y = -x + 2$

27. $y = x + \frac{1}{2}$ **29.** $y = -\frac{9}{13}x + \frac{40}{13}$

31. (a) $y = \frac{9}{2}x - \frac{5}{2}$ (b)

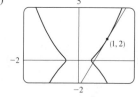

33. $-81/y^3$ **35.** $-2x/y^5$

37. (a)   Eight; $x \approx 0.42, 1.58$

(b) $y = -x + 1$, $y = \frac{1}{3}x + 2$ (c) $1 \mp \frac{1}{3}\sqrt{3}$

39. $(\pm\frac{5}{4}\sqrt{3}, \pm\frac{5}{4})$ **41.** $(x_0 x/a^2) - (y_0 y/b^2) = 1$

45.

47.

49. $\left(\pm\sqrt{3}, 0\right)$ **51.** $(-1, -1), (1, 1)$ **53.** 2

EXERCISES 3.7 ■ PAGE 179

1. (a) $3t^2 - 24t + 36$ (b) -9 ft/s   (c) $t = 2, 6$
(d) $0 \le t < 2, t > 6$
(e) 96 ft
(f)

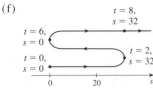

(g) $6t - 24$; -6 m/s^2

(h)

(i) Speeding up when $2 < t < 4$ or $t > 6$; slowing down when $0 \le t < 2$ or $4 < t < 6$

3. (a) $-\dfrac{\pi}{4}\sin\left(\dfrac{\pi t}{4}\right)$ (b) $-\frac18\pi\sqrt{2}$ ft/s   (c) $t = 0, 4, 8$
(d) $4 < t < 8$ (e) 4 ft
(f)

(g) $-\frac{1}{16}\pi^2\cos(\pi t/4)$; $\frac{1}{32}\pi^2\sqrt{2}$ ft/s^2
(h)

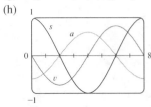

(i) Speeding up when $0 < t < 2, 4 < t < 6$; slowing down when $2 < t < 4, 6 < t < 8$
5. (a) Speeding up when $0 < t < 1$ or $2 < t < 3$; slowing down when $1 < t < 2$
(b) Speeding up when $1 < t < 2$ or $3 < t < 4$; slowing down when $0 < t < 1$ or $2 < t < 3$
7. (a) $t = 4$ s
(b) $t = 1.5$ s; the velocity has an absolute minimum.
9. (a) 5.02 m/s   (b) $\sqrt{17}$ m/s

11. (a) 30 mm^2/mm; the rate at which the area is increasing with respect to side length as x reaches 15 mm
(b) $\Delta A \approx 2x\,\Delta x$
13. (a) (i) 5π (ii) 4.5π (iii) 4.1π
(b) 4π (c) $\Delta A \approx 2\pi r\,\Delta r$
15. (a) 8π ft^2/ft   (b) 16π ft^2/ft   (c) 24π ft^2/ft
The rate increases as the radius increases.
17. (a) 6 kg/m   (b) 12 kg/m   (c) 18 kg/m
At the right end; at the left end
19. (a) 4.75 A   (b) 5 A; $t = \frac23$ s
21. (a) $dV/dP = -C/P^2$ (b) At the beginning
23. (a) 16 million/year; 78.5 million/year
(b) $P(t) = at^3 + bt^2 + ct + d$, where $a \approx 0.00129371$, $b \approx -7.061422$, $c \approx 12,822.979$, $d \approx -7,743,770$
(c) $P'(t) = 3at^2 + 2bt + c$
(d) 14.48 million/year; 75.29 million/year (smaller)
(e) 81.62 million/year
25. (a) 0.926 cm/s; 0.694 cm/s; 0
(b) 0; -92.6 (cm/s)/cm; -185.2 (cm/s)/cm
(c) At the center; at the edge
27. (a) $C'(x) = 12 - 0.2x + 0.0015x^2$
(b) \$32/yard; the cost of producing the 201st yard
(c) \$32.20
29. (a) $[xp'(x) - p(x)]/x^2$; the average productivity increases as new workers are added.
31. -0.2436 K/min
33. (a) 0 and 0   (b) $C = 0$
(c) $(0, 0), (500, 50)$; it is possible for the species to coexist.

EXERCISES 3.8 ■ PAGE 186

1. $dV/dt = 3x^2\,dx/dt$ **3.** 48 cm^2/s   **5.** $3/(25\pi)$ m/min
7. 70   **9.** $\pm\frac{46}{13}$
11. (a) The plane's altitude is 1 mi and its speed is 500 mi/h.
(b) The rate at which the distance from the plane to the station is increasing when the plane is 2 mi from the station
(c)   (d) $y^2 = x^2 + 1$
                                        (e) $250\sqrt{3}$ mi/h

13. (a) The height of the pole (15 ft), the height of the man (6 ft), and the speed of the man (5 ft/s)
(b) The rate at which the tip of the man's shadow is moving when he is 40 ft from the pole
(c)   (d) $\dfrac{15}{6} = \dfrac{x + y}{y}$ (e) $\frac{25}{3}$ ft/s

15. 65 mi/h   **17.** $837/\sqrt{8674} \approx 8.99$ ft/s
19. -1.6 cm/min   **21.** $\frac{720}{13} \approx 55.4$ km/h
23. $(10{,}000 + 800{,}000\pi/9) \approx 2.89 \times 10^5$ cm^3/min
25. $\frac{10}{3}$ cm/min   **27.** $6/(5\pi) \approx 0.38$ ft/min   **29.** 0.3 m^2/s
31. 80 cm^3/min   **33.** $\frac{107}{810} \approx 0.132$ Ω/s   **35.** 0.396 m/min
37. (a) 360 ft/s   (b) 0.096 rad/s   **39.** $\frac{10}{9}\pi$ km/min

41. $1650/\sqrt{31} \approx 296$ km/h   **43.** $\frac{7}{4}\sqrt{15} \approx 6.78$ m/s

1. $L(x) = -10x - 6$ **3.** $L(x) = -x + \pi/2$

5. $\sqrt{1-x} \approx 1 - \frac{1}{2}x$;

$\sqrt{0.9} \approx 0.95$,
$\sqrt{0.99} \approx 0.995$

7. $-1.204 < x < 0.706$ **9.** $-0.045 < x < 0.055$

11. (a) $dy = 2x(x \cos 2x + \sin 2x)\,dx$ (b) $dy = \dfrac{t}{\sqrt{1+t^2}}\,dt$

13. (a) $dy = \dfrac{-2}{(u-1)^2}\,du$ (b) $dy = -\dfrac{6r^2}{(1+r^3)^3}\,dr$

15. (a) $dy = 5/(2\sqrt{4+5x})\,dx$ (b) 0.05

17. (a) $dy = \sec^2 x\,dx$ (b) -0.2

19. $\Delta y = 0.64$, $dy = 0.8$

21. $\Delta y = -0.1$, $dy = -0.125$

23. 32.08 **25.** 4.02 **27.** $1 - \pi/90 \approx 0.965$

31. (a) 270 cm^3, 0.01, 1% (b) 36 cm^2, $0.00\overline{6}$, $0.\overline{6}\%$

33. (a) $84/\pi \approx 27$ cm^2; $\frac{1}{84} \approx 0.012$

(b) $1764/\pi^2 \approx 179$ cm^3; $\frac{1}{56} \approx 0.018$

35. (a) $2\pi rh\,\Delta r$ (b) $\pi(\Delta r)^2 h$

41. (a) 4.8, 5.2 (b) Too large

True-False Quiz

1. False   **3.** False   **5.** True   **7.** False   **9.** True
11. False

Exercises

1. (a) (i) 3 m/s   (ii) 2.75 m/s   (iii) 2.625 m/s
(iv) 2.525 m/s   (b) 2.5 m/s

3.

5. $a = f$, $c = f'$, $b = f''$

7. (a) The rate at which the cost changes with respect to the interest rate; dollars/(percent per year)
(b) As the interest rate increases past 10%, the cost is increasing at a rate of $1200/(percent per year).
(c) Always positive

9. The rate at which the total value of US currency in circulation is changing in billions of dollars per year; $22.2 billion/year

11. $f'(x) = 3x^2 + 5$ **13.** $6x(x^4 - 3x^2 + 5)^2(2x^2 - 3)$

15. $\dfrac{1}{2\sqrt{x}} - \dfrac{4}{3\sqrt[3]{x^7}}$ **17.** $\dfrac{2(2x^2+1)}{\sqrt{x^2+1}}$ **19.** $\dfrac{t^2+1}{(1-t^2)^2}$

21. $-\left(\sec^2\sqrt{1-x}\right)/(2\sqrt{1-x})$ **23.** $\dfrac{1-y^4-2xy}{4xy^3+x^2-3}$

25. $\dfrac{2\sec 2\theta\,(\tan 2\theta - 1)}{(1+\tan 2\theta)^2}$ **27.** $-(x-1)^{-2}$

29. $\dfrac{2x - y\cos(xy)}{x\cos(xy)+1}$ **31.** $-6x\csc^2(3x^2+5)$

33. $\dfrac{\cos\sqrt{x} - \sqrt{x}\sin\sqrt{x}}{2\sqrt{x}}$ **35.** $2\cos\theta\,\tan(\sin\theta)\,\sec^2(\sin\theta)$

37. $\frac{1}{5}(x\tan x)^{-4/5}(\tan x + x\sec^2 x)$

39. $\cos\left(\tan\sqrt{1+x^3}\right)\left(\sec^2\sqrt{1+x^3}\right)\dfrac{3x^2}{2\sqrt{1+x^3}}$ **41.** $-\frac{4}{27}$

43. $-5x^4/y^{11}$ **45.** 1 **47.** $y = 2\sqrt{3x+1} - \pi\sqrt{3}/3$

49. $y = 2x + 1$

51. (a) $\dfrac{10-3x}{2\sqrt{5-x}}$ (b) $y = \frac{7}{4}x + \frac{1}{4}$, $y = -x + 8$

(c)

53. $\left(\pi/4, \sqrt{2}\right)$, $\left(5\pi/4, -\sqrt{2}\right)$ **55.** $y = -\frac{2}{3}x^2 + \frac{14}{3}x$

59. (a) 2 (b) 44 **61.** $2xg(x) + x^2 g'(x)$ **63.** $2g(x)g'(x)$

65. $f'(x) = g'(g(x))g'(x)$ **67.** $f'(x) = g'(\sin x)\cdot\cos x$

69. $\dfrac{f'(x)[g(x)]^2 + g'(x)\,[f(x)]^2}{[f(x)+g(x)]^2}$

71. $f'(g(\sin 4x))g'(\sin 4x)(\cos 4x)(4)$

73. (a) $v(t) = 3t^2 - 12$; $a(t) = 6t$ (b) $t > 2$; $0 \le t < 2$
(c) 23 (d)

(e) $t > 2$; $0 < t < 2$

75. 4 kg/m   **77.** $\frac{4}{3}$ cm^2/min   **79.** 13 ft/s   **81.** 400 ft/h

83. (a) $L(x) = 1 + x$; $\sqrt[3]{1 + 3x} \approx 1 + x$; $\sqrt[3]{1.03} \approx 1.01$
(b) $-0.23 < x < 0.40$
85. $12 + \frac{3}{2}\pi \approx 16.7 \text{ cm}^2$ **87.** $\frac{1}{32}$ **89.** $\frac{1}{4}$ **91.** $\frac{1}{8}x^2$

PROBLEMS PLUS ▪ PAGE 200

1. $\left(\pm\frac{1}{2}\sqrt{3}, \frac{1}{4}\right)$
5. (a) 0   (b) 1   (c) $f'(x) = x^2 + 1$
9. $\left(0, \frac{5}{4}\right)$
11. (a) $4\pi\sqrt{3}/\sqrt{11}$ rad/s   (b) $40\left(\cos\theta + \sqrt{8 + \cos^2\theta}\right)$ cm
(c) $-480\pi \sin\theta\left(1 + \cos\theta/\sqrt{8 + \cos^2\theta}\right)$ cm/s
13. $x_T \in (3, \infty)$, $y_T \in (2, \infty)$, $x_N \in \left(0, \frac{5}{3}\right)$, $y_N \in \left(-\frac{5}{2}, 0\right)$
15. (b) (i) $53°$ (or $127°$)   (ii) $63°$ (or $117°$)
17. R approaches the midpoint of the radius AO.
19. $-\sin a$ **21.** $(1, -2), (-1, 0)$
23. $\sqrt{29}/58$ **25.** $2 + \frac{375}{128}\pi \approx 11.204 \text{ cm}^3/\text{min}$

CHAPTER 4

EXERCISES 4.1 ▪ PAGE 211

Abbreviations: abs., absolute; loc., local; max., maximum; min., minimum

1. Absolute minimum: smallest function value on the entire domain of the function; local minimum at c: smallest function value when x is near c
3. Abs. max. at s, abs. min. at r, loc. max. at c, loc. min. at b and r
5. Abs. max. $f(4) = 5$, loc. max. $f(4) = 5$ and $f(6) = 4$, loc. min. $f(2) = 2$ and $f(5) = 3$

7.   **9.**

11. (a)   (b)

(c)

13. (a)   (b)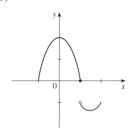

15. Abs. max. $f(1) = 5$ **17.** None
19. Abs. min. $f(0) = 0$
21. Abs. max. $f(-3) = 9$, abs. and loc. min. $f(0) = 0$
23. None   **25.** Abs. max. $f(0) = 1$
27. Abs. max. $f(3) = 2$ **29.** $-\frac{2}{5}$ **31.** $-4, 2$
33. $0, \frac{1}{2}\left(-1 \pm \sqrt{5}\right)$ **35.** $0, 2$ **37.** $0, \frac{4}{9}$ **39.** $0, \frac{8}{7}, 4$
41. $n\pi$ (n an integer)   **43.** 16   **45.** $f(0) = 5, f(2) = -7$
47. $f(-1) = 8, f(2) = -19$
49. $f(3) = 66, f(\pm 1) = 2$ **51.** $f(1) = \frac{1}{2}, f(0) = 0$
53. $f(\sqrt{2}) = 2, f(-1) = -\sqrt{3}$

55. $f(\pi/6) = \frac{3}{2}\sqrt{3}, f(\pi/2) = 0$

57. $f\left(\dfrac{a}{a + b}\right) = \dfrac{a^a b^b}{(a + b)^{a+b}}$

59. (a) $2.19, 1.81$ (b) $\frac{6}{25}\sqrt{\frac{3}{5}} + 2, -\frac{6}{25}\sqrt{\frac{3}{5}} + 2$

61. (a) $0.32, 0.00$ (b) $\frac{3}{16}\sqrt{3}, 0$ **63.** $\approx 3.9665°C$
65. Cheapest, $t \approx 0.855$ (June 1994);
most expensive, $t \approx 4.618$ (March 1998)
67. (a) $r = \frac{2}{3}r_0$ (b) $v = \frac{4}{27}kr_0^3$
(c)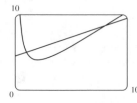

EXERCISES 4.2 ▪ PAGE 219

1. 2   **3.** $\frac{9}{4}$ **5.** f is not differentiable on $(-1, 1)$
7. $0.8, 3.2, 4.4, 6.1$
9. (a), (b)   (c) $2\sqrt{2}$

11. 0   **13.** $\sqrt{3}/9$ **15.** f is not continous at 3
23. 16   **25.** No   **31.** No

EXERCISES 4.3 ▪ **PAGE 227**

Abbreviations: inc., increasing; dec., decreasing; CD, concave downward; CU, concave upward; HA, horizontal asymptote; VA, vertical asymptote; IP, inflection point(s)

1. (a) $(1, 3), (4, 6)$ (b) $(0, 1), (3, 4)$ (c) $(0, 2)$
(d) $(2, 4), (4, 6)$ (e) $(2, 3)$

3. (a) I/D Test   (b) Concavity Test
(c) Find points at which the concavity changes.

5. (a) Inc. on $(1, 5)$; dec. on $(0, 1)$ and $(5, 6)$
(b) Loc. max. at $x = 5$, loc. min. at $x = 1$

7. $x = 1, 7$

9. (a) Inc. on $(-\infty, 3), (2, \infty)$; dec. on $(-3, 2)$
(b) Loc. max. $f(-3) = 81$; loc. min. $f(2) = -44$
(c) CU on $\left(-\frac{1}{2}, \infty\right)$; CD on $\left(-\infty, -\frac{1}{2}\right)$; IP $\left(-\frac{1}{2}, \frac{37}{2}\right)$

11. (a) Inc. on $(-1, 0), (1, \infty)$; dec. on $(-\infty, -1), (0, 1)$
(b) Loc. max. $f(0) = 3$; loc. min. $f(\pm 1) = 2$
(c) CU on $\left(-\infty, -\sqrt{3}/3\right), \left(\sqrt{3}/3, \infty\right)$;
CD on $\left(-\sqrt{3}/3, \sqrt{3}/3\right)$; IP $\left(\pm\sqrt{3}/3, \frac{22}{9}\right)$

13. (a) Inc. on $(0, \pi/4), (5\pi/4, 2\pi)$; dec. on $(\pi/4, 5\pi/4)$
(b) Loc. max. $f(\pi/4) = \sqrt{2}$; loc. min. $f(5\pi/4) = -\sqrt{2}$
(c) CU on $(3\pi/4, 7\pi/4)$; CD on $(0, 3\pi/4), (7\pi/4, 2\pi)$;
IP $(3\pi/4, 0), (7\pi/4, 0)$

15. Loc. max. $f(-1) = 7$, loc. min. $f(1) = -1$

17. Loc. max. $f\left(\frac{3}{4}\right) = \frac{5}{4}$

19. (a) f has a local maximum at 2.
(b) f has a horizontal tangent at 6.

21.

23.

25.

27. (a) Inc. on $(0, 2), (4, 6), (8, \infty)$;
dec. on $(2, 4), (6, 8)$
(b) Loc. max. at $x = 2, 6$;
loc. min. at $x = 4, 8$
(c) CU on $(3, 6), (6, \infty)$;
CD on $(0, 3)$
(d) 3   (e) See graph at right.

29. (a) Inc. on $(-\infty, -1), (2, \infty)$;
dec. on $(-1, 2)$
(b) Loc. max. $f(-1) = 7$;
loc. min. $f(2) = -20$
(c) CU on $\left(\frac{1}{2}, \infty\right)$; CD on $\left(-\infty, \frac{1}{2}\right)$;
IP $\left(\frac{1}{2}, -\frac{13}{2}\right)$
(d) See graph at right.

31. (a) Inc. on $(-\infty, -1), (0, 1)$;
dec. on $(-1, 0), (1, \infty)$
(b) Loc. max. $f(-1) = 3, f(1) = 3$;
loc. min. $f(0) = 2$
(c) CU on $\left(-1/\sqrt{3}, 1/\sqrt{3}\right)$;
CD on $\left(-\infty, -1/\sqrt{3}\right), \left(1/\sqrt{3}, \infty\right)$;
IP $\left(\pm 1/\sqrt{3}, \frac{23}{9}\right)$
(d) See graph at right.

33. (a) Inc. on $(-\infty, -2), (0, \infty)$;
dec. on $(-2, 0)$
(b) Loc. max. $h(-2) = 7$;
loc. min. $h(0) = -1$
(c) CU on $(-1, \infty)$;
CD on $(-\infty, -1)$; IP $(-1, 3)$
(d) See graph at right.

35. (a) Inc. on $(-2, \infty)$;
dec. on $(-3, -2)$
(b) Loc. min. $A(-2) = -2$
(c) CU on $(-3, \infty)$
(d) See graph at right.

37. (a) Inc. on $(-1, \infty)$;
dec. on $(-\infty, -1)$
(b) Loc. min. $C(-1) = -3$
(c) CU on $(-\infty, 0), (2, \infty)$;
CD on $(0, 2)$;
IPs $(0, 0), \left(2, 6\sqrt[3]{2}\right)$
(d) See graph at right.

39. (a) Inc. on $(\pi, 2\pi)$;
dec. on $(0, \pi)$
(b) Loc. min. $f(\pi) = -1$
(c) CU on $(\pi/3, 5\pi/3)$;
CD on $(0, \pi/3), (5\pi/3, 2\pi)$;
IP $\left(\pi/3, \frac{5}{4}\right), \left(5\pi/3, \frac{5}{4}\right)$
(d) See graph at right.

41. $(3, \infty)$
43. (a) Loc. and abs. max. $f(1) = \sqrt{2}$, no min.
(b) $\frac{1}{4}\left(3 - \sqrt{17}\right)$
45. (b) CU on $(0.94, 2.57), (3.71, 5.35)$;
CD on $(0, 0.94), (2.57, 3.71), (5.35, 2\pi)$;
IP $(0.94, 0.44), (2.57, -0.63), (3.71, -0.63), (5.35, 0.44)$
47. CU on $(-\infty, -0.6), (0.0, \infty)$; CD on $(-0.6, 0.0)$

49. (a) The rate of increase is initially very small, increases to a maximum at $t \approx 8$ h, then decreases toward 0.
(b) When $t = 8$ (c) CU on $(0, 8)$; CD on $(8, 18)$ (d) $(8, 350)$
51. $K(3) - K(2)$; CD   **53.** $f(x) = \frac{1}{9}(2x^3 + 3x^2 - 12x + 7)$

EXERCISES 4.4 ▪ PAGE 240

1. (a) As x becomes large, $f(x)$ approaches 5.
(b) As x becomes large negative, $f(x)$ approaches 3.
3. (a) ∞ (b) ∞ (c) $-\infty$ (d) 1   (e) 2
(f) $x = -1, x = 2, y = 1, y = 2$
5. 0   **7.** $\frac{3}{2}$ **9.** 0   **11.** $-\frac{1}{2}$ **13.** $\frac{1}{2}$ **15.** 2
17. 3   **19.** $\frac{1}{6}$ **21.** $\frac{1}{2}(a - b)$ **23.** ∞ **25.** $-\infty$
27. ∞ **29.** 1
31. (a), (b) $-\frac{1}{2}$ **33.** $y = 2; x = 2$
35. $y = 2; x = -2, x = 1$ **37.** $x = 5$ **39.** $y = 3$
41. $f(x) = \dfrac{2 - x}{x^2(x - 3)}$
43. $y = -1$ **45.** $y = 0$

47. $-\infty, -\infty$ **49.** $-\infty, \infty$

51.

53.

55. (a) 0   (b) An infinite number of times

57. (a) 0   (b) $\pm\infty$ **59.** 4
61. $N \geqslant 15$ **63.** $N \leqslant -6, N \leqslant -22$ **65.** (a) $x > 100$

EXERCISES 4.5 ▪ PAGE 248

1. A. $\mathbb{R}$ B. y-int. 0; x-int. 0
C. About $(0, 0)$ D. None
E. Inc. on $(-\infty, \infty)$ F. None
G. CU on $(0, \infty)$; CD on $(-\infty, 0)$;
IP $(0, 0)$
H. See graph at right.

3. A. $\mathbb{R}$ B. y-int. 2; x-int. 2, $\frac{1}{2}(7 \pm 3\sqrt{5})$
C. None   D. None
E. Inc. on $(1, 5)$;
dec. on $(-\infty, 1), (5, \infty)$
F. Loc. min. $f(1) = -5$;
loc. max. $f(5) = 27$
G. CU on $(-\infty, 3)$;
CD on $(3, \infty)$; IP $(3, 11)$
H. See graph at right.

5. A. $\mathbb{R}$ B. y-int. 0; x-int. $-4, 0$
C. None   D. None
E. Inc. on $(-3, \infty)$;
dec. on $(-\infty, -3)$
F. Loc. min. $f(-3) = -27$
G. CU on $(-\infty, -2), (0, \infty)$;
CD on $(-2, 0)$; IP $(0, 0), (-2, -16)$
H. See graph at right.

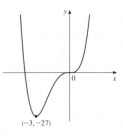

7. A. $\mathbb{R}$ B. y-int. 1
C. None   D. None
E. Inc. on $(-\infty, 0), (1, \infty)$;
dec. on $(0, 1)$
F. Loc. max. $f(0) = 1$;
loc. min. $f(1) = -2$
G. CU on $\left(1/\sqrt[3]{4}, \infty\right)$;
CD on $\left(-\infty, 1/\sqrt[3]{4}\right)$;
IP $\left(1/\sqrt[3]{4}, 1 - 9/(2\sqrt[3]{16})\right)$
H. See graph at right.

9. A. $\{x \mid x \neq 1\}$ B. y-int. 0; x-int. 0
C. None   D. VA $x = 1$, HA $y = 1$
E. Dec. on $(-\infty, 1), (1, \infty)$
F. None
G. CU on $(1, \infty)$; CD on $(-\infty, 1)$
H. See graph at right.

11. A. $\{x \mid x \neq \pm 3\}$ B. y-int. $-\frac{1}{9}$
C. About y-axis   D. VA $x = \pm 3$, HA $y = 0$
E. Inc. on $(-\infty, -3)$, $(-3, 0)$;
dec. on $(0, 3)$, $(3, \infty)$
F. Loc. max. $f(0) = -\frac{1}{9}$
G. CU on $(-\infty, -3)$, $(3, \infty)$;
CD on $(-3, 3)$
H. See graph at right.

13. A. $\mathbb{R}$ B. y-int. 0; x-int. 0
C. About $(0, 0)$ D. HA $y = 0$
E. Inc. on $(-3, 3)$;
dec. on $(-\infty, -3)$, $(3, \infty)$
F. Loc. min. $f(-3) = -\frac{1}{6}$;
loc. max. $f(3) = \frac{1}{6}$;
G. CU on $\left(-3\sqrt{3}, 0\right)$, $\left(3\sqrt{3}, \infty\right)$;
CD on $\left(-\infty, -3\sqrt{3}\right)$, $\left(0, 3\sqrt{3}\right)$;
IP $(0, 0)$, $\left(\pm 3\sqrt{3}, \pm\sqrt{3}/12\right)$
H. See graph at right.

15. A. $(-\infty, 0) \cup (0, \infty)$ B. x-int. 1
C. None   D. HA $y = 0$; VA $x = 0$
E. Inc. on $(0, 2)$;
dec. on $(-\infty, 0)$, $(2, \infty)$
F. Loc. max. $f(2) = \frac{1}{4}$
G. CU on $(3, \infty)$;
CD on $(-\infty, 0)$, $(0, 3)$; IP $\left(3, \frac{2}{9}\right)$
H. See graph at right

17. A. $\mathbb{R}$ B. y-int. 0, x-int. 0
C. About y-axis   D. HA $y = 1$
E. Inc. on $(0, \infty)$; dec. on $(-\infty, 0)$
F. Loc. min. $f(0) = 0$
G. CU on $(-1, 1)$;
CD on $(-\infty, -1)$, $(1, \infty)$; IP $\left(\pm 1, \frac{1}{4}\right)$
H. See graph at right

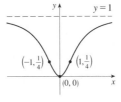

19. A. $(-\infty, 5]$ B. y-int. 0; x-int. 0, 5
C. None   D. None
E. Inc. on $\left(-\infty, \frac{10}{3}\right)$; dec. on $\left(\frac{10}{3}, 5\right)$
F. Loc. max. $f\left(\frac{10}{3}\right) = \frac{10}{9}\sqrt{15}$
G. CD on $(-\infty, 5)$
H. See graph at right.

21. A. $(-\infty, -2) \cup (1, \infty)$
B. x-int. $-2, 1$
C. None   D. None
E. Inc. on $(1, \infty)$; dec. on $(-\infty, -2)$
F. None
G. CD on $(-\infty, -2)$, $(1, \infty)$
H. See graph at right.

23. A. $\mathbb{R}$ B. y-int. 0; x-int. 0
C. About the origin
D. HA $y = \pm 1$
E. Inc. on $(-\infty, \infty)$ F. None
G. CU on $(-\infty, 0)$;
CD on $(0, \infty)$; IP $(0, 0)$
H. See graph at right.

25. A. $\left\{x \mid |x| \leq 1, x \neq 0\right\} = [-1, 0) \cup (0, 1]$
B. x-int. ± 1 C. About $(0, 0)$
D. VA $x = 0$
E. Dec. on $(-1, 0)$, $(0, 1)$
F. None
G. CU on $\left(-1, -\sqrt{2/3}\right)$, $\left(0, \sqrt{2/3}\right)$;
CD on $\left(-\sqrt{2/3}, 0\right)$, $\left(\sqrt{2/3}, 1\right)$;
IP $\left(\pm\sqrt{2/3}, \pm 1/\sqrt{2}\right)$
H. See graph at right.

27. A. $\mathbb{R}$ B. y-int. 0; x-int. 0, $\pm 3\sqrt{3}$ C. About the origin
D. None   E. Inc. on $(-\infty, -1)$, $(1, \infty)$; dec. on $(-1, 1)$
F. Loc. max. $f(-1) = 2$;
loc. min. $f(1) = -2$
G. CU on $(0, \infty)$; CD on $(-\infty, 0)$;
IP $(0, 0)$
H. See graph at right.

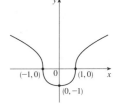

29. A. $\mathbb{R}$ B. y-int. -1; x-int. ± 1
C. About y-axis   D. None
E. Inc. on $(0, \infty)$; dec. on $(-\infty, 0)$
F. Loc. min. $f(0) = -1$
G. CU on $(-1, 1)$;
CD on $(-\infty, -1)$, $(1, \infty)$;
IP $(\pm 1, 0)$
H. See graph at right.

31. A. $\mathbb{R}$ B. y-int. 0; x-int. $n\pi$ (n an integer)
C. About the origin, period 2π D. None
E. Inc. on $(2n\pi - \pi/2, 2n\pi + \pi/2)$;
dec. on $(2n\pi + \pi/2, 2n\pi + 3\pi/2)$
F. Loc. max. $f(2n\pi + \pi/2) = 2$;
loc. min. $f(2n\pi + 3\pi/2) = -2$
G. CU on $((2n - 1)\pi, 2n\pi)$;
CD on $(2n\pi, (2n + 1)\pi)$; IP $(n\pi, 0)$
H. See graph at right.

33. A. $(-\pi/2, \pi/2)$ B. y-int. 0; x-int. 0   C. About y-axis
D. VA $x = \pm\pi/2$
E. Inc. on $(0, \pi/2)$;
dec. on $(-\pi/2, 0)$
F. Loc. min. $f(0) = 0$
G. CU on $(-\pi/2, \pi/2)$
H. See graph at right.

35. A. $(0, 3\pi)$ C. None   D. None
E. Inc. on $(\pi/3, 5\pi/3)$, $(7\pi/3, 3\pi)$;
dec. on $(0, \pi/3)$, $(5\pi/3, 7\pi/3)$
F. Loc. min. $f(\pi/3) = (\pi/6) - \frac{1}{2}\sqrt{3}, f(7\pi/3) = (7\pi/6) - \frac{1}{2}\sqrt{3}$;
loc. max. $f(5\pi/3) = (5\pi/6) + \frac{1}{2}\sqrt{3}$
G. CU on $(0, \pi)$, $(2\pi, 3\pi)$;
CD on $(\pi, 2\pi)$;
IP $(\pi, \pi/2)$, $(2\pi, \pi)$
H. See graph at right.

37. A. All reals except $(2n + 1)\pi$ (n an integer)
B. y-int. 0; x-int. $2n\pi$
C. About the origin, period 2π
D. VA $x = (2n + 1)\pi$
E. Inc. on $((2n - 1)\pi, (2n + 1)\pi)$ F. None
G. CU on $(2n\pi, (2n + 1)\pi)$; CD on $((2n - 1)\pi, 2n\pi)$;
IP $(2n\pi, 0)$
H.

39.

41.

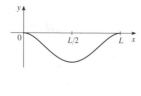

43. $y = x - 1$ **45.** $y = 2x - 2$
47. A. $\left(-\infty, \frac{1}{2}\right) \cup \left(\frac{1}{2}, \infty\right)$
B. y-int. 1; x-int. $\frac{1}{4}(5 \pm \sqrt{17})$
C. None
D. VA $x = \frac{1}{2}$; SA $y = -x + 2$
E. Dec. on $\left(-\infty, \frac{1}{2}\right)$, $\left(\frac{1}{2}, \infty\right)$
F. None
G. CU on $\left(\frac{1}{2}, \infty\right)$; CD on $\left(-\infty, \frac{1}{2}\right)$
H. See graph at right

49. A. $\{x \mid x \neq 0\}$ B. None
C. About $(0, 0)$ D. VA $x = 0$; SA $y = x$
E. Inc. on $(-\infty, -2)$, $(2, \infty)$;
dec. on $(-2, 0)$, $(0, 2)$
F. Loc. max. $f(-2) = -4$;
loc. min. $f(2) = 4$
G. CU on $(0, \infty)$; CD on $(-\infty, 0)$
H. See graph at right.

51. A. $\mathbb{R}$ B. y-int. 1; x-int. -1
C. None   D. SA $y = 2x + 1$
E. Inc. on $(-\infty, \infty)$ F. None
G. CU on $(-\infty, -\sqrt{3})$,
$(0, \sqrt{3})$;
CD on $(-\sqrt{3}, 0)$, $(\sqrt{3}, \infty)$;
IP $(\pm\sqrt{3}, 1 \pm \frac{3}{2}\sqrt{3})$, $(0, 1)$
H. See graph at right.

53.

57. VA $x = 0$, asymptotic to $y = x^3$

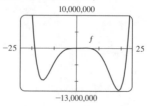

EXERCISES 4.6 ▪ **PAGE 255**

1. Inc. on $(0.92, 2.5)$, $(2.58, \infty)$; dec. on $(-\infty, 0.92)$, $(2.5, 2.58)$;
loc. max. $f(2.5) \approx 4$; loc. min. $f(0.92) \approx -5.12$, $f(2.58) \approx 3.998$;
CU on $(-\infty, 1.46)$, $(2.54, \infty)$;
CD on $(1.46, 2.54)$; IP $(1.46, -1.40)$, $(2.54, 3.999)$

3. Inc. on $(-15, 4.40)$, $(18.93, \infty)$;
dec. on $(-\infty, -15)$, $(4.40, 18.93)$;
loc. max. $f(4.40) \approx 53{,}800$; loc. min. $f(-15) \approx -9{,}700{,}000$,
$f(18.93) \approx -12{,}700{,}000$; CU on $(-\infty, -11.34)$, $(0, 2.92)$,
$(15.08, \infty)$; CD on $(-11.34, 0)$, $(2.92, 15.08)$;
IP $(0, 0)$, $\approx (-11.34, -6{,}250{,}000)$, $(2.92, 31{,}800)$,
$(15.08, -8{,}150{,}000)$

5. Inc. on $(-\infty, -1.7)$, $(-1.7, 0.24)$, $(0.24, 1)$;
dec. on $(1, 2.46)$, $(2.46, \infty)$; loc. max. $f(1) = -\frac{1}{3}$;

CU on $(-\infty, -1.7)$, $(-0.506, 0.24)$, $(2.46, \infty)$;
CD on $(-1.7, -0.506)$, $(0.24, 2.46)$; IP $(-0.506, -0.192)$

7. Inc. on $(-1.49, -1.07)$, $(2.89, 4)$; dec. on $(-4, -1.49)$,
$(-1.07, 2.89)$; loc. max. $f(-1.07) \approx 8.79$; loc. min.
$f(-1.49) \approx 8.75$, $f(2.89) \approx -9.99$; CU on $(-4, -1.28)$,
$(1.28, 4)$; CD on $(-1.28, 1.28)$; IP $(-1.28, 8.77)$, $(1.28, -1.48)$

9. Inc. on $\left(-8 - \sqrt{61}, -8 + \sqrt{61}\right)$; dec. on $\left(-\infty, -8 - \sqrt{61}\right)$,
$\left(-8 + \sqrt{61}, 0\right)$, $(0, \infty)$; CU on $\left(-12 - \sqrt{138}, -12 + \sqrt{138}\right)$,
$(0, \infty)$; CD on $\left(-\infty, -12 - \sqrt{138}\right)$, $\left(-12 + \sqrt{138}, 0\right)$

 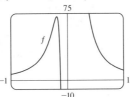

11. Loc. max. $f(-5.6) \approx 0.018$, $f(0.82) \approx -281.5$,
$f(5.2) \approx 0.0145$; loc. min. $f(3) = 0$

13. $f'(x) = -\dfrac{x(x + 1)^2(x^3 + 18x^2 - 44x - 16)}{(x - 2)^3(x - 4)^5}$

$f''(x) = 2\dfrac{(x + 1)(x^6 + 36x^5 + 6x^4 - 628x^3 + 684x^2 + 672x + 64)}{(x - 2)^4(x - 4)^6}$

CU on $(-35.3, -5.0)$, $(-1, -0.5)$, $(-0.1, 2)$, $(2, 4)$, $(4, \infty)$;
CD on $(-\infty, -35.3)$, $(-5.0, -1)$, $(-0.5, -0.1)$;
IP $(-35.3, -0.015)$, $(-5.0, -0.005)$, $(-1, 0)$, $(-0.5, 0.00001)$,
$(-0.1, 0.0000066)$

15. Inc. on $(0, 0.43)$; dec. on $(0.43, \infty)$; loc. max. $f(0.43) \approx 0.41$;
CU on $(0.94, \infty)$; CD on $(0, 0.94)$;
IP $(0.94, 0.34)$

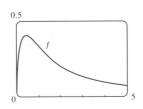

17. Inc. on $(-4.91, -4.51)$, $(0, 1.77)$, $(4.91, 8.06)$, $(10.79, 14.34)$,
$(17.08, 20)$;
dec. on $(-4.51, -4.10)$, $(1.77, 4.10)$, $(8.06, 10.79)$, $(14.34, 17.08)$;
loc. max. $f(-4.51) \approx 0.62$, $f(1.77) \approx 2.58$, $f(8.06) \approx 3.60$,
$f(14.34) \approx 4.39$;
loc. min. $f(10.79) \approx 2.43$, $f(17.08) \approx 3.49$; CU on $(9.60, 12.25)$,
$(15.81, 18.65)$;
CD on $(-4.91, -4.10)$, $(0, 4.10)$, $(4.91, 9.60)$, $(12.25, 15.81)$,
$(18.65, 20)$;
IPs at $(9.60, 2.95)$, $(12.25, 3.27)$, $(15.81, 3.91)$, $(18.65, 4.20)$

19. Max. $f(0.59) \approx 1$, $f(0.68) \approx 1$, $f(1.96) \approx 1$;
min. $f(0.64) \approx 0.99996$, $f(1.46) \approx 0.49$, $f(2.73) \approx -0.51$;
IP $(0.61, 0.99998)$, $(0.66, 0.99998)$, $(1.17, 0.72)$,
$(1.75, 0.77)$, $(2.28, 0.34)$

 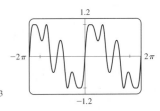

21. For $c \geqslant 0$, there is no IP and only one extreme point, the origin. For $c < 0$, there is a maximum point at the origin, two minimum points, and two IPs, which move downward and away from the origin as $c \to -\infty$.

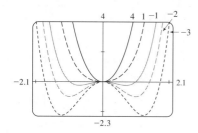

23. For $c > 0$, the maximum and minimum values are always $\pm\frac{1}{2}$, but the extreme points and IPs move closer to the y-axis as c increases. $c = 0$ is a transitional value: when c is replaced by $-c$, the curve is reflected in the x-axis.

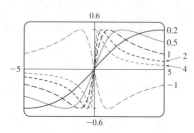

25. For $|c| < 1$, the graph has local maximum and minimum values; for $|c| \geqslant 1$ it does not. The function increases for $c \geqslant 1$ and decreases for $c \leqslant -1$. As c changes, the IPs move vertically but not horizontally.

27. (a) Positive   (b)

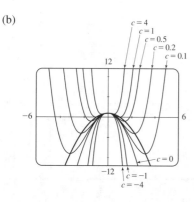

1. (a) 11, 12   (b) 11.5, 11.5   **3.** 10, 10
5. 25 m by 25 m   **7.** $N = 1$
9. (a)

(b)

(c) $A = xy$ (d) $5x + 2y = 750$ (e) $A(x) = 375x - \frac{5}{2}x^2$
(f) 14,062.5 ft^2
11. 1000 ft by 1500 ft   **13.** 4000 cm^3 **15.** \$191.28
17. $\left(-\frac{28}{17}, \frac{7}{17}\right)$ **19.** $\left(-\frac{1}{3}, \pm\frac{4}{3}\sqrt{2}\right)$ **21.** Square, side $\sqrt{2}\,r$
23. $L/2, \sqrt{3}\,L/4$ **25.** Base $\sqrt{3}\,r$, height $3r/2$
27. $4\pi r^3/(3\sqrt{3})$ **29.** $\pi r^2(1 + \sqrt{5})$ **31.** 24 cm, 36 cm
33. (a) Use all of the wire for the square
(b) $40\sqrt{3}/(9 + 4\sqrt{3})$ m for the square
35. Height = radius = $\sqrt[3]{V/\pi}$ cm   **37.** $V = 2\pi R^3/(9\sqrt{3})$
41. $E^2/(4r)$
43. (a) $\frac{3}{2}S^2 \csc\theta\,(\csc\theta - \sqrt{3}\cot\theta)$ (b) $\cos^{-1}(1/\sqrt{3}) \approx 55°$
(c) $6s[h + s/(2\sqrt{2})]$
45. Row directly to B **47.** ≈ 4.85 km east of the refinery
49. $10\sqrt[3]{3}/(1 + \sqrt[3]{3})$ ft from the stronger source
51. $(a^{2/3} + b^{2/3})^{3/2}$
53. (b) (i) \$342,491; \$342/unit; \$390/unit   (ii) 400
(iii) \$320/unit
55. (a) $p(x) = 19 - \frac{1}{3000}x$ (b) \$9.50
57. (a) $p(x) = 550 - \frac{1}{10}x$ (b) \$175   (c) \$100
61. 9.35 m   **65.** $x = 6$ in.   **67.** $\pi/6$ **69.** $\frac{1}{2}(L + W)^2$
71. (a) About 5.1 km from B (b) C is close to B; C is close to D; $W/L = \sqrt{25 + x^2}/x$, where $x = |BC|$ (c) ≈ 1.07; no such value   (d) $\sqrt{41}/4 \approx 1.6$

1. (a) $x_2 \approx 2.3, x_3 \approx 3$ (b) No   **3.** $\frac{4}{5}$ **5.** 1.1797
7. 1.1785   **9.** -1.25 **11.** 1.82056420   **13.** 1.217562
15. 0.876726   **17.** $-0.724492, 1.220744$
19. $-0.471074, 1.461070$ **21.** 0.641714
23. $-1.93822883, -1.21997997, 1.13929375, 2.98984102$
25. $-1.97806681, -0.82646233$
27. (b) 31.622777
33. (a) $-1.293227, -0.441731, 0.507854$ (b) -2.0212
35. (0.164419, 0.990958)
37. (0.410245, 0.347810)
39. 0.76286%

EXERCISES 4.9 ■ PAGE 279

1. $F(x) = \frac{1}{2}x^2 - 3x + C$ **3.** $F(x) = \frac{1}{2}x + \frac{1}{4}x^3 - \frac{1}{5}x^4 + C$

5. $F(x) = \frac{2}{3}x^3 + \frac{1}{2}x^2 - x + C$ **7.** $F(x) = 4x^{5/4} - 4x^{7/4} + C$

9. $F(x) = 4x^{3/2} - \frac{6}{7}x^{7/6} + C$

11. $F(x) = \begin{cases} -5/(4x^8) + C_1 & \text{if } x < 0 \\ -5/(4x^8) + C_2 & \text{if } x > 0 \end{cases}$

13. $F(u) = \frac{1}{3}u^3 - 6u^{-1/2} + C$

15. $G(\theta) = \sin\theta + 5\cos\theta + C$

17. $F(t) = 2\sec t + t^{1/2} + C_n$

19. $F(x) = x^5 - \frac{1}{3}x^6 + 4$ **21.** $x^3 + x^4 + Cx + D$

23. $\frac{3}{20}x^{8/3} + Cx + D$ **25.** $t^5 + \frac{1}{2}Ct^2 + Dt + E$

27. $x - 3x^2 + 8$ **29.** $4x^{3/2} + 2x^{5/2} + 4$

31. $2\sin t + \tan t + 4 - 2\sqrt{3}$

33. $2x^4 + \frac{1}{3}x^3 + 5x^2 - 22x + \frac{59}{3}$

35. $-\sin\theta - \cos\theta + 5\theta + 4$ **37.** $x^2 - 2x^3 + 9x + 9$

39. $x^2 - \cos x - \frac{1}{2}\pi x$ **41.** 10   **43.** b

45.

47.

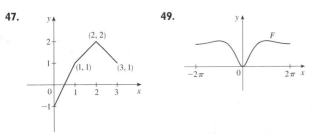

49.

51. $s(t) = 1 - \cos t - \sin t$ **53.** $s(t) = \frac{1}{6}t^3 - t^2 + 3t + 1$

55. $s(t) = -10\sin t - 3\cos t + (6/\pi)t + 3$

57. (a) $s(t) = 450 - 4.9t^2$ (b) $\sqrt{450/4.9} \approx 9.58$ s

(c) $-9.8\sqrt{450/4.9} \approx -93.9$ m/s   (d) About 9.09 s

61. 225 ft   **63.** \$742.08   **65.** $\frac{130}{11} \approx 11.8$ s

67. $\frac{88}{15} \approx 5.87$ ft/s^2 **69.** 62,500 km/h^2 ≈ 4.82 m/s^2

71. (a) 22.9125 mi   (b) 21.675 mi   (c) 30 min 33 s

(d) 55.425 mi

CHAPTER 4 REVIEW ■ PAGE 282

True-False Quiz

1. False   **3.** False   **5.** True   **7.** False   **9.** True

11. True   **13.** False   **15.** True   **17.** True   **19.** True

Exercises

1. Abs. max. $f(4) = 5$, abs. and loc. min. $f(3) = 1$;

loc. min. $f(3) = 1$

3. Abs. max. $f(2) = \frac{2}{5}$, abs. and loc. min. $f(-\frac{1}{3}) = -\frac{9}{2}$

5. Abs. max. $f(\pi) = \pi$; abs. min. $f(0) = 0$; loc. max.
$f(\pi/3) = (\pi/3) + \frac{1}{2}\sqrt{3}$; loc. min. $f(2\pi/3) = (2\pi/3) - \frac{1}{2}\sqrt{3}$

7. $\frac{1}{2}$ **9.** $-\frac{2}{3}$ **11.** $\frac{3}{4}$

13.

15.

17. A. $\mathbb{R}$ B. y-int. 2

C. None   D. None

E. Dec. on $(-\infty, \infty)$ F. None

G. CU on $(-\infty, 0)$;

CD on $(0, \infty)$; IP $(0, 2)$

H. See graph at right.

19. A. $\mathbb{R}$ B. y-int. 0; x-int. 0, 1

C. None   D. None

E. Inc. on $\left(\frac{1}{4}, \infty\right)$, dec. on $\left(-\infty, \frac{1}{4}\right)$

F. Loc. min. $f\left(\frac{1}{4}\right) = -\frac{27}{256}$

G. CU on $\left(-\infty, \frac{1}{2}\right)$, $(1, \infty)$;

CD on $\left(\frac{1}{2}, 1\right)$; IP $\left(\frac{1}{2}, -\frac{1}{16}\right)$, $(1, 0)$

H. See graph at right.

21. A. $\{x \mid x \neq 0, 3\}$

B. None   C. None

D. HA $y = 0$; VA $x = 0$, $x = 3$

E. Inc. on $(1, 3)$; dec. on $(-\infty, 0)$,

$(0, 1)$, $(3, \infty)$

F. Loc. min. $f(1) = \frac{1}{4}$

G. CU on $(0, 3)$, $(3, \infty)$; CD on $(-\infty, 0)$

H. See graph at right.

23. A. $\{x \mid x \neq -8\}$

B. y-int. 0, x-int. 0   C. None

D. VA $x = -8$; SA $y = x - 8$

E. Inc. on $(-\infty, -16)$, $(0, \infty)$;

dec. on $(-16, -8)$, $(-8, 0)$

F. Loc. max. $f(-16) = -32$;

loc. min. $f(0) = 0$

G. CU on $(-8, \infty)$; CD on $(-\infty, -8)$

H. See graph at right.

25. A. $[-2, \infty)$

B. y-int. 0; x-int. $-2, 0$

C. None   D. None

E. Inc. on $\left(-\frac{4}{3}, \infty\right)$, dec. on $\left(-2, -\frac{4}{3}\right)$

F. Loc. min. $f\left(-\frac{4}{3}\right) = -\frac{4}{9}\sqrt{6}$

G. CU on $(-2, \infty)$

H. See graph at right.

27. A. $\mathbb{R}$ B. y-int. -2
C. About y-axis, period 2π D. None
E. Inc. on $(2n\pi, (2n + 1)\pi)$, n an integer; dec. on $((2n - 1)\pi, 2n\pi)$
F. Loc. max. $f((2n + 1)\pi) = 2$; loc. min. $f(2n\pi) = -2$
G. CU on $(2n\pi - (\pi/3), 2n\pi + (\pi/3))$;
CD on $(2n\pi + (\pi/3), 2n\pi + (5\pi/3))$; IP $(2n\pi \pm (\pi/3), -\frac{1}{4})$
H.

29. Inc. on $(-\sqrt{3}, 0), (0, \sqrt{3})$;
dec. on $(-\infty, -\sqrt{3}), (\sqrt{3}, \infty)$;
loc. max. $f(\sqrt{3}) = \frac{2}{9}\sqrt{3}$,
loc. min. $f(-\sqrt{3}) = -\frac{2}{9}\sqrt{3}$;
CU on $(-\sqrt{6}, 0), (\sqrt{6}, \infty)$;
CD on $(-\infty, -\sqrt{6}), (0, \sqrt{6})$;
IP $(\sqrt{6}, \frac{5}{36}\sqrt{6}), (-\sqrt{6}, -\frac{5}{36}\sqrt{6})$

31. Inc. on $(-0.23, 0), (1.62, \infty)$; dec. on $(-\infty, -0.23), (0, 1.62)$;
loc. max. $f(0) = 2$; loc. min. $f(-0.23) \approx 1.96$, $f(1.62) \approx -19.2$;
CU on $(-\infty, -0.12), (1.24, \infty)$;
CD on $(-0.12, 1.24)$; IP $(-0.12, 1.98), (1.24, -12.1)$

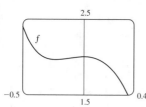

37. (a) 0   (b) CU on $\mathbb{R}$ **41.** $3\sqrt{3}r^2$
43. $4/\sqrt{3}$ cm from D **45.** $L = C$ **47.** \$11.50
49. 1.297383   **51.** 1.16718557
53. $f(x) = \frac{2}{5}x^{5/2} + \frac{3}{5}x^{5/3} + C$
55. $f(t) = t^2 + 3 \cos t + 2$
57. $f(x) = \frac{1}{2}x^2 - x^3 + 4x^4 + 2x + 1$
59. $s(t) = t^2 + \cos t + 2$
61.

63. No
65. (b) About 8.5 in. by 2 in.   (c) $20/\sqrt{3}$ in., $20\sqrt{2/3}$ in.

PROBLEMS PLUS ▪ PAGE 286

5. $(-2, 4), (2, -4)$ **7.** $\frac{4}{3}$ **9.** $(m/2, m^2/4)$
11. $-3.5 < a < -2.5$ **13.** (a) $x/(x^2 + 1)$ (b) $\frac{1}{2}$

15. (a) $-\tan \theta \left[\dfrac{1}{c}\dfrac{dc}{dt} + \dfrac{1}{b}\dfrac{db}{dt}\right]$

(b) $\dfrac{b\dfrac{db}{dt} + c\dfrac{dc}{dt} - \left(b\dfrac{dc}{dt} + c\dfrac{db}{dt}\right) \sec \theta}{\sqrt{b^2 + c^2 - 2bc \cos \theta}}$

17. (a) $T_1 = D/c_1$, $T_2 = (2h \sec \theta)/c_1 + (D - 2h \tan \theta)/c_2$,
$T_3 = \sqrt{4h^2 + D^2}/c_1$
(c) $c_1 \approx 3.85$ km/s, $c_2 \approx 7.66$ km/s, $h \approx 0.42$ km
21. $3/(\sqrt[3]{2} - 1) \approx 11\frac{1}{2}$ h

CHAPTER 5

EXERCISES 5.1 ▪ PAGE 298

1. (a) $40, 52$ (b) $43.2, 49.2$

3. (a) 0.7908, underestimate   (b) 1.1835, overestimate

5. (a) $8, 6.875$ (b) $5, 5.375$

(c) $5.75, 5.9375$

(d) M_6

7. 0.2533, 0.2170, 0.2101, 0.2050; 0.2
9. (a) Left: 0.8100, 0.7937, 0.7904;
right: 0.7600, 0.7770, 0.7804
11. 34.7 ft, 44.8 ft   **13.** 63.2 L, 70 L   **15.** 155 ft
17. $\lim\limits_{n\to\infty} \sum\limits_{i=1}^{n} \sqrt[4]{1 + 15i/n} \cdot (15/n)$ **19.** $\lim\limits_{n\to\infty} \sum\limits_{i=1}^{n} \left(\dfrac{i\pi}{2n}\cos\dfrac{i\pi}{2n}\right)\dfrac{\pi}{2n}$
21. The region under the graph of $y = \tan x$ from 0 to $\pi/4$
23. (a) $\lim\limits_{n\to\infty} \dfrac{64}{n^6} \sum\limits_{i=1}^{n} i^5$ (b) $\dfrac{n^2(n+1)^2(2n^2+2n-1)}{12}$ (c) $\frac{32}{3}$
25. $\sin b, 1$

EXERCISES 5.2 ▪ PAGE 310

1. -6
The Riemann sum represents the sum of the areas of the two rectangles above the x-axis minus the sum of the areas of the three rectangles below the x-axis; that is, the net area of the rectangles with respect to the x-axis.

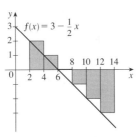

3. -0.856759
The Riemann sum represents the sum of the areas of the two rectangles above the x-axis minus the sum of the areas of the three rectangles below the x-axis.

5. (a) 4   (b) 6   (c) 10   **7.** $-475, -85$ **9.** 124.1644
11. 0.3084   **13.** 0.30843908, 0.30981629, 0.31015563
15.

n	R_n
5	1.933766
10	1.983524
50	1.999342
100	1.999836

The values of R_n appear to be approaching 2.

17. $\int_2^6 \dfrac{1-x^2}{4+x^2}\,dx$ **19.** $\int_1^8 \sqrt{2x + x^2}\,dx$ **21.** 42
23. $\frac{4}{3}$ **25.** 3.75   **29.** $\lim\limits_{n\to\infty} \sum\limits_{i=1}^{n} \dfrac{2+4i/n}{1+(2+4i/n)^5}\cdot\dfrac{4}{n}$
31. $\lim\limits_{n\to\infty} \sum\limits_{i=1}^{n}\left(\sin\dfrac{5\pi i}{n}\right)\dfrac{\pi}{n} = \dfrac{2}{5}$
33. (a) 4   (b) 10   (c) -3 (d) 2   **35.** $-\frac{3}{4}$
37. $3 + \frac{9}{4}\pi$ **39.** 2.5   **41.** 0   **43.** 3   **45.** 22.5
47. $\int_{-1}^{5} f(x)\,dx$ **49.** 122
51. $2m \le \int_0^2 f(x)\,dx \le 2M$ by Comparison Property 8
55. $3 \le \int_1^4 \sqrt{x}\,dx \le 6$ **57.** $\dfrac{\pi}{12} \le \int_{\pi/4}^{\pi/3} \tan x\,dx \le \dfrac{\pi}{12}\sqrt{3}$
59. $2 \le \int_{-1}^{1} \sqrt{1+x^4}\,dx \le 2\sqrt{2}$ **69.** $\int_0^1 x^4\,dx$ **71.** $\frac{1}{2}$

1. One process undoes what the other one does. See the Fundamental Theorem of Calculus, page 320.
3. (a) 0, 2, 5, 7, 3   (d)
(b) (0, 3)
(c) $x = 3$

5.   (a), (b) x^2

7. $g'(x) = 1/(x^3 + 1)$
9. $g'(y) = y^2 \sin y$ **11.** $F'(x) = -\sqrt{1 + \sec x}$
13. $h'(x) = -\sin^4(1/x)/x^2$ **15.** $y' = \sqrt{\tan x} + \sqrt{\tan x}\,\sec^2 x$
17. $y' = \dfrac{3(1-3x)^3}{1+(1-3x)^2}$ **19.** $\frac{3}{4}$ **21.** 63
23. $\frac{5}{9}$ **25.** $\frac{7}{8}$ **27.** $\frac{156}{7}$ **29.** $\frac{40}{3}$ **31.** 1   **33.** $\frac{49}{3}$
35. 0
37. The function $f(x) = x^{-4}$ is not continuous on the interval $[-2, 1]$, so FTC2 cannot be applied.
39. The function $f(\theta) = \sec\theta\tan\theta$ is not continuous on the interval $[\pi/3, \pi]$, so FTC2 cannot be applied.
41. $\frac{243}{4}$ **43.** 2
45. 3.75

47. $g'(x) = \dfrac{-2(4x^2 - 1)}{4x^2 + 1} + \dfrac{3(9x^2 - 1)}{9x^2 + 1}$
49. $y' = 3x^{7/2}\sin(x^3) - \dfrac{\sin\sqrt{x}}{2\sqrt[4]{x}}$ **51.** $\sqrt{257}$
53. (a) $-2\sqrt{n}, \sqrt{4n-2}$, n an integer > 0
(b) $(0, 1)$, $\left(-\sqrt{4n-1}, -\sqrt{4n-3}\right)$, and $\left(\sqrt{4n-1}, \sqrt{4n+1}\right)$,
n an integer > 0 (c) 0.74
55. (a) Loc. max. at 1 and 5; loc. min. at 3 and 7
(b) $x = 9$
(c) $\left(\frac{1}{2}, 2\right), (4, 6), (8, 9)$
(d) See graph at right.

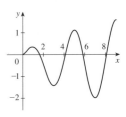

57. $\frac{1}{4}$ **65.** $f(x) = x^{3/2}, a = 9$
67. (b) Average expenditure over $[0, t]$; minimize average expenditure
69. $\ln 3$ **71.** π **73.** $e^2 - 1$

EXERCISES 5.4 ▪ PAGE 329

5. $\frac{1}{3}x^3 - (1/x) + C$ **7.** $\frac{1}{5}x^5 - \frac{1}{8}x^4 + \frac{1}{8}x^2 - 2x + C$
9. $2t - t^2 + \frac{1}{3}t^3 - \frac{1}{4}t^4 + C$ **11.** $\frac{1}{3}x^3 - 4\sqrt{x} + C$
13. $\frac{1}{2}\theta^2 + \csc\theta + C$ **15.** $\tan\alpha + C$
17. $\sin x + \frac{1}{4}x^2 + C$

19. 18   **21.** 231   **23.** 52   **25.** $\frac{256}{15}$ **27.** $-\frac{63}{4}$ **29.** $\frac{55}{63}$
31. $2\sqrt{5}$ **33.** 8   **35.** $1 + \pi/4$ **37.** $\frac{256}{5}$ **39.** 1
41. -3.5 **43.** 0, 1.32; 0.84   **45.** $\frac{4}{3}$
47. The increase in the child's weight (in pounds) between the ages of 5 and 10
49. Number of gallons of oil leaked in the first 2 hours
51. Increase in revenue when production is increased from 1000 to 5000 units
53. Newton-meters (or joules)   **55.** (a) $-\frac{3}{2}$ m   (b) $\frac{41}{6}$ m
57. (a) $v(t) = \frac{1}{2}t^2 + 4t + 5$ m/s   (b) $416\frac{2}{3}$ m
59. $46\frac{2}{3}$ kg   **61.** 1.4 mi   **63.** $58,000
65. (b) At most 40%; $\frac{5}{36}$ **67.** $-\cos x + \cosh x + C$
69. $\frac{1}{3}x^3 + x + \tan^{-1}x + C$ **71.** $\pi/6$

EXERCISES 5.5 ▪ PAGE 338

1. $\frac{1}{3}\sin 3x + C$ **3.** $\frac{2}{9}(x^3 + 1)^{3/2} + C$ **5.** $-\frac{1}{4}\cos^4\theta + C$
7. $-\frac{1}{2}\cos(x^2) + C$ **9.** $\frac{1}{63}(3x - 2)^{21} + C$
11. $\frac{1}{3}(2x + x^2)^{3/2} + C$ **13.** $-(1/\pi)\cos\pi t + C$
15. $\frac{2}{3}\sqrt{3ax + bx^3} + C$ **17.** $2\sin\sqrt{t} + C$ **19.** $\frac{1}{7}\sin^7\theta + C$
21. $\frac{1}{2}(1 + z^3)^{2/3} + C$ **23.** $-\frac{2}{3}(\cot x)^{3/2} + C$
25. $\frac{1}{3}\sec^3x + C$ **27.** $-1/(\sin x) + C$
29. $\frac{4}{7}(x + 2)^{7/4} - \frac{8}{3}(x + 2)^{3/4} + C$
31. $\frac{1}{8}(x^2 - 1)^4 + C$ **33.** $\frac{1}{4}\sin^4x + C$

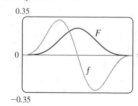

35. 0   **37.** $\frac{182}{9}$ **39.** 4   **41.** 0   **43.** 3
45. $\frac{1}{3}(2\sqrt{2} - 1)a^3$ **47.** $\frac{16}{15}$ **49.** $\frac{1}{2}(\sin 4 - \sin 1)$
51. $\sqrt{3} - \frac{1}{3}$ **53.** 6π **55.** $\dfrac{5}{4\pi}\left(1 - \cos\dfrac{2\pi t}{5}\right)$ L   **57.** 5

65. $-\frac{1}{3}\ln|5 - 3x| + C$ **67.** $\frac{1}{3}(\ln x)^3 + C$
69. $\frac{2}{3}(1 + e^x)^{3/2} + C$ **71.** $e^{\tan x} + C$
73. $\tan^{-1}x + \frac{1}{2}\ln(1 + x^2) + C$ **75.** $-\ln(1 + \cos^2 x) + C$
77. $\ln|\sin x| + C$ **79.** 2   **81.** $\ln(e + 1)$ **83.** $\pi^2/4$

CHAPTER 5 REVIEW ▪ PAGE 341

True-False Quiz

1. True   **3.** True   **5.** False   **7.** True   **9.** True
11. False   **13.** False   **15.** False

Exercises

1. (a) 8   (b) 5.7

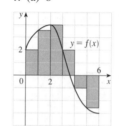

3. $\frac{1}{2} + \pi/4$ **5.** 3   **7.** f is c, f' is b, $\int_0^x f(t)\,dt$ is a
9. 37   **11.** $\frac{9}{10}$ **13.** -76 **15.** $\frac{21}{4}$ **17.** Does not exist
19. $\frac{1}{3}\sin 1$ **21.** 0   **23.** $[1/(2\pi)]\sin^2\pi t + C$
25. $\frac{1}{2}\sqrt{2} - \frac{1}{2}$ **27.** $\frac{23}{3}$ **29.** $2\sqrt{1 + \sin x} + C$ **31.** $\frac{64}{5}$
33. $F'(x) = x^2/(1 + x^3)$ **35.** $g'(x) = 4x^3\cos(x^8)$
37. $y' = \dfrac{(2\cos x - \cos\sqrt{x})}{(2x)}$ **39.** $4 \le \int_1^3 \sqrt{x^2 + 3}\,dx \le 4\sqrt{3}$
43. 0.280981
45. Number of barrels of oil consumed from Jan. 1, 2000, through Jan. 1, 2008
47. 72,400   **49.** 3   **51.** $(1 + x^2)(x\cos x + \sin x)/x^2$

PROBLEMS PLUS ▪ PAGE 345

1. $\pi/2$ **3.** $f(x) = \frac{1}{2}x$ **5.** -1 **7.** $[-1, 2]$
9. (a) $\frac{1}{2}(n - 1)n$ (b) $\frac{1}{2}[\![b]\!](2b - [\![b]\!] - 1) - \frac{1}{2}[\![a]\!](2a - [\![a]\!] - 1)$
15. $2(\sqrt{2} - 1)$

CHAPTER 6

EXERCISES 6.1 ▪ PAGE 352

1. $\frac{32}{3}$ **3.** $\frac{4}{3}$ **5.** 19.5   **7.** $\frac{1}{6}$ **9.** $\frac{4}{3}$ **11.** $\frac{1}{3}$ **13.** 72
15. $6\sqrt{3}$ **17.** $\frac{59}{12}$ **19.** $\frac{32}{3}$ **21.** $\frac{8}{3}$ **23.** $\frac{1}{2}$
25. $2 - \pi/2$ **27.** $\frac{3}{4}$ **29.** 6.5   **31.** $\frac{3}{2}\sqrt{3} - 1$
33. 0.6407   **35.** 0, 0.90; 0.04   **37.** 8.38   **39.** $12\sqrt{6} - 9$
41. $117\frac{1}{3}$ ft   **43.** 4232 cm²
45. (a) Car A   (b) The distance by which A is ahead of B after 1 minute   (c) Car A   (d) $t \approx 2.2$ min
47. $\frac{24}{5}\sqrt{3}$ **49.** $4^{2/3}$ **51.** ± 6 **53.** $\ln 2 - \frac{1}{2}$
55. $2 - 2\ln 2$

EXERCISES 6.2 ▪ PAGE 362

1. $19\pi/12$

3. $\pi/2$

5. 162π

7. $4\pi/21$

9. $64\pi/15$

11. $\pi/6$

13. $2\pi\left(\frac{4}{3}\pi - \sqrt{3}\right)$

15. $16\pi/15$

17. $29\pi/30$

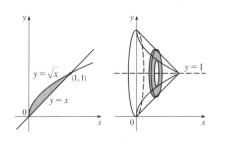

19. $\pi/7$ **21.** $\pi/10$ **23.** $\pi/2$ **25.** $7\pi/15$
27. $5\pi/14$ **29.** $13\pi/30$ **31.** $\pi \int_0^{\pi/4} (1 - \tan^3 x)^2 \, dx$
33. $\pi \int_0^{\pi} \left[1^2 - (1 - \sin x)^2\right] dx$
35. $\pi \int_{-2\sqrt{2}}^{2\sqrt{2}} \left[5^2 - \left(\sqrt{1 + y^2} + 2\right)^2\right] dy$
37. $-1.288, 0.884; 23.780$ **39.** $\frac{11}{8}\pi^2$
41. Solid obtained by rotating the region $0 \leqslant y \leqslant \cos x$,
$0 \leqslant x \leqslant \pi/2$ about the x-axis
43. Solid obtained by rotating the region above the x-axis bounded
by $x = y^2$ and $x = y^4$ about the y-axis
45. 1110 cm^3 **47.** (a) 196 (b) 838 **49.** $\frac{1}{3}\pi r^2 h$
51. $\pi h^2\left(r - \frac{1}{3}h\right)$ **53.** $\frac{2}{3}b^2 h$ **55.** 10 cm^3 **57.** 24
59. $\frac{1}{3}$ **61.** $\frac{8}{15}$
63. (a) $8\pi R \int_0^r \sqrt{r^2 - y^2} \, dy$ (b) $2\pi^2 r^2 R$
65. (b) $\pi r^2 h$ **67.** $\frac{5}{12}\pi r^3$ **69.** $8 \int_0^r \sqrt{R^2 - y^2} \sqrt{r^2 - y^2} \, dy$

EXERCISES 6.3 ▪ PAGE 368

1. Circumference $= 2\pi x$, height $= x(x - 1)^2$; $\pi/15$

3. 2π

5. 8π

7. 16π

9. $21\pi/2$

11. $768\pi/7$ **13.** $16\pi/3$ **15.** $7\pi/15$ **17.** $8\pi/3$
19. $5\pi/14$ **21.** $\int_{2\pi}^{3\pi} 2\pi x \sin x \, dx$
23. $\int_0^1 2\pi(x+1)[\sin(\pi x/2) - x^4] \, dx$
25. $\int_0^\pi 2\pi(4-y)\sqrt{\sin y} \, dy$ **27.** 3.68
29. Solid obtained by rotating the region $0 \leq y \leq x^4$, $0 \leq x \leq 3$ about the y-axis
31. Solid obtained by rotating the region bounded by
(i) $x = 1 - y^2$, $x = 0$, and $y = 0$, or (ii) $x = y^2$, $x = 1$, and $y = 0$ about the line $y = 3$
33. 0, 1.32; 4.05   **35.** $\frac{1}{32}\pi^3$ **37.** 8π **39.** $\frac{63}{2}\pi$
41. $\frac{4}{3}\pi$ **43.** $\frac{4}{3}\pi r^3$ **45.** $\frac{1}{3}\pi r^2 h$

1. 588 J   **3.** 9 ft-lb   **5.** 180 J   **7.** $\frac{15}{4}$ ft-lb
9. (a) $\frac{25}{24} \approx 1.04$ J   (b) 10.8 cm   **11.** $W_2 = 3W_1$
13. (a) 625 ft-lb   (b) $\frac{1875}{4}$ ft-lb   **15.** 650,000 ft-lb
17. 3857 J   **19.** 2450 J   **21.** $\approx 1.06 \times 10^6$ J

23. $\approx 1.04 \times 10^5$ ft-lb   **25.** 2.0 m   **29.** $Gm_1m_2\left(\dfrac{1}{a} - \dfrac{1}{b}\right)$

1. $\frac{8}{3}$ **3.** $\frac{45}{28}$ **5.** $\frac{1}{15}(26^{3/2} - 1)$ **7.** $2/(5\pi)$
9. (a) 1   (b) 2, 4   (c)

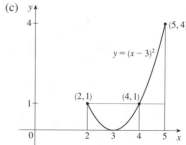

11. (a) $4/\pi$ (b) $\approx 1.24, 2.81$
(c) 3

15. $38\frac{1}{3}$ **17.** $(50 + 28/\pi)°F \approx 59°F$ **19.** 6 kg/m
21. $5/(4\pi) \approx 0.4$ L

Exercises

1. $\frac{8}{3}$ **3.** $\frac{7}{12}$ **5.** $\frac{4}{3} + 4/\pi$ **7.** $64\pi/15$ **9.** $1656\pi/5$
11. $\frac{4}{3}\pi(2ah + h^2)^{3/2}$ **13.** $\int_{-\pi/3}^{\pi/3} 2\pi(\pi/2 - x)(\cos^2 x - \frac{1}{4}) \, dx$
15. (a) $2\pi/15$ (b) $\pi/6$ (c) $8\pi/15$
17. (a) 0.38   (b) 0.87
19. Solid obtained by rotating the region $0 \leq y \leq \cos x$, $0 \leq x \leq \pi/2$ about the y-axis
21. Solid obtained by rotating the region $0 \leq x \leq \pi$, $0 \leq y \leq 2 - \sin x$ about the x-axis
23. 36   **25.** $\frac{125}{3}\sqrt{3}$ m^3 **27.** 3.2 J
29. (a) $8000\pi/3 \approx 8378$ ft-lb   (b) 2.1 ft   **31.** $f(x)$

1. (a) $f(t) = 3t^2$ (b) $f(x) = \sqrt{2x/\pi}$ **3.** $\frac{32}{27}$
5. (b) 0.2261   (c) 0.6736 m
(d) (i) $1/(105\pi) \approx 0.003$ in/s   (ii) $370\pi/3$ s ≈ 6.5 min
9. $y = \frac{32}{9}x^2$
11. (a) $V = \int_0^h \pi[f(y)]^2 \, dy$ (c) $f(y) = \sqrt{kA/(\pi C)} \, y^{1/4}$
Advantage: the markings on the container are equally spaced.
13. $b = 2a$ **15.** $B = 16A$

CHAPTER 7

EXERCISES 7.1 ▪ PAGE 391

1. (a) See Definition 1.
(b) It must pass the Horizontal Line Test.
3. No **5.** Yes **7.** No **9.** No **11.** Yes **13.** No
15. No **17.** 2 **19.** 4
21. $F = \frac{9}{5}C + 32$; the Fahrenheit temperature as a function of the Celsius temperature; $[-273.15, \infty)$
23. $f^{-1}(x) = \frac{3}{2} - \frac{1}{2}x$ **25.** $f^{-1}(x) = -\frac{1}{3}x^2 + \frac{10}{3}, \ x \geq 0$
27. $y = \left(\dfrac{1-x}{1+x}\right)^2, \quad -1 < x \leq 1$
29. $f^{-1}(x) = \sqrt[4]{x-1}$ **31.**

33. (b) $\frac{1}{12}$
(c) $f^{-1}(x) = \sqrt[3]{x}$,
domain $= \mathbb{R} =$ range
(e)

35. (b) $-\frac{1}{2}$
(c) $f^{-1}(x) = \sqrt{9-x}$,
domain $= [0, 9]$, range $= [0, 3]$
(e)

37. $\frac{1}{7}$ **39.** $2/\pi$ **41.** $\frac{3}{2}$
43.
$f^{-1}(x) = -\left(\sqrt[3]{4}/6\right)\left(\sqrt[3]{D - 27x^2 + 20} - \sqrt[3]{D + 27x^2 - 20} + \sqrt[3]{2}\right)$,
where $D = 3\sqrt{3}\sqrt{27x^4 - 40x^2 + 16}$; two of the expressions are complex.
45. (a) $g^{-1}(x) = f^{-1}(x) - c$ (b) $h^{-1}(x) = (1/c)f^{-1}(x)$

EXERCISES 7.2 ▪ PAGE 402

1. (a) $f(x) = a^x, a > 0$ (b) $\mathbb{R}$ (c) $(0, \infty)$
(d) See Figures 6(c), 6(b), and 6(a), respectively.
3.

All approach 0 as $x \to -\infty$, all pass through $(0, 1)$, and all are increasing. The larger the base, the faster the rate of increase.

5.

$y = \left(\frac{1}{3}\right)^x \quad y = \left(\frac{1}{10}\right)^x \quad y = 10^x \quad y = 3^x$

The functions with base greater than 1 are increasing and those with base less than 1 are decreasing. The latter are reflections of the former about the y-axis.

7.

$y = 4^x - 3$

9.

$y = -2^{-x}$

11.

$\left(0, \frac{1}{2}\right)$
$y = 1 - \frac{1}{2}e^{-x}$

13. (a) $y = e^x - 2$ (b) $y = e^{x-2}$ (c) $y = -e^x$
(d) $y = e^{-x}$ (e) $y = -e^{-x}$
15. (a) $(-\infty, \infty)$ (b) $(-\infty, 0) \cup (0, \infty)$
17. $f(x) = 3 \cdot 2^x$ **21.** At $x \approx 35.8$ **23.** ∞ **25.** 1
27. 0 **29.** 0 **31.** $f'(x) = e^x(x^3 + 3x^2 + 2x + 2)$
33. $y' = 3ax^2 e^{ax^3}$ **35.** $f'(u) = (-1/u^2)e^{1/u}$
37. $F'(t) = e^{t \sin 2t}(2t \cos 2t + \sin 2t)$
39. $y' = 3e^{3x}/\sqrt{1 + 2e^{3x}}$ **41.** $y' = e^{e^x}e^x$
43. $y' = \dfrac{(ad - bc)e^x}{(ce^x + d)^2}$ **45.** $y' = \dfrac{4e^{2x}}{(1 + e^{2x})^2} \sin \dfrac{1 - e^{2x}}{1 + e^{2x}}$
47. $y = 2x + 1$ **49.** $y' = (1 - 2xye^{x^2y})/(x^2 e^{x^2y} - 1)$
53. $-4, -2$ **55.** $f^{(n)}(x) = 2^n e^{2x}$ **57.** (b) -0.567143
59. (a) 1 (b) $kae^{-kt}/(1 + ae^{-kt})^2$
(c) $t \approx 7.4$ h

$p = 0.8$

61. -1 **63.** $f(2) = 2/\sqrt{e}, f(-1) = -1/\sqrt[8]{e}$
65. (a) Inc. on $(2, \infty)$; dec. on $(-\infty, 2)$
(b) CU on $(-\infty, 3)$; CD on $(3, \infty)$ (c) $(3, -2e^{-3})$
67. A. $\{x \mid x \neq -1\}$
B. y-int. $1/e$ C. None
D. HA $y = 1$; VA $x = -1$
E. Inc. on $(-\infty, -1)$, $(-1, \infty)$
F. None
G. CU on $(-\infty, -1)$, $\left(-1, -\frac{1}{2}\right)$;
CD on $\left(-\frac{1}{2}, \infty\right)$; IP $\left(-\frac{1}{2}, 1/e^2\right)$
H. See graph at right

$y = 1$
$x = -1$

69. 28.57 min, when the rate of increase of drug level in the bloodstream is greatest; 85.71 min, when rate of decrease is greatest
71. Loc. max. $f(-1/\sqrt{3}) = e^{2\sqrt{3}/9} \approx 1.5$;
loc. min. $f(1/\sqrt{3}) = e^{-2\sqrt{3}/9} \approx 0.7$;
IP $(-0.15, 1.15), (-1.09, 0.82)$

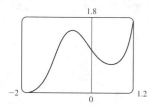

73. $\frac{1}{3}(1 - e^{-15})$ **75.** $\frac{2}{3}(1 + e^x)^{3/2} + C$
77. $\frac{1}{2}e^{2x} + 2x - \frac{1}{2}e^{-2x} + C$ **79.** $-e^{\cos x} + C$
81. $2e^{\sqrt{x}} + C$ **83.** 4.644   **85.** $\pi(e^2 - 1)/2$ **89.** $\frac{1}{2}$

EXERCISES 7.3 ■ **PAGE 409**

1. (a) It's defined as the inverse of the exponential function with base a, that is, $\log_a x = y \Leftrightarrow a^y = x$.
(b) $(0, \infty)$ (c) $\mathbb{R}$ (d) See Figure 1.
3. (a) 3   (b) -3 **5.** (a) -2 (b) 15
7. (a) 3   (b) -2
9. $3 \log_2 x + \log_2 y - 2 \log_2 z$ **11.** $10 \ln u + 10 \ln v$
13. $\log_{10}(ac/b)$ **15.** $\ln 1215$
17. $\ln \dfrac{(1 + x^2)\sqrt{x}}{\sin x}$

19. (a) 0.402430   (b) 1.454240   (c) 1.651496
21.

$y = \log_{1.5} x$ All graphs approach
$y = \ln x$ $-\infty$ as $x \to 0^+$, all pass
$y = \log_{10} x$ through $(1, 0)$, and all
$y = \log_{50} x$ are increasing. The
larger the base, the slower the rate of increase.

23. (a)

$y = \log_{10}(x + 5)$

(b)

$y = -\ln x$

25. (a) $\sqrt{e}$ (b) $-\ln 5$
27. (a) $5 + \log_2 3$ or $5 + (\ln 3)/\ln 2$ (b) $\frac{1}{2}(1 + \sqrt{1 + 4e})$
29. $-3, 0$ **31.** e^e **33.** $\ln 3$
35. (a) 0.5210   (b) 3.0949
37. (a) $x < \ln 10$ (b) $x > 1/e$
39. About 1,084,588 mi   **41.** 8.3
43. (a) $f^{-1}(n) = (3/\ln 2) \ln(n/100)$; the time elapsed when there are n bacteria   (b) After about 26.9 hours
45. $-\infty$ **47.** 0   **49.** ∞ **51.** $(-\infty, -3) \cup (3, \infty)$
53. (a) $\left(-\infty, \frac{1}{2}\ln 3\right]$ (b) $f^{-1}(x) = \frac{1}{2}\ln(3 - x^2), [0, \sqrt{3})$
55. $y = e^x - 3$ **57.** $f^{-1}(x) = \sqrt[3]{\ln x}$ **59.** $y = \dfrac{1}{10^x - 1}$

61. $\left(-\frac{1}{2}\ln 3, \infty\right)$ **63.** $(-\infty, 0), (4, \infty)$
65. (b) $f^{-1}(x) = \frac{1}{2}(e^x - e^{-x})$ **67.** f is a constant function
71. $-1 \le x < 1 - \sqrt{3}$ or $1 + \sqrt{3} < x \le 3$

EXERCISES 7.4 ■ **PAGE 419**

1. The differentiation formula is simplest.
3. $f'(x) = \dfrac{\cos(\ln x)}{x}$ **5.** $f'(x) = \dfrac{3}{(3x - 1)\ln 2}$
7. $f'(x) = \dfrac{1}{5x\sqrt[5]{(\ln x)^4}}$ **9.** $f'(x) = \dfrac{\sin x}{x} + \cos x \ln(5x)$
11. $F'(t) = \dfrac{6}{2t + 1} - \dfrac{12}{3t - 1}$ **13.** $g'(x) = \dfrac{2x^2 - 1}{x(x^2 - 1)}$
15. $f'(u) = \dfrac{1 + \ln 2}{u[1 + \ln(2u)]^2}$ **17.** $h'(t) = 3t^2 - 3^t \ln 3$
19. $y' = \dfrac{10x + 1}{5x^2 + x - 2}$ **21.** $y' = \dfrac{-x}{1 + x}$
23. $y' = \dfrac{1}{\ln 10} + \log_{10} x$ **25.** $y' = 5^{-1/x}(\ln 5)/x^2$
27. $y' = x + 2x \ln(2x); y'' = 3 + 2 \ln(2x)$
29. $y' = \dfrac{1}{\sqrt{1 + x^2}}; y'' = \dfrac{-x}{(1 + x^2)^{3/2}}$
31. $f'(x) = \dfrac{2x - 1 - (x - 1) \ln(x - 1)}{(x - 1)[1 - \ln(x - 1)]^2}$;
$(1, 1 + e) \cup (1 + e, \infty)$
33. $f'(x) = \dfrac{2(x - 1)}{x(x - 2)}; (-\infty, 0) \cup (2, \infty)$
35. $\frac{1}{2}$ **37.** $y = 3x - 2$ **39.** $\cos x + 1/x$
41. $y' = (2x + 1)^5(x^4 - 3)^6\left(\dfrac{10}{2x + 1} + \dfrac{24x^3}{x^4 - 3}\right)$
43. $y' = \dfrac{\sin^2 x \tan^4 x}{(x^2 + 1)^2}\left(2 \cot x + \dfrac{4 \sec^2 x}{\tan x} - \dfrac{4x}{x^2 + 1}\right)$
45. $y' = x^x(1 + \ln x)$
47. $y' = x^{\sin x}\left(\dfrac{\sin x}{x} + \cos x \ln x\right)$
49. $y' = (\cos x)^x(-x \tan x + \ln \cos x)$
51. $y' = (\tan x)^{1/x}\left(\dfrac{\sec^2 x}{x \tan x} - \dfrac{\ln \tan x}{x^2}\right)$
53. $y' = \dfrac{2x}{x^2 + y^2 - 2y}$ **55.** $f^{(n)}(x) = \dfrac{(-1)^{n-1}(n - 1)!}{(x - 1)^n}$
57. 2.958516, 5.290718
59. CU on $(e^{8/3}, \infty)$, CD on $(0, e^{8/3})$, IP $\left(e^{8/3}, \frac{8}{3}e^{-4/3}\right)$
61. A. All x in $(2n\pi, (2n + 1)\pi)$ (n an integer)
B. x-int. $\pi/2 + 2n\pi$ C. Period 2π D. VA $x = n\pi$
E. Inc. on $(2n\pi, \pi/2 + 2n\pi)$; dec. on $(\pi/2 + 2n\pi, (2n + 1)\pi)$
F. Loc. max. $f(\pi/2 + 2n\pi) = 0$ G. CD on $(2n\pi, (2n + 1)\pi)$
H.

63. A. $\mathbb{R}$ B. y-int 0; x-int. 0
C. About y-axis   D. None
E. Inc. on $(0, \infty)$;
dec. on $(-\infty, 0)$
F. Loc. min. $f(0) = 0$
G. CU on $(-1, 1)$; CD on
$(-\infty, -1)$, $(1, \infty)$;
IP $(\pm 1, \ln 2)$ H. See graph at right.

65. Inc. on $(0, 2.7)$, $(4.5, 8.2)$, $(10.9, 14.3)$;
IP $(3.8, 1.7)$, $(5.7, 2.1)$, $(10.0, 2.7)$, $(12.0, 2.9)$
67. (a) $y = ab^t$ where $a \approx 100.01244$ and $b \approx 0.000045146$
(b) -670.63 μA
69. $3 \ln 2$ **71.** $\frac{1}{3} \ln \frac{5}{2}$ **73.** $\frac{1}{2}e^2 + e - \frac{1}{2}$
75. $\frac{1}{3}(\ln x)^3 + C$ **77.** $-\ln(1 + \cos^2 x) + C$ **79.** $90/(\ln 10)$
83. $\pi \ln 2$ **85.** $45{,}974$ J   **87.** $\frac{1}{3}$
89. $0 < m < 1, m - 1 - \ln m$

EXERCISES 7.2* ▪ PAGE 428

1. $2 \ln r - \ln 3 - \frac{1}{2} \ln s$ **3.** $10 \ln u + 10 \ln v$

5. $\ln 1215$ **7.** $\ln \dfrac{(1 + x^2)\sqrt{x}}{\sin x}$

9.

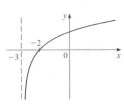

$y = -\ln x$

11.

13. $-\infty$ **15.** $f'(x) = (2 + \ln x)/(2\sqrt{x})$
17. $f'(x) = \dfrac{\cos(\ln x)}{x}$ **19.** $f'(x) = \dfrac{1}{5x\sqrt[5]{(\ln x)^4}}$
21. $f'(x) = \dfrac{\sin x}{x} + \cos x \ln(5x)$ **23.** $g'(x) = -2a/(a^2 - x^2)$
25. $F'(t) = \dfrac{6}{2t + 1} - \dfrac{12}{3t - 1}$ **27.** $g'(x) = \dfrac{2x^2 - 1}{x(x^2 - 1)}$
29. $f'(u) = \dfrac{1 + \ln 2}{u[1 + \ln(2u)]^2}$ **31.** $y' = \dfrac{10x + 1}{5x^2 + x - 2}$
33. $y' = \sec^2(\ln(ax + b)) \dfrac{a}{ax + b}$
35. $y' = x + 2x \ln(2x); y'' = 3 + 2 \ln(2x)$
37. $f'(x) = \dfrac{2x - 1 - (x - 1)\ln(x - 1)}{(x - 1)[1 - \ln(x - 1)]^2}; (1, 1 + e) \cup (1 + e, \infty)$
39. $f'(x) = -\dfrac{1}{2x\sqrt{1 - \ln x}}; (0, e]$ **41.** $\frac{1}{2}$ **43.** $\cos x + 1/x$
45. $y = 2x - 2$ **47.** $y' = \dfrac{2x}{x^2 + y^2 - 2y}$
49. $f^{(n)}(x) = \dfrac{(-1)^{n-1}(n - 1)!}{(x - 1)^n}$ **51.** $2.958516, 5.290718$
53. A. All x in $(2n\pi, (2n + 1)\pi)$ (n an integer)
B. x-int. $\pi/2 + 2n\pi$ C. Period 2π D. VA $x = n\pi$
E. Inc. on $(2n\pi, \pi/2 + 2n\pi)$; dec. on $(\pi/2 + 2n\pi, (2n + 1)\pi)$
F. Loc. max. $f(\pi/2 + 2n\pi) = 0$ G. CD on $(2n\pi, (2n + 1)\pi)$

H.

55. A. $\mathbb{R}$ B. y-int 0; x-int. 0
C. About y-axis   D. None
E. Inc. on $(0, \infty)$;
dec. on $(-\infty, 0)$
F. Loc. min. $f(0) = 0$
G. CU on $(-1, 1)$; CD on
$(-\infty, -1)$, $(1, \infty)$;
IP $(\pm 1, \ln 2)$ H. See graph at right.
57. Inc. on $(0, 2.7)$, $(4.5, 8.2)$, $(10.9, 14.3)$;
IP $(3.8, 1.7)$, $(5.7, 2.1)$, $(10.0, 2.7)$, $(12.0, 2.9)$

59. $y' = (2x + 1)^5(x^4 - 3)^6\left(\dfrac{10}{2x + 1} + \dfrac{24x^3}{x^4 - 3}\right)$

61. $y' = \dfrac{\sin^2 x \tan^4 x}{(x^2 + 1)^2}\left(2 \cot x + \dfrac{4 \sec^2 x}{\tan x} - \dfrac{4x}{x^2 + 1}\right)$

63. $3 \ln 2$ **65.** $\frac{1}{3} \ln \frac{5}{2}$ **67.** $\frac{1}{2}e^2 + e - \frac{1}{2}$ **69.** $\frac{1}{3}(\ln x)^3 + C$
71. $-\ln(1 + \cos^2 x) + C$ **75.** $\pi \ln 2$ **77.** $45{,}974$ J
79. $\frac{1}{3}$ **81.** (b) 0.405 **85.** $0 < m < 1, m - 1 - \ln m$

EXERCISES 7.3* ▪ PAGE 435

1.

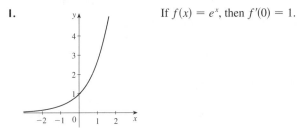

If $f(x) = e^x$, then $f'(0) = 1$.

3. (a) $\frac{1}{25}$ (b) 10 **5.** (a) $\sqrt{e}$ (b) $-\ln 5$
7. (a) $\frac{1}{3}(\ln k - 1)$ (b) $\frac{1}{2}(1 + \sqrt{1 + 4e})$
9. $-3, 0$ **11.** $\ln 3$
13. (a) 0.5210 (b) 3.0949
15. (a) $x < \ln 10$ (b) $x > 1/e$
17.

$y = e^{-x}$

19.

$y = 1$
$\left(0, \frac{1}{2}\right)$
$y = 1 - \frac{1}{2}e^{-x}$

21. (a) $\left(-\infty, \frac{1}{2}\ln 3\right]$ (b) $f^{-1}(x) = \frac{1}{2}\ln(3 - x^2), [0, \sqrt{3}]$
23. $y = e^x - 3$ **25.** $f^{-1}(x) = \sqrt[3]{\ln x}$ **27.** 1 **29.** 0
31. 0 **33.** $f'(x) = e^x(x^3 + 3x^2 + 2x + 2)$
35. $y' = 3ax^2 e^{ax^3}$ **37.** $f'(u) = (-1/u^2)e^{1/u}$
39. $F'(t) = e^{t \sin 2t}(2t \cos 2t + \sin 2t)$

41. $y' = 3e^{3x}/\sqrt{1 + 2e^{3x}}$ **43.** $y' = e^{e^x}e^x$

45. $y' = \dfrac{(ad - bc)e^x}{(ce^x + d)^2}$ **47.** $y' = \dfrac{4e^{2x}}{(1 + e^{2x})^2} \sin\dfrac{1 - e^{2x}}{1 + e^{2x}}$

49. $y = 2x + 1$ **51.** $y' = (1 - 2xye^{x^2y})/(x^2e^{x^2y} - 1)$
55. $-4, -2$ **57.** $f^{(n)}(x) = 2^n e^{2x}$ **59.** (b) -0.567143
61. (a) 1 (b) $kae^{-kt}/(1 + ae^{-kt})^2$

(c)

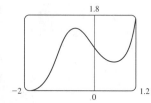

$t \approx 7.4$ h

63. -1 **65.** $f(2) = 2/\sqrt{e}, f(-1) = -1/\sqrt[8]{e}$
67. (a) Inc. on $(2, \infty)$; dec. on $(-\infty, 2)$
(b) CU on $(-\infty, 3)$; CD on $(3, \infty)$ (c) $(3, -2e^{-3})$
69. A. $\{x \mid x \neq -1\}$
B. y-int. $1/e$ C. None
D. HA $y = 1$; VA $x = -1$
E. Inc. on $(-\infty, -1), (-1, \infty)$
F. None
G. CU on $(-\infty, -1), (-1, -\frac{1}{2})$;
CD on $(-\frac{1}{2}, \infty)$; IP $(-\frac{1}{2}, 1/e^2)$
H. See graph at right

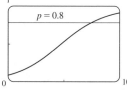

71. 28.57 min, when the rate of increase of drug level in the bloodstream is greatest; 85.71 min, when rate of decrease is greatest

73. Loc. max. $f(-1/\sqrt{3}) = e^{2\sqrt{3}/9} \approx 1.5$;
loc. min. $f(1/\sqrt{3}) = e^{-2\sqrt{3}/9} \approx 0.7$;
IP $(-0.15, 1.15), (-1.09, 0.82)$

75. $\frac{1}{3}(1 - e^{-15})$ **77.** $\frac{2}{3}(1 + e^x)^{3/2} + C$
79. $\frac{1}{2}e^{2x} + 2x - \frac{1}{2}e^{-2x} + C$ **81.** $-e^{\cos x} + C$
83. $2e^{\sqrt{x}} + C$ **85.** 4.644 **87.** $\pi(e^2 - 1)/2$ **91.** $\frac{1}{2}$

EXERCISES 7.4* ■ PAGE 445

1. (a) $a^x = e^{x \ln a}$ (b) $(-\infty, \infty)$ (c) $(0, \infty)$
(d) See Figures 1, 3, and 2. **3.** $e^{\sqrt{7} \ln 5}$ **5.** $e^{x \ln \cos x}$
7. (a) 3 (b) -3 **9.** (a) 3 (b) -2
11.

All approach 0 as $x \to -\infty$, all pass through $(0, 1)$, and all are increasing. The larger the base, the faster the rate of increase.

13. (a) 0.402430 (b) 1.454240 (c) 1.651496
15.

All graphs approach $-\infty$ as $x \to 0^+$, all pass through $(1, 0)$, and all are increasing. The larger the base, the slower the rate of increase.

17. $f(x) = 3 \cdot 2^x$ **19.** (b) About 1,084,588 mi
21. ∞ **23.** 0
25. $h'(t) = 3t^2 - 3^t \ln 3$ **27.** $y' = 5^{-1/x}(\ln 5)/x^2$
29. $f'(u) = 10 \ln 2 (2^u + 2^{-u})^9 (2^u - 2^{-u})$
31. $f'(x) = \dfrac{3}{(3x - 1) \ln 2}$ **33.** $y' = \dfrac{1}{\ln 10} + \log_{10} x$
35. $y' = x^x(1 + \ln x)$ **37.** $y' = x^{\sin x}\left(\dfrac{\sin x}{x} + \cos x \ln x\right)$
39. $y' = (\cos x)^x(-x \tan x + \ln \cos x)$
41. $y' = (\tan x)^{1/x}\left(\dfrac{\sec^2 x}{x \tan x} - \dfrac{\ln \tan x}{x^2}\right)$
43. $y = (10 \ln 10)x + 10(1 - \ln 10)$ **45.** $90/(\ln 10)$
47. $(\ln x)^2/(2 \ln 10) + C$ [or $\frac{1}{2}(\ln 10)(\log_{10} x)^2 + C$]
49. $3^{\sin \theta}/\ln 3 + C$ **51.** $16/(5 \ln 5) - 1/(2 \ln 2)$
53. 0.600967 **55.** $y = \dfrac{1}{10^x - 1}$ **57.** 8.3
59. $10^8/\ln 10$ dB/(watt/m²)
61. (a) $y = ab^t$ where $a \approx 100.01244$ and $b \approx 0.000045146$
(b) -670.63 μA

EXERCISES 7.5 ■ PAGE 453

1. About 235
3. (a) $100(4.2)^t$ (b) ≈ 7409 (c) $\approx 10,632$ bacteria/h
(d) $(\ln 100)/(\ln 4.2) \approx 3.2$ h
5. (a) 1508 million, 1871 million (b) 2161 million
(c) 3972 million; wars in the first half of century, increased life expectancy in second half
7. (a) $Ce^{-0.0005t}$ (b) $-2000 \ln 0.9 \approx 211$ s
9. (a) $100 \times 2^{-t/30}$ mg (b) ≈ 9.92 mg (c) ≈ 199.3 years
11. ≈ 2500 years **13.** (a) $\approx 137°$F (b) ≈ 116 min
15. (a) $13.\overline{3}°$C (b) ≈ 67.74 min
17. (a) ≈ 64.5 kPa (b) ≈ 39.9 kPa
19. (a) (i) $3828.84 (ii) $3840.25 (iii) $3850.08
(iv) $3851.61 (v) $3852.01 (vi) $3852.08
(b) $dA/dt = 0.05A, A(0) = 3000$

EXERCISES 7.6 ■ PAGE 461

1. (a) $\pi/3$ (b) π **3.** (a) $\pi/4$ (b) $\pi/4$
5. (a) 10 (b) $\pi/3$ **7.** $2/\sqrt{5}$ **9.** $\frac{2}{3}\sqrt{2}$
13. $x/\sqrt{1 + x^2}$

15.

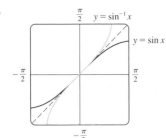

The second graph is the reflection of the first graph about the line $y = x$.

23. $y' = \dfrac{1}{2\sqrt{x}(1+x)}$ **25.** $y' = \dfrac{1}{\sqrt{-x^2-x}}$

27. $G'(x) = -1 - \dfrac{x\arccos x}{\sqrt{1-x^2}}$ **29.** $y' = -2e^{2x}/\sqrt{1-e^{4x}}$

31. $y' = -(\sin\theta)/(1+\cos^2\theta)$ **33.** $h'(t) = 0$

35. $y' = \sqrt{a^2-b^2}/(a+b\cos x)$

37. $g'(x) = 2/\sqrt{1-(3-2x)^2}; [1,2], (1,2)$ **39.** $\pi/6$

41. $1 - \dfrac{x\arcsin x}{\sqrt{1-x^2}}$ **43.** $-\pi/2$ **45.** $\pi/2$

47. At a distance $5 - 2\sqrt{5}$ from A **49.** $\frac{1}{4}$ rad/s

51. A. $\left[-\frac{1}{2}, \infty\right)$
B. y-int. 0; x-int. 0
C. None
D. HA $y = \pi/2$
E. Inc. on $\left(-\frac{1}{2}, \infty\right)$
F. None
G. CD on $\left(-\frac{1}{2}, \infty\right)$
H. See graph at right

53. A. $\mathbb{R}$
B. y-int. 0; x-int. 0
C. About $(0,0)$
D. SA $y = x \pm \pi/2$
E. Inc. on $\mathbb{R}$ F. None
G. CU on $(0, \infty)$; CD on $(-\infty, 0)$;
IP $(0,0)$
H. See graph at right.

55. Max. at $x = 0$, min. at $x \approx \pm 0.87$, IP at $x \approx \pm 0.52$
57. $\tan^{-1}x + x + C$
59. π **61.** $\pi/12$ **63.** $\tan^{-1}x + \frac{1}{2}\ln(1+x^2) + C$
65. $\ln|\sin^{-1}x| + C$ **67.** $\frac{1}{3}\sin^{-1}t^3 + C$
69. $2\tan^{-1}\sqrt{x} + C$ **73.** $\pi/2 - 1$

EXERCISES 7.7 ▪ PAGE 468

1. (a) 0 (b) 1 **3.** (a) $\frac{3}{4}$ (b) $\frac{1}{2}(e^2 - e^{-2}) \approx 3.62686$
5. (a) 1 (b) 0
21. $\operatorname{sech} x = \frac{3}{5}, \sinh x = \frac{4}{3}, \operatorname{csch} x = \frac{3}{4}, \tanh x = \frac{4}{5}, \coth x = \frac{5}{4}$
23. (a) 1 (b) -1 (c) ∞ (d) $-\infty$ (e) 0 (f) 1
(g) ∞ (h) $-\infty$ (i) 0
31. $f'(x) = x\cosh x$ **33.** $h'(x) = \tanh x$
35. $y' = 3e^{\cosh 3x}\sinh 3x$ **37.** $f'(t) = -2e^t\operatorname{sech}^2(e^t)\tanh(e^t)$

39. $y' = \dfrac{\operatorname{sech}^2 x}{1+\tanh^2 x}$ **41.** $G'(x) = \dfrac{-2\sinh x}{(1+\cosh x)^2}$

43. $y' = \dfrac{1}{2\sqrt{x}(1-x)}$ **45.** $y' = \sinh^{-1}(x/3)$

47. $y' = \dfrac{-1}{x\sqrt{x^2+1}}$

51. (a) 0.3572 (b) 70.34°
53. (b) $y = 2\sinh 3x - 4\cosh 3x$
55. $\left(\ln(1+\sqrt{2}), \sqrt{2}\right)$
57. $\frac{1}{3}\cosh^3 x + C$ **59.** $2\cosh\sqrt{x} + C$ **61.** $-\operatorname{csch} x + C$

63. $\ln\left(\dfrac{6+3\sqrt{3}}{4+\sqrt{7}}\right)$ **65.** $\tanh^{-1}e^x + C$

67. (a) 0, 0.48 (b) 0.04

EXERCISES 7.8 ▪ PAGE 478

1. (a) Indeterminate (b) 0 (c) 0
(d) ∞, $-\infty$, or does not exist (e) Indeterminate
3. (a) $-\infty$ (b) Indeterminate (c) ∞
5. 2 **7.** $\frac{9}{5}$ **9.** $-\infty$ **11.** ∞ **13.** p/q
15. 0 **17.** $-\infty$ **19.** ∞ **21.** $\frac{1}{2}$ **23.** 1
25. $\ln\frac{5}{3}$ **27.** 1 **29.** $\frac{1}{2}$ **31.** 0 **33.** $-1/\pi^2$
35. $\frac{1}{2}a(a-1)$ **37.** $\frac{1}{24}$ **39.** π **41.** 3 **43.** 0
45. $-2/\pi$ **47.** $\frac{1}{2}$ **49.** $\frac{1}{2}$ **51.** ∞ **53.** 1
55. e^{-2} **57.** e^3 **59.** 1 **61.** e^4
63. $1/\sqrt{e}$ **65.** e^2 **67.** $\frac{1}{4}$

69. A. $\mathbb{R}$ B. y-int. 0; x-int. 0
C. None D. HA $y = 0$
E. Inc. on $(-\infty, 1)$, dec. on $(1, \infty)$
F. Loc. max. $f(1) = 1/e$
G. CU on $(2, \infty)$; CD on $(-\infty, 2)$
IP $(2, 2/e^2)$
H. See graph at right.

71. A. $\mathbb{R}$ B. y-int. 0; x-int. 0 C. About $(0,0)$ D. HA $y = 0$
E. Inc. on $\left(-1/\sqrt{2}, 1/\sqrt{2}\right)$; dec. on $\left(-\infty, -1/\sqrt{2}\right), \left(1/\sqrt{2}, \infty\right)$
F. Loc. min. $f\left(-1/\sqrt{2}\right) = -1/\sqrt{2e}$; loc. max. $f\left(1/\sqrt{2}\right) = 1/\sqrt{2e}$
G. CU on $\left(-\sqrt{3/2}, 0\right), \left(\sqrt{3/2}, \infty\right)$; CD on $\left(-\infty, -\sqrt{3/2}\right), \left(0, \sqrt{3/2}\right)$;
IP $\left(\pm\sqrt{3/2}, \pm\sqrt{3/2}e^{-3/2}\right), (0,0)$
H.

73. A. $(-1, \infty)$ B. y-int. 0; x-int. 0
C. None D. VA $x = -1$
E. Inc. on $(0, \infty)$; dec. on $(-1, 0)$
F. Loc. min. $f(0) = 0$
G. CU on $(-1, \infty)$
H. See graph at right.

75. (a)

(b) $\lim_{x \to 0^+} x^{-x} = 1$

(c) Max. value $f(1/e) = e^{1/e} \approx 1.44$ (d) 1.0

77. (a)

(b) $\lim_{x \to 0^+} x^{1/x} = 0$, $\lim_{x \to \infty} x^{1/x} = 1$

(c) Max. value $f(e) = e^{1/e} \approx 1.44$ (d) IP at $x \approx 0.58, 4.37$

79.

For $c > 0$, $\lim_{x \to \infty} f(x) = 0$ and $\lim_{x \to -\infty} f(x) = -\infty$.
For $c < 0$, $\lim_{x \to \infty} f(x) = \infty$ and $\lim_{x \to -\infty} f(x) = 0$.
As $|c|$ increases, the maximum and minimum points and the IPs get closer to the origin.

81. 1   **87.** $\pi/6$ **89.** 56   **97.** $\frac{1}{3}$ **99.** (a) 0

CHAPTER 7 REVIEW ▪ PAGE 483

True-False Quiz

1. True   **3.** False   **5.** True   **7.** True   **9.** False
11. False   **13.** False   **15.** True   **17.** True

Exercises

1. No   **3.** (a) 7   (b) $\frac{1}{8}$

5.   **7.**

9.

11. (a) 9   (b) 2   **13.** $e^{1/3}$
15. ln ln 17   **17.** $\sqrt{1 + e}$
19. tan 1   **21.** $f'(t) = t + 2t \ln t$
23. $h'(\theta) = 2 \sec^2(2\theta) e^{\tan 2\theta}$ **25.** $y' = 5 \sec 5x$
27. $y' = (1 + c^2) e^{cx} \sin x$ **29.** $y' = 2 \tan x$
31. $y' = -\dfrac{e^{1/x}(1 + 2x)}{x^4}$ **33.** $y' = 3^{x \ln x}(\ln 3)(1 + \ln x)$
35. $H'(v) = (v/(1 + v^2)) + \tan^{-1}v$
37. $y' = 2x^2 \cosh(x^2) + \sinh(x^2)$
39. $y' = \cot x - \sin x \cos x$ **41.** $y' = -(1/x)[1 + 1/(\ln x)^2]$
43. $y' = 3 \tanh 3x$ **45.** $y' = (\cosh x)/\sqrt{\sinh^2 x - 1}$
47. $y' = \dfrac{-3 \sin(e^{\sqrt{\tan 3x}}) e^{\sqrt{\tan 3x}} \sec^2(3x)}{2\sqrt{\tan 3x}}$ **49.** $f'(x) = g'(x)e^{g(x)}$
51. $g'(x)/g(x)$ **53.** $2^x(\ln 2)^n$ **57.** $y = -x + 2$
59. $(-3, 0)$ **61.** (a) $y = \frac{1}{4}x + \frac{1}{4}(\ln 4 + 1)$ (b) $y = ex$
63. 0   **65.** 0   **67.** $-\infty$ **69.** -1 **71.** π **73.** 8
75. 0   **77.** $\frac{1}{2}$

79. A. $\{x \mid x \neq 0\}$ B. None
C. About $(0, 0)$ D. HA $y = 0$
E. Dec. on $(-\infty, 0)$ and $(0, \infty)$
F. None
G. CU on $(0, \infty)$; CD on $(-\infty, 0)$
H. See graph at right.

81. A. $(0, \infty)$ B. x-int. 1
C. None   D. None
E. Inc. on $(1/e, \infty)$; dec. on $(0, 1/e)$
F. Loc. min. $f(1/e) = -1/e$
G. CU on $(0, \infty)$
H. See graph at right.

83. A. $\mathbb{R}$ B. y-int. 0, x-int. 0   C. None   D. HA $y = 0$
E. Inc. on $\left(-\infty, \frac{1}{2}\right)$, dec. on $\left(\frac{1}{2}, \infty\right)$ F. Loc. max. $f\left(\frac{1}{2}\right) = 1/(2e)$
G. CU on $(1, \infty)$; CD on $(-\infty, 1)$; IP $(1, e^{-2})$
H.

85.

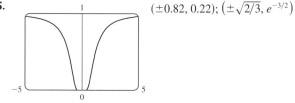

$(\pm 0.82, 0.22); (\pm\sqrt{2/3}, e^{-3/2})$

87. $v(t) = -Ae^{-ct}[c\cos(\omega t + \delta) + \omega\sin(\omega t + \delta)]$,
$a(t) = Ae^{-ct}[(c^2 - \omega^2)\cos(\omega t + \delta) + 2c\omega\sin(\omega t + \delta)]$

89. (a) $200(3.24)^t$ (b) $\approx 22{,}040$
(c) $\approx 25{,}910$ bacteria/h   (d) $(\ln 50)/(\ln 3.24) \approx 3.33$ h

91. 4.32 days   **93.** $\frac{1}{4}(1 - e^{-2})$ **95.** $\arctan e - \pi/4$

97. $2e^{\sqrt{x}} + C$ **99.** $\frac{1}{2}\ln|x^2 + 2x| + C$

101. $-\frac{1}{2}[\ln(\cos x)]^2 + C$ **103.** $2^{\tan\theta}/\ln 2 + C$

105. $-(1/x) - 2\ln|x| + x + C$ **109.** $e^{\sqrt{x}}/(2x)$

111. $\frac{1}{3}\ln 4$ **113.** $\pi^2/4$ **115.** $\frac{2}{3}$ **117.** $2/e$

121. $f(x) = e^{2x}(1 + 2x)/(1 - e^{-x})$

PROBLEMS PLUS ◾ **PAGE 487**

7. $1/\sqrt{2}$ **9.** $\frac{1}{2}$ **13.** $2\sqrt{e}$ **15.** $a \le e^{1/e}$

CHAPTER 8

EXERCISES 8.1 ◾ **PAGE 493**

1. $\frac{1}{3}x^3\ln x - \frac{1}{9}x^3 + C$ **3.** $\frac{1}{5}x\sin 5x + \frac{1}{25}\cos 5x + C$

5. $2(r - 2)e^{r/2} + C$

7. $-\dfrac{1}{\pi}x^2\cos\pi x + \dfrac{2}{\pi^2}x\sin\pi x + \dfrac{2}{\pi^3}\cos\pi x + C$

9. $\frac{1}{2}(2x + 1)\ln(2x + 1) - x + C$

11. $t\arctan 4t - \frac{1}{8}\ln(1 + 16t^2) + C$

13. $\frac{1}{2}t\tan 2t - \frac{1}{4}\ln|\sec 2t| + C$

15. $x(\ln x)^2 - 2x\ln x + 2x + C$

17. $\frac{1}{13}e^{2\theta}(2\sin 3\theta - 3\cos 3\theta) + C$

19. $\pi/3$ **21.** $1 - 1/e$ **23.** $\frac{1}{2} - \frac{1}{2}\ln 2$ **25.** $\frac{1}{4} - \frac{3}{4}e^{-2}$

27. $\frac{1}{6}(\pi + 6 - 3\sqrt{3})$ **29.** $\sin x(\ln\sin x - 1) + C$

31. $\frac{32}{5}(\ln 2)^2 - \frac{64}{25}\ln 2 + \frac{62}{125}$

33. $2\sqrt{x}\sin\sqrt{x} + 2\cos\sqrt{x} + C$ **35.** $-\frac{1}{2} - \pi/4$

37. $\frac{1}{2}(x^2 - 1)\ln(1 + x) - \frac{1}{4}x^2 + \frac{1}{2}x + \frac{3}{4} + C$

39. $(2x + 1)e^x + C$

41. $\frac{1}{3}x^2(1 + x^2)^{3/2} - \frac{2}{15}(1 + x^2)^{5/2} + C$

43. (b) $-\frac{1}{4}\cos x\sin^3 x + \frac{3}{8}x - \frac{3}{16}\sin 2x + C$

45. (b) $\frac{2}{3}, \frac{8}{15}$ **51.** $x(\ln x)^3 - 3x(\ln x)^2 + 6x\ln x - 6x + C$

53. $\frac{25}{4} - \frac{75}{4}e^{-2}$ **55.** 1.0475, 2.8731; 2.1828   **57.** $4 - 8/\pi$

59. $2\pi e$ **61.** $\frac{9}{2}\ln 3 - \frac{13}{9}$ **63.** $2 - e^{-t}(t^2 + 2t + 2)$ m
65. 2

EXERCISES 8.2 ◾ **PAGE 501**

1. $\frac{1}{5}\cos^5 x - \frac{1}{3}\cos^3 x + C$ **3.** $-\frac{11}{384}$

5. $\dfrac{1}{3\pi}\sin^3(\pi x) - \dfrac{2}{5\pi}\sin^5(\pi x) + \dfrac{1}{7\pi}\sin^7(\pi x) + C$

7. $\pi/4$ **9.** $3\pi/8$ **11.** $\frac{3}{2}\theta + 2\sin\theta + \frac{1}{4}\sin 2\theta + C$

13. $\pi/16$ **15.** $\frac{2}{45}\sqrt{\sin\alpha}(45 - 18\sin^2\alpha + 15\sin^4\alpha) + C$

17. $\frac{1}{2}\cos^2 x - \ln|\cos x| + C$ **19.** $\ln|\sin x| + 2\sin x + C$

21. $\frac{1}{2}\tan^2 x + C$ **23.** $\tan x - x + C$

25. $\frac{1}{5}\tan^5 t + \frac{2}{3}\tan^3 t + \tan t + C$ **27.** $\frac{117}{8}$

29. $\frac{1}{3}\sec^3 x - \sec x + C$

31. $\frac{1}{4}\sec^4 x - \tan^2 x + \ln|\sec x| + C$

33. $\frac{1}{6}\tan^6\theta + \frac{1}{4}\tan^4\theta + C$

35. $x\sec x - \ln|\sec x + \tan x| + C$ **37.** $\sqrt{3} - \frac{1}{3}\pi$

39. $\frac{1}{3}\csc^3\alpha - \frac{1}{5}\csc^5\alpha + C$ **41.** $\ln|\csc x - \cot x| + C$

43. $-\frac{1}{6}\cos 3x - \frac{1}{26}\cos 13x + C$ **45.** $\frac{1}{8}\sin 4\theta - \frac{1}{12}\sin 6\theta + C$

47. $\frac{1}{2}\sin 2x + C$ **49.** $\frac{1}{10}\tan^5(t^2) + C$

51. $\frac{1}{4}x^2 - \frac{1}{4}\sin(x^2)\cos(x^2) + C$ **53.** $\frac{1}{6}\sin 3x - \frac{1}{18}\sin 9x + C$

 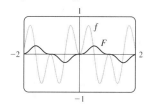

55. 0   **57.** 1   **59.** 0   **61.** $\pi^2/4$ **63.** $\pi(2\sqrt{2} - \frac{5}{2})$
65. $s = (1 - \cos^3\omega t)/(3\omega)$

EXERCISES 8.3 ◾ **PAGE 508**

1. $\sqrt{x^2 - 9}/(9x) + C$ **3.** $\frac{1}{3}(x^2 - 18)\sqrt{x^2 + 9} + C$

5. $\pi/24 + \sqrt{3}/8 - \frac{1}{4}$ **7.** $-\sqrt{25 - x^2}/(25x) + C$

9. $\ln(\sqrt{x^2 + 16} + x) + C$ **11.** $\frac{1}{4}\sin^{-1}(2x) + \frac{1}{2}x\sqrt{1 - 4x^2} + C$

13. $\frac{1}{6}\sec^{-1}(x/3) - \sqrt{x^2 - 9}/(2x^2) + C$

15. $\frac{1}{16}\pi a^4$ **17.** $\sqrt{x^2 - 7} + C$

19. $\ln\left|(\sqrt{1 + x^2} - 1)/x\right| + \sqrt{1 + x^2} + C$ **21.** $\frac{9}{500}\pi$

23. $\frac{9}{2}\sin^{-1}((x - 2)/3) + \frac{1}{2}(x - 2)\sqrt{5 + 4x - x^2} + C$

25. $\sqrt{x^2 + x + 1} - \frac{1}{2}\ln(\sqrt{x^2 + x + 1} + x + \frac{1}{2}) + C$

27. $\frac{1}{2}(x + 1)\sqrt{x^2 + 2x} - \frac{1}{2}\ln|x + 1 + \sqrt{x^2 + 2x}| + C$

29. $\frac{1}{4}\sin^{-1}(x^2) + \frac{1}{4}x^2\sqrt{1 - x^4} + C$

33. $\frac{1}{6}(\sqrt{48} - \sec^{-1} 7)$ **37.** 0.81, 2; 2.10

41. $r\sqrt{R^2 - r^2} + \pi r^2/2 - R^2\arcsin(r/R)$ **43.** $2\pi^2 R r^2$

EXERCISES 8.4 ◾ **PAGE 517**

1. (a) $\dfrac{A}{x + 3} + \dfrac{B}{3x + 1}$ (b) $\dfrac{A}{x} + \dfrac{B}{x + 1} + \dfrac{C}{(x + 1)^2}$

3. (a) $\dfrac{A}{x} + \dfrac{B}{x^2} + \dfrac{C}{x^3} + \dfrac{Dx + E}{x^2 + 4}$

(b) $\dfrac{A}{x + 3} + \dfrac{B}{(x + 3)^2} + \dfrac{C}{x - 3} + \dfrac{D}{(x - 3)^2}$

5. (a) $1 + \dfrac{A}{x-1} + \dfrac{B}{x+1} + \dfrac{Cx+D}{x^2+1}$

(b) $\dfrac{At+B}{t^2+1} + \dfrac{Ct+D}{t^2+4} + \dfrac{Et+F}{(t^2+4)^2}$

7. $x + 6\ln|x-6| + C$

9. $2\ln|x+5| - \ln|x-2| + C$ **11.** $\frac{1}{2}\ln\frac{3}{2}$

13. $a\ln|x-b| + C$ **15.** $\frac{7}{6} + \ln\frac{2}{3}$

17. $\frac{27}{5}\ln 2 - \frac{9}{5}\ln 3 \left(\text{or } \frac{9}{5}\ln\frac{8}{3}\right)$

19. $-\dfrac{1}{36}\ln|x+5| + \dfrac{1}{6}\dfrac{1}{x+5} + \dfrac{1}{36}\ln|x-1| + C$

21. $\frac{1}{2}x^2 - 2\ln(x^2+4) + 2\tan^{-1}(x/2) + C$

23. $2\ln|x| + (1/x) + 3\ln|x+2| + C$

25. $\ln|x-1| - \frac{1}{2}\ln(x^2+9) - \frac{1}{3}\tan^{-1}(x/3) + C$

27. $\frac{1}{2}\ln(x^2+1) + (1/\sqrt{2})\tan^{-1}(x/\sqrt{2}) + C$

29. $\frac{1}{2}\ln(x^2+2x+5) + \frac{3}{2}\tan^{-1}\left(\dfrac{x+1}{2}\right) + C$

31. $\frac{1}{3}\ln|x-1| - \frac{1}{6}\ln(x^2+x+1) - \dfrac{1}{\sqrt{3}}\tan^{-1}\dfrac{2x+1}{\sqrt{3}} + C$

33. $\frac{1}{4}\ln\frac{8}{3}$ **35.** $\frac{1}{16}\ln|x| - \frac{1}{32}\ln(x^2+4) + \dfrac{1}{8(x^2+4)} + C$

37. $\frac{7}{8}\sqrt{2}\,\tan^{-1}\left(\dfrac{x-2}{\sqrt{2}}\right) + \dfrac{3x-8}{4(x^2-4x+6)} + C$

39. $\ln\left|\dfrac{\sqrt{x+1}-1}{\sqrt{x+1}+1}\right| + C$

41. $2 + \ln\frac{25}{9}$ **43.** $\frac{3}{10}(x^2+1)^{5/3} - \frac{3}{4}(x^2+1)^{2/3} + C$

45. $2\sqrt{x} + 3\sqrt[3]{x} + 6\sqrt[6]{x} + 6\ln|\sqrt[6]{x}-1| + C$

47. $\ln\left[\dfrac{(e^x+2)^2}{e^x+1}\right] + C$

49. $\ln|\tan t + 1| - \ln|\tan t + 2| + C$

51. $\left(x - \frac{1}{2}\right)\ln(x^2-x+2) - 2x + \sqrt{7}\tan^{-1}\left(\dfrac{2x-1}{\sqrt{7}}\right) + C$

53. $-\frac{1}{2}\ln 3 \approx -0.55$

55. $\frac{1}{2}\ln\left|\dfrac{x-2}{x}\right| + C$ **59.** $\frac{1}{5}\ln\left|\dfrac{2\tan(x/2)-1}{\tan(x/2)+2}\right| + C$

61. $4\ln\frac{2}{3} + 2$ **63.** $-1 + \frac{11}{3}\ln 2$

65. $t = -\ln P - \frac{1}{9}\ln(0.9P + 900) + C$, where $C \approx 10.23$

67. (a) $\dfrac{24{,}110}{4879}\dfrac{1}{5x+2} - \dfrac{668}{323}\dfrac{1}{2x+1} - \dfrac{9438}{80{,}155}\dfrac{1}{3x-7} +$

$\dfrac{1}{260{,}015}\dfrac{22{,}098x + 48{,}935}{x^2+x+5}$

(b) $\dfrac{4822}{4879}\ln|5x+2| - \dfrac{334}{323}\ln|2x+1| - \dfrac{3146}{80{,}155}\ln|3x-7| +$

$\dfrac{11{,}049}{260{,}015}\ln(x^2+x+5) + \dfrac{75{,}772}{260{,}015\sqrt{19}}\tan^{-1}\dfrac{2x+1}{\sqrt{19}} + C$

The CAS omits the absolute value signs and the constant of integration.

1. $\sin x + \frac{1}{3}\sin^3 x + C$

3. $\sin x + \ln|\csc x - \cot x| + C$

5. $4 - \ln 9$ **7.** $e^{\pi/4} - e^{-\pi/4}$

9. $\frac{243}{5}\ln 3 - \frac{242}{25}$ **11.** $\frac{1}{2}\ln(x^2-4x+5) + \tan^{-1}(x-2) + C$

13. $\frac{1}{8}\cos^8\theta - \frac{1}{6}\cos^6\theta + C$ (or $\frac{1}{4}\sin^4\theta - \frac{1}{3}\sin^6\theta + \frac{1}{8}\sin^8\theta + C$)

15. $x/\sqrt{1-x^2} + C$

17. $\frac{1}{4}x^2 - \frac{1}{2}x\sin x\cos x + \frac{1}{4}\sin^2 x + C$
(or $\frac{1}{4}x^2 - \frac{1}{4}x\sin 2x - \frac{1}{8}\cos 2x + C$)

19. $e^{e^x} + C$ **21.** $(x+1)\arctan\sqrt{x} - \sqrt{x} + C$

23. $\frac{4097}{45}$ **25.** $3x + \frac{23}{3}\ln|x-4| - \frac{5}{3}\ln|x+2| + C$

27. $x - \ln(1+e^x) + C$ **29.** $15 + 7\ln\frac{2}{7}$

31. $\sin^{-1}x - \sqrt{1-x^2} + C$

33. $2\sin^{-1}\left(\dfrac{x+1}{2}\right) + \dfrac{x+1}{2}\sqrt{3-2x-x^2} + C$

35. 0 **37.** $\pi/8 - \frac{1}{4}$ **39.** $\ln|\sec\theta - 1| - \ln|\sec\theta| + C$

41. $\theta\tan\theta - \frac{1}{2}\theta^2 - \ln|\sec\theta| + C$ **43.** $\frac{2}{3}(1+e^x)^{3/2} + C$

45. $-\frac{1}{3}(x^3+1)e^{-x^3} + C$

47. $\ln|x-1| - 3(x-1)^{-1} - \frac{3}{2}(x-1)^{-2} - \frac{1}{3}(x-1)^{-3} + C$

49. $\ln\left|\dfrac{\sqrt{4x+1}-1}{\sqrt{4x+1}+1}\right| + C$ **51.** $-\ln\left|\dfrac{\sqrt{4x^2+1}+1}{2x}\right| + C$

53. $\dfrac{1}{m}x^2\cosh(mx) - \dfrac{2}{m^2}x\sinh(mx) + \dfrac{2}{m^3}\cosh(mx) + C$

55. $2\ln\sqrt{x} - 2\ln(1+\sqrt{x}) + C$

57. $\frac{3}{7}(x+c)^{7/3} - \frac{3}{4}c(x+c)^{4/3} + C$

59. $\sin(\sin x) - \frac{1}{3}\sin^3(\sin x) + C$ **61.** $2(x - 2\sqrt{x} + 2)e^{\sqrt{x}} + C$

63. $-\tan^{-1}(\cos^2 x) + C$ **65.** $\frac{2}{3}[(x+1)^{3/2} - x^{3/2}] + C$

67. $\sqrt{2} - 2/\sqrt{3} + \ln(2 + \sqrt{3}) - \ln(1 + \sqrt{2})$

69. $e^x - \ln(1+e^x) + C$

71. $-\sqrt{1-x^2} + \frac{1}{2}(\arcsin x)^2 + C$

73. $\frac{1}{8}\ln|x-2| - \frac{1}{16}\ln(x^2+4) - \frac{1}{8}\tan^{-1}(x/2) + C$

75. $2(x-2)\sqrt{1+e^x} + 2\ln\dfrac{\sqrt{1+e^x}+1}{\sqrt{1+e^x}-1} + C$

77. $\frac{2}{3}\tan^{-1}(x^{3/2}) + C$

79. $\frac{1}{3}x\sin^3 x + \frac{1}{3}\cos x - \frac{1}{9}\cos^3 x + C$ **81.** $xe^{x^2} + C$

1. $(-1/x)\sqrt{7-2x^2} - \sqrt{2}\sin^{-1}(\sqrt{2}x/\sqrt{7}) + C$

3. $\dfrac{1}{2\pi}\sec(\pi x)\tan(\pi x) + \dfrac{1}{2\pi}\ln|\sec(\pi x) + \tan(\pi x)| + C$

5. $\pi/4$ **7.** $\dfrac{1}{2\pi}\tan^2(\pi x) + \dfrac{1}{\pi}\ln|\cos(\pi x)| + C$

9. $-\sqrt{4x^2+9}/(9x) + C$ **11.** $e - 2$

13. $-\frac{1}{2}\tan^2(1/z) - \ln|\cos(1/z)| + C$

15. $\frac{1}{2}(e^{2x}+1)\arctan(e^x) - \frac{1}{2}e^x + C$

17. $\dfrac{2y-1}{8}\sqrt{6+4y-4y^2} + \frac{7}{8}\sin^{-1}\left(\dfrac{2y-1}{\sqrt{7}}\right)$

$- \frac{1}{12}(6+4y-4y^2)^{3/2} + C$

19. $\frac{1}{9}\sin^3 x\,[3\ln(\sin x) - 1] + C$

21. $\frac{1}{2\sqrt{3}}\ln\left|\dfrac{e^x + \sqrt{3}}{e^x - \sqrt{3}}\right| + C$

23. $\frac{1}{4}\tan x\sec^3 x + \frac{3}{8}\tan x\sec x + \frac{3}{8}\ln|\sec x + \tan x| + C$

25. $\frac{1}{2}(\ln x)\sqrt{4 + (\ln x)^2} + 2\ln\left[\ln x + \sqrt{4 + (\ln x)^2}\right] + C$

27. $\sqrt{e^{2x} - 1} - \cos^{-1}(e^{-x}) + C$

29. $\frac{1}{5}\ln\left|x^5 + \sqrt{x^{10} - 2}\right| + C$ **31.** $2\pi^2$

35. $\frac{1}{3}\tan x\sec^2 x + \frac{2}{3}\tan x + C$

37. $\frac{1}{4}x(x^2 + 2)\sqrt{x^2 + 4} - 2\ln\left(\sqrt{x^2 + 4} + x\right) + C$

39. $\frac{1}{10}(1 + 2x)^{5/2} - \frac{1}{6}(1 + 2x)^{3/2} + C$

41. $-\ln|\cos x| - \frac{1}{2}\tan^2 x + \frac{1}{4}\tan^4 x + C$

43. (a) $-\ln\left|\dfrac{1 + \sqrt{1 - x^2}}{x}\right| + C$;

both have domain $(-1, 0) \cup (0, 1)$

45. $F(x) = \frac{1}{2}\ln(x^2 - x + 1) - \frac{1}{2}\ln(x^2 + x + 1)$;

max. at -1, min. at 1; IP at -1.7, 0, and 1.7

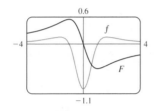

47. $F(x) = -\frac{1}{10}\sin^3 x\cos^7 x - \frac{3}{80}\sin x\cos^7 x + \frac{1}{160}\sin x\cos^5 x + \frac{1}{128}\sin x\cos^3 x + \frac{3}{256}\sin x\cos x + \frac{3}{256}x$;

max. at π, min. at 0; IP at 0.7, $\pi/2$, and 2.5

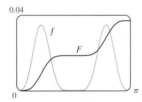

EXERCISES 8.7 ■ PAGE 541

1. (a) $L_2 = 6$, $R_2 = 12$, $M_2 \approx 9.6$
(b) L_2 is an underestimate, R_2 and M_2 are overestimates.
(c) $T_2 = 9 < I$ (d) $L_n < T_n < I < M_n < R_n$

3. (a) $T_4 \approx 0.895759$ (underestimate)
(b) $M_4 \approx 0.908907$ (overestimate)
$T_4 < I < M_4$

5. (a) 5.932957, $E_M \approx -0.063353$
(b) 5.869247, $E_S \approx 0.000357$

7. (a) 2.413790 (b) 2.411453 (c) 2.412232

9. (a) 0.146879 (b) 0.147391 (c) 0.147219

11. (a) 0.451948 (b) 0.451991 (c) 0.451976

13. (a) 4.513618 (b) 4.748256 (c) 4.675111

15. (a) -0.495333 (b) -0.543321 (c) -0.526123

17. (a) 1.064275 (b) 1.067416 (c) 1.074915

19. (a) $T_8 \approx 0.902333$, $M_8 \approx 0.905620$
(b) $|E_T| \leq 0.0078$, $|E_M| \leq 0.0039$
(c) $n = 71$ for T_n, $n = 50$ for M_n

21. (a) $T_{10} \approx 1.983524$, $E_T \approx 0.016476$;
$M_{10} \approx 2.008248$, $E_M \approx -0.008248$;
$S_{10} \approx 2.000110$, $E_S \approx -0.000110$
(b) $|E_T| \leq 0.025839$, $|E_M| \leq 0.012919$, $|E_S| \leq 0.000170$
(c) $n = 509$ for T_n, $n = 360$ for M_n, $n = 22$ for S_n

23. (a) 2.8 (b) 7.954926518 (c) 0.2894
(d) 7.954926521 (e) The actual error is much smaller.
(f) 10.9 (g) 7.953789422 (h) 0.0593
(i) The actual error is smaller.   (j) $n \geq 50$

25.

n	L_n	R_n	T_n	M_n
5	0.742943	1.286599	1.014771	0.992621
10	0.867782	1.139610	1.003696	0.998152
20	0.932967	1.068881	1.000924	0.999538

n	E_L	E_R	E_T	E_M
5	0.257057	-0.286599	-0.014771	0.007379
10	0.132218	-0.139610	-0.003696	0.001848
20	0.067033	-0.068881	-0.000924	0.000462

Observations are the same as after Example 1.

27.

n	T_n	M_n	S_n
6	6.695473	6.252572	6.403292
12	6.474023	6.363008	6.400206

n	E_T	E_M	E_S
6	-0.295473	0.147428	-0.003292
12	-0.074023	0.036992	-0.000206

Observations are the same as after Example 1.

29. (a) 19.8 (b) 20.6 (c) $20.5\overline{3}$
31. (a) 23.44 (b) $0.341\overline{3}$ **33.** $37.7\overline{3}$ ft/s
35. $10{,}177$ megawatt-hours   **37.** 828 **39.** 6.0 **41.** 59.4
43.

[graph of y vs x, with shaded regions between marks at 0.5, 1, 1.5, 2]

EXERCISES 8.8 ■ PAGE 551

Abbreviations: C, convergent; D, divergent

1. (a) Infinite interval   (b) Infinite discontinuity
(c) Infinite discontinuity   (d) Infinite interval
3. $\frac{1}{2} - 1/(2t^2)$; 0.495, 0.49995, 0.4999995; 0.5

5. $\frac{1}{12}$ **7.** D   **9.** $2e^{-2}$ **11.** D   **13.** 0   **15.** D

17. D   **19.** $\frac{1}{25}$ **21.** D   **23.** $\pi/9$

25. $\frac{1}{2}$ **27.** D   **29.** $\frac{32}{3}$ **31.** D   **33.** $\frac{75}{4}$

35. D   **37.** $-2/e$ **39.** $\frac{8}{3}\ln 2 - \frac{8}{9}$

41. e **43.** $2\pi/3$

45. Infinite area

47. (a)

t	$\int_1^t [(\sin^2 x)/x^2]\, dx$
2	0.447453
5	0.577101
10	0.621306
100	0.668479
1,000	0.672957
10,000	0.673407

It appears that the integral is convergent.

(c)

49. C   **51.** D   **53.** D   **55.** π **57.** $p < 1,\ 1/(1-p)$

59. $p > -1,\ -1/(p+1)^2$ **65.** $\sqrt{2GM/R}$

67. (a)

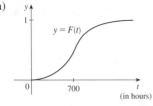

(b) The rate at which the fraction $F(t)$ increases as t increases
(c) 1; all bulbs burn out eventually

69. 1000

71. (a) $F(s) = 1/s,\ s > 0$ (b) $F(s) = 1/(s-1),\ s > 1$

(c) $F(s) = 1/s^2,\ s > 0$

77. $C = 1;\ \ln 2$ **79.** No

True-False Quiz

1. False   **3.** False   **5.** False   **7.** False

9. (a) True   (b) False   **11.** False   **13.** False

Exercises

1. $5 + 10\ln\frac{2}{3}$ **3.** $\ln 2$ **5.** $\frac{2}{15}$

7. $-\cos(\ln t) + C$ **9.** $\frac{64}{5}\ln 4 - \frac{124}{25}$

11. $\sqrt{3} - \frac{1}{3}\pi$ **13.** $3e^{\sqrt[3]{x}}\left(\sqrt[3]{x^2} - 2\sqrt[3]{x} + 2\right) + C$

15. $-\frac{1}{2}\ln|x| + \frac{3}{2}\ln|x+2| + C$

17. $x\sec x - \ln|\sec x + \tan x| + C$

19. $\frac{1}{18}\ln(9x^2 + 6x + 5) + \frac{1}{9}\tan^{-1}\left[\frac{1}{2}(3x+1)\right] + C$

21. $\ln\left|x - 2 + \sqrt{x^2 - 4x}\right| + C$

23. $\ln\left|\dfrac{\sqrt{x^2+1}-1}{x}\right| + C$

25. $\frac{3}{2}\ln(x^2+1) - 3\tan^{-1}x + \sqrt{2}\tan^{-1}(x/\sqrt{2}) + C$

27. $\frac{2}{5}$ **29.** 0   **31.** $6 - \frac{3}{2}\pi$

33. $\dfrac{x}{\sqrt{4-x^2}} - \sin^{-1}\left(\dfrac{x}{2}\right) + C$

35. $4\sqrt{1+\sqrt{x}} + C$ **37.** $\frac{1}{2}\sin 2x - \frac{1}{8}\cos 4x + C$

39. $\frac{1}{8}e - \frac{1}{4}$ **41.** $\frac{1}{36}$ **43.** D

45. $4\ln 4 - 8$ **47.** $-\frac{4}{3}$ **49.** $\pi/4$

51. $(x+1)\ln(x^2+2x+2) + 2\arctan(x+1) - 2x + C$

53. 0

55. $\frac{1}{4}(2x-1)\sqrt{4x^2-4x-3} - $
               $\ln\left|2x-1+\sqrt{4x^2-4x-3}\right| + C$

57. $\frac{1}{2}\sin x\sqrt{4+\sin^2 x} + 2\ln\left(\sin x + \sqrt{4+\sin^2 x}\right) + C$

61. No

63. (a) 1.925444   (b) 1.920915   (c) 1.922470

65. (a) $0.01348,\ n \geqslant 368$ (b) $0.00674,\ n \geqslant 260$

67. 8.6 mi

69. (a) 3.8   (b) 1.7867, 0.000646   (c) $n \geqslant 30$

71. C   **73.** 2   **75.** $\frac{3}{16}\pi^2$

1. About 1.85 inches from the center   **3.** 0

7. $f(\pi) = -\pi/2$ **11.** $(b^b a^{-a})^{1/(b-a)}e^{-1}$

13. $2 - \sin^{-1}(2/\sqrt{5})$

---

1. $4\sqrt{5}$ **3.** $\int_0^{2\pi}\sqrt{1+\sin^2 x}\,dx$ **5.** $\int_1^4\sqrt{9y^4+6y^2+2}\,dy$

7. $\frac{2}{243}(82\sqrt{82}-1)$ **9.** $\frac{1261}{240}$ **11.** $\frac{32}{3}$

13. $\ln(\sqrt{2}+1)$ **15.** $\ln 3 - \frac{1}{2}$

17. $\sqrt{1+e^2} - \sqrt{2} + \ln(\sqrt{1+e^2}-1) - 1 - \ln(\sqrt{2}-1)$

19. $\sqrt{2} + \ln(1+\sqrt{2})$ **21.** $\frac{46}{3}$ **23.** 5.115840

25. 1.569619

27. (a), (b)

$L_1 = 4,$
$L_2 \approx 6.43,$
$L_4 \approx 7.50$

(c) $\int_0^4 \sqrt{1 + [4(3 - x)/(3(4 - x)^{2/3})]^2} \, dx$ (d) 7.7988

29. $\sqrt{5} - \ln\left(\frac{1}{2}(1 + \sqrt{5})\right) - \sqrt{2} + \ln\left(1 + \sqrt{2}\right)$

31. 6

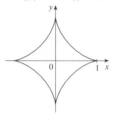

33. $s(x) = \frac{2}{27}\left[(1 + 9x)^{3/2} - 10\sqrt{10}\right]$ **35.** $2\sqrt{2}\left(\sqrt{1 + x} - 1\right)$
37. 209.1 m   **39.** 29.36 in.   **41.** 12.4

EXERCISES 9.2 ■ **PAGE 573**

1. (a) $\int_0^1 2\pi x^4 \sqrt{1 + 16x^6} \, dx$ (b) $\int_0^1 2\pi x \sqrt{1 + 16x^6} \, dx$

3. (a) $\int_0^1 2\pi \tan^{-1}x \sqrt{1 + \dfrac{1}{(1 + x^2)^2}} \, dx$

(b) $\int_0^1 2\pi x \sqrt{1 + \dfrac{1}{(1 + x^2)^2}} \, dx$

5. $\frac{1}{27}\pi\left(145\sqrt{145} - 1\right)$ **7.** $\frac{98}{3}\pi$
9. $2\sqrt{1 + \pi^2} + (2/\pi)\ln\left(\pi + \sqrt{1 + \pi^2}\right)$ **11.** $\frac{21}{2}\pi$
13. $\frac{1}{27}\pi\left(145\sqrt{145} - 10\sqrt{10}\right)$ **15.** πa^2
17. 9.023754   **19.** 13.527296
21. $\frac{1}{4}\pi\left[4\ln(\sqrt{17} + 4) - 4\ln(\sqrt{2} + 1) - \sqrt{17} + 4\sqrt{2}\right]$
23. $\frac{1}{6}\pi\left[\ln(\sqrt{10} + 3) + 3\sqrt{10}\right]$
27. (a) $\frac{1}{3}\pi a^2$ (b) $\frac{56}{45}\pi\sqrt{3}a^2$
29. (a) $2\pi\left[b^2 + \dfrac{a^2 b \sin^{-1}\left(\sqrt{a^2 - b^2}/a\right)}{\sqrt{a^2 - b^2}}\right]$

(b) $2\pi\left[a^2 + \dfrac{ab^2 \sin^{-1}\left(\sqrt{b^2 - a^2}/b\right)}{\sqrt{b^2 - a^2}}\right]$

31. $\int_a^b 2\pi[c - f(x)]\sqrt{1 + [f'(x)]^2} \, dx$ **33.** $4\pi^2 r^2$

EXERCISES 9.3 ■ **PAGE 583**

1. (a) 187.5 lb/ft²   (b) 1875 lb   (c) 562.5 lb
3. 6000 lb   **5.** 6.7×10^4 N   **7.** 9.8×10^3 N
9. 1.2×10^4 lb   **11.** $\frac{2}{3}\delta ah$ **13.** 5.27×10^5 N
15. (a) 314 N   (b) 353 N
17. (a) 5.63×10^3 lb   (b) 5.06×10^4 lb
(c) 4.88×10^4 lb   (d) 3.03×10^5 lb

19. 2.5×10^5 N   **21.** $230; \frac{23}{7}$ **23.** $10; 1; \left(\frac{1}{21}, \frac{10}{21}\right)$

25. $(0, 1.6)$ **27.** $\left(\dfrac{1}{e - 1}, \dfrac{e + 1}{4}\right)$ **29.** $\left(\frac{9}{20}, \frac{9}{20}\right)$

31. $\left(\dfrac{\pi\sqrt{2} - 4}{4(\sqrt{2} - 1)}, \dfrac{1}{4(\sqrt{2} - 1)}\right)$ **33.** $(2, 0)$

35. $60; 160; \left(\frac{8}{3}, 1\right)$ **37.** $(0.781, 1.330)$ **41.** $\left(0, \frac{1}{12}\right)$
45. $\frac{1}{3}\pi r^2 h$

EXERCISES 9.4 ■ **PAGE 589**

1. $38,000   **3.** $43,866,933.33   **5.** $407.25
7. $12,000   **9.** 3727; $37,753
11. $\frac{2}{3}(16\sqrt{2} - 8) \approx$ $9.75 million   **13.** $\dfrac{(1 - k)(b^{2-k} - a^{2-k})}{(2 - k)(b^{1-k} - a^{1-k})}$
15. 1.19×10^{-4} cm³/s
17. 6.60 L/min   **19.** 5.77 L/min

EXERCISES 9.5 ■ **PAGE 596**

1. (a) The probability that a randomly chosen tire will have a lifetime between 30,000 and 40,000 miles
(b) The probability that a randomly chosen tire will have a lifetime of at least 25,000 miles
3. (a) $f(x) \geqslant 0$ for all x and $\int_{-\infty}^{\infty} f(x) \, dx = 1$
(b) $1 - \frac{3}{8}\sqrt{3} \approx 0.35$
5. (a) $1/\pi$ (b) $\frac{1}{2}$
7. (a) $f(x) \geqslant 0$ for all x and $\int_{-\infty}^{\infty} f(x) \, dx = 1$ (b) 5
11. (a) $e^{-4/2.5} \approx 0.20$ (b) $1 - e^{-2/2.5} \approx 0.55$ (c) If you aren't served within 10 minutes, you get a free hamburger.
13. $\approx 44\%$
15. (a) 0.0668   (b) $\approx 5.21\%$
17. ≈ 0.9545
19. (b) 0; a_0 (c)

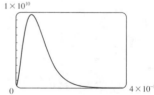

(d) $1 - 41e^{-8} \approx 0.986$ (e) $\frac{3}{2}a_0$

CHAPTER 9 REVIEW ■ **PAGE 598**

Exercises

1. $\frac{15}{2}$ **3.** (a) $\frac{21}{16}$ (b) $\frac{41}{10}\pi$ **5.** 3.292287   **7.** $\frac{124}{5}$
9. ≈ 458 lb   **11.** $\left(\frac{8}{5}, 1\right)$ **13.** $\left(2, \frac{2}{3}\right)$ **15.** $2\pi^2$
17. $7166.67

19. (a) $f(x) \geqslant 0$ for all x and $\int_{-\infty}^{\infty} f(x) \, dx = 1$
(b) ≈ 0.3455 (c) 5, yes

21. (a) $1 - e^{-3/8} \approx 0.31$ (b) $e^{-5/4} \approx 0.29$
(c) $8\ln 2 \approx 5.55$ min

PROBLEMS PLUS ▪ PAGE 600

1. $\frac{2}{3}\pi - \frac{1}{2}\sqrt{3}$

3. (a) $2\pi r(r \pm d)$ (b) $\approx 3.36 \times 10^6 \text{ mi}^2$
(d) $\approx 7.84 \times 10^7 \text{ mi}^2$

5. (a) $P(z) = P_0 + g \int_0^z \rho(x)\, dx$
(b) $(P_0 - \rho_0 gH)(\pi r^2) + \rho_0 gHe^{L/H} \int_{-r}^{r} e^{x/H} \cdot 2\sqrt{r^2 - x^2}\, dx$

7. Height $\sqrt{2}\, b$, volume $\left(\frac{28}{27}\sqrt{6} - 2\right)\pi b^3$ **9.** 0.14 m

11. $2/\pi, 1/\pi$

CHAPTER 10

EXERCISES 10.1 ▪ PAGE 607

3. (a) $\frac{1}{2}, -1$ **5.** (d)

7. (a) It must be either 0 or decreasing
(c) $y = 0$ (d) $y = 1/(x + 2)$

9. (a) $0 < P < 4200$ (b) $P > 4200$
(c) $P = 0, P = 4200$

13. (a) At the beginning; stays positive, but decreases
(c)

EXERCISES 10.2 ▪ PAGE 614

1. (a)   (b) $y = 0,$
$y = 2,$
$y = -2$

3. III **5.** IV

7.   **9.**

11.   **13.**

15.

17. $-2 \le c \le 2; -2, 0, 2$

19. (a) (i) 1.4 (ii) 1.44 (iii) 1.4641
(b)   Underestimates

(c) (i) 0.0918 (ii) 0.0518 (iii) 0.0277
It appears that the error is also halved (approximately).
21. $-1, -3, -6.5, -12.25$ **23.** 1.7616
25. (a) (i) 3 (ii) 2.3928 (iii) 2.3701 (iv) 2.3681
(c) (i) -0.6321 (ii) -0.0249 (iii) -0.0022 (iv) -0.0002
It appears that the error is also divided by 10 (approximately).
27. (a), (d) (b) 3
  (c) Yes; $Q = 3$
(e) 2.77 C

EXERCISES 10.3 ▪ PAGE 622

1. $y = Kx$ **3.** $y = K\sqrt{x^2 + 1}$
5. $y + \ln|\sec y| = \frac{1}{3}x^3 + x + C$
7. $y = \pm\sqrt{[3(te^t - e^t + C)]^{2/3} - 1}$ **9.** $u = Ae^{2t + t^2/2} - 1$
11. $y = -\sqrt{x^2 + 9}$ **13.** $\cos x + x\sin x = y^2 + \frac{1}{3}e^{3y} + \frac{2}{3}$
15. $u = -\sqrt{t^2 + \tan t + 25}$ **17.** $y = \dfrac{4a}{\sqrt{3}}\sin x - a$
19. $y = e^{x^2/2}$ **21.** $y = Ke^x - x - 1$
23. (a) $\sin^{-1}y = x^2 + C$
(b) $y = \sin(x^2)$, $-\sqrt{\pi/2} \le x \le \sqrt{\pi/2}$ (c) No

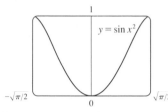

25. $\cos y = \cos x - 1$

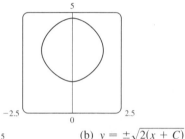

27. (a), (c)   (b) $y = \pm\sqrt{2(x + C)}$

29. $y = Cx^2$ **31.** $x^2 - y^2 = C$

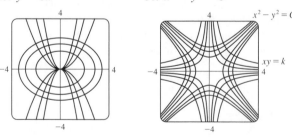

33. $Q(t) = 3 - 3e^{-4t}$; 3   **35.** $P(t) = M - Me^{-kt}$; M
37. (a) $x = a - \dfrac{4}{(kt + 2/\sqrt{a})^2}$
(b) $t = \dfrac{2}{k\sqrt{a - b}}\left(\tan^{-1}\sqrt{\dfrac{b}{a - b}} - \tan^{-1}\sqrt{\dfrac{b - x}{a - b}}\right)$
39. (a) $C(t) = (C_0 - r/k)e^{-kt} + r/k$
(b) r/k; the concentration approaches r/k regardless of the value of C_0
41. (a) $15e^{-t/100}$ kg   (b) $15e^{-0.2} \approx 12.3$ kg

43. About 4.9%   **45.** g/k
47. (a) $dA/dt = k\sqrt{A}\,(M - A)$ (b) $A(t) = M\left(\dfrac{Ce^{\sqrt{M}kt} - 1}{Ce^{\sqrt{M}kt} + 1}\right)^2$,
where $C = \dfrac{\sqrt{M} + \sqrt{A_0}}{\sqrt{M} - \sqrt{A_0}}$ and $A_0 = A(0)$

EXERCISES 10.4 ▪ PAGE 634

1. (a) 100; 0.05   (b) Where P is close to 0 or 100;
on the line $P = 50$; $0 < P_0 < 100$; $P_0 > 100$
(c)

Solutions approach 100; some increase and some decrease, some
have an inflection point but others don't; solutions with $P_0 = 20$
and $P_0 = 40$ have inflection points at $P = 50$
(d) $P = 0$, $P = 100$; other solutions move away from $P = 0$ and
toward $P = 100$
3. (a) 3.23×10^7 kg   (b) ≈ 1.55 years
5. (a) $dP/dt = \frac{1}{265}P(1 - P/100)$, P in billions
(b) 5.49 billion   (c) In billions: 7.81, 27.72
(d) In billions: 5.48, 7.61, 22.41
7. (a) $dy/dt = ky(1 - y)$ (b) $y = \dfrac{y_0}{y_0 + (1 - y_0)e^{-kt}}$
(c) 3:36 PM
11. $P_E(t) = 1578.3(1.0933)^t + 94{,}000$;
$P_L(t) = \dfrac{32{,}658.5}{1 + 12.75e^{-0.1706t}} + 94{,}000$

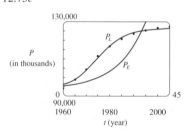

13. (a) $P(t) = \dfrac{m}{k} + \left(P_0 - \dfrac{m}{k}\right)e^{kt}$ (b) $m < kP_0$
(c) $m = kP_0$, $m > kP_0$ (d) Declining
15. (a) Fish are caught at a rate of 15 per week.
(b) See part (d)   (c) $P = 250$, $P = 750$
(d)

$0 < P_0 < 250$: $P \to 0$;
$P_0 = 250$: $P \to 250$;
$P_0 > 250$: $P \to 750$

(e) $P(t) = \dfrac{250 - 750ke^{t/25}}{1 - ke^{t/25}}$

where $k = \frac{1}{11}, -\frac{1}{9}$

17. (b)

$0 < P_0 < 200: P \to 0$;
$P_0 = 200: P \to 200$;
$P_0 > 200: P \to 1000$

(c) $P(t) = \dfrac{m(K - P_0) + K(P_0 - m)e^{(K-m)(k/K)t}}{K - P_0 + (P_0 - m)e^{(K-m)(k/K)t}}$

19. (a) $P(t) = P_0 e^{(k/r)[\sin(rt - \phi) + \sin \phi]}$ (b) Does not exist

EXERCISES 10.5 ▪ PAGE 642

1. Yes **3.** No **5.** $y = \frac{2}{3}e^x + Ce^{-2x}$

7. $y = x^2 \ln|x| + Cx^2$ **9.** $y = \frac{2}{3}\sqrt{x} + C/x$

11. $y = \dfrac{\int \sin(x^2)\,dx + C}{\sin x}$ **13.** $u = \dfrac{t^2 + 2t + 2C}{2(t + 1)}$

15. $y = -x - 1 + 3e^x$ **17.** $v = t^3 e^{t^2} + 5e^{t^2}$

19. $y = -x \cos x - x$

21. $y = \dfrac{(x - 1)e^x + C}{x^2}$

25. $y = \pm\left(Cx^4 + \dfrac{2}{5x}\right)^{-1/2}$

27. (a) $I(t) = 4 - 4e^{-5t}$ (b) $4 - 4e^{-1/2} \approx 1.57$ A

29. $Q(t) = 3(1 - e^{-4t})$, $I(t) = 12e^{-4t}$

31. $P(t) = M + Ce^{-kt}$

33. $y = \frac{2}{5}(100 + 2t) - 40{,}000(100 + 2t)^{-3/2}$; 0.2275 kg/L

35. (b) mg/c (c) $(mg/c)[t + (m/c)e^{-ct/m}] - m^2g/c^2$

EXERCISES 10.6 ▪ PAGE 648

1. (a) $x =$ predators, $y =$ prey; growth is restricted only by predators, which feed only on prey.
(b) $x =$ prey, $y =$ predators; growth is restricted by carrying capacity and by predators, which feed only on prey.

3. (a) The rabbit population starts at about 300, increases to 2400, then decreases back to 300. The fox population starts at 100, decreases to about 20, increases to about 315, decreases to 100, and the cycle starts again.

(b)

5.

9. (a) Population stabilizes at 5000.
(b) (i) $W = 0$, $R = 0$: Zero populations
(ii) $W = 0$, $R = 5000$: In the absence of wolves, the rabbit population is always 5000.
(iii) $W = 64$, $R = 1000$: Both populations are stable.
(c) The populations stabilize at 1000 rabbits and 64 wolves.

(d)

CHAPTER 10 REVIEW ▪ PAGE 651

True-False Quiz

1. True **3.** False **5.** True **7.** True

Exercises

1. (a)

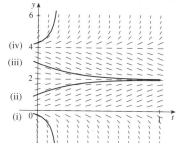

(b) $0 \le c \le 4$;
$y = 0, y = 2, y = 4$

3. (a)

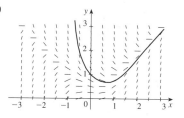

$y(0.3) \approx 0.8$

(b) 0.75676
(c) $y = x$ and $y = -x$; there is a local maximum or minimum
5. $y = (\frac{1}{2}x^2 + C)e^{-\sin x}$ **7.** $y = \pm\sqrt{\ln(x^2 + 2x^{3/2} + C)}$
9. $r(t) = 5e^{t-t^2}$ **11.** $y = \frac{1}{2}x(\ln x)^2 + 2x$ **13.** $x = C - \frac{1}{2}y^2$
15. (a) $P(t) = \dfrac{2000}{1 + 19e^{-0.1t}}$; ≈ 560 (b) $t = -10 \ln \frac{2}{57} \approx 33.5$
17. (a) $L(t) = L_\infty - [L_\infty - L(0)]e^{-kt}$ (b) $L(t) = 53 - 43e^{-0.2t}$
19. 15 days   **21.** $k \ln h + h = (-R/V)t + C$
23. (a) Stabilizes at 200,000
(b) (i) $x = 0, y = 0$: Zero populations
(ii) $x = 200,000, y = 0$: In the absence of birds, the insect population is always 200,000.
(iii) $x = 25,000, y = 175$: Both populations are stable.
(c) The populations stabilize at 25,000 insects and 175 birds.
(d)

25. (a) $y = (1/k) \cosh kx + a - 1/k$ or
$y = (1/k) \cosh kx - (1/k) \cosh kb + h$ (b) $(2/k) \sinh kb$

PROBLEMS PLUS ▪ PAGE 654

1. $f(x) = \pm 10 e^x$ **5.** $y = x^{1/n}$ **7.** 20°C
9. (b) $f(x) = \dfrac{x^2 - L^2}{4L} - \frac{1}{2}L \ln\left(\dfrac{x}{L}\right)$ (c) No
11. (a) 9.8 h   (b) $31,900\pi \approx 100,000$ ft²; 6283 ft²/h
(c) 5.1 h
13. $x^2 + (y - 6)^2 = 25$

CHAPTER 11

EXERCISES 11.1 ▪ PAGE 662

1.

3.

5. (a)

(b) $y = \frac{2}{3}x + \frac{13}{3}$

7. (a)

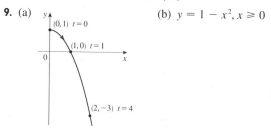

(b) $x = \frac{1}{4}(y - 5)^2 - 2$,
$-3 \le y \le 11$

9. (a)

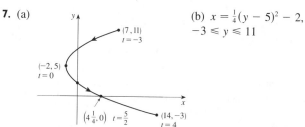

(b) $y = 1 - x^2, x \ge 0$

11. (a) $x^2 + y^2 = 1, x \ge 0$
(b)

13. (a) $y = 1/x, y > 1$
(b)

15. (a) $y = \frac{1}{2}\ln x + 1$
(b)

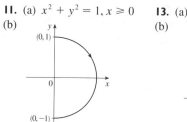

17. (a) $y^2 - x^2 = 1, y \ge 1$
(b)

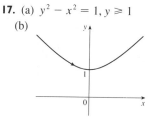

19. Moves counterclockwise along the circle
$(x - 3)^2 + (y - 1)^2 = 4$ from $(3, 3)$ to $(3, -1)$
21. Moves 3 times clockwise around the ellipse
$(x^2/25) + (y^2/4) = 1$, starting and ending at $(0, -2)$
23. It is contained in the rectangle described by $1 \leqslant x \leqslant 4$
and $2 \leqslant y \leqslant 3$.
25.

27.

29.

31. (b) $x = -2 + 5t, y = 7 - 8t, 0 \leqslant t \leqslant 1$
33. (a) $x = 2 \cos t, y = 1 - 2 \sin t, 0 \leqslant t \leqslant 2\pi$
(b) $x = 2 \cos t, y = 1 + 2 \sin t, 0 \leqslant t \leqslant 6\pi$
(c) $x = 2 \cos t, y = 1 + 2 \sin t, \pi/2 \leqslant t \leqslant 3\pi/2$
37. The curve $y = x^{2/3}$ is generated in (a). In (b), only the portion
with $x \geqslant 0$ is generated, and in (c) we get only the portion with
$x > 0$.
41. $x = a \cos \theta, y = b \sin \theta; (x^2/a^2) + (y^2/b^2) = 1$, ellipse
43.

45. (a) Two points of intersection

(b) One collision point at $(-3, 0)$ when $t = 3\pi/2$
(c) There are still two intersection points, but no collision point.
47. For $c = 0$, there is a cusp; for $c > 0$, there is a loop whose size
increases as c increases.

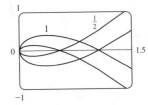

49. As n increases, the number of oscillations increases;
a and b determine the width and height.

EXERCISES 11.2 ▪ PAGE 672

1. $\dfrac{2t + 1}{t \cos t + \sin t}$ **3.** $y = -x$
5. $y = -(2/e)x + 3$ **7.** $y = 2x + 1$
9. $y = \frac{1}{6}x$

11. $1 + \frac{3}{2}t, 3/(4t), t > 0$
13. $-e^{-t}, e^{-t}/(1 - e^t), t < 0$
15. $-\frac{3}{2} \tan t, -\frac{3}{4} \sec^3 t, \pi/2 < t < 3\pi/2$
17. Horizontal at $(6, \pm16)$, vertical at $(10, 0)$
19. Horizontal at $(\pm\sqrt{2}, \pm1)$ (four points), vertical at $(\pm2, 0)$
21. $(0.6, 2); (5 \cdot 6^{-6/5}, e^{6^{-1/5}})$
23.
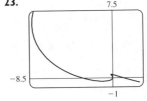
25. $y = x, y = -x$

27. (a) $d \sin \theta/(r - d \cos \theta)$ **29.** $(\frac{16}{27}, \frac{29}{9}), (-2, -4)$
31. πab **33.** $3 - e$ **35.** $2\pi r^2 + \pi d^2$
37. $\int_1^2 \sqrt{1 + 4t^2} \, dt \approx 3.1678$
39. $\int_0^{2\pi} \sqrt{3 - 2 \sin t - 2 \cos t} \, dt \approx 10.0367$ **41.** $4\sqrt{2} - 2$
43. $-\sqrt{10}/3 + \ln(3 + \sqrt{10}) + \sqrt{2} - \ln(1 + \sqrt{2})$
45. $\sqrt{2}\,(e^\pi - 1)$
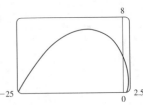

47. $e^3 + 11 - e^{-8}$

49. 612.3053   **51.** $6\sqrt{2}, \sqrt{2}$

55. (a)
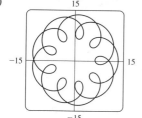
$t \in [0, 4\pi]$

(b) ≈ 294

57. $\int_0^1 2\pi(t^2 + 1)e^t\sqrt{e^{2t}(t + 1)^2(t^2 + 2t + 2)}\, dt \approx 103.5999$

59. $\frac{2}{1215}\pi(247\sqrt{13} + 64)$ **61.** $\frac{6}{5}\pi a^2$ **63.** 59.101

65. $\frac{24}{5}\pi(949\sqrt{26} + 1)$ **71.** $\frac{1}{4}$

EXERCISES 11.3 ▪ PAGE 683

1. (a)

$(2, 7\pi/3), (-2, 4\pi/3)$

(b)
$(1, 5\pi/4), (-1, \pi/4)$

(c)

$(1, 3\pi/2), (-1, 5\pi/2)$

3. (a)

$(-1, 0)$

(b)
$\left(-1, -\sqrt{3}\right)$

(c)

$\left(\sqrt{2}, -\sqrt{2}\right)$

5. (a) (i) $\left(2\sqrt{2}, 7\pi/4\right)$ (ii) $\left(-2\sqrt{2}, 3\pi/4\right)$
(b) (i) $(2, 2\pi/3)$ (ii) $(-2, 5\pi/3)$

7.

9.

11.

13. $2\sqrt{3}$ **15.** Circle, center O, radius 2
17. Circle, center $\left(0, \frac{3}{2}\right)$, radius $\frac{3}{2}$
19. Horizontal line, 1 unit above the x-axis
21. $r = 3\sec\theta$ **23.** $r = -\cot\theta\csc\theta$ **25.** $r = 2c\cos\theta$
27. (a) $\theta = \pi/6$ (b) $x = 3$

29.

31.

33.

35.

37.

39.

41.

43.

45.

47.

49.

51.

53.

55. (a) For $c < -1$, the inner loop
begins at $\theta = \sin^{-1}(-1/c)$ and
ends at $\theta = \pi - \sin^{-1}(-1/c)$;
for $c > 1$, it begins at
$\theta = \pi + \sin^{-1}(1/c)$ and
ends at $\theta = 2\pi - \sin^{-1}(1/c)$.

57. $\sqrt{3}$ **59.** $-\pi$ **61.** 1

63. Horizontal at $(3/\sqrt{2}, \pi/4)$, $(-3/\sqrt{2}, 3\pi/4)$;
vertical at $(3, 0)$, $(0, \pi/2)$

65. Horizontal at $(\frac{3}{2}, \pi/3)$, $(0, \pi)$ [the pole], and $(\frac{3}{2}, 5\pi/3)$;
vertical at $(2, 0)$, $(\frac{1}{2}, 2\pi/3)$, $(\frac{1}{2}, 4\pi/3)$

67. Horizontal at $(3, \pi/2)$, $(1, 3\pi/2)$; vertical at $(\frac{3}{2} + \frac{1}{2}\sqrt{3}, \alpha)$,
$(\frac{3}{2} + \frac{1}{2}\sqrt{3}, \pi - \alpha)$ where $\alpha = \sin^{-1}(-\frac{1}{2} + \frac{1}{2}\sqrt{3})$

69. Center $(b/2, a/2)$, radius $\sqrt{a^2 + b^2}/2$

71.

73.

75.

77. By counterclockwise rotation through angle $\pi/6$, $\pi/3$,
or α about the origin

79. (a) A rose with n loops if n is odd and $2n$ loops if n is even
(b) Number of loops is always $2n$

81. For $0 < a < 1$, the curve is an oval, which develops a dimple as
$a \to 1^-$. When $a > 1$, the curve splits into two parts, one of which
has a loop.

1. $\pi^5/10{,}240$ **3.** $\pi/12 + \frac{1}{8}\sqrt{3}$ **5.** π^2 **7.** $\frac{41}{4}\pi$
9. $\frac{9}{4}\pi$ **11.** 4

13. π **15.** 3π

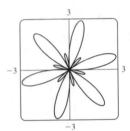

17. $\frac{1}{8}\pi$ **19.** $\frac{9}{20}\pi$ **21.** $\pi - \frac{3}{2}\sqrt{3}$ **23.** $\frac{1}{3}\pi + \frac{1}{2}\sqrt{3}$
25. $4\sqrt{3} - \frac{4}{3}\pi$ **27.** π **29.** $\frac{5}{24}\pi - \frac{1}{4}\sqrt{3}$ **31.** $\frac{1}{2}\pi - 1$
33. $\frac{1}{8}\pi - \frac{1}{4}$ **35.** $\frac{1}{4}(\pi + 3\sqrt{3})$
37. $(\frac{3}{2}, \pi/6)$, $(\frac{3}{2}, 5\pi/6)$, and the pole
39. $(1, \theta)$ where $\theta = \pi/12, 5\pi/12, 13\pi/12, 17\pi/12$
and $(-1, \theta)$ where $\theta = 7\pi/12, 11\pi/12, 19\pi/12, 23\pi/12$
41. $(\frac{1}{2}\sqrt{3}, \pi/3)$, $(\frac{1}{2}\sqrt{3}, 2\pi/3)$, and the pole
43. Intersection at $\theta \approx 0.89, 2.25$; area ≈ 3.46 **45.** π
47. $\frac{8}{3}[(\pi^2 + 1)^{3/2} - 1]$ **49.** 29.0653   **51.** 9.6884
53. $\frac{16}{3}$ **55.** (b) $2\pi(2 - \sqrt{2})$

1. $(0, 0)$, $(\frac{1}{8}, 0)$, $x = -\frac{1}{8}$ **3.** $(0, 0)$, $(0, -\frac{1}{16})$, $y = \frac{1}{16}$

5. $(-2, 3)$, $(-2, 5)$, $y = 1$

7. $(-2, -1)$, $(-5, -1)$, $x = 1$

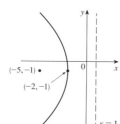

9. $x = -y^2$, focus $\left(-\frac{1}{4}, 0\right)$, directrix $x = \frac{1}{4}$

11. $(\pm 3, 0)$, $(\pm 2, 0)$

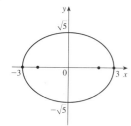

13. $(0, \pm 4)$, $\left(0, \pm 2\sqrt{3}\right)$

15. $(1, \pm 3)$, $\left(1, \pm\sqrt{5}\right)$

17. $\dfrac{x^2}{4} + \dfrac{y^2}{9} = 1$, foci $\left(0, \pm\sqrt{5}\right)$

19. $(\pm 12, 0)$, $(\pm 13, 0)$,
$y = \pm\frac{5}{12}x$

21. $(0, \pm 2)$, $\left(0, \pm 2\sqrt{2}\right)$,
$y = \pm x$

23. $(4, -2)$, $(2, -2)$;
$\left(3 \pm\sqrt{5}, -2\right)$;
$y + 2 = \pm 2(x - 3)$

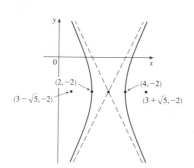

25. Parabola, $(0, -1)$, $\left(0, -\frac{3}{4}\right)$
27. Ellipse, $\left(\pm\sqrt{2}, 1\right)$, $(\pm 1, 1)$
29. Hyperbola, $(0, 1)$, $(0, -3)$; $\left(0, -1 \pm\sqrt{5}\right)$ **31.** $x^2 = -8y$
33. $y^2 = -12(x + 1)$ **35.** $y - 3 = 2(x - 2)^2$
37. $\dfrac{x^2}{25} + \dfrac{y^2}{21} = 1$ **39.** $\dfrac{x^2}{12} + \dfrac{(y - 4)^2}{16} = 1$
41. $\dfrac{(x + 1)^2}{12} + \dfrac{(y - 4)^2}{16} = 1$ **43.** $\dfrac{x^2}{9} - \dfrac{y^2}{16} = 1$
45. $\dfrac{(y - 1)^2}{25} - \dfrac{(x + 3)^2}{39} = 1$ **47.** $\dfrac{x^2}{9} - \dfrac{y^2}{36} = 1$
49. $\dfrac{x^2}{3,763,600} + \dfrac{y^2}{3,753,196} = 1$
51. (a) $\dfrac{121x^2}{1,500,625} - \dfrac{121y^2}{3,339,375} = 1$ (b) ≈ 248 mi
55. (a) Ellipse (b) Hyperbola (c) No curve
59. 9.69 **61.** $\dfrac{b^2 c}{a} + ab\ln\left(\dfrac{a}{b + c}\right)$ where $c^2 = a^2 + b^2$

EXERCISES 11.6 ▪ PAGE 704

1. $r = \dfrac{42}{4 + 7\sin\theta}$ **3.** $r = \dfrac{15}{4 - 3\cos\theta}$
5. $r = \dfrac{8}{1 - \sin\theta}$ **7.** $r = \dfrac{4}{2 + \cos\theta}$
9. (a) 1 (b) Parabola (c) $y = 1$
(d)

11. (a) $\frac{1}{4}$ (b) Ellipse (c) $y = -12$
(d)

13. (a) $\frac{1}{3}$ (b) Ellipse (c) $x = \frac{9}{2}$
(d)

15. (a) 2   (b) Hyperbola   (c) $x = -\frac{3}{8}$
(d)

17. (a) $2, y = -\frac{1}{2}$

(b) $r = \dfrac{1}{1 - 2\sin(\theta - 3\pi/4)}$

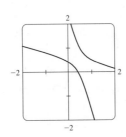

19. The ellipse is nearly circular when e is close to 0 and becomes more elongated as $e \to 1^-$. At $e = 1$, the curve becomes a parabola.

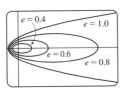

25. $r = \dfrac{2.26 \times 10^8}{1 + 0.093\cos\theta}$

27. 35.64 AU   **29.** 7.0×10^7 km   **31.** 3.6×10^8 km

CHAPTER 11 REVIEW ▪ PAGE 705

True-False Quiz

I. False   **3.** False   **5.** True   **7.** False   **9.** True

Exercises

I. $x = y^2 - 8y + 12$ **3.** $y = 1/x$

5. $x = t,\ y = \sqrt{t};\ x = t^4,\ y = t^2;$
$x = \tan^2 t,\ y = \tan t,\ 0 \leqslant t < \pi/2$

7. (a)

(b) $\left(3\sqrt{2}, 3\pi/4\right),$
$\left(-3\sqrt{2}, 7\pi/4\right)$

$\left(-2, 2\sqrt{3}\right)$

9.

II.

13.

15.

17. $r = \dfrac{2}{\cos\theta + \sin\theta}$

19.

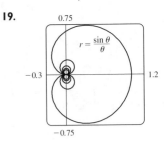

21. 2   **23.** -1

25. $\dfrac{1 + \sin t}{1 + \cos t},\ \dfrac{1 + \cos t + \sin t}{(1 + \cos t)^3}$ **27.** $\left(\frac{11}{8}, \frac{3}{4}\right)$

29. Vertical tangent at
$\left(\frac{3}{2}a, \pm\frac{1}{2}\sqrt{3}\,a\right), (-3a, 0);$
horizontal tangent at
$(a, 0), \left(-\frac{1}{2}a, \pm\frac{3}{2}\sqrt{3}\,a\right)$

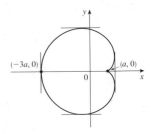

31. 18   **33.** $(2, \pm\pi/3)$ **35.** $\frac{1}{2}(\pi - 1)$
37. $2(5\sqrt{5} - 1)$

39. $\dfrac{2\sqrt{\pi^2 + 1} - \sqrt{4\pi^2 + 1}}{2\pi} + \ln\left(\dfrac{2\pi + \sqrt{4\pi^2 + 1}}{\pi + \sqrt{\pi^2 + 1}}\right)$

41. $471,295\pi/1024$

43. All curves have the vertical asymptote $x = 1$. For $c < -1$, the curve bulges to the right. At $c = -1$, the curve is the line $x = 1$. For $-1 < c < 0$, it bulges to the left. At $c = 0$ there is a cusp at $(0, 0)$. For $c > 0$, there is a loop.

45. $(\pm 1, 0), (\pm 3, 0)$ **47.** $\left(-\frac{25}{24}, 3\right), (-1, 3)$

49. $\dfrac{x^2}{25} + \dfrac{y^2}{9} = 1$ **51.** $\dfrac{y^2}{72/5} - \dfrac{x^2}{8/5} = 1$

53. $\dfrac{x^2}{25} + \dfrac{(8y - 399)^2}{160,801} = 1$ **55.** $r = \dfrac{4}{3 + \cos\theta}$

57. $x = a(\cot\theta + \sin\theta\cos\theta),\ y = a(1 + \sin^2\theta)$

PROBLEMS PLUS ▪ PAGE 708

1. $\ln(\pi/2)$

3. $\left[-\frac{3}{4}\sqrt{3}, \frac{3}{4}\sqrt{3}\right] \times [-1, 2]$

5. (a) At $(0, 0)$ and $\left(\frac{3}{2}, \frac{3}{2}\right)$
(b) Horizontal tangents at $(0, 0)$ and $\left(\sqrt[3]{2}, \sqrt[3]{4}\right)$;
vertical tangents at $(0, 0)$ and $\left(\sqrt[3]{4}, \sqrt[3]{2}\right)$
(d)   (g) $\frac{3}{2}$

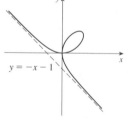

CHAPTER 12

EXERCISES 12.1 ▪ PAGE 720

Abbreviations: C, convergent; D, divergent

1. (a) A sequence is an ordered list of numbers. It can also be defined as a function whose domain is the set of positive integers.
(b) The terms a_n approach 8 as n becomes large.
(c) The terms a_n become large as n becomes large.

3. $0.8, 0.96, 0.992, 0.9984, 0.99968$ **5.** $-3, \frac{3}{2}, -\frac{1}{2}, \frac{1}{8}, -\frac{1}{40}$
7. $3, 5, 9, 17, 33$ **9.** $a_n = 1/(2n - 1)$ **11.** $a_n = 5n - 3$
13. $a_n = \left(-\frac{2}{3}\right)^{n-1}$ **15.** $\frac{1}{3}, \frac{2}{5}, \frac{3}{7}, \frac{4}{9}, \frac{5}{11}, \frac{6}{13}$; yes; $\frac{1}{2}$
17. 1   **19.** 5   **21.** 1   **23.** 1   **25.** 0   **27.** D
29. 0   **31.** 0   **33.** 0   **35.** 0   **37.** 1   **39.** e^2
41. $\ln 2$ **43.** D   **45.** D   **47.** 1   **49.** $\frac{1}{2}$
51. D   **53.** 0
55. (a) $1060, 1123.60, 1191.02, 1262.48, 1338.23$ (b) D

57. $-1 < r < 1$
59. Convergent by the Monotonic Sequence Theorem; $5 \leq L < 8$
61. Decreasing; yes   **63.** Not monotonic; no
65. Decreasing; yes   **67.** 2   **69.** $\frac{1}{2}\left(3 + \sqrt{5}\right)$
71. (b) $\frac{1}{2}\left(1 + \sqrt{5}\right)$ **73.** (a) 0   (b) 9, 11

EXERCISES 12.2 ▪ PAGE 730

1. (a) A sequence is an ordered list of numbers whereas a series is the *sum* of a list of numbers.
(b) A series is convergent if the sequence of partial sums is a convergent sequence. A series is divergent if it is not convergent.

3. $-2.40000, -1.92000,$
$-2.01600, -1.99680,$
$-2.00064, -1.99987,$
$-2.00003, -1.99999,$
$-2.00000, -2.00000$;
convergent, sum $= -2$

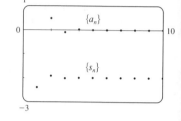

5. $1.55741, -0.62763,$
$-0.77018, 0.38764,$
$-2.99287, -3.28388,$
$-2.41243, -9.21214,$
$-9.66446, -9.01610$;
divergent

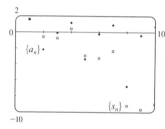

7. $0.29289, 0.42265,$
$0.50000, 0.55279,$
$0.59175, 0.62204,$
$0.64645, 0.66667,$
$0.68377, 0.69849$;
convergent, sum $= 1$

9. (a) C   (b) D   **11.** 9   **13.** D   **15.** 60   **17.** $\frac{1}{7}$
19. D   **21.** D   **23.** D   **25.** $\frac{5}{2}$ **27.** D   **29.** D
31. D   **33.** $e/(e - 1)$ **35.** $\frac{3}{2}$ **37.** $\frac{11}{6}$ **39.** $e - 1$
41. $\frac{2}{9}$ **43.** $1138/333$ **45.** $5063/3300$

47. $-3 < x < 3; \dfrac{x}{3 - x}$ **49.** $-\frac{1}{4} < x < \frac{1}{4}; \dfrac{1}{1 - 4x}$

51. All $x; \dfrac{2}{2 - \cos x}$ **53.** 1

55. $a_1 = 0, a_n = \dfrac{2}{n(n + 1)}$ for $n > 1$, sum $= 1$

57. (a) $S_n = \dfrac{D(1 - c^n)}{1 - c}$ (b) 5   **59.** $\frac{1}{2}\left(\sqrt{3} - 1\right)$

63. $\dfrac{1}{n(n + 1)}$ **65.** The series is divergent.

71. $\{s_n\}$ is bounded and increasing.

73. (a) $0, \frac{1}{9}, \frac{2}{9}, \frac{1}{3}, \frac{2}{3}, \frac{7}{9}, \frac{8}{9}, 1$

75. (a) $\frac{1}{2}, \frac{5}{6}, \frac{23}{24}, \frac{119}{120}$; $\dfrac{(n+1)! - 1}{(n+1)!}$ (c) 1

EXERCISES 12.3 ■ PAGE 739

1. C

$y = \dfrac{1}{x^{1.3}}$

a_2 a_3 a_4 a_5 ···

3. D   **5.** C   **7.** C   **9.** D   **11.** C   **13.** D   **15.** C
17. C   **19.** C   **21.** D   **23.** C   **25.** C   **27.** $p > 1$
29. $p < -1$ **31.** $(1, \infty)$
33. (a) 1.54977, error $\leqslant 0.1$ (b) 1.64522, error $\leqslant 0.005$
(c) $n > 1000$
35. 0.00145   **41.** $b < 1/e$

EXERCISES 12.4 ■ PAGE 745

1. (a) Nothing   (b) C   **3.** C   **5.** D   **7.** C   **9.** C
11. C   **13.** C   **15.** C   **17.** D   **19.** D   **21.** C
23. C   **25.** D   **27.** C   **29.** C   **31.** D
33. 1.249, error < 0.1 **35.** 0.76352, error < 0.001
45. Yes

EXERCISES 12.5 ■ PAGE 749

1. (a) A series whose terms are alternately positive and
negative   (b) $0 < b_{n+1} \leqslant b_n$ and $\lim_{n \to \infty} b_n = 0$,
where $b_n = |a_n|$ (c) $|R_n| \leqslant b_{n+1}$
3. C   **5.** C   **7.** D   **9.** C   **11.** C   **13.** D
15. C   **17.** C   **19.** D
21. 1.0000, 0.6464,
0.8389, 0.7139, 0.8033,
0.7353, 0.7893, 0.7451, 0.7821,
0.7505; error < 0.0275

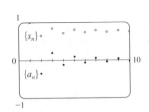

23. 5   **25.** 4   **27.** 0.9721   **29.** 0.0676
31. An underestimate   **33.** p is not a negative integer
35. $\{b_n\}$ is not decreasing

EXERCISES 12.6 ■ PAGE 755

Abbreviations: AC, absolutely convergent;
CC, conditionally convergent

1. (a) D   (b) C   (c) May converge or diverge
3. AC   **5.** CC   **7.** AC   **9.** D   **11.** AC   **13.** AC

15. AC   **17.** CC   **19.** AC   **21.** AC   **23.** D
25. AC   **27.** D   **29.** D   **31.** (a) and (d)
35. (a) $\frac{661}{960} \approx 0.68854$, error < 0.00521
(b) $n \geqslant 11, 0.693109$

EXERCISES 12.7 ■ PAGE 758

1. C   **3.** D   **5.** C   **7.** D   **9.** C   **11.** C   **13.** C
15. C   **17.** D   **19.** C   **21.** C   **23.** D   **25.** C
27. C   **29.** C   **31.** D   **33.** C   **35.** C   **37.** C

EXERCISES 12.8 ■ PAGE 763

1. A series of the form $\sum_{n=0}^{\infty} c_n(x - a)^n$, where x is a variable
and a and the c_n's are constants
3. $1, [-1, 1)$ **5.** $1, [-1, 1]$ **7.** $\infty, (-\infty, \infty)$
9. $2, (-2, 2)$ **11.** $\frac{1}{2}, \left(-\frac{1}{2}, \frac{1}{2}\right]$ **13.** $4, (-4, 4]$
15. $1, [1, 3]$ **17.** $\frac{1}{3}, \left[-\frac{13}{3}, -\frac{11}{3}\right)$ **19.** $\infty, (-\infty, \infty)$
21. $b, (a - b, a + b)$ **23.** $0, \left\{\frac{1}{2}\right\}$ **25.** $\frac{1}{4}, \left[-\frac{1}{2}, 0\right]$
27. $\infty, (-\infty, \infty)$ **29.** (a) Yes   (b) No   **31.** k^k **33.** No

35. (a) $(-\infty, \infty)$
(b), (c)

2 s_0 s_2 s_4

J_1

-8 8

-2 s_1 s_3 s_5

37. $(-1, 1), f(x) = (1 + 2x)/(1 - x^2)$ **41.** 2

EXERCISES 12.9 ■ PAGE 769

1. 10   **3.** $\displaystyle\sum_{n=0}^{\infty} (-1)^n x^n, (-1, 1)$ **5.** $2 \displaystyle\sum_{n=0}^{\infty} \frac{1}{3^{n+1}} x^n, (-3, 3)$

7. $\displaystyle\sum_{n=0}^{\infty} (-1)^n \frac{1}{9^{n+1}} x^{2n+1}, (-3, 3)$ **9.** $1 + 2 \displaystyle\sum_{n=1}^{\infty} x^n, (-1, 1)$

11. $\displaystyle\sum_{n=0}^{\infty} \left[(-1)^{n+1} - \frac{1}{2^{n+1}}\right] x^n, (-1, 1)$

13. (a) $\displaystyle\sum_{n=0}^{\infty} (-1)^n (n + 1) x^n, R = 1$

(b) $\dfrac{1}{2} \displaystyle\sum_{n=0}^{\infty} (-1)^n (n + 2)(n + 1) x^n, R = 1$

(c) $\dfrac{1}{2} \displaystyle\sum_{n=2}^{\infty} (-1)^n n(n - 1) x^n, R = 1$

15. $\ln 5 - \displaystyle\sum_{n=1}^{\infty} \frac{x^n}{n5^n}, R = 5$ **17.** $\displaystyle\sum_{n=3}^{\infty} \frac{n - 2}{2^{n-1}} x^n, R = 2$

19. $\sum_{n=0}^{\infty} (-1)^n \dfrac{1}{16^{n+1}} x^{2n+1}, R = 4$

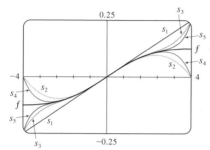

21. $\sum_{n=0}^{\infty} \dfrac{2x^{2n+1}}{2n+1}, R = 1$

23. $C + \sum_{n=0}^{\infty} \dfrac{t^{8n+2}}{8n+2}, R = 1$

25. $C + \sum_{n=1}^{\infty} (-1)^{n+1} \dfrac{x^{2n-1}}{4n^2 - 1}, R = 1$

27. 0.199989   **29.** 0.000983   **31.** 0.09531

33. (b) 0.920   **37.** $[-1, 1], [-1, 1), (-1, 1)$

EXERCISES 12.10 ▪ PAGE 782

1. $b_8 = f^{(8)}(5)/8!$ **3.** $\sum_{n=0}^{\infty} (n+1)x^n, R = 1$

5. $\sum_{n=0}^{\infty} (n+1)x^n, R = 1$

7. $\sum_{n=0}^{\infty} (-1)^n \dfrac{\pi^{2n+1}}{(2n+1)!} x^{2n+1}, R = \infty$

9. $\sum_{n=0}^{\infty} \dfrac{5^n}{n!} x^n, R = \infty$ **11.** $\sum_{n=0}^{\infty} \dfrac{x^{2n+1}}{(2n+1)!}, R = \infty$

13. $-1 - 2(x-1) + 3(x-1)^2 + 4(x-1)^3 + (x-1)^4,$ $R = \infty$

15. $\sum_{n=0}^{\infty} \dfrac{e^3}{n!} (x-3)^n, R = \infty$

17. $\sum_{n=0}^{\infty} (-1)^{n+1} \dfrac{1}{(2n)!} (x-\pi)^{2n}, R = \infty$

19. $\sum_{n=0}^{\infty} (-1)^n \dfrac{1 \cdot 3 \cdot 5 \cdot \cdots \cdot (2n-1)}{2^n \cdot 3^{2n+1} \cdot n!} (x-9)^n, R = 9$

25. $1 + \dfrac{x}{2} + \sum_{n=2}^{\infty} (-1)^{n-1} \dfrac{1 \cdot 3 \cdot 5 \cdot \cdots \cdot (2n-3)}{2^n n!} x^n, R = 1$

27. $\sum_{n=0}^{\infty} (-1)^n \dfrac{(n+1)(n+2)}{2^{n+4}} x^n, R = 2$

29. $\sum_{n=0}^{\infty} (-1)^n \dfrac{\pi^{2n+1}}{(2n+1)!} x^{2n+1}, R = \infty$

31. $\sum_{n=0}^{\infty} \dfrac{2^n + 1}{n!} x^n, R = \infty$

33. $\sum_{n=0}^{\infty} (-1)^n \dfrac{1}{2^{2n}(2n)!} x^{4n+1}, R = \infty$

35. $\dfrac{1}{2}x + \sum_{n=1}^{\infty} (-1)^n \dfrac{1 \cdot 3 \cdot 5 \cdot \cdots \cdot (2n-1)}{n! \, 2^{3n+1}} x^{2n+1}, R = 2$

37. $\sum_{n=1}^{\infty} (-1)^{n+1} \dfrac{2^{2n-1}}{(2n)!} x^{2n}, R = \infty$

39. $\sum_{n=0}^{\infty} (-1)^n \dfrac{1}{(2n)!} x^{4n}, R = \infty$

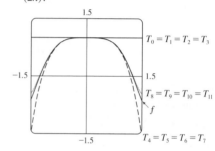

41. $\sum_{n=1}^{\infty} \dfrac{(-1)^{n-1}}{(n-1)!} x^n, R = \infty$

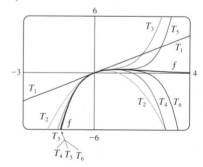

43. 0.81873

45. (a) $1 + \sum_{n=1}^{\infty} \dfrac{1 \cdot 3 \cdot 5 \cdot \cdots \cdot (2n-1)}{2^n n!} x^{2n}$

(b) $x + \sum_{n=1}^{\infty} \dfrac{1 \cdot 3 \cdot 5 \cdot \cdots \cdot (2n-1)}{(2n+1)2^n n!} x^{2n+1}$

47. $C + \sum_{n=0}^{\infty} (-1)^n \dfrac{x^{6n+2}}{(6n+2)(2n)!}, R = \infty$

49. $C + \sum_{n=1}^{\infty} (-1)^n \dfrac{1}{2n\,(2n)!} x^{2n}, R = \infty$ **51.** 0.440

53. 0.40102   **55.** $\frac{1}{3}$ **57.** $\frac{1}{120}$ **59.** $1 - \frac{3}{2}x^2 + \frac{25}{24}x^4$

61. $1 + \frac{1}{6}x^2 + \frac{7}{360}x^4$ **63.** e^{-x^4}

65. $1/\sqrt{2}$ **67.** $e^3 - 1$

XERCISES 12.11 ▪ PAGE 791

. (a) $T_0(x) = 1 = T_1(x)$, $T_2(x) = 1 - \frac{1}{2}x^2 = T_3(x)$,
$T_4(x) = 1 - \frac{1}{2}x^2 + \frac{1}{24}x^4 = T_5(x)$,
$T_6(x) = 1 - \frac{1}{2}x^2 + \frac{1}{24}x^4 - \frac{1}{720}x^6$

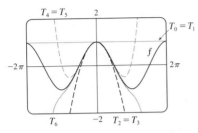

(b)

x	f	$T_0 = T_1$	$T_2 = T_3$	$T_4 = T_5$	T_6
$\frac{\pi}{4}$	0.7071	1	0.6916	0.7074	0.7071
$\frac{\pi}{2}$	0	1	−0.2337	0.0200	−0.0009
π	−1	1	−3.9348	0.1239	−1.2114

(c) As n increases, $T_n(x)$ is a good approximation to $f(x)$ on a larger and larger interval.

3. $\frac{1}{2} - \frac{1}{4}(x - 2) + \frac{1}{8}(x - 2)^2 - \frac{1}{16}(x - 2)^3$

5. $-\left(x - \frac{\pi}{2}\right) + \frac{1}{6}\left(x - \frac{\pi}{2}\right)^3$

7. $x + \frac{1}{6}x^3$

9. $x - 2x^2 + 2x^3$

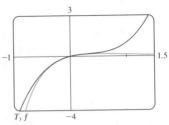

11. $T_5(x) = 1 - 2\left(x - \frac{\pi}{4}\right) + 2\left(x - \frac{\pi}{4}\right)^2 - \frac{8}{3}\left(x - \frac{\pi}{4}\right)^3$
$\qquad + \frac{10}{3}\left(x - \frac{\pi}{4}\right)^4 - \frac{64}{15}\left(x - \frac{\pi}{4}\right)^5$

13. (a) $2 + \frac{1}{4}(x - 4) - \frac{1}{64}(x - 4)^2$ (b) 1.5625×10^{-5}
15. (a) $1 + \frac{2}{3}(x - 1) - \frac{1}{9}(x - 1)^2 + \frac{4}{81}(x - 1)^3$ (b) 0.000097
17. (a) $1 + \frac{1}{2}x^2$ (b) 0.0015 **19.** (a) $1 + x^2$ (b) 0.00006
21. (a) $x^2 - \frac{1}{6}x^4$ (b) 0.042 **23.** 0.17365 **25.** Four
27. $-1.037 < x < 1.037$ **29.** $-0.86 < x < 0.86$
31. 21 m, no   **37.** (c) They differ by about 8×10^{-9} km.

CHAPTER 12 REVIEW ▪ PAGE 795

True-False Quiz

1. False   **3.** True   **5.** False   **7.** False
9. False   **11.** True   **13.** True   **15.** False
17. True   **19.** True

Exercises

1. $\frac{1}{2}$ **3.** D   **5.** 0   **7.** e^{12} **9.** 2   **11.** C
13. C   **15.** D   **17.** C   **19.** C   **21.** C   **23.** CC
25. AC   **27.** $\frac{1}{11}$ **29.** $\pi/4$ **31.** e^{-e} **35.** 0.9721
37. 0.18976224, error $< 6.4 \times 10^{-7}$
41. 4, $[-6, 2)$ **43.** 0.5, $[2.5, 3.5)$
45. $\frac{1}{2} \sum\limits_{n=0}^{\infty} (-1)^n \left[\frac{1}{(2n)!} \left(x - \frac{\pi}{6}\right)^{2n} + \frac{\sqrt{3}}{(2n + 1)!} \left(x - \frac{\pi}{6}\right)^{2n+1} \right]$
47. $\sum\limits_{n=0}^{\infty} (-1)^n x^{n+2}, R = 1$ **49.** $-\sum\limits_{n=1}^{\infty} \frac{x^n}{n}, R = 1$
51. $\sum\limits_{n=0}^{\infty} (-1)^n \frac{x^{8n+4}}{(2n + 1)!}, R = \infty$
53. $\frac{1}{2} + \sum\limits_{n=1}^{\infty} \frac{1 \cdot 5 \cdot 9 \cdot \, \cdots \, \cdot (4n - 3)}{n! 2^{6n+1}} x^n, R = 16$

55. $C + \ln|x| + \sum\limits_{n=1}^{\infty} \dfrac{x^n}{n \cdot n!}$

57. (a) $1 + \frac{1}{2}(x-1) - \frac{1}{8}(x-1)^2 + \frac{1}{16}(x-1)^3$

(b) 1.5 (c) 0.000006

59. $-\frac{1}{6}$

PROBLEMS PLUS ▪ PAGE 797

1. $15!/5! = 10,897,286,400$

3. (b) 0 if $x = 0$, $(1/x) - \cot x$ if $x \neq k\pi$, k an integer

5. (a) $s_n = 3 \cdot 4^n$, $l_n = 1/3^n$, $p_n = 4^n/3^{n-1}$ (c) $\frac{2}{5}\sqrt{3}$

9. $(-1, 1)$, $\dfrac{x^3 + 4x^2 + x}{(1 - x)^4}$ **11.** $\ln\frac{1}{2}$

13. (a) $\frac{250}{101}\pi(e^{-(n-1)\pi/5} - e^{-n\pi/5})$ (b) $\frac{250}{101}\pi$

CHAPTER 13

EXERCISES 13.1 ▪ PAGE 805

1. $(4, 0, -3)$ **3.** $Q; R$

5. A vertical plane that intersects the xy-plane in the line $y = 2 - x$, $z = 0$ (see graph at right)

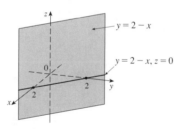

7. $|PQ| = 6$, $|QR| = 2\sqrt{10}$, $|RP| = 6$; isosceles triangle

9. (a) No (b) Yes

11. $(x - 1)^2 + (y + 4)^4 + (z - 3)^2 = 25$;
$(x - 1)^2 + (z - 3)^2 = 9$, $y = 0$ (a circle)

13. $(x - 3)^2 + (y - 8)^2 + (z - 1)^2 = 30$

15. $(3, -2, 1)$, 5

17. $(2, 0, -6)$, $9/\sqrt{2}$ **19.** (b) $\frac{5}{2}, \frac{1}{2}\sqrt{94}, \frac{1}{2}\sqrt{85}$

21. (a) $(x - 2)^2 + (y + 3)^2 + (z - 6)^2 = 36$

(b) $(x - 2)^2 + (y + 3)^2 + (z - 6)^2 = 4$

(c) $(x - 2)^2 + (y + 3)^2 + (z - 6)^2 = 9$

23. A plane parallel to the xz-plane and 4 units to the left of it

25. A half-space consisting of all points in front of the plane $x = 3$

27. All points on or between the horizontal planes $z = 0$ and $z = 6$

29. All points on or inside a sphere with radius $\sqrt{3}$ and center O

31. All points on or inside a circular cylinder of radius 3 with axis the y-axis

33. $0 < x < 5$ **35.** $r^2 < x^2 + y^2 + z^2 < R^2$

37. (a) $(2, 1, 4)$ (b)

39. $14x - 6y - 10z = 9$, a plane perpendicular to AB

EXERCISES 13.2 ▪ PAGE 813

1. (a) Scalar (b) Vector (c) Vector (d) Scalar

3. $\overrightarrow{AB} = \overrightarrow{DC}$, $\overrightarrow{DA} = \overrightarrow{CB}$, $\overrightarrow{DE} = \overrightarrow{EB}$, $\overrightarrow{EA} = \overrightarrow{CE}$

5. (a)   (b)

(c) $v + w$ (d)

7. $a = \langle -4, -2 \rangle$ **9.** $a = \langle 3, -1 \rangle$

  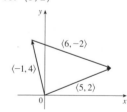

11. $a = \langle 2, 0, -2 \rangle$ **13.** $\langle 5, 2 \rangle$

15. $\langle 0, 1, -1 \rangle$

17. $\langle 2, -18 \rangle$, $\langle 1, -42 \rangle$, 13, 10

19. $-\mathbf{i} + \mathbf{j} + 2\mathbf{k}$, $-4\mathbf{i} + \mathbf{j} + 9\mathbf{k}$, $\sqrt{14}$, $\sqrt{82}$

21. $-\dfrac{3}{\sqrt{58}}\mathbf{i} + \dfrac{7}{\sqrt{58}}\mathbf{j}$ **23.** $\frac{8}{9}\mathbf{i} - \frac{1}{9}\mathbf{j} + \frac{4}{9}\mathbf{k}$

25. $\langle 2, 2\sqrt{3} \rangle$ **27.** ≈ 45.96 ft/s, ≈ 38.57 ft/s
29. $100\sqrt{7} \approx 264.6$ N, $\approx 139.1°$
31. $\sqrt{493} \approx 22.2$ mi/h, N8°W
33. $\mathbf{T}_1 \approx -196\,\mathbf{i} + 3.92\,\mathbf{j}$, $\mathbf{T}_2 \approx 196\,\mathbf{i} + 3.92\,\mathbf{j}$
35. $\pm(\mathbf{i} + 4\mathbf{j})/\sqrt{17}$ **37. 0**

39. (a), (b)   (d) $s = \frac{9}{7}, t = \frac{11}{7}$

41. A sphere with radius 1, centered at (x_0, y_0, z_0)

1. (b), (c), (d) are meaningful
3. 14   **5.** 19   **7.** 32   **9.** -15
11. $\mathbf{u} \cdot \mathbf{v} = \frac{1}{2}, \mathbf{u} \cdot \mathbf{w} = -\frac{1}{2}$
15. $\cos^{-1}\left(\dfrac{9 - 4\sqrt{7}}{20}\right) \approx 95°$ **17.** $\cos^{-1}\left(\dfrac{5}{\sqrt{1015}}\right) \approx 81°$
19. $\cos^{-1}\left(\dfrac{-1}{2\sqrt{7}}\right) \approx 101°$ **21.** $45°, 45°, 90°$
23. (a) Neither   (b) Orthogonal
(c) Orthogonal   (d) Parallel
25. Yes   **27.** $(\mathbf{i} - \mathbf{j} - \mathbf{k})/\sqrt{3}$ $\left[\text{or } (-\mathbf{i} + \mathbf{j} + \mathbf{k})/\sqrt{3}\right]$
29. $\dfrac{3}{5\sqrt{2}}, \dfrac{4}{5\sqrt{2}}, \dfrac{1}{\sqrt{2}};$ $65°, 56°, 45°$
31. $\frac{2}{7}, \frac{3}{7}, -\frac{6}{7};$ $73°, 65°, 149°$
33. $1/\sqrt{3}, 1/\sqrt{3}, 1/\sqrt{3};$ $55°, 55°, 55°$
35. $3, \langle \frac{9}{5}, -\frac{12}{5} \rangle$ **37.** $\frac{9}{7}, \langle \frac{27}{49}, \frac{54}{49}, -\frac{18}{49} \rangle$
39. $1/\sqrt{21}, \frac{2}{21}\mathbf{i} - \frac{1}{21}\mathbf{j} + \frac{4}{21}\mathbf{k}$
43. $\langle 0, 0, -2\sqrt{10} \rangle$ or any vector of the form
$\langle s, t, 3s - 2\sqrt{10} \rangle, s, t \in \mathbb{R}$
45. 144 J   **47.** $2400 \cos(40°) \approx 1839$ ft-lb   **49.** $\frac{13}{5}$
51. $\cos^{-1}(1/\sqrt{3}) \approx 55°$

1. $16\,\mathbf{i} + 48\,\mathbf{k}$ **3.** $15\,\mathbf{i} - 3\,\mathbf{j} + 3\,\mathbf{k}$ **5.** $\frac{1}{2}\mathbf{i} - \mathbf{j} + \frac{3}{2}\mathbf{k}$
7. $t^4\mathbf{i} - 2t^3\mathbf{j} + t^2\mathbf{k}$ **9. 0**   **11.** $\mathbf{i} + \mathbf{j} + \mathbf{k}$
13. (a) Scalar (b) Meaningless   (c) Vector
(d) Meaningless   (e) Meaningless   (f) Scalar
15. 24; into the page   **17.** $\langle 5, -3, 1 \rangle, \langle -5, 3, -1 \rangle$
19. $\langle -2/\sqrt{6}, -1/\sqrt{6}, 1/\sqrt{6} \rangle, \langle 2/\sqrt{6}, 1/\sqrt{6}, -1/\sqrt{6} \rangle$
27. 16   **29.** (a) $\langle 6, 3, 2 \rangle$ (b) $\frac{7}{2}$
31. (a) $\langle 13, -14, 5 \rangle$ (b) $\frac{1}{2}\sqrt{390}$
33. 82   **35.** 3   **39.** $10.8 \sin 80° \approx 10.6$ N·m
41. ≈ 417 N   **43.** (b) $\sqrt{97/3}$
49. (a) No   (b) No   (c) Yes

1. (a) True   (b) False   (c) True   (d) False   (e) False
(f) True   (g) False   (h) True   (i) True   (j) False
(k) True
3. $\mathbf{r} = (2\,\mathbf{i} + 2.4\,\mathbf{j} + 3.5\,\mathbf{k}) + t(3\,\mathbf{i} + 2\,\mathbf{j} - \mathbf{k});$
$x = 2 + 3t, y = 2.4 + 2t, z = 3.5 - t$
5. $\mathbf{r} = (\mathbf{i} + 6\mathbf{k}) + t(\mathbf{i} + 3\mathbf{j} + \mathbf{k});$
$x = 1 + t, y = 3t, z = 6 + t$
7. $x = 1 - 5t, y = 3, z = 2 - 2t; \dfrac{x - 1}{-5} = \dfrac{z - 2}{-2}, y = 3$
9. $x = 2 + 2t, y = 1 + \frac{1}{2}t,$
$z = -3 - 4t;$
$(x - 2)/2 = 2y - 2 = (z + 3)/(-4)$
11. $x = 1 + t, y = -1 + 2t, z = 1 + t;$
$x - 1 = (y + 1)/2 = z - 1$
13. Yes
15. (a) $(x - 1)/(-1) = (y + 5)/2 = (z - 6)/(-3)$
(b) $(-1, -1, 0), (-\frac{3}{2}, 0, -\frac{3}{2}), (0, -3, 3)$
17. $\mathbf{r}(t) = (2\mathbf{i} - \mathbf{j} + 4\mathbf{k}) + t(2\mathbf{i} + 7\mathbf{j} - 3\mathbf{k}), 0 \le t \le 1$
19. Parallel   **21.** Skew
23. $-2x + y + 5z = 1$ **25.** $x + y - z = -1$
27. $2x - y + 3z = 0$ **29.** $3x - 7z = -9$
31. $x + y + z = 2$ **33.** $-13x + 17y + 7z = -42$
35. $33x + 10y + 4z = 190$ **37.** $x - 2y + 4z = -1$
39.   **41.**
43. $(2, 3, 5)$ **45.** $(2, 3, 1)$ **47.** $1, 0, -1$
49. Perpendicular   **51.** Neither, $\approx 70.5°$ **53.** Parallel
55. (a) $x = 1, y = -t, z = t$ (b) $\cos^{-1}\left(\dfrac{5}{3\sqrt{3}}\right) \approx 15.8°$
57. $x = 1, y - 2 = -z$
59. $x + 2y + z = 5$ **61.** $(x/a) + (y/b) + (z/c) = 1$
63. $x = 3t, y = 1 - t, z = 2 - 2t$
65. P_1 and P_3 are parallel, P_2 and P_4 are identical
67. $\sqrt{61/14}$ **69.** $\frac{18}{7}$ **71.** $5/(2\sqrt{14})$ **75.** $1/\sqrt{6}$

1. (a) Parabola
(b) Parabolic cylinder with rulings parallel to the z-axis
(c) Parabolic cylinder with rulings parallel to the x-axis

3. Elliptic cylinder

5. Parabolic cylinder

7. Cylindrical surface

9. (a) $x = k$, $y^2 - z^2 = 1 - k^2$, hyperbola ($k \neq \pm 1$);
$y = k$, $x^2 - z^2 = 1 - k^2$, hyperbola ($k \neq \pm 1$);
$z = k$, $x^2 + z^2 = 1 + k^2$, circle
(b) The hyperboloid is rotated so that it has axis the y-axis
(c) The hyperboloid is shifted one unit in the negative y-direction

11. Elliptic paraboloid with axis the x-axis

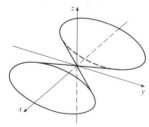

13. Elliptic cone with axis the x-axis

15. Hyperboloid of two sheets

17. Ellipsoid

19. Hyperbolic paraboloid

21. VII   **23.** II   **25.** VI   **27.** VIII

29. $-\dfrac{x^2}{9} - \dfrac{y^2}{4} + \dfrac{z^2}{36} = 1$
Hyperboloid of two sheets
with axis the z-axis

31. $\dfrac{x}{6} = \dfrac{y^2}{3} + \dfrac{z^2}{2}$

Elliptic paraboloid with vertex
$(0, 0, 0)$ and axis the x-axis

33. $x^2 + \dfrac{(y-2)^2}{4} + (z-3)^2 = 1$

Ellipsoid with center $(0, 2, 3)$

35. $(y+1)^2 = (x-2)^2 + (z-1)^2$
Circular cone with vertex $(2, -1, 1)$
and axis parallel to the y-axis

37.

39.

33. Hyperboloid of two sheets **35.** Ellipsoid

37. $4x^2 + y^2 + z^2 = 16$

1. $\left(\sqrt{3} - 1.5\right)$ m

3. (a) $(x + 1)/(-2c) = (y - c)/(c^2 - 1) = (z - c)/(c^2 + 1)$
(b) $x^2 + y^2 = t^2 + 1, z = t$ (c) $4\pi/3$

41.

$z = 2$
$z = \sqrt{x^2 + y^2}$

43. $y = x^2 + z^2$ **45.** $-4x = y^2 + z^2$, paraboloid

47. (a) $\dfrac{x^2}{(6378.137)^2} + \dfrac{y^2}{(6378.137)^2} + \dfrac{z^2}{(6356.523)^2} = 1$
(b) Circle   (c) Ellipse

CHAPTER 14

1. $(-1, 2]$ **3.** $\langle 1, 0, 0\rangle$ **5.** $\mathbf{i} + \mathbf{j} + \mathbf{k}$

51.

7.

9.

True-False Quiz

1. True   **3.** True   **5.** True   **7.** True   **9.** True
11. False   **13.** False   **15.** False   **17.** True

Exercises

1. (a) $(x + 1)^2 + (y - 2)^2 + (z - 1)^2 = 69$
(b) $(y - 2)^2 + (z - 1)^2 = 68, x = 0$
(c) Center $(4, -1, -3)$, radius 5
3. $\mathbf{u} \cdot \mathbf{v} = 3\sqrt{2}; |\mathbf{u} \times \mathbf{v}| = 3\sqrt{2}$; out of the page
5. $-2, -4$ **7.** (a) 2   (b) -2 (c) -2 (d) 0
9. $\cos^{-1}\left(\frac{1}{3}\right) \approx 71°$ **11.** (a) $\langle 4, -3, 4\rangle$ (b) $\sqrt{41}/2$
13. 166 N, 114 N
15. $x = 4 - 3t, y = -1 + 2t, z = 2 + 3t$
17. $x = -2 + 2t, y = 2 - t, z = 4 + 5t$
19. $-4x + 3y + z = -14$ **21.** $(1, 4, 4)$
23. Skew   **25.** $x + y + z = 4$
27. $22/\sqrt{26}$
29. Plane   **31.** Cone

11.

13.

$y = x^2$

15. $\mathbf{r}(t) = \langle t, 2t, 3t\rangle, 0 \leq t \leq 1$;
$x = t, y = 2t, z = 3t, 0 \leq t \leq 1$
17. $\mathbf{r}(t) = \langle 3t + 1, 2t - 1, 5t + 2\rangle, 0 \leq t \leq 1$;
$x = 3t + 1, y = 2t - 1, z = 5t + 2, 0 \leq t \leq 1$
19. VI   **21.** IV   **23.** V
25.

27. $(0, 0, 0), (1, 0, 1)$

29.

31.

33.

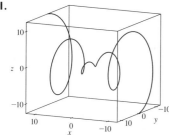

37. $\mathbf{r}(t) = t\,\mathbf{i} + \frac{1}{2}(t^2 - 1)\,\mathbf{j} + \frac{1}{2}(t^2 + 1)\,\mathbf{k}$

39. $x = 2\cos t,\ y = 2\sin t,\ z = 4\cos^2 t$ **41.** Yes

EXERCISES 14.2 ■ PAGE 864

1. (a)

(b), (d)

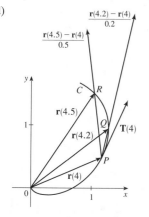

(c) $\mathbf{r}'(4) = \lim\limits_{h \to 0} \dfrac{\mathbf{r}(4 + h) - \mathbf{r}(4)}{h};\ \mathbf{T}(4) = \dfrac{\mathbf{r}'(4)}{|\mathbf{r}'(4)|}$

3. (a), (c)   (b) $\mathbf{r}'(t) = \langle 1, 2t \rangle$

5. (a), (c)   **7.** (a), (c)

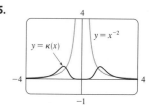

(b) $\mathbf{r}'(t) = \cos t\,\mathbf{i} - 2\sin t\,\mathbf{j}$ (b) $\mathbf{r}'(t) = e^t\,\mathbf{i} + 3e^{3t}\,\mathbf{j}$
9. $\mathbf{r}'(t) = \langle t\cos t + \sin t, 2t, \cos 2t - 2t\sin 2t \rangle$
11. $\mathbf{r}'(t) = 4e^{4t}\,\mathbf{k}$ **13.** $\mathbf{r}'(t) = 2te^{t^2}\,\mathbf{i} + [3/(1 + 3t)]\,\mathbf{k}$
15. $\mathbf{r}'(t) = \mathbf{b} + 2t\mathbf{c}$ **17.** $\left\langle \frac{1}{3}, \frac{2}{3}, \frac{2}{3} \right\rangle$ **19.** $\frac{3}{5}\,\mathbf{j} + \frac{4}{5}\,\mathbf{k}$
21. $\langle 1, 2t, 3t^2 \rangle, \langle 1/\sqrt{14}, 2/\sqrt{14}, 3/\sqrt{14} \rangle, \langle 0, 2, 6t \rangle, \langle 6t^2, -6t, 2 \rangle$
23. $x = 3 + t,\ y = 2t,\ z = 2 + 4t$
25. $x = 1 - t,\ y = t,\ z = 1 - t$
27. $x = t,\ y = 1 - t,\ z = 2t$
29. $x = -\pi - t,\ y = \pi + t,\ z = -\pi t$
31. $66°$ **33.** $4\mathbf{i} - 3\mathbf{j} + 5\mathbf{k}$ **35.** $\mathbf{i} + \mathbf{j} + \mathbf{k}$
37. $e^t\,\mathbf{i} + t^2\,\mathbf{j} + (t\ln t - t)\mathbf{k} + \mathbf{C}$
39. $t^2\,\mathbf{i} + t^3\,\mathbf{j} + \left(\frac{2}{3}t^{3/2} - \frac{2}{3}\right)\mathbf{k}$
45. $2t\cos t + 2\sin t - 2\cos t \sin t$

EXERCISES 14.3 ■ PAGE 872

1. $20\sqrt{29}$ **3.** $e - e^{-1}$ **5.** $\frac{1}{27}(13^{3/2} - 8)$ **7.** 15.3841
9. 1.2780 **11.** 42

13. $\mathbf{r}(t(s)) = \dfrac{2}{\sqrt{29}}\,s\,\mathbf{i} + \left(1 - \dfrac{3}{\sqrt{29}}\,s\right)\mathbf{j} + \left(5 + \dfrac{4}{\sqrt{29}}\,s\right)\mathbf{k}$
15. $(3\sin 1, 4, 3\cos 1)$
17. (a) $\left\langle (2/\sqrt{29})\cos t, 5/\sqrt{29}, (-2/\sqrt{29})\sin t \right\rangle$,
$\langle -\sin t, 0, -\cos t \rangle$ (b) $\frac{2}{29}$
19. (a) $\dfrac{1}{e^{2t} + 1}\left\langle \sqrt{2}e^t, e^{2t}, -1 \right\rangle, \dfrac{1}{e^{2t} + 1}\left\langle 1 - e^{2t}, \sqrt{2}e^t, \sqrt{2}e^t \right\rangle$
(b) $\sqrt{2}e^{2t}/(e^{2t} + 1)^2$
21. $2/(4t^2 + 1)^{3/2}$ **23.** $\frac{4}{25}$ **25.** $\frac{1}{7}\sqrt{\frac{19}{14}}$
27. $2/(4x^2 - 8x + 5)^{3/2}$ **29.** $15\sqrt{x}/(1 + 100x^3)^{3/2}$
31. $\left(-\frac{1}{2}\ln 2, 1/\sqrt{2}\right)$; approaches 0
33. (a) P (b) $1.3, 0.7$ **35.**

37. a is $y = f(x)$, b is $y = \kappa(x)$

39. $\kappa(t) = \dfrac{6\sqrt{4\cos^2 t - 12\cos t + 13}}{(17 - 12\cos t)^{3/2}}$

integer multiples of 2π

41. $1/(\sqrt{2}\,e^t)$ **43.** $\langle \frac{2}{3}, \frac{2}{3}, \frac{1}{3} \rangle, \langle -\frac{1}{3}, \frac{2}{3}, -\frac{2}{3} \rangle, \langle -\frac{2}{3}, \frac{1}{3}, \frac{2}{3} \rangle$

45. $y = 6x + \pi, x + 6y = 6\pi$

47. $\left(x + \frac{5}{2}\right)^2 + y^2 = \frac{81}{4}, x^2 + \left(y - \frac{5}{3}\right)^2 = \frac{16}{9}$

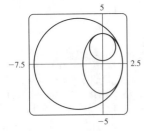

49. $(-1, -3, 1)$ **57.** $2/(t^4 + 4t^2 + 1)$

59. 2.07×10^{10} Å ≈ 2 m

EXERCISES 14.4 ■ **PAGE 882**

1. (a) $1.8\mathbf{i} - 3.8\mathbf{j} - 0.7\mathbf{k}, 2.0\mathbf{i} - 2.4\mathbf{j} - 0.6\mathbf{k},$
$2.8\mathbf{i} + 1.8\mathbf{j} - 0.3\mathbf{k}, 2.8\mathbf{i} + 0.8\mathbf{j} - 0.4\mathbf{k}$
(b) $2.4\mathbf{i} - 0.8\mathbf{j} - 0.5\mathbf{k}, 2.58$

3. $\mathbf{v}(t) = \langle -t, 1 \rangle$
$\mathbf{a}(t) = \langle -1, 0 \rangle$
$|\mathbf{v}(t)| = \sqrt{t^2 + 1}$

5. $\mathbf{v}(t) = -3\sin t\,\mathbf{i} + 2\cos t\,\mathbf{j}$
$\mathbf{a}(t) = -3\cos t\,\mathbf{i} - 2\sin t\,\mathbf{j}$
$|\mathbf{v}(t)| = \sqrt{5\sin^2 t + 4}$

7. $\mathbf{v}(t) = \mathbf{i} + 2t\,\mathbf{j}$
$\mathbf{a}(t) = 2\,\mathbf{j}$
$|\mathbf{v}(t)| = \sqrt{1 + 4t^2}$

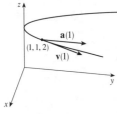

9. $\langle 2t, 3t^2, 2t \rangle, \langle 2, 6t, 2 \rangle, |t|\sqrt{9t^2 + 8}$

11. $\sqrt{2}\,\mathbf{i} + e^t\,\mathbf{j} - e^{-t}\,\mathbf{k}, e^t\,\mathbf{j} + e^{-t}\,\mathbf{k}, e^t + e^{-t}$

13. $e^t[(\cos t - \sin t)\mathbf{i} + (\sin t + \cos t)\mathbf{j} + (t + 1)\mathbf{k}],$
$e^t[-2\sin t\,\mathbf{i} + 2\cos t\,\mathbf{j} + (t + 2)\mathbf{k}], e^t\sqrt{t^2 + 2t + 3}$

15. $\mathbf{v}(t) = t\,\mathbf{i} + 2t\,\mathbf{j} + \mathbf{k}, \mathbf{r}(t) = \left(\frac{1}{2}t^2 + 1\right)\mathbf{i} + t^2\,\mathbf{j} + t\,\mathbf{k}$

17. (a) $\mathbf{r}(t) = \left(\frac{1}{3}t^3 + t\right)\mathbf{i} + (t - \sin t + 1)\mathbf{j} + \left(\frac{1}{4} - \frac{1}{4}\cos 2t\right)\mathbf{k}$
(b)

19. $t = 4$ **21.** $\mathbf{r}(t) = t\,\mathbf{i} - t\,\mathbf{j} + \frac{5}{2}t^2\,\mathbf{k}, |\mathbf{v}(t)| = \sqrt{25t^2 + 2}$

23. (a) ≈ 22 km   (b) ≈ 3.2 km   (c) 500 m/s

25. 30 m/s   **27.** $\approx 10.2°, \approx 79.8°$

29. $13.0° < \theta < 36.0°, 55.4° < \theta < 85.5°$

31. (a) 16 m   (b) $\approx 23.6°$ upstream

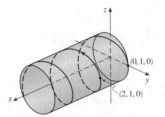

33. $6t, 6$ **35.** $0, 1$ **37.** $e^t - e^{-t}, \sqrt{2}$

39. 4.5 cm/s^2, 9.0 cm/s^2 **41.** $t = 1$

CHAPTER 14 REVIEW ■ **PAGE 886**

True-False Quiz

1. True   **3.** False   **5.** False   **7.** True
9. False   **11.** True

Exercises

1. (a)

(b) $\mathbf{r}'(t) = \mathbf{i} - \pi\sin\pi t\,\mathbf{j} + \pi\cos\pi t\,\mathbf{k},$
$\mathbf{r}''(t) = -\pi^2\cos\pi t\,\mathbf{j} - \pi^2\sin\pi t\,\mathbf{k}$

3. $\mathbf{r}(t) = 4\cos t\,\mathbf{i} + 4\sin t\,\mathbf{j} + (5 - 4\cos t)\mathbf{k}, 0 \le t \le 2\pi$

5. $\frac{1}{3}\mathbf{i} - (2/\pi^2)\mathbf{j} + (2/\pi)\mathbf{k}$ **7.** 86.631 **9.** $\pi/2$

11. (a) $\langle t^2, t, 1 \rangle / \sqrt{t^4 + t^2 + 1}$
(b) $\langle 2t, 1 - t^4, -2t^3 - t \rangle / \sqrt{t^8 + 4t^6 + 2t^4 + 5t^2}$
(c) $\sqrt{t^8 + 4t^6 + 2t^4 + 5t^2}/(t^4 + t^2 + 1)^2$

13. $12/17^{3/2}$ **15.** $x - 2y + 2\pi = 0$

17. $\mathbf{v}(t) = (1 + \ln t)\mathbf{i} + \mathbf{j} - e^{-t}\,\mathbf{k},$
$|\mathbf{v}(t)| = \sqrt{2 + 2\ln t + (\ln t)^2 + e^{-2t}}, \mathbf{a}(t) = (1/t)\mathbf{i} + e^{-t}\,\mathbf{k}$

19. (a) About 3.8 ft above the ground, 60.8 ft from the athlete
(b) ≈ 21.4 ft   (c) ≈ 64.2 ft from the athlete
21. (c) $-2e^{-t}\mathbf{v}_d + e^{-t}\mathbf{R}$

PROBLEMS PLUS ■ PAGE 888

1. (a) $\mathbf{v} = \omega R(-\sin \omega t\, \mathbf{i} + \cos \omega t\, \mathbf{j})$ (c) $\mathbf{a} = -\omega^2 \mathbf{r}$
3. (a) $90°$, $v_0^2/(2g)$
5. (a) ≈ 0.94 ft to the right of the table's edge, ≈ 15 ft/s
(b) $\approx 7.6°$ (c) ≈ 2.13 ft to the right of the table's edge
7. $56°$

CHAPTER 15

EXERCISES 15.1 ■ PAGE 901

1. (a) -27; a temperature of $-15°C$ with wind blowing at
40 km/h feels equivalent to about $-27°C$ without wind.
(b) When the temperature is $-20°C$, what wind speed gives a wind
chill of $-30°C$?   20 km/h
(c) With a wind speed of 20 km/h, what temperature gives a wind
chill of $-49°C$? $-35°C$
(d) A function of wind speed that gives wind-chill values when the
temperature is $-5°C$
(e) A function of temperature that gives wind-chill values when
the wind speed is 50 km/h
3. Yes
5. (a) 25; a 40-knot wind blowing in the open sea for 15 h will
create waves about 25 ft high.
(b) $f(30, t)$ is a function of t giving the wave heights produced by
30-knot winds blowing for t hours.
(c) $f(v, 30)$ is a function of v giving the wave heights produced by
winds of speed v blowing for 30 hours.
7. (a) 4   (b) $\mathbb{R}^2$ (c) $[0, \infty)$
9. (a) e (b) $\{(x, y, z) \mid z \geq x^2 + y^2\}$ (c) $[1, \infty)$
11. $\{(x, y) \mid y \geq -x\}$

13. $\{(x, y) \mid \frac{1}{9}x^2 + y^2 < 1\}$

15. $\{(x, y) \mid -1 \leq x \leq 1, -1 \leq y \leq 1\}$

17. $\{(x, y) \mid y \geq x^2, x \neq \pm 1\}$

19. $\{(x, y, z) \mid x^2 + y^2 + z^2 \leq 1\}$

21. $z = 3$, horizontal plane

23. $4x + 5y + z = 10$, plane

25. $z = y^2 + 1$, parabolic cylinder

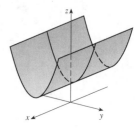

27. $z = 4x^2 + y^2 + 1$
elliptic paraboloid

29. $z = \sqrt{x^2 + y^2}$,
top half of cone

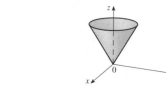

31. $\approx 56, \approx 35$ **33.** Steep; nearly flat

35.

37.

51.

53.

55. (a) C (b) II   **57.** (a) F   (b) I
59. (a) B (b) VI
61. Family of parallel planes
63. Family of hyperboloids of one or two sheets with axis the y-axis
65. (a) Shift the graph of f upward 2 units
(b) Stretch the graph of f vertically by a factor of 2
(c) Reflect the graph of f about the xy-plane
(d) Reflect the graph of f about the xy-plane and then shift it upward 2 units

39. $(y - 2x)^2 = k$

41. $y = \ln x + k$

43. $y = ke^{-x}$

45. $y^2 - x^2 = k^2$

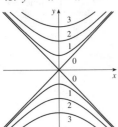

47. $x^2 + 9y^2 = k$

67.

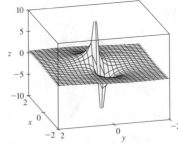

f appears to have a maximum value of about 15. There are two local maximum points but no local minimum point.

69.

The function values approach 0 as x, y become large; as (x, y) approaches the origin, f approaches $\pm\infty$ or 0, depending on the direction of approach.
71. If $c = 0$, the graph is a cylindrical surface. For $c > 0$, the level curves are ellipses. The graph curves upward as we leave the origin, and the steepness increases as c increases. For $c < 0$, the level curves are hyperbolas. The graph curves upward in the y-direction and downward, approaching the xy-plane, in the x-direction giving a saddle-shaped appearance near $(0, 0, 1)$.
73. $c = -2, 0, 2$ **75.** (b) $y = 0.75x + 0.01$

49.

EXERCISES 15.2 ▪ PAGE 913

1. Nothing; if f is continuous, $f(3, 1) = 6$ **3.** $-\frac{5}{2}$

5. 1   **7.** $\frac{2}{7}$ **9.** Does not exist   **11.** Does not exist

13. 0   **15.** Does not exist   **17.** 2   **19.** 1

21. Does not exist

23. The graph shows that the function approaches different numbers along different lines.

25. $h(x, y) = (2x + 3y - 6)^2 + \sqrt{2x + 3y - 6}$; $\{(x, y) \mid 2x + 3y \geq 6\}$

27. Along the line $y = x$ **29.** $\{(x, y) \mid y \neq \pm e^{x/2}\}$

31. $\{(x, y) \mid y \geq 0\}$ **33.** $\{(x, y) \mid x^2 + y^2 > 4\}$

35. $\{(x, y, z) \mid y \geq 0, y \neq \sqrt{x^2 + z^2}\}$

37. $\{(x, y) \mid (x, y) \neq (0, 0)\}$ **39.** 0   **41.** -1

43.

f is continuous on $\mathbb{R}^2$

EXERCISES 15.3 ▪ PAGE 924

1. (a) The rate of change of temperature as longitude varies, with latitude and time fixed; the rate of change as only latitude varies; the rate of change as only time varies.
(b) Positive, negative, positive

3. (a) $f_T(-15, 30) \approx 1.3$; for a temperature of $-15°$C and wind speed of 30 km/h, the wind-chill index rises by 1.3°C for each degree the temperature increases. $f_v(-15, 30) \approx -0.15$; for a temperature of $-15°$C and wind speed of 30 km/h, the wind-chill index decreases by 0.15°C for each km/h the wind speed increases.
(b) Positive, negative   (c) 0

5. (a) Positive   (b) Negative

7. (a) Positive   (b) Negative

9. $c = f, b = f_x, a = f_y$

11. $f_x(1, 2) = -8 =$ slope of C_1, $f_y(1, 2) = -4 =$ slope of C_2

13. $f_x = 2x + 2xy, f_y = 2y + x^2$

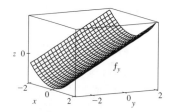

15. $f_x(x, y) = -3y, f_y(x, y) = 5y^4 - 3x$

17. $f_x(x, t) = -\pi e^{-t} \sin \pi x, f_t(x, t) = -e^{-t} \cos \pi x$

19. $\partial z/\partial x = 20(2x + 3y)^9, \partial z/\partial y = 30(2x + 3y)^9$

21. $f_x(x, y) = 2y/(x + y)^2, f_y(x, y) = -2x/(x + y)^2$

23. $\partial w/\partial \alpha = \cos \alpha \cos \beta, \partial w/\partial \beta = -\sin \alpha \sin \beta$

25. $f_r(r, s) = \dfrac{2r^2}{r^2 + s^2} + \ln(r^2 + s^2), f_s(r, s) = \dfrac{2rs}{r^2 + s^2}$

27. $\partial u/\partial t = e^{w/t}(1 - w/t), \partial u/\partial w = e^{w/t}$

29. $f_x = z - 10xy^3z^4, f_y = -15x^2y^2z^4, f_z = x - 20x^2y^3z^3$

31. $\partial w/\partial x = 1/(x + 2y + 3z), \partial w/\partial y = 2/(x + 2y + 3z), \partial w/\partial z = 3/(x + 2y + 3z)$

33. $\partial u/\partial x = y \sin^{-1}(yz), \partial u/\partial y = x \sin^{-1}(yz) + xyz/\sqrt{1 - y^2z^2}, \partial u/\partial z = xy^2/\sqrt{1 - y^2z^2}$

35. $f_x = yz^2 \tan(yt), f_y = xyz^2t \sec^2(yt) + xz^2 \tan(yt), f_z = 2xyz \tan(yt), f_t = xy^2z^2 \sec^2(yt)$

37. $\partial u/\partial x_i = x_i/\sqrt{x_1^2 + x_2^2 + \cdots + x_n^2}$

39. $\frac{1}{5}$ **41.** $\frac{1}{4}$

43. $f_x(x, y) = y^2 - 3x^2y, f_y(x, y) = 2xy - x^3$

45. $\dfrac{\partial z}{\partial x} = \dfrac{3yz - 2x}{2z - 3xy}, \dfrac{\partial z}{\partial y} = \dfrac{3xz - 2y}{2z - 3xy}$

47. $\dfrac{\partial z}{\partial x} = \dfrac{1 + y^2z^2}{1 + y + y^2z^2}, \dfrac{\partial z}{\partial y} = \dfrac{-z}{1 + y + y^2z^2}$

49. (a) $f'(x), g'(y)$ (b) $f'(x + y), f'(x + y)$

51. $f_{xx} = 6xy^5 + 24x^2y, f_{xy} = 15x^2y^4 + 8x^3 = f_{yx}, f_{yy} = 20x^3y^3$

53. $w_{uu} = v^2/(u^2 + v^2)^{3/2}, w_{uv} = -uv/(u^2 + v^2)^{3/2} = w_{vu}, w_{vv} = u^2/(u^2 + v^2)^{3/2}$

55. $z_{xx} = -2x/(1 + x^2)^2, z_{xy} = 0 = z_{yx}, z_{yy} = -2y/(1 + y^2)^2$

61. $12xy$, $72xy$

63. $24\sin(4x + 3y + 2z)$, $12\sin(4x + 3y + 2z)$

65. $\theta e^{r\theta}(2\sin\theta + \theta\cos\theta + r\theta\sin\theta)$ **67.** $4/(y + 2z)^3$, 0

69. ≈ 12.2, ≈ 16.8, ≈ 23.25 **81.** R^2/R_1^2

87. No   **89.** $x = 1 + t$, $y = 2$, $z = 2 - 2t$

93. -2

95. (a)

(b) $f_x(x, y) = \dfrac{x^4y + 4x^2y^3 - y^5}{(x^2 + y^2)^2}$, $f_y(x, y) = \dfrac{x^5 - 4x^3y^2 - xy^4}{(x^2 + y^2)^2}$

(c) $0, 0$ (e) No, since f_{xy} and f_{yx} are not continuous.

EXERCISES 15.4 ▪ PAGE 935

1. $z = -8x - 2y$

3. $x + y - 2z = 0$

5. $z = y$

7.   **9.**

11. $2x + \frac{1}{4}y - 1$ **13.** $\frac{1}{9}x - \frac{2}{9}y + \frac{2}{3}$ **15.** $1 - \pi y$

19. $-\frac{2}{3}x - \frac{7}{3}y + \frac{20}{3}$; $2.84\overline{6}$ **21.** $\frac{3}{7}x + \frac{2}{7}y + \frac{6}{7}z$; 6.9914

23. $4T + H - 329$; $129°F$

25. $dz = 3x^2\ln(y^2)\,dx + (2x^3/y)\,dy$

27. $dm = 5p^4q^3\,dp + 3p^5q^2\,dq$

29. $dR = \beta^2\cos\gamma\,d\alpha + 2\alpha\beta\cos\gamma\,d\beta - \alpha\beta^2\sin\gamma\,d\gamma$

31. $\Delta z = 0.9225$, $dz = 0.9$ **33.** 5.4 cm^2 **35.** 16 cm^3

37. 150 **39.** $\frac{1}{17} \approx 0.059\ \Omega$ **41.** 2.3%

43. $\varepsilon_1 = \Delta x$, $\varepsilon_2 = \Delta y$

EXERCISES 15.5 ▪ PAGE 943

1. $(2x + y)\cos t + (2y + x)e^t$

3. $[(x/t) - y\sin t]/\sqrt{1 + x^2 + y^2}$

5. $e^{y/z}[2t - (x/z) - (2xy/z^2)]$

7. $\partial z/\partial s = 2xy^3\cos t + 3x^2y^2\sin t$,
$\partial z/\partial t = -2sxy^3\sin t + 3sx^2y^2\cos t$

9. $\partial z/\partial s = t^2\cos\theta\cos\phi - 2st\sin\theta\sin\phi$,
$\partial z/\partial t = 2st\cos\theta\cos\phi - s^2\sin\theta\sin\phi$

11. $\dfrac{\partial z}{\partial s} = e^r\left(t\cos\theta - \dfrac{s}{\sqrt{s^2 + t^2}}\sin\theta\right)$,

$\dfrac{\partial z}{\partial t} = e^r\left(s\cos\theta - \dfrac{t}{\sqrt{s^2 + t^2}}\sin\theta\right)$

13. 62 **15.** $7, 2$

17. $\dfrac{\partial u}{\partial r} = \dfrac{\partial u}{\partial x}\dfrac{\partial x}{\partial r} + \dfrac{\partial u}{\partial y}\dfrac{\partial y}{\partial r}$, $\dfrac{\partial u}{\partial s} = \dfrac{\partial u}{\partial x}\dfrac{\partial x}{\partial s} + \dfrac{\partial u}{\partial y}\dfrac{\partial y}{\partial s}$,

$\dfrac{\partial u}{\partial t} = \dfrac{\partial u}{\partial x}\dfrac{\partial x}{\partial t} + \dfrac{\partial u}{\partial y}\dfrac{\partial y}{\partial t}$

19. $\dfrac{\partial w}{\partial x} = \dfrac{\partial w}{\partial r}\dfrac{\partial r}{\partial x} + \dfrac{\partial w}{\partial s}\dfrac{\partial s}{\partial x} + \dfrac{\partial w}{\partial t}\dfrac{\partial t}{\partial x}$,

$\dfrac{\partial w}{\partial y} = \dfrac{\partial w}{\partial r}\dfrac{\partial r}{\partial y} + \dfrac{\partial w}{\partial s}\dfrac{\partial s}{\partial y} + \dfrac{\partial w}{\partial t}\dfrac{\partial t}{\partial y}$

21. $85, 178, 54$ **23.** $\frac{9}{7}, \frac{9}{7}$ **25.** $36, 24, 30$

27. $\dfrac{4(xy)^{3/2} - y}{x - 2x^2\sqrt{xy}}$ **29.** $\dfrac{\sin(x - y) + e^y}{\sin(x - y) - xe^y}$

31. $\dfrac{3yz - 2x}{2z - 3xy}$, $\dfrac{3xz - 2y}{2z - 3xy}$

33. $\dfrac{1 + y^2z^2}{1 + y + y^2z^2}$, $-\dfrac{z}{1 + y + y^2z^2}$

35. $2°C/s$ **37.** ≈ -0.33 m/s per minute

39. (a) 6 m^3/s   (b) 10 m^2/s   (c) 0 m/s

41. ≈ -0.27 L/s   **43.** $-1/(12\sqrt{3})$ rad/s

45. (a) $\partial z/\partial r = (\partial z/\partial x)\cos\theta + (\partial z/\partial y)\sin\theta$,
$\partial z/\partial\theta = -(\partial z/\partial x)r\sin\theta + (\partial z/\partial y)r\cos\theta$

51. $4rs\,\partial^2z/\partial x^2 + (4r^2 + 4s^2)\partial^2z/\partial x\,\partial y + 4rs\,\partial^2z/\partial y^2 + 2\,\partial z/\partial y$

EXERCISES 15.6 ▪ PAGE 956

1. ≈ -0.08 mb/km   **3.** ≈ 0.778 **5.** $2 + \sqrt{3}/2$

7. (a) $\nabla f(x, y) = \langle 2\cos(2x + 3y), 3\cos(2x + 3y)\rangle$
(b) $\langle 2, 3\rangle$ (c) $\sqrt{3} - \frac{3}{2}$

9. (a) $\langle e^{2yz}, 2xze^{2yz}, 2xye^{2yz}\rangle$ (b) $\langle 1, 12, 0\rangle$ (c) $-\frac{22}{3}$

11. $23/10$ **13.** $-8/\sqrt{10}$ **15.** $4/\sqrt{30}$ **17.** $9/(2\sqrt{5})$

19. $2/5$ **21.** $4\sqrt{2}$, $\langle -1, 1\rangle$ **23.** 1, $\langle 0, 1\rangle$

25. 1, $\langle 3, 6, -2\rangle$ **27.** (b) $\langle -12, 92\rangle$

29. All points on the line $y = x + 1$

31. (a) $-40/(3\sqrt{3})$

33. (a) $32/\sqrt{3}$ (b) $\langle 38, 6, 12\rangle$ (c) $2\sqrt{406}$ **35.** $\frac{327}{13}$

39. (a) $x + y + z = 11$ (b) $x - 3 = y - 3 = z - 5$

41. (a) $4x - 5y - z = 4$ (b) $\dfrac{x - 2}{4} = \dfrac{y - 1}{-5} = \dfrac{z + 1}{-1}$

43. (a) $x + y - z = 1$ (b) $x - 1 = y = -z$

45.   **47.** $\langle 2, 3\rangle$, $2x + 3y = 12$

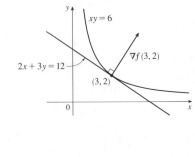

53. No   **59.** $x = -1 - 10t$, $y = 1 - 16t$, $z = 2 - 12t$

63. If $\mathbf{u} = \langle a, b\rangle$ and $\mathbf{v} = \langle c, d\rangle$, then $af_x + bf_y$ and $cf_x + df_y$ are known, so we solve linear equations for f_x and f_y.

1. (a) f has a local minimum at $(1, 1)$.
(b) f has a saddle point at $(1, 1)$.
3. Local minimum at $(1, 1)$, saddle point at $(0, 0)$
5. Maximum $f\left(-1, \frac{1}{2}\right) = 11$
7. Minima $f(1, 1) = 0$, $f(-1, -1) = 0$, saddle point at $(0, 0)$
9. Saddle points at $(1, -1)$, $(-1, 1)$
11. Minimum $f(2, 1) = -8$, saddle point at $(0, 0)$
13. None   **15.** Minimum $f(0, 0) = 0$, saddle points at $(\pm 1, 0)$
17. Minima $f(0, 1) = f(\pi, -1) = f(2\pi, 1) = -1$,
saddle points at $(\pi/2, 0)$, $(3\pi/2, 0)$
21. Minima $f(1, \pm 1) = 3$, $f(-1, \pm 1) = 3$
23. Maximum $f(\pi/3, \pi/3) = 3\sqrt{3}/2$,
minimum $f(5\pi/3, 5\pi/3) = -3\sqrt{3}/2$, saddle point at (π, π)
25. Minima $f(-1.714, 0) \approx -9.200$, $f(1.402, 0) \approx 0.242$,
saddle point $(0.312, 0)$, lowest point $(-1.714, 0, -9.200)$
27. Maxima $f(-1.267, 0) \approx 1.310$, $f(1.629, \pm 1.063) \approx 8.105$,
saddle points $(-0.259, 0)$, $(1.526, 0)$,
highest points $(1.629, \pm 1.063, 8.105)$
29. Maximum $f(2, 0) = 9$, minimum $f(0, 3) = -14$
31. Maximum $f(\pm 1, 1) = 7$, minimum $f(0, 0) = 4$
33. Maximum $f(3, 0) = 83$, minimum $f(1, 1) = 0$
35. Maximum $f(1, 0) = 2$, minimum $f(-1, 0) = -2$
37.

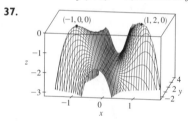

39. $\sqrt{3}$ **41.** $\left(2, 1, \sqrt{5}\right), \left(2, 1, -\sqrt{5}\right)$ **43.** $\frac{100}{3}, \frac{100}{3}, \frac{100}{3}$
45. $8r^3/\left(3\sqrt{3}\right)$
47. $\frac{4}{3}$ **49.** Cube, edge length $c/12$
51. Square base of side 40 cm, height 20 cm   **53.** $L^3/\left(3\sqrt{3}\right)$

1. $\approx 59, 30$
3. No maximum, minima $f(1, 1) = f(-1, -1) = 2$
5. Maxima $f(\pm 2, 1) = 4$, minima $f(\pm 2, -1) = -4$
7. Maximum $f(1, 3, 5) = 70$, minimum $f(-1, -3, -5) = -70$
9. Maximum $2/\sqrt{3}$, minimum $-2/\sqrt{3}$
11. Maximum $\sqrt{3}$, minimum 1
13. Maximum $f\left(\frac{1}{2}, \frac{1}{2}, \frac{1}{2}, \frac{1}{2}\right) = 2$,
minimum $f\left(-\frac{1}{2}, -\frac{1}{2}, -\frac{1}{2}, -\frac{1}{2}\right) = -2$
15. Maximum $f\left(1, \sqrt{2}, -\sqrt{2}\right) = 1 + 2\sqrt{2}$,
minimum $f\left(1, -\sqrt{2}, \sqrt{2}\right) = 1 - 2\sqrt{2}$
17. Maximum $\frac{3}{2}$, minimum $\frac{1}{2}$
19. Maxima $f\left(\pm 1/\sqrt{2}, \mp 1/\left(2\sqrt{2}\right)\right) = e^{1/4}$,
minima $f\left(\pm 1/\sqrt{2}, \pm 1/\left(2\sqrt{2}\right)\right) = e^{-1/4}$
27–37. See Exercises 39–49 in Section 15.7.
39. $L^3/\left(3\sqrt{3}\right)$

41. Nearest $\left(\frac{1}{2}, \frac{1}{2}, \frac{1}{2}\right)$, farthest $(-1, -1, 2)$
43. Maximum ≈ 9.7938, minimum ≈ -5.3506
45. (a) c/n (b) When $x_1 = x_2 = \cdots = x_n$

True-False Quiz

1. True   **3.** False   **5.** False   **7.** True   **9.** False
11. True

Exercises

1. $\{(x, y) \mid y > -x - 1\}$ **3.**

5.

7.

9. $\frac{2}{3}$
11. (a) $\approx 3.5°C/m$, $-3.0°C/m$ (b) $\approx 0.35°C/m$ by
Equation 15.6.9 (Definition 15.6.2 gives $\approx 1.1°C/m$.)
(c) -0.25
13. $f_x = 1/\sqrt{2x + y^2}$, $f_y = y/\sqrt{2x + y^2}$
15. $g_u = \tan^{-1}v$, $g_v = u/(1 + v^2)$
17. $T_p = \ln(q + e^r)$, $T_q = p/(q + e^r)$, $T_r = pe^r/(q + e^r)$
19. $f_{xx} = 24x$, $f_{xy} = -2y = f_{yx}$, $f_{yy} = -2x$
21. $f_{xx} = k(k - 1)x^{k-2}y^lz^m$, $f_{xy} = klx^{k-1}y^{l-1}z^m = f_{yx}$,
$f_{xz} = kmx^{k-1}y^lz^{m-1} = f_{zx}$, $f_{yy} = l(l - 1)x^ky^{l-2}z^m$,
$f_{yz} = lmx^ky^{l-1}z^{m-1} = f_{zy}$, $f_{zz} = m(m - 1)x^ky^lz^{m-2}$
25. (a) $z = 8x + 4y + 1$ (b) $\dfrac{x - 1}{8} = \dfrac{y + 2}{4} = 1 - z$
27. (a) $2x - 2y - 3z = 3$ (b) $\dfrac{x - 2}{4} = \dfrac{y + 1}{-4} = \dfrac{z - 1}{-6}$
29. (a) $4x - y - 2z = 6$
(b) $x = 3 + 8t$, $y = 4 - 2t$, $z = 1 - 4t$
31. $\left(2, \frac{1}{2}, -1\right)$, $\left(-2, -\frac{1}{2}, 1\right)$
33. $60x + \frac{24}{5}y + \frac{32}{5}z - 120$; 38.656
35. $2xy^3(1 + 6p) + 3x^2y^2(pe^p + e^p) + 4z^3(p \cos p + \sin p)$
37. $-47, 108$ **43.** $ze^{x\sqrt{y}}\left\langle z\sqrt{y}, xz/\left(2\sqrt{y}\right), 2\right\rangle$ **45.** $\frac{43}{5}$
47. $\sqrt{145}/2, \left\langle 4, \frac{9}{2}\right\rangle$ **49.** $\approx \frac{5}{8}$ knot/mi

51. Minimum $f(-4, 1) = -11$
53. Maximum $f(1, 1) = 1$; saddle points $(0, 0)$, $(0, 3)$, $(3, 0)$
55. Maximum $f(1, 2) = 4$, minimum $f(2, 4) = -64$
57. Maximum $f(-1, 0) = 2$, minima $f(1, \pm 1) = -3$,
saddle points $(-1, \pm 1)$, $(1, 0)$
59. Maximum $f(\pm\sqrt{2/3}, 1/\sqrt{3}) = 2/(3\sqrt{3})$,
minimum $f(\pm\sqrt{2/3}, -1/\sqrt{3}) = -2/(3\sqrt{3})$
61. Maximum 1, minimum -1
63. $\left(\pm 3^{-1/4}, 3^{-1/4}\sqrt{2}, \pm 3^{1/4}\right), \left(\pm 3^{-1/4}, -3^{-1/4}\sqrt{2}, \pm 3^{1/4}\right)$
65. $P(2 - \sqrt{3}), P(3 - \sqrt{3})/6, P(2\sqrt{3} - 3)/3$

PROBLEMS PLUS ■ **PAGE 984**

1. $L^2W^2, \frac{1}{4}L^2W^2$ **3.** (a) $x = w/3$, base $= w/3$ (b) Yes
7. $\sqrt{6}/2, 3\sqrt{2}/2$

CHAPTER 16

EXERCISES 16.1 ■ **PAGE 994**

1. (a) 288   (b) 144
3. (a) $\pi^2/2 \approx 4.935$ (b) 0
5. (a) -6 (b) -3.5
7. $U < V < L$
9. (a) ≈ 248 (b) 15.5
11. 60   **13.** 3
15. 1.141606, 1.143191, 1.143535, 1.143617, 1.143637, 1.143642

EXERCISES 16.2 ■ **PAGE 1000**

1. $500y^3, 3x^2$ **3.** 10   **5.** 2   **7.** 261,632/45   **9.** $\frac{21}{2}\ln 2$
11. 0   **13.** π **15.** $\frac{21}{2}$ **17.** $9\ln 2$
19. $\frac{1}{2}(\sqrt{3} - 1) - \frac{1}{12}\pi$ **21.** $\frac{1}{2}(e^2 - 3)$
23.

25. 47.5   **27.** $\frac{166}{27}$ **29.** 2   **31.** $\frac{64}{3}$
33. $21e - 57$

35. $\frac{5}{6}$
37. Fubini's Theorem does not apply. The integrand has an infinite discontinuity at the origin.

EXERCISES 16.3 ■ **PAGE 1008**

1. 32   **3.** $\frac{3}{10}$ **5.** $e - 1$ **7.** $\frac{4}{3}$ **9.** π **11.** $\frac{1}{2}e^{16} - \frac{17}{2}$
13. $\frac{1}{2}(1 - \cos 1)$ **15.** $\frac{147}{20}$ **17.** 0   **19.** $\frac{7}{18}$ **21.** $\frac{31}{8}$
23. 6   **25.** $\frac{128}{15}$ **27.** $\frac{1}{3}$ **29.** 0, 1.213, 0.713   **31.** $\frac{64}{3}$
33.

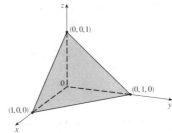

35. 13,984,735,616/14,549,535   **37.** $\pi/2$
39. $\int_0^2 \int_{y^2}^4 f(x, y) \, dx \, dy$ **41.** $\int_{-3}^3 \int_0^{\sqrt{9-x^2}} f(x, y) \, dy \, dx$

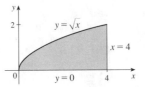

43. $\int_0^{\ln 2} \int_{e^y}^2 f(x, y) \, dx \, dy$

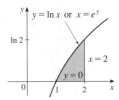

45. $\frac{1}{6}(e^9 - 1)$ **47.** $\frac{1}{3}\ln 9$ **49.** $\frac{1}{3}(2\sqrt{2} - 1)$ **51.** 1
53. $(\pi/16)e^{-1/16} \leq \iint_Q e^{-(x^2+y^2)^2} \, dA \leq \pi/16$ **55.** $\frac{3}{4}$
59. 8π **61.** $2\pi/3$

EXERCISES 16.4 ■ **PAGE 1014**

1. $\int_0^{3\pi/2} \int_0^4 f(r\cos\theta, r\sin\theta) r \, dr \, d\theta$ **3.** $\int_{-1}^1 \int_0^{(x+1)/2} f(x, y) \, dy \, dx$
5. $33\pi/2$

7. 0   **9.** $\frac{1}{2}\pi\sin 9$ **11.** $(\pi/2)(1 - e^{-4})$ **13.** $\frac{3}{64}\pi^2$
15. $\pi/12$ **17.** $\frac{1}{8}(\pi - 2)$ **19.** $\frac{16}{3}\pi$ **21.** $\frac{4}{3}\pi$
23. $\frac{4}{3}\pi a^3$ **25.** $(2\pi/3)\left[1 - (1/\sqrt{2})\right]$
27. $(8\pi/3)(64 - 24\sqrt{3})$
29. $\frac{1}{2}\pi(1 - \cos 9)$ **31.** $2\sqrt{2}/3$
33. 1800π ft^3 **35.** $\frac{15}{16}$ **37.** (a) $\sqrt{\pi}/4$ (b) $\sqrt{\pi}/2$

EXERCISES 16.5 ▪ PAGE 1024

1. $\frac{64}{3}$ C   **3.** $\frac{4}{3}, (\frac{4}{3}, 0)$ **5.** $6, (\frac{4}{7}, \frac{3}{2})$

7. $\frac{1}{4}(e^2 - 1), \left(\dfrac{e^2 + 1}{2(e^2 - 1)}, \dfrac{4(e^3 - 1)}{9(e^2 - 1)} \right)$

9. $L/4$, $(L/2, 16/(9\pi))$ **11.** $(\frac{3}{8}, 3\pi/16)$ **13.** $(0, 45/(14\pi))$

15. $(2a/5, 2a/5)$ if vertex is $(0, 0)$ and sides are along positive axes

17. $\frac{1}{16}(e^4 - 1), \frac{1}{8}(e^2 - 1), \frac{1}{16}(e^4 + 2e^2 - 3)$

19. $7ka^6/180$, $7ka^6/180$, $7ka^6/90$ if vertex is $(0, 0)$ and sides are along positive axes

21. $m = \pi^2/8$, $(\bar{x}, \bar{y}) = \left(\dfrac{2\pi}{3} - \dfrac{1}{\pi}, \dfrac{16}{9\pi} \right)$, $I_x = 3\pi^2/64$,

$I_y = \frac{1}{16}(\pi^4 - 3\pi^2)$, $I_0 = \pi^4/16 - 9\pi^2/64$

23. $\rho bh^3/3$, $\rho b^3h/3$; $b/\sqrt{3}$, $h/\sqrt{3}$

25. $\rho a^4 \pi/16$, $\rho a^4 \pi/16$; $a/2$, $a/2$

27. (a) $\frac{1}{2}$ (b) 0.375 (c) $\frac{5}{48} \approx 0.1042$

29. (b) (i) $e^{-0.2} \approx 0.8187$

(ii) $1 + e^{-1.8} - e^{-0.8} - e^{-1} \approx 0.3481$ (c) $2, 5$

31. (a) ≈ 0.500 (b) ≈ 0.632

33. (a) $\iint_D (k/20)[20 - \sqrt{(x - x_0)^2 + (y - y_0)^2}] \, dA$, where D is the disk with radius 10 mi centered at the center of the city

(b) $200\pi k/3 \approx 209k$, $200(\pi/2 - \frac{8}{9})k \approx 136k$, on the edge

EXERCISES 16.6 ▪ PAGE 1034

1. $\frac{27}{4}$ **3.** 1 **5.** $\frac{1}{3}(e^3 - 1)$ **7.** $-\frac{1}{3}$ **9.** 4 **11.** $\frac{65}{28}$

13. $8/(3e)$ **15.** $\frac{1}{60}$ **17.** $16\pi/3$ **19.** $\frac{16}{3}$ **21.** 36π

23. (a) $\int_0^1 \int_0^x \int_0^{\sqrt{1-y^2}} dz\,dy\,dx$ (b) $\frac{1}{4}\pi - \frac{1}{3}$

25. 60.533

27.

29. $\int_{-2}^{2} \int_0^{4-x^2} \int_{-\sqrt{4-x^2-y}/2}^{\sqrt{4-x^2-y}/2} f(x, y, z) \, dz\,dy\,dx$

$= \int_0^4 \int_{-\sqrt{4-y}}^{\sqrt{4-y}} \int_{-\sqrt{4-x^2-y}/2}^{\sqrt{4-x^2-y}/2} f(x, y, z) \, dz\,dx\,dy$

$= \int_{-1}^1 \int_0^{4-4z^2} \int_{-\sqrt{4-y-4z^2}}^{\sqrt{4-y-4z^2}} f(x, y, z) \, dx\,dy\,dz$

$= \int_0^4 \int_{-\sqrt{4-y}/2}^{\sqrt{4-y}/2} \int_{-\sqrt{4-y-4z^2}}^{\sqrt{4-y-4z^2}} f(x, y, z) \, dx\,dz\,dy$

$= \int_{-2}^2 \int_{-\sqrt{4-x^2}/2}^{\sqrt{4-x^2}/2} \int_0^{4-x^2-4z^2} f(x, y, z) \, dy\,dz\,dx$

$= \int_{-1}^1 \int_{-\sqrt{4-4z^2}}^{\sqrt{4-4z^2}} \int_0^{4-x^2-4z^2} f(x, y, z) \, dy\,dx\,dz$

31. $\int_{-2}^{2} \int_{x^2}^{4} \int_0^{2-y/2} f(x, y, z) \, dz\,dy\,dx$

$= \int_0^4 \int_{-\sqrt{y}}^{\sqrt{y}} \int_0^{2-y/2} f(x, y, z) \, dz\,dx\,dy$

$= \int_0^2 \int_0^{4-2z} \int_{-\sqrt{y}}^{\sqrt{y}} f(x, y, z) \, dx\,dy\,dz$

$= \int_0^4 \int_0^{2-y/2} \int_{-\sqrt{y}}^{\sqrt{y}} f(x, y, z) \, dx\,dz\,dy$

$= \int_{-2}^2 \int_0^{2-x^2/2} \int_{x^2}^{4-2z} f(x, y, z) \, dy\,dz\,dx$

$= \int_0^2 \int_{-\sqrt{4-2z}}^{\sqrt{4-2z}} \int_{x^2}^{4-2z} f(x, y, z) \, dy\,dx\,dz$

33. $\int_0^1 \int_{\sqrt{x}}^1 \int_0^{1-y} f(x, y, z) \, dz\,dy\,dx$

$= \int_0^1 \int_0^{y^2} \int_0^{1-y} f(x, y, z) \, dz\,dx\,dy$

$= \int_0^1 \int_0^{1-z} \int_0^{y^2} f(x, y, z) \, dx\,dy\,dz$

$= \int_0^1 \int_0^{1-y} \int_0^{y^2} f(x, y, z) \, dx\,dz\,dy$

$= \int_0^1 \int_0^{1-\sqrt{x}} \int_{\sqrt{x}}^{1-z} f(x, y, z) \, dy\,dz\,dx$

$= \int_0^1 \int_0^{(1-z)^2} \int_{\sqrt{x}}^{1-z} f(x, y, z) \, dy\,dx\,dz$

35. $\int_0^1 \int_y^1 \int_0^y f(x, y, z) \, dz\,dx\,dy = \int_0^1 \int_0^x \int_0^y f(x, y, z) \, dz\,dy\,dx$

$= \int_0^1 \int_z^1 \int_y^1 f(x, y, z) \, dx\,dy\,dz = \int_0^1 \int_0^y \int_y^1 f(x, y, z) \, dx\,dz\,dy$

$= \int_0^1 \int_0^x \int_z^x f(x, y, z) \, dy\,dz\,dx = \int_0^1 \int_z^1 \int_z^x f(x, y, z) \, dy\,dx\,dz$

37. $\frac{79}{30}, (\frac{358}{553}, \frac{33}{79}, \frac{571}{553})$ **39.** $a^5, (7a/12, 7a/12, 7a/12)$

41. $I_x = I_y = I_z = \frac{2}{3}kL^5$ **43.** $\frac{1}{2}\pi kha^4$

45. (a) $m = \int_{-3}^{3} \int_{-\sqrt{9-x^2}}^{\sqrt{9-x^2}} \int_1^{5-y} \sqrt{x^2 + y^2} \, dz\,dy\,dx$

(b) $(\bar{x}, \bar{y}, \bar{z})$, where

$\bar{x} = (1/m) \int_{-3}^{3} \int_{-\sqrt{9-x^2}}^{\sqrt{9-x^2}} \int_1^{5-y} x\sqrt{x^2 + y^2} \, dz\,dy\,dx$

$\bar{y} = (1/m) \int_{-3}^{3} \int_{-\sqrt{9-x^2}}^{\sqrt{9-x^2}} \int_1^{5-y} y\sqrt{x^2 + y^2} \, dz\,dy\,dx$

$\bar{z} = (1/m) \int_{-3}^{3} \int_{-\sqrt{9-x^2}}^{\sqrt{9-x^2}} \int_1^{5-y} z\sqrt{x^2 + y^2} \, dz\,dy\,dx$

(c) $\int_{-3}^{3} \int_{-\sqrt{9-x^2}}^{\sqrt{9-x^2}} \int_1^{5-y} (x^2 + y^2)^{3/2} \, dz\,dy\,dx$

47. (a) $\frac{3}{32}\pi + \frac{11}{24}$

(b) $(\bar{x}, \bar{y}, \bar{z}) = \left(\dfrac{28}{9\pi + 44}, \dfrac{30\pi + 128}{45\pi + 220}, \dfrac{45\pi + 208}{135\pi + 660} \right)$

(c) $\frac{1}{240}(68 + 15\pi)$

49. (a) $\frac{1}{8}$ (b) $\frac{1}{64}$ (c) $\frac{1}{5760}$

51. $L^3/8$

53. The region bounded by the ellipsoid $x^2 + 2y^2 + 3z^2 = 1$

EXERCISES 16.7 ▪ PAGE 1040

1. (a)

$(\sqrt{2}, \sqrt{2}, 1)$ $(2, -2\sqrt{3}, 5)$

3. (a) $(\sqrt{2}, 7\pi/4, 4)$ (b) $(2, 4\pi/3, 2)$

5. Vertical half-plane through the z-axis   **7.** Circular paraboloid

9. (a) $z = r^2$ (b) $r = 2\sin\theta$

11.

13. Cylindrical coordinates: $6 \le r \le 7, 0 \le \theta \le 2\pi, 0 \le z \le 20$

15.

$64\pi/3$

17. 384π **19.** $\pi(e^6 - e - 5)$ **21.** $2\pi/5$
23. (a) 162π (b) $(0, 0, 15)$
25. $\pi Ka^2/8, (0, 0, 2a/3)$ **27.** 0
29. (a) $\iiint_C h(P)g(P) \, dV$, where C is the cone
(b) $\approx 3.1 \times 10^{19}$ ft-lb

EXERCISES 16.8 ▪ PAGE 1046

1. (a)

$(0, 0, 1)$

(b)

$\left(\tfrac{1}{2}\sqrt{2}, \tfrac{1}{2}\sqrt{6}, \sqrt{2}\right)$

3. (a) $(4, \pi/3, \pi/6)$ (b) $\left(\sqrt{2}, 3\pi/2, 3\pi/4\right)$
5. Half-cone
7. Sphere, radius $\tfrac{1}{2}$, center $\left(0, \tfrac{1}{2}, 0\right)$
9. (a) $\cos^2\phi = \sin^2\phi$ (b) $\rho^2(\sin^2\phi \cos^2\theta + \cos^2\phi) = 9$
11.

$\rho = 2$

13.

$\phi = \dfrac{3\pi}{4}$

$\rho = 1$

15. $0 \le \phi \le \pi/4, 0 \le \rho \le \cos\phi$

17.

$(9\pi/4)\left(2 - \sqrt{3}\right)$

19. $\int_0^{\pi/2} \int_0^3 \int_0^2 f(r\cos\theta, r\sin\theta, z) \, r \, dz \, dr \, d\theta$
21. $312{,}500\,\pi/7$ **23.** $15\pi/16$ **25.** $1562\pi/15$
27. $\left(\sqrt{3} - 1\right)\pi a^3/3$ **29.** (a) 10π (b) $(0, 0, 2.1)$
31. $\left(0, \tfrac{525}{296}, 0\right)$
33. (a) $\left(0, 0, \tfrac{3}{8}a\right)$ (b) $4K\pi a^5/15$
35. $(2\pi/3)\left[1 - (1/\sqrt{2})\right], \left(0, 0, 3/\left[8(2 - \sqrt{2})\right]\right)$
37. $5\pi/6$ **39.** $\left(4\sqrt{2} - 5\right)/15$
41.

43. $136\pi/99$

EXERCISES 16.9 ▪ PAGE 1056

1. 16 **3.** $\sin^2\theta - \cos^2\theta$ **5.** 0
7. The parallelogram with vertices $(0, 0), (6, 3), (12, 1), (6, -2)$
9. The region bounded by the line $y = 1$, the y-axis, and $y = \sqrt{x}$
11. -3 **13.** 6π **15.** $2\ln 3$
17. (a) $\tfrac{4}{3}\pi abc$ (b) 1.083×10^{12} km^3
19. $\tfrac{8}{5}\ln 8$ **21.** $\tfrac{3}{2}\sin 1$ **23.** $e - e^{-1}$

CHAPTER 16 REVIEW ▪ PAGE 1057

True-False Quiz

1. True **3.** True **5.** True **7.** False

Exercises

1. ≈ 64.0 **3.** $4e^2 - 4e + 3$ **5.** $\tfrac{1}{2}\sin 1$ **7.** $\tfrac{2}{3}$
9. $\int_0^\pi \int_2^4 f(r\cos\theta, r\sin\theta) \, r \, dr \, d\theta$
11. The region inside the loop of the four-leaved rose $r = \sin 2\theta$ in the first quadrant
13. $\tfrac{1}{2}\sin 1$ **15.** $\tfrac{1}{2}e^6 - \tfrac{7}{2}$ **17.** $\tfrac{1}{4}\ln 2$ **19.** 8
21. $81\pi/5$ **23.** 40.5 **25.** $\pi/96$ **27.** $\tfrac{64}{15}$ **29.** 176
31. $\tfrac{2}{3}$ **33.** $2ma^3/9$
35. (a) $\tfrac{1}{4}$ (b) $\left(\tfrac{1}{3}, \tfrac{8}{15}\right)$
(c) $I_x = \tfrac{1}{12}, I_y = \tfrac{1}{24}; \bar{\bar{y}} = 1/\sqrt{3}, \bar{\bar{x}} = 1/\sqrt{6}$
37. $(0, 0, h/4)$
39. 97.2 **41.** 0.0512
43. (a) $\tfrac{1}{15}$ (b) $\tfrac{1}{3}$ (c) $\tfrac{1}{45}$
45. $\int_0^1 \int_0^{1-z} \int_{-\sqrt{y}}^{\sqrt{y}} f(x, y, z) \, dx \, dy \, dz$ **47.** $-\ln 2$ **49.** 0

PROBLEMS PLUS ▪ PAGE 1060

1. 30 **3.** $\tfrac{1}{2}\sin 1$ **7.** (b) 0.90

CHAPTER 17

1.

3.

5.

7.

9.

11. II **13.** I **15.** IV **17.** III
19. The line $y = 2x$

21. $\nabla f(x, y) = (xy + 1)e^{xy}\,\mathbf{i} + x^2 e^{xy}\,\mathbf{j}$

23. $\nabla f(x, y, z) = \dfrac{x}{\sqrt{x^2 + y^2 + z^2}}\,\mathbf{i}$

$+ \dfrac{y}{\sqrt{x^2 + y^2 + z^2}}\,\mathbf{j} + \dfrac{z}{\sqrt{x^2 + y^2 + z^2}}\,\mathbf{k}$

25. $\nabla f(x, y) = 2x\,\mathbf{i} - \mathbf{j}$

27.

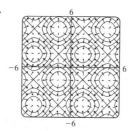

29. III **31.** II **33.** (2.04, 1.03)
35. (a) (b) $y = 1/x, x > 0$

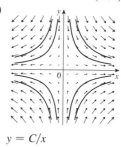

$y = C/x$

1. $\frac{1}{54}(145^{3/2} - 1)$ **3.** 1638.4 **5.** $\frac{243}{8}$ **7.** $\frac{17}{3}$ **9.** $\sqrt{5}\,\pi$
11. $\frac{1}{12}\sqrt{14}(e^6 - 1)$ **13.** $\frac{1}{5}$ **15.** $\frac{97}{3}$
17. (a) Positive (b) Negative
19. 45 **21.** $\frac{6}{5} - \cos 1 - \sin 1$ **23.** 1.9633 **25.** 15.0074
27. $3\pi + \frac{2}{3}$

29. (a) $\frac{11}{8} - 1/e$ (b)

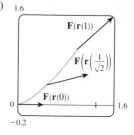

31. $\frac{172,704}{5,632,705}\sqrt{2}(1 - e^{-14\pi})$ **33.** $2\pi k, (4/\pi, 0)$
35. (a) $\bar{x} = (1/m)\int_C x\rho(x, y, z)\,ds,$
$\bar{y} = (1/m)\int_C y\rho(x, y, z)\,ds,$
$\bar{z} = (1/m)\int_C z\rho(x, y, z)\,ds,$ where $m = \int_C \rho(x, y, z)\,ds$
(b) $(0, 0, 3\pi)$
37. $I_x = k\left(\frac{1}{2}\pi - \frac{4}{3}\right), I_y = k\left(\frac{1}{2}\pi - \frac{2}{3}\right)$
39. $2\pi^2$ **41.** 26 **43.** 1.67×10^4 ft-lb **45.** (b) Yes
47. ≈ 22 J

EXERCISES 17.3 ▪ PAGE 1089

1. 40 **3.** $f(x, y) = x^2 - 3xy + 2y^2 - 8y + K$
5. $f(x, y) = e^x \sin y + K$ **7.** $f(x, y) = ye^x + x \sin y + K$
9. $f(x, y) = x \ln y + x^2 y^3 + K$
11. (b) 16 **13.** (a) $f(x, y) = \frac{1}{2} x^2 y^2$ (b) 2
15. (a) $f(x, y, z) = xyz + z^2$ (b) 77
17. (a) $f(x, y, z) = xy^2 \cos z$ (b) 0
19. 2 **21.** 30 **23.** No **25.** Conservative
29. (a) Yes (b) Yes (c) Yes
31. (a) Yes (b) Yes (c) No

EXERCISES 17.4 ▪ PAGE 1096

1. 8π **3.** $\frac{2}{3}$ **5.** 12 **7.** $\frac{1}{3}$ **9.** -24π **11.** $\frac{4}{3} - 2\pi$
13. $\frac{625}{2}\pi$ **15.** $-8e + 48e^{-1}$ **17.** $-\frac{1}{12}$ **19.** 3π **21.** (c) $\frac{9}{2}$
23. $(4a/3\pi, 4a/3\pi)$ if the region is the portion of the disk
$x^2 + y^2 = a^2$ in the first quadrant

EXERCISES 17.5 ▪ PAGE 1104

1. (a) $-x^2 \mathbf{i} + 3xy \mathbf{j} - xz \mathbf{k}$ (b) yz
3. (a) $(x - y)\mathbf{i} - y\mathbf{j} + \mathbf{k}$ (b) $z - 1/(2\sqrt{z})$
5. (a) $\mathbf{0}$ (b) $2/\sqrt{x^2 + y^2 + z^2}$
7. (a) $\langle 1/y, -1/x, 1/x \rangle$ (b) $1/x + 1/y + 1/z$
9. (a) Negative (b) curl $\mathbf{F} = \mathbf{0}$
11. (a) Zero (b) curl $\mathbf{F}$ points in the negative z-direction
13. $f(x, y, z) = xy^2 z^3 + K$ **15.** $f(x, y, z) = x^2 y + y^2 z + K$
17. Not conservative **19.** No

EXERCISES 17.6 ▪ PAGE 1114

1. P: no; Q: yes
3. Plane through $(0, 3, 1)$ containing vectors $\langle 1, 0, 4 \rangle$, $\langle 1, -1, 5 \rangle$
5. Hyperbolic paraboloid
7.

9.

11.

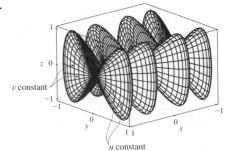

13. IV **15.** II **17.** III
19. $x = 1 + u + v, y = 2 + u - v, z = -3 - u + v$
21. $x = x, z = z, y = \sqrt{1 - x^2 + z^2}$
23. $x = 2 \sin \phi \cos \theta, y = 2 \sin \phi \sin \theta,$
$z = 2 \cos \phi, 0 \le \phi \le \pi/4, 0 \le \theta \le 2\pi$
$\left[\text{or } x = x, y = y, z = \sqrt{4 - x^2 - y^2}, x^2 + y^2 \le 2 \right]$
25. $x = x, y = 4 \cos \theta, z = 4 \sin \theta, 0 \le x \le 5, 0 \le \theta \le 2\pi$

29. $x = x, y = e^{-x} \cos \theta,$
$z = e^{-x} \sin \theta, 0 \le x \le 3,$
$0 \le \theta \le 2\pi$

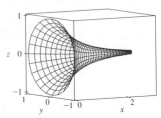

31. (a) Direction reverses (b) Number of coils doubles
33. $3x - y + 3z = 3$ **35.** $-x + 2z = 1$ **37.** $3\sqrt{14}$
39. $\frac{4}{15}(3^{5/2} - 2^{7/2} + 1)$ **41.** $(2\pi/3)(2\sqrt{2} - 1)$
43. $(\pi/6)(17\sqrt{17} - 5\sqrt{5})$
45. $\frac{1}{2}\sqrt{21} + \frac{17}{4}[\ln(2 + \sqrt{21}) - \ln \sqrt{17}]$ **47.** 4
49. 13.9783
51. (a) 24.2055 (b) 24.2476
53. $\frac{45}{8}\sqrt{14} + \frac{15}{16} \ln[(11\sqrt{5} + 3\sqrt{70})/(3\sqrt{5} + \sqrt{70})]$
55. (b)

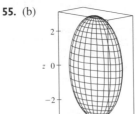

(c) $\int_0^{2\pi} \int_0^\pi \sqrt{36 \sin^4 u \cos^2 v + 9 \sin^4 u \sin^2 v + 4 \cos^2 u \sin^2 u} \, du \, dv$
57. 4π **59.** $2a^2(\pi - 2)$

EXERCISES 17.7 ▪ PAGE 1127

1. 49.09 **3.** 900π **5.** $171\sqrt{14}$ **7.** $\sqrt{3}/24$
9. $5\sqrt{5}/48 + 1/240$ **11.** $364\sqrt{2}\pi/3$
13. $(\pi/60)(391\sqrt{17} + 1)$ **15.** 16π **17.** 12

19. $\frac{713}{180}$ **21.** $-\frac{1}{6}$ **23.** $-\frac{4}{3}\pi$ **25.** 0 **27.** 48

29. $2\pi + \frac{8}{3}$ **31.** 0.1642 **33.** 3.4895

35. $\iint_S \mathbf{F} \cdot d\mathbf{S} = \iint_D [P(\partial h/\partial x) - Q + R(\partial h/\partial z)]\, dA$,
where D = projection of S on xz-plane

37. $(0, 0, a/2)$

39. (a) $I_z = \iint_S (x^2 + y^2)\rho(x, y, z)\, dS$ (b) $4329\sqrt{2}\,\pi/5$

41. 0 kg/s **43.** $\frac{8}{3}\pi a^3 \varepsilon_0$ **45.** 1248π

3. 0 **5.** 0 **7.** -1 **9.** 80π

11. (a) $81\pi/2$ (b)

(c) $x = 3\cos t$, $y = 3\sin t$,
$z = 1 - 3(\cos t + \sin t)$,
$0 \le t \le 2\pi$

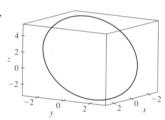

17. 3

5. 2 **7.** $9\pi/2$

9. 0 **11.** $32\pi/3$ **13.** 0

15. $341\sqrt{2}/60 + \frac{81}{20}\arcsin(\sqrt{3}/3)$ **17.** $13\pi/20$

19. Negative at P_1, positive at P_2

21. div $\mathbf{F} > 0$ in quadrants I, II; div $\mathbf{F} < 0$ in quadrants III, IV

True-False Quiz

1. False **3.** True **5.** False **7.** True

Exercises

1. (a) Negative (b) Positive **3.** $6\sqrt{10}$ **5.** $\frac{4}{15}$

7. $\frac{110}{3}$ **9.** $\frac{11}{12} - 4/e$ **11.** $f(x, y) = e^y + xe^{xy}$ **13.** 0

17. -8π **25.** $\frac{1}{6}(27 - 5\sqrt{5})$

27. $(\pi/60)(391\sqrt{17} + 1)$ **29.** $-64\pi/3$

33. $-\frac{1}{2}$ **37.** -4 **39.** 21

CHAPTER 18

1. $y = c_1 e^{3x} + c_2 e^{-2x}$ **3.** $y = c_1 \cos 4x + c_2 \sin 4x$

5. $y = c_1 e^{2x/3} + c_2 x e^{2x/3}$ **7.** $y = c_1 + c_2 e^{x/2}$

9. $y = e^{2x}(c_1 \cos 3x + c_2 \sin 3x)$

11. $y = c_1 e^{(\sqrt{3}-1)t/2} + c_2 e^{-(\sqrt{3}+1)t/2}$

13. $P = e^{-t}\left[c_1 \cos(\frac{1}{10}t) + c_2 \sin(\frac{1}{10}t)\right]$

15.

All solutions approach either 0 or $\pm\infty$ as $x \to \pm\infty$.

17. $y = 2e^{-3x/2} + e^{-x}$ **19.** $y = e^{x/2} - 2xe^{x/2}$

21. $y = 3\cos 4x - \sin 4x$ **23.** $y = e^{-x}(2\cos x + 3\sin x)$

25. $y = 3\cos(\frac{1}{2}x) - 4\sin(\frac{1}{2}x)$ **27.** $y = \dfrac{e^{x+3}}{e^3 - 1} + \dfrac{e^{2x}}{1 - e^3}$

29. No solution

31. $y = e^{-2x}(2\cos 3x - e^\pi \sin 3x)$

33. (b) $\lambda = n^2\pi^2/L^2$, n a positive integer; $y = C \sin(n\pi x/L)$

1. $y = c_1 e^{-2x} + c_2 e^{-x} + \frac{1}{2}x^2 - \frac{3}{2}x + \frac{7}{4}$

3. $y = c_1 + c_2 e^{2x} + \frac{1}{40}\cos 4x - \frac{1}{20}\sin 4x$

5. $y = e^{2x}(c_1 \cos x + c_2 \sin x) + \frac{1}{10}e^{-x}$

7. $y = \frac{3}{2}\cos x + \frac{11}{2}\sin x + \frac{1}{2}e^x + x^3 - 6x$

9. $y = e^x(\frac{1}{2}x^2 - x + 2)$

11.

The solutions are all asymptotic to $y_p = \frac{1}{10}\cos x + \frac{3}{10}\sin x$ as $x \to \infty$. Except for y_p, all solutions approach either ∞ or $-\infty$ as $x \to -\infty$.

13. $y_p = Ae^{2x} + (Bx^2 + Cx + D)\cos x + (Ex^2 + Fx + G)\sin x$

15. $y_p = Ax + (Bx + C)e^{9x}$

17. $y_p = xe^{-x}[(Ax^2 + Bx + C)\cos 3x + (Dx^2 + Ex + F)\sin 3x]$

19. $y = c_1 \cos(\frac{1}{2}x) + c_2 \sin(\frac{1}{2}x) - \frac{1}{3}\cos x$

21. $y = c_1 e^x + c_2 x e^x + e^{2x}$

23. $y = c_1 \sin x + c_2 \cos x + \sin x \ln(\sec x + \tan x) - 1$

25. $y = [c_1 + \ln(1 + e^{-x})]e^x + [c_2 - e^{-x} + \ln(1 + e^{-x})]e^{2x}$

27. $y = e^x\left[c_1 + c_2 x - \frac{1}{2}\ln(1 + x^2) + x\tan^{-1}x\right]$

1. $x = 0.35\cos(2\sqrt{5}\,t)$ **3.** $x = -\frac{1}{5}e^{-6t} + \frac{6}{5}e^{-t}$ **5.** $\frac{49}{12}$ kg

7.

13. $Q(t) = (-e^{-10t}/250)(6 \cos 20t + 3 \sin 20t) + \frac{3}{125}$,
$I(t) = \frac{3}{5}e^{-10t} \sin 20t$

15. $Q(t) = e^{-10t}\left[\frac{3}{250} \cos 20t - \frac{3}{500} \sin 20t\right]$
$- \frac{3}{250} \cos 10t + \frac{3}{125} \sin 10t$

EXERCISES 18.4 ▪ PAGE 1173

1. $c_0 \sum\limits_{n=0}^{\infty} \dfrac{x^n}{n!} = c_0 e^x$ **3.** $c_0 \sum\limits_{n=0}^{\infty} \dfrac{x^{3n}}{3^n n!} = c_0 e^{x^3/3}$

5. $c_0 \sum\limits_{n=0}^{\infty} \dfrac{(-1)^n}{2^n n!} x^{2n} + c_1 \sum\limits_{n=0}^{\infty} \dfrac{(-2)^n n!}{(2n+1)!} x^{2n+1}$

7. $c_0 + c_1 \sum\limits_{n=1}^{\infty} \dfrac{x^n}{n} = c_0 - c_1 \ln(1 - x)$ for $|x| < 1$

9. $\sum\limits_{n=0}^{\infty} \dfrac{x^{2n}}{2^n n!} = e^{x^2/2}$

11. $x + \sum\limits_{n=1}^{\infty} \dfrac{(-1)^n 2^2 5^2 \cdot \ldots \cdot (3n-1)^2}{(3n+1)!} x^{3n+1}$

CHAPTER 18 REVIEW ▪ PAGE 1174

True-False Quiz

1. True   **3.** True

Exercises

1. $y = c_1 e^{5x} + c_2 e^{-3x}$ **3.** $y = c_1 \cos(\sqrt{3}x) + c_2 \sin(\sqrt{3}x)$

5. $y = e^{2x}(c_1 \cos x + c_2 \sin x + 1)$

7. $y = c_1 e^x + c_2 x e^x - \frac{1}{2} \cos x - \frac{1}{2}(x + 1) \sin x$

9. $y = c_1 e^{3x} + c_2 e^{-2x} - \frac{1}{6} - \frac{1}{5}x e^{-2x}$

11. $y = 5 - 2e^{-6(x-1)}$ **13.** $y = (e^{4x} - e^x)/3$

15. $\sum\limits_{n=0}^{\infty} \dfrac{(-2)^n n!}{(2n+1)!} x^{2n+1}$

17. $Q(t) = -0.02e^{-10t}(\cos 10t + \sin 10t) + 0.03$

19. (c) $2\pi/k \approx 85$ min   (d) $\approx 17{,}600$ mi/h

APPENDIXES

EXERCISES A ▪ PAGE A9

1. 18   **3.** π **5.** $5 - \sqrt{5}$ **7.** $2 - x$

9. $|x + 1| = \begin{cases} x + 1 & \text{for } x \geqslant -1 \\ -x - 1 & \text{for } x < -1 \end{cases}$ **11.** $x^2 + 1$

13. $(-2, \infty)$

15. $[-1, \infty)$

17. $(3, \infty)$

19. $(2, 6)$

21. $(0, 1]$

23. $\left[-1, \frac{1}{2}\right)$

25. $(-\infty, 1) \cup (2, \infty)$

27. $\left[-1, \frac{1}{2}\right]$

29. $(-\infty, \infty)$

31. $(-\sqrt{3}, \sqrt{3})$

33. $(-\infty, 1]$

35. $(-1, 0) \cup (1, \infty)$

37. $(-\infty, 0) \cup \left(\frac{1}{4}, \infty\right)$

39. $10 \leqslant C \leqslant 35$ **41.** (a) $T = 20 - 10h, 0 \leqslant h \leqslant 12$
(b) $-30°C \leqslant T \leqslant 20°C$ **43.** $\pm\frac{3}{2}$ **45.** $2, -\frac{4}{3}$
47. $(-3, 3)$ **49.** $(3, 5)$ **51.** $(-\infty, -7] \cup [-3, \infty)$
53. $[1.3, 1.7]$ **55.** $[-4, -1] \cup [1, 4]$
57. $x \geqslant (a + b)c/(ab)$ **59.** $x > (c - b)/a$

EXERCISES B ▪ PAGE A15

1. 5   **3.** $\sqrt{74}$ **5.** $2\sqrt{37}$ **7.** 2   **9.** $-\frac{9}{2}$

17.

19.

21. $y = 6x - 15$ **23.** $2x - 3y + 19 = 0$
25. $5x + y = 11$ **27.** $y = 3x - 2$ **29.** $y = 3x - 3$
31. $y = 5$ **33.** $x + 2y + 11 = 0$ **35.** $5x - 2y + 1 = 0$
37. $m = -\frac{1}{3}$,   **39.** $m = 0$,   **41.** $m = \frac{3}{4}$,
$b = 0$ $b = -2$ $b = -3$

43.

45.

47.

49.

51.
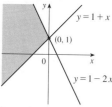

53. $(0, -4)$ **55.** (a) $(4, 9)$ (b) $(3.5, -3)$ **57.** $(1, -2)$
59. $y = x - 3$ **61.** (b) $4x - 3y - 24 = 0$

EXERCISES C ▪ PAGE A23

1. $(x - 3)^2 + (y + 1)^2 = 25$ **3.** $x^2 + y^2 = 65$

5. $(2, -5), 4$ **7.** $\left(-\frac{1}{2}, 0\right), \frac{1}{2}$ **9.** $\left(\frac{1}{4}, -\frac{1}{4}\right), \sqrt{10}/4$

11. Parabola

13. Ellipse

15. Hyperbola

17. Ellipse

19. Parabola

21. Hyperbola

23. Hyperbola

25. Ellipse

27. Parabola

29. Parabola

31. Ellipse

33.

35. $y = x^2 - 2x$
37.

39.

EXERCISES D ▪ PAGE A32

1. $7\pi/6$ **3.** $\pi/20$ **5.** 5π **7.** $720°$ **9.** $75°$
11. $-67.5°$ **13.** 3π cm **15.** $\frac{2}{3}$ rad $= (120/\pi)°$
17.

19.

21.
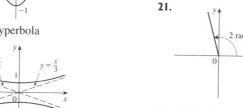

23. $\sin(3\pi/4) = 1/\sqrt{2}$, $\cos(3\pi/4) = -1/\sqrt{2}$, $\tan(3\pi/4) = -1$,
$\csc(3\pi/4) = \sqrt{2}$, $\sec(3\pi/4) = -\sqrt{2}$, $\cot(3\pi/4) = -1$
25. $\sin(9\pi/2) = 1$, $\cos(9\pi/2) = 0$, $\csc(9\pi/2) = 1$, $\cot(9\pi/2) = 0$,
$\tan(9\pi/2)$ and $\sec(9\pi/2)$ undefined
27. $\sin(5\pi/6) = \frac{1}{2}$, $\cos(5\pi/6) = -\sqrt{3}/2$, $\tan(5\pi/6) = -1/\sqrt{3}$,
$\csc(5\pi/6) = 2$, $\sec(5\pi/6) = -2/\sqrt{3}$, $\cot(5\pi/6) = -\sqrt{3}$
29. $\cos \theta = \frac{4}{5}$, $\tan \theta = \frac{3}{4}$, $\csc \theta = \frac{5}{3}$, $\sec \theta = \frac{5}{4}$, $\cot \theta = \frac{4}{3}$
31. $\sin \phi = \sqrt{5}/3$, $\cos \phi = -\frac{2}{3}$, $\tan \phi = -\sqrt{5}/2$, $\csc \phi = 3/\sqrt{5}$,
$\cot \phi = -2/\sqrt{5}$

33. $\sin \beta = -1/\sqrt{10}$, $\cos \beta = -3/\sqrt{10}$, $\tan \beta = \frac{1}{3}$,
$\csc \beta = -\sqrt{10}$, $\sec \beta = -\sqrt{10}/3$

35. 5.73576 cm   **37.** 24.62147 cm   **59.** $\frac{1}{15}(4 + 6\sqrt{2})$

61. $\frac{1}{15}(3 + 8\sqrt{2})$ **63.** $\frac{24}{25}$ **65.** $\pi/3, 5\pi/3$

67. $\pi/4, 3\pi/4, 5\pi/4, 7\pi/4$ **69.** $\pi/6, \pi/2, 5\pi/6, 3\pi/2$

71. $0, \pi, 2\pi$ **73.** $0 \le x \le \pi/6$ and $5\pi/6 \le x \le 2\pi$

75. $0 \le x < \pi/4, 3\pi/4 < x < 5\pi/4, 7\pi/4 < x \le 2\pi$

77.

79.

81.

89. 14.34457 cm^2

EXERCISES E ■ PAGE A38

1. $\sqrt{1} + \sqrt{2} + \sqrt{3} + \sqrt{4} + \sqrt{5}$ **3.** $3^4 + 3^5 + 3^6$

5. $-1 + \frac{1}{3} + \frac{3}{5} + \frac{5}{7} + \frac{7}{9}$ **7.** $1^{10} + 2^{10} + 3^{10} + \cdots + n^{10}$

9. $1 - 1 + 1 - 1 + \cdots + (-1)^{n-1}$ **11.** $\sum_{i=1}^{10} i$

---

13. $\sum_{i=1}^{19} \frac{i}{i+1}$ **15.** $\sum_{i=1}^{n} 2i$ **17.** $\sum_{i=0}^{5} 2^i$ **19.** $\sum_{i=1}^{n} x^i$

21. 80   **23.** 3276   **25.** 0   **27.** 61   **29.** $n(n+1)$

31. $n(n^2 + 6n + 17)/3$ **33.** $n(n^2 + 6n + 11)/3$

35. $n(n^3 + 2n^2 - n - 10)/4$

41. (a) n^4 (b) $5^{100} - 1$ (c) $\frac{97}{300}$ (d) $a_n - a_0$

43. $\frac{1}{3}$ **45.** 14   **49.** $2^{n+1} + n^2 + n - 2$

EXERCISES G ■ PAGE A55

1. $8 - 4i$ **3.** $13 + 18i$ **5.** $12 - 7i$ **7.** $\frac{11}{13} + \frac{10}{13}i$

9. $\frac{1}{2} - \frac{1}{2}i$ **11.** $-i$ **13.** $5i$ **15.** $12 + 5i, 13$

17. $4i, 4$ **19.** $\pm\frac{3}{2}i$ **21.** $-1 \pm 2i$

23. $-\frac{1}{2} \pm (\sqrt{7}/2)i$ **25.** $3\sqrt{2}[\cos(3\pi/4) + i\sin(3\pi/4)]$

27. $5\{\cos[\tan^{-1}(\frac{4}{3})] + i\sin[\tan^{-1}(\frac{4}{3})]\}$

29. $4[\cos(\pi/2) + i\sin(\pi/2)], \cos(-\pi/6) + i\sin(-\pi/6)$,
$\frac{1}{2}[\cos(-\pi/6) + i\sin(-\pi/6)]$

31. $4\sqrt{2}[\cos(7\pi/12) + i\sin(7\pi/12)]$,
$(2\sqrt{2})[\cos(13\pi/12) + i\sin(13\pi/12)], \frac{1}{4}[\cos(\pi/6) + i\sin(\pi/6)]$

33. -1024 **35.** $-512\sqrt{3} + 512i$

37. $\pm 1, \pm i, (1/\sqrt{2})(\pm 1 \pm i)$ **39.** $\pm(\sqrt{3}/2) + \frac{1}{2}i, -i$

41. i **43.** $\frac{1}{2} + (\sqrt{3}/2)i$ **45.** $-e^2$

47. $\cos 3\theta = \cos^3\theta - 3\cos\theta \sin^2\theta$,
$\sin 3\theta = 3\cos^2\theta \sin\theta - \sin^3\theta$

INDEX

RP denotes Reference Page numbers.

SPECIAL FUNCTIONS

POWER FUNCTIONS $f(x) = x^a$

(i) $f(x) = x^n$, n a positive integer

n even

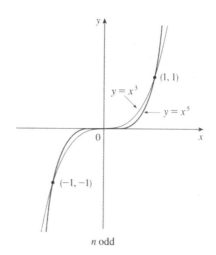

n odd

(ii) $f(x) = x^{1/n} = \sqrt[n]{x}$, n a positive integer

$f(x) = \sqrt{x}$

$f(x) = \sqrt[3]{x}$

(iii) $f(x) = x^{-1} = \dfrac{1}{x}$

INVERSE TRIGONOMETRIC FUNCTIONS

$\arcsin x = \sin^{-1}x = y \iff \sin y = x$ and $-\dfrac{\pi}{2} \le y \le \dfrac{\pi}{2}$

$\arccos x = \cos^{-1}x = y \iff \cos y = x$ and $0 \le y \le \pi$

$\arctan x = \tan^{-1}x = y \iff \tan y = x$ and $-\dfrac{\pi}{2} < y < \dfrac{\pi}{2}$

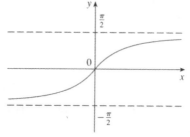

$y = \tan^{-1}x = \arctan x$

$\lim\limits_{x \to -\infty} \tan^{-1}x = -\dfrac{\pi}{2}$

$\lim\limits_{x \to \infty} \tan^{-1}x = \dfrac{\pi}{2}$

SPECIAL FUNCTIONS

EXPONENTIAL AND LOGARITHMIC FUNCTIONS

$\log_a x = y \iff a^y = x$

$\ln x = \log_e x,$ where $\ln e = 1$

$\ln x = y \iff e^y = x$

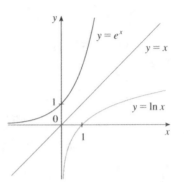

Cancellation Equations

$\log_a(a^x) = x \qquad a^{\log_a x} = x$

$\ln(e^x) = x \qquad e^{\ln x} = x$

Laws of Logarithms

1. $\log_a(xy) = \log_a x + \log_a y$

2. $\log_a\left(\dfrac{x}{y}\right) = \log_a x - \log_a y$

3. $\log_a(x^r) = r\log_a x$

$\lim_{x \to -\infty} e^x = 0 \qquad\qquad \lim_{x \to \infty} e^x = \infty$

$\lim_{x \to 0^+} \ln x = -\infty \qquad \lim_{x \to \infty} \ln x = \infty$

Exponential functions

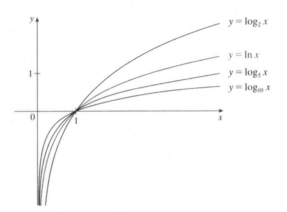

Logarithmic functions

HYPERBOLIC FUNCTIONS

$\sinh x = \dfrac{e^x - e^{-x}}{2} \qquad\qquad \operatorname{csch} x = \dfrac{1}{\sinh x}$

$\cosh x = \dfrac{e^x + e^{-x}}{2} \qquad\qquad \operatorname{sech} x = \dfrac{1}{\cosh x}$

$\tanh x = \dfrac{\sinh x}{\cosh x} \qquad\qquad \coth x = \dfrac{\cosh x}{\sinh x}$

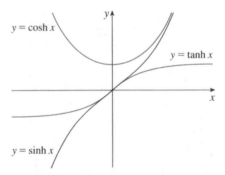

INVERSE HYPERBOLIC FUNCTIONS

$y = \sinh^{-1}x \iff \sinh y = x \qquad\qquad \sinh^{-1}x = \ln\left(x + \sqrt{x^2 + 1}\right)$

$y = \cosh^{-1}x \iff \cosh y = x \ \text{ and }\ y \geq 0 \qquad \cosh^{-1}x = \ln\left(x + \sqrt{x^2 - 1}\right)$

$y = \tanh^{-1}x \iff \tanh y = x \qquad\qquad \tanh^{-1}x = \tfrac{1}{2}\ln\left(\dfrac{1 + x}{1 - x}\right)$

DIFFERENTIATION RULES

GENERAL FORMULAS

1. $\dfrac{d}{dx}(c) = 0$

2. $\dfrac{d}{dx}[cf(x)] = cf'(x)$

3. $\dfrac{d}{dx}[f(x) + g(x)] = f'(x) + g'(x)$

4. $\dfrac{d}{dx}[f(x) - g(x)] = f'(x) - g'(x)$

5. $\dfrac{d}{dx}[f(x)g(x)] = f(x)g'(x) + g(x)f'(x)$ (Product Rule)

6. $\dfrac{d}{dx}\left[\dfrac{f(x)}{g(x)}\right] = \dfrac{g(x)f'(x) - f(x)g'(x)}{[g(x)]^2}$ (Quotient Rule)

7. $\dfrac{d}{dx}f(g(x)) = f'(g(x))g'(x)$ (Chain Rule)

8. $\dfrac{d}{dx}(x^n) = nx^{n-1}$ (Power Rule)

EXPONENTIAL AND LOGARITHMIC FUNCTIONS

9. $\dfrac{d}{dx}(e^x) = e^x$

10. $\dfrac{d}{dx}(a^x) = a^x \ln a$

11. $\dfrac{d}{dx}\ln|x| = \dfrac{1}{x}$

12. $\dfrac{d}{dx}(\log_a x) = \dfrac{1}{x \ln a}$

TRIGONOMETRIC FUNCTIONS

13. $\dfrac{d}{dx}(\sin x) = \cos x$

14. $\dfrac{d}{dx}(\cos x) = -\sin x$

15. $\dfrac{d}{dx}(\tan x) = \sec^2 x$

16. $\dfrac{d}{dx}(\csc x) = -\csc x \cot x$

17. $\dfrac{d}{dx}(\sec x) = \sec x \tan x$

18. $\dfrac{d}{dx}(\cot x) = -\csc^2 x$

INVERSE TRIGONOMETRIC FUNCTIONS

19. $\dfrac{d}{dx}(\sin^{-1}x) = \dfrac{1}{\sqrt{1 - x^2}}$

20. $\dfrac{d}{dx}(\cos^{-1}x) = -\dfrac{1}{\sqrt{1 - x^2}}$

21. $\dfrac{d}{dx}(\tan^{-1}x) = \dfrac{1}{1 + x^2}$

22. $\dfrac{d}{dx}(\csc^{-1}x) = -\dfrac{1}{x\sqrt{x^2 - 1}}$

23. $\dfrac{d}{dx}(\sec^{-1}x) = \dfrac{1}{x\sqrt{x^2 - 1}}$

24. $\dfrac{d}{dx}(\cot^{-1}x) = -\dfrac{1}{1 + x^2}$

HYPERBOLIC FUNCTIONS

25. $\dfrac{d}{dx}(\sinh x) = \cosh x$

26. $\dfrac{d}{dx}(\cosh x) = \sinh x$

27. $\dfrac{d}{dx}(\tanh x) = \operatorname{sech}^2 x$

28. $\dfrac{d}{dx}(\operatorname{csch} x) = -\operatorname{csch} x \coth x$

29. $\dfrac{d}{dx}(\operatorname{sech} x) = -\operatorname{sech} x \tanh x$

30. $\dfrac{d}{dx}(\coth x) = -\operatorname{csch}^2 x$

INVERSE HYPERBOLIC FUNCTIONS

31. $\dfrac{d}{dx}(\sinh^{-1}x) = \dfrac{1}{\sqrt{1 + x^2}}$

32. $\dfrac{d}{dx}(\cosh^{-1}x) = \dfrac{1}{\sqrt{x^2 - 1}}$

33. $\dfrac{d}{dx}(\tanh^{-1}x) = \dfrac{1}{1 - x^2}$

34. $\dfrac{d}{dx}(\operatorname{csch}^{-1}x) = -\dfrac{1}{|x|\sqrt{x^2 + 1}}$

35. $\dfrac{d}{dx}(\operatorname{sech}^{-1}x) = -\dfrac{1}{x\sqrt{1 - x^2}}$

36. $\dfrac{d}{dx}(\coth^{-1}x) = \dfrac{1}{1 - x^2}$

TABLE OF INTEGRALS

BASIC FORMS

1. $\int u\, dv = uv - \int v\, du$

2. $\int u^n\, du = \dfrac{u^{n+1}}{n+1} + C, \quad n \neq -1$

3. $\int \dfrac{du}{u} = \ln|u| + C$

4. $\int e^u\, du = e^u + C$

5. $\int a^u\, du = \dfrac{a^u}{\ln a} + C$

6. $\int \sin u\, du = -\cos u + C$

7. $\int \cos u\, du = \sin u + C$

8. $\int \sec^2 u\, du = \tan u + C$

9. $\int \csc^2 u\, du = -\cot u + C$

10. $\int \sec u \tan u\, du = \sec u + C$

11. $\int \csc u \cot u\, du = -\csc u + C$

12. $\int \tan u\, du = \ln|\sec u| + C$

13. $\int \cot u\, du = \ln|\sin u| + C$

14. $\int \sec u\, du = \ln|\sec u + \tan u| + C$

15. $\int \csc u\, du = \ln|\csc u - \cot u| + C$

16. $\int \dfrac{du}{\sqrt{a^2 - u^2}} = \sin^{-1}\dfrac{u}{a} + C$

17. $\int \dfrac{du}{a^2 + u^2} = \dfrac{1}{a}\tan^{-1}\dfrac{u}{a} + C$

18. $\int \dfrac{du}{u\sqrt{u^2 - a^2}} = \dfrac{1}{a}\sec^{-1}\dfrac{u}{a} + C$

19. $\int \dfrac{du}{a^2 - u^2} = \dfrac{1}{2a}\ln\left|\dfrac{u + a}{u - a}\right| + C$

20. $\int \dfrac{du}{u^2 - a^2} = \dfrac{1}{2a}\ln\left|\dfrac{u - a}{u + a}\right| + C$

FORMS INVOLVING $\sqrt{a^2 + u^2}$, $a > 0$

21. $\int \sqrt{a^2 + u^2}\, du = \dfrac{u}{2}\sqrt{a^2 + u^2} + \dfrac{a^2}{2}\ln\left(u + \sqrt{a^2 + u^2}\right) + C$

22. $\int u^2 \sqrt{a^2 + u^2}\, du = \dfrac{u}{8}(a^2 + 2u^2)\sqrt{a^2 + u^2} - \dfrac{a^4}{8}\ln\left(u + \sqrt{a^2 + u^2}\right) + C$

23. $\int \dfrac{\sqrt{a^2 + u^2}}{u}\, du = \sqrt{a^2 + u^2} - a\ln\left|\dfrac{a + \sqrt{a^2 + u^2}}{u}\right| + C$

24. $\int \dfrac{\sqrt{a^2 + u^2}}{u^2}\, du = -\dfrac{\sqrt{a^2 + u^2}}{u} + \ln\left(u + \sqrt{a^2 + u^2}\right) + C$

25. $\int \dfrac{du}{\sqrt{a^2 + u^2}} = \ln\left(u + \sqrt{a^2 + u^2}\right) + C$

26. $\int \dfrac{u^2\, du}{\sqrt{a^2 + u^2}} = \dfrac{u}{2}\sqrt{a^2 + u^2} - \dfrac{a^2}{2}\ln\left(u + \sqrt{a^2 + u^2}\right) + C$

27. $\int \dfrac{du}{u\sqrt{a^2 + u^2}} = -\dfrac{1}{a}\ln\left|\dfrac{\sqrt{a^2 + u^2} + a}{u}\right| + C$

28. $\int \dfrac{du}{u^2\sqrt{a^2 + u^2}} = -\dfrac{\sqrt{a^2 + u^2}}{a^2 u} + C$

29. $\int \dfrac{du}{(a^2 + u^2)^{3/2}} = \dfrac{u}{a^2\sqrt{a^2 + u^2}} + C$

TABLE OF INTEGRALS

FORMS INVOLVING $\sqrt{a^2 - u^2}$, $a > 0$

30. $\displaystyle\int \sqrt{a^2 - u^2}\, du = \frac{u}{2}\sqrt{a^2 - u^2} + \frac{a^2}{2}\sin^{-1}\frac{u}{a} + C$

31. $\displaystyle\int u^2\sqrt{a^2 - u^2}\, du = \frac{u}{8}(2u^2 - a^2)\sqrt{a^2 - u^2} + \frac{a^4}{8}\sin^{-1}\frac{u}{a} + C$

32. $\displaystyle\int \frac{\sqrt{a^2 - u^2}}{u}\, du = \sqrt{a^2 - u^2} - a\ln\left|\frac{a + \sqrt{a^2 - u^2}}{u}\right| + C$

33. $\displaystyle\int \frac{\sqrt{a^2 - u^2}}{u^2}\, du = -\frac{1}{u}\sqrt{a^2 - u^2} - \sin^{-1}\frac{u}{a} + C$

34. $\displaystyle\int \frac{u^2\, du}{\sqrt{a^2 - u^2}} = -\frac{u}{2}\sqrt{a^2 - u^2} + \frac{a^2}{2}\sin^{-1}\frac{u}{a} + C$

35. $\displaystyle\int \frac{du}{u\sqrt{a^2 - u^2}} = -\frac{1}{a}\ln\left|\frac{a + \sqrt{a^2 - u^2}}{u}\right| + C$

36. $\displaystyle\int \frac{du}{u^2\sqrt{a^2 - u^2}} = -\frac{1}{a^2 u}\sqrt{a^2 - u^2} + C$

37. $\displaystyle\int (a^2 - u^2)^{3/2}\, du = -\frac{u}{8}(2u^2 - 5a^2)\sqrt{a^2 - u^2} + \frac{3a^4}{8}\sin^{-1}\frac{u}{a} + C$

38. $\displaystyle\int \frac{du}{(a^2 - u^2)^{3/2}} = \frac{u}{a^2\sqrt{a^2 - u^2}} + C$

FORMS INVOLVING $\sqrt{u^2 - a^2}$, $a > 0$

39. $\displaystyle\int \sqrt{u^2 - a^2}\, du = \frac{u}{2}\sqrt{u^2 - a^2} - \frac{a^2}{2}\ln\left|u + \sqrt{u^2 - a^2}\right| + C$

40. $\displaystyle\int u^2\sqrt{u^2 - a^2}\, du = \frac{u}{8}(2u^2 - a^2)\sqrt{u^2 - a^2} - \frac{a^4}{8}\ln\left|u + \sqrt{u^2 - a^2}\right| + C$

41. $\displaystyle\int \frac{\sqrt{u^2 - a^2}}{u}\, du = \sqrt{u^2 - a^2} - a\cos^{-1}\frac{a}{|u|} + C$

42. $\displaystyle\int \frac{\sqrt{u^2 - a^2}}{u^2}\, du = -\frac{\sqrt{u^2 - a^2}}{u} + \ln\left|u + \sqrt{u^2 - a^2}\right| + C$

43. $\displaystyle\int \frac{du}{\sqrt{u^2 - a^2}} = \ln\left|u + \sqrt{u^2 - a^2}\right| + C$

44. $\displaystyle\int \frac{u^2\, du}{\sqrt{u^2 - a^2}} = \frac{u}{2}\sqrt{u^2 - a^2} + \frac{a^2}{2}\ln\left|u + \sqrt{u^2 - a^2}\right| + C$

45. $\displaystyle\int \frac{du}{u^2\sqrt{u^2 - a^2}} = \frac{\sqrt{u^2 - a^2}}{a^2 u} + C$

46. $\displaystyle\int \frac{du}{(u^2 - a^2)^{3/2}} = -\frac{u}{a^2\sqrt{u^2 - a^2}} + C$

TABLE OF INTEGRALS

FORMS INVOLVING $a + bu$

47. $\displaystyle\int \frac{u\,du}{a + bu} = \frac{1}{b^2}\left(a + bu - a\ln|a + bu|\right) + C$

48. $\displaystyle\int \frac{u^2\,du}{a + bu} = \frac{1}{2b^3}\left[(a + bu)^2 - 4a(a + bu) + 2a^2\ln|a + bu|\right] + C$

49. $\displaystyle\int \frac{du}{u(a + bu)} = \frac{1}{a}\ln\left|\frac{u}{a + bu}\right| + C$

50. $\displaystyle\int \frac{du}{u^2(a + bu)} = -\frac{1}{au} + \frac{b}{a^2}\ln\left|\frac{a + bu}{u}\right| + C$

51. $\displaystyle\int \frac{u\,du}{(a + bu)^2} = \frac{a}{b^2(a + bu)} + \frac{1}{b^2}\ln|a + bu| + C$

52. $\displaystyle\int \frac{du}{u(a + bu)^2} = \frac{1}{a(a + bu)} - \frac{1}{a^2}\ln\left|\frac{a + bu}{u}\right| + C$

53. $\displaystyle\int \frac{u^2\,du}{(a + bu)^2} = \frac{1}{b^3}\left(a + bu - \frac{a^2}{a + bu} - 2a\ln|a + bu|\right) + C$

54. $\displaystyle\int u\sqrt{a + bu}\,du = \frac{2}{15b^2}(3bu - 2a)(a + bu)^{3/2} + C$

55. $\displaystyle\int \frac{u\,du}{\sqrt{a + bu}} = \frac{2}{3b^2}(bu - 2a)\sqrt{a + bu} + C$

56. $\displaystyle\int \frac{u^2\,du}{\sqrt{a + bu}} = \frac{2}{15b^3}(8a^2 + 3b^2u^2 - 4abu)\sqrt{a + bu} + C$

57. $\displaystyle\int \frac{du}{u\sqrt{a + bu}} = \frac{1}{\sqrt{a}}\ln\left|\frac{\sqrt{a + bu} - \sqrt{a}}{\sqrt{a + bu} + \sqrt{a}}\right| + C,\quad \text{if } a > 0$

$\displaystyle\qquad\qquad = \frac{2}{\sqrt{-a}}\tan^{-1}\sqrt{\frac{a + bu}{-a}} + C,\qquad \text{if } a < 0$

58. $\displaystyle\int \frac{\sqrt{a + bu}}{u}\,du = 2\sqrt{a + bu} + a\int \frac{du}{u\sqrt{a + bu}}$

59. $\displaystyle\int \frac{\sqrt{a + bu}}{u^2}\,du = -\frac{\sqrt{a + bu}}{u} + \frac{b}{2}\int \frac{du}{u\sqrt{a + bu}}$

60. $\displaystyle\int u^n\sqrt{a + bu}\,du = \frac{2}{b(2n + 3)}\left[u^n(a + bu)^{3/2} - na\int u^{n-1}\sqrt{a + bu}\,du\right]$

61. $\displaystyle\int \frac{u^n\,du}{\sqrt{a + bu}} = \frac{2u^n\sqrt{a + bu}}{b(2n + 1)} - \frac{2na}{b(2n + 1)}\int \frac{u^{n-1}\,du}{\sqrt{a + bu}}$

62. $\displaystyle\int \frac{du}{u^n\sqrt{a + bu}} = -\frac{\sqrt{a + bu}}{a(n - 1)u^{n-1}} - \frac{b(2n - 3)}{2a(n - 1)}\int \frac{du}{u^{n-1}\sqrt{a + bu}}$

TABLE OF INTEGRALS

TRIGONOMETRIC FORMS

63. $\displaystyle\int \sin^2 u \, du = \tfrac{1}{2}u - \tfrac{1}{4}\sin 2u + C$

64. $\displaystyle\int \cos^2 u \, du = \tfrac{1}{2}u + \tfrac{1}{4}\sin 2u + C$

65. $\displaystyle\int \tan^2 u \, du = \tan u - u + C$

66. $\displaystyle\int \cot^2 u \, du = -\cot u - u + C$

67. $\displaystyle\int \sin^3 u \, du = -\tfrac{1}{3}(2 + \sin^2 u)\cos u + C$

68. $\displaystyle\int \cos^3 u \, du = \tfrac{1}{3}(2 + \cos^2 u)\sin u + C$

69. $\displaystyle\int \tan^3 u \, du = \tfrac{1}{2}\tan^2 u + \ln|\cos u| + C$

70. $\displaystyle\int \cot^3 u \, du = -\tfrac{1}{2}\cot^2 u - \ln|\sin u| + C$

71. $\displaystyle\int \sec^3 u \, du = \tfrac{1}{2}\sec u \tan u + \tfrac{1}{2}\ln|\sec u + \tan u| + C$

72. $\displaystyle\int \csc^3 u \, du = -\tfrac{1}{2}\csc u \cot u + \tfrac{1}{2}\ln|\csc u - \cot u| + C$

73. $\displaystyle\int \sin^n u \, du = -\frac{1}{n}\sin^{n-1}u \cos u + \frac{n-1}{n}\int \sin^{n-2}u \, du$

74. $\displaystyle\int \cos^n u \, du = \frac{1}{n}\cos^{n-1}u \sin u + \frac{n-1}{n}\int \cos^{n-2}u \, du$

75. $\displaystyle\int \tan^n u \, du = \frac{1}{n-1}\tan^{n-1}u - \int \tan^{n-2}u \, du$

76. $\displaystyle\int \cot^n u \, du = \frac{-1}{n-1}\cot^{n-1}u - \int \cot^{n-2}u \, du$

77. $\displaystyle\int \sec^n u \, du = \frac{1}{n-1}\tan u \sec^{n-2}u + \frac{n-2}{n-1}\int \sec^{n-2}u \, du$

78. $\displaystyle\int \csc^n u \, du = \frac{-1}{n-1}\cot u \csc^{n-2}u + \frac{n-2}{n-1}\int \csc^{n-2}u \, du$

79. $\displaystyle\int \sin au \sin bu \, du = \frac{\sin(a-b)u}{2(a-b)} - \frac{\sin(a+b)u}{2(a+b)} + C$

80. $\displaystyle\int \cos au \cos bu \, du = \frac{\sin(a-b)u}{2(a-b)} + \frac{\sin(a+b)u}{2(a+b)} + C$

81. $\displaystyle\int \sin au \cos bu \, du = -\frac{\cos(a-b)u}{2(a-b)} - \frac{\cos(a+b)u}{2(a+b)} + C$

82. $\displaystyle\int u \sin u \, du = \sin u - u \cos u + C$

83. $\displaystyle\int u \cos u \, du = \cos u + u \sin u + C$

84. $\displaystyle\int u^n \sin u \, du = -u^n \cos u + n\int u^{n-1}\cos u \, du$

85. $\displaystyle\int u^n \cos u \, du = u^n \sin u - n\int u^{n-1}\sin u \, du$

86. $\displaystyle\int \sin^n u \cos^m u \, du = -\frac{\sin^{n-1}u \cos^{m+1}u}{n+m} + \frac{n-1}{n+m}\int \sin^{n-2}u \cos^m u \, du$

$\displaystyle\qquad = \frac{\sin^{n+1}u \cos^{m-1}u}{n+m} + \frac{m-1}{n+m}\int \sin^n u \cos^{m-2}u \, du$

INVERSE TRIGONOMETRIC FORMS

87. $\displaystyle\int \sin^{-1}u \, du = u \sin^{-1}u + \sqrt{1-u^2} + C$

88. $\displaystyle\int \cos^{-1}u \, du = u \cos^{-1}u - \sqrt{1-u^2} + C$

89. $\displaystyle\int \tan^{-1}u \, du = u \tan^{-1}u - \tfrac{1}{2}\ln(1+u^2) + C$

90. $\displaystyle\int u \sin^{-1}u \, du = \frac{2u^2-1}{4}\sin^{-1}u + \frac{u\sqrt{1-u^2}}{4} + C$

91. $\displaystyle\int u \cos^{-1}u \, du = \frac{2u^2-1}{4}\cos^{-1}u - \frac{u\sqrt{1-u^2}}{4} + C$

92. $\displaystyle\int u \tan^{-1}u \, du = \frac{u^2+1}{2}\tan^{-1}u - \frac{u}{2} + C$

93. $\displaystyle\int u^n \sin^{-1}u \, du = \frac{1}{n+1}\left[u^{n+1}\sin^{-1}u - \int \frac{u^{n+1}\,du}{\sqrt{1-u^2}}\right], \quad n \neq -1$

94. $\displaystyle\int u^n \cos^{-1}u \, du = \frac{1}{n+1}\left[u^{n+1}\cos^{-1}u + \int \frac{u^{n+1}\,du}{\sqrt{1-u^2}}\right], \quad n \neq -1$

95. $\displaystyle\int u^n \tan^{-1}u \, du = \frac{1}{n+1}\left[u^{n+1}\tan^{-1}u - \int \frac{u^{n+1}\,du}{1+u^2}\right], \quad n \neq -1$

TABLE OF INTEGRALS

EXPONENTIAL AND LOGARITHMIC FORMS

96. $\displaystyle\int ue^{au}\,du = \frac{1}{a^2}(au-1)e^{au} + C$

97. $\displaystyle\int u^n e^{au}\,du = \frac{1}{a}u^n e^{au} - \frac{n}{a}\int u^{n-1}e^{au}\,du$

98. $\displaystyle\int e^{au}\sin bu\,du = \frac{e^{au}}{a^2+b^2}(a\sin bu - b\cos bu) + C$

99. $\displaystyle\int e^{au}\cos bu\,du = \frac{e^{au}}{a^2+b^2}(a\cos bu + b\sin bu) + C$

100. $\displaystyle\int \ln u\,du = u\ln u - u + C$

101. $\displaystyle\int u^n \ln u\,du = \frac{u^{n+1}}{(n+1)^2}[(n+1)\ln u - 1] + C$

102. $\displaystyle\int \frac{1}{u\ln u}\,du = \ln|\ln u| + C$

HYPERBOLIC FORMS

103. $\displaystyle\int \sinh u\,du = \cosh u + C$

104. $\displaystyle\int \cosh u\,du = \sinh u + C$

105. $\displaystyle\int \tanh u\,du = \ln\cosh u + C$

106. $\displaystyle\int \coth u\,du = \ln|\sinh u| + C$

107. $\displaystyle\int \operatorname{sech} u\,du = \tan^{-1}|\sinh u| + C$

108. $\displaystyle\int \operatorname{csch} u\,du = \ln\left|\tanh \tfrac{1}{2}u\right| + C$

109. $\displaystyle\int \operatorname{sech}^2 u\,du = \tanh u + C$

110. $\displaystyle\int \operatorname{csch}^2 u\,du = -\coth u + C$

111. $\displaystyle\int \operatorname{sech} u\tanh u\,du = -\operatorname{sech} u + C$

112. $\displaystyle\int \operatorname{csch} u\coth u\,du = -\operatorname{csch} u + C$

FORMS INVOLVING $\sqrt{2au-u^2}$, $a>0$

113. $\displaystyle\int \sqrt{2au-u^2}\,du = \frac{u-a}{2}\sqrt{2au-u^2} + \frac{a^2}{2}\cos^{-1}\left(\frac{a-u}{a}\right) + C$

114. $\displaystyle\int u\sqrt{2au-u^2}\,du = \frac{2u^2-au-3a^2}{6}\sqrt{2au-u^2} + \frac{a^3}{2}\cos^{-1}\left(\frac{a-u}{a}\right) + C$

115. $\displaystyle\int \frac{\sqrt{2au-u^2}}{u}\,du = \sqrt{2au-u^2} + a\cos^{-1}\left(\frac{a-u}{a}\right) + C$

116. $\displaystyle\int \frac{\sqrt{2au-u^2}}{u^2}\,du = -\frac{2\sqrt{2au-u^2}}{u} - \cos^{-1}\left(\frac{a-u}{a}\right) + C$

117. $\displaystyle\int \frac{du}{\sqrt{2au-u^2}} = \cos^{-1}\left(\frac{a-u}{a}\right) + C$

118. $\displaystyle\int \frac{u\,du}{\sqrt{2au-u^2}} = -\sqrt{2au-u^2} + a\cos^{-1}\left(\frac{a-u}{a}\right) + C$

119. $\displaystyle\int \frac{u^2\,du}{\sqrt{2au-u^2}} = -\frac{(u+3a)}{2}\sqrt{2au-u^2} + \frac{3a^2}{2}\cos^{-1}\left(\frac{a-u}{a}\right) + C$

120. $\displaystyle\int \frac{du}{u\sqrt{2au-u^2}} = -\frac{\sqrt{2au-u^2}}{au} + C$